John Platter
SOUTH AFRICAN
WINES
2 0 0 5

THE GUIDE TO CELLARS, VINEYARDS

WINEMAKERS, RESTAURANTS

AND ACCOMMODATION

The John Platter SA Wine Guide (Pty) Ltd
www.platterwineguide.com

Publisher
Andrew McDowall

Editor
Philip van Zyl

Tasters
Michael Fridjhon, Angela Lloyd, Jabulani Ntshangase, Jeremy Borg, Neil Pendock, Dave Swingler, Cathy van Zyl; Cape Wine Masters Tim James, Tony Mossop, Irina von Holdt & Christine Rudman; honorary member of the Institute of Cape Wine Masters David Hughes; Master of Wine Richard Kelley

Contributors
Lindsaye McGregor, Lynne Kloot, Wendy Toerien-Bristow, Pippa de Bruyn & David Biggs

Advertising
Linda Ransome   021 438·6161
Young Media   011 648·3869

Sales
Alison Worrall   083 530·9761

Co-ordination
Meryl Weaver, Ina de Villiers & Ann Bomford

Maps & typesetting
Gawie du Toit

Photography
Dennis Gordon

© The John Platter SA Wine Guide (Pty) Ltd 2005
PO Box 1466 Hermanus 7200

Tel: 028 313·1281
Fax: 028 312·1395

publisher@platterwineguide.co.za
www.platteronline.com

ISBN 0-9584506-3-3

Typeset by Zebra Publications, Hout Bay

Contents

Foreword

Conventional wine wisdom holds that Europe is the Old World, while SA, among others, is the New. By extension, the Old World is blessed with 'old' terroir. (Terroir, loosely, is the combination of vineyard-site-specific elements which affect the resultant wine.) The New World makes do with terroir that is less venerable, less 'authentic' and 'valuable'. It is a perception which condemns the New World to perpetual subordination. For, in wine-making, terroir matters — you need great terroir to make great wine. If there is a passionate winemaker who doesn't believe this, I have yet to meet her or him. Less certain is the relative importance of the various elements that constitute terroir. Winemakers appear to agree on two — climate and soil — as having a special significance. Climate is mercurial, cantankerous, it threatens, forgives, never rests. Soil is the bedrock of winemaking dreams; its age affects structure and fertility, in turn shaping the character and flavour of the wine. Through spectacular bumping and grinding below the bedclothes of time we in southern Africa have inherited some of the most ancient soil in the world, traceable back to the first super continent, 1 000m years ago. Our geology is like a craggy, sun-etched Wild West gunslinger — impossible to cram more character into one face. In soil terms, *we* are the Old World — this makes our wines different. When you capture that spirit of place in a wine it resonates with authentic brilliance. The wine echoes around your soul; maybe even your DNA.

Terroir, it is sometimes said, is influenced by the history and culture of the people who work the land. Reason is because humans affect how nature transforms the elements into life and visa versa. (Ever felt tense before a thunderstorm? Or spoken to your plants?) Europe, with its ancient and magnificent farming traditions, makes the link between man and terroir plausible. And yet, even here the evidence suggests that parts of Africa were cultivated before Europe. So even in this sense the Old World probably cannot claim supremacy over the New.

Ensconced in the cytoplasm of our cells are small structures called mitochondria which help the cells use oxygen. Mitochondria contain specific, identifiable DNA. This DNA is passed only from mother to child, and only from a female to the next generation — mitochondria reside only in the egg (not the sperm) from which we grow. Because of the inheritance pattern of mitochondrial DNA, we can track — with certainty — our maternal genetic ancestors back to a common ur-mother, the Mitochondrial Eve, who lived in southern Africa around 150 000 to 200 000 years ago. Which means the first and longest lasting interaction between man, sun and soil happened here in the collective cradle of humankind — southern Africa, the true 'old' terroir.

It doesn't end there. The complexities of our climate and unique geology have resulted in the most diverse winegrowing region in the world. It's reflected in the Cape Floral Kingdom, with over 9 600 species, the richest on earth. Next time you fly from Cape Town, get a window seat. You take off over the Cape Fold Mountains, the ruffles of a ball-gown hurriedly discarded on the floor of the world. The ridges dance across and alongside each other, as if God played noughts and crosses in liquid granite. There are unexpected soft corners and kloofs — the gown's fabulous folds tell a story of passion — the land is alive. Like a million goodnight kisses all blown at once, steep slopes turn the sighs of a huge, warming continent into torrents of rushing air. As a winemaker looking down on this magnificence, you might be forgiven for recognising the wrinkles at the edges of your lover's eyes, welcoming and about to smile. Authentic South African wine should trumpet our African Renaissance, but to the whole world it will also whisper 'Welcome Home'.

Bruce Jack, **Somerset West**

Wines of the Year

In the course of tasting and rating more than 5 000 wines for each edition, members of our team individually identify a limited number showing exceptional quality. These are entered into a second round of tasting, open only to finished/bottled wines, available during the currency of the book. The shortlisted wines are retasted 'blind' (without sight of the label) by an assembled panel, and those regarded as superlative in an SA context are awarded the guide's highest grading — five stars. For the current guide, 67 wines were shortlisted and 17 selected for the top rating. These standouts are listed below under the heading 'Five Stars'. For the first time, the highest scoring five-star wines were subjected to a further tasting to determine the overall top scorer. The wine which emerged from this stringent selection represents the pinnacle of SA winemaking and is the recipient of the guide's highest accolade: Wine of the Year.

Also for the first time this year, we publish the names of the candidates which did not make the five-star selection but which are also extremely fine and collectible in their own right. We list them below as our Highly Recommended wines of the year. Some longevity is implicit in wines of this calibre, and all should improve with further cellaring — say 8-10 years or more in the case of the reds and fortifieds, and around 6-8 for the whites. (Proper storage is, of course, vital for sound maturation.) Beyond the Five Stars and Highly Recommended wines, a number of other vintages tasted for this edition also showed particular potential for ageing. These are listed separately under the heading 'Buy Now, Drink Later'. Further details about all releases listed below will be found under the names of the relevant producers in the A-Z section. The 2005 five-star tasting was audited by Fisher Hoffman PKF (Cape Town) Inc.

■ Wine of the Year

- Jean Daneel Signature Chenin Blanc 2003

■ Five Stars

Chardonnay
- Hamilton Russell Vineyards 2003
- Jordan Nine Yards Reserve 2003

Chenin Blanc
- Jean Daneel Signature 2003

Pinot Noir
- Hamilton Russell Vineyards 2003

Port
- Axe Hill Cape Vintage 2002
- Boplaas Cape Vintage Reserve 2002

Red Blends
- Ernie Els 2002
- Kaapzicht Steytler Vision 2001
- Rust en Vrede Estate Wine 2001

Sauvignon Blanc
- Steenberg Reserve 2004

Semillon
- Cape Point Vineyards 2003
- Vergelegen CWG 2003

Shiraz
- Boekenhoutskloof Syrah 2002
- Sadie Family Columella 2002

Unfortified Desserts
- Joostenberg Chenin Blanc Noble Late Harvest 2003
- Robertson Winery Wide River Reserve Noble Late Harvest 2001

White Blends
- Vergelegen White 2003

■ Highly Recommended

Cabernet Franc
- Zorgvliet Silvermyn 2003

Cabernet Sauvignon
- Blue Creek 2002
- Boekenhoutskloof 2002
- Rudera CWG Auction Reserve 2002
- Rustenberg Peter Barlow 2002
- Springfield Méthode Ancienne 1999

Chardonnay
- Springfield Méthode Ancienne 2002
- Thelema 2003
- Vergelegen Reserve 2003
- Weltevrede Poet's Prayer 2002

Gewürztraminer
- Zevenwacht 2003

Méthode Cap Classique
- Bon Courage Blanc de Blancs MCC 2000

Petit Verdot
- Simonsig CWG Auction Reserve 2002

Pinotage
- Diemersfontein Carpe Diem 2001

Port
- Boplaas Cape Vintage Reserve CWG 2002
- De Krans Vintage Reserve 2001

Red Blends
- Boekenhoutskloof Chocolate Block 2003
- Clos Malverne Auret Cape Blend Limited Release 2001
- De Toren Fusion V 2002
- Glen Carlou Grand Classique 2002
- Kanonkop Paul Sauer 2001
- Morgenhof Première Sélection 2001
- Morgenster Lourens River Valley 2002
- Paradyskloof Kallista 2001
- Spice Route Malabar 2002
- Vergelegen 'Vergelegen' 2002
- Warwick Trilogy 2002
- Waterford CWG Blend 2003

Sauvignon Blanc
- Fleur du Cap Unfiltered Limited Release 2004
- Iona 2004
- Nitida 2003
- Nitida Club Select 2004
- Vergelegen Schaapenberg (wooded) 2004
- Vergelegen Reserve ('Schaapenberg' unwooded) 2004

Semillon
- Steenberg 2004

Shiraz
- Annandale 2001
- Anthony de Jager Homtini 2003
- Glen Carlou 2003
- Hartenberg CWG Auction Reserve Gravel Hill 2002
- Simonsig Merindol Syrah 2001
- The Foundry Syrah 2002
- The Observatory Syrah 2002
- Topaz Syrah 2003

Unfortified Desserts
- Bon Courage Noble Late Harvest 2004
- Darling Cellars Noble Late Harvest 2002
- Fairview La Beryl Blanc 2003
- Klein Constantia Vin de Constance 1999
- Rudera CWG Auction Reserve Chenin Blanc Noble Late Harvest 2002
- Signal Hill Mathilde Aszú 6 Puttonyos 2002

White Blends
- Sadie Family Palladius 2002

■ Buy Now, Drink Later

Cabernet Sauvignon
- Alto 2001
- Le Riche Reserve 2001
- Saxenburg Private Collection 2001
- Vergelegen 'V' 2001
- Webersburg 2001

Chardonnay
- De Wetshof Bateleur 2003
- Glen Carlou 2003 & Black Label 2003
- Neil Ellis Elgin 2003

Chenin Blanc
- Robusto 2002
- Rudera 2003

Pinotage
- Beyerskloof Reserve 2003
- DeWaal (Uiterwyk) Top of the Hill 2001
- Graham Beck Old Road 2001
- Jacobsdal 2000
- L'Avenir 2003

Port
- Boplaas CWG Auction Vintage 2002
- JP Bredell Cape Vintage Reserve 1998

- Overgaauw Cape Vintage 1997
- Vergenoegd Old Cape Colony 2001

Red Blends

- Cordoba Crescendo 2002
- Beyerskloof 2002
- Buitenverwachting Christine 2000
- Delheim Grand Reserve 2001
- DeWaal (Uiterwyk) Cape Blend 2001
- Fairview Caldera NV
- Jean Daneel Wines Cabernet Sauvignon-Merlot 2001
- Kaapzicht CWG Auction Reserve Blend 2001
- Meerlust Rubicon 2000
- Meinert Synchronicity 2001
- Morgenster 2001
- Nico van der Merwe Mas Nicolas 2001
- Remhoogte Estate Wine 2002
- Rustenberg John X Merriman 2002
- Simonsig Frans Malan 2002
- Simonsig Tiara 2002
- Vergenoegd Estate Wine 2001
- Welgemeend Estate Reserve 2001

Riesling

- Klein Constantia Weisser Riesling 2004
- Paul Cluver Weisser Riesling 2004
- Thelema 2003

Sauvignon Blanc

- Nitida Cellars 2004
- Vergelegen Schaapenberg (wooded) 2003

Shiraz

- Delheim Vera Cruz 2001
- Graham Beck The Ridge Syrah 2002
- Saxenburg Shiraz Select 2001
- Stellenzicht Vineyards Syrah 2002

Unfortified Desserts

- Klein Constantia Vin de Constance 1998
- Paul Cluver Weisser Riesling NLH 2003

Top Performers at a Glance

The following are SA's top wines as measured by their showing in selected wine competitions and professional tastings, as well as this guide. The list covers the following results (latest available): Veritas 2003 (www.veritas.co.za) — we indicate only double-gold medals; Fairbairn Capital Trophy Wine Show 2004 (www.trophywineshow.co.za) — gold medals and trophies; Michelangelo International Wine Awards 2003 (www.michelangelo-int-wine-awards.co.za) — double-golds; SA *Wine* magazine (www.winemag.co.za) — 4½ and 5 stars Jun 2003-04; UK *Decanter* magazine (www.decanter.com) — 4-5 stars Jun 2003-04; US *Wine Spectator* magazine (www.winespectator.com) — 90-100 points Jun 2003-04. See section on SA wine competitions for more details. Our own 4½ and 5 star ratings are also shown. The results below, as well as rankings in other local and international competitions are included in the A-Z section under the relevant producers and brands. Be aware that some wineries do not enter competitions and might not be represented here.

	Vintage	Platter	Veritas	Wine	FCTWS	Michelangelo	Decanter	Wine Spectator	IWC	IWSC
Cabernet Franc										
Raats	01		DG							
Warwick	01	4½								
Cabernet Sauvignon										
Anura Reserve	01		DG							
Asara	98	4½								
Ashanti	00						4			
Backsberg	01						4			
Bilton	01						4			
Boekenhoutskloof	01	4½								
Boekenhoutskloof Porcupine Ridge	02							G		
BoweJoubert	01		DG							
Carisbrooke	00	4½								
Cederberg V Generations	00			4½						
Cederberg V Generations	01	4½								
Cloof	00						5			
De Trafford	01	4½								
Delaire	00	4½								
Devon Hill	02		DG							
Diemersfontein Carpe Diem	01							G		
Dieu Donné Reserve	99						4			
EagleVlei	00						4			
Fairview	01						4			
Flagstone The Music Room	00						4			
Havana Hills Du Plessis Reserve	00						4			
Jean Daneel Signature	00						4			
Jordan	00							G		
Jordan	01		DG							
Kaapzicht	01	4½								
Kanu Limited Release	98						4			
Kanu Limited Release	01	4½								
KWV Cathedral Cellar	00	4½		4½						

	Vintage	Platter	Veritas	Wine	FCTWS	Michelangelo	Decanter	Wine Spectator	IWC	IWSC
La Motte	99						4			
Laibach Friedrich Laibach	00						4			
L'Avenir	99						4			
Le Riche	00	4½								
Le Riche Reserve	01	4½								
Linton Park Reserve	01	4½								
Meerlust Rubicon	98						4			
Meinert	00						4			
Middelvlei	00						4			
Middelvlei	01				G					
Mischa Eventide	00						4			
Mont du Toit	00						4			
Môreson Pinehurst	99						4			
Morgenhof	94			4½						
Morgenhof	00						4			
Morgenhof Reserve	01	4½								
Neil Ellis	00						4			
Neil Ellis Stellenbosch	01	4½						90		
Neil Ellis Vineyard Selection	00		DG	4½			4		G	
Neil Ellis Vineyard Selection	01	4½						90		
Overgaauw	00						4			
Overgaauw	01	4½								
Paul Cluver	99						4			
Remhoogte	00						4			
Rudera	00	4½								
Ruitersvlei Reserve	98						4			
Rupert & Rothschild Baron Edmond	99						4			
Rust en Vrede	99						4			
Rust en Vrede	00							90		
Rustenberg Peter Barlow	99			4½			5			
Rustenberg Peter Barlow	01	4½						92		
Rustenberg Peter Barlow	02				G					
Savanha Naledi	00								G	
Springfield Méthode Ancienne	98	4½								
Springfield Whole Berry	01	4½								
Stark-Condé Condé	01	4½						92		
Stark-Condé Stark	00	4½						91		
Swartland Indalo	01						4			
Swartland Indalo	02		DG							
Thelema	00						4			
Thelema	01	4½						91		
Vergelegen	98				T					
Vergelegen	01	5								
Vergelegen 'V'	01	5								
Wamakersvallei La Cave	01									G
Yonder Hill	01						4			

	Vintage	Platter	Veritas	Wine	FCTWS	Michelangelo	Decanter	Wine Spectator	IWC	IWSC
Carignan										
Fairview Pegleg	02								G	
Chardonnay										
Boland	02		DG							
Boschendal	02								G	
Bouchard Finlayson Missionvale	02							90		
Danie de Wet Unoaked Sur Lie	03		DG							
Dieu Donné	02		DG							
Direct Wines/Wilson's Oak Fermented	01					DG				
Durbanville Hills Rhinofields	01	4½								
Fairview Akkerbos	01		DG							
Fleur du Cap Unfiltered	02	4½		4½						
Glen Carlou	02							91		
Glen Carlou Reserve	02	4½								
Groote Post	03			G						
Hamilton Russell Vineyards	02	4½						91		
Jordan	02	4½								
Jordan Nine Yards	02	4½								
Kumala Journey's End	02	5								
Longridge	01	4½				DG				
Mulderbosch	01							92		
Mulderbosch	02							92		
Mulderbosch Barrel Fermented	03				T					
Neethlingshof Lord Neethling	02	4½								
Neil Ellis Elgin	02							91		
Rijk's	02				T					
Rupert & Rothschild	02	4½								
Rustenberg Stellenbosch	02							90		
Rustenberg Five Soldiers	01							91		
Stellenzicht Golden Triangle	01					DG				
Vergelegen Reserve	02	4½								
Vinfruco Rock Ridge	03		DG							
Woolworths Limestone Hill	02	4½								
Woolworths Signature	02	4½								
Chenin Blanc										
Boschendal	03					DG				
Cederberg	03		DG							
De Trafford	03							90		
Kanu Limited Release Wooded	02			5				90		
Ken Forrester Forrester-Meinert	02	4½		5						
Post House	02	4½								
Raats	02							91		
Rijk's Barrel Fermented	02		DG			DG				
Spice Route	03	4½								
Spier Private Collection	01			4½						
SylvanVale	00	4½								

	Vintage	Platter	Veritas	Wine	FCTWS	Michelangelo	Decanter	Wine Spectator	IWC	IWSC
Colombard										
Perdeberg	03		DG							
Fortified desserts										
Avondale Muscat Blanc	01		DG							
Barrydale Seven Falls White Muscadel	00					DG				
Botha Hanepoot Jerepiko	00					DG				
Jonkeer White Muscadel	00					DG				
Monis Red Muscadel	92	4½		4½						
Nuy White Muscadel	01		DG							
Nuy White Muscadel	02		DG							
Rietvallei Muscadel	02		DG							
Weltevrede Ouma se Wyn	01					DG				
Weltevrede Oupa Se Wyn	01		DG							
Malbec										
Nederburg Private Bin	01		DG							
Merlot										
Avondale Les Pleurs	00	4½								
Cordoba	01	4½								
Du Preez Estate Reserve	01				T					
Fairview	02		DG							
Groote Post	01		DG							
Hartenberg	00		DG							
Hartenberg	01		DG							
KWV Cathedral Cellar	00	4½	DG							
Linton Park	01			4½						
Linton Park Reserve	01	4½		4						
L'Ormarins	01		DG							
Meerlust	00	4½								
Morgenhof Reserve	01	4½								
Overgaauw	01	4½								
Quoin Rock	01	4½								
Remhoogte	00								G	
Rickety Bridge Paulinas Reserve	01	4½								
Slaley Reserve	99	4½								
Spice Route Flagship	01	4½								
Steenberg	02	4½								
Stellenbosch Vineyards Genesis	01	4½								
Thelema	01								90	
Thelema Reserve	00			4½						
Thelema Reserve	01	4½								
Vergelegen	01	4½								
Vergenoegd	00		DG							
Yonder Hill	01								G	
Méthode Cap Classique										
Villiera Brut Natural	01	5								

	Vintage	Platter	Veritas	Wine	FCTWS	Michelangelo	Decanter	Wine Spectator	IWC	IWSC
Villiera Monro Premier Cuvée Brut	97		DG							
Petit Verdot										
Nederburg Private Bin	01		DG							
Pinot Noir										
Bouchard Finlayson Galpin Peak Tête	01	5							G	
Bouchard Finlayson Galpin Peak Tête	02	4½								
Flagstone Poetry Collection	00	4½								
Hamilton Russell Vineyards	02	4½								
Meerlust	00	4½								
WhaleHaven	01	4½								
Pinotage										
Allée Bleue	02		DG							
Bellevue	02	4½	DG							
Bellevue PK Morkel	02	4½								
Bergsig	02	4½								
Beyerskloof Reserve	01									G
DeWaal/Uiterwyk	01	4½								
DeWaal/Uiterwyk Top of the Hill	01	4½								
Diemersfontein	03					T				
Diemersfontein Carpe Diem	02	4½								
Fairview Primo	02	4½								G
Kaapzicht Steytler	01	5								
Kanonkop	01	4½						91		
Kanonkop CWG	01	4½								
L'Avenir CWG	02	4½								
Laibach Unfiltered	01	4½								
L'Avenir	00									G
L'Avenir	01									G
Longridge	01								G	
Neethlingshof Lord Neethling	00	4½								
Rijk's	02		DG							
Sentinel	03					T				
Simonsig Redhill	01	4½								
Southern Right	02	4½								
Spice Route Flagship	00	4½								
Stellenbosch Vineyards Kumkani	02	4½								
Tukulu	01									G
Tukulu	02	4½								
Umkhulu	02	4½								
Van Zylskloof	02		DG							
Woolworths Reserve	01	4½								
Port										
Allesverloren	97	4½								
Axe Hill	01	4½								
Boplaas Cape Vintage Reserve	01	4½	DG					90		
Boplaas CWG Auction Reserve	01	5								

	Vintage	Platter	Veritas	Wine	FCTWS	Michelangelo	Decanter	Wine Spectator	IWC	IWSC
Boplaas CWG Auction Reserve	02			4½						
De Krans Vintage Reserve	01	4½	DG					91		
Domein Doornkraal Tawny	92		DG							
JP Bredell Cape Vintage Reserve	95				T					
Monis Tawny	93		DG							
Rooiberg	97					DG				
Red Blends										
Asara	98	4½								
Assegai	01	4½								
Avondale 'Avondale'	01	4½								
Beyerskloof	99									G
Beyerskloof	01	4½								
Beyerskloof Synergy Reserve	01		DG							
Boschendal	00	4½								
Buitenverwachting	00	4½								
Clos Malverne Auret Limited Release	01	4½								
Cordoba Crescendo	00	5								
Cordoba Crescendo	01	4½								
Darling Cellars	01	4½								
De Toren Fusion V	01	4½		4½			4	91		
De Trafford Elevation 393	00							93		
DeWaal/Uiterwyk	02	4½								
Durbanville Hills Caapmans	99	4½								
Ernie Els	01	5		4½				93		
Fairview Goat Roti	02							91		
Fairview SMV	02		DG							
Glen Carlou Grand Classique	01		DG							
Graham Beck	00	4½								
Grangehurst	00	4½								
Guardian Peak SMG	01		DG							
Havana Hills Du Plessis Reserve	01				T					
Havana Hills Du Plessis Reserve	02	4½								
High Constantia	01	4½								
Jordan Cobblers Hill	00							90		
Jordan CWG	01	4½								
Kaapzicht Steytler	01	4½								
Kanonkop CWG	99	4½								
Kanonkop Paul Sauer	98									G
Kanonkop Paul Sauer	00	4½	DG					92		
Klein Gustrouw	01	4½								
KWV Cathedral Cellar Triptych	00		DG							
L'Ormarins	00	4½								
Meerlust Rubicon	00	4½								
Mont Destin 1482	01	4½	DG							
Mont du Toit	00	4½								
Mont du Toit Le Sommet	00	4½								

	Vintage	Platter	Veritas	Wine	FCTWS	Michelangelo	Decanter	Wine Spectator	IWC	IWSC
Môreson	00	4½								
Morgenhof Première Sélection	99			4½						
Morgenhof Première Sélection	00	4½								
Mulderbosch Faithful Hound	01							90		
Neethlingshof Lord Neethling Laurentius	98	4½				DG				
Nico van der Merwe	01	4½								
Overgaauw Shiraz-Cabernet	01		DG							
Overgaauw Tria Corda	01	4½	DG							
Raka Biography	02		DG							
Rupert & Rothschild Baron Edmond	99									G
Rupert & Rothschild Baron Edmond	01	4½								
Rust en Vrede 'Estate'	98			4½						
Rust En Vrede 'Estate'	00	5		4½				92		
Rustenberg John X Merriman	01	4½						91		
Simonsig Frans Malan	00		DG					90		
Simonsig Frans Malan	01		DG							
Springfield	01	4½								
Vergelegen CWG Blend	01	5								
Vergelegen Mill Race	00								G	
Vergelegen 'Vergelegen'	00									G
Vergelegen 'Vergelegen'	01	4½								
Vergenoegd	01	4½								
Von Ortloff	00	4½								
Warwick Three Cape Ladies	01							91		
Warwick Trilogy/Estate Reserve	01	4½						90		
Welgemeend	00	4½								
Woolworths Signature	01	4½								
Zonnebloem	01	4½								
Sauvignon Blanc										
Bartho Eksteen Premier Choix	03	4½								
Boschendal Jean le Long	03		DG			DG				
Buitenverwachting	96				T					
Buitenverwachting	03							90		
Flagstone Free Run	02								G	
Fleur Du Cap Unfiltered Limited Release	03		DG							
Fleur du Cap Unfiltered Reserve	03	4½								
Fryer's Cove	03	4½								
Graham Beck	03		DG							
Hillcrest	03	4½								
Jason's Hill	03		DG							
KWV Reserve	03		DG							
Mulderbosch	03	4½						92		
Nederburg Private Bin D234	03		DG							
Neethlingshof	03	4½								
Neil Ellis (Sainsbury's) Sincerely Sauvignon	02									G
Neil Ellis Groenekloof	02							90		

	Vintage	Platter	Veritas	Wine	FCTWS	Michelangelo	Decanter	Wine Spectator	IWC	IWSC
Neil Ellis Groenekloof	03	4½								
Nelson Estate	03					DG				
Savanha	03		DG							
Spier Private Collection	03	4½								
Steenberg Reserve	03	5	DG	4½						
Thelema	03							90		
Vergelegen	03	4½								
Vergelegen CWG	02	4½								
Warwick Prof Black	03		DG					91		
Semillon										
Boekenhoutskloof	01	4½								
Fairview	02	4½								
Fairview Oom Pagel	02	4½		5						
Rijk's	02				T					
Steenberg	03	5		4½						
Stellenzicht Reserve	02	4½								
Vergelegen	99				T					
Shiraz										
Anthony de Jager Homtini	02	4½								
Avondale	01		DG							
Avondale Les Pleurs	01	4½	DG							
Beaumont	02	4½								
Bilton	01								G	G
Boekenhoutskloof	01	4½		5						
Boland	00									G
Boschkloof	01	4½								
Camberley	02	4½								
Cederberg	02				T					
Coleraine Culraithin	01		DG							
Coleraine Culraithin	02	4½								
De Trafford	01			4½				94		
De Trafford	02	4½								
Delheim Vera Cruz	00							91		
Delheim	01	4½						90		
DeWaal/Uiterwyk	01	4½								
Dispore Kamma Wines	02				T					
Domaine Brahms	02	4½								
Fairview Cyril Back	01							90		
Fairview Jakkalsfontein	02							92		
Fairview Solitude	02	4½								
Fairview The Beacon	01								G	
Fairview The Beacon	02	4½						93		
Glen Carlou	02								G	
Graham Beck The Ridge	00								G	
Graham Beck The Ridge	01	4½								
Hartenberg	01	4½								

	Vintage	Platter	Veritas	Wine	FCTWS	Michelangelo	Decanter	Wine Spectator	IWC	IWSC
Hartenberg CWG Gravel Hill	00			4½						
Kanu	02							90		
Kloovenburg	02	4½								
KWV Cathedral Cellar	00	4½								
Lievland Syrah	00	4½								
Luddite	02	4½								
Middelvlei	00									G
Middelvlei	01									G
Muratie	01		DG							
Neil Ellis Vineyard Selection	01	4½						90		
Rickety Bridge	01	4½								
Rust en Vrede	00	4½	DG					90		
Sadie Family	01	4½								
Saxenburg	01	4½								
Sentinel	02	4½								
Simonsig CWG	02	4½								
Simonsig Merindol	01		DG			DG				
Simonsig Merindol	02				G					
Spice Route Flagship	01	4½						91		
Spier Private Collection	00								G	
Stellenbosch Vineyards Genesis	01	4½								
Stellenzicht	01	4½								
Stellenzicht Golden Triangle	01		DG							
Stony Brook Reserve	02	4½								
The Foundry	01	5								
The Observatory	01	4½		4½						
Thelema	01							91		
Vergelegen	01	4½								
Waterford	02	4½								
Zorgvliet Silver Myn	02				G					

Tinta Barocca

	Vintage	Platter	Veritas	Wine	FCTWS	Michelangelo	Decanter	Wine Spectator	IWC	IWSC
Allesverloren	01		DG							

Unfortified Desserts

	Vintage	Platter	Veritas	Wine	FCTWS	Michelangelo	Decanter	Wine Spectator	IWC	IWSC
Asara Sauvignon Blanc NLH	02									G
Boekenhoutskloof NLH	02	4½								
Bon Courage NLH	01		DG							
Bon Courage Weisser Riesling Natural Sweet	03		DG							
Botha Hanepoot Jeripigo	00		DG							
Darling Cellars NLH	02	4½								
De Trafford Vin de Paille	01			5						
De Trafford Vin de Paille	02	4½								
Fairview La Beryl Vin de Paille	02	4½								
Joostenberg Chenin Blanc NLH	03				T					
Ken Forrester 'T' NLH	01	5			G			91		
Klein Constantia Sauvignon Blanc NLH	98			4½						
Klein Constantia Vin de Constance	98			4½				93		

	Vintage	Platter	Veritas	Wine	FCTWS	Michelangelo	Decanter	Wine Spectator	IWC	IWSC
Klein Constantia Vin de Constance	99			4½						
Nederburg NLH	01									G
Neethlingshof NLH	03	4½								
Paul Cluver Weisser Riesling NLH	03	5								
Rudera Chenin Blanc NLH	03							92		
Rustenberg Straw Wine	02	4½								
Signal Hill Crème de Tête Muscat NLH	00			4½						
Signal Hill Mathilde Aszú	02	4½				DG		91		
Villiera Inspiration NHL	01							90		
White Blends										
Bon Courage Colombard-Chardonnay	03		DG							
Fleur Du Cap VCSS Limited Release	02		DG							
Sadie Family Palladius	02	4½								
Slanghoek Vinay	NV		DG							
Vergelegen	02	5		4½						
Vergelegen	03				T					

Editor's Note

This was supposed to be the Year of the Great Contraction – the year the swaggering, Texas-sized rand roughed up our sparkly wine export business, and down-in-doldrums domestic consumption delivered an ill-timed blow to the home market. But no. The undiminished rise in wine start-ups (again more than 50 this edition) and the pumped-up, let's go get 'em attitude of longer-established winegrowers suggest 2004/5 is more consolidation than convulsion. Certainly, the happy if extended 2004 harvest, second auspicious vintage in a row, will do much to help producers' flagging spirits – if not necessarily sales. Still, market conditions are a way off ideal, and this is reflected in unusually high number of unsold wines, which we retasted for this edition and re-rated as necessary. (Some wines improved in bottle, as one would have hoped, while others, especially lower-priced whites, tended to benefit rather less.) A generally positive trend, from the consumer's standpoint, is the slower rate of price inflation. We adjusted our value-for-money thresholds accordingly, and we feel that the wines flagged with either the good-value symbol (✓, indicating wines of 3½-star quality and better) or the super-quaffing icon (☺, identifying best-buys at 3 stars and below) represent excellent value in a buyer's market.

We've revived a previous section of the guide, Wines of the Year, and included therein the top-ranked wines of 2005 (the five stars and Highly Recommended 4½-starred wines), and investment wines to lay down for future enjoyment. Also reintroduced by popular demand is the Top Performers table, showing wines which rated highest in competitions and tastings in the past twelve months. We hope the resuscitated Wines of the Year section will be the first stop for readers wanting advice on what to drink and what to the cellar in 2005, no matter what their taste or budget. Those who require more detailed information about particular wines or wineries will find it in the A-Z.

Readers may wonder how we arrive at our star ratings. Each year, a team of internationally experienced tasters mobilises in an attempt to assess every bottled or boxed wine on sale locally as well as overseas. (Unavoidably examples slip past us, and of course we try to incorporate these and any new releases in the next edition.) The results of our tastings are reflected in the A-Z section, along with news about the wineries and winemakers, general information about products, vinification facilities, vineyards, amenities available to visitors and more. The ratings are also summarised in the General Index. In line with heightened international interest in SA wine, we continue to highlight names of brands and alternative labels used by local producers for overseas markets (these are also cross-referenced for convenience). Also featured in the A-Z are general style indicators; technical details – alcohol, acid, sugar levels, time in wood etc – are provided only where they are useful in giving clues to the character of the wine.

For visitors in search of wine-route information, the maps section has been completely overhauled and now not only shows the names of the farms on the maps themselves but also gives extra information about the wineries in the particular area, including an indication of whether or not they are open on weekends and public holidays, offer meals or refreshments, specifically cater for children, and are disabled-friendly in the opinion of our wheelchair-borne consultant Guy Davies. For this edition Guy had intended visiting the new wineries mentioned in the A-Z, as well as established farms that had upgraded their visitor facilities since the last edition. Unfortunately he was hospitalised mid-year, and this had to be postponed. He can be contacted for more information on tel 872·1101 or 083·289·1199, fax 872·9675; email east19@telkomsa.net and website www.disabilty-solutions.co.za.

Also of interest to tourists and wine-ramblers is the ever-expanding Eat-out and Stay-over sections, wherein providers of various sorts and styles of hospitality describe their attractions in their own words.

Our ranking system remains largely the same as last year. We cover the full spectrum, from wines we consider 'somewhat less than ordinary' (and award 0 stars) to 'superlative Cape classics', worthy of a full 5. Wines rated ★★★✰ or higher are usually listed first in each entry, with a general rating in the margin, denoting the wine's track record over two or more vintages. Wines ranked 4 stars or more are set in red type. Vintages deviating from the general rating are individually starred in the text. Good everyday-drinking wines and more modest examples (★★★ or fewer) are included in the 'run-on' listings at the end of entries. For easy identification, the quaffing best-buys are both boxed together and individually labelled with the wallet-cordial ☺ sign. See also the section on How to use the guide.

Because of deadlines, many wines in the guide are tasted freshly bottled or as works-in-progress; any considered unrateable as a result are noted as such in the text. It's worth mentioning that we tasted from the end of June to early August 2004. Except for the bottlings re-assessed for five stars (see the preamble to the Wines of the Year), all wines were tasted 'sighted' (with labels exposed), necessarily so, given the high number of unfinished wines submitted for rating. Because of the subjective element associated with wine assessment, we strongly recommend you view our rankings as adjuncts to the tasting notes rather than as oracular pronouncements. For this purpose we include the results of other professional tastings and competitions in both the wine descriptions and the Top Performers table.

Wines featured in the guide were assessed by our team of internationally experienced tasters whose professionalism and unflagging enthusiasm we again gratefully acknowledge. Our slightly enlarged team this edition included Michael Fridjhon, Dave Hughes, Tim James, Angela Lloyd, Tony Mossop, Jabulani Ntshangase, Neil Pendock, Dave Swingler, Irina von Holdt, Richard Kelley, Christine Rudman, Jeremy Borg and Cathy van Zyl. Their initials appear below the wines they tasted.

Warm thanks to the rest of the splendid team: multi-role-playing Tim James; Lindsaye McGregor, Lynne Kloot, Wendy Toerien-Bristow, Pippa de Bruyn and David Biggs; Ina de Villiers; Meryl Weaver, Ann 'Blompot' Bomford and the elves of Cat's Pee Corner; Alison Worrall, Linda Ransom, Sally Young; Dennis Gordon; Gawie du Toit; Mark White; Hanneli Smit & co at Vin Lab; Ryk Taljaard. And Bruce Jack of Flagstone Winery for his foreword.

High fives to wife Cathy and son Luke, inveterate Star Trekkers, no doubt delighted to have a real Borg on the team.

Special thanks to SA's wine producers, without whose support the book could not be produced. And a standing invitation to visit our website, www.platteronline.com, for the latest updates, interactive wine-touring maps and search tools, and other features.

How to Use This Guide

Ratings (*Subjective choices in a South African wine context*)

★★★★★ Superlative. A Cape classic   ★★★★ Outstanding

   ★★★★ Excellent   ★★★☆ Very good/promising

     ★★★ Characterful, appealing   ★★☆ Good everyday drinking

       ★★ Pleasant drinking   ★☆ Casual quaffing

         ★ Plain and simple   ☆ Very ordinary

                     No star Somewhat less than ordinary

✓   Good value   ☺   Exceptionally drinkable and well priced

All wines rated 4 stars or more are set in red type.

Symbols & abbreviations

▌	Bottles own wine on property	&	Wheelchair-friendly (as rated, based on per-
▌	Visiting hours, tasting details		sonal inspection, by the our consultant
	(no tasting fee unless noted)		Guy Davies)
▐◉	Restaurant/refreshments	◉◉	Other tourist attractions/amenities on the
▊	Accommodation		property
✆	Telephone number	📠	Fax number

Visitable wineries in the A-Z open on public holidays unless noted

All dialling codes (021) unless noted

Abbreviations

% alc	Percentage alcohol by volume	MCC	Méthode cap classique
1stB	First bottled vintage	MIWA	Michelangelo Int. Wine Awards
BYO	Bring your own (wine, picnic)	NLH	Noble Late Harvest
Bdx	Bordeaux	NV	Non-vintage. Year of harvest not
Cs	Cases		stated on label
CWG	Cape Winemakers Guild	RS	Residual sugar
CWT	Classic Wine Trophy	SAA	South African Airways (selected
Est	Date established		for First/Business Class)
FCTWS	Fairbairn Capital Trophy Wine	SAYWS	SA Young Wine Show
	Show	SLH	Special Late Harvest
G/ℓ	Grams per litre	*Veritas*	SA National Bottled Wine Show
IWC	International Wine Challenge	VG	Veritas gold medal
IWSC	International Wine & Spirit	VDG	Veritas double-gold medal
	Competition	*Wine*	SA *Wine* magazine
JCMA	Juliet Cullinan Masters Award	WO	Wine of Origin
LBV	Late Bottled Vintage	WOM	Wine of the Month Club
Malo	Malolactic fermentation	*WS*	*Wine Spectator*

Assumptions

Unless stated otherwise, the following are implied:

- Cabernet/cab = cabernet sauvignon; pinot = pinot noir; chenin = chenin blanc; sauvignon = sauvignon blanc; riesling = Rhine/weisser riesling; touriga = touriga nacional; tinta = tinta barocca (tinta r = tinta roriz; tinta f = tinta francisca)
- Red wines wooded (in 225/300ℓ barrels); Fr = French, Am = American oak; whites unoaked
- Case = 12 × 750ml bottles
- All wines dry unless noted

See also Editor's Note and top of the A-Z section for more about using the guide

The SA Wine Industry

■ The industry in brief

In terms of world wine production, in 2001 (latest available year) South Africa ranked 10th, behind Portugal and ahead of Chile — its 647m litres representing 2.5% of the world total. Official SA statistics show that in 2003 there were 4 435 primary wine producers, and 505 wine cellars crushing grapes — 89 and 77 more, respectively, than the previous year. There were 66 co-operatives, 93 officially recognised 'estates', 330 private cellars and 16 producing wholesalers.

1990

15%

85%

2003

40%

60%

Red ● and white ○ grape varieties as % of total area

The vineyards

International demand continues to drive the change in the national vineyard, primarily from white to red grapes, and to a greater concentration on the 'noble' varieties. The grape most enthusiastically planted in 2003 was again cab (a sizeable ±1 000 ha). Chenin, still the number one in terms of total hectarage (17%), has the distinction of being both the 2nd most planted variety and, by a big margin, the most uprooted. Significantly, the percentage of young, scarcely productive vines continues to decline, albeit slowly. In 2003, ±14.5% of vines were under 4 years of age; another ±37.5% were 4–10 years old. Only ±20% of SA vineyards were 20 years or older.

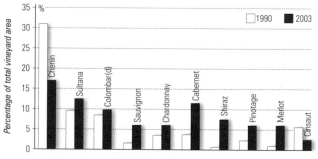

Top 5 white and top 5 red varieties

Exports

Exports of Cape wine are one of the major economic success stories of post-1994 SA (see graph). Buoyed by the then still favourable exchange rate, wine exports jumped 30% in 2003 alone. Unsurprisingly, chenin was the most exported noble variety in 2003, followed by chardonnay. Sauvignon continued its rapid rise in the export stakes, topping cab as the third most exported variety. Overseas shipments of fortified wine recovered very slightly in 2003, and bubblies continued to sparkle, rising to more than 1.6m litres.

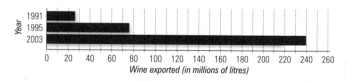

Wine exported (in millions of litres)

Local consumption

As exports soared, SA per-capita wine consumption slumped to 7.92ℓ in 2003, the lowest in decades. Compared with 2002, per-capita consumption of fortified wine was slightly higher while sparkling was unchanged. SA now slots in near the US at No 31 in world wine-drinking (Luxembourg, at over 64ℓ/liver, convincingly tops the log). Of the natural wine sold on the local market, about 39% is in glass containers – and close to 60% of this comes in the standard 750ml bottle.

New dispensation for estates

Changes have been made to the Wine of Origin (WO) regulations relating to 'estates'. These were originally the smallest category of the WO system, and denoted, in theory at least, single, continuous pieces of land, within whose confines wines were grown, vinified and bottled. Exceptions diluted the concept virtually from the outset, however, and more recently the estate image was eroded further by the defection of several high-profile properties (Fairview, Rustenberg and others), and by the increasing international fascination with single-vineyard and terroir-specific wines.

The newly introduced reforms do away with traditional 'estates' and instead focus on the notion of 'estate wines'. These must be produced in contiguous vineyards, farmed as single units and equipped with facilities that enable all processes up to final certification. All previously recognised estates (there are close to 100, though some do not produce under their own label and some do not make wine at all) have been automatically registered as Units for the Production of Estate Wine. They are now able, for the first time, to use their names to brand their total output – 'estate' as well as non-estate, though only certified estate wine may be labelled and advertised as such. As for wineries not historically registered as estates, they are now free to apply to be recognised as estate-wine producing units and to put 'estate wines' onto the market. How these changes will be received by the wine-consuming public, and how they will be viewed against pending legislation permitting single-vineyard identification on front-labels, remains to be seen. Note: in this guide, only registered production units are referred to as 'estates', to distinguish them from what in official parlance are 'private wine cellars', 'co-operatives' and 'producing wholesalers'.

Units registered for the production of estate wine

Akkerdal, Frhoek	Excelsior, Rbtsn	Keerweder, Frhoek
Allesverloren, Swtlnd	Fort Simon, Stbosch	Klawervlei, Stbosch
Alto, Stbosch	Goede Hoop, Stbosch	Klein Constantia, Constia
Altydgedacht, Dbnvlle	Goedvertrouw, Bot R	Klein Gustrouw, Stbosch
Ardein, Rbtsn	Goedverwacht, Rbtsn	Kloofzicht, Tbgh
Asara, Stbosch	Graham Beck Wines,	Kranskop, Rbtsn
Avontuur, Stbosch	Frhoek & Rbtsn	L'Avenir, Stbosch
Bellevue, Stbosch	Grande Provence, Stbosch	Le Bonheur, Stbosch
Bergsig, Wrcstr	Groot Constantia, Constia	Le Grand Chasseur, Rbtsn
Bloemendal, Dbnvlle	Hamilton Russell, W Bay	Lemberg, Tbgh
Bon Courage, Rbtsn	Hartenberg, Stbosch	Lievland, Stbosch
Bonfoi, Stbosch	Hildenbrand, Wellngtn	Loopspruit, Mpumalanga
Boschendal, Grt Drknstn	Hillcrest, Dbnvlle	Lushof, Stbosch
Cabrière, Frhoek	Jacaranda, Paarl	Manley, Tbgh
De Heuvel, Tbgh	Jacobsdal, Stbosch	Meerendal, Dbnvlle
De Wetshof, Rbtsn	Jasonsfontein (Jason's	Meerlust, Stbosch
De Zoete Inval, Paarl	Hill), Wrcstr	Middelvlei, Stbosch
Deetlefs, Wrcstr	Johann Graue	Mischa, Wellngtn
Devonvale, Stbosch	(Nederburg), Paarl	Mon Don, Rbtsn
Diemersdal, Dbnvlle	Joubert, Stbosch	Mons Ruber, L Karoo
Du Preez, Wrcstr	Kaapzicht, Stbosch	Mont Blois, Rbtsn
Elsenburg, Stbosch	Kanonkop, Stbosch	Monterosso, Stbosch

Mooiplaas, Stbosch	Opstal, Wrcstr	Slaley, Stbosch
Morgenhof, Stbosch	Oubenheim, Olfnts R	Springfield, Rbtsn
Morgenster, Stbosch	Oude Nektar, Stbosch	Theuniskraal, Tbgh
Mount Rozier, Stbosch	Oude Wellington, Wellngtn	Twee Jonge Gezellen, Tbgh
Muratie, Stbosch	Overgaauw, Stbosch	Uiterwyk, Stbosch
Neethlingshof, Stbosch	Paul Cluver, Elgin	Uitkyk, Stbosch
Nelson's, Paarl	Rainbow's End, Stbosch	Upland, Wellngtn
Nicholaas L Jonker	Remhoogte, Stbosch	Van Zylshof, Rbtsn
(Jonkheer), Rbtsn	Rietvallei, Rbtsn	Vera Cruz, Stbosch
Niel Joubert, Paarl	Rust en Vrede, Stbosch	Vergenoegd, Stbosch
Nieuwedrift, Swtlnd	Schalkenbosch, Tbgh	Warwick, Stbosch
Onverwacht, Wellngtn	Seidelberg, Paarl	Waterford, Stbosch

Doubting sauvignon

National newspaper *Business Day* sparked a furore in November 2003 by going public with long-circulating rumours of illegal use of flavourings in sauvignon. Citing 'an increasing number of Doubting Thomases, well-informed but strangely silent commentators', the author of the report, internationally respected wine critic (and taster for this guide), Michael Fridjhon asserted it was unlikely that the more opulent fruit flavours noted in the country's top 2003 sauvignons could have been obtained naturally even in the that most auspicious of vintages. In words quoted extensively here and overseas, Fridjhon declared: 'The shadow of counterfeit wine production hangs over the Cape wine industry like a pall.'

While sauvignon producers, who had seen exports jump in recent years to more than 11m litres, scrambled to minimise the fallout, the watchdog Wine & Spirit Board (W&SB) responded with a statement by its management committee head, Jakob Deist. Affirming that the addition of flavouring was both illegal in SA and 'patently unethical', Deist vowed to do 'everything possible to identify wrongdoers and bring them before the law'. In February, a follow-up communiqué said an extensive testing programme covering all growing areas had been launched. Teams of W&SB inspectors were being dispatched to draw samples prior to fermentation. These would be compared with finished wines to highlight any inconsistencies. These, if found, would be followed by forensic audits of 'not only the suspected wines ... but the entire Sauvignon blanc production'. Wineries found guilty of using additives 'could be criminally prosecuted ... and prevented from having their wines certified'.

The board has since issued no further statements, and our questions about the number of samples taken and whether or not suspicious samples had been found remained unanswered at press time. In an ironic twist, vintage 2004 played straight into the hands of the sceptics by delivering not the usual one but two aroma-stripping heatwaves — the first struck unusually early, in January, just as early-ripening sauvignon approached maturity. Resulting quietness on nose and palate will no doubt be greeted with many an (undeserved?) raised eyebrow.

■ Wine industry organisations

ARC Infruitec-Nietvoorbij Director: Johan van Zyl ■ PR: Karlien Breedt ✆ **809·3100/ 809·3524** 🖷 809·3000 ■ breedtk@infruit.agric.za ■ www.arc.agric.za
Internationally-regarded one-stop research institute, generating advanced technology for deciduous fruit- and grape-growers and related processors.

Cape Estate Wine Producers' Association (CEWPA) Chair: Braam van Velden ✆ **881·3815** 🖷 881·3436 ■ info@overgaauw.co.za ■ Manager: Pierre Loubser ✆ 855·1128 ■ 855·4351 ■ pierre.l@mweb.co.za

Cape Winemakers Guild (CWG) See separate entry in A-Z section

Chenin Blanc Association (CBA) Chair: Zakkie Bester ✆ (022) 448·1213 🖷 448·1281 ■ zakkie@riebeekcellars.co.za ■ Manager: Andries van der Walt ✆ **424·6883/** 082·882·9022 🖷 426·1967 ■ avdwalt@inds-ct.co.za ■ www.chenin.co.za

Méthode Cap Classique Producers' Association Chair: Jeff Grier ✆ **865·2002** 🖷 865·2314 ■ wine@villiera.com

Muscadel Association Chair: Swepie le Roux ℂ **(044) 251·6715** 🖷 (044) 241·2548 ▪ swepie@odn.co.za ▪ Vice-Chair: Willem Joubert ℂ **(023) 615·1135** (023) 615·1284 ▪ ashkel@mweb.co.za

Pinotage Association Chair: Beyers Truter ℂ **865·1235** 🖷 865·2683 ▪ beyers@beyerskloof.co.za ▪ Manager: Pierre Loubser ℂ **855·1128** 🖷 855·4351 ▪ pierre.l@mweb.co.za ▪ www.pinotage.co.za

Shiraz Association Chair: Jacques Borman ℂ **881·3268** ▪ 🖷 881·3032 ▪ jborman@adept.co.za

SA Port Producers' Association (SAPPA) Chair: Tony Mossop ℂ/🖷 **780·1178** ▪ tony@axehill.co.za

SA Wine & Brandy Company (SAWB) CEO Johan van Rooyen ▪ johan@sawb.co.za or lcoetzee@sawb.co.za ▪ www.sawb.co.za ℂ **886·8992** 🖷 882·9510
Section-21 company uniting growers, cellars, labour and merchants in a bid to make the wine and brandy industries more globally competitive through implementation of the Wine Industry Strategy Plan (WIP).

SA Wine Industry Trust Chair: Gavin Pieterse ℂ **(011) 726·7830** 🖷 (011) 726·8790 ▪ gavinp@arim.co.za ▪ Administration: ℂ **809·3047** 🖷 889·5900 ▪ sawit@infruit.agric.za ▪ www.sawit.co.za
Focuses on transforming the wine industry through its Section-21 companies: BUSCO (Wine Industry Business Support Company), concentrating on research, development and technology transfer as well as generic local and export marketing; DEVCO (Wine Industry Development Company), focusing on establishment of new wine farmers from previously disadvantaged groups, support/upliftment of farm workers and communities, and black economic empowerment within the wine industry; and WEF (Wine Education Fund).

Wine Industry Ethical Trade Association (WIETA) CEO: Nicky Taylor ℂ **447·5660** 🖷 447·5662 ▪ nicky@wieta.org.za; anisa@wieta.org.za
Non-profit, voluntary organisation established in 2002 to promote ethical trade in the wine industry. WIETA has adopted a code of labour standards for the industry, and its main task is to conduct ethical audits to assess members' compliance with the code.

Wine & Spirit Board Chair: Njabulo Nduli ▪ Secretary: Hugo van der Merwe ℂ **889·6555** 🖷 889·5823 ▪ hugo@infruit.agric.za; alicia@infruit.agric.za
Mainly administers the Wine of Origin (WO), estate brandy and Integrated Production of Wine (IPW) schemes.

Wines of South Africa (WOSA) Chair: Paul Cluver Snr ℂ/🖷 **844·0605** ▪ drcluver@cluver.co.za ▪ CEO: Su Birch ℂ **883·3860** 🖷 883·3861 ▪ info@wosa.co.za ▪ www.wosa.co.za
Generic marketing organisation, responsible for raising the profile of SA wine in key export markets.

■ Winegrowing areas

Note: The area maps in this section are not to the same scale

From a 17th-century experimental vineyard in the Dutch East India Company's gardens below Table Mountain, SA's vignoble over more than 340 vintages has spread over a wide area. Grapes are now grown in over 60 official appellations covering some 110 000ha. Since the introduction of the Wine of Origin (WO) scheme in 1972/3, production zones have been designated 'regions', 'districts' and 'wards'. The latter, following recent amendments to the laws governing estates (see The industry in brief, above) are now the smallest category of the WO system. Below are the most important grape cultivation zones. Note: Figures mentioned here are supplied by SA Wine Industry Information & Systems (www.sawis.co.za), and reflect the latest available (2003) status for the WO areas.

Cape Point Promising, if viticulturally challenging, cool-climate area on the western and southern slopes of the Cape Peninsula. Recognised for sauvignon and semillon; the first red-wine vineyards have just come on-stream. Major varieties (ha): sauvignon (11), cab (10), shiraz (4), pinot (4), chardonnay (3).

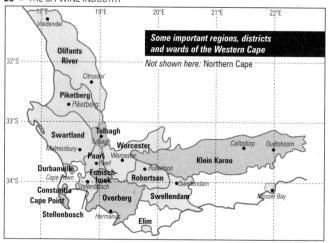

Some important regions, districts and wards of the Western Cape

Not shown here: Northern Cape

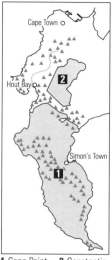

1 Cape Point **2** Constantia

Constantia Premier viticultural area on the eastern slopes of the Cape Peninsula, summer-cooled by south-easterly breezes off False Bay. Recognised for whites generally, notably sauvignon, semillon and muscat. Sauvignon (124), cab (59), chardonnay (56), merlot (42), shiraz (26).

Darling This area around the eponymous town has been hived off Swartland and is now a standalone district. Its showpiece is the higher-lying Groenekloof ward, long the source of top-class sauvignon, also showing promise with reds such as shiraz. Cab (518), shiraz (258), chenin (251), sauvignon (244), pinotage (238).

Durbanville This southern portion of the Tygerberg district has a reputation for striking sauvignons and merlots. Important quality factors include deep, moisture-retaining soils, cooling summer night-time mists and proximity to the ocean. Cab (328), sauvignon (253), shiraz (215), merlot (211), pinotage (99).

Elim Maritime vineyards around the old mission village of Elim near Cape Agulhas, Africa's most southerly point. Officially a standalone ward within the WO scheme, its still tiny hectarage is among the most closely watched in the Cape. Sauvignon (26), cab (17), merlot (3), semillon (1), petit verdot (1).

Little Karoo This semi-arid scrubland is ideal for ostrich farmers but something of a challenge for winegrowers, who rely on irrigation. Similarities (in climate, if not soil) with the Douro Valley of Portugal have inspired some local growers, principally around the village of Calitzdorp, to apply their talents to 'port' with results that impress even the Portuguese. Also recognised for fortifieds generally. Colombard (777), chenin (641), hanepoot (278), chardonnay (205), ruby cab (135).

Lower Orange This hot-climate stretch along the Orange River is the Cape's most northerly, and the 4th largest overall in terms of hectarage (15 000, close to 15% of the total). Overwhelmingly a white-grape area but red plantings are increasing. Sultana (10 559), colombard (2 550), chenin (861), hanepoot (382), ruby cab (190).

Olifants River Quality moves are afoot in this north-westerly Cape grape-growing area, both in the low-lying Olifants Valley and the cooler upland wards of Cederberg and

1 Swartland   4 Philadelphia
2 Darling
3 Durbanville

1 Olifants River   4 Citrusdal Mntn
2 Bamboes Bay   5 Lutzville Valley
3 Citrusdal Valley   6 Piekenierskloof

Piekenierskloof. Recognised mainly for everyday reds and fortified. A climate conducive to organic cultivation is now beginning to be exploited to that end. Major varieties (ha): chenin (2 085), colombard (1 914), shiraz (983), hanepoot (680), pinotage (616).

Paarl This district has many mesoclimates, soils and aspects, and thus succeeds with a variety of styles and grapes. Paarl proper is recognised for shiraz and, more recently, viognier and mourvèdre grown on warmer slopes. Chenin (1 744), cab (1 292), shiraz (790), cinsaut (575); pinotage (563). The ward of Wellington is showing promise, especially with shiraz and gutsy red blends generally. Chenin (1 202), cab (822), cinsaut (524), shiraz (449), merlot (351). Franschhoek, founded by 17th-century French Huguenots and now a millionaire's playground, is recognised for cab and semillon. Sauvignon (227), cab (222), chardonnay (177), merlot (136), shiraz (126). Recently proclaimed Simonsberg-Paarl, on the slopes of the Simonsberg, is recognised for red blends and chardonnay. Cab

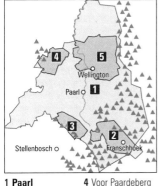

1 Paarl   4 Voor Paardeberg
2 Franschhoek   5 Wellington
3 Simonsberg-Paarl

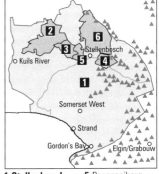

1 Stellenbosch   5 Papegaaiberg
2 Bottelary   6 Simonsberg-
3 Devon Valley   Stellenbosch
4 Jonkershoek
  Valley

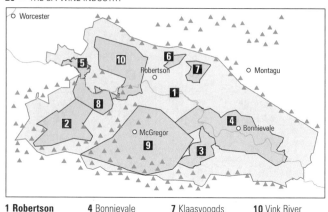

1 Robertson   **4** Bonnievale   **7** Klaasvoogds   **10** Vink River
2 Agterkliphoogte   **5** Eilandia   **8** Le Chasseur
3 Boesmans River   **6** Hoops River   **9** McGregor

(410), chardonnay (239), merlot (172), chenin (160), sauvignon (158). Voor Paardeberg, another newish ward, has long been a source of top-notch grapes for merchants and private cellars; noted for shiraz, pinotage and chenin. Cab (386), pinotage (202), chenin (193), shiraz (183), merlot (178).

Philadelphia Brand-new ward north of Durbanville, cooled by the Atlantic and already highly regarded as the home of Havana Hills, famed for its Cab, Merlot and red blends. Varietal breakdown unavailable at press time.

Robertson Though a warmer area, the 'valley of vines and roses' has traditionally been white-wine country. But there are now flashes of red-wine brilliance, especially shiraz and cab. Recognised for chardonnay, sauvignon, everyday whites and sparkling. Colombard (2 158), chenin (1830), chardonnay (1 677), cab (1327), sauvignon (1 040).

Stellenbosch To many, this intensively farmed district is the red wine capital of SA. Yet many of its whites, bubblies and fortifieds also feature in the SA first league. Key contributors to quality are the cooler mountain slopes, varied soil types and breezes off False Bay which moderate summer temperatures. Jonkershoek Valley, a ward east of Stellenbosch town, is recognised for cab and cab blends. Cab (58), merlot (26), chardonnay (23), pinotage (20), chenin (18), sauvignon (17). Simonsberg-Stellenbosch, encompassing the south-western foothills of the Simonsberg mountain, is especially recognised for cab, cab blends, pinotage and reds generally. Cab (301), merlot (156), sauvignon (154), shiraz (130), chardonnay (114), pinotage (110). North-west of Stellenbosch town are three adjoining wards: Bottelary, noted for pinotage, shiraz and warm-blooded blends. Chenin (549), cab (465), sauvignon (312), shiraz (280), pinotage (268); Devon Valley, recognised mainly for red blends. Cab (196), merlot (159), shiraz (115), pinotage (82), sauvignon (73); and Papegaaiberg. The remainder of the district, as yet unappellated, includes Stellenboschberg, Helderberg and Faure, recognised for red blends, chenin and sauvignon. Cab (2 374), shiraz (1 262), merlot (1 211), sauvignon (1097), chenin (1035).

Swartland Traditionally associated with beefy reds, especially pinotage and shiraz, this sunny area north of Cape Town has two designated wards, Malmesbury and Riebeekberg, plus a large appellated area. Riebeekberg: chenin (247), shiraz (175), cab (168), pinotage (167), chardonnay (161). Malmesbury: cab (709), chenin (588), shiraz (500), pinotage (492), merlot (299). Swartland: chenin (2 728), pinotage (883), cab (153), shiraz (615), sauvignon (390).

Tulbagh This landlocked district, traditionally known for sparkling and lightish whites, is steadily moving towards reds. Major varieties: chenin (582), colombard (331), cab (153), shiraz (132), pinotage (107).

Walker Bay Since the 1980s, some of the Cape's finest wines have come from this maritime area south-east of Cape Town, recently 'upgraded' from a ward to a district. Upland Elgin is now a ward within the Overberg district. Recognised for pinot, aromatic pinotage, sauvignon and chardonnay. The latest varietal breakdown not available; previously Walker Bay: sauvignon (68), cab (50), merlot (45), pinotage (40), shiraz (39). Elgin: sauvignon (58), cab (41), merlot (35), pinot (28), chardonnay (18).

1 Elim   **2** Kleinrivier   **3** Walker Bay

Worcester Still the largest winegrowing area, measured by number of vines (62m, nearly 20% of the total), producing chiefly for brandy-making and the merchant trade, but small quantities are bottled under own labels and these often represent good value. Recognised for everyday reds/whites and fortifieds. Chenin (4 218), colombard (2 431), chardonnay (1 381), cab (1 294), sauvignon (1 214).

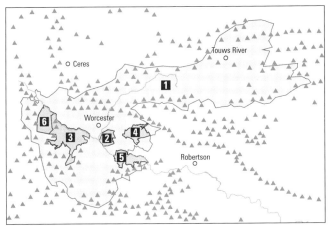

| **1 Worcester** | 3 Goudini | 5 Scherpenheuvel |
| 2 Aan-de-Doorns | 4 Nuy | 6 Slanghoek |

Wine of Origin-defined production areas
(New appellations in **bold**.)

Region	District	Ward
Breede River Valley	Robertson	Agterkliphoogte
		Bonnievale
		Boesmansrivier
		Eilandia
		Hoopsrivier
		Klaasvoogds
		Le Chasseur
		McGregor
		Vinkrivier

Region	District	Ward
Breede River Valley (*continued*)	Swellendam	Buffeljags
		Stormsvlei
	Worcester	Aan-de-Doorns
		Goudini
		Nuy
		Scherpenheuvel
		Slanghoek
Little Karoo	—	Montagu
	—	Tradouw
	Calitzdorp	—
	—	**Upper Langkloof**
	—	**Outeniqua**
Coastal	Cape Point	—
	—	Constantia
	Darling	Groenekloof
	Paarl	Franschhoek Valley
		Wellington
		Simonsberg-Paarl
		Voor Paardeberg
	Tygerberg	Durbanville
		Philadelphia
	Stellenbosch	Jonkershoek Valley
		Papegaaiberg
		Simonsberg–Stellenbosch
		Bottelary
		Devon Valley
	Swartland	Malmesbury
		Riebeekberg
	Tulbagh	—
Olifants River	Citrusdal Mountain	Piekenierskloof
	—	Bamboes Bay
	Citrusdal Valley	—
	Lutzville Valley	Koekenaap
	—	Spruitdrift
	—	Vredendal
—	Overberg	Elgin
—	Walker Bay	**Kleinrivier**
—	Douglas*	—
—	—	Cederberg
—	—	Ceres
—	—	Elim
—	—	Hartswater*
—	—	Herbertsdale
—	—	Lower Orange*
—	—	Prince Albert Valley
—	—	Rietrivier (Free State)*
—	—	Ruiterbosch
—	—	Swartberg

Boberg (fortified wines from Paarl & Tulbagh)

*Production zones within the officially designated Northern Cape Geographical Unit; all other areas are part of the Western Cape Geographical Unit. Source: SAWIS

◼ Grape varieties

Legislation requires the presence in the wine of 75% of the stated variety (85% if exported). Blends may only name component parts if those components were vinified separately, prior to blending; then they are listed with the larger contributor(s) named first. If one of the blend partners is less than 20%, percentages for all the varieties must be given. Figures given for proportion of the national vineyard are for 2003.

Red-wine varieties

Cabernet sauvignon Adaptable and internationally planted black grape making some of the world's finest and longest-lasting wines. And retaining some of its inherent qualities even when overcropped in less suitable soils and climates. Can stand alone triumphantly, but frequently blended with a wide range of other varieties: traditionally, as in Bordeaux, with cab franc, merlot and a few minor others, but also in SA sometimes partnering varieties such as shiraz and pinotage. Number of different clones, with differing characteristics. 11.7% of total vineyard area, steadily increasing (3.8% in 1990).

Cabernet franc Like its descendant cabernet sauvignon, with which it is often partnered, a classic part of the Bordeaux blend, but in SA and elsewhere also used for varietal wines – particularly on the Loire. Tiny vineyard area (0.8%), increasing.

Carignan Hugely planted in the south of France, where it is not much respected. But there, as in SA, older, low-yielding vines can produce pleasant surprises. Insignificant vineyard area.

Cinsaut Cinsault in France. Another of the mass, undistinguished plantings of southern France, which only occasionally comes up trumps. Used to be known locally as hermitage, the name reflected in its offspring (with pinot noir), pinotage. 2.7% of vineyard area, decreasing (5.7% in 1990).

Gamay noir Although it produces some serious long-lived wines in Beaujolais, its use for (mainly) early- and easy-drinking 'nouveau' wines there, often using carbonic maceration, is the model mostly copied in SA. Insignificant vineyard area.

Grenache (noir) The international (ie French) name for the Spanish grape garnacha. Widespread in Spain and southern France, generally used in blends (as in Rioja and Châteauneuf), but occasionally solo. A favourite for rosés. When vigour restrained, capable of greatness, but this is rare. Tiny plantings here. (White/pink versions also occur.)

Malbec Once a significant part of Bordeaux's blend, now most important in Cahors in western France (where it is known as cot), and as Argentina's signature variety. In SA a few varietal and blended examples; very small plantings.

Merlot Classic blending partner (as in Bordeaux) for cabernet, fashionable around the world, where it tends to be seen as an 'easier' version of cab – although this is perhaps because it is often made in a less ambitious manner. Merlot varietal wines increasingly common in SA too. 6% of vineyard area, increasing (0.9% in 1990).

Mourvèdre Internationally known by its French name, though originally Spanish (monastrell). In Australia and California also called mataro – which was, until recently, its official name in SA. Particularly successful in some serious southern French blends, and increasingly modish internationally. Minuscule plantings here.

Nebbiolo Perhaps the greatest red grape to have scarcely ventured from its home – Piedmont in this case, where it makes massive, tannic, long-lived wines. Minute plantings here.

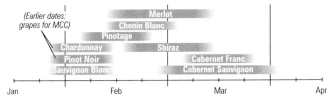

Approximate ripening dates in the Stellenbosch area for some important grape varieties

Petit verdot Use of this excellent variety in the Médoc limited by its late ripening. Now appearing in some local blends, and a few varietals. Tiny but increasing quantities.

Pinotage A 1920s cross between pinot noir and cinsaut ('hermitage'). Made in a range of styles, from simply fruity to ambitious, well-oaked examples. 6% of vineyard area, decreasing (6.5% in 2001).

Pinot noir Notoriously difficult grape to succeed with outside its native Burgundy, but SA, along with the rest of the New World, now producing some excellent examples, especially as use of BK5 'champagne' clone wanes. Usually matured in wood; seldom at a bargain price. Still very small proportion of the vineyard (0.5%).

Ruby cabernet US cross between cabernet sauvignon and carignan, designed for heat tolerance. Rather rustic, used mostly in cheaper blends. 2.3% of vineyard area.

Shiraz Better known as syrah outside SA and Australia (and on some local labels too). Internationally increasing in popularity, with northern Rhône and now also Australia as its major domiciles. Clearly happy in warmer climates, shiraz is seen by many as the great hope for SA wine. Made here in a variety of styles – generally wooded, often with American oak. 7.7% of vineyard area, sharply up from 0.7% in 1990.

Tinta barocca Elsewhere spelt 'barroca'. One of the important Portuguese port-making grapes, which is now its primary role in SA, usually blended. Also used for some varietal unfortified wines, and namelessly in some 'dry reds'. Insignificant vineyard area.

Touriga nacional Important Portuguese port-making grape, now usefully grown here for similar ends, along with tinta francisca, tinta roriz (tempranillo) and souzão. Tiny plantings.

Zinfandel The quintessential Californian grape (of European origin, and the same as Italy's primitivo), used here in a small way for some big wines. Tiny plantings.

White wine varieties

Chardonnay In the Cape, as elsewhere, many new vineyards of this grape have come on-stream in recent years, with wines showing a wide range of styles, quality and price. Generally used varietally, but also in blends. Often heavily wooded in more ambitious wines. 5.9% of vineyard area, has increased greatly (1.5% in 1990), now stabilising.

Chenin blanc SA has more chenin (locally also called steen) than even France's Loire Valley, the variety's home. Used here for everything from generic 'dry whites' to ambitious sweet wines, to brandy. Some notable table-wine successes in recent years, in a sea of overcropped mediocrity. 17.1% of vineyard area, still declining (31.9% in 1990).

Colombar(d) One of the mainstays of brandy production in the Cape, colombard (usually without the 'd' in SA) also used for numerous varietal and blended wines, ranging from dry to sweet – seldom wooded. 9.8% of vineyard area, declining.

Gewürztraminer Readily identifiable from its rose-petal fragrance, best known in its Alsatian guise. In the Cape usually made in sweeter styles. Insignificant vineyard area.

Hanepoot Traditional Afrikaans name for muscat d'Alexandrie, the Cape's most planted muscat variety (see also muscadel below). 2.7% of vineyard area (some for raisins and table grapes), declining.

Muscadel Name used here for both muscat de Frontignan and muscat blanc à petits grains (both red and white versions). The grape associated with the famous Constantia dessert wines of the 18th century today is used chiefly for dessert and fortified wines and for touching up blends. Red and white versions total ±1% of vineyard area.

Muscat See Hanepoot and Muscadel.

Riesling The name a source of confusion to consumers, and of distress to the producers of what is known in its great homeland, Germany, simply as riesling and here officially as Rhine or weisser riesling. In SA, standing alone, 'riesling' usually, and officially, refers to Cape riesling (sometimes called Paarl or SA riesling), a much inferior grape properly known as crouchen blanc, mostly used here anonymously in blends, and sometimes varietally. Rhine/weisser riesling frequently in off-dry style here, in blends or varietally, some noteworthy botrytised dessert examples – developing terpene character much earlier in SA than in cooler climates. Cape riesling: 1.2% of vineyard area, decreasing; Rhine: stable at 0.3%. Note: in this guide 'riesling' without qualification refers to the latter.

Sauvignon blanc Prestigious vine most associated with eastern Loire regions, Bordeaux and, increasingly, New Zealand – whose wines have helped restore fashionability to the grape. The Cape version no longer a poor relation of these. Usually dry, but some sweet wines; sometimes wooded, more often not (former sometimes called fumé blanc/blanc fumé). 6.1% of vineyard area, increasing.

Semillon Spelt sémillon in French. The present small hectarage devoted to semillon in SA is a far cry from the early 19th century, when the grape, also known as 'groen' (green), a reference to its bright foliage, represented 93% of all Cape vines. Now only 0.9%. Sometimes heavily wooded.

Viognier Increasingly fashionable variety internationally, spreading out from its home in the northern Rhône, now showing promise here. Usually wooded. Still just 0.3% of total SA vineyard.

■ SA wine competitions & awards

An increasing number of wine competitions are run by liquor industry bodies, independent companies, publishing houses and individuals. Below are the main national events:

ABSA Bank-SA Pinotage Producers' Association Top Ten Run annually by the local pinotage producers' body and a major financial institution to help set international quality targets for growers of pinotage. Local judges.

Classic Wine Trophy Staged under rules of the Office Internationale de la Vigne et du Vin (OIV), recognising ageworthy, Old World-inclined SA wines. Overseas judges.

Diners Club Winemaker of the Year Inaugurated 1981, this prestigious competition features a different category each year. Local panel with some overseas representation.

Fairbairn Capital Trophy Wine Show Launched 2002 to identify the best wines in SA and award trophies to the top wines in each of the major classes, as well as the top producer overall. Local and international evaluators.

Juliet Cullinan Wine Masters Awards National competition organised by local wine-entrepreneur Juliet Cullinan and judged by a panel of Cape Wine Masters.

Michelangelo International Wine Awards Well-established event (1997); selections made by a combo of local and international judges. Trophy and medal winners are shown at public tastings in Cape Town and Johannesburg.

Peter Schulz Excellence Awards for Port Hosted annually by the SA Port Producers' Association, SA *Wine* and importer-wholesaler NMK Schulz to select the best wine in each of the various port categories, and an overall winner. Local judges.

SAA Selections Annual singling-out of wines to fly with the national carrier, SA Airways (drinkability in flight conditions an important consideration). The top red, white, bubbly and port each receive a trophy. Local & overseas palates.

SA Young Wine Show Inaugurated 1975 to gauge the quality of embryo wines, prior to finishing and bottling, thereby also recognising wineries that sell their products in bulk. The grand champion receives the General Smuts Trophy. Local judges.

Swiss International Air Lines Wine Awards First run in 2003 in conjunction with Cape Town's annual Good Food & Wine Show; local/international panel chaired by UK wine critic Robert Joseph.

Wine Magazine-Amorim Cork Cap Classique Challenge Annual competition to anoint SA's top bottle-fermented sparkling wines. Local judges.

Wine Magazine Best Value Awards SA judges gather annually to select the best value wines based on quality vs price. Results published in Wine's *Best Value Wine Guide*.

Wine Magazine-Tops at Spar Chenin Blanc Challenge Annual event in which wooded and unwooded chenins in the drier spectrum (max 20g/ℓ sugar) are assessed by a mostly SA panel.

Wine Magazine-Tops at Spar Shiraz Challenge Another SA *Wine*/Tops at Spar collaboration, uncovering benchmark SA wines made from shiraz/syrah. Local judges.

Wine Magazine-Tops at Spar Value for Money Pinotage Awards Reconfigured Pinotage Champion of the Year competition, now dedicated to showcase the best-value pinotages of a given vintage. SA judges.

Veritas Hosted by the SA National Wine Show Association, recognising top market-ready wines across a range of categories. Double-gold, gold, silver and bronze medals are awarded. Local palates with some overseas input.

> **Note:** For a list of wines rated highest in selected professional tastings and competitions in the past year, plus our own 4½ and 5-star ratings, see Top Performers.

■ Wine education

Cape Wine Academy General education organisation, with a hub in Stellenbosch and satellites in Johannesburg, Durban, Pretoria, Windhoek and Harare. Runs theory and tasting courses with examinations at several levels. Other courses include wine service, introduction to wines of the world, and skills workshops for front-of-house sales people. New in 2004: basic winemaking, olive oil and wine retailing courses, and becoming an approved program provider for the British WSET advanced certificate course. The principal is Marilyn Cooper and managing director Reinier Matthee.

Stellenbosch ✆ **(021) 809·7597/7547** 🖷 883·9179 ▪ Johannesburg ✆ (011) 783·4585/6 🖷 (011) 883·2356 ▪ Durban ✆/🖷 (031) 564·5067 ▪ Pretoria ✆/🖷 (012) 333·1978 ▪ Windhoek ✆ (09264) 6·125·8758 🖷 (09264) 6·122·4768 ▪ Harare ✆ (09263) 9·135·3840 ▪ info@cwa.org.za ▪ www.capewineacademy.co.za

Cape Wine Master Successful completion of examinations set since 1983 by the Cape Wine & Spirit Education Trust and, latterly, the Cape Wine Academy, have qualified 54 Cape Wine Masters (3 are honorary). Their Institute holds seminars, runs tasting workshops, charts trends and names a Wine Personality of the Year. The chair is Cornel Spies. For details, contact Margie Barker ✆ **809·7598**; mbarker@cwa.org.za. The Institute's current members are (latest inductees in bold):

Chris Bargmann ▪ **Berenice Barker** ▪ Margie Barker ▪ FC 'Duimpie' Bayly ▪ Paul Benade ▪ Cathy Brewer ▪ Robin Brown ▪ Sue Brown ▪ Michael Claasens ▪ Marilyn Cooper ▪ Henry Davel ▪ Dick Davidson ▪ Greg de Bruyn ▪ **Heidi Duminy** ▪ Stephan du Toit ▪ Pieter Esbach ▪ **Margie Fallon** ▪ Colin Frith (Hon) ▪ Margaret Fry ▪ Peter Gebler ▪ Penny Gold ▪ Jeff Grier ▪ Phyllis Hands (Hon) ▪ Bennie Howard ▪ Dave Hughes (Hon) ▪ Dave Johnson ▪ Val Kartsounis ▪ Peter Koff ▪ Gerald Ludwinski ▪ Marietjie Marais-Brown ▪ Alf Mauff ▪ Tony Mossop ▪ Allan Mullins ▪ Boets Nel ▪ Carel Nel ▪ Elsie Pels ▪ **Jenny Ratcliffe** ▪ Christine Rudman ▪ Lynne Sheriff ▪ **Caroline Snyman** ▪ Cornel Spies ▪ Clive Torr ▪ Charl van Teijlingen ▪ Sue van Wyk ▪ **Junel Vermeulen** ▪ Irina von Holdt ▪ Cathy White ▪ Geoff Willis. Gert Burger CWM passed away in May 2004 after a short illness.

■ Selected wine shops

The following retail outlets stock a wide range of fine-wines and/or provide specialised services to the wine-consuming public. 'Bricks-and-mortar' shops are listed first, by area, followed by on-line emporia.

Eastern Cape

Da Vino's Cnr Beach Hotel, Marine Drive, Summerstrand, Port Elizabeth ▪ Mon-Fri 9-6 Sat 8.30-5 Closed public holidays ✆ **(041) 583·2166** 🖷 (041) 583·6220

Makro Port Elizabeth Cnr Cape Rd & Samantha Way, Kabega ▪ Mon/Tue, Thu/Fri 8.30-5. 30 Wed 9-5.30 Sat 8-5 Public holidays 9-4 ▪ cbarton@makro.co.za ▪ www.makro.co.za ✆ **(041) 360·0605** 🖷 (041) 360·0647

Prestons 121 Main Road, Walmer ▪ Mon-Fri 9-6 Sat 8.30-4 (phone ahead on public holidays) ▪ www.eliquor.co.za ✆/🖷 **(041) 581·1993**

Ultra Liquors East London 250 Oxford Str, East London ▪ Mon-Fri 9-6 Sat 9-5 Public holidays 9-2 ▪ Closed Easter Fri, Dec 25 & Jan 1 ▪ eastlondon@ultraliquors.co.za ▪ www.ultraclub.co.za ✆ **(043) 743·5174/722·3476** 🖷 (043) 743·4283

Ultra Liquors Newton Park 140 Hurd Str, Newton Park ▪ Mon-Fri 9-6 Sat 9-5 Public holidays 9-2 ▪ Closed Easter Fri, Dec 25 & Jan 1 ▪ newtonpark@ultraliquors.co.za ▪ www.ultraclub.co.za ✆ **(041) 364·1103** 🖷 (041) 364·2277

Free State

Liquor City Bloemfontein 6 Showgrounds Shopping Centre, Currie Ave, Bloemfontein Open Mon-Sat, call store for trading hours ✆ **(051) 448·6222**

Ultra Liquors Bloemfontein Cnr Markgraaf & St Andrew Strs, Bloemfontein ▪ Mon-Fri 9-6 Sat 9-5 Public holidays 9-2 ▪ Closed Easter Fri, Dec 25 & Jan 1 ▪ bloem@ultraliquors.co.za ▪ www.ultraclub.co.za ✆ **(051) 447·3328** 🖷 (051) 447·3600

Gauteng

Bamboo-WINE+ Bamboo Centre, 53 Rustenburg Road, Cnr 9th St, Melville ▪ Mon-Fri 10-6 Sat 9-4 ▪ wine@wineplus.co.za ▪ www.bamboo-online.co.za ✆ **(011) 482·1020** 🖷 (011) 482·5958

Central Liquors @ The Square Cnr Rietfontein & Rigg Rds, Boksburg ▪ Mon-Fri 9-7 Sat & public holidays 9-5 ▪ val@centralliquors.co.za ▪ www.centralliquors.co.za ✆ **(011) 826·5070** 🖷 (011) 826·7151 Also Central Liquors 47 Fourth St, Springs ✆ **(011) 812·1428/9** 🖷 (011) 812·1910

Glenfair Wine & Liquor Shop 53/54, Glenfair Centre, Lynnwood Rd, Lynnwood Manor, Pretoria ▪ Mon-Fri 8.30-6 Sat 8-3 Public holidays 9-1 ▪ Closed religious holidays ▪ mickey@glenfairliquor.co.za ▪ www.glenfairliquor.co.za ✆ **(012) 361·4509/4563** 🖷 (012) 361·4509

John Wilson Sandton City Shop L68, Sandton City, cnr Rivonia Rd & 5th Ave, Sandton ▪ Mon-Thu 9-7 Fri 9-8 Sat 9-5 Public holidays 10-5 ▪ Closed Good Fri & Dec 25 ▪ sandton@wpcellars.co.za ✆ **(011) 783·7035** (011) 783·7036

Alberts Liquors Braam Pretorius Rd, Magalieskruin, Pretoria Open Mon-Sat, call store for trading hours ✆ **(012) 543·0813**

Alpha Liquor Store Cnr Main Reef Rd & Willem van Reekum Str, Roodepoort Open Mon-Sat, call store for trading hours ✆ **(011) 766·1086**

Liquor City Bassonia Comaro View Shopping Centre, Comaro Rd, Bassonia Open Mon-Sat, call store for trading hours ✆ **(011) 432·0457**

Liquor City Boksburg Cnr Rondebult & McGaghy Strs, Parkdene, Boksburg Open Mon-Sat, call store for trading hours ✆ **(011) 917·0866**

Liquor City Boksburg West 53 Rietfontein Rd, Boksburg West Open Mon-Sat, call store for trading hours ✆ **(011) 826·2336**

Liquor City Brackengate Cnr Andries Ave & Waal Str, Brackendowns, Alberton Open Mon-Sat, call store for trading hours ✆ **(011) 900·4493**

Liquor City Brixton 121 High Str, Brixton, Johannesburg Open Mon-Sat, call store for trading hours ✆ **(011) 837·7079**

Liquor City Broadacres Cnr Valley Rd & Cedar Ave, Broadacres, Randburg Open Mon-Sat, call store for trading hours ✆ **(011) 465·3795**

Liquor City Cleo's Cnr Kingfisher & Heidelburg Strs, Elspark, Boksburg Open Mon-Sat, call store for trading hours ✆ **(011) 916·2358**

Liquor City Cornwall View Cnr Boeing & Piering Strs, Elardus Park, Pretoria Open Mon-Sat, call store for trading hours ✆ **(012) 345·5198**

Liquor City Crystal Park Cnr Totius & Strand Strs, Crystal Park, Benoni Open Mon-Sat, call store for trading hours ✆ **(011) 969·3700**

Liquor City Dawnpark Cnr Gallahad Way & Hassink Highway, Dawn Park Shopping Centre, Dawn Park, Boksburg Open Mon-Sat, call store for trading hours ✆ **(011) 862·2044**

Liquor City Fourways Cnr Uranium & Buchwillow, Fourways Open Mon–Sat, call store for trading hours ✆ **(011) 465·6910**

Liquor City Geduld Cnr 4th & 6th Streets, Geduld, Springs Open Mon–Sat, call store for trading hours ✆ **(011) 811·5869**

Liquor City Glen Marais Cnr Dann & Veld Strs, Glen Marais Shopping Centre, Kempton Park Open Mon–Sat, call store for trading hours ✆ **(011) 391·6005**

Liquor City Glen Marais Hyper Shop 7 Glen Acres Shopping Centre, Cnr Dann & Monument Strs, Kempton Park Open Mon–Sat, call store for trading hours ✆ **(011) 391·7819**

Liquor City Glen Nerine Shop 1 Glen Nerine Shopping Centre, Cnr Witkoppen & Nerine Drive, Douglas Dale Open Mon–Sat, call store for trading hours ✆ **(011) 658·1706**

Liquor City Highlands Shop 1, Phase 2 Highlands Shopping Centre, Cnr Rabie & Glover Strs, Lyttleton Manor, Centurion Open Mon–Sat, call store for trading hours ✆ **(012) 664·3424**

Liquor City Jean·Len Shop 8 Jealen Shopping Centre, Cnr Jean & Lenchen Strs, Centurion Open Mon–Sat, call store for trading hours ✆ **(012) 663·9389**

Liquor City Joubert Street 15 Joubert Str, Johannesburg Open Mon–Sat, call store for trading hours ✆ **(011) 838·6703**

Liquor City Lambton 6 Piercy Ave, Parkhills Garden, Lambton, Germiston Open Mon–Sat, call store for trading hours ✆ **(011) 827·4566**

Liquor City Leondale Cnr Curry & Blaauwbok Ave, Leondale Open Mon–Sat, call store for trading hours ✆ **(011) 865·1690**

Liquor City Lonehill Shop 1 Lonehill Shopping Centre, Lonehill Boulevard, Lonehill, Sandton Open Mon–Sat, call store for trading hours ✆ **(011) 467·9887**

Liquor City Montana Shop 3 Montana Corner Shopping Centre, Cnr Zambesi & Dr Swanepoel, Montana, Pretoria Open Mon–Sat, call store for trading hours ✆ **(012) 548·7780**

Liquor City Moreleta Cnr Garsfontein & Rubenstein Strs, Moreleta Park, Pretoria Open Mon–Sat, call store for trading hours ✆ **(012) 993·0201**

Liquor City Northpoint Cnr Trichardt & Findel Strs, Impala Park, Boksburg Open Mon–Sat, call store for trading hours ✆ **(011) 864·1672**

Liquor City Princess Crossing Shop 39 Princess Crossing Shopping Centre, Ondekkers Rd, Roodepoort Open Mon–Sat, call store for trading hours ✆ **(011) 768·6813**

Liquor City Radiokop Honey Junction Shopping Centre, Cnr John Vorster & Christiaan de Wet Str, Roodepoort Open Mon–Sat, call store for trading hours ✆ **(011) 675·0493**

Liquor City Rooihuiskraal Shop 72 The Mall @ Reds Shopping Centre, Cnr Hendrik Verwoerd & Rooihuiskraal Ave, Centurion, Pretoria Open Mon–Sat, call store for trading hours ✆ **(012) 656·8835**

Liquor City Ruimsig Cnr Hendrik Potgieter & Peters Str, Ruimsig, Roodepoort Open Mon–Sat, call store for trading hours ✆ **(011) 958·2453**

Liquor City Ryngate Cnr Pretorius & Vlei, Rynfield, Benoni Open Mon–Sat, call store for trading hours ✆ **(011) 969·1559**

Liquor City Satelite Cnr 11th Ave & Charl Cilliers Str, Boksburg North Open Mon–Sat, call store for trading hours ✆ **(011) 917·0791**

Liquor City Selcourt 197 Nigel Rd, Selcourt Open Mon–Sat, call store for trading hours ✆ **(011) 818·2961**

Liquor City Towers Shop 3 Towers Shopping Centre, North Rand Rd, Boksburg North Open Mon–Sat, call store for trading hours ✆ **(011) 823·5221**

Liquor City Triomf Cnr Edward & Muller Strs, Triomf, Johannesburg Open Mon–Sat, call store for trading hours ✆ **(011) 673·1893**

Liquor City V.C. Shop 3 V.C. Centre, 3 Craigholm Str, Dalview, Brakpan Open Mon–Sat, call store for trading hours ✆ **(011) 744·0776**

Liquor City Waverley Cnr Hertzog & Codonia Strs, Waverley, Pretoria Open Mon–Sat, call store for trading hours ✆ **(012) 332·0535**

Liquor City Westwood Shop 7 Westwood Shopping Centre, Atlas Road, Westwood, Boksburg Open Mon–Sat, call store for trading hours ✆ **(011) 894·6567**

Liquor City Woodhill 948 St. Bernard Str, Woodhill Park, Garsfontein Open Mon-Sat, call store for trading hours ✆ **(012) 993·5042**

Liquor Inn Heidelberg 50 Voortrekker Str, Heidelberg Open Mon-Sat, call store for trading hours ✆ **(016) 341·2343**

Liquor World Camaro Square, Boundary Lane & Hartjies Rd, Oakdene Open Mon-Sat, call store for trading hours ✆ **(011) 436·1776**

Lynnridge Wine & Liquor Shop 46 Lynnridge Mall, Lynnwood Rd, Lynnwood Ridge, Pretoria ▪ Mon-Fri 8.30-6 Sat 8-3 Public holidays 9-1 ▪ Closed religious holidays ▪ mickey@glenfairliquor.co.za ▪ www.glenfairliquor.co.za ✆/🖷 **(012) 348·3456**

Makro Centurion 2 Bloukranz St, Highveld Ext 2, Centurion ▪ Mon-Fri 9-6 Sat 8-4 Public holidays 9-4 ▪ E-mail and website as per Makro Port Elizabeth ✆ **(0860) 305·999** 🖷 (0860) 405·999

Makro Crown Mines Cnr Main Reef Rd & Hanover St, Selby, Crown Mines ▪ Mon-Fri 8.30-5.30 Sat 8-4 Public holidays 9-4 ▪ E-mail and website as per Makro Port Elizabeth ✆ **(011) 309·1108** 🖷 (011) 309·1089

Makro Germiston 16 Herman Rd, Meadowdale, Germiston ▪ Moni 9-5.30 Tue-Fri 8.30-5 Sat 8-4 Public holidays 9-4 ▪ E-mail and website as per Makro Port Elizabeth ✆ **(011) 372·0314** 🖷 (011) 453·1698

Makro Wonderboom Stand 95, Lavender West Road, Annlin West, Wonderboom ▪ Mon 9-5.30 Tue-Fri 8.30-5.30 Sat 8-5 Public holidays 9-4 ▪ E-mail and website as per Makro Port Elizabeth ✆ **(0860) 306·999** 🖷 (0860) 406·999

Makro Strubens Valley Cnr Christiaan de Wet & Hendrik Potgieter Rds, Roodepoort ▪ Mon-Fri 8.30-5.30 Sat 8-4 Public holidays 9-4 ▪ E-mail and website as per Makro Port Elizabeth ✆ **(011) 671·8375** 🖷 (011) 671·8480

Makro Woodmead Waterfall Crescent South, Woodmead Ext 5, Woodmead, Sandton ▪ Mon-Fri 9-6 Sat 8-4 Public holidays 9-4 ▪ E-mail and Website as per Makro Port Elizabeth ✆ **(011) 208·9169** 🖷 (011) 208·9092

Norman Goodfellow's 192 Oxford Road, Illovo, Johannesburg ▪ Mon-Fri: 8.30-6 Sat 8.30-2 ▪ goodfellow@icon.co.za ✆ **(011) 788·4814** 🖷 (011) 442·8868

Norman Goodfellow's Hyde Park Lower level, Hyde Park Shopping Centre, Johannesburg ▪ Mon-Fri: 8.30-6 Sat 8.30-2 ▪ goodfellow@icon.co.za ✆ **(011) 325·6462** 🖷 (011) 325·5450

Picardi Rebel Fine Wines & Liquors Village Walk Centre, 125 Rivonia Rd, Sandton ▪ Mon-Fri 9-6.30 Sat 8.30-4 ▪ region.ga@picardirebel.co.za ✆ **(011) 884·2151** 🖷 (011) 884·1067

Rivonia Cellars 349 Rivonia Boulevard, Rivonia ▪ Mon-Fri 9-6 Sat 9-2 Closed religious holidays ▪ rcellars@global.co.za ✆ **(011) 803·6121/2** 🖷 (011) 803·7600

The Wine Room Bryanston Wedge Shopping Centre, Cnr Main & Post House Rds, Bryanston, Johannesburg ▪ Mon-Fri 10-6 Sat 9-3 ▪ wineroom@iafrica.com ▪ www.wineroom.co.za ✆ **(011) 463·2394** 🖷 (011) 706·7198

Ultra Liquors Corlett Drive Cnr Louis Botha Ave & Corlett Drive, Bramley ▪ Mon-Fri 9-6 Sat 9-5 Public holidays 9-2 ▪ Closed Easter Fri, Dec 25 & Jan 1 ▪ corlett@ultraliquors.co.za ▪ www.ultraclub.co.za ✆ **(011) 887·1001/2/3** 🖷 (011) 887·4947

Vintages – The Wine Seller Shop 30 Sandton Square ▪ Daily 9-midnight ▪ Closed Dec 25th/26th, Jan 1st/2nd ▪ thebutchershop@mweb.co.za ▪ www.thebutchershop.co.za ✆ **(011) 784·8676/7** 🖷 (011) 784·8674

Wine Direct Unit F76, Allandale Park, Le Roux Ave, Midrand ▪ Mon-Fri 8-5 ▪ wine@winedirectonline.co.za ▪ www.winedirectonline.co.za ✆ **(011) 315·3088** 🖷 (011) 315·3098

Garden Route

The Lagoon Wine Shop Market Square, Beacon Way, Plettenberg Bay ▪ Mon-Sat 9-8 in season, otherwise 9-6 ▪ lagoonwine@mweb.co.za ✆ **(044) 533·2440** 🖷 (044) 533·2442

Kwazulu-Natal

Buxtons La Cave Liquors buxton@3i.co.za 🖳 (031) 561·1252 ■ Buxtons Village, Umhlanga: Mon-Fri 8-7 Sat 8-5 Closed Good Fri, Dec 25th ✆ **(031) 561·6791/2** ■ La Lucia Mall: Mon-Fri 9-6 ✆ **(031) 572·6073/4** The Pavilion, Westville: Mon-Thu 9-6 Fri 9-7 Sat 8-5 ✆ **(031) 265·0571**

Canaan Cellars 23 Springfield Rd, Winterton ■ Mon-Fri 9-4.30 Sat 9-1 ■ wine@canaancellars.co.za ■ www.canaancellars.co.za ✆/🖳 **(036) 488·1988**

Makro Pietermaritzburg 5 Barnsley Rd, Campsdrift Industrial Park ■ Mon-Fri 9-6 Sat 8-5 Public holidays 9-4 ■ E-mail and website as per Makro Port Elizabeth ✆ **(033) 346·0220** 🖳 (033) 386·8120

Makro Rossburgh 101 Archary Rd (off Edwin Swales VC Drv, Clairwood ■ Hours, e-mail and website as per Makro Pietermaritzburg ✆ **(031) 480·7096** 🖳 (031) 480·7060

Makro Springfield 90 Electron Rd, Springfield ■ Hours, e-mail and website as per Makro Pietermaritzburg ✆ **(031) 203·2800** 🖳 (031) 263·1304

Parklane Cellars 237 Greyling Str, Pietermaritzburg ■ Mon-Fri 9-6 Sat 8.30-1 ■ Closed public holidays ■ min@satweb.co.za ✆ **(033) 394·1691** 🖳 (033) 394·1623

The Village Vineyard Shop 25, Kloof Village Mall, Kloof ■ Mon-Fri 9-7 Sat 8-5 Public holidays 9-5 Closed religious holidays ✆ **(031) 764·6679** 🖳 (031) 764·7196

The Wine Cellar Midlands Meander, Old Main Road (R103), Rosetta ■ Daily 9-4.30 (Wed/Thu during school term by appointment only) ■ winecellar@ebucksmail.com ■ www.thewinecellar.co.za ✆/🖳 **(033) 267·7044**

The Wine Domain 22 Salisbury Ave, Westville, Durban ■ Mon-Fri 9-5.30 Sat 9-2.30 ■ Closed public holidays ■ sales@winedomain.co.za ✆ **(031) 266·4394** 🖳 (031) 266·6124 ■ Also at 137 Windermere Road, Morningside, Durban ■ windermere@winedomain.co.za ✆ **(031) 303·7010** 🖳 (031) 303·7752

Ultra Liquors Tollgate 39 Jan Smuts Highway, Mayville ■ Mon-Fri 9-6 Sat 9-5 Public holidays 9-2 ■ Closed Easter Fri, Dec 25 & Jan 1 ■ tollgate@ultraliquors.co.za ■ www.ultraclub.co.za ✆ **(031) 261·2233/67** 🖳 (031) 261·7980

Ultra Liquors Westville 40A Buckingham Terrace, Westville ■ Mon-Fri 9-6 Sat 9-5 Public holidays 9-2 ■ Closed Easter Fri, Dec 25 & Jan 1 ■ westville@ultraliquors.co.za ■ www.ultraclub.co.za ✆ **(031) 266·4364/60** 🖳 (031) 266·4300

Mpumalanga

Big M Liquor Store Cnr 1st & 3rd Strs, Delmas Open Mon–Sat, call store for trading hours ✆ **(013) 665·2461**

Hi·Octane Store Secunda Plaza, Cnr Ettienne Rossouw & Frans du Toit Rds, Secunda Open Mon–Sat, call store for trading hours ✆ **(017) 634·7033**

Liquor City Nelspruit Shop 14 Nelspruit Crossing Shopping Centre, Cnr N4 & General Dann Pienaar Rd, Nelspruit Open Mon–Sat, call store for trading hours ✆ **(013) 752·2034**

Liquor City White River Shop 2 White River Square, Cnr Kruger Park & Hennie van Till Strs, White River Open Mon–Sat, call store for trading hours ✆ **(013) 750·2184**

Windmill Wine Shop R536 between Hazyview & Sabie ■ Mon-Sat 9-5 ■ scrumpys@mweb.co.za ✆ **(013) 737·8175** 🖳 (013) 737·8966

Northern Cape

Zebrani Liquor City Shop No. 10 Pick 'n Pay Kalahari Centre, 29A Le Roux Str, Upington Open Mon–Sat, call store for trading hours ✆ **(054) 332·3131**

North West

De Wijnwinkel & Deli 4 Leask Str, Wolmaransstad ■ Mon-Sat 9-7 Sun & public holidays 10-4 ✆ **083·262·0387** 🖳 (018) 596·2890

Liquor City Bushveld Bushveld Pick 'n Pay Centre, Cnr Potgieter & Marx Strs, Warmbaths Open Mon–Sat, call store for trading hours ✆ **(014) 736·3215**

Liquor City Euronooi Cnr Lombard Drive & Wilkson, Mooinooi, Brits Open Mon–Sat, call store for trading hours ✆ **(014) 574·3060**

Liquor City Geelhout Cnr Manuka & Wisteria Strs, Geelhout, Rustenburg Open Mon-Sat, call store for trading hours ✆ **(014) 594·1768**

Liquor City Mafikeng 7 Robinson Str, Mafikeng Open Mon-Sat, call store for trading hours ✆ **(018) 381·2326/7**

Liquor City Rustenburg Square Cnr Wolmerans & Von Willigh Strs, Rustenburg Open Mon-Sat, call store for trading hours ✆ **(014) 594·2531**

Liquor City Safari Tuine Cnr Arend & Boekenhout Strs, Safari Tuine, Rustenburg Open Mon-Sat, call store for trading hours ✆ **(014) 533·3467**

Western Cape

Aroma Fine Wine Centres Info@aroma.co.za ✆ **981·4510/0800·224·880** 🖷 981·5411 ▪ Outlets: Constantia (Aroma Alphen Cellars): Old Village Shopping Centre, Spaanschemat Rd ▪ Mon-Thu 9-6 Fri 9-6.30 Sat 8.30-5 ▪ alphen@aroma.co.za ✆ **794·8693** ▪ Canal Walk: Shop 277, Entrance 1 ▪ Aromacwa@aroma.co.za ✆ **551·7511** ▪ Mon-Fri 10-7 Sat 9-5 Sun 10-5 ▪ Somerset Mall, Somerset West: Mon-Fri 9-8 Sat 8.30-5 ▪ Aromasom@aroma.co.za ✆ **852·7551**

Caroline's Fine Wine Cellar Owner Caroline Rillema ▪ carowine@mweb.co.za ▪ www.carolineswine.com ▪ City Bowl: 15 Long Street, Cape Town ▪ Open Mon-Fri 9-6 Sat 9-1 ▪ Closed Sunday & public holidays ✆ **419·8984** 🖷 419·8985 ▪ V&A Waterfront: Shop KWH8 ▪ Open Mon-Sun 9-9 ▪ carowine3@mweb.co.za ✆ **425·5701** 🖷 425·5702 Also see Eat-out section.

Cellar in the City @ Cape Town Tourism Cnr Burg & Castle Streets, Cape Town ▪ Mon-Fri 9-5 Sat 9-1 Closed Dec 25th, Good Fri ▪ cellarinthecity@cape-town.org ✆ **426·2295**

Chapmans Peak Wine & Spirits Main Road, Hout Bay ▪ Mon-Fri 9-6.30 Sat 8.30-4 Closed Sun & religious holidays ▪ lidian@iafrica.com ✆ **790·1088** 🖷 790·1089

Darling Wine Shop on Route 27 Vyge Valley, Darling ▪ Mon-Fri 9-6 Sat 9-5 Sun 10-4 Closed religious holidays ▪ darlingwines@westc.co.za ✆ **(022) 492·3740** 🖷 (022) 492·3524

De Oude Paarl Wijn Boutique 132 Main Road, Paarl ▪ Mon-Sat 10-8 Sun 10-3 ▪ info@deoudepaarl.com ✆ **872·1002** 🖷 872·1003

De Wijngarten Boetiek Main Road, Bonnievale ▪ Mon-Fri 9-5 Sat 9-1 ▪ timjan@lando.co.za ✆ **(023) 616·2367** 🖷 (023) 616·3160

DonVino, The Wine Merchant Shop 581A, Tyger Valley Centre, Willie van Schoor Drive, Bellville ▪ Mon-Fri 9-7 Sat 9-5 ▪ Donvino@mweb.co.za ✆ **914·6952** 🖷 914·6951

Harbour Road Wines Harbour Road, Kleinmond ▪ Mon-Fri 10-5 Sat 9-5 Sun 10-4 ▪ ✆/🖷 **(028) 271·5151**

I Love Wine 40A Main Str, Paarl ▪ Mon-Sat 9-5 ▪ Closed Dec 25/26 & Jan 1 ▪ info@ilovewine.co.za ✆/🖷 **863·2375**

La Cotte Inn Wine Sales 35 Main Rd, Franschhoek ▪ Mon-Fri 9-6.30 Sat 9-1 ▪ info@lacotte.co.za ▪ www.lacotte.co.za ✆ **876·3775** 🖷 876·3036

Main Ingredient Shop 5, Nedbank Centre, 15 Kloof Rd, Sea Point, Cape Town ▪ Mon-Fri 9.30-6 Sat 9.30-1 ▪ Closed Easter Fri/Sat, Dec 25/26, Jan 1 ✆ **439 5169** 🖷 439 3169

Makro Milnerton Montague Drive, Montague Gardens, Cape Town ▪ Mon-Fri 9-6 Sat 8.30-4 Public holidays 9-4 ▪ E-mail and website as per Makro Port Elizabeth ✆ **550·6348** 🖷 551·1637

Makro Ottery Cnr Ottery & Old Strandfontein Rds, Ottery ▪ Mon-Fri 9-6 Sat 8.30-5 Public holidays 9-4 ▪ E-mail and website as per Makro Port Elizabeth ✆ **703·6852** 🖷 703·2508

Manuka Fine Wines Shop C6, Steenberg Village, Reddam Ave, Tokai ▪ Mon-Fri 8-7 Sat 8-5 ▪ Closed Christmas Day, New Year's Day, Good Friday ▪ info@manuka.co.za ▪ www.manuka.co.za

Mooiberge Cnr Annandale Road & R44, Stellenbosch ▪ Daily 8-6 ▪ ✆ **881·3222** 🖷 881·3656

Picardi Rebel Fine Wines & Liquors 218 Main Rd, Claremont ∎ Mon-Thu 9-6 Fri 8.30-6.30 Sat 8.30-5 ∎ ℂ **671·9918** 🖷 683·9025

Riedel@Aroma Old Village Shopping Centre, Spaanschemat Rd, Constantia ∎ Mon-Thu 9-6 Fri 9-6.30 Sat 9-5 ∎ riedel@aroma.co.za ℂ **794·8693** 🖷 794·8694

Spier Wine Centre R310 Lynedoch Rd, Stellenbosch ∎ Daily 9-5 ∎ info@spier.co.za ∎ www.spier.co.za ℂ **809·1100** 🖷 881·3634

Stellenbosch Wine Export Centre 86-88 Dorp Street, Stellenbosch ∎ Mon-Fri 9-7 Sat 9-5 Closed Dec 25 ∎ WineCape@global.co.za ∎ ℂ/🖷 **883·3814**

Steven Rom Wine Merchants & Exporters Checkers Galleria Centre, 76 Regent Rd, Sea Point, Cape Town ∎ wine@stevenrom.co.za ∎ www.stevenrom.co.za ∎ Mon-Fri 9-6 Sat 9-4 ℂ **439·6043** 🖷 434·0401 ∎ Three Anchor Bay: Bay Point, Cnr Beach & Stanley Rds, Cape Town ∎ Mon-Fri 9-7 Sat 9-5 ℂ **434·0001** ∎ New wine depot, The Cape Grape & Wine Co: Polkadraai Rd (M12), Stellenbosch (next to Amani) ℂ **0860·10·30·34** / **905·0290** 🖷 905·0293 ∎ info@capegrape.co.za ∎ www.capegrape.co.za

The Cape Grape & Wine Company See Steven Rom Wine Merchants & Exporters

The Palms World of Wine Palms Décor & Lifestyle Centre, 145 Sir Lowry Road, Cape Town ∎ Mon-Fri 9-5 Sat 10-2 Closed public holidays ∎ info@waterfrontworldofwine.com ∎ www.waterfrontworldofwine.com ℂ **461·7266** 🖷 461·9547

The Vineyard Connection Delvera, cnr R44 & Muldersvlei Rd, Muldersvlei ∎ Mon-Fri 8-5 Sat 9-5 Sun 10-5 ∎ info@vineyardconnection.co.za ∎ www.vineyardconnection.co.za ℂ **884·4360** 🖷 884·4361

The Wine Shop at Constantia Uitsig Constantia Uitsig Farm, Spaanschemat River Rd, Constantia ∎ Mon-Fri 9-5 Sat, Sun & public holidays 10-4 Closed Good Fri, Dec 25 & 26 ∎ thewineshop@uitsig.co.za ∎ www.uitsig.co.za ℂ **794·1810** 🖷 794·1812

34° South Wine Shop Shop 19, Knysna Quays, Waterfront Drive, Knysna ∎ Open restaurant hours ∎ wine@34-south.com ∎ www.34-south.com ℂ/🖷 **(044) 382·7331**

Ultra Liquors George 7 Courtenay Str, George ∎ Mon-Fri 9-6 Sat 9-5 Public holidays 9-2 ∎ Closed Easter Fri, Dec 25 & Jan 1 ∎ george@ultraliquors.co.za ∎ www.ultraclub.co.za ℂ **(044) 874·5514** 🖷 (044) 874·5511

Ultra Liquors Greenpoint 122 Main Rd & Varney Str, Greenpoint ∎ Mon-Fri 9-6 Sat 9-5 Public holidays 9-2 ∎ Closed Easter Fri, Dec 25 & Jan 1 ∎ greenpoint@ultraliquors.co.za ∎ www.ultraclub.co.za ℂ **(021) 434·4847/4302/4838** 🖷 (021) 434·7548

Ultra Liquors Parow 305 Voortrekker Rd, Parow ∎ Mon-Fri 9-6 Sat 9-5 Public holidays 9-2 ∎ Closed Easter Fri, Dec 25 & Jan 1 ∎ parow@ultraliquors.co.za ∎ www.ultraclub.co.za ℂ **(021) 930·2415/6** 🖷 (021) 930·4007

Ultra Liquors Wynberg Cnr Malton & 300 Main Str, Wynberg ∎ Mon-Fri 9-6 Sat 9-5 Public holidays 9-2 ∎ Closed Easter Fri, Dec 25 & Jan 1 ∎ wynburg@ultraliquors.co.za ∎ www.ultraclub.co.za ℂ **(021) 762·5885/1473** 🖷 (021) 761·6005

Vaughan Johnson's Wine & Cigar Shop V&A Waterfront Pierhead, Cape Town ∎ Mon-Fri 9-6 Sat 9-5 Sun 10-5 ∎ vjohnson@mweb.co.za ∎ www.vaughanjohnson.com ℂ **419·2121** 🖷 419·0040

Vino Pronto 42 Orange Str, Gardens, Cape Town ∎ Mon-Fri 10-8 Sat 10-5 ∎ Closed Dec 25th, Jan 1st & Good Fri ∎ vinopronto@global.co.za ℂ **424·5587** 🖷 423·5707

Wine Cellar (incl insulated/secure maturation cellars) Unit 4, Prices Park, Nelson Road, Observatory, Cape Town ∎ Mon-Fri 8-5 Sat by appointment ∎ info@winecellar.co.za ∎ www.winecellar.co.za ℂ **448·4105 / (028) 312·1663**

Wine & Company 7 High St, Hermanus ∎ Mon-Fri 9-6 Sat 9-2 Closed public holidays ∎ winenco@telkomsa.net ℂ **(028) 313·2047** 🖷 (028) 312·4029

Wine Concepts Cardiff Castle, Cnr Kildare Rd & Main St, Newlands, Cape Town. Also at Lifestyle on Kloof, 50, Kloof St, Gardens, Cape Town ∎ Mon-Fri 9-8 Sat 9-5 (doors close hour earlier in winter) Closed religious holidays ∎ Newlands: sales@wineconcepts.co.za ∎ www.wineconcepts.co.za ℂ **671·9030** 🖷 671·9031 Gardens: kloofst@wineconcepts.co.za ℂ **426·4401** 🖷 426·4402

Wine Village-Hermanus Hemel-en-Aarde Village, Cnr Hemel-en-Aarde and Sandbaai crossing, Hermanus ∎ Mon-Fri 9-6 Sat 9-5 Sun 10-3 Closed Easter Fri, Dec 25 ∎ wine@

hermanus.co.za winenews@hermanus.co.za ▪ www.wine-village.co.za 🕾 **(028) 316·3988** 🖷 (028) 316·3989

Online Wine Shops

Cybercellar fiona@cybercellar.co.za ▪ www.cybercellar.co.za 🕾/🖷 **874·2106**

Wine.co.za info@wine.co.za ▪ www.wine.co.za 🕾 **855·0509** 🖷 855·0519

Wine Direct See listing under Gauteng above

Winemail winemail@rsp.co.za ▪ www.winemail.co.za 🕾 **883·9398** 🖷 883·8075

Wineseller-Fine Wine On-Line orders@wineseller.co.za ▪ www.wineseller.co.za 🕾 **905·0290** 🖷 905·0293

Wine with Personality hello@winewithpersonality.co.za ▪ www.winewithpersonality.co.za 🕾 **082·371·5017** 🖷 086·671·8358

Vintages & Styles

■ Recent Cape vintages

SA wines do not exhibit the major vintage variations seen in cooler northern regions such as Burgundy or Bordeaux. There are, nevertheless, perceptible differences from year to year. These, in terms of reds, relate more to relative ageing potential than the declaration of generally poor vintages; whites, if anything, are more prone to vintage variation, summer heatwaves robbing them of freshness and flavour. Dry, hot summers are the norm but a variety of factors make generalisations difficult and dangerous.

2004 Long and late, bedevilled by uneven berry-set and an early aroma-stripping heatwave. Still, cooler dry conditions yielded healthy, elegant, possibly ageworthy wines with lower alcs and yielding tannins. Chardonnay, merlot and shiraz especially promising.

2003 Hailed as an outstanding year, with concentrated, structured and generous reds as well as whites. The general euphoria tempered by some difficulties with late-ripening varieties in certain areas.

2002 Challenging and patchy year, marred by disease and high harvest temperatures. Generally, individual producers' track record rather than variety or terroir should guide the purchase/cellaring decision.

2001 Hot, dry, largely disease-free vintage, yielding some excellent reds — fruity and concentrated, possibly long-lived. White-wine producers who picked between heatwaves delivered flavourful if alcoholic wines.

2000 Another hot year with predictably powerful, concentrated reds, sometimes with big tannins. The best should keep very well. Whites, by contrast, generally less stellar and not for long ageing.

1999 Near-perfect ripening conditions meant fat, alcoholic reds with ripe fruit for earlier drinking. Some attractive, fruity whites from chardonnay, semillon and chenin, but generally not too much excitement.

1998 Excellent vintage. Deep, lusty (sometimes tannic) reds with enough fruit for extended cellaring. Whites somewhat less sexy; some good fuller-bodied versions but even these not for keeping.

1997 One of the coolest and latest on record. Serious problems with downy mildew. Slender, supple (rather than light) reds, the best showing pristine fruit, smooth tannins and elegance. Some excellent, stylish whites with beautiful aromas and balance.

1996 A large crush spoiled, for the most part, by damp weather. Generally awkward reds, lacking fruit and concentration; not for keeping. Ditto whites, which should have consumed by now, except for NLHs, which benefited from botrytis-favouring conditions.

■ Older vintages

1995 Very dry and hot; ripe, big but concentrated reds with good maturation potential. **1994** Hottest, driest vintage in decades; variable quality, though new-clone cabernets and early ripening reds fared well. **1993** Year without serious mishaps; some excellent sauvignons; above-average reds. **1992** Coolish year favouring whites, especially sauvignon; reds also very good to outstanding; first-rate pinotage vintage. **1991** Dry, warm to hot year, favouring early to mid-season ripeners; some exceptionally concentrated, long-lasting reds. **1990** Uneven year, alternately cool and warm; average whites; middling reds with some very characterful examples; good cabs. The **1980s**: as a rough rule, even years usually more favourable for reds (82, 84, 86); uneven years, marginally cooler, favoured whites, but uneven 'white' years 87 and especially 89 produced some remarkable reds. The **1970s**: again, even years generally favoured reds. The best of the 70s was undoubtedly 74; but top wines from some other vintages are delicious now. The **1960s** and earlier years of mainly academic interest now, though some reds have aged astonishingly well.

■ SA wine styles

Blanc de blancs White wine made from white grapes only; also used for champagne and méthode cap classique.

Blanc fumé or **fumé blanc** Dry white from sauvignon, not necessarily finished in wood (nor smoked, smoky).

Blanc de noir A pink wine (shades range from off-white through peach to pink) made from red grapes.

Brut See sugar or sweetness, sparkling wine.

Cap classique See Méthode cap classique.

Cape Blend Evolving term, increasingly used to denote a (red) blend with pinotage, the 'local' grape making up 30%-70% of the assemblage; sometimes simply a blend showing a distinct 'Cape' character.

Carbonated See Sparkling wine.

Cultivar Grape variety (a contraction of 'cultivated variety').

Cuvée French term for the blend of a wine.

Demi-sec See Sugar or sweetness.

Dessert wine A sweet wine, often to accompany the dessert but sometimes pleasurably prior, as in the famous Sauternes/foie gras combo.

Dry to sweet See sugar or sweetness.

Fortified wines Increased in alcoholic strength by the addition of spirits, by SA law to minimum 15% alcohol by volume.

Grand cru See Premier Grand Cru

Jerepiko or **jerepigo** Red or white wine, produced without fermentation; grape juice is fortified with grape spirit, preventing fermentation; very sweet with considerable unfermented grape flavours.

Late Harvest Sweet wine from late -harvested and therefore sweeter grapes. See Sugar or sweetness.

Méthode cap classique (MCC) See Sparkling wine.

Noble Late Harvest (NLH) Sweet dessert wine exhibiting a noble rot (botrytis) character, from grapes infected by the *botrytis cinerea* fungus. This mould, in warm, misty autumn weather, attacks the skins of ripe grapes, causing much of the juice to evaporate. As the berries wither, their sweetness and flavour become powerfully concentrated. SA law dictates that grapes for NLH must be harvested at a minimum of 28° Balling and residual sugar must exceed 50g/ℓ.

Nouveau Term originated in Beaujolais for fruity young and light red, usually from gamay and made by the carbonic maceration method. Bottled a few weeks after vintage to capture the youthful, fresh flavour of fruit and yeasty fermentation.

Perlant, perlé, pétillant Lightly sparkling, carbonated wine.

Port Fortified dessert with improving quality record in Cape since late 1980s, partly through efforts of SA Port Producers' Association which recommends use of word 'Cape' to identify the local product. Following are SAPPA-defined styles: **Cape White**: non-muscat grapes, wood-aged min 6 mths, any size vessel; **Cape Ruby**: blended, fruity, components aged min 6 mths, up to 3 years depending on size of vessel. Average age min 1 year. **Cape Vintage**: fruit of one harvest; dark, full-bodied, vat-aged (any size); **Cape Vintage Reserve**: fruit of one harvest in year of 'recognised quality'. Preferably aged min 1 year, vats of any size, sold only in glass; **Cape Late Bottled Vintage** (LBV): fruit of single 'year of quality', dark, full-bodied, slightly tawny colour, aged 3-6 years (of which min 2 years in oak); **Cape Tawny**: wood-matured, amber-orange (tawny) colour, smooth, slightly nutty taste (white grapes not permitted); **Cape Dated Tawny**: single-vintage tawny.

Premier Grand Cru Unlike in France, not a quality rating in SA —usually an austerely dry white.

Residual sugar See Sugar or sweetness.

Rosé Pink wine, made from red or a blend of red and white grapes. The red grape skins are removed before the wine takes up too much colouring.

Sparkling wine Bubbly, or 'champagne', usually white but sometimes rosé and even red, given its effervescence by carbon dioxide – allowed to escape in the normal winemaking process. **Champagne** undergoes its second fermentation in the bottle. Under an agreement with France, SA does not use the term which describes the sparkling wines from the Champagne area. Instead, **méthode cap classique** (MCC) is the SA term to describe sparkling wines made by the classic method. **Charmat** undergoes its second, bubble-forming fermentation in a tank and is bottled under pressure. **Carbonated** sparklers are made by the injection of carbon dioxide bubbles (as in fizzy soft drinks). See also Sugar or sweetness.

Special Late Harvest (SLH) SA designation for a lighter dessert style wine. There is no longer a legal stipulation for residual sugar content, but if the RS is below 20g/ℓ, the label must state 'extra dry', 'dry', 'semi-dry' or 'sweet', as the case may be. The minimum alcohol content has been raised from 10% to 11% by volume.

Stein Semi-sweet white wine, usually a blend and often confused with steen, a grape variety (chenin blanc), though most steins are made partly from steen grapes.

Sugar or sweetness In still wines: extra-dry or bone-dry wines have less than 2.5g/ℓ residual sugar, undetectable to the taster. A wine legally is dry up to 5g/ℓ. Taste buds will begin picking up a slight sweetness, or softness, in a wine – depending on its acidity – at about 6g/ℓ, when it is still off-dry. By about 8-9g/ℓ a definite sweetness can usually be noticed. However, an acidity of 8-9g/ℓ can render a sweet wine fairly crisp even with a sugar content of 20g/ℓ plus. Official sweetness levels in SA wine are:

Still wines	Sugar (g/ℓ)	Sparkling wines	Sugar (g/ℓ)
Extra dry	$\leq 2,5$	Extra dry/brut	≤ 15
Dry	≤ 5	Dry/sec	15-35
Semi-dry	$5 \leq 12$	Semi-sweet/demi-sec	35-50
Semi-sweet	$< 5 < 30$	Sweet/doux	50
Late Harvest	≥ 20		
Special Late Harvest (SLH)	—		
Natural Sweet (or Sweet Natural)	> 20		
Nobel Late Harvest	> 50		
Naturally dried grape wine (straw wine)	> 30		

Varietal wine From single variety of grape. In SA must consist of 75% or more of the stated grape – but 85% or more if exported.

Vintage In SA primarily used to denote year of harvest. Not a substantive quality classification (a 'vintage' port in Europe means one from an officially declared great port grape year).

Frequently Used Words & Phrases

■ Winetasting terms

Short of a ready description? Here are a few frequently-used words, phrases and explanations that may be helpful. See also Winemaking terms; SA wine styles.

Accessible, approachable Flavours and feel of the wine are harmonious, easily recognised; it is ready to drink.

Aftertaste The lingering flavours and impressions of a wine; its persistence – the longer, the better.

Alcoholic 'Hot' or, in excess, burning character caused by imbalanced or excessive alcohol. Also simply spirituous.

Astringent Mouth-puckering sensation in the mouth, associated with high tannin (and sometimes acid); also bitter, sharp.

Aroma Smells in the bouquet, or nose, especially the odours associated with the grape rather than the winemaking process.

Attack First sensations on palate/nose – pungent, aggressive, quiet etc.

Austere Usually meaning unyielding, sometimes harsh. Sometimes, more favourably, to imply a notable restraint/refinement.

Backbone The wine is well formed, firm, not flabby or insipid.

Baked 'Hot', earthy quality. Usually from scorched/shrivelled grapes which have been exposed too long to the sun, or from too warm a barrel fermentation, especially in some whites.

Balance Desirable attribute. The wine's chief constituents – alcohol, acid, tannin, fruit and wood (where used) – are in harmony.

Bead Bubbles in sparkling wine; a fine, long-lasting bead is the most desirable. See also Mousse.

Big Expansive in the mouth, weighty, full-bodied, as a result of high alcohol or fruit concentration.

Bite or **grip** Imparted by tannins and acids (and alcohol in fortified wines); important in young wines designed for ageing. If overdone can impart undesirable bitterness, harshness or spirity 'glow'.

Bitter Sensation perceived mainly on the back of the tongue, and in the finish of the wine. Usually unpleasant, though an accepted if not immediately admired character of certain Italian wines. Sometimes more positively associated with the taste of a specific fruit or nut, such as cherry-kernel or almond.

Body Fullness on the palate.

Botrytis/ed Exhibits a noble rot/botrytis character, from grapes infected by the *botrytis cinerea fungus.*

Bottle age Negative or positive, depending on context. Positively describes development of aromas/flavours (ie complexity) as wine moves from youth to maturity. Much-prized attribute in fine whites and reds. Negatively, bottle age results in a wine with stale, empty or even off odours.

Buttery Flavour and texture associated with barrel-fermented white wines, especially chardonnays; rich, creamy smoothness.

Charming Usually used in the context of lighter, simpler wines. Sometimes synonymous with 'sweet' (both as in 'sugary' and 'dear').

Claret Another name for a dry red Bordeaux or Bordeaux-like red

Classic Showing characteristics of the classics of Bordeaux, Burgundy etc; usually implying balance, elegance, subtlety.

Coarse Rough, unbalanced tannins, acid, alcohol or oak.

Complexity Strong recommendation. A complex wine has several layers of flavour, usually developing with age/maturation. See Bottle age.

Concentration See Intensity.

Confected Over-elaborately constructed, artificial, forced; also overly sweet.

Corked Wine is faulty; its flavours have been tainted by yeast, fungal or bacterial infections, often but not necessarily from the cork. It smells damp and mouldy in its worst stages – but sometimes it's barely detectable. In a restaurant, a corked wine should be rejected and returned immediately; producers are honour-bound to replace corked wine.

Creamy Not literally creamy, of course; more a silky, buttery feel and texture.

Crisp Refers to acidity. Positively, means fresh, clean; negatively, too tart, sharp.

Deep and depth Having many layers; intense; also descriptive of a serious wine.

Dense Well-padded texture, flavour-packed.

Deposits (also sediment or crust) Tasteless and harmless tartrates, acid crystals or tannin in older red wines. Evidence that wine has not been harshly fined, filtered or cold-stabilised.

Dried out Bereft of fruit, harder constituents remaining; tired.

Earthy Usually positive, wine showing its origins from soil, minerally, damp leaves, mushrooms etc.

Easy Undemanding (and hopefully inexpensive).

Elegant Stylish, refined, 'classic'.

Esters Scents and smells usually generated by alcohols and acids in wine. A wine may be 'estery' when these characteristics are prominent.

Extract An indication of the 'substance' of a wine, expressed as sugar-free or total extract (which would include some sugars). 18g/ℓ would be low, light; anything much above 23g/ℓ in whites is significant; the corresponding threshold for reds is around 30g/ℓ.

Fat Big, full, ample in the mouth.

Finesse Graceful, polished. Nothing excessive.

Finish The residual sensations – tastes and textures – after swallowing. Should be pleasant (crisp, lively) and enduring, not short, dull or flat. See also Length.

Firm Compact, has good backbone.

Flabby Usually, lacking backbone, especially acid.

Flat Characterless, unexciting, lacks acid. Or bubbly which has lost its fizz.

Fleshy Very positive, meaning a wine is well fleshed out with texture and grape flavours.

Flowery Floral, flower-like (i.e. the smell of rose, honeysuckle, jasmine etc). Distinct from 'fruity' (ie smell/taste of papaya, cantaloupe, grape! etc)

Forward rather than shy; advancing in age too; mature.

Fresh Lively, youthful, invigorating. Closely related to the amount of acid in the wine and absence of oxidative character: a big, intensely sweet dessert without a backbone of acidity will taste flat and sickly; enough acid and the taste is fresh and uncloying.

Fruity See floral.

Full High in alcohol and extract.

Gamey Overripe, decadent; not universally unattractive.

Gravel/ly With suggestions of minerally, earthy quality; also firm texture.

Green Usually unripe, sour; sometimes simply youthful.

Grip Often almost literally gripping, firm on palate, in finish. Acid, tannin, alcohol are contributors.

Heady Usually refers to the smell of a wine. High in alcohol; intense; high-toned.

Herbaceous Grassy, hay-like, heathery; can also indicate under-ripeness.

Hollow Lacking substance, flavours.

Honey or **honeyed** Sometimes literally a honey/beeswax taste or flavour; a sign of developing maturity in some varieties or more generally a sign of bottle age.

Hot Burning sensation of alcohol in finish.

Intensity No flab, plenty of driving flavour; also deep colour.

Lean Thin, mean, lacking charm of ample fruit; also, more positively, compact, sinewy.

Lees/leesy Taste-imparting dead yeast cells (with grape skins and other solid matter) remaining with wine in tank/barrel (or bottle in the case of *méthode champenoise* sparkling wines) after fermentation. The longer the wine is 'on its lees' (sur lie) the more richness and flavour it should absorb.

Light/lite Officially wines under 10% alcohol by volume, also light in body (and often short on taste); a health-conscious trend in both reds and whites.

Lively Bouncy, fresh flavours.

Long or **length** Enduring; wine's flavours reverberate in the palate long after swallowing.

Maderised Oxidised and flat; colour is often brownish. Over-mature.

Meaty Sometimes suggesting a general savouriness; but also literally the aroma of meat – raw, smoked etc.

Mousse Fizz in sparkling wines; usually refers also to quality, size and effervescence of the bubbles. See also Bead.

Mouthfeel, **mouthfilling** Texture, feel; racy, crispness (fine with appropriate dishes) or generous, supple, smooth.

Neutral What it says, neither here nor there.

New World Generally implies accessible, bold, often extrovert (in terms of fruit and use of oak). **Old World** embraces terms like subtle, complex, less oaky, more varied and generally more vinous (than fruity). See also Classic.

Oaky Having exaggerated oak aromas/flavours (vanilla, spice, char, woodsmoke etc). Oak balanced by fruit in young wines may lessen with age, but over-oaked young wines (where fruit is not in balance) will become over-oaked old wines.

Palate Combination of flavour, taste and texture of a wine.

Pebbly See Gravelly.

Perfumed or **scented** Strong fragrances (fruity, flowery, animal etc)

Plump Well fleshed in a charming, cherubic way.

Porty Heavy, over-ripe, stewed; a negative in unfortified wine.

Rich Flavourful, intense, generous. Not necessarily sweet.

Robust Strapping, full-bodied (but not aggressive).

Rough Bull-in-a-china-shop wine, or throat sand-papering quality.

Round Well balanced, without gawkiness or jagged edges.

Sharp or **tart** All about acid, usually unbalanced. But occasionally sharpish, fresh wine is right for the occasion.

Short or **quick** Insubstantial wine, leaving little impression.

Simple One-dimensional or no flavour excitement.

Stalky Unripe, bitter, stemmy.

Stewed Over-ripe, cooked, soft, soggy fruit.

Structure Vague word, usually refers to the wine's make up (acid, tannin, alcohol) in relation to its ageing ability; if a wine is deemed to have 'the structure to age' it suggests these principal preservatives are in place.

Stylish Classy, distinguished; also voguish.

Supple Very desirable (not necessarily subtle), yielding, refined texture and flavours. See also Mouthfeel.

Tannic Tannins are prominent in the wine, imparting, positively, a mouth-puckering, grippy, tangy quality; negatively, a harsh, unyielding character.

Tension Racy, nervous fruity-acid play on the palate.

Terpene(s)/terpenoid Strong, floral compounds influencing the aromas of especially riesling, gewürztraminer and the muscats; with bottle-age, terpenes often develop a pungent resinous oiliness.

Texture Tactile 'feel' in the mouth: hard, acidic, coarse and alcoholic; or, smooth, velvety, 'warm'.

Toasty Often used for barrel-fermented and aged wines showing a pleasant biscuity, charry character.

Vegetal Grassy, leafy, herby – in contrast to fruity, flowery, oaky. Overdone, a no-no.

Yeasty Warm bakery smells, often evident in barrel-fermented whites and *méthode champenoise* sparkling wines, where yeasts stay in contact with the wine after fermentation.

■ Winemaking terms

A few brief reference explanations. See also sections Winetasting terms, SA wine styles.

Acid and **acidity** The fresh − or, in excess, sharp or tart − taste of wine. Too little acid and the wine tastes dull and flat. In SA, winemakers are permitted to adjust acidity either by adding acid − at any stage before bottling − or by lowering the acid level with a de-acidifier. See also Volatile acid and Malolactic.

Alcohol Essential component of wine, providing fullness, richness and, at higher levels, sometimes an impression of sweetness. Also a preservative, helping keep wines in good condition. Produced by yeasts fermenting the sugars in the grape. Measured by volume of the total liquid. Most unfortified table wines in SA have between 11% and 14% alc by vol; fortifieds range from about 16% to 21%.

Barrels (**barrel-aged**; **barrel-fermented**) Wines are transferred into barrels to age, pick up oaky flavours etc. When must or fermenting must is put into barrels, the result-ing wine is called barrel-fermented. A barrel or cask is generally a 225-500ℓ oak con-tainer; *barrique* is a French word for a 225ℓ barrel; a pipe, adapted from the Portuguese *pipa*, usually indicates a vessel of 530-630ℓ; vat is a term generally used for larger (2 000-5 000ℓ) wooden vessels.

Bottles While the 750ml (75cl) bottle is now the most widely used size of container for wine, it is by no means the only one. Smaller bottles (375 & 500ml) are popular with restaurants and airlines, and larger sizes are prized by collectors because of their nov-elty value and/or their tendency to promote slower wine ageing. The following are the larger bottle sizes (note: some no longer in production):

Capacity		Bordeaux	Champagne/Burgundy
litres	bottles		
1.5	2	magnum	magnum
3	4	double magnum	Jéroboam
4.5	6	Jéroboam	Rehoboam
6	8	Impériale	Methuselah
9	12	−	Salmanazar
12	16	−	Balthazar
15	20	−	Nebuchadnezzar

Batonnage See Lees.

Biodynamic See Organic.

Blend A wine made from two or more different grape varieties, vintages, vineyards or containers. Some of the world's finest wines are blends.

Carbonic maceration or **maceration carbonique** Method of fermenting wine without first crushing the grapes. Whole clusters with stalks etc are put into closed vat; intracellular fermentation occurs within the grape berries, which then burst.

Chaptalisation Originally French term for the addition of sugar to grape must to raise the alcohol of a wine. Selectively legal in northern Europe, where acid adjustments are not allowed as they are in SA. Winemakers in both hemispheres bend the rules.

Charmat Method of making sparkling wine in a sealed tank (*cuvée close)* under pres-sure. Easier, cheaper than méthode champenoise.

Chips See Oak chips

Cold ferment 'Cold' is a relative term; applied to fermentation of mainly white wines in temperature-controlled tanks, it refers to a temperature around usually 13-16°C. The benefits, especially important in a warm country, include conserving the primary fruit aromas and ensuring fermentation is carried out steadily and thoroughly.

Cold soak or **cold maceration**. Red winemaking method carried out prior to fermenta-tion. Skins and juice are held, usually for a few days, at a sufficiently cool temperature to prevent fermentation. The theory is that this extracts more favourable colour and aromas than after fermentation.

Cold stabilisation Keeping a wine at about -4°C for a week or more to precipitate tartaric acid and 'clean up' the wine, preventing later formation of (harmless) tartrate crystals in bottle. Some winemakers believe this process damages flavour and prefer to avoid it.

Dosage The sugar added to sparkling wine after the second fermentation.

Fermentation The conversion of sugar in grapes into alcohol and carbon dioxide, a function of enzymes secreted by yeasts. Wild yeasts occur in vineyards and wineries, but in modern Cape winemaking cultured yeasts are normally added to secure the process. Beyond about 15% of alcohol, yeasts are overwhelmed and fermentation ceases, although it usually is stopped (for instance by cooling, filtration or the addition of alcohol) before this stage. See also Malolactic.

Filtration Removes last impurities including **yeast** cells. Done excessively, can thin a wine. Some traditionalists bottle without cold- or protein-stabilisation or filtration.

Fining and **protein stabilisation** Fining is ridding wine of suspended particles by adding substances that attract and draw the particles from the wine.

Free run After grapes have been de-stalked and crushed, juice runs freely.

Garage wine Generic term for wine made in minuscule quantities, sometimes literally in a garage; grower of such wine sometimes called a *garagiste*.

Glycerol Minor product of alcoholic fermentation; from the Greek for sweet. Has an apparent sweetening effect on even dry wines and also gives a viscous, mouthfilling character.

Icewine Sweet, concentrated wine from grapes picked and pressed while frozen. Not a recognised category for SA wine production.

Leafroll virus Virus (or complex of viruses), widespread throughout the winegrowing world, which causes the vine to perform below its potential and thereby produce wine which is lower in colour, body and flavour than that derived from virus-free or 'cleaned-up' plants.

Lees Spent yeast cells and other matter which collect at the bottom of any container in winemaking. Yeast autolysis, or decomposition, can impart richness and flavour to a wine, sometimes referred to as leesy. Lees stirring or *batonnage* involves mixing the bed of lees in a barrel or tank through the wine, which is said to be sur lie; it is employed primarily on barrel-fermented white wines. The main effects of mixing lees and wine are to prevent off-odours developing from lack of oxygen, to limit the amount of wood tannin and flavour extracted, and to increase flavour.

Malolactic fermentation (malo) Occurs when bacteria convert malic into lactic acids. This reduces the acidity of a wine, a normal and healthy process, especially in reds — provided, of course, it occurs before bottling.

Maturation Ageing properties are closely related to tannin and/or fixed acid content of a wine. A relatively full red wine with tannin has lasting power. With age, it may develop complexity, subtlety and smooth mellowness. Lighter wines with lower tannins are drinkable sooner but probably will not reach the same level of complexity. A number of Cape whites, especially chardonnays and rieslings, now mature well over several years, but most are best drunk in their fruity youth, up to 18 months.

Méthode champenoise Classic method of making champagne by inducing secondary fermentation in the bottle and producing fine bubbles. Due to French restrictions on terminology, Cape sparkling wines made in this way are called méthode cap classique (MCC).

Micro-oxygenation Relatively new (1990) technique enabling introduction of precise, controlled doses of oxygen to must/wine. Advocates claim softer tannins, more stable colours and other advantages.

Oak chips, either in older barrels or stainless steel tanks, are used increasingly in SA, as are oak **staves**. Still frowned on by some purists, the 'additives' approximate the flavour effects of a new barrel, far more cheaply, more easily handled.

Oak-matured See Barrels.

Organic viticulture/winemaking Increasingly popular alternative to 'conventional' or 'industrialised' winegrowing, emphasising natural and sustainable farming methods and cellar techniques. A variant is biodynamic viticulture, influenced by anthroposophy, focused on improving wine quality through harmony with nature and its rhythms.

Oxidation Change (usually for the worse) due to exposure to air, in whites often producing dark yellow or yellowish colour (called maderisation), altering, 'ageing' the taste. Controlled aeration is used to introduce acceptable and desirable development in wine.

pH A chemical notation, used in winemaking and evaluation. The pH of a wine is its effective, active acidity – not in volume but by strength or degree. The reading provides a guide to a wine's keepability. The optimum pH in a wine is somewhere between 3.1 and 3.4 – which significantly improves a wine's protection from bacterial spoilage, so permitting it to mature and develop if properly stored.

Racking Drawing or pumping wine off from one cask or tank to another, to leave behind the deposit or lees.

Reductive Wine in an unevolved, unoxidised state is said to be 'reductive'; usually with a tight, sometimes unyielding character. The absence of air (in a bottled wine) or the presence of substantial sulphur dioxide (anti-oxidant) levels, will inhibit both oxidation and reduction processes, which are linked and complementary.

Skin contact After crushing and de-stemming, white grapes may be left for a period with the juice, remaining in contact with skins (before being moved into the press, from which the grape juice is squeezed). Some winemakers believe the colours and flavours in and under the grape skins should be maximised in this way; others believe extended (or any) contact can lead to coarseness, even bitterness.

Sur lie See Lees.

Tannin Vital preservative in wine, which derives primarily from the grape skins. Necessary for a red wine's longevity. A young wine's raw tannin can give it a harshness, but no red wine matures into a great one without tannin, which itself undergoes change, combines with other substances and mellows. Tannin leaves a mouth-puckering dryness about the gums, gives 'grip' to a wine. A wooded wine will also contain some wood tannin. Various types or qualities of tannin are increasingly commented on.

Tartrates Harmless crystals formed by tartaric acid precipitating in non-cold- stabilised wine. Because of lack of public acceptance, usually avoided through cold stabilisation.

Unfiltered See Filtration.

Virus or **virused** See Leafroll.

Volatile acid (VA) The part of the acidity which can become volatile. A high reading indicates a wine is prone to spoilage. Recognised at high levels by a sharp, 'hot', vinegary smell. In SA, most wines must by law be below 1.2g/ℓ of VA; in practice, the majority are well below 1g/ℓ.

Whole-bunch pressing or **cluster pressing** Some SA cellars use this age-old process of placing whole bunches directly in the press and gently squeezing. The more usual method is to de-stem and crush the grapes before pressing. Whole-bunch pressing is said to yield fresher, cleaner must, and wine lower in polyphenols which, in excess, tend to age wines faster and render them coarser.

Wood-fermented/matured See Barrels.

Yeasts Micro-organisms that secrete enzymes which convert or ferment sugar into alcohol. See fermentation.

Touring Wine Country

■ Wine routes, trusts & associations

For localised information about regional official wine routes and wineries, contact these organisations:

Breedekloof Wine and Tourism ✆ (023) 349·1791 🖷 (023) 349·1720
info@breedekloof.co.za ▪ www.breedekloof.co.za

Calitzdorp Wine Route ✆ (044) 213·3775 🖷 (044) 213·3302
calitzdorpinfo@kannaland.co.za ▪ www.calitzdorp.co.za

Constantia Wine Route ✆ (021) 794·5190 (Lars Maack) 🖷 (021) 794·1351
ars@buitenverwachting.co.za

Darling Wine Experience ✆ (022) 492·3361 🖷 (022) 492·3430
mclaughlin@worldonline.co.za ▪ www.darlingtourism.co.za

Durbanville Wine Valley Association ✆ 083·310·1228 🖷 (021) 976·1467
nitida@mweb.co.za

Franschhoek See Vignerons de Franschhoek

Helderberg Wine Route ✆ (021) 852·6166 🖷 (021) 852·6168
hwr@mweb.co.za ▪ www.helderbergwineroute.co.za

Little Karoo Wine Route ✆/🖷 (028) 572·1284 (Ellen Marais)
info@kleinkaroowines.co.za ▪ www.kleinkaroowines.co.za

Northern Cape Wine Association ✆ (054) 337·8800 (Gabi Gosling)
🖷 (054) 332·4408 ▪ marketing@owk.co.za

Olifants River Wine Route ✆/🖷 (027) 213·3126/083·652·3158
olifantsrivwineroute@kingsley.co.za

Outeniqua Wine Route ✆/🖷 (044) 873·4212/072·833·8223
harpie@xsinet.co.za

Paarl Vintners ✆ (021) 863·4886 🖷 (021) 863·4883
paarl@wine.co.za ▪ www.paarlwine.co.za

Rawsonville Wine Route See Breedekloof Wine & Tourism

Robertson Wine Valley ✆ (023) 626·3167/083·701·5404 🖷 (023) 626·1054
robertsonvalley@wine.co.za ▪ www.robertsonwinevalley.co.za

Stellenbosch Wine Route ✆ (021) 886·4310 🖷 (021) 886·4330
info@wineroute.co.za ▪ www.wineroute.co.za

Swartland Wine Route ✆ (022) 487·1133 🖷 (022) 487·2063
swartlandinfo@westc.co.za ▪ www.swartlandwineroute.co.za

Tulbagh Wine Route ✆/🖷 (023) 230·1348
info@tulbaghwineroute.com ▪ www.tulbaghwineroute.com

Vignerons de Franschhoek ✆ (021) 876·3062 🖷 (021) 876·2964
franschhoek@wine.co.za ▪ www.franschhoekwines.co.za

Walker Bay Wine Wander ✆ (028) 316·3988 🖷 (028) 316·3989
wine@hermanus.co.za

Wellington Wine Route ✆ (021) 873·4604 🖷 (021) 873·4607
welltour@mweb.co.za ▪ www.visitwellington.com

Worcester Winelands ✆ (023) 342·8710 🖷 (023) 342·2294
manager@worcesterwinelands.co.za ▪ www.worcesterwinelands.co.za

---

■ Winelands tourism offices

For additional accommodation options, brochures and local advice, contact the information offices and/or publicity associations of the wine areas you plan to visit.

Franschhoek Vallée Tourisme ✆ (021) 876·3063 🖷 (021) 876·276
info@franschhoek.org.za ▪ www.franschhoek.org.za

Helderberg Tourism Bureau ✆ (021) 851·4022 🖷 (021) 851·1497
info@helderbergtourism.co.za ▪ www.helderbergtourism.co.za

Hermanus Tourism Bureau ✆ (028) 312·2629 📠 (028) 313·0305
  infoburo@hermanus.co.za
McGregor Tourism Bureau ✆/📠 (023) 625·1954
  mcgregortour@telkomsa.net ▪ www.mcgregor.org.za
Northern Cape Tourism ✆ (053) 832·2657 📠 (053) 831·2937
  tourism@northerncape.org.za ▪ www.northerncape.org.za
Paarl Tourism Bureau ✆ (021) 872·4842 📠 (021) 872·9376
  paarl@cis.co.za ▪ www.paarlonline.com
Robertson Tourism Bureau ✆ (023) 626·4437 📠 (023) 626·4290
  info@robertson.org.za ▪ www.robertsonr62.com
Stellenbosch Tourism Info Bureau ✆ (021) 883·3584 📠 (021) 883·8017
  info@stellenboschtourism.co.za ▪ www.stellenboschtourism.co.za
Wellington Tourism Bureau ✆ (021) 873·4604 📠 (021) 873·4607
  welltour@mweb.co.za ▪ www.visitwellington.com
West Coast Peninsula Tourism Bureau ✆ (022) 714·2088 📠 (022) 714·4240
  bureau@kingsley.co.za
Worcester Tourism Bureau ✆ (023) 348·2795 📠 (023) 347·4678
  tourism@worcesterwinelands.co.za ▪ www.worcestertourism.co.za

■ Specialist wine tours

Adamastor & Bacchus John Ford conducts tailor-made tours for small groups to wine farms not usually accessible to the public. Tours can be conducted in German and Norwegian. ▪ johnford@iafrica.com ✆ **439·5169/083·229·1172** 📠 439·3169

Amber Wine Tours Lesley Cox specialises in tailor-made, private wine tours by luxury vehicle for small groups or individuals. Only registered guides with wine knowledge conduct the tours. ▪ amberwines@wol.co.za ▪ www.amberwines.co.za ✆ **083·448·7016**

Gourmet Wine Tours Exploratory tours for individuals or small groups covering principal Cape wine areas and properties, plus meals in top restaurants. By Stephen Flesch, registered guide and Cape Town Slow Food Convivium secretary. Some French, German spoken. ▪ sflesch@iafrica.com ▪ www.gourmetwinetours.co.za ✆ **705·4317/083·229·3581** 📠 **706·0766**

Gudrun Grünewald Conducts tailor-made, personalised wine and gourmet tours to carefully-selected wine farms and restaurants. German, English and Afrikaans spoken. happyholiday@adept.co.za ▪ www.happyholiday.co.za ✆/📠 **880 1201/082·699·3098**

It Just Did! The wine tourism specialists. Memories and fun are all part of their personalised private wine tours. Meet the winemakers. Township tastings, harvest tours, wine and river tastings and much more. ▪ info@itjustdid.com ✆ **082·390·6092**

Judy's Tours Judy Krohn, experienced (RSA, Europe & Australia) specialist registered wine guide personally conducts private tours to all Cape wine regions. Day or overnight itineraries to suit individual requests, emphasis on fine food and wine (German & English). ▪ judyk@zsd.co.za ✆ **084·500·1941/851·4205**

Ocean & Vine Tours Wayne Donaldson, registered specialist guide offers private, tailor-made tours to all of the Cape wine regions. Wine, golf and fly-fishing combination options also offered. ▪ wayne@wine.co.za ✆ **082·900·6999**

Redwood Tours Daily wine tours by Keith van der Schyff, specialist guide who is privileged to live on a wine farm in Stellenbosch. Private and tailor-made tours to suit all tastes and interests. ▪ rwt@adept.co.za ▪ www.redwoodtours.co.za

Southern Destinations Vanessa Ratcliffe and her team add innovative and creative flair to a Cape winelands experience. Wine- and food-intensive itineraries designed for those travelling solo, with friends, or as a corporate group. French spoken. ▪ vanessa@ southerndestinations.co ▪ www.southerndestinations.com ✆ **422·3233/083·309·3331**

The Capevine Special-interest tour operator Annette Stals organises the consummate winelands experience for groups of 7 or more, to facilitate your enjoyment of wine, architecture, history, gardens, regional cuisine and beautiful scenery. ▪ capevine@iafrica.com ℂ 913·6611 🖷 913·4580

Vineyard Ventures First — and, for a long time, only — specialist wine tour company. Gillian Stoltzman (082·893·5387) and Glen Christie (082·920·2825) use their matchless contacts and all-inclusive costing to customise sipping-safaris to visitors' tastes — off the tourist beat. ▪ vinven@iafrica.com ▪ www.vineyardventures.co.za ℂ 434·8888 🖷 434·9999

Vintage Cape Tours Private and tailor-made tours for the discerning food and wine lover, conducted by specialist wine guides in English, German, French and Afrikaans. ▪ info@vintagecape.co.za ▪ www.vintagecape.co.za ℂ 872·9252/082·553·8928/082·656·3994 🖷 862·1484

Vintour Helmut Feil, qualified guide with 37 years' experience in the wine industry, offers small tailor-made tours for the serious wine and food connoisseur or professional, in German or English. ▪ helmut@vintour.co.za ℂ/🖷 976·5709/083·626·0029

Walker Bay Wine Destination Full and half-day tours to the Walker Bay wine region and surrounds. Twenty-five of SA's highly rated wine producers, at the centre of the fynbos kingdom, on the edge of the best whale watching town in the world. ▪ wine@hermanus.co.za ℂ (028) 316·3988

Wellington Wine Walk Three-day guided hiking trail through the Wellington winelands, including accommodation at comfortable guest houses and luggage portage between overnight stops. Enjoy wine, olive and cheese tastings en route. ▪ judy@winescapetours.co.za ℂ 083·313·8383 🖷 461·5555

Window on Cape Wine With more than 50 new wine producers this year, Meryl Weaver offers up to date, quality and tailor-made 'edutainment'. Full/half-day tours; tutored wine tastings for corporate or tour groups. Registered specialist guide, CWM student and wine lecturer. ▪ mvweaver@iafrica.com ℂ/🖷 866·1002/082·782·5198

Wine Desk Exclusive wine tour specialists, offering advice on what to do, where to go and where to stay in the winelands. Complimentary tastings daily. Situated at Waterfront Information Centre and Visitor's Centre at Canal Walk. ℂ 405·4550/082·822·6127 winedesk@tourcapetown.com ligia@winedesk.co.za ▪ www.winedeskwaterfront.co.za

▦ Stay-overs in the winelands and Cape Town

Featured below are some guest lodges, hotels, country inns, B&Bs and self-catering cottages in the winelands, many of them on wine farms (look for the 🛏 symbol beside the individual entries in the A-Z section of this guide). Unless stated to the contrary, all speak English and Afrikaans, have parking, gardens/-terraces, swimming pools and televisions. Rates are for standard double rooms unless otherwise specified — for example per person (pp) or breakfast included (B&B). Establishments new to the guide are indicated in bold type below. **Note: the stay-overs featured here describe their own attractions.**

Index of stay-overs
Listed alphabetically, with region. New names in **bold**.

Iris Cottage . . . . Franschhoek
Ivory Heights Gst
  House . . . . Somerset West
Kleine Zalze Lodges . . . . Stellenbosch
Klippe Rivier Cntry Hse . . Swellendam
Knorhoek Guest
  House . . . . Stellenbosch
La Bonne Auberge . . . . Somerset West
La Couronne Hotel . . . . . Franschhoek
La Fontaine Gst Hse . . Franschhoek
La Maison Bleue . . . . Franschhoek
La Petite Ferme . . . . Franschhoek
L'Avenir Wine Estate
  Gst Hse . . . . Stellenbosch
Le Manoir de Brendel . Franschhoek
Lemberg Gst Hse . . . . . . Tulbagh
Marianne Wine Farm
  Guest Apartments . . . Stellenbosch
Mimosa Lodge . . . . Montagu
Montagu Cntry Hotel . . Montagu
Montmartre Luxury
  Lodges . . . . Franschhoek
Mooi Bly . . . . Paarl
Muratie Wine Estate . . Stellenbosch
Natte Valleij Farm . . . . . . Stellenbosch
NH The Lord Charles
  Hotel . . . . Somerset West
Oak Tree Lodge . . . . . . Paarl

Ons Genot Cntry
  House . . . . Stellenbosch
Papyrus House . . . . Stellenbosch
Plumwood Inn . . . . Franschhoek
Pontac Manor Hotel . . . . . Paarl
Rijk's Cntry Hotel . . . . . Tulbagh
Riviera House . . . . Hermanus
Schulphoek Seafront
  Guesthouse . . . . Hermanus
Somerton Manor . . . . Somerset West
Sonop Gst Hse . . . . Paarl
Steenberg Hotel . . . . Constantia
Summerwood Gst Hse . . . Stellenbosch
The Cellars-Hohenort
  Hotel . . . . Constantia
The Old Mill Lodge . . . . . . McGregor
The Retreat at
  Groenfontein . . . . Calitzdorp
The Village Hotel
  at Spier . . . . Stellenbosch
Tierhoek Cottages . . . . . . Robertson
Weltevrede Wine Farm
  Guest Cottages . . . . . . Bonnievale
Weltevrede Guest Farm . . Robertson
Zandberg Farm Cntry
  Hse . . . . Somerset West
Zevenwacht Cntry Inn . . . Kuils River

Bonnievale

Weltevrede Wine Estate Guest Cottages Weltevrede Wine Estate, Bonnievale ▪ R200–R320 per cottage ▪ Major credit cards accepted ▪ No pool, TV ▪ Owners Philip & Lindelize Jonker ▪ info@weltevrede.com ▪ www.weltevrede.com ✆ **(023) 616·2141** 🖷 (023) 616·2460

   Two self-catering cottages situated on Weltevrede Wine Estate. Braai or sip sundowners on the stoep, overlooking the vista of vineyards and the Breede River winding through it. In winter there is a fireplace or wood stove to warm you. This is a bird-watcher's paradise with walks through the vineyards and along the banks of the river. Bring your own canoe, mountain bike or fishing rod for bass. Breakfast on request. The Weltevrede Restaurant is open for lunch in summer. Come and enjoy the romance of living on a wine estate for a few days. (See also Eat-out section for Under the Vines Bistro and A-Z section.)

Bot River

Beaumont Guest Cottages Compagnes Drift Farm, Main Road, Bot River ▪ From R190–R300 pp ▪ Major credit cards accepted ▪ Self-catering ▪ No pool/TV ▪ Owners Beaumont family ▪ beauwine@netactive.co.za ▪ www.beaumont.co.za, www.wheretostay.co.za ✆ **(028) 284·9194 / -9370 a/h** 🖷 (028) 284·9733

   The historic farm Compagnes Drift (circa early 1700s) in the heart of the Bot River valley is home to internationally renowned Beaumont wines. Enjoy the tranquil ambience of a bygone era in the country comfort of the Mill House and Peppertree Cottage — an authentic farm experience which offers much to wine tasters, bird watchers, artists, ramblers, horse riders and those who simply need a guaranteed quiet 'getaway'. ▪ (See also A-Z section.)

Calitzdorp

The Retreat at Groenfontein Groenfontein Farm, 20 km NE of Calitzdorp, 59 km NW of Oudtshoorn ▪ R450 pp DB&B, luxury rooms R500–R550 pp DB&B ▪ Visa & MasterCard accepted ▪ French, German, Italian & Swedish spoken ▪ Owners Grant & Marie Burton ▪ groenfon@iafrica.com ▪ www.groenfontein.com ✆/🖷 **(044) 213·3880**

Victorian farmhouse, 7 comfortable en-suite rooms, lovely lounge and dining room overlooking sweeping lawns and majestic Swartberg. Three- and 4-star graded accommodation. Winner AA Accommodation Award 2003 & 2004. Grant and Marie pamper guests with hearty breakfasts and tasty dinners. Enjoy peaceful walks or challenging trails, or simply relax at the pool and let the peace and silence soak into your soul.

Constantia

Constantia Uitsig Country Hotel Spaanschemat River Road, Constantia ▪ R2 800 per room B&B ▪ Major credit cards accepted ▪ Cricket oval ▪ Conference venue ▪ Owners David & Marlene McCay ▪ reservations@uitsig.co.za ▪ www.uitsig.co.za ✆ **(021) 794·6500** 🖷 (021) 794·7605

Set amongst the vineyards of a private wine estate in the shadow of Table Mountain, the highly acclaimed hotel is just 20 minutes from the city centre and Waterfront. Renowned for its atmosphere of quiet elegance and gracious hospitality. The hotel has 16 individually decorated garden rooms, each with a private patio and sweeping views of the Constantia Valley. (See also Eat-out section for Constantia Uitsig & La Colombe, and A-Z section.)

Hampshire House 10 Willow Road, Constantia ▪ R700 per room B&B ▪ Visa & MasterCard accepted ▪ Air-conditioning ▪ Owners Ricky & Carole Chapman ▪ stay@hampshirehouse.co.za ▪ www.hampshirehouse.co.za ✆ **(021) 794·6288** 🖷 (021) 794·2934

Set in the Constantia wine valley, this 4-star guesthouse was a finalist in the AA Accommodation Awards three years running. It provides the perfect base from which to explore the Cape Peninsula, with easy motorway access to Table Mountain, the Waterfront, winelands, beaches and local restaurants. Five individually decorated en-suite bedrooms have king-sized or twin ¾ beds, satellite TV, CD player, hairdryer and many other amenities. Swimming pool and secure off-street parking. English and continental buffet breakfasts served. The Hampshire Arms is a cosy pub with an interesting winelist.

Steenberg Hotel Steenberg Estate, Tokai Road, Constantia Valley ▪ From R1 530 per room B&B ▪ Major credit cards accepted ▪ Air-conditioning ▪ Relaxation room & gym ▪ German spoken ▪ Owner Mantis Collection ▪ info@steenberghotel.com ▪ www.steenberghotel.com ✆ **(021) 713·2222** 🖷 (021) 713·2251

The 5-star Steenberg Hotel is situated on the Cape's oldest wine farm, a mere 20 minutes from Cape Town. Legendary elegance and traditions of the 17th century combine with the most refined luxuries and conveniences of a modern boutique hotel. Catharina's (see Eat-out section) is open for breakfast, lunch and dinner 7 days a week. The restaurant is located in the original winery built in 1682 and now tastefully redecorated. Gourmet cuisine served in international fine-dining style. Cigar lounge. (See also A-Z section.)

The Cellars-Hohenort Hotel 93 Brommersvlei Road, Constantia ▪ R2 500 B&B ▪ Major credit cards accepted ▪ Air-conditioning ▪ French, German, Italian & Xhosa spoken ▪ Owner Liz McGrath ▪ cellars@relaischateaux.com ▪ www.collectionmcgrath.com ✆ **(021) 794·2137** 🖷 (021) 794·2149

The hotel is next to the world-famous Kirstenbosch Botanical Gardens and minutes away from the Constantia wine route. It has 9 acres of splendid landscaped gardens and a small vineyard. In its renaissance as one of the great country house hotels of the Cape, the 5-star Cellars-Hohenort is a member of the International Relais & Châteaux Association. (See also Eat-out section for The Greenhouse & The Cape Malay Restaurant.)

Durbanville

D'Aria Guest Cottages D'Aria Vineyards, Race Course Road, Durbanville ▪ R520 per cottage ▪ Major credit cards accepted ▪ Air-conditioning ▪ Owner D'Aria ▪ living@daria.co.za ▪ www.daria.co.za ✆ **(021) 975·5802** 🖷 (021) 975·5740

An award-winning restaurant, D'Aria Poplars Restaurant, D'Aria Sensorium Function Venue and 12 guest cottages situated among the vineyards, all await you at D'Aria. The cottages are semi self-catering units, each with their own braai area on the verandah. Each cottage offers the comfort of air-conditioned rooms, telephones, TV with 6 channels, heated towel rails in the bathrooms, as well as a mini-bar fridge. Follow your heart and experience it yourself. (See also Eat-out section for D'Aria Poplars Restaurant.)

Franschhoek

Akademie Street Guest Houses 5 Akademie Street, Franschhoek ■ R600–R1 700 per room B&B ■ Visa, MasterCard & American Express accepted ■ Air-conditioning ■ Owners Katherine & Arthur Mc William Smith ■ info@aka.co.za ■ www.aka.co.za ✆ **(021) 876·3027** 🖶 (021) 876·3293

Five-star, 2004 highly commended in AA Accommodation 'South Africa's Best' awards, the guest houses are within easy, safe walking distance to most of the great village restaurants. Each house has its own private garden and pool. They all join onto pathways leading through lush gardens to the Cape Dutch home, Twyfeling, where breakfasts are served under a vine-covered patio. Oortuiging, the restored 1860s cottage, has two private bedrooms and sleeps three. Vreugde is an intimate garden suite which sleeps two. Gelatenheid, with wide balconies and superb mountain views, is a spacious double-storey villa which sleeps two.

Auberge Clermont Robertsvlei Road, Franschhoek ■ R980 per room B&B ■ Major credit cards accepted ■ Owner Penny Gordon ■ clermont@mweb.co.za ■ www.clermont.co.za ✆ **(021) 876·3700** 🖶 (021) 876·3701

Delightful Provençal-style auberge in stunning setting surrounded by chardonnay vineyards and ancient oaks. Lavender, rosemary and rose bushes perfume the air. Beautiful pool and tennis court, and great vineyard walks. Six stylish rooms, splendid en-suite bathrooms plus a three-bedroom self-catering villa beside a formal French garden. Associate guesthouse of the award-winning Haute Cabrière Cellar Restaurant (see also Eat-out section for Haute Cabrière Cellar Restaurant and French Connection Bistro).

Auberge du Quartier Français cnr Berg & Wilhelmina streets, Franschhoek ■ R2 500 ■ Major credit cards accepted ■ Air-conditioning ■ French spoken ■ Owner Susan Huxter ■ res@lqf.co.za ■ www.lequartier.co.za ✆ **(021) 876·2151** 🖶 (021) 876·3105

Embraced by majestic mountain views, Le Quartier Français lies at the heart of the enchanting village of Franschhoek, Cape winelands. Six luxurious suites, two with private pool, and 15 elegantly decorated en-suite bedrooms overlook a central garden. Here, the old world meets the new in a marriage of sophistication and comfort. In the famous restaurant, experience award-winning cuisine from Margot Janse — 2004 Top Chef South Africa. (See also Eat-out section for Le Quartier Français Restaurant, Bread & Wine and Delicious.)

Burgundy Bourgogne Manor House & Cottages Burgundy Bourgogne Farm, Excelsior Road, Franschhoek ■ From R342-R1 140 pp ■ Visa & MasterCard accepted ■ Owner Trevor Kirsten ■ burgundybourgogne@saol.com ■ www.burgundybourgogne.co.za ✆ **(021) 876·4623** 🖶 (021) 876·3817

Need a refreshing break where you can savour true Huguenot history? Set amidst olive orchards and centuries old oaks, Burgundy Bourgogne Manor House & Cottages charmingly recapture the style and atmosphere of life on a 1694 Huguenot wine farm. Furnished to perfection, these homesteads incorporate all the amenities you'll need as you relish the tranquillity and peace of Franschhoek's picturesque valley and mountains. (See also Eat-out section for Haute Cabrière Cellar Restaurant and French Connection Bistro.)

Franschhoek Country House & Villas Main Road, Franschhoek ■ From R495-R995 pp sharing B&B ■ Major credit cards accepted ■ Air-conditioning ■ Owner Jean-Pierre Snyman ■ info@fch.co.za ■ www.fch.co.za ✆ **(021) 876·3386** 🖶 (021) 876·2744

Situated in the picturesque valley of Franschhoek, this upmarket country house offers luxury and indulgence. The restored manor house has 14 rooms and suites with all the expected luxuries and amenities. The newly built villa suites offer the most luxurious stay in Franschhoek. A swimming pool is surrounded by gardens with beautiful mountain vistas. The in-house Monneaux Restaurant, famous for its exquisite menu and wine selection, is voted as one of South Africa's best! (See also Eat-out section for Monneaux Restaurant.)

Grande Provence Guest House Grande Provence Estate, Main Road, Franschhoek ■ R2 000 per room B&B ■ Major credit cards accepted ■ Air-conditioning ■ Owner Grande

Provence Properties Ltd ▪ guesthouse@agustawines.co.za ▪ www.agustawines.co.za ℭ **(021) 876·2163** 🖷 (021) 876·4204

Grande Provence Estate is just a 5-minute drive from the charming village of Franschhoek and yet easily a destination in its own right. Guests find it hard to leave the grounds, let alone to return to the real world once their stay draws to a close. Housed within a small complex of historic Cape Dutch buildings, guests enjoy every comfort, privacy and a gracious style of hospitality. (See also Eat-out section for Grande Provence Restaurant and A-Z section for Agusta Wines.)

Iris Cottage 56 Akademie Street, Franschhoek ▪ From R500 per room (low season) to R800 per room (high season) ▪ Self-catering ▪ Visa & MasterCard accepted ▪ Dutch & German spoken ▪ Owners Tom & Heidi Clode ▪ iris@plumwoodinn.com ▪ www.cape-venues. co.za/iris.htm ℭ **(021) 876·3883** 🖷 (021) 876·3803

Charming Cape Dutch cottage in tranquil part of Franschhoek village, just a short walk from the art galleries, restaurants and shops. Two bedrooms, kitchen, lounge with fireplace and patio opening onto the verandah. Flower-filled garden and delightful pool. Iris Cottage is the perfect place from which to enjoy all the area has to offer.

La Couronne Hotel Dassenberg Road, Franschhoek ▪ From R1 100 per room B&B ▪ Major credit cards accepted ▪ Air-conditioning ▪ Gym ▪ Health & beauty facility ▪ German & Xhosa spoken ▪ Owners Erwin Schnitzler & Miko Rwayitare ▪ reservations@lacouronnehotel.co. za ▪ www.lacouronnehotel.co.za ℭ **(021) 876·2770** 🖷 (021) 876·3788

La Couronne, 'the crown' of Franschhoek, is positioned in what is undoubtedly one of the most beautiful settings in the world. This small luxury hotel, set among the vines, offers a complete winelands experience. Activities in the area include horse riding, fly-fishing, hiking, walking, mountain biking, winetasting and fine dining (see also Eat-out section).

La Fontaine Guest House 21 Dirkie Uys Street, Franschhoek ▪ R350 B&B pp sharing ▪ Visa & MasterCard accepted ▪ Air-conditioning ▪ Owner Linquenda Guest House cc ▪ lafontaine@wam.co.za ▪ www.lafontainefranschhoek.co.za ℭ/🖷 **(021) 876·2112**

A short stroll to restaurants, shops and galleries, La Fontaine has nine spacious en-suite double rooms; five upstairs in the house, three set in peaceful garden, pool and courtyard surroundings and one family garden suite. Winetasting, golf, fly-fishing, horse riding and hiking are all nearby. Swimming pool, off-street parking and beautiful mountain views. Delicious buffet breakfasts.

La Maison Bleue 30 Uitkyk Street, Franschhoek ▪ R300 pp self-catering ▪ No credit card facilities Children 12+ welcome ▪ No smoking ▪ German & Dutch spoken ▪ Owners Richard & Rebekah Kelley rosemary_beetge@absamail.co.za ℭ/🖷 **(021) 876·3849; 083·456·9371** (Contact person: Rosemary)

SA residence of Platter Guide contributor and Master of Wine Richard Kelley. La Maison Bleue is situated in a quiet location on the edge of the village. The house has an extensive living area with 3 bedrooms (2 doubles, 1 twin), well-equipped kitchen and garden with mountain views, terrace, pool and *petanque piste*. Long- or short-term lets.

La Petite Ferme Pass Road, Franschhoek ▪ R1 200 per room B&B ▪ Major credit cards accepted ▪ Air-conditioning ▪ Basic German spoken ▪ Owners Dendy Young family ▪ lapetite@iafrica.com ℭ **(021) 876·3016** 🖷 (021) 876·3624

La Petite Ferme is nestled on the Middagkrans mountain high above Franschhoek with breathtaking views of vineyards and the lush valley below. Luxury, elegance and comfort are paramount, with 5 individually decorated suites set among the vineyards. Each free-standing suite features a private patio, garden and plunge pool. The spacious interiors have a fireplace, TV, mini bar, air-conditioning and en-suite bathroom with oval bathtub and shower. (See also Eat-out section.)

Le Manoir de Brendel R45, Main Road, Franschhoek ▪ Major credit cards accepted ▪ Conference facilities ▪ Spa Restaurant ▪ Chapel ▪ Wine Tasting & Sales daily 11:00–17:00 (export brand: Wine 4 U) ▪ Owners Christian & Maren Brendel ▪ lemanoir@brendel.co.za ▪ www.le-manoir-de-brendel.com ℭ **(021) 876·4525** 🖷 (021) 876·4524

This Victorian 5-star Guesthouse (twinned with a Hunting and Guest Lodge in Namibia) has air-conditioned suites, some facing the pool and the vineyards, and others picturesque gardens. Energetic activities such as the gym, tennis court, swimming pool and walking trail along the vineyards are offered. Leisurely breakfasts and lunches are served in our intimate restaurant. (See also A-Z section.)

Montmartre Luxury Lodges Pass Road, Franschhoek ▪ R399 pp B&B ▪ Major credit cards accepted ▪ Owners Franschhoek Water (Pty) Ltd ▪ peter@montmartre.co.za ▪ www.montmartre.co.za ✆ (021) 876·3614 ✆ (021) 876·3620

Montmartre Luxury Lodges are set high on the northern slopes of the magnificent Franschhoek mountains in a beautiful garden which extends upwards into the Cape's unique *fynbos*. Overlooking a trout-filled lake and the charming village of Franschhoek below, it is an ideal setting for a relaxing weekend of leisure. Each lodge has its own unique decor.

Plumwood Inn 11 Cabrière Street, Franschhoek ▪ From R550 per room B&B low season & R850 high season ▪ 5-course dinner on request ▪ Visa & MasterCard accepted ▪ Dutch & German spoken ▪ Owners Lucienne & Roel Rutten ▪ info@plumwoodinn.com ▪ www.plumwoodinn.com ✆ (021) 876·3883 ✆ (021) 876·3803

Situated on the quiet outskirts of Franschhoek, Plumwood Inn overlooks plum trees and dramatic mountains. Each room has a unique sense of style and design, and is equipped with TV, hairdryer, mini-safe, soft gowns, heater, air-conditioning and en-suite bathroom. Enjoy a sumptuous poolside alfresco breakfast with homemade marmalades, bread and other delights. Guests can relax and unwind beside the heated salt-water swimming pool.

Hermanus

Riviera House No 4 12th Avenue, Voëlklip, Hermanus ▪ From R1 313–R1 616 per room B&B (seasonal) ▪ Major credit cards accepted ▪ Air-conditioning ▪ German spoken ▪ Owners John & Sue Lederle ▪ Manager Lauren Kleynhaus ▪ reservations@rivierahouse.co.za ▪ www.rivierahouse.co.za ✆ (028) 314·0972 ✆ (028) 314·0973

An expression of good taste and Caribbean grace, this exclusive 5-star guesthouse boasts one of the most splendid views of Walker Bay in Hermanus and is only a stone's throw away from our own Blue Flag Grotto Beach. Five luxurious en-suite rooms, restful nooks and sprawling verandahs allow for quiet repose and uninterrupted sea views. Enjoy the tranquillity over a chilled bottle of Cape wine while experiencing the traditionally warm Cape hospitality.

Schulphoek Seafront Guesthouse & Restaurant 44 Marine Drive, Sandbaai, Hermanus ▪ Luxury & standard: R610-R826 B&B (plus complimentary 4-course meal for first night); incentive rates for longer stays ▪ Major credit cards accepted (excl Amex) ▪ Restaurant ▪ Wine cellar ▪ Jacuzzi & heated pool ▪ Satellite TV & video/dvd ▪ Library ▪ Hosts Petro & Mannes van Zyl ▪ schulphoek@hermanus.co.za ▪ www.schulphoek.co.za ✆ (028) 316·2626 ✆ (028) 316·2627

This 5-star establishment is situated at Schulphoek, a beautiful quiet bay with spectacular sea views, 5km from Hermanus' centre. Individually styled suites are luxurious and spacious. The lounge and dining room have magnificent uninterrupted seascapes. The kitchen, staffed by a chef, offers a four-course menu du jour, with herbs and vegetables picked daily from the potager. Choose from 7 000 bottles of South African wine. Diners Club Platinum cellar award 02. (See also Eat-out section.)

Kuils River

Zevenwacht Country Inn Zevenwacht Wine Farm, Langverwacht Road, Kuils River ▪ Country Inn R1 080 B&B per room; Cottages R350 B&B pp sharing ▪ Major credit cards accepted ▪ Air-conditioning (excl cottages) ▪ German spoken ▪ Owner Harold Johnson ▪ reservations@zevenwacht.co.za ▪ www.zevenwacht.co.za ✆ (021) 903·5123 ✆ (021) 906·1570

Zevenwacht, on the Stellenbosch wine route, is home not only to reputed wines but also many other attractions, including the Country Inn, offering accommodation in 13 luxury suites or 7 vineyard cottages. Dining options include the Historic Manor House Restaurant, open daily for breakfast, lunch, dinner and picnics. Our Country Inn has unsurpassed ocean views of Table Bay and False Bay. Other features include a sauna and floodlit tennis court, winetastings, facilities for weddings, product launches and conferences (a 64-seat auditorium is housed in the Country Inn), a cheesery and a chefs' school. (See also Eat-out and A-Z sections.)

McGregor

The Old Mill Lodge Mill Street, McGregor ▪ R880 DB&B/R690 B&B per room, R80 single supplement ▪ Major credit cards accepted ▪ Owners Spencer & Karen Hill ▪ info@ oldmilllodge.co.za ▪ www.oldmilllodge.co.za ✆ **(023) 625·1841** 🖷 (023) 625·1941

Restored country house, tranquil and relaxing, with cosy lounge, fully stocked bar and elegant restaurant, all overlooking the lodge's vineyard and the Langeberg mountains. Separate thatched cottages, en suite, are set in beautiful gardens. A short walk through the olive groves takes you to the secluded swimming pool, fishing dam and nature reserve, conference centre and complementary healing room. Diner's Club 1997, 2001 Merit awards and Diner's Club 2002 Platinum award. 2003 AA Finalist Award. (See also Eat-out section.)

Montagu

Mimosa Lodge Church Street, Montagu ▪ Seasonal rates from R280 pp B&B ▪ Major credit cards accepted ▪ French, German & Italian spoken ▪ mimosa@lando.co.za ▪ www. mimosa.co.za ✆ **(023) 614·2351** 🖷 (023) 614·2418

Firmly established in Montagu, this carefully restored lodge exudes charm, warmth and friendliness. The decor is vibrant and colourful. The 9 comfortable en-suite bedrooms have modern facilities, while the 6 garden suites offer luxury and tranquillity. The garden with its black-marbled pool is surrounded by the lodge's own apricot orchards. There's also a boules pitch. Renowned for its creative cuisine and extensive wine cellar. The acclaimed table d'hôte changes daily, and special dietary requirements are gladly catered for.

Montagu Country Hotel 27 Bath Street, Montagu ▪ R365 pp B&B ▪ Major credit cards accepted ▪ Air-conditioning ▪ Owner GP Lubbe ▪ montinn@iafrica.com ▪ www. montagucountryhotel.co.za ✆ **(023) 614·3125** 🖷 (023) 614·1905

Montagu is situated on the legendary 'Route 62', between Cape Town and the Garden Route. The Hotel's Colonial 'Art Deco' style is based on 1920's Paris design. We specialise in traditional cuisine, with top quality wines of the region. Experience our Wellness Centre and the healing waters of our mineral pool. Montagu, where the isolation and beauty of untouched landscapes can quench the soul. (See also Eat-out section for Wild Apricot Restaurant.)

Paarl

Grande Roche Hotel Plantasie Street, Paarl ▪ Terrace Suite R2 500-R3 500 B&B ▪ Major credit cards accepted ▪ Air-conditioning ▪ German, Dutch & French spoken ▪ General Manager Horst Frehse ▪ reserve@granderoche.co.za ▪ www.granderoche.com ✆ **(021) 863·2727** 🖷 (021) 863·2220

Grande Roche has become a legend in South Africa with an array of awards including Satour's first Hotel of the Year Award for 'incredible attention to detail, impeccable grounds, excellent food and superb levels of luxury' as well as the American-based international Andrew Harper Award given to outstanding country estates exuding warmth, charm and excellence. This South African gem overlooks vineyards and rugged mountains, and its sprawl of individually decorated suites are a gentle alternative to the hurly-burly of big city life. Relax in the pools, go biking or play tennis on site, enjoy excellent golf nearby, visit the fitness centre or the hotel's private masseur. It's the ideal base from which to explore the entire Cape region. (See also Eat-out section for Bosman's Restaurant).

Mooi Bly Horseshoe at Bo Dal Pad, Dal Josafat, Paarl ▪ From R150-R300 pp ▪ Self-catering, B&B on request ▪ Visa & MasterCard accepted ▪ Dutch (French & German if required)

spoken ■ Owners Luc Wouters & family ■ info@mooibly.com ■ www.mooibly.com 📞/
🖷 **(021) 868-2808**

Mooi Bly estate offers 5 unique self-catering cottages in the middle of its vineyards. Each cottage has its own private stoep, garden and braai, and a view over the farm dam, vineyards or Paarl valley. Daily serviced cottages from 2 up to 6 persons; 45 minutes from Cape Town and airport. This year they will make their wine in the new cellar on the farm. Recommendable restaurants nearby. Close to several renowned boutique wineries. (See also A-Z section.)

Oak Tree Lodge 32 Main Street, Paarl ■ R275-R425 pp B&B ■ Major credit cards accepted ■ Air-conditioning ■ Owners Yvette & Gerd Baudewig ■ info@oaktreelodge.co.za ■ www.oaktreelodge.co.za 📞 **(021) 863-2631** 🖷 (021) 863-2607

Oak Tree Lodge is centrally situated in the historic winelands town of Paarl. Spacious en-suite bedrooms offer TV with satellite and German satellite channels, telephone, air-conditioning, underfloor heating, bar fridge, hairdryer and tea trays. Choose between standard rooms or newly built luxury garden rooms next to the pool with lovely vineyard and mountain views. Restaurants and winetasting within walking distance.

Pontac Manor Hotel 16 Zion Street, Paarl ■ From R465 B&B pp sharing ■ Major credit cards accepted ■ Air-conditioning ■ Owners Deseré & Tim Orrill-Legg ■ orrill-legg@pontac. com ■ www.pontac.com 📞 **(021) 872-0445** 🖷 (021) 872-0460

This beautifully restored Victorian manor today houses a gracious 4-star hotel, offering luxurious accommodation in 23 tastefully decorated rooms. Facilities include plush guest lounges, gourmet dining in 'The Restaurant at Pontac' (see Eat-out section), light dining in Café du Pontac and Duke's Bar, swimming pool and wrap-around verandah overlooking the valley. The beautiful grounds harbour ancient oaks and a classical rose garden. Private functions for up to 80 guests. Conference facilities for up to 45 delegates. Just 55 km from Cape Town on the N1 motorway, the town of Paarl is an easily accessible destination in the heart of the winelands.

Sonop Guest House Sonop Wine Farm, Voorpaardeberg Road, Paarl ■ R250 B&B pp sharing ■ Major credit cards accepted ■ Air-conditioning ■ Conference facilities ■ French spoken ■ Owner Jacques Germanier ■ office@african-terroir.co.za ■ www.african-terroir. co.za 📞 **(021) 869-8103** 🖷 (021) 869-8104

Sonop Guest House is a quaint 4-bedroomed B&B situated on one of the few organic wine farms in South Africa. In addition, African Terroir Winery is in walking distance from the guesthouse making it an exceptional stay-over. The location at the foot of the Paardeberg mountains adds to the serenity of idyllic scenery and ambience. (See also A-Z section for African Terroir.)

Robertson

Fraai Uitzicht 1798 Klaas Voogds East, on Route 62 between Robertson & Montagu ■ From R400 B&B pp sharing ■ Major credit cards accepted ■ German, French, Swedish & Xhosa spoken ■ Owners Axel Spanholtz & Mario Motti ■ info@fraaiuitzicht.com ■ www. fraaiuitzicht.com 📞/🖷 **(023) 626-6156**

Nestling among the majestic Langeberg hills, in the heart of the Robertson Valley, the historic wine and guest farm with an award-winning restaurant welcomes you to the real vineyard experience! Stylishly appointed guest cottages and suites, set amid vineyards and orchards, offer luxurious comfort with spectacular views. Attentive hosts ensure fine dining in the award-winning restaurant. Fraai Uitzicht 1798 offers a tranquil retreat, balm for the soul, the ideal place to spend a relaxing, comfortable and culinary few days. (See also Eat-out and A-Z sections.)

Weltevrede Guest Farm Weltevrede, Eilandia, Robertson ■ R60-R80 pp sharing. R100 pp single (all meals on request) ■ Visa, MasterCard & Diners Club accepted ■ Owner Tina du Preez ■ weltevrede.guestfarm@intekom.co.za ■ www.weltevredegf.co.za 📞 **(023) 626-2073** 🖷 (023) 626-1895

Enjoy wine farm hospitality and real country food at a safe private organic wine farm on the Breede River. Fully equipped self-catering cottages. Antique chapel for intimate weddings with catering facilities. Conference facilities 10⁺ up to 100. (See also Eat-out section and A-Z section for Bon Cap Organic Wines.)

Tierhoek Cottages Tierhoek Farm, Noree Valley, Robertson ▪ R150 pp ▪ Self-catering, B& B on request ▪ No credit card facilities ▪ Owners Bruce & Alison Gilson ▪ gilson@intekom. co.za ▪ www.tierhoekcottages.co.za Ⓒ/🖷 **(023) 626·1191**

Pepper Tree, Lucky Bean and Tierhoek House are private, self-catering cottages situated on a working fruit and vine farm. Enjoy spectacular scenery in your own private valley. Walk in the mountains and enjoy the abundance of bird and wildlife. Elegantly furnished, well-equipped, romantic cottages with open fireplaces, private verandahs and braai areas. Use of own private pools. Breakfast and dinner 'baskets' on request.

Somerset West & Environs

Assegai Guest Lodge 10 Harewood Avenue, Helderberg Estate, Somerset West ▪ From R260–R320 B&B pp sharing (double); R290–R350 B&B pp (single) ▪ German spoken ▪ Owners Sue and Raimund Buchner ▪ rbuchner@worldonline.co.za ▪ www.members.afrika-adventure.org/a/assegai/ Ⓒ **(021) 855·2249** 🖷 (021) 855·4924

Come and enjoy a secluded and private atmosphere surrounded by trees and abundant bird life. Centrally situated in the winelands, only 10 minutes drive to Stellenbosh or the False Bay beaches, with Cape Town and its International airport 30 minutes away. The lodge, because of its size, is a 'home from home' yet spacious and charming. Tiled floors with tastefully furnished reception rooms and bedrooms all en-suite with fridge and television. Pool and barbeque facilities in tranquil gardens. Winetasting as well as arranged wine cellar and golf tours. (See also A-Z section.)

Die Ou Pastorie Country House 41 Lourens Street, Somerset West ▪ From R625 pp B& B, R1 250 per room B&B ▪ Major credit cards accepted ▪ info@dieoupastorie.co.za ▪ www.dieoupastorie.co.za Ⓒ **(021) 850·1660** 🖷 (021) 851·3710

This historic monument with its gracious antiques dates back to 1819, yet offers every modern convenience plus easy access to Cape Town and the winelands. The 16 en-suite bedrooms are decorated in Victorian style and set in manicured gardens. The restaurant, situated in the original *pastorie* (parsonage), has a warm and intimate atmosphere, and features contemporary style cuisine and an acclaimed winelist (see also Eat-out section).

Ivory Heights Guest House 17 Louis Botha Avenue, Somerset West ▪ R780 per room B&B ▪ Major credit cards accepted ▪ Air-conditioning ▪ Xhosa spoken ▪ Owners André & Sonnia du Plessis ▪ info@ivoryheights.co.za ▪ www.ivoryheights.co.za Ⓒ **(021) 852·8333** 🖷 (021) 852·8886

Indulge in world-class service, luxurious accommodation, loads of living areas, panoramic mountain and sea views, and ultimate comfort. Ivory Heights offers top-class facilities to pamper our discerning guests. Heated pool, tennis and squash courts, gym, home cinema and video conferencing. Close to all major attractions, Ivory Heights is the ideal base for a memorable holiday in the Cape. Golf courses, wine estates, white sandy beaches and nature trails are on our doorstep. AA Quality Assured, Portfolio Collection and 5-star TGSA.

La Bonne Auberge 21 Van Zyl Street, cnr Drama Street, Somerset West ▪ R350 pp sharing B&B ▪ 5 Suites B&B; 1 Petite Maisonette (self-catering) ▪ Major credit cards accepted ▪ Owners Yvonne & Frederick Thermann ▪ info@labonneauberge.co.za ▪ www. labonneauberge.co.za Ⓒ **(021) 852·0078** 🖷 (021) 850·0460

Under the oak trees in a leafy suburb with views of the Helderberg mountains, the restored, sunny Cape Dutch manor house bids you a warm welcome. The new garden cottage and suites are stylishly decorated and have private entrance, patio, fridge, safe, TV, air-conditioning/heating. Enjoy a continental breakfast under the trees, swimming in the large pool and relaxing in the garden. Ideally situated for exploring the famous wine estates and fine restaurants of the Stellenbosch area. Professional, friendly service, comfort and value for money are what we are about. (See also Eat-out & A-Z sections for L'Auberge du Paysan.)

NH The Lord Charles Hotel cnr Faure & Stellenbosch roads (R44), Somerset West ▪ From R787–50 B&B pp sharing excl 1% tourism levy ▪ Major credit cards accepted ▪ Air-conditioning ▪ Airport shuttle ▪ Gym ▪ Tennis courts ▪ Dutch, German & Spanish spoken ▪ Managing director (SA) Erik Jansen ▪ info@nh-hotels.co.za ▪ www.nh-hotels.co.za ✆ **(021) 855·1040** 📠 (021) 855·1107

Nestled amid the breathtaking surroundings of the famous Cape winelands, NH The Lord Charles Hotel is situated conveniently a mere 30 minutes from the Cape Town International Airport. Guests enjoy all the attractions of city life such as the best shopping and a variety of restaurants without losing the appeal and peacefulness of the countryside. Our property boasts 188 air-conditioned rooms and 9 luxurious suites, all tastefully decorated, in a harmonious setting for relaxation or business. Many rooms have their own private terrace leading out onto our splendid 9-hectare estate. All have a magnificent view of our mandated gardens, majestic Helderberg mountains or a panoramic sea view over False Bay. (See also Eat-out section for La Vigna Restaurant, Garden Terrace & St Andrew's 19th Hole.)

Somerton Manor 13 Somerset Street, Somerset West ▪ R380 pp B&B ▪ Major credit cards accepted ▪ Air-conditioning ▪ Dutch & German spoken ▪ Owner Antonie van den Hurk ▪ info@somerton.co.za ▪ www.somerton.co.za ✆ **(021) 851·4682** 📠 (021) 851·4672

Set in a large garden with a winding mountain stream. Relax around the heated swimming pool with jacuzzi, sauna and fully equipped gymnasium. Enjoy fine wine from the cellar in the lapa or around the billiard table. Luxurious en-suite bedrooms have satellite TV and telephone. Situated in the Helderberg with its beaches, wine routes and restaurants. Four-star grading. Reduced green fees at Erinvale golf club.

Zandberg Farm Country House 96 Winery Road, off R44 between Stellenbosch & Somerset West ▪ From R550 per room B&B low season – R1 300 B&B ▪ Major credit cards accepted ▪ Dutch & German spoken ▪ Owner Hilary Beal ▪ info@zandberg.co.za ▪ www.zandberg.co.za ✆/📠 **(021) 842·2945**

'A perfect little paradise', the farm dates back to 1690, with 11 beautifully installed cottages and 2 large suites in main house. Set in 4 acres of old park-like gardens, lake, swimming pool, wellness studio, gym, putting green and fine restaurant '96 Winery Road' on site, 10 minutes to beaches and golf course. Children under 12 stay free. Champagne breakfasts.

Stellenbosch & Environs

33 Stellenbosch Vlottenburg Road (off R310), Vlottenburg, 5 km from Stellenbosch ▪ From R280 pp sharing ▪ Breakfast R50 pp ▪ Major credit cards accepted ▪ No pool ▪ Air-conditioning ▪ Airport transfers ▪ French & German spoken ▪ Owner Simon Lavarack ▪ info@33.co.za ▪ www.33.co.za ✆ **(021) 881·3792** 📠 (021) 881·3140

33 Stellenbosch is an immaculately restored homestead, situated in the very heart of the historic and picturesque Stellenbosch winelands. 33 caters for every need, from that of the discerning traveller seeking sumptuous old world guesthouse facilities, or companies seeking elegant, yet professional conferencing facilities, to guests who demand uncompromising culinary excellence at all times. We invite you to enjoy our unique brand of hospitality and cuisine to delight your senses (see also Eat-out section).

Dankbaarheid Apartments Eikendal Road (off R44 between Stellenbosch & Somerset West) ▪ Price per unit from R290 (studio) to R800 (luxury apartment) ▪ Self-catering ▪ Owners Kristo & Tita Truter ▪ dankbaar@adept.co.za ▪ www.dankbaar.co.za ✆ **(021) 855·3051/082·850·1512** 📠 (021) 855·4907

Voted one of SA's best farm stays in the latest AA Awards and 3-star rated by the Tourism Grading Council, Dankbaarheid wine farm is set in the 'golden triangle' wine area of Stellenbosch and offers 4 comfortable self-catering apartments (sleeping 2-5) with quality fixtures, automatic shutters, braai, private patios, secure parking, views and more. Resident owners and hosts Kristo and Tita Truter give their guests personal attention.

De Goue Druif 110 Dorp Street, Stellenbosch ▪ R375 B&B pp sharing ▪ Visa & MasterCard accepted ▪ Air-conditioning ▪ French, German & Flemish spoken ▪ Owner Katrien Cools ▪

gouedruif@new.co.za ▪ http://gouedruif.hypermart.net ✆ **(021) 883·3555** 🖷 (021) 883·3588

A 4-star graded guesthouse in a national monument situated in the centre of Stellenbosch. Restaurants in walking distance. Cape history is gracefully blended with luxury. The suites have all modern facilities: air-conditioning, heating, superb breakfast, gym, sauna, steam bath, pool, lush garden, undercover parking. Impressive collection of South African wines.

Devon Valley Hotel Devon Valley Road, Stellenbosch ▪ From R700 per room B&B ▪ Major credit cards accepted ▪ Air-conditioning ▪ German spoken ▪ Owner LGI Hotels & Vineyards ▪ info@devonvalleyhotel.com ▪ www.devonvalleyhotel.com ✆ **(021) 865·2012** 🖷 (021) 865·2610

This much-loved Stellenbosch landmark has recently been rejuvenated. Over 50 years old, the charming Devon Valley Hotel offers spectacular valley and mountain views, 38 stylishly decorated rooms, innovative contemporary Cape cuisine and an award-winning winelist. Walk through beautiful gardens, swim in one of the two pools, gaze over their own vineyards or just sit on the terrace, admire the view and enjoy their award-winning SylvanVale wines. At night, relax in front of the log fire in the Cedarwood Lounge and savour one of the largest collections of single malt whiskies in the country. (See also Eat-out section for Flavours and A-Z for SylvanVale.)

d'Ouwe Werf Country Inn 30 Church Street, Stellenbosch ▪ R990 per room B&B ▪ Major credit cards accepted ▪ Air-conditioning ▪ French, German, Italian & Spanish spoken ▪ ouwewerf@iafrica.com ▪ www.ouwewerf.com ✆ **(021) 887·4608** 🖷 (021) 887·4626

Established 1802, d'Ouwe Werf has defined hospitality and fine dining for centuries. Relax in luxurious accommodation consisting of 31 en-suite bedrooms, all individually decorated and with modern facilities. The hotel prides itself on its friendly, personal yet professional service. The '1802 Restaurant' is renowned as a culinary destination. Situated in the heart of historical Stellenbosch and within easy walking distance of shops, museums and art galleries.

Kleine Zalze Lodges Kleine Zalze Wine Farm/De Zalze Golf Estate, Technopark turn-off, Strand Road (R44), Stellenbosch ▪ From R250–R600 pp for various units & facilities ▪ Self-catering ▪ Major credit cards accepted ▪ Air-conditioning ▪ Terroir Restaurant ▪ Conference & wedding facilities ▪ De Zalze Golf Course – special guest rates ▪ German spoken ▪ Owner Kleine Zalze Lodges (Pty) Ltd ▪ accommodation@kleinezalze.co.za ▪ www.kleinezalze.com ✆ **(021) 880·0740** 🖷 (021) 880·2215

Our four-star rated stylishly decorated self-catering guest lodges overlook the De Zalze Golf Course and Kleine Zalze vineyards. Units range in size from one to four bedrooms, all en-suite, with fireplace and lounge area leading onto a private patio with barbecue facilities overlooking the golf course. All lodges are fully equipped with full- or half-kitchens with cutlery and crockery, DSTV, mini bar, microwave, tea and coffee facilities, and are serviced. Single bedroom units are also available. (See also Eat-out & A-Z sections.)

Knorhoek Guest House & Wines Knorhoek Farm, Knorhoek Road, off R44, Koelenhof ▪ From R283 B&B pp sharing ▪ Major credit cards accepted ▪ Owners Carol & Ingrid van Niekerk ▪ guesthouse@knorhoek.co.za ▪ www.knorhoek.co.za ✆/🖷 **(021) 865·2114/5**

Picture yourself lounging under an ancient oak tree, sipping award-winning Knorhoek wines, gazing over paddocks, gardens, vineyards and the mountain changing from blue to purple. Savour the tranquillity of this magnificent setting; 8 rooms tastefully decorated with Victorian touches; tea trays, TV with M-Net, underfloor heating, cosy lounge, dinner (Mon-Thu) and breakfast alfresco in summer. (See also Eat-out and A-Z sections.)

L'Avenir Wine Estate Guest House Klapmuts Road (R44), Stellenbosch ▪ R600–R900 per room B&B (seasonal) ▪ Major credit cards accepted ▪ Ceiling fans ▪ French & German spoken ▪ Owner L'Avenir Wine Estate (Pty) Ltd ▪ lavenir@adept.co.za ▪ www.lavenir.co.za ✆ **(021) 889·5001** 🖷 (021) 889·5258

This is a winelover's heaven: 9 en-suite bedrooms around a large pool on a wine estate with 70 hectares of prime vineyards to wander in, cellar tours and award-winning wines at cellar prices. Relaxed and unhurried luxury, only 5 minutes from Stellenbosch, 20 minutes from the airport and the beaches of the Strand, 50 minutes from Cape Town. Conference facilities are available. (See also A-Z section.)

Marianne Wine Farm Guest Apartments Marianne Wine Farm, Valley Road, off R44, between Stellenbosch & Klapmuts ▪ R690 B&B ▪ Major credit cards accepted ▪ German spoken ▪ destin@adept.co.za ✆ **(021) 875·5040** 🖷 (021) 875·5036

Surrounded by citrus orchards and vineyards, our spacious and comfortable apartments are uniquely African in style. Relax at the swimming pool while watching the sun setting over distant Table Mountain. Braai facilities at the pool. Enjoy scenic walks through the vineyards, mountain biking or explore the Western Cape. Breakfast is served at the nearby waterside restaurant — Olivello — which offers Cape comfort food enhanced by delicious Mediterranean flavours. Children are welcome. Secure parking. TGCSA 4-star. (See also Eat-out section for Olivello)

Muratie Wine Estate Knorhoek Road, off R44, Koelenhof ▪ Seasonal rates ▪ Major credit cards accepted ▪ Owners Melck family ▪ muratie@kingsley.co.za ▪ www.muratie.co.za ✆ **(021) 865·2330/6** 🖷 (021) 865·2790

Self-catering cottage for two. Become part of the magic of Muratie. Experience life on a real working wine estate in the Stellenbosch wine region and stay over in the studio of the famous SA artist GP Canitz. (See also A-Z section.)

Natte Valleij Farm Klapmuts Road (R44), 12 km north of Stellenbosch towards Paarl ▪ R225 pp B&B ▪ Self-catering: Vineyard Cottage from R475 per cottage pd; Cellar Cottage R420 per cottage pd ▪ Owners Charles & Charlene Milner ▪ milner@intekom.co.za ▪ www. nattevalleij.co.za ✆ **(021) 875·5171** 🖷 (021) 875·5475

Situated below the Simonsberg mountains in the prime winegrowing Muldersvlei bowl where the Stellenbosch wine route meets the Paarl wine route, Charles and Charlene Milner's historic farm, the first land grant of the area, offers a B&B option as well as self-catering. Vineyard Cottage can sleep 6 in 3 double bedrooms, with 2 bathrooms, sitting room and dining room; Cellar Cottage sleeps 2 with the option of 2 extra beds in the sitting room. Both cottages have their own stoep (patio) and braai (bbq). There is a secluded swimming pool in the large garden and horse riding can be done from the farm. Outrides go through vineyards and mountain foothills in the most beautiful surroundings.

Ons Genot Country Lodge Bottelary Road, Stellenbosch ▪ From R290 pp B&B (low season) to R450 pp B&B (high season) ▪ Major credit cards accepted ▪ Tennis court ▪ Air-conditioning ▪ Dutch, French & German spoken ▪ Owners Eric & Marleen Bovijn ▪ info@onsgenot.com ▪ www.onsgenot.com ✆ **(021) 865·2233** 🖷 (021) 865·2250

Ons Genot is an exclusive 4-star country retreat on the outskirts of historic Stellenbosch, and a finalist in the AA Accommodation Awards 2002, 2003 & 2004. Features include luxury en-suite air-conditioned rooms with private terrace and attractive garden, television, mini-bar, wall safe, phone, bathroom with bath and shower. In addition, the honeymoon suite has a private jacuzzi. The restaurant at Ons Genot offers breakfast, lunch and dinner (see also Eat-out section).

Papyrus Lodge Winery Road, off R44 between Stellenbosch & Somerset West ▪ From R600 B&B pp sharing ▪ Visa & MasterCard accepted ▪ Lake ▪ Swiss German, German & Italian spoken ▪ Owners Stefan & Kristin Heusser ▪ info@papyruslodge.co.za ▪ www. papyruslodge.co.za ✆ **(021) 842·3606** 🖷 (021) 842·3607

Papyrus Lodge: A unique experience of life at the waterside. Spectacular location, well maintained gardens, lush vineyards, stunning views, own lake. Romantic wooden chalets, built on stilts with a big deck overhanging the water. Spacious and luxury suites in the Cape Dutch Main Lodge. A resting place, an inspiration and a treat for your soul, mind and body … a true little paradise. Swimming, fishing, rowing, bird-watching. Excellent restaurant adjacent. Swiss hosts.

Summerwood Guest House 28 Jonkershoek Road, Stellenbosch ▪ R1 300 per room B&B ▪ Major credit cards accepted ▪ Dutch & French spoken ▪ Owners Ann & Christian Baret ▪

summerwood@mweb.co.za ▪ www.summerwood.co.za ✆ **(021) 887·4112** 📠 (021) 887·4239

A short stroll from Stellenbosch, Summerwood, built in 1903 and now beautifully restored as a 5-star graded guesthouse, consists of 9 tastefully furnished air-conditioned en-suite rooms, guest lounge and sunny breakfast room leading onto a terrace. Beautiful grounds with a large pool contribute to the tranquillity for which it's renowned. Ann and Christian delight in helping their guests appreciate this special corner of South Africa.

The Village Hotel at Spier Lynedoch Road (R310), Stellenbosch ▪ R1 382 per room B&B ▪ Major credit cards accepted ▪ 5 Restaurants ▪ 7 Swimming pools ▪ 3 Tennis courts (one floodlit) ▪ Camelot Spa ▪ Cheetah Outreach Centre & Eagle Encounters ▪ Air-conditioning ▪ Banqueting & conference facilities ▪ Xhosa spoken ▪ info@spier.co.za ▪ www.spier.co.za ✆ **(021) 809·1100** 📠 (021) 881·3141

With 155 rooms nestled in traditional Cape-styled buildings centred around 6 private courtyards, the Village offers a total escape to those in need of some time out from the world. Figaro's Restaurant is situated adjacent to the reception area of the hotel and offers a breathtaking view of the surrounding Helderberg mountains. (See also Eat-out & A-Z sections).

Swellendam

Klippe Rivier Country House From N2 take R60, turn left at 4-way stop, Swellendam district ▪ R895 B&B pp sharing, R850 B&B pp for 2 or more nights ▪ Major credit cards accepted ▪ Air-conditioning ▪ Children 8+ welcome ▪ German spoken ▪ Owner Liz Westby-Nunn ▪ info@klipperivier.com ▪ www.klipperivier.com ✆ **(028) 514·3341** 📠 (028) 514·3337

A magnificent Cape Dutch country house. Converted 'waenhuis' and stables have 6 luxury air-conditioned bedrooms. Three downstairs rooms have an open fireplace, dressing room and generous bathroom with separate shower and toilet. Loft rooms, under thatch, have private bathrooms and balconies with mountain views. Three cottages with mountain views, one of which is secluded and ideal for honeymooners.

Tulbagh

Lemberg Guest House Off the R46, 4 km west of Tulbagh ▪ R250 pp B&B (May–Sep) – R300 pp B&B (Oct–Apr) ▪ Major credit cards accepted ▪ German spoken ▪ Owners Klaus & Uschi Schindler ▪ schindler@lando.co.za ▪ www.kapstadt.de/lemberg ✆ **(023) 230·0659** 📠 (023) 230·0661

Set fairly privately in the lush garden of this boutique wine estate, a stylish and spacious rondavel offers discerning guests (up to 4 people) a perfect and peaceful retreat. Overlooking the lake with plenty of birds and panoramic mountain views for an unforgettable delicious breakfast experience in the garden. Gourmet evening dinners are served in the rondavel (self-catering option). Pre-booked lunches for day visitors also available. German owner (professional hunter) offers hunting trips (one or more days) to nearby hunting farms. (See also A-Z section.)

Rijk's Country Hotel Rijk's Private Cellar, Rijk's Farm, Tulbagh ▪ From R600 per room B&B ▪ Major credit cards accepted ▪ Owner Neville Dorrington ▪ bookings@rijks.co.za ▪ www.rijks.co.za ✆ **(023) 230·1006** 📠 (023) 230·1125

Rijk's is a winelands getaway of charm and tranquillity, set on the outskirts of the historic and picturesque Tulbagh village. Enjoy a light lunch on the lakeside terrace, with magnificent views of the Winterhoek mountains. Rijk's Restaurant has a warm and intimate atmosphere, and offers excellent country cuisine with friendly personal service. Our award-winning winelist complements all meals and provides a memorable dining experience. Relax in front of crackling log fires, memories will linger on … (See also A-Z section.)

Wellington

Diemersfontein Wine & Country Estate Jan van Riebeeck Drive, R301 between Paarl & Wellington ▪ R450 pp B&B ▪ Major credit cards accepted ▪ Owners David & Susan

Sonnenberg ▪ hospitality@diemersfontein.co.za ▪ www.diemersfontein.co.za © **(021) 873·2671** 🖷 (021) 873·4526

We warmly invite you to share with us the tranquil spirit of Diemersfontein, whether you are conferencing, marrying, staying for a few days of leisure (or even permanently) — or taking some of it home in a bottle! Diemersfontein is known for its beauty, informal elegance and grace — an idyllic country destination only 45 minutes' drive from Cape Town. (See also Eat-out section for Seasons at Diemersfontein and A-Z section.)

▪ Eat-outs in the winelands and Cape Town

Below are some dining out options in Cape Town and the winelands. For more eat-outs among the vines, consult the A-Z section of the guide for wineries which offer light lunches, picnics etc. Look for the 🍽 symbol beside the individual entries. Unless stated to the contrary, all allow you to bring your own (BYO) wine — the corkage fee is indicated at the start of each entry. Restaurants new to the guide are indicated in bold type below. Any claims to disabled-friendliness are unverified by the publishers of the guide. **Note: the eat-outs featured here describe their own culinary styles, menus and attractions.**

Index of eat-outs

The Blue Danube
  Restaurant . . . . Cape Town
The Cape Malay
  Restaurant . . . . Constantia
The Duck Pond . . . . Stellenbosch
The Gallery Café . . . . Stellenbosch
The Greenhouse . . . . Constantia
The Guinea Fowl
  Restaurant . . . . Kuils River
The Nose Restaurant &
  Wine Bar. . . . . Cape Town

The Old Mill Lodge . . . . . . McGregor
The Restaurant at Pontac. Paarl
Under the Vines Bistro . Bonnievale
Wakame Restaurant . . . Cape Town
Wasabi Restaurant . . . . Constantia
Weltevrede Restaurant . . Robertson
Wijnhuis . . . . Stellenbosch
Wild Apricot
  Restaurant . . . . Montagu
Zevenwacht Restaurant . Kuils River

Bonnievale

Under the Vines Bistro Weltevrede Wine Estate, Bonnievale ▪ Country cuisine ▪ Open Tue-Sat 10:00-16:00 ▪ Closed June, July, Good Friday, Christmas, Boxing & New Year's days ▪ Booking advised for large groups ▪ Children welcome ▪ Wheelchair-friendly ▪ Major credit cards accepted ▪ No BYO ▪ Owner Lindelize Jonker ▪ info@weltevrede.com ▪ www. weltevrede.com ✆ **(023) 616·2141** 📠 (023) 616·2460

When you visit the Bistro at Weltevrede wine estate expect a warm welcome and delicious food. Farm bread is baked every day and our menu always offers something new. Our food is lovingly prepared while you drink in the calm atmosphere and sip the wines of Weltevrede. In summer, tables are moved outside to enjoy the beautiful vista over the vineyards. On cold days, we have a roaring fire and slow-cooked home foods to savour. If it sounds good, come and visit us! (See also Stay-over & A-Z sections.)

Cape Town

Aubergine Restaurant 39 Barnet Street, Gardens ▪ Continental cuisine with Asian influences ▪ Lunch on Thu; 'Cinq à Sept' daily 17:00-19:00 & dinner Mon-Sat 19:00-22:00 ▪ Closed Sun ▪ Booking advised ▪ Children welcome ▪ Wheelchair-friendly ▪ Major credit cards accepted ▪ Corkage R40 ▪ Owner Harald Bresselschmidt ▪ aubergin@mweb.co.za ▪ www.aubergine.co.za ✆ **(021) 465·4909** 📠 (021) 461·3781

Aubergine Restaurant offers innovative continental cuisine with Asian influences. Our original concept 'Cinq-A-Sept', served between 5 & 7pm, is a sophisticated solution to rush hour traffic or for early evening relaxation, offering delectable hors d'ouevres, drinks and ambrosial desserts on the elegant garden terrace, or in the lounge. Our culturally diverse dinner menu bursts with colours, aromas and flavours to tantalise even the seasoned palate. Our 5-Star winelist features 300 wines!

Balducci's Shop 6162, Victoria Wharf, V&A Waterfront ▪ Cal-Med cuisine ▪ Open daily 9am till late ▪ Booking advised ▪ Children welcome (but no under 12 at night) ▪ Wheelchair-friendly ▪ Major credit cards accepted ▪ Corkage R30 ▪ Owners Ian Halfon & Doron Duveen ▪ debbyd@stelmos.co.za ▪ www.balduccis.co.za ✆ **(021) 421·6002/3** 📠 (021) 421·6010

Balducci's, overlooking the harbour, is an award-winning international café-restaurant situated in the V&A Waterfront. This elegant sit-down eatery has an understated European grace which complements an outstanding menu and attentive service. Balducci's Royal Sushi Bar situated adjacent to the restaurant is internationally acclaimed and regarded as one of the best around.

Belthazar Restaurant & Wine Bar Shop 153, Victoria Wharf, V&A Waterfront ▪ Grill & seafood ▪ Open daily 12:00-late ▪ Booking advised ▪ Children 12+ welcome ▪ Wheelchair-friendly ▪ Major credit cards accepted ▪ No BYO ▪ Owners Ian Halfon, Doron Duveen & Jonathan Steyn ▪ debbyd@stelmos.co.za ▪ www.belthazar.co.za ✆ **(021) 421·3753/6** 📠 (021) 421·3748

Belthazar, the biggest wine-by-the-glass bar in the world, is a totally new concept in wining and dining. Experienced sommeliers expertly serve up to 100 of the Cape's finest wines by the glass and advise customers on a winelist of up to 600 fine wines and sought-after rare vintages. Indulge your palate, enjoy the best in life – from the slick service to superb Karan beef aged in our butcher's shop, a variety of South African game, export quality Mozambican seafood and the freshest South African seafood.

Cara Lazuli 11 Buiten Street, Cape Town ▪ North African & modern Moroccan ▪ Open Mon-Sat 19:00-23:00, reservations from 11am ▪ Booking essential ▪ Major credit cards accepted ▪ Corkage R20 (limited to 1 bottle/4 people) ▪ Owner Richard Griffin ▪ www.eatingout.co.za ✆ **(021) 426·2351** 🖷 (021) 422·4554

A gateway to Morocco on Cape Town's Buiten Street, Cara Lazuli is an intimate labyrinth of candlelit corners and petal-strewn tables. Award-winning owner/chef Richard Griffin engages the sumptuous flavours of North Africa in a feast of exotica. Fragrant traditional tagines share space with modern classics, while nightly specials like the sesame and honey coated seared Scottish salmon on a ceviche of kingklip, or the springbok shanks braised in harissa, honey and cinnamon, ensnare and delight the senses.

Caroline's Cape Kitchen Caroline's Fine Wine Cellar, 15 Long Street, Cape Town ▪ Cape country cuisine ▪ Lunch Mon-Fri, dinner bookings for groups of 30+ ▪ Closed Sat & Sun, public holidays, first week Jan ▪ Booking advised ▪ Wheelchair-friendly ▪ Major credit cards accepted ▪ No BYO ▪ Owner Caroline Rillema ▪ caroline@carolineswine.com ▪ www.carolineswine.com ✆ **(021) 419·8984** 🖷 (021) 419·8985

Caroline's Fine Wine Cellar is a well-established specialist wine shop in the Cape Town CBD. Proprietor Caroline Rillema has 25 years' experience in the wine trade and manages this store personally. She has converted their large wine cellar adjoining the shop into a restaurant where diners can enjoy lunch at tables surrounded by large stocks of the finest of Cape wines. Delicious homemade lunches are prepared in an open kitchen and six different wines can be tasted by the glass. A special tasting at R50 per person can be arranged before lunch, booking essential.

Chef 3 Rose Street, Green Point ▪ Italian cuisine ▪ Lunch Mon-Fri 12:00-15:00; dinner Tue-Sat 19:00-22:00 ▪ Booking advised ▪ Children welcome ▪ Major credit cards accepted ▪ Corkage R30 ▪ Owner Nicolai Guiseppe Pareti ✆ **(021) 419·6767**

Dine at one of SA's Top 100 Restaurants… At Chef, enjoy a different menu every evening, depending on the weather, seasonal availability and chef's whim. Watch chef/owner Nicolai Guiseppe Pareti prepare your meal in our open kitchen while you're being enchanted by the music of our pianist. A perfect venue for romantic dinners or functions for up to 30 people.

Emily's Top Floor, Clock Tower Centre, V&A Waterfront ▪ SA cuisine with an African reference ▪ Lunch Mon-Sat, dinner Mon-Sun ▪ Closed Good Friday & Christmas day ▪ Booking advised ▪ Children welcome ▪ Wheelchair-friendly ▪ Major credit cards accepted ▪ Corkage R50 ▪ Owner Peter Veldsman ▪ caia@mweb.co.za ▪ www.emily-s.com ✆ **(021) 421·1133** 🖷 (021) 421·1131

During the past 13 years, Emily's has earned a multitude of prestigious awards for both food and wine. The innovative cuisine is contemporary South African with reference to the rest of Africa. Emily's goes to great lengths to source the best ingredients and finest, well-matured red meat. Oysters, fresh or baked; gravad of crocodile, harissa-flavoured African red soup with corn-off-the-cob ice cream; grilled crayfish with linefish ragoût, vapeur of calamari on skate wing; newly recreated old traditional dishes like bobotie and denningvleis; game such as ostrich, impala, gemsbok, kudu, wildebeest and kid; creative desserts; an extensive collection of cheese and a choice of more than 2 000 wines and spirits — all of this awaits the visitor to Emily's.

Madame Zingara 192 Loop Street, Cape Town ▪ Modern eclectic, Italian-based cuisine ▪ Open Mon-Sat 19:00-23:00, reservations from 11am ▪ Booking imperative ▪ Major credit cards accepted ▪ Corkage R20 (limited to 1 bottle/4 people) ▪ Owner Richard Griffin ▪ www.eatingout.co.za ✆ **(021) 426·2458** 🖷 (021) 422·4554

Prepare to be enchanted from your first footfall across the petal-cushioned threshold of Madame Zingara. Rich in ambience, owner/chef Richard Griffin's creation remains a beloved Cape Town institution. A firm nod to the Mediterranean, fused with the unexpected, the menu is a sensual treat. House standards like the starter of tiger prawns with arborio, jeera and cayenne and the now famous chocolate chilli fillet, as well as 15 nightly specials ensure that no palate goes undelighted.

Savoy Cabbage Restaurant & Champagne Bar 101 Hout Street, Cape Town ▪ Contemporary ▪ Lunch Mon-Fri 12:00-14:30, dinner Mon-Sat 19:00-22:30 ▪ Closed Sun ▪ Booking essential ▪ Major credit cards accepted ▪ Air-conditioned ▪ Smoking section ▪ Secure parking ▪ Corkage R20 ▪ Owner Caroline Bagley ▪ savoycab@iafrica.com ✆ **(021) 424·2626** 🖷 (021) 424·3366

Winner of a string of accolades, including CNN's only 'Hot Spot' for Cape Town and a place in every annual *Wine* Top 100 Restaurants ranking to date, this city-centre establishment offers gracious dining in impressive surroundings featuring historic brick, concrete and glass. Impeccable service and attention to detail are hallmarks. The daily-changing menu is inspired by the freshest produce and known to feature game, offal and good vegetarian dishes. Boutique winelist.

The Blue Danube Restaurant 102 New Church Street, Tamboerskloof, Cape Town ▪ Continental ▪ Lunch Tue-Fri 12:00-14:30, dinner Mon-Sun 18:30-23:00 ▪ Booking advised ▪ Children welcome ▪ Major credit cards accepted ▪ Corkage R30 ▪ Owners Thomas & Britta Sinn ▪ danube@iafrica.com ▪ http://www.bluedanube.co.za www.bluedanube.co.za ▪ ✆/🖷 **(021) 423·3624**

Experience exquisite European-style cuisine with an African edge. Situated in Tamboerskloof, one of the Cape's most beautiful and historic suburbs, this unique establishment offers a comprehensive choice of delicious food and fine South African wines. Austrian-born chef Thomas Sinn is both consistent and innovative, treating diners to truly superior culinary delights. Currently recognised as one of the top 10 restaurants in South Africa, with its prestigious reputation, award-winning menu and winelist, world-class chef and subtle, sophisticated atmosphere, The Blue Danube Restaurant will appeal to, and satisfy, anyone with a discerning palate.

The Nose Restaurant & Wine Bar Cape Quarter, Dixon Street, Green Point, Cape Town ▪ Rustic, wine-friendly cuisine ▪ Mon-Sun 11:00-late ▪ Booking advised ▪ Children welcome daytime only ▪ Wheelchair-friendly ▪ Major credit cards accepted ▪ No BYO ▪ Owners Cathy & Kevin Marston ▪ info@thenose.co.za ▪ www.thenose.co.za ✆ **(021) 425·2200** 🖷 (021) 425·2210

Thirty-five wines by the glass, many more by the bottle, first releases, South African exclusives, unusual grape varieties, wineries you've never even heard of – you don't know Cape wine until you've picked The Nose! And if all that isn't enough, they also offer a full menu of delicious homemade food – including Thai fish cakes, Cape Malay chicken curries, innovative salads, steaks, linefish – plus their signature platters of tasty finger food to accompany your glass of wine. Full bar also available. The Nose is situated on a beautiful open-air piazza in Cape Town's trendiest area – De Waterkant. It's laidback, friendly and relaxed – the perfect place to enjoy the finer things of life. Cheers!

Wakame Restaurant Cnr Beach Road & Surrey Place, Mouille Point, Cape Town ▪ Pacific Rim blended with Asian fusion and a hint of French & Western influence; sushi bar ▪ Mon-Sun 12:00-15:00 & 18:00-22:30 ▪ Closed Christmas & New Year's days ▪ Booking advised ▪ Children welcome ▪ Major credit cards accepted ▪ Corkage R25, French R65 ▪ Owners Greg Slotar, Deon Berg & Roy de Gouveia ▪ info@wakame.co.za ▪ www.wakame.co.za ✆ **(021) 433·2377** 🖷 (021) 434·5148

From the lighthouse in Mouille Point to the lights of Table Bay, Wakame's breathtaking views add a unique dimension to the epicurean delights that await you. Pacific Rim blended with Asian fusion and a hint of French and Western influences are what hold true to form in the kitchen.

Constantia

Buitenverwachting Restaurant Klein Constantia Road, Constantia ▪ European cosmopolitan cuisine ▪ Open for lunch & dinner Tue-Fri (all year) & Mon-Sat (Oct-Mar) ▪ Closed Sun, Mon (Apr-Sep), some public holidays & ±8 weeks Jun-Aug (TBC) ▪ Booking advised ▪ Children 12+ welcome ▪ Wheelchair-friendly ▪ Major credit cards accepted ▪ Corkage R35

▪ Owner Lars Maack ▪ restaurant@buitenverwachting.com ▪ www.buitenverwachting. co.za © **(021) 794·3522** 🖷 (021) 794·1351

Overlooking a panorama of vines and mountain slopes, this well-known sophisticated restaurant has a degustation menu that is as exotic as it is continental. The exclusive ambience and dedication to quality by executive chef Edgar Osojnik make this restaurant in Constantia an absolute must. (See also A-Z section.)

Catharina's Restaurant Steenberg Estate, Tokai Road, Constantia Valley ▪ Contemporary Cape Colonial cuisine ▪ Open daily 7:00–23:00 ▪ Booking advised ▪ Children welcome ▪ Wheelchair-friendly ▪ Major credit cards accepted ▪ Corkage R35 ▪ Owner The Mantis Collection ▪ info@steenberghotel.com ▪ www.steenberghotel.com © **(021) 713·2222** 🖷 (021) 713·2251

The restaurant is located in the original winery, built in 1682, and now tastefully decorated in Cape colonial mode to enhance the historical architectural features. Gourmet cuisine features Cape continental dishes presented and served in international fine-dining style. Cigar lounge and breakfast patio. (See also Stay-over & A-Z sections.)

Constantia Uitsig Restaurant Spaanschemat River Road, Constantia ▪ Mediterranean cuisine ▪ Mon-Sun lunch 12:30–14:00, dinner 19:30–21:00 ▪ Closed New Year's day ▪ Booking advised ▪ Children welcome ▪ Wheelchair-friendly ▪ Major credit cards accepted ▪ Corkage R25 (wine), R50 (Champagne) ▪ Owners Marlene & David McCay ▪ frank@uitsig. co.za ▪ www.uitsig.co.za © **(021) 794·4480** 🖷 (021) 794·3105

Constantia Uitsig Restaurant, housed in the original 19th-century manor house, offers varied and innovative Mediterranean cuisine. Since its inception 10 years ago, it has consistently featured among the Top 10 Restaurants in South Africa. (See also Stay-over & A-Z sections.)

La Colombe Restaurant Spaanschemat River Road, Constantia ▪ Southern-inspired French cuisine ▪ Mon-Sun lunch 12:30–14:00, dinner 19:30–21:00 ▪ Closed Sun eve (winter) ▪ Booking advised ▪ Children welcome ▪ Wheelchair-friendly ▪ Major credit cards accepted ▪ Corkage R25 ▪ Owners Marlene & David McCay ▪ www.lacolombe.co.za © **(021) 794·2390** 🖷 (021) 794·7914

La Colombe Restaurant has been voted *top restaurant in South Africa* for three years, and serves traditional French-Provençal cuisine of the very highest standard. French-born chef Franck Dangereux changes the menu daily to incorporate fresh seasonal ingredients with natural sun-ripened flavors. (See also Stay-over section for Constantia Uitsig Country Hotel & A-Z section.)

Peddlars on the Bend 3 Spaanschemat River Road, Constantia ▪ Cosmopolitan cuisine ▪ Open daily 11:00–23:00 (bar), 12:00–23:00 (kitchen) ▪ Closed Christmas & New Year's days ▪ Booking advised ▪ Children welcome ▪ Wheelchair-friendly ▪ Major credit cards accepted ▪ Corkage R15 from 2nd bottle ▪ peddlars@mweb.co.za © **(021) 794·7747/50** 🖷 (021) 794·2730

Peddlars is popular with locals and visitors alike. Warm country charm, a lovely garden setting, and a reputation for quality food and service, are all part of the attraction. The menu is prepared from fresh ingredients daily, and the kitchen is open all day for those who would like a late lunch or early dinner. Specialities include great steaks, seafood and hearty country-style dishes. The award-winning winelist showcases the local wineries and offers a good selection of cognac, malt whisky, cigars and liqueurs. Peddlars is a non-smoking restaurant and has a small smoking area. Pub menu available for bar and garden area. The bar draws an eclectic crowd who mix well and know how to party. Plenty of free parking available.

The Cape Malay Restaurant The Cellars-Hohenort Hotel, 93 Brommersvlei Road, Constantia ▪ Traditional Malay cuisine ▪ Open 7 days a week for breakfast 7:00–10:00, lunch 12:00–14:30, dinner 19:00–21:30 ▪ Booking advised ▪ Wheelchair-friendly ▪ Major credit cards accepted ▪ Corkage R30 ▪ Owner Liz McGrath ▪ cellars@relaischateaux.com ▪ www. collectionmcgrath.com © **(021) 794·2137** 🖷 (021) 794·2149

Cape Malay cuisine is unique to the Western Cape. It dates back to the 17th century and has evolved to reflect the influences of the times. Martha Williams, Cape Malay head chef, lovingly prepares authentic boboties, smoorsnoek, samoosas and a variety of other dishes. Relax in the 'spice' colours of the décor; the friendly and well-informed staff will put you at ease in this five-star luxury hotel, The Cellars-Hohenort. (See also Stay-over section.)

The Greenhouse The Cellars-Hohenort Hotel, 93 Brommersvlei Road, Constantia ▪ Global/international fine dining ▪ Open 7 days a week for breakfast 7:00–10:00, lunch 12:00–14:30, dinner 19:00–21:30 ▪ Booking advised ▪ Wheelchair-friendly ▪ Major credit cards accepted ▪ Corkage R30 ▪ Owner Liz McGrath ▪ cellars@relaischateaux.com ▪ www.collectionmcgrath.com ℂ **(021) 794·2137** 🖷 (021) 794·2149

The new and exciting 'Greenhouse' restaurant, with an emphasis on the indigenous, the organic and the fresh, offers a different dining experience in Cape Town. Regarded as one of the top 10 restaurants, it is spacious, with sweeping views through clear plate-glass windows of beautiful gardens right up to the 200-year-old camphor trees. The award-winning winelist features some 300 wines selected by a professional sommelier. (See also Stay-over section.)

Wasabi Restaurant Shop 17, Old Village Centre, Constantia ▪ Asian with Western influence and sushi bar ▪ Mon-Sun 12:00–15:00 & 18:00–22:30 ▪ Booking advised ▪ Children welcome ▪ Wheelchair-friendly ▪ Major credit cards accepted ▪ Corkage R19 ▪ Owners Greg Slotar & Roy de Gouveia ▪ info@wasabi.co.za ▪ www.wasabi.co.za ℂ **(021) 794·6546** 🖷 (021) 434·5148

Breaking through the boundaries of life, the owners of Wasabi decided to take their patrons on a different trip to Asia. Simplicity is the order of the day, and the attention to detail and relentless effort put into preparing and cooking the food to perfection are Wasabi's greatest assets.

Darling

Groote Post Restaurant Groote Post Wine Cellar, Darling Hills Road, Darling ▪ Modern country cuisine ▪ Open Wed-Sat 12:00–14:30 ▪ Closed Sun-Tue & July ▪ Booking advised ▪ Children welcome ▪ Wheelchair-friendly ▪ Major credit cards accepted (excl Amex) ▪ No BYO ▪ Owner Shaun McLaughlin ▪ mclaughlin@worldonline.co.za ▪ www.grootepost.co.za ℂ **(022) 492·2825** 🖷 (022) 492·3430

The restaurant is located in the historic Manor House on this wine farm just outside Darling. Voted best New Restaurant on the West Coast, this winelands eatery serves modern country cuisine using the freshest of ingredients prepared daily by chef Debbie McLaughlin. Come and experience Darling at its best! (See also A-Z section.)

Durbanville

@ The Hills Durbanville Hills Winery, Tygerberg Valley Road, Durbanville ▪ Contemporary SA ▪ Lunch Tue-Sun 12:00–15:00 ▪ Closed Mon, Good Friday, Easter Sunday, Christmas & New Year's eves, 25 Dec, 1 & 2 Jan ▪ Booking advised ▪ Children welcome ▪ Wheelchair-friendly ▪ Visa & MasterCard accepted ▪ No BYO ▪ Restaurateur Marlene Brynand ▪ info@durbanvillehills.co.za ▪ www.durbanvillehills.co.za ℂ **(021) 558·1300** 🖷 (021) 559·8169

From its outlook on the Luipardsberg, this contemporary restaurant offers panoramic views of Table Bay, Table Mountain, the Atlantic Ocean and the Durbanville Hills vineyards. Modern-style regional food with Mediterranean nuances is presented in an innovative way. The menu changes regularly to reflect the seasons and is designed to complement the cellar's award-winning wines. Specialities include smoked kudu salad, biltóng and blue cheese soup, lamb neck in red wine sauce, the catch of the day and the popular sago pudding. (See also A-Z section.)

D'Aria Poplars Restaurant D'Aria Vineyards, Race Course Road, Durbanville ▪ Open Mon-Sat 9:00–22:30, Sun 9:00–15:30 ▪ Closed Sun eve ▪ Booking advised ▪ Children welcome ▪ Wheelchair-friendly ▪ Major credit cards accepted ▪ Corkage R20 ▪ poplars@daria.co.za ▪ www.daria.co.za ℂ **(021) 975·5736** 🖷 (021) 975·5740

In the heart of one of the most exciting modern wine regions in the Cape, we have the opportunity to add to the history and reputation of Durbanville. At D'Aria we offer you the award-winning Poplars Restaurant, D'Aria Sensorium Function Venue and D'Aria Guest Cottages, 12 cottages situated among the vineyards (see separate Stay-over entry). In winter we have cosy fireplaces in the dining rooms, and in summer enjoy a meal on our open patio. Our exciting à la carte menu offers a wide selection of international cuisine. Light meals include caramelised onion tart with goats' feta and peppadew salsa, panfried tuna steak with gherkins, pickled ginger and beetroot mayonnaise. Awards: Winelist (Diners Club 02 and 03), Top 100 restaurants.

Franschhoek & Environs

Boschendal You'll be spoilt for choice with three culinary options on this historic wine farm: Boschendal Restaurant, Le Café and Le Pique-Nique. (See separate listings.)

Boschendal Restaurant Pniel Road (R310), 1,5 km from junction with R45, Groot Drakenstein ▪ Cape-French cuisine ▪ Open 7 days a week, 12:15 for 12:30, guests to be seated by 13:30 ▪ Closed Good Friday, 1 May & 16 Jun ▪ Chaîne des Rôtisseurs blazon ▪ Booking advised ▪ Children welcome ▪ Wheelchair-friendly ▪ Major credit cards accepted ▪ No BYO ▪ Owners Boschendal Ltd ▪ reservations@boschendal.com ▪ www.boschendal. com ℂ **(021) 870·4274** ☎ (021) 874·2137

Housed in the beautifully restored original cellar, the Boschendal Restaurant serves buffet-style lunches featuring Cape-French cuisine (steaming roasts, local seafood specialities, salads, desserts and much more) complemented by Boschendal wines (the Jean le Long range, only available here) and a Diners Club-applauded winelist (98-01 Merit; 02 Platinum). The nearby Manor House is a national monument and museum showcasing historic artworks, Cecil Rhodes memorabilia, furniture and displays.

Bread & Wine Môreson Wine Farm Happy Valley Road, La Motte, Franschhoek ▪ Modern country fare ▪ Open Wed-Sun 12:00-17:00 (except during season) ▪ Booking advised ▪ Children welcome ▪ Wheelchair-friendly ▪ Major credit cards accepted ▪ No BYO ▪ Owner Richard Friedman ▪ breadandwine@moreson.co.za ▪ www.lequartier.co.za ℂ/☎ **(021) 876·3692**

Bread & Wine vineyard restaurant offers a new genre of Cape country cuisine, reflecting the global return to cuisine du terroir. Imaginative mixes of local ingredients are skillfully presented and complemented. The innovative menu tempts you to explore a range of tastes and textures, while lingering over Môreson's fine wine, served by the glass or bottle. (See also Stay-over section for Auberge du Quartier Français and A-Z section for Môreson.)

Chamonix Restaurant Uitkyk Street, Franschhoek ▪ French cuisine ▪ Open daily 12:00-16:00 & Fri eve from 18:30 ▪ Booking advised ▪ Children welcome ▪ Wheelchair-friendly ▪ Major credit cards accepted ▪ Complimentary wine tasting ▪ Owner Don Newton ▪ dnewton@mweb.co.za ▪ www.chamonix-restaurant.co.za / www.eatingout.co.za/online/chamonix.co.za ℂ/ ☎ **(021) 876·2393**

Classic French cuisine in the heart of Franschhoek. Glorious views of the valley as you dine alfresco on our garden terrace or enjoy a gastronomic treat next to a warm log fire. We are renowned for our hospitality and award-winning estate wines. Free winetasting for diners.

Delicious 38 Huguenot Street, Franschhoek ▪ Deli & espresso bar ▪ Open daily 7:30-17:00 & Wed eve (booking advised) ▪ Children welcome ▪ Major credit cards accepted ▪ No BYO ▪ Owner Susan Huxter ▪ linda@lqf.co.za ℂ **(021) 876·4004** ☎ (021) 876·3105

For those special breakfasts, picnic delights, lunches and take-outs, this is where the locals meet, relax and indulge in hot gossip. (See also Stay-over section for Auberge du Quartier Français.)

French Connection Bistro 48 Huguenot Street, Franschhoek ▪ French bistro style ▪ Open daily for lunch 12:00-15:30 & dinner 18:30-21:30 ▪ Closed Christmas eve ▪ Booking advised ▪ Children welcome ▪ Wheelchair-friendly ▪ Major credit cards accepted ▪ Corkage R20 ▪ Matthew Gordon & Trevor Kirsten ▪ french@worldonline.co.za ℂ **(021) 876·4056** ☎ (021) 876·4036

Master chef Matthew Gordon's stylish and exciting bistro offers simple, delicious, informal French fare. The ambience is that of a typical French bistro with a classic interior and friendly service. Superb food and Franschhoek Valley winelist. BYO discouraged. (See also Stay-over section for Auberge Clermont and Burgundy Bourgogne Manor House & Cottages.)

Grande Provence Restaurant Grande Provence Estate, Main Road, Franschhoek ▪ Open Tue-Sun 10:00-22:00 ▪ Children welcome ▪ Wheelchair-friendly ▪ Major credit cards accepted ▪ Corkage R15 ▪ Owner Grande Provence Properties Ltd ▪ restaurant@agustawines.co.za ▪ www.agustawines.co.za ✆ **(021) 876·4143** 🖷 (021) 876·3118

A gentle stroll within the estate brings you to Grande Provence Restaurant where you will find menus designed for sophisticated yet unpretentious dining. Our chefs work with the very best fresh market produce and our food reflects a strong emphasis on seasonal flavours. Dining at Grande Provence also provides a unique opportunity to familiarise yourself with some of the estate's finest vintages complemented by stylish food and excellent service. (See also Stay-over section and A-Z for Agusta Wines.)

Haute Cabrière Cellar Restaurant Pass Road, Franschhoek ▪ International cuisine ▪ Lunch daily; dinner Oct-Apr (daily) & May-Sep (Fri & Sat) ▪ Booking advised ▪ Children welcome ▪ Wheelchair-friendly ▪ Major credit cards accepted ▪ No BYO ▪ Owners Matthew & Nicky Gordon ▪ hautecab@iafrica.com ▪ www.hautecabriere.com ✆ **(021) 876·3688** 🖷 (021) 876·3691

High up on the Franschhoek pass two unique talents, cellarmaster Achim von Arnim and chef-patron Matthew Gordon, reinvent the eating-out experience. It's a gastronomic adventure with a menu created to complement the Haute Cabrière wines and Pierre Jourdan Cap Classiques. No starters or main courses, just a variety of dishes in full and half portions to pair with the wines. (See also Stay-over section for Auberge Clermont and Burgundy Bourgogne Manor House & Cottages.)

La Couronne Restaurant Dassenberg Road, Franschhoek ▪ Classic European cuisine ▪ Open daily breakfast 07:00-11:00, lunch 12:00-15:00 & dinner 19:00-21:30 ▪ Booking advised ▪ Children welcome ▪ Wheelchair-friendly ▪ Major credit cards accepted ▪ Corkage R25 ▪ Owners Erwin Schnitzler & Miko Rwayitare ▪ reservations@lacouronnehotel.co.za ▪ www.lacouronnehotel.co.za ✆ **(021) 876·2770** 🖷 (021) 876·3788

High in the Franschhoek foothills, blessed with magnificent views, this small luxury hotel boasts one of the 50 most exciting restaurants in the world, according to *Condé Nast Traveller*. 'Classic international' is the tone. The extensive winelist and imaginative cuisine may be enjoyed on the terrace in summer or beside the fire in winter. This must be one of the most romantic settings on the planet. (See also Stay-over section.)

La Petite Ferme Restaurant Pass Road, Franschhoek ▪ French country cuisine ▪ Lunch daily from 12:00-16:00 ▪ Closed 25 Dec & 1 Jan ▪ Booking advised ▪ Children welcome ▪ Major credit cards accepted ▪ Corkage R12 ▪ Owners Dendy Young family ▪ lapetite@iafrica.com ✆ **(021) 876·3016** 🖷 (021) 876·3624

Magnificent views, innovative cuisine and warm hospitality have established this restaurant as one of *Wine* Magazine's Top 10 restaurants in their 10-year anniversary edition. Three generations of the Dendy Young family have been involved here. Natalie Edgcumbe runs the restaurant and guest suites with the help of Adéle Kirsten, allowing Mark Dendy Young to concentrate on the increased wine production. The wines are available on the winelist (all by the glass) or in limited quantities to patrons. The all-girl kitchen is headed up by Olivia Mitchell, assisted by Carina Bouwer. Together they bring an innovative dimension to a menu rooted in French country cuisine with African, Malay and international influences. (See also Stay-over & A-Z sections.)

Le Café Boschendal Pniel Road (R310), 1,5 km from junction with R45, Groot Drakenstein ▪ Cape-French light lunches ▪ Open Mon-Sun 10:00-17:00 ▪ Closed Good Friday, 1 May & 16 June ▪ Children welcome ▪ Wheelchair-friendly ▪ Major credit cards accepted ▪ Indoor/outdoor seating ▪ No BYO ▪ Owners Boschendal Ltd ▪ reservations@boschendal.com ▪ www.boschendal.com ✆ **(021) 870·4282/3** 🖷 (021) 874·2137

Tucked away in the original slave quarters, Le Café serves tasty light lunches and country-style teas with the best scones in the valley. Enjoy traditional bobotie in the cosy restaurant in winter; in summer, relax outdoors with a glass of wine, a slice of quiche, or a baguette and a salad under the dappled shade of ancient oaks.

Le Pique-Nique Boschendal Pniel Road (R310), 1,5 km from junction with R45, Groot Drakenstein ■ French-style picnic hampers ■ Open Mon-Sun, mid-Oct to mid-May. Collect picnic baskets from 12:15–13:30 ■ Closed mid-May to mid-Oct; Good Friday & 1 May ■ Booking advised ■ Special children's hampers ■ Wheelchair-friendly ■ Major credit cards accepted ■ No BYO ■ Owners Boschendal Ltd ■ reservations@boschendal.com ■ www. boschendal.com ℭ **(021) 870· 4274** ≣ (021) 874·2137

In summer Le Pique-Nique, at the foot of the Simonsberg mountains, provides a relaxed and family-friendly setting for alfresco lunches. Collect your hamper of pâtés, French baguettes, home-cured cold meats and crispy salads from the gazebo and spread your picnic at tables in the shade of pine trees or on the lawn beside a pond. Ice-cream desserts and coffees are served from the gazebo. Guests may linger in the gardens as long as they wish.

Le Quartier Français 'The Tasting Room' 16 Huguenot Street, Franschhoek ■ Contemporary cuisine ■ Open Mon-Sun for breakfast 7:30–10:30; lunch 12:00–14:30, dinner 19:00–21:00 ■ Booking advised ■ Children welcome ■ Wheelchair-friendly ■ Major credit cards accepted ■ Corkage R30 ■ Owner Susan Huxter ■ linda@lqf.co.za ■ www.lequartier. co.za ℭ **(021) 876·2151** ≣ (021) 876·3105

Cutting edge experience in this exciting refurbished restaurant. Specialising in unique 6- and 8-course tasting menus (dinners only), excitingly complemented by regional wines. Alongside enjoy honest, good food prepared with the finest seasonal produce, cooked in a wood-burning oven. Bar area and terrace open for lighter meals 11:00 till late. (See also Stay-over section for Auberge du Quartier Français.)

Monneaux Restaurant Franschhoek Country House, Main Road, Franschhoek ■ Contemporary cuisine ■ Open 7 days a week for breakfast, lunch & dinner ■ Booking advised ■ Children welcome ■ Wheelchair-friendly ■ Major credit cards accepted ■ Corkage R25 ■ Owner Jean-Pierre Snyman ■ info@fch.co.za ■ www.fch.co.za ℭ **(021) 876·3386** ≣ (021) 876·2744

Voted as one of the top restaurants in South Africa, the contemporary cuisine is innovative, prepared with fresh well-sourced ingredients and exquisitely presented. Lunches are served under spreading pepper trees in the garden while dinner is served in the understated yet elegant dining room or enclosed verandah. The winelist with its wide variety emphasises local wines of the area. (See also Stay-over section for Franschhoek Country House.)

Hermanus

B's Steakhouse No 5 Hemel & Aarde Village, National Road (R43), Sandbaai, Hermanus ■ Classic SA steakhouse ■ Open Tue-Sat 18:30-late, Sun 12–14:30, 18:30-late ■ Closed Mon (except school holidays) ■ Booking advised ■ Children 12+ welcome ■ Wheelchair-friendly ■ Major credit cards accepted ■ Corkage R20 ■ Owners Bruce & Christine Henderson ■ www.eating-out.co.za ℭ **(028) 316·3625**

Life is too short to eat bad food! That's the motto at B's, a family-run restaurant with a relaxed, friendly atmosphere and an emphasis on good food, wine and service. They go to great lengths to purchase the best cuts of well-aged meat and serve only fresh fish. Their attention to detail has won them Steakhouse of the Year (Southern & Western Cape regions) and three Diners Club Platinum winelist awards.

Schulphoek Seafront Guesthouse & Restaurant 44 Marine Drive, Sandbaai, Hermanus (entrance off Piet Retief Crescent) ■ Global cuisine ■ Restaurant for stay-over guests only ■ Closed May ■ Booking advised ■ Children welcome by arrangement ■ Major credit cards accepted (excl Amex) ■ No BYO ■ Hosts Petro & Mannes van Zyl ■ schulphoek@hermanus.co. za ■ www.schulphoek.co.za ℭ **(028) 316·2626** ≣ (028) 316·2627

Situated at Schulphoek, a beautiful quiet bay with spectacular sea views, 5km from Hermanus' centre. The dining room with its uninterrupted seascapes is staffed by a chef, offers a four-course menu du jour, delectable seafood and venison dishes, fresh herbs and vegetables from the potager and over 7 000 bottles of regional wine. One of the best fitted restaurant kitchens in the country. For stay-over guests a complimentary 4-course dinner on date of arrival is included. (See also Stay-over section.)

Kuils River

The Guinea Fowl Restaurant Polkadraai Road (M12), Kuils River ▪ Continental cuisine ▪ Lunch Wed-Mon, dinner Wed-Sat ▪ Closed Tue & Jun-Aug ▪ Booking advised ▪ Children welcome ▪ Wheelchair-friendly ▪ Major credit cards accepted ▪ Owners Adrian & Birgit Bührer ▪ guineaf@mweb.co.za ▪ www.saxenburg.co.za ✆ **(021) 906·5232** 🖷 (021) 906·0489

Well-known restaurateur Leo Romer has the pleasure of welcoming connoisseurs to the Guinea Fowl for the best fish in town. After satisfying patrons for 16 years at Le Chalet, he's now cheffing up a storm on Saxenburg wine farm. New are the light lunches in the garden *lapa*, a convivial venue for private functions and weddings. 'There are lots of restaurants – like sand on the beach,' Romer says. 'But no-one is closer to the fish than we are!' (See also A-Z section for Saxenburg.)

Zevenwacht Restaurant Zevenwacht Wine Farm, Langverwacht Road, Kuils River ▪ Global cuisine ▪ Open year-round for breakfast, lunch & dinner ▪ Booking advised ▪ Children welcome ▪ Wheelchair-friendly ▪ Major credit cards accepted ▪ No BYO ▪ restaurant@ zevenwacht.co.za ▪ www.zevenwacht.co.za ✆ **(021) 903·5123** 🖷 (021) 903·5257

The restaurant is housed in the elegant Cape Dutch manor house in a tranquil setting overlooking the lake. Global cuisine is served in a friendly, relaxed atmosphere. Quality picnic baskets are available in the gardens. (See also Stay-over & A-Z sections.)

McGregor

The Old Mill Lodge Mill Street, McGregor ▪ Eclectic country cuisine ▪ Open daily for breakfast 8:30–10:00 & dinner from 19:30 ▪ Booking advised ▪ Children welcome ▪ Wheelchair-friendly ▪ Major credit cards accepted ▪ Corkage R12 ▪ Owners Spencer & Karen Hill ▪ info@oldmilllodge.co.za ▪ www.oldmilllodge.co.za ✆ **(023) 625·1841** 🖷 (023) 625·1941

The restaurant at the lodge offers fine dining by candlelight, overlooking the vineyard and distant Langeberg mountains. A la carte four-course meals overseen by owner-chef Spencer Hill showcase the lodge's own vegetable and herb gardens. Friendly service, choice wines from the multi-Diners Club awarded list (most recent award Platinum 02), fully licensed bar and cosy lounge with fireplace guarantee a memorable visit. (See also Stay-over section.)

Montagu

Wild Apricot Restaurant 27 Bath Street, Montagu ▪ Traditional SA cuisine ▪ Open daily 07:00–22:00 ▪ Booking advised ▪ Children welcome ▪ Major credit cards accepted ▪ Corkage R10 ▪ Owner Gert Lubbe ▪ montinn@iafrica.com ▪ www.montagucountryhotel.co.za ✆ **(023) 614·3125** 🖷 (023) 614·1905

The restaurant is fully air-conditioned for the hot summers, with cosy log fires to warm you in winter. We specialise in traditional cuisine complemented by top quality wines from the region. Golden oldies played on a baby grand piano take you on a nostalgic trip down memory lane. (See also Stay-over section for Montagu Country Hotel.)

Paarl & environs

Bosman's Restaurant & Tarantella Bar Plantasie Street, Paarl ▪ Global cuisine ▪ Breakfast 7:00–10:30, lunch 12:00–14:00 & dinner 19:00–21:00; Tarantella Bar 11:00–close ▪ Closed 15 May-31 Jul ▪ Booking advised ▪ Children welcome (4+ for dinner) ▪ Wheelchair-friendly ▪ Major credit cards accepted ▪ No BYO ▪ Restaurant manager & cellarmaster Kent Scheermeyer ▪ reserve@granderoche.co.za ▪ www.granderoche.com ✆ **(021) 863·2727** 🖷 (021) 863·2220

Wind your way through the winelands and stop at Bosman's for light, elegant, informal lunches complemented by splendid wines from the superbly stocked cellar (Diners Club Winelist Diamond awards 00, 01, 02, 03 and 04; awarded the Best Winelist in South Africa by *Wine* magazine in 2003). Bosman's is a world-class restaurant providing contemporary Cape gourmet cuisine in the gracious atmosphere of a magnificent manor house. The Grande Roche, a 5-star estate hotel (see separate Stay-over entry), has become a legend on the hospitality scene, winning a formidable array of awards and culinary accolades. Besides receiving Satour's first Hotel of The Year award for its 'incredible attention to detail, impeccable grounds, excellent food and superb levels of luxury', its latest achievements include the *Business Day* Restaurant of the Year Award in 2002, being the only South African restaurant to be ranked among the top 10 in the world in the Malaysian newspaper, *New Strait Times*, as well as being on the Top 10 list of wine country hotels of the world in America's *Food & Wine* magazine. It is also the first and only hotel-restaurant on the African continent to achieve Relais Gourmand status, one of the world's highest Relais & Chateaux culinary appellations.

De Leuwen Jagt Restaurant Seidelberg Wine Farm, Suid Agter-Paarl Road, Suider-Paarl ▪ SA cuisine ▪ Open daily 09:00–18:00 (Oct-Mar) & 10:00–17:00 (Apr-Sep) ▪ Booking advised ▪ Children welcome ▪ Wheelchair-friendly ▪ Major credit cards accepted ▪ No BYO ▪ Owner Herman Kotze ▪ deleuwenjagt@seidelberg.co.za ▪ www.seidelberg.co.za ℂ **(021) 863·5222** ▦ (021) 863·3797

De Leuwen Jagt restaurant is situated on the breathtaking Seidelberg wine estate. As if winning wines, appetising fare and beautiful glass art were not enough, unbelievable views and three centuries of tradition add to the attractions. The stunning mountainside location of the restaurant, combined with delectable cuisine, superb Seidelberg wines, tasteful surroundings and attentive service, make it a favourite with visitors and locals alike. There's bobotie, ostrich and venison to tempt tourists, backed by fabulous salads and lighter fare. Seidelberg is a family-friendly estate – a children's menu, jungle gym and farm animals keep small fry occupied. Take exit 47 from the N1, then follow the signs to neighbouring Fairview. (See also A-Z section.)

Lilly Pad Anura Wine Farm, Simondium Road, Klapmuts ▪ Contemporary African cuisine ▪ Open Tue-Sun 10:00–16:00 ▪ Closed Mon ▪ Children welcome ▪ No BYO ▪ Owners Tymen & Jenny Bouma ▪ info@anura.co.za ▪ www.anura.co.za ℂ **(021) 875·5360** ▦ (021) 875·5657

The restaurant has breathtaking views of the Simonsberg and is surrounded by vineyards. We serve light lunches made from fresh products through to three-course meals. Functions welcome (40-60 seater), or enjoy coffee and scones in front of the fireplace. (See also A-Z section for Anura Vineyards.)

Marc's 129 Main Road, Paarl ▪ Mediterranean cuisine ▪ Open daily for lunch; dinner Mon-Sat; light meals served in afternoons ▪ Booking advised ▪ Children welcome ▪ Wheelchair-friendly ▪ Major credit cards accepted ▪ Corkage R20 ▪ Owner Marc Friederich ▪ ℂ **(021) 863·3980** ▦ (021) 863·3990 chezmarc@mweb.co.za

Situated on the historical Main Street of Paarl, Marc's Mediterranean Cuisine & Garden is the 2003 winner of the *Eat Out* Johnnie Walker best new restaurant in the winelands award. Owner and award-winning sommelier Marc Friederich and Austrian chef Thomas Talkner will delight you with their fresh, simple and imaginative food. Also worth a mention is their daily fresh bread baked in a wood-fired oven, the warm elegant lounge, and future wine and cigar bar.

Rhebokskloof Restaurant Rhebokskloof Private Cellar, Wine Route No 8, Agter-Paarl Road, Windmeul ▪ Global cuisine ▪ Open 7 days a week: Thu-Mon am-late; Tue & Wed am-lunch (closed for dinner) ▪ Booking advised ▪ Children welcome ▪ Wheelchair-friendly ▪ Major credit cards accepted ▪ No BYO ▪ Owners Rhebokskloof Farming & Trading ▪ restaurant@rhebokskloof.co.za ▪ www.rhebokskloof.co.za ℂ **(021) 869·8606** ▦ (021) 869·8906

Rhebokskloof Restaurant offers an unforgettable journey to enjoy top-quality wines from an award-winning winelist which highlights Rhebokskloof's own wines, combined with excellent innovative global cuisine created by our executive chef in one of South Africa's Top 100 kitchens, in one of the most beautiful locations in the winelands. Come and enjoy a journey of the senses. (See also A-Z section.)

The Restaurant at Pontac 16 Zion Street, Paarl ▪ International cuisine with local flair ▪ Open daily for lunch & dinner ▪ Booking advised ▪ Children welcome ▪ Wheelchair-friendly ▪ Major credit cards accepted ▪ Corkage R30 ▪ Owners Tim & Deseré Orrill-Legg ▪ orrill-legg@pontac.com ▪ www.pontac.com ✆ **(021) 872·0445** 🖷 (021) 872·0460

Part of a beautifully restored historic estate, which today also houses a 23-room boutique hotel, The Restaurant at Pontac is renowned for its provocative cuisine and delightful ambience. Patrons dine alfresco on a whitewashed patio, or inside in a restaurant decorated in original Cape vernacular. With classical French roots, the culinary style is enhanced by local influences and flavours, and everything on the menu is available in full or half portions. Smoking section. (See also Stay-over section.)

Robertson

Fraai Uitzicht 1798 Klaas Voogds East, on Route 62 between Robertson & Montagu ▪ Contemporary country cuisine ▪ Open Wed-Sun from 11:00 ▪ Closed Mon & Tue; Jun & Jul; 24, 25 & 31 Dec, 1 Jan ▪ Booking advised ▪ Wheelchair-friendly ▪ Major credit cards accepted ▪ No BYO ▪ Owners Axel Spanholtz & Mario Motti ▪ info@fraaiuitzicht.com ▪ www.fraaiuitzicht.com ✆/🖷 **(023) 626·6156**

Fraai Uitzicht 1798, the historic wine and guest farm with restaurant, welcomes you to a real vineyard experience. Attentive hosts provide a relaxed ambience for a fine wine and dine experience in the award-winning restaurant. Contemporary country cuisine, prepared with personal attention using fresh produce from the vegetable and herb garden, is complemented by a selection of the best wines the Robertson valley of wine and roses has to offer. (See also Stay-over and A-Z sections.)

Weltevrede Restaurant Weltevrede, Eilandia, Robertson ▪ Country cuisine ▪ Open daily from 6:00-20:30 ▪ Booking advised ▪ Children welcome ▪ Wheelchair-friendly ▪ Major credit cards accepted ▪ No BYO ▪ Owner Tina du Preez ▪ weltevrede.guestfarm@intekom.co.za ▪ www.weltevredegf.co.za ✆ **(023) 626·2073** 🖷 (023) 626·1895

In the hustle bustle of today's busy life, it is always good to hear people say 'everything here is so tranquil, quiet, and away from the rush of city life'. If this is how our guests see our establishment, we have accomplished more than what we bargained for. Our food is traditional home-style food – proudly South African. (See also Stay-over section and A-Z section for Bon Cap Organic Wines.)

Simon's Town

Bon Appétit Restaurant 90 St George's Street, Simon's Town ▪ French cuisine ▪ Open Tue-Sat for lunch 12:00-14:00; dinner 18:30-22:00 ▪ Closed Sun & Mon ▪ Booking advised ▪ Wheelchair-friendly ▪ Major credit cards accepted ▪ Corkage R20 ▪ Owners Judith & Manu Guillet ▪ www.eating-out.com ✆/🖷 **(021) 786·2412**

Michelin-trained French chef Manu Guillet produces fine French cuisine, prepared to order from the freshest local ingredients. Listed as one of SA's Top 100 restaurants for five years running and awarded 5-stars by *Wine* magazine for outstanding cheffing ability. Bon Appétit is located on the main road in Simon's Town in the 1902 British Hotel building.

Somerset West & Environs

96 Winery Road Restaurant Zandberg Farm, Winery Road (off R44), Firgrove ▪ Upmarket, rustic country cuisine ▪ Lunch daily from 12:00-15:00, dinner Mon-Sat from 19:00 ▪ Closed Sun eve ▪ Booking advised ▪ Children welcome ▪ Wheelchair-friendly ▪ Major credit cards accepted ▪ Corkage R25 ▪ Owners Ken Forrester, Martin Meinert, Allan Forrester & Natasha Harris ▪ wineryrd@mweb.co.za ▪ www.96wineryroad.co.za ✆ **(021) 842·2020** 🖷 (021) 842·2050

From the start in May 1996 it has been our goal to delight each guest with a superb dining experience in our warm, relaxing venue in the heart of the Helderberg winelands. Nominated a Top 10 restaurant in the 2004 Eat Out awards, 96 has become a sort of HQ for local and international wine luminaries. Food is fresh, colourful, uncomplicated, and cooked with care and generosity. The menu changes frequently according to the whim and creativity of chef Natasha Harris and Mother Nature. The winelist is extensive with choices from the Helderberg region and the 'rest of the world', with something to suit every pocket and palate.

Die Ou Pastorie 41 Lourens Street, Somerset West ▪ Contemporary cuisine ▪ Lunch Tue-Fri 12:00-14:00, dinner Mon-Sat 19:00-close ▪ Closed Sun ▪ Booking advised ▪ Children 12+ welcome ▪ Major credit cards accepted ▪ Corkage R30 ▪ info@dieoupastorie.co.za ▪ www.dieoupastorie.co.za ✆ **(021) 850·1660** 🖷 (021) 851·3710

Good food, excellent service and dedication to guests' satisfaction are the cornerstones of this restaurant, among the finest in the Western Cape. Die Ou Pastorie offers an innovative and modern à la carte menu which changes seasonally. This and the award-winning winelist make Die Ou Pastorie an unforgettable experience. (See also Stay-over section.)

Garden Terrace NH The Lord Charles Hotel, cnr Faure & Stellenbosch roads, Somerset West ▪ Eastern, Oriental, Global & African cuisine ▪ Open daily for breakfast & dinner ▪ Booking advised ▪ Children welcome ▪ Wheelchair-friendly ▪ Major credit cards accepted ▪ Corkage R25 ▪ Managing director (SA) Erik Jansen ▪ info@nh-hotels.co.za ▪ www.nh-hotels.co.za ✆ **(021) 855·1040** 🖷 (021) 855·1107

The Garden Terrace offers all our guests the comfort and grace of a relaxed, uncluttered, airy dining room where the breakfast and dinner buffets are meticulously assembled to give our guests the freshest and tastiest produce from surrounding areas. With the hands-on interaction between the chefs and our guests, the live action stations of the show kitchen have become a focal point in this restaurant. Get creative and design your own hot breakfast, or ask the chefs to turn your dinner into a taste and flavour tour from around the world. Special sauces and spices from the four corners of the earth add to the excitement of the themed evenings in the Garden Terrace. Fresh oysters, Eastern curries, Oriental stir-fries, rare roast beef carveries, traditional barbeques and lavish desserts offer our guests a variety of choices to suit any palate. (See also Stay-over section.)

La Vigna NH The Lord Charles Hotel, cnr Faure & Stellenbosch roads, Somerset West ▪ Eastern, Oriental, Global & African cuisine ▪ Open daily for lunch & dinner ▪ Booking advised ▪ Children welcome ▪ Wheelchair-friendly ▪ Major credit cards accepted ▪ Corkage R25 ▪ Managing Director (SA) Erik Jansen ▪ info@nh-hotels.co.za ▪ www.nh-hotels.co.za ✆ **(021) 855·1040** 🖷 (021) 855·1107

Join us for an à la carte lunch or dinner in our newly renovated, stylish restaurant. Chef Llewellyn Hurter has created a culinary tour de force with a simple yet varied menu which will tantalise all palates. With the recent renovation of the restaurant, emphasis was placed on modernising it with minimalist lines, varied textures and eclectic table settings. While more contemporary in style, we have gone to great lengths to maintain that warm, welcoming feeling synonymous with NH The Lord Charles. The adjacent wine cellar, which houses our award-winning wines, can be used as a private dining or meeting room for up to 14 guests. Be it a formal three or four-course dinner or a quick salad for lunch, La Vigna will cater for all your gastronomic needs. (See also Stay-over section.)

L'Auberge du Paysan Raithby Road, off the R44 between Somerset West & Stellenbosch ▪ French cuisine ▪ Lunch Tue-Sun 12:00-14:00, dinner Tue-Sat 19:00-22:00 ▪ Closed Sat lunch & all day Mon ▪ Booking advised ▪ Children 6+ welcome ▪ Wheelchair-friendly ▪ Major credit cards accepted ▪ Corkage R35 ▪ Owners Frederick Thermann & Michael Kovensky ▪ www.aubergedupaysan.co.za ✆/🖷 **(021) 842·2008**

Patron Frederick Thermann's style and panache highlight the discreet charms of this chic French country restaurant, acknowledged to be among the finest in the country. The elegant appointments, decor and ambience complement the traditional French menu with specialities from Alsace, Burgundy and Provence. In summer, sip pre-dinner cocktails on the patio, and in winter, wine and dine in the romantic warmth of the open log fire. Sizzling escargots, lean, crispy roast duckling and the finest crème brûlée are the house specialities. In winter, oysters, venison and game birds, and in summer, crustaceans and fresh berries from Stellenbosch are seasonal delights. For the grande finale, treat yourself to crêpes Suzette prepared at your table. Superb winelist. (See also Stay-over section for La Bonne Auberge & A-Z section.)

NH The Lord Charles Hotel There are three venues featured at this Helderberg hotel — Garden Terrace, La Vigna and St Andrews 19th Hole. (See separate listings.)

St Andrews 19th Hole NH The Lord Charles Hotel, cnr Faure & Stellenbosch roads, Somerset West ▪ Eastern, Oriental, Global & African cuisine ▪ Open daily from 17:00-24:00 ▪ Wheelchair-friendly ▪ Major credit cards accepted ▪ Managing director (SA) Erik Jansen ▪ info@nh-hotels.co.za ▪ www.nh-hotels.co.za ℂ **(021) 855·1040** 📠 (021) 855·1107

Fashioned on its renowned namesake, The Royal and Ancient golf course in Scotland, St Andrews pub has become a sought-after venue for smaller get-togethers in the Helderberg area. With authentic memorabilia from bygone days, the warm and inviting ambience of this pub is a welcome respite after the day's activities. (See also Stay-over section.)

The Avontuur Restaurant Avontuur Wine Estate, Stellenbosch Road (R44), Somerset West ▪ Contemporary country cuisine ▪ Open Mon-Fri 9:00-17:00, Sat & Sun 9:00-16:00 ▪ Closed Good Friday & Christmas day ▪ Booking essential ▪ Children welcome ▪ Wheelchair-friendly ▪ Major credit cards accepted ▪ No BYO ▪ Owners/chefs Zunia Boucher-Myers & Melanie Paltoglou (restaurant) ▪ info@avontuurestate.co.za ▪ www.avontuurestate.co.za ℂ **(021) 855·4296** 📠 (021) 855·4600

Set adjacent to the wine cellar, this intimate restaurant with views of the vineyards, ocean and Table Mountain specialises in fresh, uncomplicated and generous meals with emphasis on using local and, where possible, organic ingredients. The à la carte menu boasts three delectable breakfast choices, a full Traditional, Greek meze and a health option. The lunch menu comprises a mouthwatering selection, from soup, quiche, platters and sandwiches to a specials blackboard listing the chefs' choices of the day — succulent beef fillet accompanied by a cream and mushroom brandy sauce, fresh linefish with peppadews and capers, and ending off with our renowned crème brûlée — all to be enjoyed beside the log fire or out in the sun-drenched garden. (See also A-Z section.)

Stellenbosch & Environs

33 Stellenbosch Vlottenburg Road (off R310), Stellenbosch ▪ Mediterranean cuisine ▪ Open for lunch Wed-Fri & Sun 12:00-14:30 (Sat — functions only), dinner Tue-Sat from 19:00 (Mon by prior arrangement) ▪ Free courtesy transport (booked in advance to/from guesthouses/hotels in central Stellenbosch) ▪ Booking advised ▪ Children welcome ▪ Wheelchair-friendly ▪ Major credit cards accepted ▪ Corkage R25 (wine) & R50 (Champagne, MCC & functions) ▪ French & German spoken ▪ Owners Simon Lavarack & Louise Obertüfer ▪ info@33.co.za ▪ www.33.co.za ℂ **(021) 881·3793** 📠 (021) 881·3140

33 Stellenbosch is an immaculately restored homestead, situated in the very heart of the Stellenbosch winelands. Visitors are captivated not only by the stunning courtyard and fountain for alfresco dining in summer but also by the elegant ambience and charm exuded with comfortable sofas and a roaring fire in winter. The restaurant has been crowned with numerous accolades and is considered by many as the 'best kept secret in Stellenbosch'. We invite you to enjoy our unique brand of hospitality. (See also Stay-over section.)

De Oewer Aan de Wagenweg (next to De Volkskombuis), Stellenbosch ▪ Global cuisine ▪ Lunch 7 days a week 12:00-15:00, dinner Mon-Sat 18:30-22:00 & Sun (Sep-May) ▪ Closed Good Friday, 26 Dec & 1 Jan ▪ Booking advised ▪ Wheelchair-friendly ▪ Major credit cards accepted ▪ Corkage R15 ▪ Owners Dawid & Christelle Kriel ▪ mail@volkskombuis.co.za ▪ www.deoewer.co.za ℂ **(021) 886·5431** 📠 (021) 883·3413

Settled on the banks of the Eerste River under venerable oaks, this restaurant is well known for its alfresco-style lunches and barbeque menus. Wide selection of Mediterranean dishes and an extensive winelist. Ideal for functions.

De Volkskombuis Aan de Wagenweg, Stellenbosch ▪ SA cuisine ▪ Lunch 7 days a week 12:00-15:00, dinner Mon-Sat 18:30-22:00 & Sun (Jun-Aug) ▪ Closed Good Friday, 26 Dec & 1 Jan ▪ Booking advised ▪ Wheelchair-friendly ▪ Major credit cards accepted ▪ Corkage

R15 ▪ Owners Dawid & Christelle Kriel ▪ mail@volkskombuis.co.za ▪ www.volkskombuis. co.za ℂ **(021) 887·2121/887·5239** 🖷 (021) 883·3413

Situated in the heart of Stellenbosch, just off Dorp Street, De Volkskombuis has specialised in traditional fare for a quarter-century. Dawid and Christelle Kriel took over the family business in 2001 and with their personal touch, their passion for food, wine and people, De Volkskombuis is — more than ever — the place to go for a good meal in good company, seven days a week. Diners Club Platinum 02 award-winning winelist.

Fishmonger Stellenbosch NPK Building, cnr Ryneveld & Plein streets, Stellenbosch ▪ Mediterranean seafood ▪ Mon-Sat 12:00–22:00, Sun 12:00–21:00 ▪ Closed Christmas, New Year & Good Friday ▪ Booking advised ▪ Children welcome ▪ Wheelchair-friendly ▪ Major credit cards accepted ▪ Corkage R8 ▪ Owners André Viljoen, Craig Seaman & Nico Strydom ▪ fishmonger@adept.co.za ℂ **(021) 887·7835** 🖷 (021) 887·7834

Fishmonger is a bustling Mediterranean-style alfresco taverna in the heart of the winelands, where patrons enjoy the best and freshest seafood (sushi an added attraction), with service to match. The winelist showcases local producers and changes seasonally. Good food, good service and good wine are the watchwords here.

Flavours Devon Valley Hotel, Devon Valley Road, Stellenbosch ▪ Contemporary Cape cuisine ▪ Open daily for breakfast 07:00–11:00, lunch & dinner 11:00–22:00 ▪ Booking advised ▪ Children welcome ▪ Wheelchair-friendly ▪ Major credit cards accepted ▪ Corkage R20 ▪ Owner LGI Hotels & Vineyards ▪ info@devonvalleyhotel.com ▪ www. devonvalleyhotel.com ℂ **(021) 865·2012** 🖷 (021) 865·2610

The Devon Valley Hotel's restaurant, formerly known as 'The Vineleaf', has been newly christened 'Flavours', and promises to offer guests and visitors authentic, contemporary Cape cuisine with an award-winning winelist to complement a memorable dining experience. The restaurant has a gentle and homely ambience, affording any special occasion understated elegance in a picturesque setting. Leisurely light lunches on the terrace in summer and cosy fireside dinners in winter are a firm favourite. The focus is on bold flavours, celebrating classic, uncomplicated dishes and fresh clean tastes. (See also Stayover section.)

Hermitage at Hazendal Bottelary Road (M23), Stellenbosch ▪ Russian, SA & Mediterranean cuisine ▪ Mon-Sun 9:00–14:30 ▪ Closed Good Friday, Christmas & New Year's days ▪ Booking advised ▪ Children welcome ▪ Wheelchair-friendly ▪ Major credit cards accepted ▪ No BYO ▪ Owner Dr Mark Voloshin ▪ restaurant@hazendal.co.za ▪ www.hazendal.co.za ℂ **(021) 903·5112** 🖷 (021) 903·0057

This intimate restaurant is situated between the original cellar, which has now been renovated into a tasting centre and restaurant, and the new state-of-the-art cellar, built in 1996. A lovely fireplace in the lounge creates a warm welcome and is a great place to relax after mealtimes. There's seating for some 50 people in the restaurant, with two adjoining courtyards. Outdoor seating on the patios affords beautiful views of the surrounding mountains and hills. Meals vary from light fresh salads, hearty homemade soups and specialities, to pasta and traditional Cape Malay dishes. Hazendal also offers this superb venue for functions. Russian-born owner Dr Mark Voloshin's passion for his homeland's culture saw him establish the Marvol Museum of Russian Art, which is situated inside the wine cellar, along with the conference facility, which hosts up to 40 people. Here you can see a display of Russian icons and paintings by well-known Russian artists — Mark Voloshin's private collection of Fabergé eggs and jewellery are also on permanent display. (See also A-Z section.)

Jonkershuis Restaurant Spier Estate, Lynedoch Road (R310), Stellenbosch ▪ Cape-Malay buffet ▪ Open daily for lunch 12:30–15:30, dinner Tue-Sat 18:30–22:00 (summer), Wed-Sat 19:00–22:00 (winter) ▪ Booking advised ▪ Children welcome ▪ Wheelchair-friendly ▪ Major credit cards accepted ▪ No BYO ▪ info@spier.co.za ▪ www.spier.co.za ℂ **(021) 809·1100** 🖷 (021) 881·3634

Offering a traditional Cape Malay buffet which includes soup, farm breads, cold dishes, stews, curries, Malay specialities, Cape cheeses, and hot and cold desserts. Enjoy your meal inside the 150-year-old Jonkershuis or out on the oak-shaded terrace, the favoured summer venue. A veritable feast awaits you here. (See also Stay-over section for The Village Hotel and A-Z section.)

Knorhoek Lapa Restaurant Knorhoek Road, off R44, Stellenbosch ▪ Traditional cuisine with Mediterranean flair ▪ Open Tue-Sun 12:00-15:00 ▪ Closed Jun-Aug & religious holidays ▪ Booking advised ▪ Children welcome ▪ Major credit cards accepted ▪ No BYO ▪ Owner Knorhoek Wine Estate ▪ office@knorhoek.co.za ▪ www.knorhoek.co.za ✆/ 🖷 **(021) 865-2958**

Wander amongst oaks, poplars and nasturtiums. Be delighted by birdcalls and a gurgling mountain stream. Clink wine glasses and enjoy the best of local cuisine within a Mediterranean flavour to complete the *lapa* experience. (See also Stay-over and A-Z section.)

Morgenhof Restaurant Klapmuts Road, Stellenbosch ▪ Country cuisine ▪ Open Mon-Sun 12:00-14:30 ▪ Closed Good Friday, Christmas & New Year's days ▪ Booking advised ▪ Children welcome ▪ Wheelchair-friendly ▪ Major credit cards accepted ▪ No BYO ▪ Owner Anne Cointreau-Huchon ▪ info@morgenhof.com ▪ www.morgenhof.com ✆ **(021) 889-5510** 🖷 (021) 889-5266

Enjoy mouthwatering food with a glass of one of Morgenhof's award-winning wines. Summer lunches are served in our garden under the shade of the oak and mulberry trees. In winter, relax alongside a roaring log fire in the warmth of our Gazebo restaurant. We also have a coffee shop which is open daily for breakfasts. (See also A-Z section.)

Moyo at Spier Spier Estate, Lynedoch Road (R310), Stellenbosch ▪ Modern sophisticated African cuisine ▪ Open daily for lunch 12:00-14:00, dinner 18:00-23:00 ▪ Booking advised ▪ Children welcome ▪ Wheelchair-friendly ▪ Major credit cards accepted ▪ No BYO ▪ info@spier.co.za ▪ www.spier.co.za ✆ **(021) 809-1100** 🖷 (021) 881-3634

Lunch or dine in uniquely Cape African surroundings, and relish the diversity and excitement of a truly African experience. Select your meal from the sumptuous buffet menu, and be entertained royally by performers showcasing Cape Town's cultural talent; with a programme of theatre, and dance staged from noon to midnight. (See also Stay-over section for The Village Hotel & A-Z section.)

Olivello Restaurant Marianne Wine Farm, Valley Road (R44), Klapmuts, Stellenbosch ▪ Cape Mediterranean ▪ Seasonal opening times, generally closed Mon & Tues ▪ Booking advised (essential weekends) ▪ Children welcome ▪ Wheelchair-friendly ▪ Major credit cards accepted ▪ Corkage R30 ▪ Owners Laurille Krug & Lynne Aberdeen ▪ restaurant@olivello.co.za ▪ www.olivello.co.za www.olivello.co.za ✆ **(021) 875-5443** 🖷 (021) 875-5483

Ex Café Paradiso partners Laurille and Lynne couldn't resist the opportunity to put their passion to work in these picturesque surroundings. They take great pride in ensuring that friendly service, delicious food and a magnificent setting next to the lake will be a total feast for the senses. Their Sunday speciality is a Mediterranean Table, laid out buffet-style in the kitchen. Sit back, relax, play boules, row the boat or just laze on the lawns. Olivello is the perfect setting for celebrations such as weddings, birthdays or corporate events with every detail enthusiastically co-ordinated by them. English, Afrikaans, German and French spoken. (See also Stay-over section for Marianne Wine Farm Guest Apartments)

Ons Genot Restaurant Bottelary Road, Stellenbosch ▪ Local cuisine with Belgian flair ▪ Open Wed-Mon for breakfast, lunch & dinner ▪ Closed Tue ▪ Booking advised ▪ Children welcome ▪ Wheelchair-friendly ▪ Major credit cards accepted ▪ Corkage R20 ▪ Owners Jef & Ilse van Nuffelen ▪ info@onsgenot.com ▪ www.onsgenot.com ✆ **(021) 865-2233** 🖷 (021) 865-2250

Ons Genot Restaurant is on the outskirts of historic Stellenbosch, the heart of the Cape winelands. The combination of local ingredients and Belgian cuisine makes dining at Ons Genot an unforgettable experience. Enjoy your meal inside in the cosy dining room or outside on the wooden deck overlooking the dam. Jef and Ilse will give you a warm welcome. Ons Genot Restaurant, where friends meet for good food and wine! (See also Stay-over section.)

Sir Herbert's Wine Cottage & Red Pepper Deli Aan de Wagenweg @ Volkskombuis, Stellenbosch ▪ Mon-Fri 9:00-17:30, Sat 9:00-13:00 ▪ Closed Sun & public holidays ▪ No

BYO ▪ Owners Marlé Fourie & Dawid Kriel ▪ mail@volkskombuis.co.za ℂ **(021) 883·9119** 🖷 (021) 883·3413

As part of De Volkskombuis, brother-and-sister team Dawid Kriel and Marlé Fourie have opened a delicatessen and wine shop next to the restaurant. Famous for their catering services, quiches and stuffed breads, they also do winetastings and private cheffing for house parties. Best of local wines available, gourmet cooking for take-aways.

Spier Three restaurants – Jonkershuis, Moyo & Taphuis – and The Village Hotel feature at this pleasure resort on a wine estate. (See separate listings.)

Taphuis Restaurant Spier Estate, Lynedoch Road (R310), Stellenbosch ▪ Grill room ▪ Open daily for lunch 11:00–16:00, dinner 18:00–22:00 (summer); dinner Thu-Sat 18:00–21:00 (winter) ▪ Booking advised ▪ Children welcome ▪ Wheelchair-friendly ▪ Major credit cards accepted ▪ No BYO ▪ info@spier.co.za ▪ www.spier.co.za ℂ **(021) 809·1100** 🖷 (021) 881·3634

This riverside informal restaurant has a festive atmosphere and offers a wide variety of good foods, including fish and pasta, plus an enchanting view. A good spot for families (ask for the special kiddies menu) and rendezvous for friends or colleagues. (See also Stay-over section for The Village Hotel & A-Z section.)

Terroir Kleine Zalze Wine Farm, Techno Park turn-off, Strand Road (R44), Stellenbosch ▪ Classic Provençal with contemporary Cape influences ▪ Open for lunch Tue-Sun, dinner Tue-Sat ▪ Closed Mon, Good Friday, Christmas & New Year's days ▪ Booking advised ▪ Children welcome ▪ Wheelchair-friendly ▪ Major credit cards accepted ▪ No BYO ▪ Owner Terroir Restaurant (Pty) Ltd ▪ terroir@kleinezalze.co.za ▪ www.kleinezalze.com ℂ **(021) 880·8167** 🖷 (021) 880·0862

A modern take on Provençal classics is what chefs Michael Broughton and Nic van Wyk are producing at this new restaurant under the oaks on the Kleine Zalze estate. Matched with excellent wines from the region and beyond, 'deceptively simple' dishes such as confit of duck, prawn risotto, wood-roasted springbuck and lemon tart form part of an innovative chalkboard menu inspired by the best of what's fresh, seasonal and local. Eat outdoors in summer, indoors at the fire in winter. The same talented team caters for larger private parties and weddings in the function venue (up to 150 guests). Suspended above the wine cellar, this attractive room offers a fascinating view into the heart of the winemaking process through floor-to-ceiling glass walls, and fantastic views of the vineyards and golf course from the large balcony, particularly at sunset. (See also Stay-over & A-Z sections.)

The Duck Pond Welmoed Winery – Stellenbosch Vineyards, R310, Lynedoch ▪ Country cuisine ▪ Open daily for lunch 12:00–15:00, breakfast 09:00–11:30 (by appointment only) ▪ Closed Tue (Jun-Aug) ▪ Booking advised ▪ Children welcome ▪ Wheelchair-friendly ▪ Major credit cards accepted ▪ Corkage R10 ▪ Owner Ronel van der Walt ▪ charlene_ronel@hotmail.com ▪ www.duckpond.co.za ℂ/🖷 **(021) 881·3310**

The restaurant is situated inside the winetasting building at Welmoed Winery. Ronel van der Walt had managed the restaurant since 1999 and became the proud owner in 2001. Her sister, Charlene, is the assistant manageress. Both have many years of experience in the hospitality trade and are putting it to good use at The Duck Pond. Up to 50 people can be accommodated inside the restaurant. The lawn in front can seat a further 60 people on wooden benches and can also be used for marquee functions for bigger groups. A self-contained paved island in the middle of the pond (reached by a footbridge) can accommodate approximately 80 people and may be used for functions and barbeques. The Duck Pond serves country style food focusing on a lighter, healthier approach while using the freshest ingredients from the area. (See also A-Z section.)

The Gallery Café 2a Ryneveld Street, Stellenbosch ▪ Global cuisine with SA influences ▪ Open Mon-Sat 10:00–after movies/concerts; Sun by appointment (functions only) Booking advised ▪ Children welcome ▪ Wheelchair-friendly ▪ Major credit cards accepted ▪ Corkage R35, R50 for sparkling/magnum ▪ Owners PeterPaul & Ilse Schermers ▪ pps@adept.co.za ▪ www.dorpstreetgallery.co.za ℂ **(021) 887·9560** 🖷 (021) 887·2256

Fine food, fine wine and fine art are combined in an open and relaxed setting, linked with and next to The Dorp Street Gallery. The idea is to serve honest, nourishing, no-nonsense food, or as Sir Conran puts it: to be able to see and taste what you eat. We leave out the frills, and use daily fresh and mostly local products. A limited but carefully chosen selection of good wines *only* from Stellenbosch is available. Both meals and wines are offered at a reasonable price. Regular theme events are held, like Shiraz & Jazz, Chocolate & Tango, as well as live music performances at The Dorp Street Gallery. Booking for all events is essential.

Wijnhuis Cnr Church & Andringa streets, Stellenbosch ▪ Mediterranean ▪ Open 8am-12pm daily ▪ Closed Good Friday & Christmas Day ▪ Corkage R20 ▪ Owners Paolo & Baylon Sandri ▪ wijnhuis@mweb.co.za ℂ **887·5844/33** 🖷 (021) 887·8078

Make the Wijnhuis your first stop when visiting Stellenbosch and the winelands. In a convivial and informative environment you can taste a wide daily selection of 20 wines per glass and more than 300 to buy and take home. Or stay and enjoy a bottle or two in the bustling restaurant. A branch in the Kildare Centre, cnr Kildare Road and Mains Street, Newlands (closed on Sundays) brings this winelands experience to the city.

Tulbagh

Readers Restaurant 12 Church Street, Tulbagh ▪ Global fusion cuisine ▪ Wed-Mon 12:30-14:30, 19:00-21:30 ▪ Closed Tue ▪ Booking advised ▪ Children welcome ▪ Major credit cards accepted (excl Amex) ▪ Corkage R10 ▪ Owner Carol Collins ▪ readers@iafrica.com ℂ/🖷 **(023) 230·0087** Cell 082·894·0932

Small and welcoming, this restaurant-cum-art gallery is run by Silwood-trained Carol Collins, who offers simple yet outstanding local and global cuisine. Her appetising menus incorporate the best country ingredients and, though some dishes have become trademarks, the focus remains on variety – in terms of both fusions of flavours and imaginative combinations of unusual ingredients.

Wellington

Seasons at Diemersfontein Diemersfontein Wine & Country Estate, R301, Wellington ▪ Contemporary cuisine with SA flair ▪ Open daily for lunch 12:00-15:00, dinner 19:00-21:30 ▪ Booking advised ▪ Children welcome ▪ Major credit cards accepted ▪ Corkage R20 ▪ Owners David & Susan Sonnenberg ▪ hospitality@diemersfontein.co.za ▪ www.diemersfontein.co.za ℂ **(021) 864·5060** 🖷 (021) 864·2095

Surrounded by magnificent mountains and picturesque gardens is this contemporary restaurant, celebrating the simplicity of nature in its superb presentation and quality of cuisine. Chef Brigitte Rosemann and her team create innovative dishes for all seasons complemented by award-winning wines and excellent service. (See also Stay-over & A-Z sections.)

■ Wine & food partners

Here are some recommendations on matching cuisine and wine:

Artichokes Make most wines taste metallic. Drink water or squeeze lemon onto the chokes, which seems to tone down the tinny edges, and team with a high-acid, fresh dry white.

Asparagus A difficult customer. A dry white with lots of flavour like fresh sauvignon.

Avocado Riesling, white port.

Barbecue See Braai below.

Beef Roast: Cape Bdx blend, cab, cab franc, merlot, pinot; just about any serious red. Cold roast beef: room for a bit of light here, reds that can take a spot of chilling, pinot; also rosé, blanc de noir, sparkling dry rosé. See also Stews below.

Biltong (savoury air-dried meat snack, usually sliced) Not usually partnered with wine, but try robust shiraz (or beer).

Bobotie (spicy ground-meat, usually lamb) Many possible wine-partners: try dry sparkling, fresh young chenin, riesling, pinotage or other fruity, easy-drinking reds.

Bouillabaisse Fresh young white, sauvignon, dry rosé.

Braai (the traditional barbecue, a national institution) Depends on what's being braaied, but whether meat, fish or fowl, choose a wine with character and muscle, not a fragile little thing that would be overwhelmed by the smoke for a start.

Carpaccio Meat: Just about any red. Fish: chardonnay, MCC.

Charcuterie Simple fresh reds.

Cheese A good cheddar can be excellent with an elegant red or ruby port. Cream cheese is better with full-bodied whites — try semillon or chardonnay. Goat's cheese: full-bodied white or dry red. Blue cheese: as long as it's not too powerful, good with rich dessert whites such as NLH and port.

Chicken Roast: best red or white. Pie: try light to medium shiraz or young pinotage.

Chinese MCC, dry (or dryish) white with flavour; riesling.

Chocolate Difficult. Demi-sec bubbly, fruity dry red, red muscadel, Cape Pineau des Charentes. Or wait and have a glass of dry bubbly after the choc mousse.

Crudités Simple dry white.

Curry Fish curry: wooded chardonnay is good, especially when coconut milk is an ingredient. A cheerful, slightly off-dry (and slightly pétillant) chenin blend is fine too. Also blanc de noir. Sweetish Cape Malay curries: try matching the spice with gewürz or young riesling, or contrasting with sauvignon.

Desserts See Chocolate above.

Duck Fruity young red, champagne, shiraz, off-dry riesling, pinot.

Eggs Not great for or with any wine, but a simple omelette calls for a simple glass of red.

Foie gras Sweet white, NLH/SLH, MCC, merlot.

Fruit MCC, sweet sparkling wine, Late or Special Late Harvest, hanepoot jerepiko or rosé. Strawberries: with cream: NLH; without cream: light red.

Game birds Rosé, pinot or Cape Bdx blend. Remember, the darker the meat, the darker/stronger the wine. Guinea fowl: pinot, merlot or powerful oaked chenin.

Ham Young pinot; fresh, juicy red.

Hamburgers Dry, simple red.

Ice-cream (If not too sweet) Good bubbly.

Kidneys Full red, riesling, chardonnay.

Lamb and **mutton** Roast: best red (cabernet, merlot etc). Chops: shiraz or young cab. Try to avoid mint sauce — it distorts the taste of even minty, new-clone contenders. Stews: light red.

Liver Fruity, forceful young red such as pinotage.

Mushrooms Pinot or just about any well-aged red.

Mustard sauce Light red, pinotage.

Nuts Port after a meal; sherry before; nutty desserts: MCC.

Oxtail Shiraz, zinfandel.

Pasta Seafood: sauvignon, down-table chardonnay; cream, cheese, egg, meat, tomato sauces: sturdy red.

Pastries and **cakes** SLH.

Pâté Champagne, gewürz, riesling, pinot.

Phutu or mealie meal (SA equivalent of **polenta**) Sturdy red.

Pizza Depends on ingredients, but also see pasta above.

Pork Off-dry white, fruity red, rosé, zinfandel. Pinotage with spare ribs. In Portugal, roast sucking pig is often teamed with bubbly.

Quiche Full fruity white, riesling, gewürz, sylvaner.

Rabbit Depends on how it's cooked, and the ingredients. Anything from great to simple, red or white.

Ratatouille Light, fruity red, rosé, blanc de noir.

Risotto Fish: medium-bodied dry white; mushrooms: pinot.

Salads Go easy on the vinaigrette — vinegar affects wine. A prickly fresh white or rosé with a salade niçoise. Chardonnay with a grand shellfish salad. Or something non-serious like a blanc de noir. Or top up one's water table.

Seafood

- **Fish** Dry sparkling, MCC or dry white (sauvignon or chardonnay, or a chardonnay blend) are safe choices for saltwater; more delicate white or MCC for freshwater. Grilled: sauvignon; cream sauce: chardonnay, chardonnay blend. With red-wine sauce: red used in recipe or pinot. Smoked: crisp aromatic white, sauvignon, full-bodied (wooded) chardonnay, gewürz or riesling, dry or with a touch of sugar. Sushi: a not-too-grand (or too rich) chardonnay, brut sparkling.
- **Shellfish** Grilled, boiled, steamed or cold (with mayonnaise): sauvignon, crisp young chenin or off-dry riesling. Rich sauce: MCC or chardonnay-semillon blend. Piri-piri: this spicy/hot sauce calls for a light pétillant white.
- **Calamari** (squid) Sauvignon, dry white blend or light red.
- **Cape salmon** (geelbek) Racy sauvignon.
- **Caviar** MCC.
- **Crab** Riesling or off-dry chenin.
- **Crayfish** (Cape rock lobster or *kreef)* Sauvignon or chardonnay.
- **Elf** (shad) Chardonnay, dry chenin or Cape riesling.
- **Galjoen** Sauvignon, chardonnay or full-flavoured blanc de noir.
- **Kingklip** Chardonnay or wood-matured white.
- **Langoustine** (deep-sea, from SA's East Coast) MCC, chardonnay.
- **Mussels** Sauvignon or chenin. Smoked: wooded chardonnay
- **Oysters** MCC, sauvignon, lightly wooded or unwooded chardonnay.
- **Perlemoen** (abalone) Chardonnay or sauvignon.
- **Prawns** Chardonnay or sauvignon.
- **Salmon** Chardonnay or fruity non-tannic young red.
- **Sardines** (grilled) Crisp pétillant white, young red.
- **Smoorvis** (braised fish, usually lightly spicy) Frisky (off-dry) chenin, chardonnay or young pinotage.
- **Snoek** Assertive dry white, young red or pinotage.
- **Sole** Grilled: sauvignon or Cape riesling. Sauced: chardonnay.
- **Trout** Young riesling

Snacks Of the canapé sort: aperitif white, fruity, dry to off-dry, kir, sparkling white/rosé, blanc de noir, dry sherry.

Snails Chardonnay, pinot, dry riesling.

Sosaties Local version of the south-east Asian satay; as for curry.

Soufflés Cheese: red; fish: white; dessert: dessert white.

Steak Red wine: cab, merlot, shiraz – take your pick. Pepper steak: somehow smoothes tannins, so doesn't need a mellow old bottle.

Stews and **bredies** Hearty red. Fish casserole: fresh young white, sauvignon or dry rosé. Waterblommetjie bredie: sauvignon, chardonnay, young pinotage or merlot.

Sweetbreads Chardonnay, fine claret, pinot.

Thai Draughts of cool fresh dry white for the chilli-hot dishes. Lemongrass, coconut milk and good (wooded) chardonnay go surprisingly well together. A chilled nouveau style could hold its own. Or riesling.

Tongue Gently dry white, fruity red.

Tripe Hearty red, simple dry white or dry rosé. With tomato: dry red. With onions or white sauce: off-dry chenin or chenin-blend.

Turkey Zinfandel, dry rosé, pinot.

Veal Take your pick, depending on preparation. With vitello tonnato try a chilled, light red.

Vegetables Sauvignon, probably.

Venison Powerful pinot, pinotage, shiraz or mature Cape Bdx blend.

Winelands Maps

The maps in this section (starting on page 98) show locales where wine is available for tasting/sale either at set times or by appointment. The larger-scale map below shows the areas covered by the maps, and the table starting on the opposite page lists some details for prospective visitors.

Areas covered by the maps

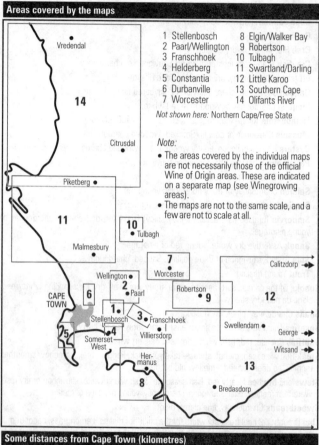

1 Stellenbosch
2 Paarl/Wellington
3 Franschhoek
4 Helderberg
5 Constantia
6 Durbanville
7 Worcester
8 Elgin/Walker Bay
9 Robertson
10 Tulbagh
11 Swartland/Darling
12 Little Karoo
13 Southern Cape
14 Olifants River

Not shown here: Northern Cape/Free State

Note:
- The areas covered by the individual maps are not necessarily those of the official Wine of Origin areas. These are indicated on a separate map (see Winegrowing areas).
- The maps are not to the same scale, and a few are not to scale at all.

Some distances from Cape Town (kilometres)

Calitzdorp	370	Paarl	60	Tulbagh	120
Franschhoek	75	Robertson	160	Vredendal	300
Hermanus	120	Stellenbosch	45	Worcester	110

Key for maps

- Main access roads
- Roads
- Gravel roads
- R62 R60 Road numbers
- Towns

Details of locales shown on maps

The table below summarises the following details by region: map grid-reference if applicable; whether open by appointment only (*℃*), open on Saturdays, Sundays (✓ = at set times; *℃* = by appointment), public holidays (✗ = closed all public holidays; otherwise assume open all or some holidays); availability of meals/refreshments, accommodation, cellar tours, facilities for children; and disabled friendliness, as audited by our disability consultant. For more information, see the A-Z directory and the Eat-out/Stay-over sections.

	Grid ref	Open by appt only	Open Saturdays	Open Sundays	Open pub. holidays	Meals/refreshments	Accommodation	Cellar tours	Disabled friendly	Child friendly
Constantia/Cape Point										
No wine route office. Phone the respective wineries.										
Ambeloui		*℃*				*℃*		*℃*		
Buitenverwachting			✓		✗	✓		*℃*	✓	
Cape Point Vineyards		*℃*								
Constantia Uitsig			✓	✓		✓	✓			
Groot Constantia			✓	✓		✓		✓	✓	
High Constantia			✓	✓		✓		✓		
Klein Constantia			✓		✗				✓	
Steenberg			✓			✓	✓	*℃*	✓	
Durbanville/Philadelphia										

Durbanville Wine Valley Association
No office hours, but phone anytime.   *℃* 083·310·1228

	Grid ref	Open by appt only	Open Saturdays	Open Sundays	Open pub. holidays	Meals/refreshments	Accommodation	Cellar tours	Disabled friendly	Child friendly
Altydgedacht			✓					*℃*		
Bloemendal			✓	✓		✓				
Capaia		*℃*								
Diemersdal			✓			✓		*℃*		
Durbanville Hills			✓	✓		✓		✓	✓	✓
Havana Hills		*℃*								
Hillcrest			✓	✓		✓		*℃*		
Meerendal			✓	✓		✓			✓	
Nitida			✓			✓		*℃*	✓	
Elgin/Walker Bay										

Walker Bay Wine Wander
(028) 316·3988
Weekdays: 09:00–18:00 ▪ Sat: 09:00–17:00 ▪ Sun: 10:00–15:00 ▪ Holidays: Normal opening hours ▪ Easter Fri & 25 Dec

	Grid ref	Open by appt only	Open Saturdays	Open Sundays	Open pub. holidays	Meals/refreshments	Accommodation	Cellar tours	Disabled friendly	Child friendly
Bartho Eksteen/Urbane			✓			*℃*			✓	
Beaumont			*℃*			✓	✓	✓	✓	
Bouchard Finlayson			✓		✗				✓	
Dispore Kamma		*℃*								
Gerhard Britz		*℃*								
Goedvertrouw		*℃*				✓	✓			✓
Hamilton Russell			✓			*℃*		*℃*		
Hemelzicht			✓		✗					
Iona						✓	✓	✓		
Luddite		*℃*								
Mauroma		*℃*					✓			

	Grid ref	Open by appt only	Open Saturdays	Open Sundays	Open pub. holidays	Meals/refreshments	Accommodation	Cellar tours	Disabled friendly	Child friendly
Newton Johnson/Cape Bay			✓		✗	✓			✓	
Oak Valley										
Paul Cluver/Thandi			✓			✓	✓		✓	
Raka			✓			✓		©		
Ross Gower/Elgin Vintners					✗	✓	✓	©		
Sumaridge			✓	✓		✓	✓			
WhaleHaven			✓			✓		©		
Wildekrans (Farm/Cellar)					✗	✓	✓	©		✓
Wildekrans (Orchard Farm Stall)			✓	✓						✓

Franschhoek

Vignerons de Franschhoek © **(021) 876·3062**
Weekdays: 09:00–18:00 (Oct–Apr); 09:00–17:00 (May–Sep) ■ Sat: 10:00–17:00 ■ Sun &
Holidays: 10:00–16:00 ■ Closed: Good Fri, 25 Dec

	Grid ref	Open by appt only	Open Saturdays	Open Sundays	Open pub. holidays	Meals/refreshments	Accommodation	Cellar tours	Disabled friendly	Child friendly
Agusta			✓	✓		✓	✓	©	✓	
Akkerdal		©	✓		✗	✓				
Allée Bleue/Meerrust			✓	✓		✓				
Blueberry Hill		©					✓			
Boekenhoutskloof		©								
Boschendal			✓	✓		✓		©	✓	
Cabrière			✓			✓		©	✓	
Cape Chamonix			✓	✓		✓	✓	©	✓	
Dieu Donné			✓	✓		✓		©		
Eikehof		©								
Franschhoek Vineyards			✓	✓		✓				✓
La Bri					✗					
GlenWood			✓	✓		✓		✓		
Graham Beck Wines			✓					©		
Haut Espoir		©								
Keerweder		©								
L'Ormarins			✓			✓				
La Couronne			©		✗	✓	✓	©		✓
La Motte			✓			✓			✓	
La Petite Ferme			✓	✓		✓	✓			
Landau du Val		©								
Le Manoir de Brendel			✓			✓	✓			
Lynx Wines		©					✓			
Mont Rochelle			✓	✓		✓		✓		
Môreson			✓	✓		✓		©	✓	
Plaisir de Merle			✓		✗		✓	©		
Rickety Bridge			✓			✓		©		
Stony Brook			✓							
Von Ortloff		©						©		

	Grid ref	Open by appt only	Open Saturdays	Open Sundays	Open pub. holidays	Meals/refreshments	Accommodation	Cellar tours	Disabled friendly	Child friendly

Helderberg

Helderberg Wine Route   © (021) 852·6166
No office hours, but phone anytime

	Grid ref	Open by appt only	Open Saturdays	Open Sundays	Open pub. holidays	Meals/refreshments	Accommodation	Cellar tours	Disabled friendly	Child friendly
Assegai		©					✓			
Avontuur			✓	✓		✓		©	✓	
Cape First		©								
Cordoba					✗			©		
Dellryst			©		✗			©	✓	✓
Eikendal			✓	✓		✓	✓	✓	✓	✓
Flagstone			✓	✓				©		
Grangehurst			✓				✓			
Helderberg/Stbosch Vyds			✓							
Ingwe		©								
JP Bredell					✗			©		
Ken Forrester/Meinert/Zandberg (96 Wnry Rd)			✓	✓		✓	✓	©	✓	
L'Auberge						✓			✓	
Longridge			✓			✓			✓	
Lourensford			✓			✓		✓		
Lushof					✗			©		
Lyngrove		©					✓			
Morgenster					✗			©		
Mount Rozier		©			✗			©		
Onderkloof							✓	©		
Post House			©							
Romond		©								
Somerbosch/Agterplaas			✓					©	✓	
Stonewall		©	©							
Vergelegen			✓	✓		✓		✓	✓	
Wedderwill		©								
Yonder Hill					✗			✓		

Little Karoo

Little Karoo Wine Route   © (028) 572·1284
No office hours, but phone anytime

Calitzdorp Wine Route © (044) 213·3775
Weekdays: 09:00-12:00; 14:00-17:00 (Oct-Apr); 09.30-12:00; 14:00-17:00 (May-Sep) ▪ Sat, Sun & Holidays: 09:00-12:00; 14:00-17:00 (Oct-Apr); 09.30-12:00; 14:00-17:00 (May-Sep)

Outeniqua Wine Route   © 072·833·8223/(044) 873·4212
No office hours, but phone anytime

	Grid ref	Open by appt only	Open Saturdays	Open Sundays	Open pub. holidays	Meals/refreshments	Accommodation	Cellar tours	Disabled friendly	Child friendly
Axe Hill		©								
Barrydale				✓		✓		©		
Bloupunt				✓			✓	©		
Boplaas				✓		©		©		
Calitzdorp				✓		✓		©		
De Krans				✓		✓		©	✓	

	Grid ref	Open by appt only	Open Saturdays	Open Sundays	Open pub. holidays	Meals/refreshments	Accommodation	Cellar tours	Disabled friendly	Child friendly
Domein Doornkraal			✓			✓		©		
Grundheim			✓							
Herold		©								
Joubert-Tradauw			✓			✓	✓	©		✓
Kango			✓			©		©		
Ladismith						✓		©		
Schoonberg		©								
Mons Ruber			✓				✓			
Montagu			✓		✗	✓			✓	
Rietrivier					✗	✓		©		
Uitvlucht			✓						✓	
Withoek						✓	✓	©		

Northern Cape/Free State/North West

Northern Cape Wine Association © (054) 337·8800
Weekdays: 07:30-17:00 ▪ Sat: 09:00-12:00

	Grid ref	Open by appt only	Open Saturdays	Open Sundays	Open pub. holidays	Meals/refreshments	Accommodation	Cellar tours	Disabled friendly	Child friendly
Douglas Cellar					✗	✓		©		
Goudveld			©							
Groblershoop			✓		✗			✓		
Grootdrink			✓		✗			✓		
Hartswater			©			✓		©		
Kakamas			✓		✗			✓		
Keimoes			✓		✗			✓		
Landzicht			✓		✗	✓		©		✓
Oranjerivier/Upington			✓		✗			✓	✓	

Olifants River

Olifants River Wine Route © (027) 213·3126
Weekdays: 08:00-17:00 ▪ Sat: 08:00-13:00

	Grid ref	Open by appt only	Open Saturdays	Open Sundays	Open pub. holidays	Meals/refreshments	Accommodation	Cellar tours	Disabled friendly	Child friendly
Cederberg			✓			✓	✓	✓		
Citrusdal Cellars			✓			✓	✓	©	✓	
Excelsious			✓							
Klawer			✓		✗	✓			✓	
Lutzville			✓		✗	✓		©	✓	
Stellar Winery			✓					©		
Van Zylskloof		©								
WestCorp/Vredendal			✓		✗	©		©	✓	

Paarl & Wellington

Paarl Vintners © (021) 872·3605
Weekdays: 09:00-17:00 ▪ Sat: 09:00-13:00 ▪ Holidays: Normal opening hours ▪ Closed: Easter Fri-Mon & 25 Dec

Wellington Wine Route © (021) 873·4604
Weekdays: 08:00-17:00 ▪ Sat: 09:00-14:00 ▪ Closed: Religious holidays

	Grid ref	Open by appt only	Open Saturdays	Open Sundays	Open pub. holidays	Meals/refreshments	Accommodation	Cellar tours	Disabled friendly	Child friendly
African Terroir	C1	©				✓	✓	©		
Anura	C7		✓	✓		✓		©		
Ashanti	F5		✓	✓		✓		©	✓	
Avondale	F6		✓					©	✓	

	Grid ref	Open by appt only	Open Saturdays	Open Sundays	Open pub. holidays	Meals/refreshments	Accommodation	Cellar tours	Disabled friendly	Child friendly
Avondvrede	C8	◷				◷		◷		
Backsberg	D8		✓	✓		✓		✓	✓	✓
Bergheim	E5	◷						◷		
Bernheim	E3		✓			✓		◷	✓	
Black Pearl	D5	◷						◷		✓
Blyde Wines	E5							◷		
Boland	E4		✓					◷		
Bovlei	G2		✓					◷	✓	
Coleraine	D6	◷				✓		◷		
Cowlin	D8		✓	✓		✓	✓	◷		✓
Crows Nest/De Reuck	D3	◷	✓			✓		✓		✓
De Compagnie	H1					◷		◷		
De Zoete Inval	E6	◷	✓			✓		◷	✓	
Détendu	C1	◷								
Diemersfontein	F2		✓	✓		✓	✓	◷		
Domaine Brahms	C3		◷					◷		
Doolhof	H1	◷								
Drakensig	D8		✓							
Eshkol	F1					✓		◷		
Fairview/Spice Route/Goats do Roam	D6		✓						✓	
Frost Vineyards	D1	◷								
Gallop Hill	D4	◷				✓				
Glen Carlou	D7		✓					◷	✓	
Hildenbrand	G2		✓	✓		✓	✓	◷		
Horse Mountain	D1	◷	✓			✓				
I Love Wine	E6		✓			✓				
Jacaranda	F1		✓			✓	✓	✓		
Joostenberg	B7		✓					✓		
Niel Joubert	D8	◷								
Kleine Draken	D6				✗	✓		◷	✓	
Kleine Parys	E5									
Kleinvallei	F4	◷								
Klompzicht	F7				✗	✓				
Kosie Möller	E6					✓				✓
KWV	E6		✓	✓		✓		✓	✓	
Laborie	E6		✓	✓		✓		◷	✓	
Landskroon	D6		✓			✓	✓	◷		✓
Leidersburg	B7	◷								
Lindhorst	D7			✓		✓	✓			✓
Linton Park	G1					✓		◷		
Main Street	E5	◷						◷		
Mason's Hill	E5	◷						◷		
Mellasat	G5	◷				✓				
Mijn-Burg	A7	◷						◷		
Mischa	F1	◷			✗	◷		◷		

	Grid ref	Open by appt only	Open Saturdays	Open Sundays	Open pub. holidays	Meals/refreshments	Accommodation	Cellar tours	Disabled friendly	Child friendly
Mont Destin	C8	©								
Mont du Toit	G2	©								
Mooi Bly	F4	©					✓			
Mount Vernon	C7	©				✓				
Nabygelegen	H1		✓			✓		©		
Napier	G2	©								
Nederburg	F5		✓	✓		✓		©	✓	
Nelson/New Beginnings	D3		✓	©		✓		✓	✓	✓
Oude Wellington	G2	©				✓	✓			✓
Perdeberg	B2				✗			©		
Rhebokskloof	D3		✓	✓		✓		©	✓	✓
Ridgeback	D3		✓	✓		✓		©		
Ruitersvlei	D6		✓	✓		✓		©	✓	✓
Rupert & Rothschild	D8									
Scali	C1	©					✓			
Seidelberg	D6		✓	✓		✓		✓		✓
Simonsvlei/Lost Horizons	D7		✓	✓		✓		©	✓	✓
Smook Wines	C1	©								
Upland	G2	©					✓			
Veenwouden	E2			✗				©		
Vendôme	E6		✓	✗				©	✓	
Vrede en Lust	D8		✓	✓		✓	✓	©		✓
Wamakersvallei	E2		✓		✗	✓		©		
Welgegund	G2	©					✓			
Welgeleë	D7	©								
Welgemeend	C7		✓		✗				✓	
Wellington	E2									
Welvanpas	H1		✓							
William Everson Wines	E6	©				✓		©		
Windmeul	D3		✓		✗			©		

Robertson

Robertson Wine Valley   © (023) 626-3167
Weekdays: 08:00–13:00; 14:00–17:00 ▪ Further opening times: enquire at Tourism Office

			Open Saturdays	Open Sundays	Open pub. holidays	Meals/refreshments	Accommodation	Cellar tours	Disabled friendly	Child friendly
Agterkliphoogte								©	✓	
Angora			©		✗					
Arendsig			©			✓				
Ashton			✓		✗	✓		©		
Bon Cap			✓	✓		✓	✓	✓		✓
Bon Courage			✓			✓			✓	✓
Bonnievale			✓	✓				©	✓	
Clairvaux			✓			✓		©	✓	
Cloverfield			✓							
De Wetshof			✓					©		
Fraai Uitzicht			✓			✓	✓	©		

	Grid ref	Open by appt only	Open Saturdays	Open Sundays	Open pub. holidays	Meals/refreshments	Accommodation	Cellar tours	Disabled friendly	Child friendly
Goedverwacht			✓			✓		©		
Graham Beck			✓					©		
Janéza		©				✓				
Jonkheer		©			✗					
Kranskop			✓			©		✓		✓
Langverwacht					✗			©	✓	
Le Grand			✓			✓		©		
Major's Hill			✓					©		
McGregor			✓						✓	
Merwespont					✗	✓		©	✓	
Mooiuitsig							✓	©		
Nordale					✗	✓		©		
Quando		©								
Rietvallei			✓			✓				✓
Robertson			✓			✓		©		
Roodezandt			✓					©	✓	
Rooiberg			✓			✓		©	✓	✓
Rusticus			✓			✓		©		
Springfield			✓			✓				
Tanagra			✓	✓		✓				✓
Van Loveren			✓			✓			✓	
Van Schoor			✓			✓		©		
Van Zylshof			✓					©		
Viljoensdrift			✓	©		✓		©		
Weltevrede			✓			✓	✓	©		
Wolvendrift			✓			✓		©	✓	
Zandvliet			✓			✓			✓	
Southern Cape										
Andy Mitchell	・	©								
Jean Daneel		©								
Oewerzicht		©				✓	✓			
Stellenbosch										

Stellenbosch Wine Route   © 021 886-4310
Weekdays: 8:30–17:00 ▪ Sat: 09:00–17:00 (Oct–Apr); 09:30–14:00 (May–Sep) ▪ Sun: 10:00–16:00 (Oct–Apr); 10:00–14:00 (May–Sep) ▪ Holidays: 10:00–16:00 ▪ Closed: Good Fri, 25 Dec & 1 Jan

	Grid ref	Open by appt only	Open Saturdays	Open Sundays	Open pub. holidays	Meals/refreshments	Accommodation	Cellar tours	Disabled friendly	Child friendly
Alto	E8		✓							
Amani	B6		©		✗			©	✓	
Annandale	E8		✓					©	✓	
Asara	D6		✓			✓	✓	©		
Audacia	E7		✓					©	✓	
Bein	B6	©								
Bellevue/Middelpos	C3		✓							
Bergkelder	E5		✓					✓	✓	
Beyerskloof	E3		✓			✓			✓	

	Grid ref	Open by appt only	Open Saturdays	Open Sundays	Open pub. holidays	Meals/refreshments	Accommodation	Cellar tours	Disabled friendly	Child friendly
Bilton	E8		✓		✗	✓	✓		✓	
Blaauwklippen	E6		✓	✓		✓		ⓒ	✓	
Blue Creek	E7	ⓒ								
Bonfoi	C5		✓		✗	✓			✓	
Boschkloof	C6	ⓒ	ⓒ					ⓒ		
Bowe Joubert	B6	ⓒ					✓			
Camberley	H5		✓	ⓒ			✓	ⓒ		
Carisbrooke	C6		✓							
Clos Malverne	D4		✓			✓		ⓒ		
Clouds	G5	ⓒ				ⓒ	✓			
Clovelly	D3	ⓒ								
Sentinel	E3	ⓒ								
De Meye	E1		✓					ⓒ		
De Toren	B6	ⓒ								
De Trafford	G8		✓					ⓒ		
Delaire	G5		✓	✓				ⓒ	✓	
Delheim	F2		✓	✓		✓		✓	✓	
Devon Hill	D4		ⓒ		✗			ⓒ	✓	
Dombeya	E8		✓			✓				
Dornier Wines	F7		✓				✓	ⓒ		
Ernie Els	F8		✓							
Fort Simon	C4		✓			ⓒ		ⓒ	✓	
Goede Hoop	C3				✗	✓		✓		
Graceland	E7	ⓒ			✗		✓			
Groenland	B3		✓			✓		ⓒ		
Hartenberg	D3		✓			✓				
Hazendal	B3		✓	✓		✓		✓		
Helderkruin	E8		✓		✗	✓		✓	✓	
Helshoogte Vyds	H4	ⓒ								
Hoopenburg	E1		✓			✓		ⓒ		
JC le Roux	D4		✓	✓		✓			✓	
Jordan	C5		✓			✓		ⓒ	✓	
Kaapzicht	B4		✓			✓	✓	ⓒ		
Kanonkop/Bouwland	F2		✓			✓			✓	
Kanu	C6		✓		✗					
Klawervlei	D1		✓					ⓒ	✓	
Klein Gustrouw	G6	ⓒ						ⓒ		
Kleine Zalze	E6		✓	✓		✓	✓	ⓒ	✓	✓
Knorhoek	F3		✓			✓	✓		✓	✓
Koelenhof	D1		✓			✓			✓	✓
L'Avenir	E3		✓			✓	✓	ⓒ		✓
Laibach	F1		✓					ⓒ		
Lanzerac	G5		✓	✓		✓	✓	✓	✓	
Le Bonheur	F1		✓			ⓒ				
Le Riche	G6				✗		✓			

	Grid ref	Open by appt only	Open Saturdays	Open Sundays	Open pub. holidays	Meals/refreshments	Accommodation	Cellar tours	Disabled friendly	Child friendly
Lievland	F1		✓	✓		✓		©	✓	
Louiesenhof	E4		✓	✓		✓			✓	✓
Louisvale	D4		✓			✓		©	✓	
Marklew	F1	©								
Meerlust/The Foundry	B8	©			✗			©		
Middelvlei	E5		✓					©	✓	
Monterosso	E4		✓					©		
Mooiplaas	B4		✓			✓				
Morgenhof	F3		✓	✓		✓			✓	
Mostertsdrift	E4	©				©				
Mulderbosch	E3	©								
Muratie	F3		✓	✓		✓	✓	©		
Neethlingshof	D5		✓	✓		✓		©	✓	✓
Neil Ellis	G6		✓							
Nietvoorbij	F4		©		✗					
Overgaauw	D6		✓					©	✓	
Quoin	F3	©						©		
Raats Family	B6	©								
Rainbow's End	H5	©								
Remhoogte	F3	©						©		
Reyneke	B6	©					✓			
Rozendal	G5	©				✓	✓	©		
Rust & Vrede	E8		✓					✓		
Rustenberg	G4		✓						✓	
Saxenburg	A6		✓	✓		✓				
Sentinel	E3		✓	✓		✓				✓
Simonsig	E2		✓			✓		✓	✓	✓
Slaley	E2		✓					©		
Spier/Savanha	C7		✓	✓		✓	✓	©	✓	
Stark-Condé	G6	©								
Stellekaya/Anatu	E5		✓		✗	©				
Stellenbosch Hills	D6		✓							
Stellenzicht	E7		✓	✓						
Sterhuis	C4	©								✓
SylvanVale (Devon Valley Hotel)	D4		✓	✓		✓	✓	©	✓	✓
Thelema	H4		✓		✗	✓			✓	
Tokara	G4		✓		✗	✓		©	✓	
Uiterwyk/DeWaal	C5		✓							
Uitkyk	F2		✓	✓		✓			✓	
Vergenoegd	B8		✓		✗			©	✓	
Villiera	D1		✓			✓		✓	✓	
Vredenheim/Stellendrift	D6		✓			✓			✓	
Paradyskloof/Vrieshof	F7	©				©		©		
Warwick	F1		✓	✓		✓		©		
Waterford	F7		✓						✓	

	Grid ref	Open by appt only	Open Saturdays	Open Sundays	Open pub. holidays	Meals/refreshments	Accommodation	Cellar tours	Disabled friendly	Child friendly
Webersburg	E8	©			X					
Welmoed/Stbosch Vyds	C7		✓	✓		✓				
Westbridge	E1		✓				✓			
Zevenwacht	A5		✓	✓		✓	✓	©	✓	
Zorgvliet	H4		✓	✓		✓	✓	©		✓

Swartland/Darling

Swartland © (022) 487·1133
Weekdays: 08:30-17:30 ▪ Sat: 08:30-13:00 ▪ Holidays: 08:30-13:00 ▪ Closed: Good Fri, 25 Dec & 1 Jan

Darling Wine Experience
Weekdays: 09:00-16:30 ▪ Sat: 09:00-2.30 ▪ Holidays: Normal hours ▪ Easter Fri-Mon

Ormonde			✓	✓		©		©		✓
Allesverloren			✓			✓		©		✓
Cloof			©			✓			✓	
Darling Cellars			✓			✓		©	✓	
Groote Post			✓			✓		©	✓	✓
Kloovenburg			✓			✓		©		
Lammershoek			©	©		✓		©		
Nieuwedrift		©	©			©	✓			✓
Porterville						©		©		
Pulpit Rock			✓			✓		©		
Riebeek			✓			✓		©		
Sadie Family		©								
Swartland			✓			✓		©		✓
Winkelshoek			✓			✓				

Tulbagh

Tulbagh Wine Route © (023) 230·1348
Weekdays: 09:00-17:00 ▪ Sat: 10:00-16:00 ▪ Sun: 11:00 -16:00 ▪ Holidays: 10:00-16:00 ▪ Closed: Good Fri, 25 Dec & 1 Jan

Alter Ego			✓			©				
Blue Crane		©								
Bianco			✓					✓		
Drostdy			✓						✓	
Lemberg			✓	✓		✓	✓	✓		
Manley			✓	✓		✓	✓	✓		
Montpellier de Tulbagh			✓	✓		✓	✓	✓		✓
Montpellier du Sud		©								
Paddagang			✓	✓		✓	✓			
Rijk's			✓			✓	✓	✓	✓	
Saronsberg			✓			✓		©		
Schalkenbosch			✓	✓		✓		©		
Theuniskraal			✓			✓			✓	
Tulbagh			✓		X				✓	
Tulbagh Mountain Vineyards		©						©		
Twee Jonge Gezellen			✓					✓		

Worcester/Breedekloof

Worcester ℂ **(023) 342·8710**
Weekdays: 08:00-17:00 ▪ Sat: 09:00-16:00▪ Sun: 10:00-15:00 ▪ Holidays: 09:00-16:00

Rawsonville/Breede Valley Wine Route ℂ **(023) 349·1791**
Weekdays: 08:30-16:30 ▪ Sat: 09:00-16:00 ▪ Sun: 10:00-16:00 ▪ Closed: Good Fri & 25 Dec

	Grid ref	Open by appt only	Open Saturdays	Open Sundays	Open pub. holidays	Meals/refreshments	Accommodation	Cellar tours	Disabled friendly	Child friendly
Aan de Doorns					✗			ℂ	✓	
Aufwaerts		ℂ								
Badsberg			✓			✓		ℂ		✓
Bergsig			✓			✓		ℂ		
Botha			✓			✓		ℂ		✓
De Doorns			✓							
De Wet					✗	✓			✓	
Deetlefs			✓			ℂ		✓		
Du Preez/Rockfields						✓		ℂ	✓	✓
Du Toitskloof			✓			✓		ℂ	✓	
Goudini			✓			✓				
Groot Eiland					✗	ℂ		ℂ	✓	
Jason's Hill			✓	ℂ		✓		✓		✓
Lateganskop								ℂ		
Daschbosch								ℂ		✓
Merwida/Riverstone			✓				✓			
Mountain Oaks		ℂ				✓		ℂ		
Nuy			✓			✓			✓	
Opstal			✓			✓		ℂ		
Overhex					✗	✓		ℂ	✓	
Romansrivier			✓			✓		ℂ		
Slanghoek			✓		✗	✓		ℂ	✓	
Waboomsrivier			✓		✗	✓		ℂ	✓	

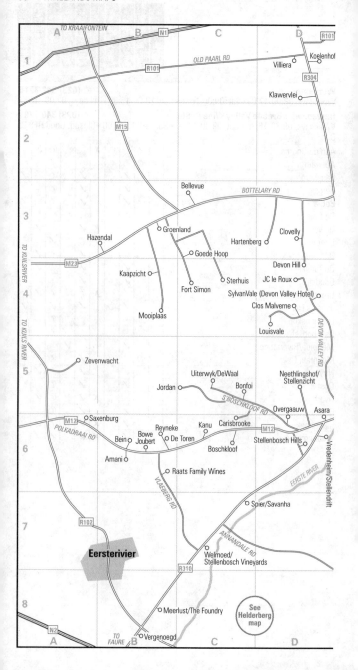

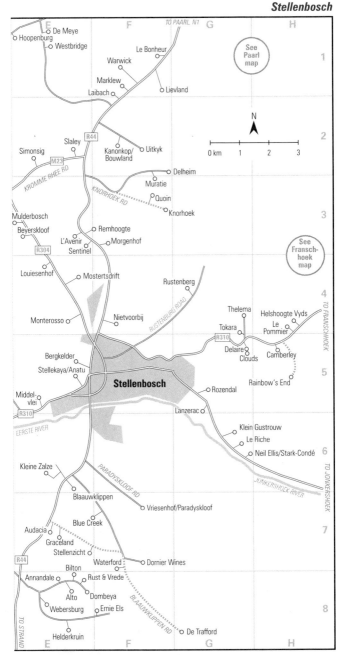

TO PAARL, N1

See Paarl map

De Meye
Hoopenburg
Westbridge
Le Bonheur
Warwick
Marklew
Lievland
Laibach

N

0 km   1   2   3

R44
Slaley
Simonsig
M23
Kanonkop/Bouwland
Uitkyk
KROMME RHEE RD
Delheim
Muratie
KNORHOEK RD
Quoin
Knorhoek

Mulderbosch
Beyerskloof
Remhoogte
L'Avenir
Morgenhof
R304
Sentinel

See Fransch-hoek map

Louiesenhof
Mostertsdrift
Rustenberg

RUSTENBURG ROAD

Monterosso
Nietvoorbij
Thelema
Helshoogte Vyds
Tokara
Le Pommier
R310
Delaire
Clouds
Camberley

Bergkelder
Stellekaya/Anatu

Stellenbosch

Rainbow's End

Middel-vlei
R310
Rozendal
EERSTE RIVER
Lanzerac

Klein Gustrouw
Le Riche
Neil Ellis/Stark-Condé

TO FRANSCHHOEK

TO JONKERSHOEK

Kleine Zalze
PARADYSKLOOF RD
JONKERSHOCK RIVER

Blaauwklippen
Vriesenhof/Paradyskloof
Blue Creek
Audacia
Graceland
Stellenzicht
R44
Waterford
Dornier Wines
Bilton
Annandale
Rust & Vrede
Alto
Dombeya
Webersburg
Ernie Els
BLAAUWKLIPPEN RD
Helderkruin
De Trafford

TO STRAND

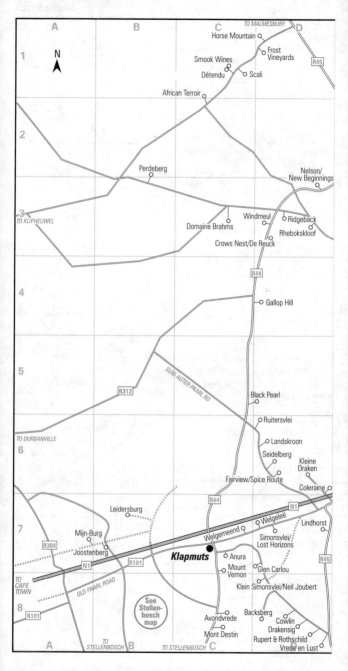

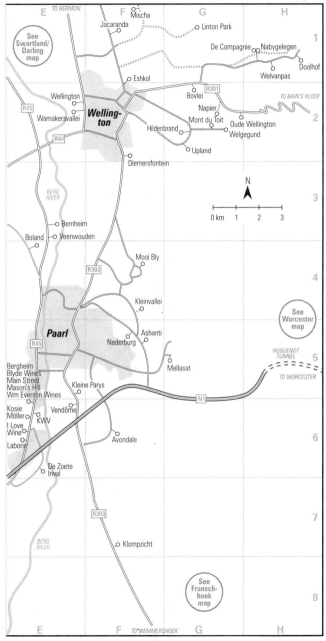

See
Swartland/
Darling
map

TO HERMON

Mischa
Jacaranda
Linton Park
De Compagnie Nabygelegen
Doolhof
Welvanpas
Eshkol
R301
Bovlei
TO BAIN'S KLOOF
Wellington
R45
Napier
Wamakersvallei
Oude Wellington
Wel**ling-
ton**
Mont du Toit
R44
Hildenbrand
Welgegund
Upland
Diemersfontein

N

BERG
RIVER

0 km   1   2   3

Bernheim
Boland   Veenwouden

See
Worcester
map

Mooi Bly

R303

Kleinvallei

Paarl

HUGUENOT
TUNNEL

Ashanti
R45
Nederburg
Mellasat
TO WORCESTER
Bergheim
Blyde Wines
Main Street
Mason's Hill
Wm Everson Wines
Kleine Parys
Kosie
Möller
Vendôme
N1
I Love
Wine   KWV
Laborie
Avondale

De Zoete
Inval

R303

BERG
RIVER

Klompzicht

See
Fransch-
hoek
map

TO WEMMERSHOEK

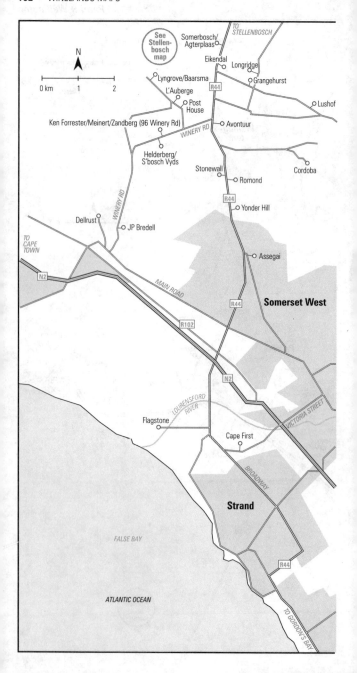

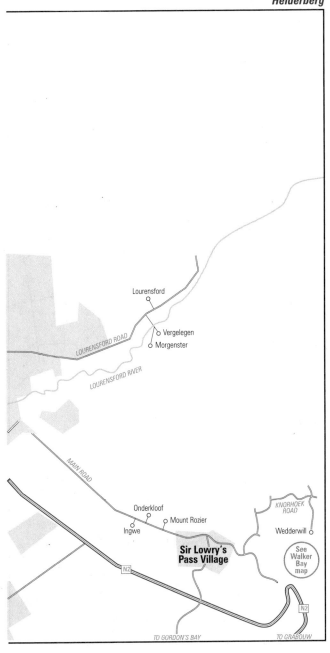

Lourensford

Vergelegen

Morgenster

LOURENSFORD ROAD

LOURENSFORD RIVER

MAIN ROAD

Onderkloof

Mount Rozier

Ingwe

Sir Lowry's
Pass Village

KNORHOEK
ROAD

Wedderwill

See
Walker
Bay
map

N2

N2

TO GORDON'S BAY

TO GRABOUW

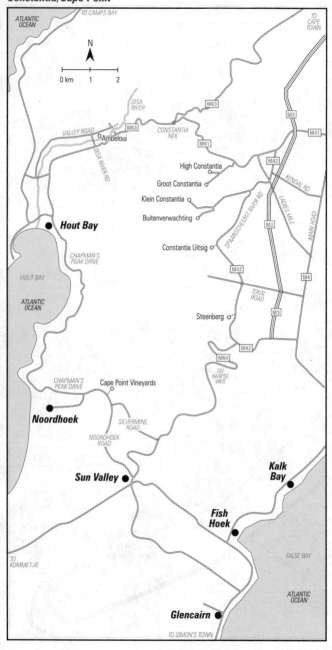

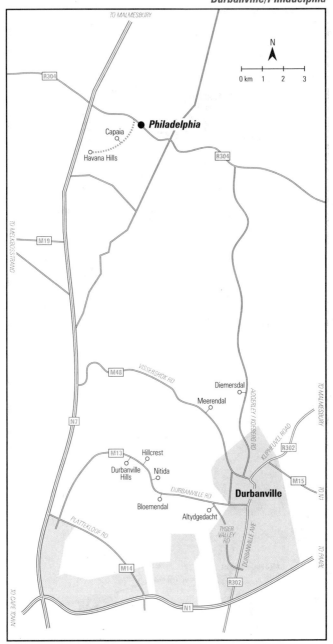

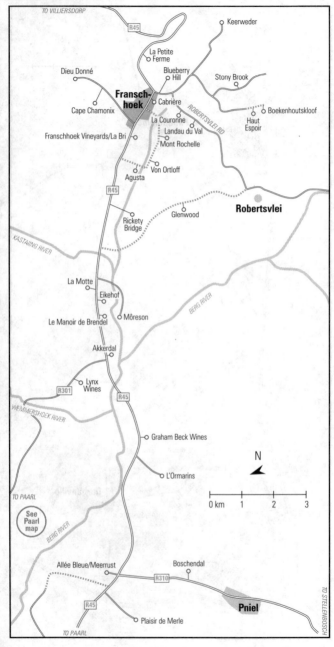

Elgin/Walker Bay

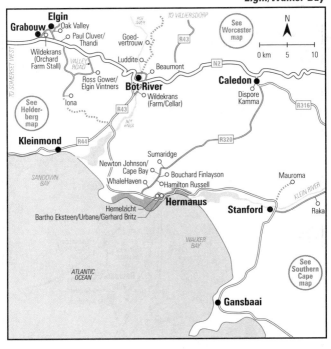

TO VILLIERSDORP

Elgin

Grabouw

Oak Valley

Paul Cluver/
Thandi

Goed-
vertrouw

See
Worcester
map

N

0 km   5   10

R43

Wildekrans
(Orchard
Farm Stall)

VALLEY
ROAD

Luddite

Beaumont

N2

TO SOMERSET WEST

Ross Gower/
Elgin Vintners

Iona

Bot River

Wildekrans
(Farm/Cellar)

Caledon

Dispore
Kamma

R316

See
Helder-
berg
map

R43

BOT
RIVER

R320

Kleinmond

R44

Sumaridge

Newton Johnson/
Cape Bay

WhaleHaven

Bouchard Finlayson

Hamilton Russell

Mauroma

KLEIN RIVER

SANDOWN
BAY

Hemelzicht

Hermanus

Bartho Eksteen/Urbane/Gerhard Britz

Stanford

Raka

WALKER
BAY

ATLANTIC
OCEAN

See
Southern
Cape
map

Gansbaai

Southern Cape

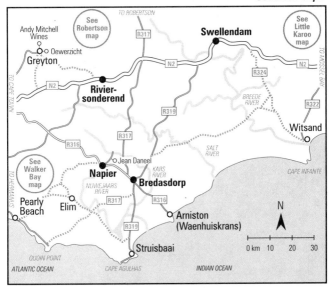

TO ROBERTSON

See
Robertson
map

R317

Swellendam

See
Little
Karoo
map

Andy Mitchell
Wines

Oewerzicht

Greyton

N2

N2

TO MOSSEL BAY

R324

BREEDE
RIVER

R322

Rivier-
sonderend

R319

Witsand

TO CAPE TOWN

R317

SALT
RIVER

R316

Jean Daneel

KARS
RIVER

CAPE INFANTE

See
Walker
Bay
map

Napier

Bredasdorp

NUWEJAARS
RIVER

R317

R316

N

Pearly
Beach

Elim

Arniston
(Waenhuiskrans)

0 km 10   20   30

R319

QUOIN POINT

Struisbaai

ATLANTIC OCEAN

CAPE AGULHAS

INDIAN OCEAN

TO HERMANUS

Worcester & Breedekloof

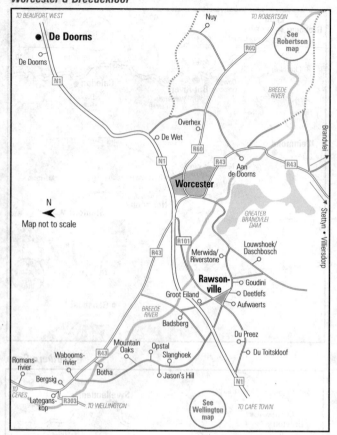

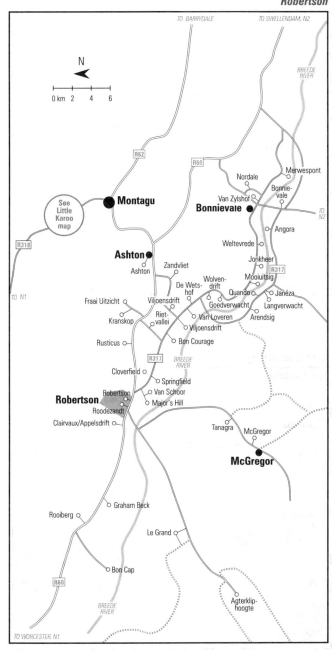

N

0 km 2   4   6

TO BARRYDALE

TO SWELLENDAM, N2

BREEDE RIVER

R62

R60

See Little Karoo map

R318

TO N1

Montagu

Nordale

Merwespont

Van Zylshof

Bonnievale

Bonnievale

Angora

TO N2

Weltevrede

Ashton

Zandvliet

Jonkheer

R317

Ashton

De Wets-hof

Wolven-drift

Mooiuitsig

Fraai Uitzicht

Viljoensdrift

Quando

Janéza

Langverwacht

Goedverwacht

Kranskop

Riet-vallei

Van Loveren

Arendsig

Viljoensdrift

Rusticus

Bon Courage

R317

BREEDE RIVER

Cloverfield

Springfield

Van Schoor

Robertson

Robertson

Major's Hill

Roodezandt

Clairvaux/Appelsdrift

Tanagra

McGregor

McGregor

Graham Beck

Rooiberg

Le Grand

R60

Bon Cap

BREEDE RIVER

TO WORCESTER, N1

Agterklip-hoogte

Tulbagh

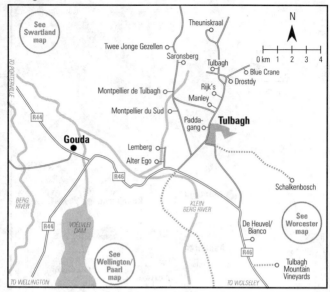

Swartland/Darling

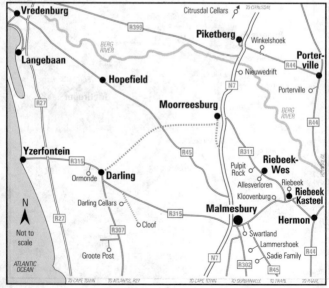

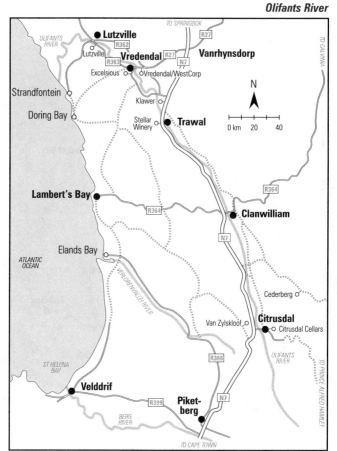

Little Karoo

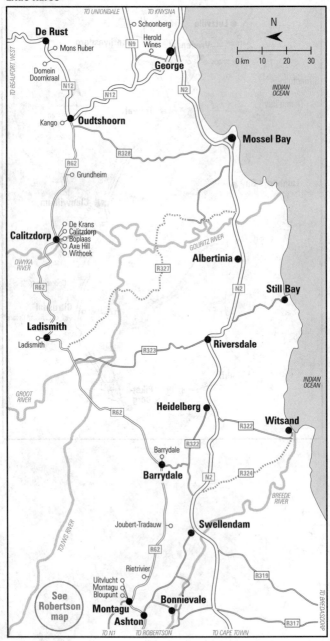

Northern Cape, Free State, North West

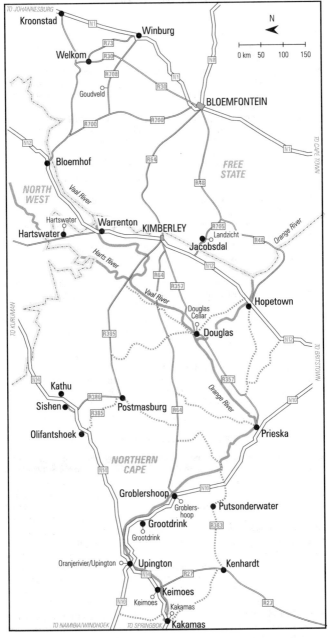

A–Z of Cape Wines

Wines in this section are entered under the name of the private producer, estate, co-operative winery or brand name of a merchant, and listed alphabetically. Entries feature
some or all of the following:

- Producer's name; only officially recognised wine 'estates' identified as such.
- Official Wine of Origin region, district or ward where winery or main vinification facility
  is situated; assume all wines described/rated bear this WO certification, unless noted.
- Date of establishment (Est).
- Date of first bottling (1stB); if bottling on property, we show the 🍷 icon.
- Tasting, sales and cellar tour times — wineries which may be visited at set hours or by
  appointment highlighted (🍷), and, where possible, reflected in the Maps section. Open
  on public holidays unless noted.
- Other attractions or activities available on the property briefly described and flagged
  thus: meals, refreshments, BYO picnics etc (🍽); accommodation (🛏); 'other' eg fes-
  tivals, function venues, walks, exhibits etc (👁👁).
- Properties audited by the guide and deemed disabled-friendly (♿).
- Name of owner.
- Name of winemaker, viticulturist and consultant, if applicable; year/month of appoint-
  ment in brackets.
- Hectares under vine (not necessarily in production); main varieties planted.
- Production, in tons and/or 12 x bottle cases (cs) and red:white ratio.
- Compliance, where applicable, with internationally recognised quality assurance and
  food safety standards such as ISO (International Standards Organisation), HACCP (Haz-
  ard Analysis & Critical Control Point) and BRC (British Retail Consortium).
- Postal and e-mail address, website, phone and fax number.

Entries may also include a brief introduction/news update, as well as listings of wines
available during the currency of the book. We give some or all of the following details:

- Wine name; vintage, colour and style;
- Grape variety/ies and fruit-source — assume own vineyards unless stated; bottlings
  certified as 'estate wine' flagged as 'EW'; bottlings made by registered estates not cer-
  tified as estate-made flagged as 'NE'. See The SA Wine Industry for more details.
- Selected recent awards and our star rating (four stars and above in red type). See Top
  Performers for a consolidated listing of recent competitions and tastings.

Refer to the section How to use this guide for further assumptions and abbreviations.

All dialling codes (021) unless noted

Aan de Doorns Co-operative Winery 🍷♿

*Worcester ▪ Est 1954 ▪ Tasting & sales Mon–Fri 8-5 ▪ Closed public holidays ▪ Tours during har-
vest by appt ▪ Owners 56 members ▪ Cellarmaster Johan Morkel (Nov 1993) ▪ Winemakers
Gert van Deventer (Sept 1997), with Nevin du Toit (Dec 2001) ▪ 1 200 ha (pinotage, chard,
chenin, colombard) ▪ 20 000 tons 5 300 cs own label ▪ PO Box 235 Worcester 6849 ▪ aded@
intekom.co.za ☏ (023) 347·2301 🖷 (023) 347·4629*

Established half a century ago and named for the thorn trees lining the nearby reaches of
the Aan De Doorn River, this Worcester co-op is now 56 growers strong. In line with the
goal he's voiced in the past ('To establish our label abroad'), cellarmaster Johan Morkel
has of late been seeing to certification from the British Retail Consortium, which sets
standards for suppliers of branded food products to the UK market. The 2004 harvest was
17% up on the previous year's, with better quality whites (and average reds).

★★★☆ **Red Muscadel** ✓ **02** fortified dessert maturing but still delectably drinkable;
plum & strawberry tones with slight spiciness, hint of good bottle-age, all buoyed
by fresh spirit. Could be cellared further. 16.9% alc.

Blanc de Noir ☺ ★★★ **04** Natural Sweet-style blush with coppery sheen, lovely ripe tropical fruit aromas, upbeat finish. Sample tasted.

Latest versions of **Pinotage** (★★★) & **Doornroodt** (★★★ dry red) not ready for tasting. **Colombar** ★★ Drink-now steely dry white; **04** lightish, with pretty bouquet of tropical fruit & honeysuckle. **Colombar-Chardonnay** ★★ **04** uncomplicated early drinking blend (80/20), fresh tropical fruit flavours, ends dry with delicate citrus tang. **Colombar Effe Soet** ★★★ Lightish-bodied, flavourful **04** (sample), similar to Dry above but sugar lifts the palate. **Sparkling** ★★★ Latest Demi-sec-style NV carbonated bubbly not tasted. **Muscat d'Alexandrie** ★★★ **02** fortified dessert with sweet notes of muscat & honeysuckle, unusual rose-petal hint, clean lingering finish. 16.3% alc. **Port** ★★★ Old-Cape fortified from tinta; **99** medicinal & whiffs eucalyptus, very sweet & raisiny. 16.5% alc. — *DH*

Adler   [NEW]

*Est/1stB 2004 ▪ Closed to public ▪ Owners/winemakers Oliver Meckler & Hans J Mamsell ▪ 200 cs 100% red ▪ oliver@olimeck.co.za ▪ PO Box 490 Riverclub 2149 ℂ **(011) 691·2964** 🖷 (011) 691·2962*

Following a tradition passed through many generations, from Hungary to Germany and now SA, Geisenheim-trained Oliver Meckler has teamed up with long-time friend Hans Mamsell to make wine under the family's Adler ('Eagle') label. Their first release is Modus M, an equal cab-merlot blend from Wellington fruit, vinified at Mischa. Having worked the last 8 years in SA for a wine (and beverage/food) equipment supplier, Meckler's philosophy is reassuringly pragmatic: 'Use only as much technology as necessary'.

Adventure see Kango
A Few Good Men see Riebeek Cellars
Affinity see African Terroir
African Collection see Rooiberg
African Gold see Old Bridge
African Horizon see Origin Wine

African Pride Wines

*Constantia ▪ Est/1stB 2002 ▪ Closed to public ▪ Owner Afrifresh Holdings ▪ Winemaker Mike Graham (May 2002) ▪ 60% red 40% white ▪ PO Box 518 Constantia 7848 ▪ info@ africanpridewines.co.za ▪ www.africanpridewines.co.za ℂ **794·0323** 🖷 794·0344*

This Constantia-based, export-oriented wine company has added a single-vineyard flagship label, Lady Anne Barnard, to its portfolio. Widely travelled winemaker Mike Graham also collects grapes from contracted growers for the single-varietal Footprint, maritime-influenced Cape Maclear and Chacma's Bark ranges destined for Europe, Hong Kong, Singapore and the US. Conducting commercial affairs is new appointee, former Vinfruco and KWV marketing man Bennie van Rensburg.

Lady Anne Barnard range
Cabernet Sauvignon ★★★★ Elegant wine, understated. Grassy/herbaceous nose, hints wet heath & leafy footpath; tone continues on **02** palate with underlying red berries; ripe tannins, supple but structured to age few yrs. 18 mths Fr oak. **Shiraz** ★★★★ **02** creamy mulberry aroma, lively, juicy palate characterised by excellent ripe Hldrberg fruit, well expressed. 16 mths oak, new/2nd fill. **Chardonnay** ★★★★ Statement wine with big oak presence; **03** flavours of lemon, lime & buttered toast; fleeting peachy whiffs. Another yr should help integrate oak & fruit, & possibly up the star rating. Fermented/9 mths new Fr oak, portion native yeasts. These WO Stbosch, all below W-Cape.

Footprint range
Cabernet Sauvignon ★★★ Spicy black plum aromas in **03**, light textured but juicy, nicely fruited. **Shiraz** ★★★ Fynbos & spice bouquet, savoury woodsmoke pervades palate, **03**

accessible, ready to drink. ±14% alc. **Chardonnay** ★★★ Preview **04** aromatic & lively on nose; succulent mid-palate zested with lime acidity, sweet finish. 10% barrel fermented. **Sauvignon Blanc** ★★★ Attractive edginess to **04**, early harvested for piercing grassiness, forthcoming, herbaceous tone repeats on palate to thirst-quenching finish.

Cape MacLear range

Shiraz-Cabernet Sauvignon ★★★ Shiraz dominated (66%) unwooded blend with smoked meat aromas, sweet ripe-fruit tastes; **03** soft, approachable, easy drinking. **Chenin Blanc-Chardonnay** ★★★ Some peach & fruit salad aromas; rounded peach flavours, **04** lively & juicy 60/40 blend. — *CR/TM*

■ *African Sky* see Drostdy

African Terroir

Paarl • Est 1991 • 1stB 1991 • Visits Mon-Fri 9-5 by appt • Fee R15 refunded on purchase of 2+ btls • Closed Dec 25/26 & Jan 1 • Picnic baskets, platters & beverages by appt; or BYO • Guest house • Tourgroups • Conferencing • Owner Jacques Germanier • Winemakers Helène van der Westhuizen, with Matthieu Lebaki (Jan 2003/May 2004) • Viti consultant s Thys Greef & Francois Brink (Sep 2000/Dec 2002) • 75 ha (own vyds: cab, shiraz) • 400 tons • BRC & HACCP certified; ISO 9001:2000 in progress • Ranges for customers: Indaba, Mooiberge, Unity & Affinity • PO Box 2029 Windmeul 7630 • office@african-terroir.co.za • www.african-terroir.co.za © 869·8103 ◻ 869·8104

New stock is taking root in this terroir: Olivier Glannaz has taken over as MD, Guy Smith steps into the sales director's slot and Helène van der Westhuizen (neé Carstens) takes on the mantle of chief winemaker for this well-established Swiss negociant business, with a quartet of vinification facilities in the Boland. One of these, at Sonop farm in Paarl, has a brand new cellar and 'wine desk', where the produce may be tasted. There's also a guest house on the property as well as a travel agency, one of whose staff conducts tours of the vineyards and cellars. Taking a wider view, there's a new look, too, to the packaging of the Out of Africa and Sonop wines, and both ranges have been extended. An upper tier of Diamond wines gets added to Out of Africa; Sonop now includes Standard, Organic and Winds of Change/Fairtrade bottlings. Winds of Change is also the title of an empowerment project pioneered on Sonop. The concept has now been extended to the company's Cilmor farms in Worcester, where 250 farm workers will benefit.

Diemersdal range

★★★☆ **Cabernet Sauvignon** Pvs were silky wines showing good balance. Minerally **02** retasted for last ed was noted as turning savoury, needed early enjoyment. **03** (★★★) not up to bar; bouillon notes on nose/palate; quite lean, carries too much oak (yr Fr).

★★★☆ **Merlot 02** offered copybook ripe plums & violets; sweet fruit still controlled by firmish tannins, needing yr/2 to settle. **03** spicy currant character, touch creamy oak; youthful yet already softer than siblings below, more giving. Oak as above.

★★★☆ **Pinotage** Round, early approachable yet seriously structured. **02** sweet fruited, supple & plummy. **03** shy mulberry whiffs, slight pinot-like forest floor hint; moderately refined, elegant; oak as above.

★★★★ **Shiraz** Last tasted was **02**, seamless combo of ripe fruit & peppery seasoning; boldly structured yet without aggression.

★★★☆ **Harmony 02** switched to Bdx blend cab, merlot, cab f (pvs added shiraz &/or pinotage). Generously & sweetly fleshed. Yr Fr oak; same claret make-up (60/30/10) & oak for **03**, endowed with blackcurrant & cedar aromas; medium body, tight & withdrawn mid-2004, only hinting at dark plummy fruit. 14% alc.

★★★★ **Chardonnay** Well-structured, satisfying, with house's supple textures. Buttery grapefruit aromas in **03**, long fresh-fruit finish. **04** ☺ shy, hint resinous oak over peach fruit; light-bodied, minerally, elegant, not overblown.

Sauvignon Blanc ★★★ **04** fragrant, hints guava/gooseberry; bright bone-dry minerally palate, soft yet very dry. All above EW.

Elixir range

★★★☆ **Sauvignon Blanc Noble Late Harvest** Soft, silky **00**, striking orange-gold colour; fairly developed aromas, some dried apricot whiffs & good botrytis dusting; clean fruity acidity controls the crème brûlée richness. Yr barrel aged. 15% alc. Grapes ex-Dbnvlle.

Milton Grove range

Chardonnay ★★★ **04** shy green melon notes on nose; supple & dry flavours; soft lemon-zesty finish.

Shiraz ★★★★ **04** shy stewed plum nose, touch white pepper; appealing plummy shiraz fruit, leathery whiff; good juice & suppleness. ±14% alc. **Semillon-Charonnay** ★★☆ Semillon in lead this yr (70/30); **04** fragrant nose with hint peach; dry flavours with citrus suppleness, creamy apple finish.

Out of Africa range

★★★★ **Cabernet Sauvignon Unfiltered 03** characterised by sweet berries & spice, rotundness for early drinking. **04** (★★★) has braaivleis whiffs over blackcurrant, quite dry fennel flavours.

★★★☆ **Pinotage 03** had a fairly lively palate with slight creamy hint. **04** continues the vibrant mode with bright mulberry nose; soft, sweetish entry; ripe but not over the top; soft, easy-drinking.

★★★★ **Shiraz** Supercharged fruit & aromas characterised punchy **03**. Similar New World exuberance displayed in **04** (sample), plummy, plump, juicy, silky. 14.6% alc.

★★★☆ **Chardonnay 03** was similar to Organic version, though slightly higher (Fr) oaked portion (30%) imparted spice to clean white-peach fruit. **04** (sample) creamy melon aromas, again hint peach; flavourful citrus crème brûlée on finish.

Merlot ★★★ **04** leafy undergrowth & hint meat, medium body; savoury dark-choc flavours. Combo Vdal/Dbnvlle fruit. **Diamond Collection Shiraz 03** more Old World than above; heathery whiffs & some pepper; mid-weight fruit, slight earthiness, dry savoury finish, quite elegant. Provisional ★★★★. **Diamond Collection Chardonnay 04** (sample) peaches & custard aromas, hint of resinous oak; quite firm, substantial; provisional ★★★★. Barrel fermented/4 mths matured. **Sauvignon Blanc** ★★★ **04** water-white; quite forthcoming peardrop & marzipan aromas, flinty grapefruit palate. Dbnvlle fruit. 12% alc.

Sonop Organic range   [NEW]

All **04**. **Cabernet Sauvignon** ★★★ Fairly closed mid-2004, though evinces good varietal character (hallmark of all these Organics); clean cassis fruit, hint of sweetness, dry finish. **Merlot** ★★★ Bright plum-jam-on-toast fruit on nose; plump, soft & chocolatey flavour. **Pinotage** ★★★ Shy pinot-like character: light-textured/coloured, muted earthiness; some grainy tannins; appealingly different from the blockbuster style. **Shiraz** ★★★ Deeply coloured; smoky/peppery damsons on nose; taut & dry with espresso flavour; elegant despite big alc 14.2%. **Chardonnay** ★★★ Spicy baked apple intro; apple again in soft & juicy palate, slightly sweet finish with hint of jasmine. **Sauvignon Blanc** ★★☆ Light bodied & not unpleasantly austere; flinty, dusty, lemon-dry flavours.

Tribal range

African Red ☺ ★★★ Latest NV shows understated plum jam aromas; livelier mulberry flavour, low tannins for easy/early drinking.

Rosé ★★ Light-bodied pink from pinotage. cinsaut, pinot; NV; muted cherry aromas, fairly succulent cherry palate, food-friendly dry finish. **African White Semi Sweet** ★ Latest version shade off the mark; shy, lightly fruited, quick finishing. Above available in glass &

1ℓ flexible packs. **Sparkling White Off-Dry** ★★ Light semi-sweet fizz with dusty pear whiffs & hint marzipan, soft lingering sweetness. All NV/uncertified.

Winds of Change range

Pinotage-Cabernet Sauvignon ★★★ **04** pinotage's smoky mulberry fruit to fore (70/30 blend); soft, silky & lightly spicy. **Shiraz-Merlot** ★★★ 70/30 blend in **04**, smoked meat, touch white pepper; soft, ripe & drinkable. 14% alc. **Chardonnay** ★★☆ Partly oaked, so wood presence minimal in **04**, green sheen; grapefruit & dried herb aromas; lean, minerally, citrus flavours, bone-dry. **Sauvignon Blanc** ★★ 04 pale, shy; some pear/peach deciduous fruit on nose; flinty, austere palate; needs a braaied snoek. Fruit for these ranges widely sourced; WOs include W-Cape, Paarl & Dbnvlle. **Azania**, **Bredasdorp**, **Kersfontein** & **Cape Soleil** ranges discontinued. — *TM*

African Treasure see Vin-X-Port
African Wine Adventure see Mooiuitsig

African Wines & Spirits

Cape Town ▪ Est 1999 ▪ Closed to public ▪ Owners Edward Snell & Co Director: David Hooper ▪ 40% red 60% white ▪ PO Box 389 Constantia 7848 ▪ aws@awsomedrinks.com ▪ www.africanwine.co.za ℂ 680·9300 ✆ 680·9386

This wholesaling and marketing company, headquartered in Newlands, is now owned by Edward Snell & Co, and its wine ranges, including Craighall and South, South West (aka SSW), are made to spec by Stellenbosch Vineyards. Other brands in the stable include Cinzano Spumante, and the Bertrams reds and Port. See separate entries.

Africa Vineyards see Winecorp

Agterkliphoogte Winery ♟&

Robertson ▪ Est 1965 ▪ 1stB 1986 ▪ Tasting, sales & tours Mon-Fri 8-5 ▪ Closed Easter Fri-Mon, May 1, Dec 25/26 & Jan 1 ▪ Tours by appt ▪ Owners 22 members ▪ Winemaker Helmard Hanekom, with Tiaan Blom (Jan 1986/Dec 2003) ▪ Viti consultant Briaan Stipp (1995) ▪ 448 ha (cab, cinsaut, merlot, pinotage, semillon) ▪ 6 440 tons ±10 000 cs own label 50% red 50% white ▪ PO Box 267 Robertson 6705 ▪ akhwyn@lando.co.za ℂ (023) 626·1103 ✆ (023) 626·3329

Kosie Möller Wines exports almost all of the co op's harvest — a record 6 440 tons last season, which saw deliveries halted for a week because of lack of storage space. Post-crush, top of Helmard Hanekom's to-do list was expansion of the cellar and installation of extra tanks. Their own-wine goes to the 22 members or is sold to visitors (not that there are many, Hanekom notes, as the winery's off any main route). Agterkliphoogte's label is Wandsbeck, a not unusual name for farms in the area (it's an old family name in Europe). The range comprises a Chenin, a chenin, colombard blend called Sunay, same blend under the name of Chenay, Shiraz, Ruby Cab and Muscadel.

Agterplaas

Stellenbosch ▪ Est/1stB 2003 ▪ Visits by appt ▪ Owner/winemaker James Basson ▪ PO Box 863 Stellenbosch 7599 ▪ 4.5 tons 250 cs ▪ agterplaas@webmail.co.za ℂ/✆ 886·9015

Something was always brewing in the backyard of the suburban home of James Basson ('Agterplaas', as his friends fondly refer to him). This isn't a Herman Charles Bosman story, and the brew wasn't firewater. It was beer for starters, then, from 2003, wine. Soon his backyard operation was the most progressive in Parow. Now he's relocated to more commodious premises in the corner of his friends' cellar at Somerbosch. This has allowed the enterprising *garagiste*, who earns a living designing wine cellars, among other things, to expand his output to 250 cases.

Mike's Red ★★☆ Reprises an old-Cape formula — cab/cinsaut (79/21) in **03**. Cab the senior partner taste-wise, too, cool cedar notes, softish tannins & fresh acidity. 8 mths used Fr oak. 13.5% alc. **Sauvignon Blanc** ★★☆ Assertive **04** — lean, bone-dry with brisk acid, rapier direct. — *IvH*

Agulhas see Merwespont

Agusta Wines

Franschhoek ▪ Est 1998 ▪ Tasting & sales daily: summer 10-6; winter 9-5 ▪ Fee R12 ▪ Closed Easter Fri & Dec 25 ▪ Tours by appt ▪ Grande Provence Restaurant & Guest House ▪ Gifts ▪ Tourgroups ▪ Winemaker Jaco Marais (Oct 2003) ▪ Farm manager Anton Olivier, advised by Kevin Watt (2000/2001) ▪ 22 ha (cab, merlot, shiraz, chenin, sauvignon) ▪ 250 tons 22 000 cs own labels 35% red 55% white 10% rosé ▪ ISO 14001 certified ▪ PO Box 102 Franschhoek 7690 ▪ orders@agustawines.co.za ▪ www.agustawines.co.za ✆ 876·3195 🖷 876·3118

The consortium of European businessmen who bought this Franschhoek property from Count Riccardo Agusta mean business. They blazed in with architects, then an international interior design team to totally revamp the restaurant, tasting room and guesthouse. Even the cellar has been upgraded (again). 'All the philosophies available have been claimed by the winemakers out there. I just do my job,' says businesslike incoming cellar chief Jaco Marais (previously at Excelsior). From this vintage, grapes will be sourced from prime Coastal region vineyards, while most of their own fruit will be sold off. A Sauvignon, Shiraz and red blend will be added to the Count Agusta range, and the popular Angels Tears Red makes a comeback, no doubt delighting its many fans.

Count Agusta range

★★★★ **Cabernet Sauvignon** Temporarily out of stock. We last assessed the **01**, showing a high-extract, muscular style, with sumptuous flavours & spicing.

★★★★ **Chardonnay 01**, trophy at 2003 FCTWS, super, steely, complex offering, with subtle yet flavoursome oak condiment. **02** (★★★★) too blockbuster-ish for its own good; all new oak (9 mths; pvs combo new/2nd fill) an overpowering presence, as is 15% alc; they negate considerable charms of sweet-ripe fruit, delicate glacé pineapple tone. But will doubtless have adherents. Own & Frhoek grapes.

Agusta range

These closed with screwcaps. **Cabernet Sauvignon** ★★★ Last tasted was the **02**, elegant, with bright flavours & fine tannins. **Merlot** ★★★ **02**, forceful (14.3% alc), taut & reserved when reviewed last ed, still not quite settled/knit; good core ripe cassis fruit augurs well, however. 8 mths Fr oak, 30% new. Own, Stbosch fruit. **Shiraz** To date the robust, Ribena-toned **03**, tasted as sample & provisionally rated ★★★★. **Chardonnay** ★★★ **03** changes to unwooded (pvsly tiny portion wood-fermented); shy melon/tropical aromas/flavours, easy & undemanding. 13.7% alc. Own & Frhoek grapes. **Sauvignon Blanc 04** (unrated work in progress) bracing & pungent; passionfruit & lime flavours shot through with rivetting acidity. Pvs **03** (★★★) followed house-style lime profile, with mineral-zesty finish. Own grapes.

Angels Tears range

> **Red** ☺ ★★★ Entente cordiale between merlot & cab; supple, rounded; flavours of pristine, vital red berries. So delicious, has to be good for you.

Pink 🆕 From chenin with dollop pinotage, off-dry. Not ready for tasting. **White** ★★☆ Something of a benchmark in off-dry, fruity white genre; chenin/hanepoot melded subtly into supple, juicy, pink-sweets-toned mouthful. All in this range NV, WO W-Cape. — *CR*

Aigle Noir see Remhoogte

Akkerdal Estate

Franschhoek ▪ Est 2000 ▪ 1stB 2001 ▪ Tasting & sales Sat 9-1; Mon-Fri 8-5 by appt ▪ Sales also at Franschhoek Vineyards (see A-Z entry) & La Cotte Inn Wine Sales (see Wine shops section) ▪ Closed public holidays ▪ Self-catering guest house ▪ Owner/winemaker/viticulturist Pieter Hanekom, advised by Eben Archer & Dawid Saayman ▪ 18 ha (malbec, merlot, mourvèdre, petit v, pinotage, shiraz, chard, sauvignon, semillon, viognier) ▪ ±750 cs own label 95% red 5% white ▪ ISO certification in progress ▪ PO Box 36 La Motte 7691 ▪ wine@akkerdal.co.za ▪ www.akkerdal.co.za © 876·3481 ☎ 876·3189

Pieter Hanekom survived harvest 2004, a full month later than usual, with his enthusiasm undiminished and a trust in his gut-feel when working with his portfolio of less widely planted varieties (the newest include nouvelle and tempranillo). Now he's more intent on micro-managing his domain, down to adjusting the spacing of vines within rows — all to further his goal of growing 'a unique range of bottled art and poetry'. The new tasting area, encircled by vineyards and mountains, is an idyllic place, the owner/winemaker declares.

★★★★ **Merlot 03** (★★★★) savoury notes, green olive, some herbal whiffs, dry herbaceous finish, heightened by 18 mths older barrels. No **02** — went into Passion, below. Follows plummy, accessible yet elegant **01**.

★★★★ **Syrah** 🆕 Ripe but elegant **02** (13.2% alc), softened with drop viognier, silky allspice, persistent, harmonious. Oaking as above.

★★★★ **Wild Boar** 🆕 **02** blend equal parts malbec, mourvèdre, merlot. Gamey with earth/mineral notes, smoky whiffs, dry tannins, restrained. 14 mths older Fr oak.

★★★ **Passion** 🆕 ★★★ Plum almond notes on **02** merlot-based blend with 12% shiraz; fine light tannins, spicy marzipan finish. Well integrated 18 mths Fr oak. Accessible, very easy drinking. — MF

Alexanderfontein see Ormonde
Alexander von Essen see Buitenverwachting

Allée Bleue

Franschhoek ▪ Est 2000 ▪ 1stB 2001 ▪ Tasting & sales daily 9-5 ▪ Café Allée Bleue (Tue-Sun 9-5) & other attractions (see intro) ▪ Tourgroups ▪ Owners Dauphin Enwickling (Germany) ▪ Winemaker Gerda Willers (Dec 2001) ▪ Viti consultant Rob Meihuizen (2001) ▪ 30 ha (cab, merlot, pinotage, shiraz, sauvignon, semillon) ▪ 88% red 9% white 3% rosé ▪ PO Box 100 Groot Drakenstein 7680 ▪ info@meerrust.com ▪ www.meerrust.com © 874·1021 ☎ 874·1850

A disappointing harvest, generally, in 2004, laments general manager JC de Wet. Meerrust farm's own vines are on their way into production (no more buying-in soon) and in the meanwhile freelance winemaker Gerda Willers is working on the first red blend in the Allée Bleue range. Her maiden wine here, the Pinotage, was validated by Veritas judges in 2003, who awarded it a double-gold. De Wet has identified the East as a possible export market and a Cape Blend as a possible product for export. Back home, the local business continues to grow, with a new café and nursery added to its conference facilities and sale of organic herbs and mushrooms.

★★★★★ **Pinotage** Earthy, sweet fruited aromas, dense textures on mouthfilling **03**, 60% new wood adding structure. 13% alc. From single Piekenklf (Ctrsdal) vyd. **02**'s richer more tannic, sumptuous fruit conceals 15% alc. VDG, ABSA Pinotage Top Ten. **01** (★★★★) evolving well, though with mouth-puckering tannins & 14.8% alc dominating berry fruit. VDG.

★★★★ **Shiraz 02** clove whiffs, white pepper, raspberry all feature in this ripe (14.5% alc) yet elegant wine. 50% new wood. Swiss gold.

★★★★ **Isabeau** Fine blend semillon/chardonnay (60/40). Intense **03** offers thatch, lime, lanolin & new-oak seasoning seamlessly integrated. Dry, persistent — elegant despite robust flavours. **02** is further evolved, with oak notes concealing 14.3% alc.

Cabernet Sauvignon ★★★ **03** youthful, almost herbaceous aromas, chunky tannins, slightly rustic austerity, demands bottle ageing. 50% new oak. 13.8% alc. From single

Stbosch vyd. **Pinotage Natural Sweet** ★★ Dense tannins of powerful **03** conceal 22g/ℓ sugar. Notably unaromatic; rather gauche in its bigness (15.5% alc). From Ctrsdal fruit. 50% new oak maturation. All ⬛ɴᴇᴡ. — MF

Allesverloren Estate

Swartland ▪ Est 1704 ▪ Tasting & sales Mon-Fri 8.30-5 Sat 8.30-2 Phone ahead on public holidays ▪ Tours by appt ▪ BYO picnic ▪ Play area for children ▪ Conservation area ▪ Owner/winemaker/viticulturist Danie Malan (Nov 1987) ▪ 187 ha (cab, shiraz & various port varieties) ▪ 50 000 cs 100% red ▪ PO Box 23 Riebeek West 7306 ▪ info@allesverloren.co.za ▪ www.allesverloren.co.za ℭ (022) 461·2320 🖷 (022) 461·2444

Danie Malan is present holder of a torch that's been passed through winemaking generations since wine was first made on this three-centuries-old farm in 1806. A couple of years ago Malan made the first Touriga Nacional, an 00, and released it quietly through their tasting room. Now there's a new vintage, the 03, and its being given national distribution by Distell. While his wines are all matured at Bergkelder in Stellenbosch, a barrelling facility on the farm in the Swartland ('shiraz country', avers Malan) is on the drawing board. The Allesverloren style is 'strong and distinctive, with huge ripeness', and it's much appreciated by northern European consumers like the Swedes.

★★★★ **Cabernet Sauvignon** These respected as fine examples, style established & reliable. **01** (★★★) in somewhat leaner, earthier mode; firm acidity & tannin; probably not for extended cellaring. **00** youthfully reticent last yr, firm & dry but hinting at good future. 18 mths Fr oak, 30% new.

★★★★ **Shiraz** Difficult red vintage reflected in **02** (★★★☆), 'hot', plummy nose with red fruits, firm acidity with drying finish. May need time. 14% alc. **01** showed familiar Allesverloren clout (14.3% alc), generous build, chunky ripe fruit. ±18 mths oak, some new, mainly Fr.

★★★★ **Tinta Barocca** ✓ Leading example from among handful of producers soldiering on with variety. **01** (★★★★) medium-intensity game/fungus hints to savoury black fruit; quite firm & restrained, touch rustic. 14.2% alc. Contrast with **00**, which had attractive plump fruit leavened by tangy acid. Fr oak 18 mths, 50/50 2nd/3rd fill.

★★★★☆ **Port** An enduring favourite, on restaurant lists from Aggenys to Zastron. Reliable LBV style; **98** rich prune/savoury nose with salty madeira-like tang; sweet & deliciously forward flavour. A 'quaffing' Port, if there is such a thing. **97** was drier (82g/ℓ sugar) than pvs, still recognisably Allsvrlrn, if more delicate. Souzão, pontac, touriga & trio of tintas (roriz introduced into pvs **96**). Old-oak aged.

Touriga Nacional ⬛ɴᴇᴡ ★★★ Youthful raspberry tone to **03**; light, sweet & taut palate, admirably low in alc (12.5%). Traditionally styled, may develop interestingly. — RK/JB

Alphen Hill see Kosie Möller Wines

Alter Ego Wines

Tulbagh ▪ Est 2001 ▪ 1stB 2002 ▪ Visits Mon-Sat 9-5 by appt ▪ Meals by appt or BYO ▪ Mountain biking by appt ▪ Owner Vin de Parr cc ▪ Winemaker/viticulturist John Parr (Sep 2001) ▪ 4 ha (cabs s/f, merlot, pinotage, chard) ▪ 35 tons 2 000 cs 50% red 40% white 10% port ▪ PO Box 364 Tulbagh 6820 ▪ playberg@icon.co.za ▪ www.kloofzichtwines.co.za ℭ (023) 230·0658 🖷 (023) 230·0774

'We always know how old our first wine is because our son Ethan Asher was born on the day we harvested,' says John Parr. That was three years ago, just after he and wife Beverley had bought the Kloofzicht property in Tulbagh. Looking back, they're pleased to have survived 'doing things our way with no mega-wealthy backer'. They now find themselves in the enviable position of sell out of wine across the range. 'Our wine is made exactly how I want to make it. Individuality sells', continues John P, who, somewhat to his surprise, is just as comfortable wearing his marketer's cap as he is in his winemaker's boots. 'I would like to reach the stage with our retailers and customers where we are honest about the quality of wines on a yearly basis, with prices dropping or rising accordingly.' Now there's a refreshing attitude.

Ethan Asher ★★★★ 'Cape blend' pinotage, cab, merlot (50/40/10), 14 mths Fr/Am oak, **02** retasted, full-flavoured, rich, ripe fruit still in grip of tannins; give few yrs to soften & open. **Old Parr's Head Semillon** ★★★ New in the guide, **03** expresses the variety well & indivdually; notes of lime & lemon, smoky whiff (though unoaked), hint honey; very attractive now – suggest drink fairly soon. Modest 12.7% alc. **Alter Ego Elroy's Pawt 00** unrated sweet fortified from cab & merlot, 'made with a few eucalyptus leaves in barrel'. Like the Labrador it's named for, brimming with personality. 375ml. 17% alc. – *DH*

Alto Estate

Stellenbosch ▪ Est 1906 ▪ 1stB 1918 ▪ Tasting & sales Mon-Fri 9-5 Sat & public holidays 10-1 ▪ Fee R10 (R20 incl glass) ▪ Owner Lusan Premium Wines ▪ Winemaker Schalk van der Westhuizen (Jul 2000) ▪ Viti consultant Eben Archer (2002) ▪ 93 ha ▪ 25 000 cs 100% red ▪ PO Box 104 Stellenbosch 7599 ▪ info@alto.co.za ▪ www.alto.co.za ① 881·3884 ▤ 881·3894

The name refers to more than the farm's high-lying position on the granite slopes of the Helderberg: its wines (notably the iconic Alto Estate, in process of reverting to its original name, 'Rouge') are award-winners and its ambitions are lofty. A replanting programme involving Eben Archer, now associate professor of Viticulture & Oenology at Stellenbosch University and full-time viticulturist for the Lusan group wineries, aims to up the annual output from 350 to 600 tons, with an average yield of 6 tons/ha. Also advising winemaker Schalk van der Westhuizen is French oenologist Pascal Chatonnet, an international specialist in barrel-ageing. A new wood management policy has resulted in the introduction of oak from Eastern Europe, which adds fresh nuances as well as containing prices.

★★★★ **Cabernet Sauvignon** Very much a *vin de garde*, & well worth the wait; that slow-maturing character epitomised by **01** (★★★★★), on par with outstanding **98**, **95**. Youthful red fruits on nose; forthcoming, juicy flavours, amply concentrated & structured for the long haul. **00** was something of an anomaly – less obviously tannic, more accessible, beautifully poised. **99** lighter, elegant. Oaking regimen 18-24 mths 300ℓ Fr oak, 50% new, rest 2nd/3rd fill.

★★★★ **Shiraz** Off 8 yr old unirrigated vyd, 400-450m up the Helderberg. Well-tamed **01** was first; big, but not bold, rather more elegant than powerful despite ±14% alc. Follow-up **02** has similar vanilla-washed ripe redcurrant tone; very nice. 'Great with braaied boerewors,' says down-to-earth winemaker. 18 mths new oak 60% Am. Still youthful, could do with 3-4 yrs, will last 5-7 min. Am/Fr oak (60/40), 18 mths.

★★★★ **Alto Estate** One of Cape's oldest & best-loved labels. Has morphed from cab, cinsaut of yesteryear via traditional Bdx blend to current merlot, cabs s/f, shiraz mix (48/22/15/15). **02** attractively rustic & organic with high-toned nose/palate; gripping tannins & firm acidity, but a promising future. **01** soft & touch light in comparison; faintly 'hot' & not as complex. 18 mths oak, mainly Fr, 1st-3rd fill. – *RK*

Altydgedacht Estate

Durbanville ▪ Est 1698 ▪ 1stB 1981 ▪ Tasting & sales Mon-Fri 9-5 Sat 9-3 ▪ Closed Easter Fri, Dec 25 & Jan 1 ▪ Tours by appt ▪ Pampoenkraal boma-style function restaurant ① ·913·4962/3 ▪ Conferencing ▪ Conservation area ▪ Owners Parker family ▪ Winemaker Oliver Parker, with Mark Carmichael-Green ▪ Viticulturists John Parker, with Adanté Roux (2002) ▪ 158 ha (12 varieties, r/w) ▪ 1 250 tons ±5 000 cs own label 60% red 40% white ▪ Export label: Tygerberg ▪ PO Box 213 Durbanville 7551 ▪ altydgedacht@mweb.co.za ▪ www. altydgedacht.co.za ① 976·1295 ▤ 976·4318 /8521

Oliver Parker has had a good year. The 5th-generation winemaker celebrated 20 years of marriage, his mother's 80th birthday (in her day, Jean P was one of a tiny handful of female winemakers), and what Ollo P describes as the most stress-free harvest to date. Dry conditions made for exceedingly healthy grapes, and the long ripening season put paid to the usual mad rush to pick all the grapes in time. He's particularly delighted with the first crop from what used to be grainland, transformed into a sauvignon vineyard. It has produced the most wonderful flavours, proof again for this anti-process winemaker that 'what matters is where the grapes are grown. Even more than whether wine is officially recognised as 'estate' or not'.

★★★★ **Cabernet Sauvignon** Reserved but forceful, **01** follows through well on its spice, tobacco, cassis aromas. Savoury fruit underpinned by serious tannin, well-balanced 13% alc. Yr Fr/Am oak, 20% new. Like chunky **00**, would benefit from yr/2 in bottle.

★★★★ **Barbera** Ever-engaging, appropriately not too serious SA pioneer of this Italian grape. Still youthful **01** (retasted) big, richly textured, with boiled sweet flavours, structured more by acid than tannin. **02** maintains tradition, but a little lighter, leaner, less sweet, more tannic – & perhaps more interesting. Alc up from 14 to 14.5%. Mix Fr/Am oak, quarter new.

★★★★ **Merlot** Pleasant, plummy **03** has lightish colour & fruit, with minty herbal note; clean bright finish. From mix open fermenters & steel tanks; then yr in 90% new Fr oak. Alc 13% – welcomely modest, these days.

★★★★ **Pinotage** ✓ Following path of attractively rich & plush **00**, latest **01** full, juicy, succulent, bags of generous bright fruit, ripe tannin in support. Slight bitter twist to finish adds interest rather than problem at this stage. Well-integrated oak, 25% new, Fr/15% Am.

★★★★ **Shiraz** ✓ Still satisfying, **01** quite elegantly balances aromatic, sweet redcurrant fruit, oak (16 mths 60/40 Fr/Am oak, 20% new) & gently gripping tannins. 14.% alc.

★★★★ **Sauvignon Blanc 04** with ripe, overt tropical fruit-salad character, packed with flavour, freshly & fruitily succulent, plus ingratiating 3.4g/ℓ sugar. 13.5% alc.

★★★★ **Chardonnay** Mostly oak-fermented/aged 5 mths. Round, pleasant, fresh **03** well balanced, though coconutty oak still apparent, along with citrus fruit. No **04**.

Gewürztraminer ★★★ Lunchtime-light & appealing **04** (12.5% alc) just dry; with evanescent rose-petal & spice charm. **Chatelaine** ★★ Pot-pourri, flowery scents on **04** blend gewürz, riesling, with soft, light-bodied (12% alc) & light-hearted pleasantness. – *TJ*

Amabokobokho see Bovlei
Amalienstein see Ladismith
Amandalia see Rooiberg

Amani Vineyards

Stellenbosch ▪ Est/1stB 1997 ▪ Tasting & sales Mon-Fri 10-4 Sat by appt ▪ Fee R10 ▪ Closed public holidays ▪ Tours by appt ▪ African artefacts display ▪ Owner Jim Atkinson ▪ Winemaker Danelle van Rensburg (Feb 2003) ▪ Viticulturist/GM Rusty Myers (Oct 2002), advised by Kevin Watt ▪ 23 ha (cab f, merlot, shiraz, chard, sauvignon) ▪ 8 000 cs 30% red 70% white ▪ PO Box 12422 Die Boord 7613 ▪ wine@amani.co.za ▪ www.amani.co.za ℂ 905·1126 ⊞ 905·4404

Music made light work of long hours at this Polkadraai Hills cellar last harvest. Farm manager Rusty Myers and his family, jazz and country music fans from Oklahoma, had a portable CD crank out their favourite tunes. A new sorting table was inaugurated, reports winemaker Danelle van Rensburg, though as it turned out the smaller-than-usual harvest produced mostly clean and healthy grapes. New vineyards are being established under the guidance of consultant Kevin Watt, including shiraz, cab, viognier and mourvèdre – building blocks of an exotic-sounding future blend. Work has also begun on experimental high-density blocks, the vines closely planted to produce smaller, more flavourful berries. A new label, Atkinson Ridge (untasted), starts on a high note with a limited-quantity Chardonnay.

★★★★ **Merlot** Since **01**, double-gold at MIWA 2002, a classy act; ±30% new barriques, 11-18 mths; usually with splash cab s or f for complexity/stiffening. **03** (★★★☆) taut & elegant; balanced, well-paced flavours though perhaps lacking complexity, conviction of standout **02**, which had grassy top-notes to meaty black fruit. These approachable on release, stamina for min 3-4 yrs. ±13.5% alc.

★★★★ **Chardonnay** Excellent track record since maiden **98**. **02** had more citrus tones than the usual peach; buttered toast richness from classy oak (fermented/aged ±10 mths Fr barrels, some new). Similar wooding for latest **03** (★★★★), eager, juicy & easy drinking, notes of grapefruit & apple (possibly from soupçon chenin); fresh crunchy texture from 26% unwooded portion & racy 7g/ℓ acid. At ±14% alc, as expansive as **01**, but controlled.

Sauvignon Blanc ★★★ Green-tinged **03** acquiring attractive grapefruit bottle-age, clean mineral note on finish. Best enjoyed before end of the yr, while still zingy. — *TM*

Amarava Wines

Stellenbosch ▪ *Est 1999* ▪ *1stB 2004* ▪ *Closed to public* ▪ *Owner Bernard Rodenberg* ▪ *Vini/ viti consultants Teddy Hall & Dawie le Roux (2003/2002)* ▪ *17 ha (cabs s/f, merlot, shiraz, sauvignon)* ▪ *2 tons* ▪ *PO Box 1083 Somerset West 7129* ▪ *Smit@amaravawines.com* ▪ *www.amaravawines.com* ℭ *084·587·7270*

Bernard Rodenberg fell in love with the Cape winelands after an introduction by friend Otto Lenseling of Dutch wine merchant Fourcroy Lenseling, a major importer of SA wine. Since acquiring Portion 12 of Knorhoek Farm on the Sir Lowry's Pass side of the Helderberg, Rodenberg has established a vineyard, intending to make a blended red under the Amarava label (Zulu equivalent of 'Eve'; mother of nations). But the False Bay-facing Schaapenberg slopes, an exciting sauvignon site, delivered the fine 04 below. (A Blanc de Noir has been exported to the Netherlands.) Farm manager Louis Smit and viticulturist Dawie le Roux oversee 'very well-managed' vineyards, says Rudera's Teddy Hall, who makes the wine as 'a friendly arrangement'.

★★★★ **Sauvignon Blanc** Arresting fruity style; **04** loads of gooseberry, lime & passion fruit, tangy sweet-sour tussle, high acid (8g/ℓ) easily absorbed by concentrated fruit. Stbosch grapes. Promising debut. 13% alc. — *IvH*

■ *Ama Ulibo* see Goedverwacht

Ambeloui Wine Cellar 🍴🍷⊚

Hout Bay (see Constantia map) ▪ *Est 1995* ▪ *1stB 1998* ▪ *Visits by appt* ▪ *Lunches for groups by appt* ▪ *Owners Nick & Ann Christodoulou* ▪ *Winemaker/viticulturist Nick Christodoulou* ▪ *0.6 ha (pinot, chard)* ▪ *600 cs 100% MCC* ▪ *PO Box 26800 Hout Bay 7872* ▪ *ambeloui@icon.co.za* ▪ *www.ambeloui.co.za* ℭ *082·441·6039* 🖷 *790·7873*

February 2 is when materfamilias Ann Christodoulou celebrates her birthday. In 2002, it was also the day the Christodoulou family harvested the chardonnay and pinot growing on their not-even-a-hectare farm on the banks of Hout Bay's Disa River. Given that their vintages have family names, there are no prizes for guessing whose name the latest bubbly bears. 'We ran out of family when it came to naming the 2004 vintage,' confides Ann C, 'but our loyal and dedicated children produced our first grandchild on the first day of the harvest. We're looking forward to introducing everyone to Alex in two years' time.' Another Christodoulou tradition is that the new vintage is brought out of the cellar for sale on the first Saturday of November of each year. And breaking away from the customary, Ann is now serving Mediterranean-style picnic lunches under the trees next to the vineyard, on Fridays and Saturdays from November to April, with a cellar tour thrown in. Bookings are obligatory.

★★★★ **MCC** Classy, hand-crafted brut from chardonnay/pinot; vintages named for family members. **01** 'Alexis' (★★★★★) 36 mths on lees, nuanced biscuit/Granny Smith apple/honey nose & weighty palate from 60% pinot. Like chardonnay-dominated (66%) **02** 'Ann', 10% barrel-fermented, degorged 2004. Latter more evolved, grippier despite 12 mths less on lees, delicious brioche flavour. These will reward cellaring. Untasted **02** 'Ann Reserve' (50/50) & **02** Rosé to follow. Sugars ±9g/ℓ, alcs 12%. ±400 cs. — *CvZ*

Anatu Wines

Stellenbosch ▪ Est/1stB 2002 ▪ Visits by appt ▪ Owners André & Freda Hamersma, Wickus & Anina Guelpa, Dries van Zyl ▪ Winemaker Anina Guelpa ▪ 270 cs 80% red 20% white ▪ PO Box 5792 Cresta 2118 ▪ wickus.g@adept.co.za ▪ www.anatu.co.za ✆ (021) 889·8398

What started as jocular dinner-table talk among friends ended up as a full-fledged (albeit pocket-sized) winemaking venture. Johannesburg-based André and Freda Hamersma and Dries van Zyl, and Wickus and Anina Guelpa had dreamed of making wine for some time when, in 2002, one of them announced a suitable parcel of grapes had become available. Suddenly their what if? turned into what now?! Two fermentation bins, three barrels and 'lots of red wine on the walls' later, they produced an experimental Shiraz. Next vintage, Stellekaya's Dave Lello offered his modern facilities in Stellenbosch and the friends were 'able to create wines as we envisaged them'. Fruits of this era are another Shiraz and a Viognier. Now they've taken the plunge, cost and effort are not considerations in their pursuit of small quantities of 'unique, handcrafted' wines.

★★★★ **Shiraz** Robust **03**, deep flavoured & husky, but not without charm. Warm, sweet black cherries, spicy oak & whiff smoke; ripe tannins linger in finish. Dbnvlle grapes, fermented in open-ended barrels with punch-downs. No filtering/ fining. 14 mths oak, 50% new Fr/Am. 15%alc. MIWA 2004 *garagiste* trophy.—*IvH*

Ancient Africa see Baarsma
Andrew Bain see Cape Vineyards

Andy Mitchell Wines

Greyton ▪ Est/1stB 2003 ▪ Visits by appt ▪ Owners/winemakers Andy & Vikki Mitchell ▪ Vini consultants Terroir Wines ▪ 150 cs 100% red ▪ PO Box 543 Paarden Eiland 7420 ▪ andy@za.northsails.com ✆/🖷 (028) 254·9045

It's a change from water to wine for the Mitchells, now Greyton *garagistes* as well as sailmakers for upscale yachts from a Cape Town factory. Their country property, adjoining a nature reserve, is at the highest point of the Greyton-McGregor trail and has staggering views. Winemaker Andy and assistant Vikki set up a well-equipped boutique operation there in 2003, replete with temperature-controlled barrel area below the production cellar which gave them their first 150 cases of red last season. The top-quality wines they hope will flow are destined for Overberg eateries, the tourist trade and specialist wine shops overseas. 'We will expand our range next season to include a white variety,' says Andy M. 'Ultimately we would also like to do a Bordeaux blend as well as co-ferment a little viognier with our shiraz, if we can persuade nature to co-operate with harvest dates.'

Breakfast Rock Syrah 03 still in barrel, perhaps ★★★ on release. Raspberry, pepper notes prelude to still oaky palate (will be 15 mths Fr oak, 33% new). Super-ripe, hand-sorted, cold-soaked, heavily extracted Hldrberg fruit, giving massive 15% alc.—*MF*

Angels Tears see Agusta

Angora Estate

Robertson ▪ Est/1stB 2002 ▪ Tasting & sales by appt ▪ Closed public holidays ▪ Owner Gerrit Joubert ▪ Winemakers Gerrit Joubert & sons, with Danie Slabber ▪ Viticulturist Danie Slabber ▪ 16 ha (cab; port varieties, ruby cab, shiraz, chenin, muscadel) ▪ 300 tons 300 cs own label 100% red ▪ PO Box 343 Bonnievale 6730 ▪ chris.joubert@gilga.com ✆ 881·3475 🖷 881·3248

Bit by bit, the Jouberts are building up the old family farm they rescued some years ago — 'When we have money we build'. That includes building up the vineyards — in 2004, more shiraz went into the ground and sizeable plantings of chenin and chardonnay are planned over the next 2 years. The first Shiraz from winemaking brothers Chris and Johan has been labelled and released.

Shiraz ★★★ **02** spiced peppery whiffs & gamey hints with mineral/earth layers; has rounded out with yr in bottle, accessible soft tannins, dry oaky finish. 15 mths seasoned Fr barrels. 13.8% alc. — *DS*

Annandale Wines

Stellenbosch ▪ Est/1stB 1996 ▪ Tasting & sales Mon-Sat 9-5 (Sep-May, else 10-4) ▪ Fee R10 refundable on purchase ▪ Closed Christian holidays ▪ Tours by appt ▪ Collection of antique wine objects ▪ Owner/winemaker/viticulturist Hempies du Toit ▪ 45 ha (cabs s/f, merlot, shiraz) ▪ 5 000 cs own label ▪ 100% red ▪ PO Box 12681 Die Boord 7613 ▪ annandale@telkomsa.net ▪ www.annandale.co.za © *881·3560* 🖷 *881·3562*

'Truly a harvest that gives one something to look forward to,' enthuses Hempies du Toit. 'Like 1974, 2004 was an unbelievable year.' This golden vintage saw the last of his newer (1999) vineyards come into production, and the release of the beefy owner/winemaker/viticulturist's Shiraz 01: 'Very special; it's dedicated to five generations of Du Toit winemakers.' The sixth generation, in the person of son Gerhard, has graduated from Stellenbosch and, after a spell at Waterford, is off to France for further maturation. Look out for a very special release down the line — an 'Old Cape Blend'.

★★★★ **Cabernet Sauvignon** These elegantly structured cabs, from own vyds since **01**, improving in bottle; fascinating trio: **97, 98** & **99**, all available. **97** marginally lighter bodied, fragrant, elegant, alc. 13%; **98** touch organic, savoury, rich, vigorous (yet moderate alc 12.5%); **99** silk-textured, seamless & richly but firmly flavoured (blackberries & cherries), alc 13.5%. These carefully oaked (2 yrs new Fr). No **00**.

★★★★★ **Shiraz 01** only vintage to date, beautifully packaged in extra-heavyweight bottle, neck hand-dipped in wax. Class hinted at last yr more fully realised. Warm spicy intensity, properly dry, neither over-rich nor showy, quintessentially Cape shiraz. Tannins cleverly manipulated to allow for earlier drinking, but also long cellaring. 30 mths 2nd fill barrels, all Fr. Deserves time, as do all HdT's wines, 5-7 yrs min.

★★★★ **Cavalier** Blend changes to merlot, cab s & f, shiraz (40/25/25/10) in **01**, 36 mths oak, all Fr (this is the *least* serious of du Toit's wines!). Slowly unfurls to show finely judged fruit & clean spicy oak; balanced, classy, unshowy, real substance. **99** was 70/30 shiraz cab. No **00**.

★★★★ **CVP** Acronym (for Cape Vintage Port) calculated to avoid inflaming EU sensibilities. To date appealingly unclassic **01**, from shiraz; sweet & delicious, flew out of the cellar. Ready, but better to cellar another 5-7 yrs. No **02**. Next is **03**. — *IvH*

AntHill Wines

Somerset West ▪ Est/1stB 2000 ▪ Tasting by appt ▪ Owners Mark Howell & Hylton Schwenk ▪ Winemaker Mark Howell ▪ 300 cs 100% red ▪ 14 Somerset Street, Somerset West 7130 ▪ anthill@absamail.co.za © *855·4275/082·895·9008* 🖷 *855·5086*

In between rolling out barrels to the local industry, Mark Howell keeps his antennae tuned and his pincers unfurled to pounce on promising looking grape parcels to vinify for his and Hylton Schwenk's boutique wine brand, AntHill. (Fermentation and ageing is done, by arrangement of course, in the nooks and crannies of some of the Cape's most vaunted cellars.) What began as a lone Pinotage has grown into a small product colony, from everyday quaffers (under the Termite's Tipple label) to the top-of-the-heap Pangolin. The wines were not ready for tasting this year, but Howell assures that the Sauvignon, diverted from a Piekenierskloof vineyard, is 'a stunner'. Also incubating are a Cab, wooded Chardonnay and a new vintage of the Pinotage.

Anthony de Jager Wines

Paarl ▪ Est/1stB 2001 ▪ Closed to public ▪ Owner/winemaker Anthony de Jager ▪ 175 cs 100% red ▪ PO Box 583 Suider-Paarl 7624 ▪ homtini@absamail.co.za © *863·2450* 🖷 *863·2591*

There is no doubt that Anthony de Jager has boundless energy — how many winemakers find time for both their own label and a large, internationally acclaimed concern such as Fairview? But AdJ's watchword is 'fun', and he wants to make and drink it. So he's conscious of not overextending himself, he says, focusing instead on making a consistently superb Shiraz, in limited quantities of course. Which left him with just enough time to paddle out and make the 2004 semi-finals of the annual Vintners Surf Classic.

★★★★☆ **Homtini Shiraz** ✓ **03** approaches spectacular form of debut **00** (★★★★★); great depth, personality. Striking yet almost ethereal lifted spice, red fruits, lily scents. Fine presence with delicate mouthfeel; poised freshness emphasises silky, sweet-fruited layers. Beautifully balanced, destined for magnificent maturity; pretty good in youth too. Fermented/18 mths matured in older oak; 14.5% alc. **02**, good poise, balance if bigger (15% alc), less concentrated than **00**. No **01**. All these include 5-7% viognier. 20-25 yr-old vines on Paarl Mountain. — *AL*

Anura

Paarl ▪ Est 1990 ▪ 1stB 2001 ▪ Tasting & sales daily 9-5 ▪ Closed Easter Fri/Mon, Dec 25/26 & Jan 1 ▪ Fee R15 (cheese & wine) ▪ Lilly Pad Restaurant (see Eat-out section) ▪ Tours by appt ▪ Farm produce sold ▪ Owners Tymen & Jenny Bouma ▪ Winemakers Tymen Bouma & Carla van der Mescht (Jan 2002) ▪ Viticulturist Hannes Kloppers (Oct 1997) ▪ 118 ha (cab, malbec, merlot, mourvèdre, sangiovese, shiraz) ▪ 580 tons 20 000 cs own label 75% red 20% white ▪ PO Box 244 Klapmuts 7625 ▪ info@anura.co.za sales@anura.co.za ▪ www. anura.co.za ☏ 875·5360 🖷 875·5657

Hand-crafted wines with an intense and uniquely SA flavour are what Tymen Bouma and Carla van der Mescht aim for. (Occasionally feet as well as hands are used to achieve the goal: last year 500ℓ of cab were crushed in a good old-fashioned foot-stomp. The results are so promising, reports Bouma, 'we're holding our breath'.) Cellar capacity has been enlarged to 400 tons and a second barrel cellar constructed. Believing 'the wow factor' essential to success in an overtraded market, they are launching a rare-in-SA Sangiovese and a Mourvèdre to spice up their varietal range. They're also experimenting with a new European-style blend. If you haven't sampled their award-winning Forest Hill camembert or brie, the new restaurant on this amphibian-themed property, the Lilly Pad, is the place to order a cheese platter.

★★★★ **Cabernet Sauvignon Reserve** Retasting **01** mid-2004 shows further maturation — shy cassis, violet bouquet, whiffs expensive cigarbox, followed by sweet, vanilla-spiced fruit, tapering evenly to dry finish. 13 mths new Fr oak. VDG. **02** sample similarly styled but less opulent, some black cherry among the cassis, more juicy, less tannin. These no shrinking violets at around 15% alc; worth cellaring 6-7 yrs.

★★★★ **Merlot** Second-release **02**, discreet dark choc & black cherry richness; fragrant, sleek & elegant; shows softer, silky tannins of the variety, oft trumpeted in SA but seldom achieved. Delicate mint on dry finish. 18 mths Fr oak, 40% new. 15% alc.

★★★☆ **Chardonnay** Expansive barrel & natural yeast (20%) fermented **03** quietly evolving in bottle, burgeoning complexity to dried peach, ripe citrus fruit backed by subtle oak. All components for 3-4 yrs, plus tad sugar (5.3g/ℓ) & 15% alc.

★★★☆ **Chenin Blanc** Bold, big **03**, deep fruited, still unfolding after 9 mths oak, 10% new Fr. Dry, spicy baked apple & creamy length with notable tannins. Watch hefty alc at 15.1%, not your average tipple. Could age attractively 3-4 yrs.

Pinotage ★★★ **01** lightish style intended for easy quaffing but tannins still grippy. Shows smoky, almost tarry, rustic notes. Mix Am/Fr oak (20% new Am). **02** sample sweeter mulberry fruit, softer tannins, though with hallmark tarry whiffs. **Shiraz** ★★★ **02** well-bred dry, dense & compact black berry fruit, firmish tannins; classic, no concessions to modernity. Touch earthy on very dry finish. 20% barrel fermented, all Fr, 50% new. Alc 14.5%. **Syrah-Mourvèdre** NEW Signals yet another attempt at making wines with more interest. Good depth to **03** (sample) with loads of dark berried juiciness. Provisional ★★★☆; supple but also with enough grip to please the classicists. 20% natural yeast fermentation, 18 mths Fr barriques, 40% new. **Sauvignon Blanc** ★★★ **03** bone-dry with firm-fleshed appeal, shows some grassy complexity, biggish build. Ideal food wine, build to hold 2-3 yrs. 13.7% alc.

Frog Hill range

Chenin Blanc NEW ☺ ★★★ Zesty, lively addition to Frog family with **03**, explosion of spiced melon, passionfruit flavour, bursting with freshness & self importance. Alc 13%.

Merlot-Shiraz-Cabernet Sauvignon NEW ★★★☆ Weight, richness in **03**; meaty, muscular feel/flavour. Well oaked, 8 mths 10% new Fr. Alc 14.6%. Better than everyday. — *IvH*

Appelsdrift see Clairvaux
Aprilskloof see Lammershoek
Arcady see Bovlei

Arendsig

Robertson ▪ Est/1stB 2004 ▪ Visits by appt ▪ BYO picnic ▪ Walks ▪ Owner GF van der Westhuizen Trust ▪ Winemaker Lourens van der Westhuizen ▪ 15 ha (cab, shiraz, chard, sauvignon, viognier) ▪ 15 tons ±500 cs ▪ PO Box 170 Robertson 6705 ▪ lourens@starmail. com © (023) 616·2835 🖷 (023) 616·2090

As a youth Lourens van der Westhuizen explored the hills that sweep down to the banks of the Breede River. He was in fact scrambling over rich, well-drained terrain, often shrouded with winter mists and cooled by summer breezes — the perfect environment to nurture a winemaker. And here he is, a graduate of Elsenburg, returned to the family farm to make their own-wine. Crushes at Glen Carlou in Paarl and Copain Wines in California were still fresh in his mind when in 2004 he picked and vinified small parcels of shiraz and chardonnay (the remainder went to the co-op, as usual). Extending his vinegrowing ambitions, he's now planted 12ha with specially selected varieties. Small beginnings....

Shiraz 500 cs made in **04**, still maturing in Fr oak (40% new) at press time. **Chardonnay** ★★★ A pure & confident expression of the variety in **04**, fermented/6 mths Fr barrels. Ripe peach & melon aromas, lively citrus flavours, fruity zest maintained through to clean, dry conclusion. Unfiltered/fined. — *CR*

Arlington Beverage Group

Est 1996 ▪ 1stB 1997 ▪ Closed to public ▪ Owner Richard Addison ▪ 200 000 cs 45% red 55% white ▪ UK head office: 162-164 Arthur Rd, London SW19 8AQ ▪ PO Box 1376 Stellenbosch 7599 ▪ sarah@arlingtonbeverage.com ▪ www.arlingtonbeverage.com

Arlington markets and sells SA wines to countries such as the UK, Ireland and Argentina. With local partners, it has built a number of successful on-trade brands including Broken Rock, Landsdowne, Millbrook and Rocheburg. The new year will see the launch of a new brand for the UK. Arlington also represents a number of leading Cape properties in the international markets, including Riebeek and Ridgeback.

Arniston Bay see Vinfruco

Asara Estate

Stellenbosch ▪ Est 1691 ▪ 1stB 1970 ▪ Tasting & sales Mon-Fri 9-5 Sat 10-5 (Nov-Apr), 10-2 (May-Oct) ▪ Fee R15 ▪ Closed Easter Fri, Dec 25/26 & Jan 1 ▪ Tours by appt ▪ BYO picnic ▪ Owner Markus & Christiane Rahmann ▪ Winemaker Jan van Rooyen (Oct 1999) ▪ Viticulturist Pieter Rossouw (1995) ▪ 120 ha (cab, merlot, shiraz, chard, sauvignon) ▪ 450 tons 20 000 cs 75% red 29% white 1% rosé ▪ PO Box 882 Stellenbosch 7599 ▪ info@AsaraWine.com ▪ www.AsaraWine.com © 888·8000 🖷 888·8001

'The word "estate" on the front-label should tell consumers that there are no external variables which can interfere with the promise of top-quality that we make,' says winemaker Jan van Rooyen. 'We are in full control.' Though in 2004 April showers came their way, these didn't put a damper on a 'good, clean, healthy, fun harvest', as the grapes were already safely in the cellar, recently overhauled and running like clockwork. Whites bursting with flavour, and 'very berryful' reds are the result. 'The noble harvest (botrytis) thankfully visited us once again, so an NLH was made,' reports JvR, 'and we made a port-style chenin for the first time in 5 years.' A handsome stone entrance now leads visitors down a new driveway lined with young pin-oaks. At the end of it, guests will find a tasting room with a generous outdoor area where they can picnic and enjoy the views.

★★★★ Bell Tower Collection Estate Wine Sets the tone of restrained, classic-mindedness of this estate's reds. Splendid, serious **98** (★★★★★) 70/30 cab/merlot had fine fruit & balanced structure, judicious wooding. 90% cab in **99**, with splashes merlot, cab f, petit v, malbec, in same classy tradition, but a trifle lighter in feel despite bigger 14.5% alc. Integrated support from 2 yrs Fr oak, 50% new. Excellent drinking now, these should see out their decades comfortably.

★★★★ Carillon No follow-up yet to **98**'s alternative merlot/cab (64/36) blend, more immediately charming than above, & a touch less grand, but finely balanced.

★★★★☆ Cabernet Sauvignon Retasted, immaculately, classically structured **98** still offers finesse, ripe, dark fruit with mineral streak & strong, savoury structure. 22 mths Fr oak, third new. 14% alc.

★★★★ Merlot 98 was ample but elegant, well structured. Lightly but firmly knit **99** has choc-mint notes, graceful tannins, well-managed 18 mths Fr oak. Concours Mondial gold. Ready, will keep well few more yrs. Like most of these, also in 375ml.

★★★★ Cape Blend NEW 01 has equal proportions merlot, cab & the vital pinotage, which offers whiffs of red fruit wildness. Some of estate's customary elegance structuring ripe berry fruits, but rather softer — richness here a little (deliciously) decadent, though tannins ripely firm, finish dry. Unobtrusive 18 mths oak. 13.5% alc.

★★★☆ Pinotage 01 continues juicy & extrovert yet delicate, well-balanced. 13.5% alc just lighter than **00**'s, where plentiful red/black berries meld in maturing bouquet & flavours. These stress Burgundian part of grape's parentage. Both yr Fr oak, third new.

★★★★ Shiraz Ripely, engagingly forward, but still with house-style drinkability & restraint (despite 14.5% alc), maiden **01** developing well, with rich fruit. Full, long-flavoured palate, with softly firm tannin. Yr Fr/Am oak, portion new. Still time to go.

★★★★ Chardonnay Reserve 03 open, generous nose, with citrus, spicy wood, oatmeal. Elegant palate, silky, well balanced, though big 14.5% alc; long dry finish. Fine food wine. Fermented/yr Fr oak — well integrated. **02** (★★★★) rather less intense.

★★★★★ Noble Late Harvest Luscious dessert from barrel-fermented chenin. Deep amber **02** (★★★★) particularly rich & sweet, with raisin, honey, marmalade: unctuous & lingering. **03** closer to **01** in elegant intensity, with honeyed apricot/pineapple, gorgeous flavours governed by lightish 11.5% alc, fine acidity. 130g/ℓ sugar.

★★★☆ Spirit of Chenin Unusual, successful fortified chenin; mature **98** petrol notes, nuts, tinned peaches. Fat, unctuous, 132g/ℓ sugar. 15 mths new Fr oak; 17% alc.

Ebony ★★★ 00 everyday blend shiraz, pinotage, gamay with moderate structure, flavour. Light wooding. Still enjoyable, but drink soon. **Rosé ★★★** Current, lightly red-gleaming NV from dark grapes only. Full-bodied (14% alc), full-flavoured, delightfully savoury & dry. **Chardonnay Unwooded ★★★** Steely, Chablis-style alternative to wooded version. Dry, well-balanced; some citrus, greengage notes, but essentially vinous. 14% alc. **Chenin Blanc Reserve Selection ★★★** Appealing spicy, peachy aromas, but **01** a little ungenerous; integrated 18 mths older Fr oak. **Ivory ★★★** Suitably ultra-pale **04** mostly sauvignon, with chardonnay, semillon; grass, pear-drop aromas/flavours; textured, crisp, freshly balanced. **Sauvignon Blanc ★★★** Refined, crisply dry & steely **04**, with straw, tropical fruit notes. 13.5% alc. **Gamay Noir** discontinued. — *TJ*

Ashanti

Paarl ▪ Est 1997 ▪ 1stB 1998 ▪ Tasting & sales daily 10-4 Sep-May (closed Sat/Sun Jun-Aug) ▪ Fee R10 ▪ Closed Easter Fri-Mon, Dec 25 & Jan 1 ▪ Tours by appt ▪ Restaurant at Ashanti *lunches Tue-Fri 11-4 year-round; in season also Sat dinners/sundowners 6.30pm-9pm & Sun à la carte lunches; booking advised* ▪ *Owner Ashanti Estates* ▪ *Winemaker Nelson Buthelezi (1999)* ▪ *Manager/viticulturist Johan Cronjé (Dec 2002)* ▪ *96 ha* ▪ *70 000 cs* ▪ *PO Box 934 Huguenot 7645* ▪ *info@ashantiwines.com* ▪ *www.ashantiwines.com* © *862·0789* 🖷 *862·2864*

Nelson Buthelezi, for several years winemaking assistant here, is now in charge of this cellar. Originally from KwaZulu-Natal, he's a man with a plan – a 3-year one, to be exact – aimed at raising the bar across the board. Attention to the vineyards, particularly new chenin, chardonnay and sauvignon; more thoughtful use of wood; and an altered pricing structure are all part of the focus. A friendly welcome remains a given, including at the country-style bistro, where light lunches or sundowners and tapas to a backdrop of birdsong are the order of the day.

★★★★ **Chiwara** Attractively different blend of mainly pinotage, cab, shiraz in **01**, delivering appetising, plump, ripe red fruit flavours. **02** more elegant, still full of taste, life; delicious crushed red berry/cedar tone; approachable with potential over possibly 5-6 yrs. ±15 mths Fr oak.

★★★★ **Pinotage** Fruity & modern, lots of flesh to match the chewy tannins; **03** appealing plum pudding & custard tone; quite firm mid-2004; could do with another yr or so. Last vintage tasted was **01**, similar juicy, perfumed fruit to pvs, sturdy but fine tannic backbone. 10–12 mths Fr oak.

Cabernet Sauvignon ★★★ **02** shows vintage's lighter, earlier-peaking qualities; mocha/choc aromas, red berry fruitiness, tannins softer than when tasted for last ed. 13% alc. 14 mths Fr oak. **Malbec** ★★★★ Last tasted was **02**, with veritable berry-orchard of fruit. **Merlot** 🆕 ★★★ Elegant **02** newcomer bears basket of fresh cassis/raspberry fruit; also fairly contrasting firm dry tannins, which another yr's ageing should help soften. **Zinfandel** ★★★ Last featured was **02**, which had fine character but didn't shout the variety. **Sangiovese** ★★★ Sympathetically oaked **02** was the last we tasted. **Shiraz** ★★★★ **03** bigger than pvs (14% alc), plenty of extract, accessible flavours spiced with white pepper & heather; creamy tone from 10 mths Fr barriques.

Concept wines

Joseph's Hat ★★★ Rich fruitcake aroma in **03**, comfortable tannins & lively texture make this a pleasing standalone drink. 10 mths Fr oak. 13.5% alc. **Sunset Hat** ★★★ Bone-dry rosé with tangy dried-fruit taste; **04** unusually subdued on nose for this label. **Nicole's Hat** ★★★ Chardonnay-based aperitif with pretty pineapple/passionfruit fragrances in **04**; good flavour & character; tasty fruity blend. – *CR*

Ashton Winery

Ashton ▪ *Est 1962* ▪ *1stB ca 1970* ▪ *Tasting & sales Mon-Thu 8-5.30 Fri 8-5 Sat 8.30-12.30* ▪ *Closed public holidays* ▪ *Tours by appt* ▪ *BYO picnic* ▪ *Owners 68 members* ▪ *Winemakers Philip Louw (Aug 2000) & André Scriven (Jan 2003)* ▪ *Viticulturist Hennie Visser (Jan 2002)* ▪ *1 864 ha (cab, ruby cab, shiraz, chard)* ▪ *18 000 tons (6 000 cs own label) 35% red 65% white* ▪ *PO Box 40 Ashton 6715* ▪ *ashkel@mweb.co.za* © *(023) 615·1135/7* 🖷 *(023) 615·1284*

The pinotage 2004 crop was somewhat disappointing here but the other varieties satisfied winemakers Philip Louw and André Scriven, resulting in 'fruitier and vibrant wines'. Vinifying fruit supplied by close to 70 growers, the Ashton cellar is 'focused on cultivating the best possible quality at the most advantageous yield' – an objective which they believe can only be attained through top-notch viticultural input.

Cabernet Sauvignon Reserve ★★★★ ✓ **00** retasted; classic cassis-cigarbox combo, balanced Old World style gaining complexity. 18 mths Fr barriques, none new. **Cabernet Sauvignon** ★★★ **02** version Fr oak staved (pvs raised in barrel); eucalyptus hint; grainy tannins matched by ripe fruit. **Pinot Noir** 🆕 ★★★ **03** (sample) impressive dark colour, huge alc (15%); soft, agreeable without being pinot-like. 7 mths 4th fill casks. **Shiraz** ★★★★ Good match for char-grilled foods – chunky, savoury; **03** (sample) one of their best: rich plum colour; harmonious dark fruit; closed mid-2004 but good potential. Yr Fr oak, none new. 14% alc. **Blanc de Noir** ★★★ Charming, off-dry picnic-partner from red muscadel. Pale salmon hued **04** has sweet talcum nose, soft strawberry palate. **Chardonnay Reserve** NEW ★★★ 6 mths 1st/2nd fill Fr oak for **03**, giving soft coconut tone; unsophisticated yet appealing. **Sauvignon Blanc** ★★★ Always early-picked for lively crispness. Lightish **04** flinty pear-drop fruit, bone-dry. **Colombar-Chardonnay** ★★ **04** (sample) attractive easy-drinker with light floral scents, well-shaped body. **Pétillant Blanc** ★★ Soft, lowish alc (±12%) blend colombard, white muscadel under screwcap; vigorous prickle in latest NV (04), fairly muted aromas. **Late Harvest** ★★★ Non-spritzy version of above; spicy almond hint in **04**; fuller than alc would suggest (11.7%); manageably sweet. **Special Late Harvest** ★★ Lightish **04** from white muscadel; honeysuckle wafts, very soft & supple, subtle muscat tones. **Red Muscadel** ★★★ ✓ **03** more structured than pvs (partly due to higher 18.5% alc); spicy tea-leaf/orange blossom fragrance, firmish potpourri taste. **White Muscadel** ★★★ ✓ Fast-forward from **97** to current **02**, jasmine & honeysuckle billow from glass; silky peach & honey flavours. Luxurious. 16.8% alc. **Port** ★★★ Not a classical style, but pleasant, fairly dry. Ruby cab joins pinotage in **01**, giving pronounced fruitiness which should settle with time; gamey/raisiny whiffs.

Satyn Rooi ☺ ★★★ As smooth as name suggests; equal blend ruby cab/pinotage, unoaked; **03** deftly executed; supple & juicy, medium bodied. Also in 6x500ml packs. **Chardonnay Unwooded** NEW ☺ ★★★ **04** (sample) fruity, very mouthfilling (14.7% alc) but bright; pear & passionfruit tones. **Colombard** ☺ ★★★ **04** arrived in cellar under blanket of dry ice to preserve fruity zing; sample shows alluring guava notes, touch quince; bone dry, refreshingly austere. Only ±12% alc. — TM

Assegai Selection

Stellenbosch (see Helderberg map) ▪ Est 1999 ▪ Tasting & sales by appt ▪ Assegai Guest Lodge ▪ Owner Woodlands Import Export ▪ 15 000 cs 80% red 20% white ▪ 10 Harewood Ave Somerset West 7130 ▪ rbuchner@worldonline.co.za ✆ 855·2249 🖷 855·4924

An export label featuring that ancient African weapon, the long throwing spear or assegai. Owner Raimund Buchner has established markets in Austria, Switzerland and many other European countries, and now has his sights set on the US and Canada. Also in his armoury are the Patrys and Tarentaal brands, described separately.

★★★★☆ **Ineva** ✓ The flagship, a succulent, well-judged blend merlot, cab, pinotage; elegantly showy. Fr oak 6 mths. 51/40/9 ratio in **01**, with hints cigarbox & lovely sweet berry fruits. **02** (★★★★) closed & tight; plums & spice glimpses; ripe cassis fruit; toasty slightly resinous finish, should be aged further. **03** more expressive; perfumed with violets & blackcurrants; has elegance & verve, deserves more time. **Cabernet Sauvignon** ★★★☆ ✓ Classically styled, 18 mths Fr/Am oak, barrels only. **01** rich fruitcake aromas, generous rounded cassis flavour; well-weighted & refreshingly unalcoholic, as are most of these. **Pinotage** ★★★☆ ✓ **02** wet heath aromas, succulent wild berry flavour; good quaffing style, well behaved. 6-18 mths Fr oak, ˈstaves/casks. **Merlot** ★★★☆ ✓ Well-fleshed **01**, choc/mocha notes, creamy liquorice in full, round & soft palate. Tasty. 18 mths Fr/Am oak, none new; same regimen for... **Shiraz** ★★★ Well-structured, flavourful **02**, whiffs strawberry, red cherry & savoury; fresh-picked berry flavour, good dry finish; probably for earlier drinking. **Merlot-Pinotage** NEW ★★★ **01** has Bovril & smoked meat on nose with sweet spicing; juicy; oak (combo staves/barrels 9 mths) doesn't interfere with enjoyment. Could take further cellaring. **Chardonnay** ★★★☆ Seamlessly wooded **03**, soft, appealing peach/honey palate verging on voluptuous. Big step up on pvs. **Chenin Blanc Barrel Fermented** NEW ★★★☆ ✓ Melon/hay aromas with buttery touch; weighty & ripe, deftly wooded. Delicious **03**. **Chenin Blanc** ★★ **04** fruit salad tones with attractive lime top-note, rather more foursquare palate. **Sauvignon Blanc** ★★★ Still-youthful **03** has green fig & melon tones, crisp herby palate, refreshing. As Raimund B's notes: 'Ideal table companion.' All above EW, WO Stbosch. — CR

Astonvale see Zandvliet
Atkinson Ridge see Amani

At The Limiet

Wellington ▪ Est/1stB 2002 ▪ Closed to public ▪ See Siyabonga for details

One of winelands eminence Graham Knox's many and varied vineyard ventures. This always a cliff-hanger. Old hárslevelü and chenin in small blocks on Wellington neighbour James McKenzie's farm are left to hang until sugar levels have reached their zenith or summer ends (whichever comes first). Shrivelling golden berries are harvested in stages (about a dozen pickings), transported to Knox's nearby Siyabonga cellar and transformed into a tiny quantity of opulent nectar. Worth the risk? Sybarites sigh: yes, please!

★★★★ **Natural Sweet** Burnished gold **03**, silky-rich layers spicy apricot & pear; great focus, purity; fruity persistence encouraged by mellowing 58g/ℓ sugar. Touch softer than luscious, tangy **02**, also with semillon. 14.5% alc. 500ml. Barrel-fermented/yr sur lie.—*AL*

Auberge du Paysan

Stellenbosch (see Helderberg map) ▪ Est 1995 ▪ 1stB 1998 ▪ Tasting & sales during restaurant hours (see Eat-out section) ▪ Closed Easter Fri-Mon, Dec 25/26, Jan 1 ▪ Art gallery ▪ Owners Frederick Thermann & Michael Kovensky ▪ Winemaker/viticulturist Tjuks Roos, with Ricardo Adams ▪ 3.8 ha (merlot, pinotage) ▪ 14 tons ±1 250 cs 100% red ▪ PO Box 315 Somerset West 7129 ©/🖰 842·2008

'Best-balanced wines since 98,' recounts Frederick Thermann, Helderberg vintner and co-owner of the French-glossed L'Auberge du Paysan restaurant, of his 2004 vintage. At present the whole crush is pinotage (which experience has taught Thermann to decant well ahead of time so that maximum softness is achieved), but a new small block of merlot is expected to yield from 2006. Also new on the property is Froggies Bistro & Tastevin, a playful variation on the Gallic theme. See the Eat-out section for details.

★★★★ **Pinotage** Trio of recent vintages tasted this ed; **02** pinot side of grape showing: forest floors & sweet fruit, elegantly mouthcoating. **01** gamey & earthy, raspberry toned, promising; both 14% alc. **00** strawberry jam whiffs, softer, obvious bottle-age, tannins turning grainy — suggest drink fairly soon. 13.5%. — *TM*

Audacia Wines

Stellenbosch ▪ Est 1930 ▪ Tasting & sales Mon-Fri 9-5 Sat 10-3 ▪ Fee R10 refunded on purchase ▪ Closed Easter Fri/Sun, Dec 25/26 & Jan 1 ▪ Tours by appt ▪ Gift shop ▪ Owners Strydom & Harris families ▪ GM/winemaker Elsa Carstens (Apr 1999), with Louis van Zyl ▪ Viticulturist Elsa Carstens ▪ 20 ha (cab, merlot, shiraz) ▪ 80 tons 6 000 cs 100% red ▪ PO Box 12679 Die Boord 7613 ▪ info@audacia.co.za ▪ www.audacia.co.za © 881·3052 🖰 881·3137 ·

It's been five years since Elsa Carstens, the first female lecturer at Elsenburg, climbed behind the wheel of this specialist red-wine cellar and, after a harvest detour to Cakebread Cellars in California, steered it into a new era. As if in celebration, their 4 year old vineyards (merlot, shiraz, cabernet franc and roobernet) delivered a better-than-expected first crop, and the Shiraz was chosen as one of eight representing SA in that category at the 2004 Tri-Nations Wine Challenge. Interestingly, you won't find any of these wines on local shelves, but you may well meet them over dinner: Audacia allocates most of its production to an exclusive restaurant clientele.

★★★★ **Cabernet Sauvignon** Current **01**, local Young Wine Show class champ, offers bramble fruit, pleasant earthiness (thread running through all these); grainy tannins still need to settle, harmonise; could mature profitably. 14.4% alc. **00** now shade drier & leaner, more curranty, possibly needs drinking. Yr Fr oak, 20% new.

★★★☆ **Merlot** Well-proportioned **01**, revisited for this ed, still an elegant, satisfying drink; light bottle-age patina to leafy plum tones; could go another few yrs. Yr Fr barrels, 2nd/3rd fill.

★★★☆ **Shiraz 01** SAYWS gold medallist that yr; big, bold & spicy style (14.8% alc). Yr 2nd-fill Fr oak. 01 retaste: pronounced Ribena aromas; sweetish choc flavours, quite assertive. Start drinking. More savoury **02** (★★★), lighter colour/body, slightly less fruit backing up the fireworks but still tasty.

Coeur de Rouge ★★★ Cab/merlot partnership (80/20), seasoned in Fr oak, 2nd-4th fill. **01** shows some good mature touches to bright cassis fruit, prominent tobacco/cigarbox characters. 14% alc. — *TM*

Aufwaerts Co-op

Rawsonville ▪ Visits by appointment ▪ PO Box 15 Rawsonville ▪ aufwaerts@breede.co.za
℗ **(023) 349·1202/082·349·4001** 🖷 *(023) 349·1202*
This well-established winery, owned by the De Villiers family, now markets a portion of its bulk production under an own-label, and invites visitors to pop in anytime for a tasting of the Dry Red and Dry White. ('Best to phone ahead though,' says Hennie de V, 'as we bottle very small batches at a time.') Also available is the Twee Eeue 5-year-old potstill brandy.

Autumn Harvest

Forerunner of SA's mid-priced wines. **Crackling** ★★ Lively, lightly petillant blend chenin, colombard, crouchen, with fresh fruit salad tones. NV under screwcap, by Distell. — *CR*

Avoca see Douglas Winery

Avondale

Paarl ▪ Est 1997 ▪ 1stB 1999 ▪ Tasting & sales Mon-Sat & public holidays 10-4 ▪ Fee R8, refunded on purchase ▪ Tours by appt ▪ Conferencing ▪ Owner John Grieve/Avondale Trust ▪ Winemaker Bertus Albertyn, with Corné Marais (Jun/Jan 2004) ▪ Viticulturist Jonathan Grieve (2000) ▪ 86 ha (cab, merlot, shiraz, chard, chenin) ▪ 290 tons 15 000 cs 74% red 20% white 6% fortified ▪ PO Box 602 Suider-Paarl 7624 ▪ wine@avondalewine.co.za
℗ **863·1976** 🖷 *863·1534*
The first small crop of organically farmed shiraz — showing 'individual character' — augurs well for this winery on Paarl's Klein Drakenstein slopes. The variety is a métier (two vintages in the shortlist of the Paarl Shiraz Challenge, one won). But expect new winemaker Bertus Albertyn (predecessor Dewaldt Heyns is kick-starting Saronsberg in Tulbagh) to up the ante on cab, after a stint with Sonoma specialist Geyser Peak. Young vineyards of mourvèdre, malbec and viognier will soon spice up an already attractive range. There's nothing faddish about the Grieve family's commitment to organic farming: their business background lies in a well-known health product range.

★★★★ **Avondale** Flagship from vintage's best reds. Retasted maiden **00** harmonious meld of cabs s/f, merlot, shiraz (45/19/18/18). Developing mature Bdx aromas of tomato & 'oyster shell'; savoury tannins from shiraz, well-infused. Drink now till ±2005/6. 16 mths new Fr oak. ±14.5% alc. VDG. Release of shiraz-led **01** (★★★★☆) held back — not re-tasted; last yr showed multi-layered flavours, tapered length; 70% new wood.

Les Pleurs range

★★★★★ **Merlot** A wine for romantics. **00**, retasted mid-04, understated, seamless. Spiced dried fruits & rain forest; sumptuous; extraordinary long, fennel finish adding gloss. Fermented new Fr oak; 13.8% alc.

★★★★★ **Syrah** From single-vyd; if regular version is rough diamond, this a polished jewel. Rich savouriness, blood-warming alc (14.5%) an Avondale signature. **02** spicy, floral, dried sage aromas; supple & svelte. Will improve ± 5yrs. Released ahead of **01** (deemed unready). Tasted mid-2003 showed smoked meat aromas, dense savoury flavours. VDG. Fr cask-fermented/aged, 80% new, 17 mths.

Avondale range

★★★★ **Cabernet Sauvignon** Demanding, warm-climate cab, usually unready on release but promising good development. **00** included soupçon cab f. After 2 yrs in bottle, developing wet earth tertiary notes; tannins still strong & finish austere (character of vintage). Hold off ± 2 yrs. Unblended **01**, for May 2005 release, has herbaceous cassis notes. Opulent, riper tannins than pvs. **02** lighter, softer. These ±14.5% alc. Fermented/matured ±14 mths Fr oak, 55–65% new.

★★★★ **Shiraz** Not for faint-hearted: beefy 14.5% alc in current **02** & strapping 15% in **01**, exuberant nose & palate. **02** sage/lavender whiffs, grippy tannins & enlivening acid. Wealth of roast-spice, meat, black pepper tones in **01**. Dryness a surprising contrast. VDG. Barrel-fermented/aged new/used oak, 15% Am.

★★★★ **Julia** Uncomplicated red sipper, blend changes with vintage. **01** cab, merlot & shiraz (39/37/32) with dot cab f. Drinkable now. **02** from fruity cab, shiraz, merlot (41/34/14) plus dollops cab f & ruby cab. Elegantly rustic. Alc (14.9%) way up on pvs 13.5%. Fr/Am oak, some new.

★★★★ **Chenin Blanc** Delicate **04** (★★★) heralds change in style: no longer with ±10% oak-fermented portion; now has 5% sauvignon, spends 3 mths on fine lees. Vibrant fruit but lacks intensity on palate.

★★★★ **Sauvignon Blanc** ✓ Classy, unwooded act from Stbosch/Mbury grapes. Intense, Loire-like **04** has 'wet pebble' flavours/textures; easily clears bar raised by mouthwatering **03**, despite lower alc (12.5% vs 13.7%). **03** showed greengage/quince coolness. Good for 2-3 yrs. No **02**.

★★★★ **Muscat Rouge** ✓ Single-vyd fortified dessert, harvested relatively early to retain fruit, minimise sweetness. From red muscat de F in **02**, light-hued (barely coppery); vivid litchi aroma; pithy tannin belies 186g/ℓ sugar. 9% barrel-fermented. 500ml.

★★★★ **Muscat Blanc** ✓ Hand-crafted nightcap. **02** pale, with appropriately delicate spanspek/litchi bouquet; more ethereal sweetness (192g/ℓ sugar) than **03** (205g/ℓ). **01**, with marmalade hue/tang, seemed rather too sumptuous. VDG. 16% alc. From low-cropped (3–4 t/ha) single block muscat de F. 500ml.

Chardonnay ★★★ Appealing **04** with clotted cream/custard tones, touch grapefruit; good oak/acid balance, though lacking intensity. 14.5% alc. 50% Fr oak, 6 mths. — *CvZ*

Avondvrede Private Wine Farm

Paarl ▪ Est 1995 ▪ 1stB 1999 ▪ Tasting, sales, cellar tours & light lunches by appt ▪ Tourgroups ▪ Function room ▪ Owners John & Christine Enthoven ▪ Winemaker John Enthoven ▪ 4 ha (cabs s/f, merlot) ▪ 20 tons ±3 600 cs 100% red ▪ PO Box 152 Klapmuts 7625 ✆ **083·658·0595** 🖷 *875·5609*

At this small winery below the Simonsberg, 'vine' and not 'hectare' is the unit of measurement when planning and carrying out vineyard development. All remaining old vines were taken out last year, and 500 cab franc *stokkies* planted. And, from the 500 chardonnay vines established in 1999, a second small quantity has been vinified. Small is the way John and Christine Enthoven intend to stay, but they also want to improve the quality of their wine and then 'maintain a high standard'. Their Koningshof Cab and Merlot Cuvée Marie Christine were not ready for tasting this edition.

Avontuur Estate

Stellenbosch (see Helderberg map) ▪ Est 1850 ▪ 1stB 1990 ▪ Tasting & sales Mon-Fri 8.30-5 Sat & Sun 8.30-4 ▪ Fee R20 for 5 tastings, incl glass ▪ Closed Easter Fri/Sun, Dec 25, Jan 1 ▪ Tours by appt ▪ The Avontuur Restaurant (see Eat-out section) ▪ Owner Tony Taberer ▪ Winemaker Willie Malherbe (Jul 2002) ▪ Viticulturist Pippa Mickleburgh (Sep 1999) ▪ 50 ha (cab s/f, merlot, pinot, pinotage, shiraz, chard, sauvignon) ▪ 20 000 cs own label 70% red 30% white ▪ Export brand: Klein Avontuur ▪ PO Box 1128 Somerset West 7129 ▪ info@ avontuurestate.co.za ▪ www.avontuurestate.co.za ✆ **855·3450** 🖷 *855·4600*

Partnering with restaurateur Al Robertson, owner Tony Taberer has extended the Avontuur brand (and the food-and-wine experience available on the estate) with the opening of an eponymous restaurant at the entrance to Cape Town's V&A Waterfront; the attached tasting area's metropolitan moniker is 'wine bar'. A new wine is on offer whether you're in the city or at the estate on the slopes of the Helderberg: the Vintner's Blend, from pinot combined with chardonnay. Back home on the farm — an elegant spread of studlands and vineyards — a new experience has been put together for visitors: a Thoroughbred Stud Farm Tour.

★★★★ **Baccarat** Brooding blend cabs s/f, merlot; **01** still remarkably deep & dark despite its age; some bottle-age revealed on nose via forest-floor hint. Seductive oak almost masks layers cassis, plum & spice; firm yet elegant palate; drinks well, should improve for 5+ yrs. 16 mths new Fr oak. 14% alc. **00** fragrant & seriously structured.

★★★☆ **Cabernet Sauvignon 00** flamboyant last yr, retasted mid-2004 more subdued; on nose, hints blackberries & charred beef. Balanced, seamless tannins. Yr used Fr oak. 15% alc.

★★★☆ **Merlot** From **99**, more Rubens than early Picasso. Confident **00** brimful with choc/spice, maraschino cherries. Light oaking (±yr older Fr barrels) for early drinking but has potential for 4-7 yrs cellaring. 13.5% alc.

★★★★ **Pinotage** Attractive **01** a fine Cape offering. Vivid raspberry, strawberry & vanilla-cream flavours backed by judicious wood (±18 mths Fr, some new). Drink over ±2-5 yrs. 14% alc. **00** luscious but burly tannins demand time.

★★★★ **Shiraz 03** poles apart from maiden **02**; the latter fruit-powered (plums/cherries), the former gamey & savoury. Tannins on **03** sweet, approachable thanks to new Am oak (50%). Noticeable 14.5% alc.

★★★★ **Cabernet Franc 00** shows characteristic tea-leaf, bramble nose; raspberry fruit just tickled by ±yr older oak. **01** lighter textured from shorter wooding. Attractive fresh compost fragrance; nimble tannins spotlight gentle, perky flavours.

★★★★★ **Luna de Miel** Oaked chardonnay; last-tasted **01** has dense lemon/lime texture, rich lees, toasty hazelnut. **03** (★★★★) similar bouquet, with over-ripe tangerine whiffs; palate dominated by caramelised oak, furry finish from lees maturation. Fairly individual style, will have its adherents.

★★★☆ **Chenin Blanc Barrel Select** None since FCTWS trophy-winning **01**.

★★★★★ **Above Royalty** Outstanding riesling NLH. Last-tasted **01** had huge flavour concentration expanded by uncloying sweetness. Fermented/9 mths in oak.

★★★★ **Brut Cap Classique** ✓ **99** from chardonnay, on lees 5 yrs. Exuberant bubbles, forward toffee-apple nose, weighty palate from extended bottle-maturation, impression of sweetness though no sugar-containing *liqueur d'expedition* added at degorgement. Pvs was NV, from pinot/chardonnay.

Vintner's Red ☺ ★★★ Fruity palate/wallet-pleaser. **03** 50/50 blend cab f/s, with dusty nose from cab franc & oak (6 mths older Fr).

Cabernet Sauvignon-Merlot ★★★ Lighter in style than the single-variety bottlings. Mélange black/red fruits for drinking now. **01**'s firm ripe tannins promise 2-3 yr longevity. Yr used Fr oak. 14% alc. **Chardonnay** ★★★ **03** for early drinking; uncomplicated tropical fruit flavours with hint of oak; light textured/bodied. **Sauvignon Blanc** ★★★ Lightish **04** (sample) offers complex cat's pee, grass, boiled sweet bouquet; arresting acid backbone & gravelly finish. 3½ mths on lees. **Vintner's White** ★★ Unpretentious, lightish easy-drinker from chardonnay & pinot blanc; **04** (sample) fragrant & musky. 3 mths older Fr oak. **Vintner's Pinotage** 🆕 ★★★ Gluggable, mulberry-hued & raspberry-toned **03**; fruit not subdued by yr older wood. The following Natural Sweets are lightish-bodied, NV: **Dolce Vita Red** ★★ Cab, merlot, ruby cab run riot in this sweet, friendly glassful. Enjoy chilled, as soon as possible after purchasing. **Dolce Vita White** ★★ Not tasted this issue. Last gave fruity, uncomplicated enjoyment. — *CvZ*

Axe Hill

Calitzdorp (see Little Karoo map) ▪ Est 1993 ▪ 1stB 1997 ▪ Open by appt ▪ Sales from Queens Bottle Store, Voortrekker Road (R62), Calitzdorp ▪ Owners Axe Hill Trust ▪ Winemaker Tony Mossop ▪ 1.3 ha (touriga, tinta, souzão) ▪ 6-7 tons; 400-450 cs; 100% port ▪ PO Box 43942 Scarborough 7975 ▪ tony@axehill.co.za © **780·1051/(044) 213·3585/082·490·4248** 🖷 *780·1178*

Tony Mossop's milestones these past 12 months? 'My 100th column for SA *Wine*, my 20th year as Cape Wine Master, and becoming a grandfather to Saskia' (daughter of Tokara winemaker Miles Mossop). This prolific wine man (and taster for this guide), with wife and co-owner Lynn, continues to pursue the perfect port at their tiny, tin-roofed *quinta* just outside Calitzdorp. Tweaking an already outstanding product, they're picking earlier, fermenting cooler, blending souzão to the established touriga/tinta mix, and experimenting with natural-yeast fermentation. In a different take on the theme, they're also vinifying (for the 2nd year) chenin for a solera-aged dry white port. And, tucked into a corner till 2006 ('but we'll drink it ourselves if it's too good — or too bad'), an unfortified red from port mainstay-grape touriga. Not forgetting their home-pressed olive oil....

★★★★★ **Cape Vintage Port** Latest five-star ranking in the guide, for **02**, entrenches this label as indisputably SA's top Port. Marked by balance rather than opulence; traditionally vinified touriga/tinta blend (±75/25) from low-yielding (±6 t/ha) vyds. 10-14 mths seasoned casks. ±20% alc. elegant dry finish. **02** gorgeous elderberry & spice character; serious yet restrained, best cellared 3-5 yrs. **01** (★★★★) unflamboyant, quite spirity. Less voluptuous than **00** FCTWS trophy winner.— *RK*

■ *Azania* see African Terroir

Baarsma SA

Stellenbosch ▪ Owner Baarsma's Holdings ▪ MD Chris Rabie (since Jul 2001) Cellarmaster: Conrad Vlok (since Sep 2002) ▪ See Lyngrove for contact details

Baarsma SA, headquartered in Stellenbosch, is a major exporter of SA wines, shipping more than 1m cases a year to the major international wine markets, notably Europe. Ranges owned or exported include Ancient Africa, Blydskap, Boschveld, Goede Moed, Goedgenoegen, Jacobus de Wet, Kaapse Pracht, Lazy Bay, Lyngrove (see entry), Meerland, Podium, Rotsvast, The Mask, Veelplesier, Volmaak, Voorspoed, Vreughvol, Welgedacht. Baarsma also represents a number of top SA brands in Europe.

■ *Babbling Brook* see Makro
Babylons Toren see Backsberg

Backsberg Cellars

Paarl ▪ Est 1916 ▪ 1stB 1970 ▪ Tasting & sales Mon-Fri 8-5 Sat 8-2 Sun 11-2 (Nov-Apr only) ▪ Fee R10 refunded on purchase ▪ Closed Easter Fri, Dec 25 & Jan 1 ▪ Self-guided tours during tasting hours ▪ Tables at Backsberg Restaurant Tue-Sun 10-3 (parties, weddings etc by appt) © *875·5952 ▪ Play area for children ▪ Maze ▪ Gifts ▪ Conferencing by appt ▪ Owner Backsberg Estate Cellars ▪ Winemaker Alicia Rechner (Dec 2001) ▪ Viticulturist Clive Trent (Jul 1992) ▪ 130 ha (cab, merlot, shiraz, chard) ▪ 1 000 tons ±80 000 cs 69% red 30% white 1% rosé ▪ Export label: Babylons Toren ▪ ISO certification in progress ▪ PO Box 537 Suider-Paarl 7624 ▪ info@backsberg.co.za ▪ www.backsberg.co.za* © **875·5141** 🖷 *875·5144*

The day after winemaker Alicia Rechner concluded the 2004 crush, she produced — a baby boy! Having spent a large portion of the previous year sorting out the new-look labels and packaging, she was delighted to find herself back in the winemaking seat. She claims the range can never be too big and, as if to prove the point, launched a new pair of kosher wines and a further two products specifically targeting the gay market. But the winemaker intimates that she's ready to slow down on product range novelties and start concentrating her energies on the high-end Babylonstoren wines. She is proud of Backsberg's commitment to their workers. Staff are regularly sent on training courses, and the last remaining group became owners of new houses last year. Add to this a clutch of awards and it would seem that for Rechner & co, the sky's no limit.

Elba ⊞ **03** 'international' mix malbec, shiraz, mourvèdre, sangiovese. Unfinished/unrated sample promising mouthful chewy choc, black fruits, chunky pliable tannins.

Babylons Toren range

★★★★ **Cabernet Sauvignon-Merlot 02**'s serious demeanour keeps this flagship blend at top spot. Still youthfully unevolved. Healthy ruby sheen; deep dark berry scents with expensive new oak trim; rich flavours still guarded by vibrant tannins. Most ageworthy of range; should peak around 2008-09. 14% alc. 16 mths Fr oak, 50% new.

★★★★ **Chardonnay 03** picks up where modern, sleek **02** left off. Touch more elegance to buttered toast, citrusy abundance. Full, creamily rich flavours, freshened, lengthened by fine, natural acid thread. Judicious oaking complements characterful style. Fermented/matured Fr oak, 70% new; malo. 14% alc.

★★★★ **Viognier 03** was notable newcomer; typical peach-kernel, dried-apricot woven into heavy-satin mouthfeel; dry, intensely long. 14.5%. 100% barrel-fermented/matured. Barrel sample **04** bigger (15.5% alc), sweeter, more juicily luscious.

Black Label range

★★★★ **Klein Babylonstoren 02** cabs s & f, merlot mix now settled into classy, modern mould. Forward but not showy amalgam ripe, vanilla-laced dark berries. Creamy, mouthfilling sweet fruit wrapped in firm yet comfortable tannin. Elegant 14% alc. Built for another 3-4 yrs. Fr oak matured, 50% new, 16 mths.

★★★☆ **Pumphouse Shiraz** Oak, fruit, rounded tannins meshed in gently expressive **02**, with 15% malbec. Elegant lily/red fruits fragrance, lithe, light-textured palate belie robust 14.5% alc. Enjoy while present harmony lasts, ±2 yrs; 16 mths oak, 15% Am.

John Martin Sauvignon Blanc ★★★ **03** mellowing quince, pear, oak spice harmony balanced with still lively palate. Good medium-bodied aperitif; can stand up to lighter summer dishes. 30% oaked 6 wks. 13.5% alc.

Varietal range

★★★☆ **Cabernet Sauvignon** ✓ **02** has developed bright, lifted plum/mulberry bouquet. Supple, substantial but not overly dense mouthful; ripe, softening tannin support. Probably at best for ±18 mths. 13.6% alc. Oak-matured. **01** *Decanter* ★★★★.

★★★☆ **Merlot** ✓ **03** sample suggests easy-going, satisfying style of **02**. Oak-brushed, bright red plum generosity; touch sugar balances weighty 14.2% alc. **02** smoothly ready, has substance for 3-4 yrs. Yr Fr oak, 25% new.

★★★★ **Organic Chardonnay** Fresh earthy attractions with lively lime/butterscotch on characterful **03**. Medium body, balanced creamy/crisp contrast, roundly dry. 14.2% alc.

> **Chardonnay** ☺ ★★★ **03** in unshowy style of **02**. Butterscotch/hazelnut nose, ripe limey tail; oak still apparent; has body to benefit from yr/2. 14% alc. 50% Fr oak.

Malbec ★★☆ Yr on, **01** wet-earth bouquet more subdued; open soon to enjoy minerally red fruits at best. **Pinotage** ★★★ Billowing red plums/raspberries on **02** reprised in **03**; friendly, juicy glugging (but NB 14.2% alc), unobtrusive tannin, oak. **Dry Red** ★★☆ NV Sweet-fruited (though technically dry) unoaked, everyday drinking. Touch of mint adds to fresh appeal, early enjoyment. **Rosé** ★★ Cherry-pink **04**; tangy red fruit hints in substantial, sweet mouthful. 14% alc. **Chenin Blanc** ★★★ **04** gentle tropical tones; limey enlivenment from splash chardonnay; bracing finish leavened by 4g/ℓ sugar. 13.5% alc. **Sauvignon Blanc** ★★☆ Subdued ripe tropical character on lightish, crisp **04**. WO W-Cape (Paarl, Rbtsn, Wrcstr).

Camp range

Chardonnay ★★★ Generous, tropical, pickled lime array on unwooded **04**. Well-balanced, agreeable without great complexity. **Cabernet Sauvignon** ★★★ **02** straightforward scented soft black berries; with 15% merlot for extra juicy palate. Flourish toasty oak in tail. 14% alc.

Kosher range

Chardonnay ★★★ **03** holding creamy, citrusy notes well on mellowing bouquet; crisp balance, 5.6g/ℓ sugar more evident in tail. Oak-influenced. **Pinotage, Merlot** NEW, **Sauvignon Blanc** NEW all **04**, not ready for tasting. Made under supervision of Cape Town Beth Din Mevushal.

Discontinued: **Special Late Harvest**, **Sparkling Brut**. — AL

Badsberg Co-op Winery 🍷 🍽 👁👁

*Worcester ▪ Est 1951 ▪ Tasting & sales Mon-Fri 8-5 Sat 10-1 ▪ Closed Easter Fri/Sun, Aug 9, Dec 25, Jan 1 ▪ Tours by appt during Dec ▪ BYO picnic ▪ Tourgroups ▪ Play area for children ▪ Gifts ▪ Conferencing ▪ Walks ▪ Conservation area ▪ Owners 26 members ▪ Winemakers Willie Burger & Henri Swiegers, with Johann Fourie (Jan 1998/Dec 2002/Dec 2003) ▪ 1 000 ha ▪ 16 000 tons 40% red 40% white 10% rosé 10% fortified ▪ PO Box 72 Rawsonville 6845 ▪ enquiries@badsberg.co.za ▪ www.badsberg.co.za © **(023) 344·3021** 🖷 (023) 344·3023*

It's been a great year for this Rawsonville winery, with a creditable showing at the Vinalies Internationales competition in Paris, the Pietman Hugo Trophy for the best group of five wines at the Worcester Young Wine Show and a gold medal from the SA Muscadel Association. New projects in the cellar include experiments with reverse-osmosis and thermo-vinification. All this following the longest and biggest grape harvest ever.

> **Pinotage** ☺ ★★★ **02** still crammed with ripe plums & mulberries; smooth, long & fruity; decidedly quaffable. **Chenin Blanc** ☺ ★★★ **03** retasted, rather understated tropical nose; livelier palate: full, smooth, drinks really well now. **Special Late Harvest** ☺ ★★★ Hanepoot & chenin do the floral thing in **04** (sample), honeysuckle & ripe tropical fruit, deliciously fresh & summery.

Merlot ★★ **02** mirrors pvs's austere, super-dry tones; extra yr in bottle hasn't really smoothed or added flesh. **Shiraz** ★★★ Debut **02** retasted, nose reveals dark berry with slight peppery hint & touch vanilla; lively tannins still, would benefit from further cellaring. Yr Fr oak. **Rosé** ★★★ Sunset-pink **03** switches to off-dry (pvs semi-sweet), with pretty ripe-plum flavours. **Chardonnay Sur Lie** ★★★ Barrel-matured **02** vanilla, lemon & lees to start; then smooth suggestion of honeyed development; not for further keeping. **Sauvignon Blanc** ★★★ **04** offers cut grass & nettles, fresh intensity, brightness; delightful in its youth. **Noble Late Harvest** ★★★★ From chenin & hanepoot (50/50), warmly acclaimed, including Rendez-vous du Chenin 2004; **03** citrus aromas & whiffs jasmine, muted botrytis character; powerfully sweet (128g/ℓ RS) without real intensity. 11.2% alc. **Vin Doux Sparkling** ★★★ Summer picnic bubbles for the sweeter-inclined; **03** delightful creamy, mouthfilling mousse. **Red Muscadel** ★★★★ **03** glows pale coppery pink; muscat, honeysuckle & peach aromas; intense sweetness saved by lively alc (16.5%) & acidity. **Red Jerepigo** ★★★★ ✓ **02** pinotage's plums & mulberry on nose, lavender whiffs, sweet but leavened with alc (15.6%); lovely warming fruity finish. **Hanepoot Jerepigo** ★★★ **03** oozes hanepoot; youthfully spiritous but delightful. 17% alc. **Port** ★★ **01** unclassic mix shiraz, cab f, ruby cab, Fr-oaked; plain but pleasantly plummy. 17.8% alc. — DH

Bain's Way see Wamakersvallei
Bakenskop see Jonkheer
Balance see Overhex
Baobab see Stettyn
Barefoot Wine Company see BWC
Baron van Imhoff see Swartland Wine Cellar

Barrydale Wine Cellar

Little Karoo ▪ Est 1940 ▪ 1stB 1976 ▪ Tasting & sales Mon-Fri 8-5 Sat 9-1 ▪ Closed Easter Fri-Mon, Dec 25 & Jan 1 ▪ Book day ahead for tours ▪ BYO picnic ▪ Heritage garden (see intro) ▪ Owners 25 members ▪ Winemaker Riaan Marais , with Ferdie Smit (Jan 1999/May 1985) ▪ Viti consultant Willem Botha (2000) ▪ 152 ha (cab, merlot, ruby cab, shiraz, chard, colombard, sauvignon) ▪ 2 000 tons 50% red 35% white 5% other ▪ Range for customer: Decent Red ▪ PO Box 59 Barrydale 6750 ▪ info@barrydalewines.co.za ▪ www.barrydalewines.co.za © (028) 572·1012 ☏ (028) 572·1541

Riaan Marais, Barrydale winemaker and manager (now also overseer of Ladismith Co-op), admits that brandy is close to his heart. He enjoys making it as much as he loves tasting it. And his two potstill versions, Joseph Barry and Barry & Nephews, are selling so fast he's had to step up production to meet the demand. On the wine front a Rosé has been added to their Misty Point range. And they've opened a heritage garden beside the tasting room, creating pleasant spot for a BYO picnic.

Tradouw range

Cabernet Sauvignon ★★★ Second-release **02** offers firm, sweet-fruited satisfaction; blackberries & minty whiff; gentle oaking (new/2nd fill barrels); legs for 3/4-yrs. **Merlot ★★★ 02** Fr-oaked, still plummy, flavoursome & smooth, could go few more yrs. 14% alc. **Pinot Noir ★★★ 02** bold (14.5% alc) & fruity, not great pinot but tasty dry red; light tannins with boiled sweet/candyfloss touch. 14.5% alc. **Chardonnay ★★** Blend barrel-fermented/aged (11 mths, malo) & unwooded components; **03** peaches & cream character with lots of vanilla; lively elegance; brisk citrus acidity. **Sauvignon Blanc ★★★ 03** retains its unusual & quite distinctive fynbos bouquet, pear-drop taste; nicely rounded yet still brisk. 13.5% alc.

Seven Falls range

Shiraz ★ 01 offers variety's smoky fruit in a quiet, no-frills package. **Shiraz-Cabernet Sauvignon NEW ★★★ 02** fresh & fruity personality; lively plums & ripe tannins for immediate enjoyment. 14% alc. **Chardonnay-Sauvignon Blanc ★ 03** plain & simple dry blend (60/40) with light tropical tone. 13.5% alc.

Misty Point range

Red ☺ ★★☆ 02 gulpability increased with extra yr in bottle; now mellow & quaffably smooth. Ruby cab/merlot, briefly oaked, 14% alc.

Pinotage ★★☆ 02 has settled, tannins comfortably soft; a pleasant quick-quaff. **White ★★** Unflashy **02** still enjoyable but drink soon. Chenin, colombard, gewürz. — DH

Bartho Eksteen Family Wines

Walker Bay ▪ Est/1stB 1998 ▪ Tasting & sales Mon-Fri 9-5.30 Sat 9-2 at Wine & Company, 7 High Street, Hermanus ▪ Fee for groups R15 ▪ Closed Easter Sun/Mon, Dec 25/26 & Jan 1 ▪ Light meals by appt ▪ Deli produce & wine gifts ▪ Owners Bartho Eksteen & Ailsa Butler (UK) ▪ Winemaker Bartho Eksteen ▪ 30 tons 2 000 cs 20% red 80% white ▪ Suite 47, Private Bag X15, Hermanus 7200 ▪ winenco@telkomsa.net © (028) 313·2047 ☏ (028) 312·4029

The 2004 harvest provoked 'mixed feelings' in Bartho Eksteen, but it also produced 'exceptional' sauvignon (ruthless selective harvesting saw the yield down an agonising 60%). This sauvignon (and shiraz) specialist says he's amused by the current preoccupation with sauvignon-semillon blends, especially the so-called novelty of wood-ageing the semillon portion. 'I've been doing this since 1998,' he laughs, 'but we all know that winemakers who work in high-profile cellars get all the attention while we puppies get ignored.' Benchmarking is an abiding emphasis, and partly for this purpose Eksteen holds a Sauvignon Celebration on the 2nd Friday of December (max 40; booking essential). Another annual challenge is seeing if he can still squeeze through the manhole of a storage tank: 'I don't know how many winemakers my age still do this themselves — or can.'

★★★★★ **Premier Choix Sauvignon Blanc** ✓ Selected Vdorp fruit, so WO Overberg. **03** styled like standard version, with semillon touch, but extra authority, intensity. Retasted, gorgeous & forceful but elegant, with yrs to go — an advertisement for waiting. Gooseberry, grass, passionfruit. 13% alc. Only in exceptional yrs; no **04**.

★★★★ **Sauvignon Blanc** ✓ Fine rich **03** even better after yr; lovely tropical fruit a part of the vinous whole. Round, balanced, with ripe, savoury acid, 13% alc. From various vyds, with 5% wood-fermented semillon. Tank sample **04** finer; perhaps ★★★★★.

★★★★ **Shiraz** Always exuberant & flamboyant, from mix Dbnvlle, W Bay grapes. **02** plentifully fruited, with blackberry & spice lurking beneath roast coffee aromas/flavours from yr oak, small % Am. **03** similar profile; lingering, well-balanced (again, those enjoying woody influence will particularly revel). At 14.5% alc, a little bigger than pvs. Few yrs ageing will benefit these; should keep 5 more at least. — *TJ*

Bartinney Cellars

Stellenbosch ▪ Est/1stB 1999 ▪ Sales Mon-Fri 9-5 ▪ Tours by appt ▪ Owner Thabana Li Meli (Pty) Ltd ▪ Winemaker/viticulturist Carl Potgieter (1999) ▪ 13 ha (cab, chard, sauvignon) ▪ 4 000 cs 33.3% red 66.6% white ▪ PO Box 2297 Dennesig 7601 ▪ thabana@mweb.co.za ✆ 885·1013 🖷 885·2852

When Sam Montsi and Prof Zackarias Sundström hooked up in Lesotho (both part of the team that wrote the Kingdom's constitution), little did they know that 20 years later they would purchase a farm together. In spite of the booming fruit industry, they instructed manager Carl Potgieter ('sold along with the gateposts') to replant the entire farm with vineyards. Trained as a horticulturist and civil engineer, Potgieter knew nothing about making wine (though a fair bit about drinking it). Yet the owners' gamble paid off. In 1999 Potgieter, mobile phone on speed-dial to consultant Jean Daneel, made his first Chardonnay. No-nonsense Potgieter has since added two whites to the range, and last year a Cab.

Thabana Li Meli range

Vin Rouge ★★ Light-textured multi-vintage (**NV**) cab, 70% 02, 30% 03; some new Fr oak; evocative spice shop scents over ripe red fruit; palate less alluring: muddled flavours, dry tannins. **Chardonnay** ★★★ Simple but satisfying **03**; light green-gold hues prefacing creamy pineapple aromas; intense & generous flavours considering unwooded, thanks to 8 mths on lees. **Sauvignon Blanc** ★★ *Sur lie* treatment as for Chard, but **02** shows its age; asparagus & lemon aromas, persistent sauvignon flavours. 13.4% alc. **Select** ★★★ Fruity blend chardonnay, sauvignon, 10% aged in new oak 8 mths. Well stuffed but noticeably sweet (±5g/ℓ sugar), lacks refreshment. 13.9% alc. — *JB*

Barton Farm

Walker Bay ▪ Est 2001 ▪ 1stB 2003 ▪ Not open to the public ▪ Owners Peter Neill & Charles Lousada ▪ Vini consultants Danie Truter & Niels Verburg ▪ Viticulturist Eric Brown ▪ 10 ha (cab, merlot, shiraz, chenin, sauvignon, semillon) ▪ 2430 cs ▪ PO Box 368 Caledon 7230 ▪ Peterjneill@aol.com ✆ (028) 284·9776

A day before returning home from a holiday in Hermanus, British businessman Peter Neill visited the barber. What he got was Barton Farm. (The salon queue was too long, so he wandered into an estate agency.) Six months later, manager Hein Swart was installed to tend the 10-ha vineyard and nectarine/plum orchard. Continuing to supply Villiersdorp Cellar was uneconomical, but after roping in UK partner Charles Lousada a year later, it was deemed viable to hook up with Danie Truter at Onderkloof in Sir Lowry's Pass Village to vinify some 2003 Chenin. Fellow Overberger Niels Verburg of Luddite Wines blended their cabernet with bought-in shiraz.

Shiraz-Cabernet Sauvignon ★★★ Spicy plum, red berry fruit on **03**, marzipan mid-palate with fine light tannins. Moderate 13.3% alc accentuates refinement, adds to accessibility, food-friendliness. **Chenin Blanc** ★★★ **03** smoky mocha notes dominate succulent tropical flavours; concentrated, persistent & rich. Lightly wood chipped. 13.2% alc. From mature W Bay vyds. **Chenin Blanc Reserve** ★★★ **03** succulent selection of above, showing fine lime & pineapple hints; elegant & lingering. — *MF*

Bastiaans Klooff see Lateganskop
Bats Rock see Lutzville
Baynsvalley see Bovlei
Bay View see Longridge
BC Wines see Brandvlei
B&E Negotiants see Urbane Wines
Beacon Hill see Jonkheer
Beaufort see Ultra Liquors

Beaumont Wines

Bot River (see Walker Bay map) ▪ Est 1750 ▪ 1stB 1994 ▪ Tasting, sales & tours Mon-Fri 9.30-12.30; 1.30-4.30 Sat by appt ▪ Fee R20 for groups of 10+ ▪ Closed Easter Sat/Sun, Dec 25 & Jan 1 ▪ Meals for small groups by appt ▪ 2 self-catering guest houses ▪ Art/jewellery exhibits ▪ Conservation area ▪ Owners Raoul & Jayne Beaumont ▪ Winemaker Sebastian Beaumont (Aug 2003) ▪ Viticulturist Leon Engelke (May 2003) ▪ 34 ha (pinotage, shiraz, chard, chenin) ▪ 200 tons 12 000 cs 60% red 40% white ▪ Export brand: Jackals River ▪ PO Box 3 Bot River 7185 ▪ beauwine@netactive.co.za ▪ www.beaumont.co.za ✆ **(028) 284·9194** 🖷 (028) 284·9733

Tell us about your first solo vintage here, we asked Sebastian Beaumont. 'Uber lekker, super cool, alles klaar.' And? 'The chenin really impressed; there's a delicious zippiness on the sauvignon, the chardonnay's showing great balance, and the reds have soft ripe tannins and full-bodied fruit.' Any other harvest news? 'Our German agent, Marcus van Riesen, a workaholic hotelier from Hamburg, helped out and I was hard-pushed to beat him to the cellar each morning.' Young malbec and petit verdot yielded a first crop, and an NLH was made after skipping the too-perfect (for noble rot) 2003 vintage. Amidst all the activity time was found to celebrate 10 years of Beaumont Wines — Sebastian B's parents Raoul and Jayne, sister Ariane and brother Lucian could look to back on a decade of growth and a steadily rising stature. And welcome a new Beaumont to the clan, Sebastian's caterer wife Nicola Weijburg.

★★★★ **Pinotage** In pinotage's rainbow, this is cool indigo, ripened slowly in temperate W Bay. Traditional open *kuip* cold soak/ferment. **03** not as bold as pvs, yet solid enough to carry 14.5% alc. Lighter hue & more delicate flavours — muted spice & strawberries, fine tannins. Whisper of vanilla from 25% Am oak. Excellent now; will improve over 2-3 yrs. **02** hallmark forward mulberry fruit, soft yet grainy tannins.

★★★★ **Mourvèdre** SA's first varietal bottling. As expected from this grape, always four-square, high alc (15.1%) & substantial tannin. These qualities & more in **03**: scrub & raspberries aromas, pervasive savouriness tempered by 16 mths Fr oak (20% new). Powerful yet balanced, needs time to ease into its frame, as did sweet-fruited, satisfying **02**, promising yrs of life.

★★★★ **Shiraz** ✓ Unlike many super-charged versions, this has never sacrificed finesse at the altar of ultra-ripe fruit. Expressive & spicy, **03** emulates **02** with dense black fruit flavours, hint smoked meat & rich, intriguing fennel-laced finish. Includes touch mourvèdre. Despite 14.8% alc, focused & balanced. Yr oak, 25% new, 25% Am.

★★★★ **Ariane 03** (★★★★) distinct step up for this Bdx blend merlot, cab, cab f (40/40/20). Generous merlot plum nose/flavours; typical cab backbone, powdery tannins; enticing cab f herbal whiffs. 14 mths Fr oak, 25% new, easily absorbed by ripe, punchy fruit. 14.5% alc.

★★★★ **Hope Marguerite Chenin Blanc Barrel Reserve** Gremlins had last yr's entry as **03** — in fact, **02**, given full-bore treatment. (Actual) **03** also single-vyd selection from old vines — some 40 yrs. Subdued nose, pithy finish followed by rush of grape's racy acidity. Should develop complexity with bottle-age. New Fr oak, 14 mths. Serious, steely wine 'for serious chenin fans'; potentially long-lived.

★★★★ **Chenin Blanc** ✓ Benchmark example from old vines. Initially shy, **04** opens up to spicy floral notes; bruised apple & citrus flavours. Includes small portion botrytised grapes, though these masked by (temporary) guava-like fermentation odours. 15% barrel-fermented portion adds to mouth-filling structure. **03** restrained melon & cream flavours. These worth a few yrs in the cellar.

★★★★ **Chardonnay** Big, rounded chardonnay, fermented/10 mths Fr oak, 25% new. Freshly-squeezed lime & orange tones in **03**; wheat & toffee instead of usual buttered toast. Oak dominates nose but appears more muted on creamy, lemon biscuit palate. These age with benefit.

★★★☆ **Sauvignon Blanc** With obvious cat's pee aromas, 'wet pebble' finish, **04** a departure from signature gooseberry style. For early drinking.

★★★☆ **Goutte d'Or** Sauternes-style botrytised semillon/sauvignon blend (80/20). 10 mths oak (some new). **03**, with higher sugar (135g/ℓ) than usual, candied peaches & pears, dried apricots. Luscious weighty palate but arresting acidity, persistent finish.

Raoul's Old Basket Press Rustic Red ☺ ★★★ As colourful & full of bravado as Raoul B himself; mainly tinta (with some merlot, shiraz), contrasting floral/spicy, dusty/fruity tones. Unwooded. High alc (14.5%) not for swigging.

Cape Vintage ★★★ 50/50 tinta/pinotage gives foot in both Cape & Portuguese camps — foot-trodden it was, too, before two yrs in old casks. Full 20% alc. **02** sweet vanilla & bread pudding nose layered with dark black plums. Sweet finish despite relatively low 84g/ℓ sugar.

Jackal's River range

For UK market. **Pinotage** ★★★ **02** was last tasted; silky, seductive, with firm finish. **Unwooded Chardonnay** ★★★ **04** shy with refined chardonnay perfume, fine lime & grapefruit palate. 12.5% alc. — *CvZ*

Bein Wine 🍷

Stellenbosch ▪ Est/1stB 2002 ▪ Open by appt only ▪ Owners/ winemakers/viticulturists Luca & Ingrid Bein ▪ 2.2 ha (merlot) 1 000 cs 100% red ▪ PO Box 3408 Matieland 7602 ▪ lib@beinwine.com ▪ www.beinwine.com ©/🖷 881·3025

What was it that prompted Luca and Ingrid Bein to trade a secure, happy life as veterinary doctors in Switzerland for the vagaries of winegrowing in the Cape (last year, they report, was particularly difficult)? Quite simply: love. Smitten by a farm in the Polkadraai Hills with its own little vineyard, they bought and systematically fine-tuned it to perform like clockwork. Their vines are now virus-free, the trellising fully upgraded and a computerised weather station installed. What has not changed is their philosophy: using the best to create the best without any compromise. 'Chips, staves, flavourings and any practices other than used in traditional winemaking will never be used for our wine', they declare. At press time a long dreamt-of own-cellar was being readied for harvest.

★★★☆ **Merlot** Ripe, fragrant **02** still forthrightly engaging a year on. Silky, fresh & elegant; firmly but restrainedly supported; balanced 13.4% alc; sensitively oaked — yr Fr, 35% new. One to watch, we said: justified by sample of **03**, similarly styled (but alc 13.8%) yet more roundness, fruit depth; charming, not frivolous; should be ★★★★. — *TJ*

Belbon Hills

Worcester ▪ Est/1stB 1999 ▪ Closed to public ▪ Directors Mirella Corsetti Kruger & Pedro Estrada Belli ▪ 30 ha (cab, pinotage, ruby cab, shiraz, chenin, colombard, sauvignon) ▪ 260 tons 10 000 cs own label 60% red 40% white ▪ PO Box 457 Bloubergstrand 7436 ▪ winery@belbonhills.com © 557·7143 🖷 557·1351

Partners-in-wine Pedro Estrada Belli and Mirella Corsetti Kruger are still on track with developing their 100ha Breede River Valley farm, which includes renovating the 80 year old cellar. Progress is slow – their import-export business makes them part-timers – but they promise local wine lovers some action this year. Their own-label wines head off-shore – to Canada, Sweden, Greece and Italy (both have Italian, and winemaking, roots); a local co-op is catchment for the rest.

Cabernet Sauvignon ★★★ **03** big step up on pvs; expansive red berry & cherry flavours sprinkled with sweetish spice, extended finish. Could develop further. 14% alc. **Ruby Cabernet** ★★★ We last tasted round & sweet-fruited **01**. **Shiraz** ★★★ Light-toned & bodied **01**, yr on shows touch of good maturity; herby whiff; supple & ready. **Red** NEW ★★★ Shiraz, pinotage, ruby cab blend (40/30/30), unwooded; fruity, juicy – slips down easily. 13.5% alc. **Blanc de Noir** NEW ★★☆ Appealingly fresh & balanced **03**, with ripe summer pudding tones; gently dry; from cab. **Chenin Blanc** NEW ★★★ **03** guava & banana whiffs, sweet ripe fruit & pleasantly contrasting acidic zing. 14.5% alc. **Sauvignon Blanc** ★★★☆ Last tasted was aromatic, medium-bodied **02**. **White** NEW ★★★ Chenin/sauvignon mix (70/30); as label says: 'tropical tone with lime & lemon'; **02** clean lemon-zest finish. WO W-Cape. – DH

Bellevue Estate

Stellenbosch ▪ Est 1701 ▪ 1stB 1999 ▪ Tasting Mon-Fri 10-4 Sat & non-religious public holidays 10-3 ▪ Owner Dirkie Morkel ▪ Winemaker Wilhelm Kritzinger (Feb 2002) ▪ Viticulturist Dirkie Morkel (1979) ▪ 193 ha (14 varieties, incl 5 Bdx reds; pinot, pinotage; chard, chenin, semillon, sauvignon) ▪ 13 000 cs own label 97% red 3% white ▪ PO Box 3 Koelenhof 7605 ▪ bellevue1@global.co.za © 865-2055 ✉ 882-2899

PK Morkel was the first (along with Paul Sauer of Kanonkop) to plant pinotage commercially, a bold move which paid off – in 1959 it won him the best wine trophy at the Cape Wine Show. Fifty years later these same vines, now presided over by his nephew Dirkie, are still producing an award-winning Pinotage. To celebrate their long history (Dirkie is the fourth generation to farm here), all Bellevue wines will now be marketed under the name Morkel, including 'Rozanne' – launched in 2004 and named after Dirkie's eldest daughter. Last year was not an easy harvest, with unpredictable ripening and sporadic sunburn, but Dirkie's winemaker Wilhelm Kritzinger is still brimming with enthusiasm, not least about the three new wines to be released this year: Petit Verdot, Malbec Limited Release and Pinot Noir.

Morkel range

★★★★☆ **PK Morkel Pinotage** Single-vyd selection, worthily representing world's first commercial pinotage partly grown here (released **61** under Lanzerac label). **02** (★★★★) combines power with elegance, still quite closed mid-2004 but class very apparent; red- & black-berried fruits have absorbed wood with ease (yr new Fr), savoury acid, ripe tannins. Preview of **03** dark sultry beauty, crammed with sleek, intense fruit, great presence, looks to join **01** in stellar league. Alc. 14.5%

★★★★ **Tumara** Label migrated to range with **02** vintage. Full house of Bdx vaieties – cabs s/f, merlot, malbec, petit verdot (66/15/4/10/5). Sleek, elegantly crafted & stylish, immaculate winemaking, not a tannin out of place. Dark choc & black cherry invitation, oak woven into the very fabric of the wine, good dry finish. Yr 50/50 new/2nd fill barrels. Alc 13.5%.

★★★★☆ **Malbec 03** interesting whiff smoked beef & mint, good follow-through onto palate, mélange of red & black berried fruits; soft tannins the distinctive feature from this variety. Alc 14%.

★★★★ **Sauvignon Blanc** ✓ **04** announces itself as serious sauvignon, from first whiff of fig-leaf & gooseberry to huge concentration of deep-fruited flavour, sweet sour tussle, ultra-long finish. A sauvignon with presence. 'Made as reductively as you can go!" says winemaker. Bone dry, unwooded, alc 14%.

Limited Release Malbec NEW Wafting vanilla (barrel sample) to minted black plum fruit, -grained tannins, savoury finish; **03** beautiful concentration in lengthy finish. 100%

new Fr oak 10 mths. Provisional ★★★★. **Petit Verdot** 🆕 (Sample) **03** attractive whiff vanilla oak, deep coloured, very youthful. Elegant & fresh faced, good red-berried fruit given fine oak treatment, fresh acidity. Elegant, if one-dimensional. Provisional rating ★★★☆. **Pinot Noir** ★★★ **02** rather more vinous than varietal; hints beetroot & strawberry but mainly good oak . Soft berry palate, then grippy tannins gather momentum to finish. All Fr oak, Burgundian coopers, third each new-3rd fill. Alc 13.5%.

Bellevue range

★★★★ **Tumara** Deep-coloured, extracted, modern Bdx-style blend, with extra satin smoothness for earlier approachability, though structured to keep 5+ yrs. Revisited for this ed confirms longevity. Cool cedar intro to **01** but sumptuous cassis fruit evokes deep-pile luxury. Generously, expensively oaked (yr Fr, 50% new); blend of cabs s/f, merlot, malbec (67/11/15/7). **02** See above.

★★★★ **Pinotage** ✓ This too in bright, modern guise, more immediately accessible than version above. **02** soft plushy, plummy fruit almost ready. Slight sweetness to fruit hauled back by firmish oak tannins, adding needed texture, dryness. Am oak, 11 mths, 50% new. VDG 2003, Pinotage Top Ten same yr.

★★★☆ **Shiraz 01** showing sleek dark-berried fruit when retasted mid-2004, tannins suave & smooth, too. Has developed into something of a charmer. MIWA gold 2002. **02** shade riper, more fleshy, both feature warm spiced plum, luscious & rather more 'red wine' than classically 'shiraz'. Yr Fr oak, 50% new.

Malbec ★★★ Softly structured rustic charmer, most accessible label from this cellar. **02** with choc-mint flavours, soft tannins. Ready or keep yr only. 14% alc. **Rozanne** 🆕 ★★★ **03** charming & fruity blend merlot, shiraz, pinotage 59/22/19, lightish, less serious, everyday quaffer with sprig of mint; will find many friends. Staves, alc 13.5%. **Atticus** ★★★ Retasted **01** for this ed, ripely fruity blend cab/pinotage (60/40), for drinking now & over next 2 yrs. 13.3% alc. **Sauvignon Blanc** ★★★ **03** mid-2004 shows slight fading to brash tropical & grassy notes, still a good accompaniment to anything fishy. Bone-dry.—*IvH*

Bellingham

Wellington ▪ Est 1693 ▪ 1stB 1947 ▪ Closed to public ▪ Owner DGB ▪ Winemakers Niël Groenewald & Lizelle Gerber, with Mario Damon (Jul/Aug 2004, Jan 2002) ▪ Viti consultants Johan Wiese & Kevin Watt (1994/2002) ▪ 5 000 tons 350 000 cs 50% red 49% white 1% rosé ▪ HACCP & ISO 9002:2000 certified ▪ PO Box 79 Groot Drakenstein 7680 ▪ bellingham@dgb.co.za ▪ www.bellingham.co.za ✆ 874·1011 🖷 874·1690

Niël Groenewald, chief winemaker recently arrived from Perdeberg (Graham Weerts having emigrated to Kendall-Jackson in the US), had a good first season (the second for the imposing new cellar): 'Heavier alcohols, elegant fruit and wonderful mid-palate flavours are to be expected.' Looking ahead, he's already nailed his colours to the mast: 'Bellingham will be the leading SA brand locally and overseas,' he declares. Lending credence to his intent is the appointment of Lizelle Gerber, ex-Eikendal and Avontuur, to the team. Adding to his local experience, assistant winemaker Mario Damon worked a second crush in France in 2004. As far as international aspirations go, the Bellingham name is already familiar in almost 50 export markets across Africa, Europe, North America and the East; the brand accounts for close to 30% of all SA wines sold in the huge UK market for more than £5. Groenewald identifies black economic empowerment as a challenge for the future and, on a deliciously mysterious note, promises that something momentous 'will be announced in the John Platter 2006 edition'.

Spitz range

★★★★ **Cabernet Franc** As with all in this premium range, only made when quality deemed worthy. None since **99**, pvsly noted as sensuous, elegant. Bottelary fruit.

★★★★ **Pinotage** Last **99**, not retasted 2004, had savoury tones, mulberry fruit, spicy vanilla sweetness on finish. 13% alc.

★★★★ **Merlot** 🆕 **02** weighty offering of distinction shows brooding dark fruit under wraps of chewy tannins, bolstered by 15% alc. Fruit intensity promises opening of choc-tar richness, development over 2-4 yrs. Pdberg grapes. 14 mths new Fr oak.

★★★★ **Chardonnay 03** extends lineage of seriously elegant wine; stony ring to creamy — not broad — texture, fine-grained in svelte finish. Now Stbosch fruit, labelled Coastal as was debut **02** from W Bay & Darling grapes: marzipan notes, concentrated grapefruit profile, seamless acidity. Natural ferment; yr new Fr oak. 14% alc.

Maverick range

★★★★ **Syrah** 🆕 First red iconoclast pushes into deep, dark, purple violets territory. **02** handsome fruit, floral tints spiced up with tensioned mulberry fruits; sweet tannins. Definitely sexy; perk from 10% native-ferment viognier. 14 mths Fr wood. 14.8% alc.

★★★★ **Chenin Blanc 03** in similar style to debut **02**. low-cropped bushvine grapes 50/50 Fr oak/tank-fermented, stirred on lees 3 mths. Revisited for this ed; delicate fruit somewhat overwhelmed by showy vanilla oak & strapping 14.5% alc.

★★★★ **Viognier** Boldly barrel-fermented with native yeasts, aged 6 mths 2nd-fill oak. **03**'s promise fulfilled: intense peach characters mingled with pistachio/roast cashew flavours, sumptuous tropical farewell carries 6g/ℓ sugar & 14.5% alc.

Our Founders (varietal) range

★★★★ **Shiraz** ✓ Higher Fr oak contribution (75%, rest Am; 30% new, 13 mths) since punchy, peppery **02** shows in subtle toasty nuances, with finely-tuned blackcurrant & loganberry to the fore. **03** palpably delicious; plumply juiced fruits remarkably accessible within sustaining tannic core, even in young sample. 14.5% alc.

★★★★ **Cabernet Sauvignon** Sample **03** cements promise of acceleration from **01**; shows cab fruit nestled into powdery tannins; fine-gained & dry, will need up to 5 yrs to show its best. **02** sweetly-fruited, concentrated, ripe; this too will last a while. Extended maceration, malo in wood, 14 mths Fr oak, 30% new. 14.8% alc.

★★★☆ **Merlot** Sample **03** presents all the varietal hallmarks: supple plummy fruit, velvet-curtain mouthfeel, gently-oaked finish (Fr, 30% new, 14 mths). Plush, modern style, 14.5% alc sits neatly within foursquare structure. As ebullient as pvs.

Pinotage ★★★ **03** fruit-driven, sappy style; overt vanilla from 50% Am oak fraction. Ripe mulberry flavours lend concentration to easy-tannin finish. 14.5% alc. **Chardonnay** ★★★ **03** Obvious oak (30% new Fr/Am fermented/matured), straightforward lemony fruit. 14% alc. **Sauvignon Blanc** ★★☆ **03** developed scrub-herb notes, sweetness cut by bracing acidity.

The Blends range

Sauvignon Blanc-Chardonnay (Sauvenay) ☺ ★★☆ Still benchmark in this easy-going style. **04** polished as ever; bright pear, med-bodied, dry-enough tail.

Cabernet Sauvignon-Merlot (Classic) ★★★ **02** 50/50 blend spotlighting latter's choc coating melded with plump cab cassis. Soft tannins afford imminent drinkability. Oak staves 3 mths. 14% alc. **Rosé** ★★ The first Cape rosé. **04** from pinotage, coral-ruby hue; candyfloss nose, sappy sweet send-off. **Chardonnay-Semillon** ★★☆ Export only. Dry, unwooded **03** full & firm, ripe figgy flesh with citric tension, sweetish finish. **Premier Grand Cru** ★★ Crisp & dry NV blend (including crouchen, chenin, sauvignon, colombard), delivering the goods consistently since 1951. **Johannisberger** ★★ Launched 1957, still SA's biggest semi-sweet. Light-bodied NV (11.7% alc); aromatic floral whiffs, sweet but tangy tail. — *DS*

▧ *Bell Tower* see Asara
Ben du Toit see Helderkruin

Bergheim

*Paarl ▪ Est/1stB 2000 ▪ Visits by appt; tasting/sales also at I Love Wine (see Wine shops section) ▪ Owners E&H Jordaan ▪ Winemaker Edwin Jordaan ▪ 200 cs 100% red ▪ PO Box 6020 Main Street Paarl 7622 © **082·770·8001** 🖷 862·7852*

Being a *garagiste* is a bit like being a general practitioner, believes Paarl doctor Edwin 'Jorries' Jordaan, whose theatre of vinous operations is a communal cellar on Paarl's Main Street. 'Overheads are massive, you work long hours for little financial gain, but there's job satisfaction in curing *parskoors* (harvest fever). And if you run into problems, you can always consult a specialist.' Last year Jordaan made a Shiraz for the first time – a doddle, in his diagnosis, compared to Pinotage.

Pinotage ★★★ Now in full-throated style: **03** (sample) barrel-aged (Fr/Am, some new, 15 mths), extracted, dense. Chewy palate; pungent stewed mulberry & toast aromas, volatile touch. Leaves nothing to the imagination. 14.5% alc. WO Voor Pdberg. – *TM* –

Bergkelder

Stellenbosch ▪ Tasting & sales Mon-Fri 8-5 Sat 9-3 ▪ Fee R20 ▪ Open public holidays ▪ Tours Mon-Fri 10 (Eng or Afr), 10.30 (Eng, Ger or Fr), 3 (Eng or Afr); Sat 10 (Eng or Afr), 10.30 (Eng, Ger or Fr), 12 (Eng or Afr); incl AV presentation available in 7 languages (7 tours a day in Dec/ Jan) Bookings: tours@bergkelder.co.za ▪ Special group tours, private functions by appt ▪ Owner Distell ▪ Cellar manager Coenie Snyman ▪ Senior winemakers Thinus Krüger (reds, 2002) & Kobus Gerber (whites, 2001) ▪ Viticulturist Bennie Liebenberg ▪ PO Box 184 Stellenbosch 7599 ▪ www.bergkelder.co.za © 809·8492 ✆ 883·813

Literally 'Mountain Cellar', after the maturation halls cut into Stellenbosch's Papegaaiberg, Bergkelder is responsible for Fleur du Cap, listed separately.

Bergschaduw see Vinfruco

Bergsig Estate

Worcester ▪ Est 1843 ▪ 1stB 1977 ▪ Tasting & sales Mon-Sat 8-5 ▪ Tasting fee for groups ▪ Closed Easter Fri-Sun, Dec 25 ▪ Tours by appt ▪ BYO picnic ▪ Owners Lategan family ▪ Winemaker De Wet Lategan (Jan 1989), with Chris du Toit (Jul 2003) ▪ 253 ha (cab, pinotage, shiraz, chard, chenin, sauvignon) ▪ 3 200 tons 50 000 cs own label ▪ 35% red 60% white 4% rosé 1% port ▪ Exported as Lategan & White River ▪ PO Box 15 Breede River 6858 ▪ wine@bergsig.co.za ▪ www.bergsig.co.za © (023) 355·1603 ✆ (023) 355·1658

It was a year of extremes, says winemaker De Wet Lategan of the 2004 harvest: 'Patience was the watchword'. Its reward? 'Close to ideal chardonnay', similar to their benchmark 2000 vintage. By contrast, Lategan considers much of the 2004 pinotage as 'extremely disappointing' (happily, the older, later-harvested blocks are full of promise). His standards are high – he does, after all, have to reach the Woolworths bar as producer of several of the retail group's popular labels – and he has a 10-medal haul in the recent past. Changes on the estate include an upgrade of the tasting area, and the appointment of Chris du Toit, with several crushes behind him, locally and in Germany.

★★★★ **Pinotage** ✓ Elegant, minerally wine, from selected ±30-yr-old shy-bearing vyds. **00** rich & mellow; ripe-berry nose; drinking well; **01** flinty edge to the berries; fuller, bigger, slightly more tannins; should develop beautifully; current **02** (★★★★★) biggest & ripest of these; retasted mid-2004, confirms its class; plummy, sweet-fruited; still fairly obvious tannins suggesting peak 3-5 yrs away. 10-15 mths oak, 50% new. 12.8-13.8% alc.

★★★★ **Cabernet Sauvignon** From **02**, more serious; rich red-berry fruit, spicy oak background (yr 2nd/3rd fill barrels); full & round, distinct but supple tannins. Good ageing potential. Big 14% alc. **03** (★★★★★) clean minerally nose, firm, more midweight (13.5% alc), fairly quick; for earlier drinking.

★★★★ **Chardonnay** ✓ Numerous local/overseas awards for this barrel fermented/aged version, including Chardonnay-du-Monde 2004 for **02**. Retasted, shows very attractive bottle-development, still has its signature peachy tone with a delicate honey-eyed touch. **03** more concentration of ripe peach, vanilla & butterscotch; full & round, lively acidic bite. ±9 mths new Fr oak.

★★★☆ **Sauvignon Blanc Brut** ✓ **03** energetic carbonated dry sparkler, dew-fresh & smilingly priced. Could even be aged a bit. Current version exactly as expected, lively & rounded with clean tropical fruit nose, refreshing finish.

★★★★ **Noble Late Harvest** ✓ Current **99** mostly sauvignon (40%) with buket, chenin, gewürz; retasted mid-2004 pronounced honeyed overlay; at peak, should continue to give pleasure for a few more yrs. 11.8% alc. 375ml.

★★★★ **Cape Ruby** ✓ Latest version of this multi-vintage NV blend from tinta not tasted.

★★★★ **Cape Late Bottled Vintage** ✓ **97** nicely rounded, shows well matched tannin & alc; could be cellared further. 95g/ℓ sugar, ±18% alc, 36 mths oak-matured; **98** richer, full & round, slightly firmer tannin; higher alc (±20%) longer cask-ageing (48 mths). Should mature with great interest/benefit.

★★★★ **Cape Vintage** ✓ Tinta, open-tank-fermented, fortified with brandy spirit, 36 months oak; **98** mulberries & sweet spice; mid-2004 very youthful still: muscular tannins & tightly coiled palate, but some very attractive secondary characters creeping in; deserves further cellaring. ±98g/ℓ sugar, 19.8% alc. **99** sweeter fruit, bigger alc, plums, damson, some cherry, very youthful; more elegant than **98**; even at high alc (20.9%), tastes sweeter. Could mature into ★★★★★ (or better) quality.

Shiraz Rosé ☺ ★★★ Bone-dry, food-cordial style, med-bodied; **04** red berries & lavender scents, strawberry flavours. Quaffable, consistent blush from shiraz. **Ruby Cabernet-Merlot** ☺ ★★★ Always a happy marriage here. **03** crammed with ripe plum & cherries, some dried fruit & grassy notes; juicy tannins. 13.5% alc.

Chenin Blanc ★★★ **03** slight tropical tone; pleasant rounded mouthfeel; fruit fading a bit; suggest drink soon. **Sauvignon Blanc** ★★★ Always a more genteel expression of the variety; **03** very appealing, still sprightly, zesty & light. **Gewürztraminer** ★★★☆ Charming sweetish summer aperitif; **04** signature rose-petals & litchis, tropical background; rounded but fresh, crisp, fragrant farewell. **Weisser Riesling** ★★★ Yr in bottle has been good to **03**; ripe pineapple, even hint mango, touch litchi; well rounded, enough acid for lively dry mouthfeel; could take further cellaring. **Bouquet Light** ★★ Latest version of this semi-sweet perlé from morio muscat not tasted. — DH

Bergwater Vineyards　　　　　　　　　　　NEW

Prince Albert ▪ Est 1999 ▪ 1stB 2002 ▪ Closed to public ▪ Owners Heimie & Stephan Schoeman & DKPG (Dutch Investors Group) ▪ Winemaker Mariska Schreuder (Jan 2003) ▪ Viti advisers VinPro (1999) ▪ 68 ha (cab, merlot, shiraz, sauvignon) ▪ 90% red 10% white ▪ PO Box 40 Prince Albert 6930 ▪ wine@bergwater.co.za ▪ www.princealbertvalley.com ✆ (023) 541·1703 🖷 (023) 541·1081

Introducing a new winery in Prince Albert Valley, a new wine ward and the latest best-kept secret among rat-race escapees. Backed by Dutch investors, Heimie and Stephan Schoeman are re-introducing winemaking to this Victorian-era enclave (old cement and even clay fermenters still found on some of the farms). The Schoemans have 48ha under vine; they plan to expand to an eventual 95ha and build an architect-designed winery in time for the 2006 crush. The facility will have a capacity of 1 500 tons (enough, incidentally, to vinify the whole valley's production). Also on the completed premises will be a restaurant, farmstall, conferencing, picnics, hikes and more. Small batches of wine were made in 2001 and 2002 but not marketed; the first commercial releases are 03s, made by Mariska Schreuder with Pierre Marais of Bergkelder, from high-lying (900m) Swartberg vineyards. The six wines are standard and reserve Merlots and Shirazes, a Royal Reserve blend, and a Cab. Most is exported, chiefly to the US and the Netherlands, though small quantities are distributed to local restaurants and hotels.

Bernheim Wines　　　　　　　　　　　

Paarl ▪ Est/1stB 2004 ▪ Tasting & sales Mon-Fri 8.30-5 Sat 9-12 ▪ Fee R5 refunded with purchase ▪ Closed Christian holidays ▪ Tours by appt ▪ Owners Pieter & Anneke Taljaard, Hermann

Helmbold, Jacques Kruger/Pacas Winery (Pty) Ltd ▪ Winemaker Jacques Kruger (Feb 2004) ▪ Viti consultant Gawie Kriel (Mar 2004) ▪ 11 ha (cabs s/f, merlot, pinotage, shiraz, chenin) ▪ 6 000 cs 70% red 25% white 5% rosé ▪ PO Box 7274 Noorder-Paarl 7623 ▪ bernheim@iafrica. com ▪ www.bernheimwines.com © 872·8358 ▤ 872·5618

Heard the one about the Accountant, the Engineer and the Winemaker? Late in January 2004 Jacques Kruger (the Winemaker, with wine-fluent wife Adna) heard that Bernheim was for sale. For years he and friends Pieter Taljaard (the Accountant) and Hermann Helmbold (the Engineer) had been dreaming about starting a small winery. By mid-Feb their offer had been accepted, and Kruger took over with most of the crop still on the vines. Despite his experience at Blaauwklippen and Long Mountain, Kruger says he was both frightened and excited by this new challenge. The cellar doors were closed for most of 2004 while they replanted old vineyards, upgraded the winery and nurtured the new wines. 'While other farms experienced problems, all our grapes were harvested ripe, proving to us that the terroir (the farm neighbours Veenwouden) has huge potential.'

Following all **04**, all tasted as samples. **Pinotage** ★★ Uncomplicated, rosé-like pasta partner with youthful mulberry bouquet; juicy, somewhat savoury dry palate. Chill in summer. **Merlot-Cabernet Sauvignon** ★★ Muted aromas of plum & woodsmoke, mid-2004 oak obvious on still fairly taut palate. 60/40 blend, fermented/aged with Fr staves, 4 mths. **Rosé** ★★★ Juicy, balanced strawberry flavours, dry finish; lightish equal colombard/chenin, dollop cab for colour. **Chenin Blanc** ★★ Shy pear-drop aroma with leesy note, bone dry. 12.4% alc. **Chenin Blanc Oak** ★★ Slightly floral nose, marginally fuller than unwooded version, very dry finish. **Late Vintage** ★★ Medium-bodied semi-sweet with hint of clove. **Cabernet Sauvignon** & **Shiraz** Not ready for tasting. – *TM*

Bertrams Wines

Venerable brand established by Robert Fuller Bertram at the end of the 19th century; now under aegis of African Wines & Spirits.

★★★★ **Cabernet Sauvignon** We last tasted 99, which had acquired an attractive 'old style' bouquet with light savoury/floral accent.

★★★★ **Shiraz** ✓ 01 comfortable traditional-style fireside red, not a fruit-bomb. Xmas-cake whiffs, slight peppery notes & hint vanilla; dry savoury finish. 14% alc (which hardly 'traditional'). Pvs 99 (★★★★) was soft, balanced, if quiet. WO Stbosch.

★★★★ **Robert Fuller Reserve** Classically minded Bdx blend, usually lightish, balanced & satisfying. **02** is a cab f/merlot blend, with gentle chamomile whiffs; aromatic rather than fruity; refined & elegant in leaner mode.13.5% alc.

Ruby Port ★★★ NV, usually from pinotage; latest limpid ruby hues, ripe plum notes, hint raisin; silky & dry tasting; grip from 19.5% alc. This, wine above, WO W-Cape. – *TM*

Beyerskloof

Stellenbosch ▪ Est 1988 ▪ 1stB 1989 ▪ Tasting & sales Mon-Fri 8.30-4.30 Sat 10-2 ▪ Closed Easter Fri/Sun/Mon, Dec 25/26 & Jan 1 ▪ Farm produce ▪ Owners Beyers Truter & Simon Halliday ▪ Winemaker Beyers Truter, with Anri Truter (Jan 2004) ▪ Viti consultant Johan Pienaar (2000) ▪ 70 ha (cab, merlot, pinotage) ▪ 490 tons 100 000 cs + 225 000ℓ for customers ▪ 98% red 2% white ▪ PO Box 107 Koelenhof 7605 ▪ wine@beyerskloof.co.za © 865·2135 ▤ 865·2683

A methodical build-up reached the point in 2004 where one of the Cape's most colourful and respected winemakers arrived 'home'. After 20 vintages, Beyers Truter presented Kanonkop's cellar keys to new chatelain, Abrie Beeselaar, to devote his substantial energies to Beyerskloof. Kanonkop's Kriges have sold their stake; Beyerskloof partner/UK importer Simon Halliday has upped his. A steadily increasing output has reached 100 000 cases. A 150-ton cellar, with four open fermenters and double the barrels (800) handled the 2004 harvest. (It was the first vinified on-site since 1995.) Having fledgling winemaker son Anri's assistance made Truter prouder than being shortlisted for the IWSC Winemaker of the Year award or being named SA Producer of the Year.

★★★★★ **Beyerskloof** Fine, modern blend cab, merlot, from 5ha planted 80/20, harvested en-bloc, vinified traditionally, 2+ yrs new Fr oak. Cedary wood & big smooth tannins still obvious on youthful **01**, but so is plenteous red fruit & mineral streak. **02**'s 15% alc higher than pvs, adding to forceful, macho presence; darkly savoury, yet sweet-fruited. These need vigorous decanting in youth — but 8-10 yrs in bottle even better.

★★★★ **Synergy** 'Cape blend', with cab & merlot in varying, but fairly equal, proportions with pinotage. Maiden **01** was succulent, refined. ± yr Fr oak, some new. **02** (★★★★) spicy, ripely soft attractions; decently structured, well balanced, but not very serious or conclusive.

★★★★ **Synergy Reserve** Cab in majority here, pinotage 37%, merlot 8%. So maiden **01** firmer, more linear than version above; yr Fr oak, half new. VDG. Fresh, dynamic **02** (★★★★★) with meaty, smoky nose is forceful but focused, with delicious rich-fruited savouriness, firmly & gently underpinned by tannin. Already enjoyable, should develop well over 5+ yrs.

★★★★ **Pinotage** ✓ Outgoing, delicious — & available in attractively priced quantity. Tasty, fresh **03** (★★★★) has enough ripe firmness to hold the fruit in well-calculated grip. Eminently drinkable, with appropriate 14% alc. Unobtrusive light oaking. **02** was ripe, bold (14% alc) & velvety.

★★★★★ **Pinotage Reserve** More serious, suavely refined evidence of the Pinotage King's varietal control. 2002 ABSA Top Ten for maiden **01**. IWC 2004 & IWSC 2003 golds for **02**, also top-ranked in *Wine*. Some sombre, forest-floor/earthy notes apparent now, with dense fruit over strong dry tannins; 14% alc. **03** lighter-hearted, with lovely scented nose (inc spicy wood), deep dark cherry fruit. Sophisticated yet like-able, intense & well-formed.

Rosé ★★★ From pinotage, unsurprisingly; last tasted was clean, dry, mild **03**. — *TJ*

Bianco Wines

Tulbagh ▪ Est/1stB 1997 ▪ Tasting & sales Mon-Fri 8.30-5 Sat 9-2 ▪ Fee R10 p/p for groups ▪ Closed Easter Fri/Sun, Dec 25 & Jan 1 ▪ Tours Mon-Fri 9-4.30 ▪ Olive oil/olive products for sale ▪ Owner Toni Bianco ▪ Winemaker Toni Bianco, with Lizette Steyn (Jan 2004) ▪ Viticulturist Craig Bianco (1999) ▪ 16 ha (cab, nebbiolo, pinotage, shiraz) ▪ 70 tons 2 000 cs 70% red 30% white ▪ PO Box 103 Tulbagh 6820 ▪ bianco@lando.co.za ▪ www.bianco.co.za ✆ (023) 231·0350 ☐ (023) 231·0938

With his Italian ancestry, it's understandable that Toni Bianco feels the industry's biggest challenge is to get more South Africans drinking wine. So they'd be more like the Europeans and Canadians who tuck into Bianco's wines with gusto (almost half the farm's production is exported). He recently appointed Lizette Steyn as his assistant in the cellar. Maybe their new early-drinking red wine will help to win SA palates.

Cabernet Sauvignon ★★★ **02** markedly fruitier, more generous than pvs; dark berry lusciousness kept in trim by big, dry, dusty tannins from 16 mths Fr oak. **Pinotage** ★★★ **02** less abrasive than range-mates (but would still benefit from 2/3 yrs bottle-ageing); fairly deep plum/cherry flavour with savoury edge. Aged in barriques, some new. **Shiraz** ★★★★ **02**, pvsly sampled from barrel, shows herby dark berries manfully facing off charry oak & very dry food-craving tannins. **Joya** NEW ★★★★ A 'Cape blend', **04** (sample) mainly pinotage (50%) with shiraz, cab; brash modern styling; ripe summer-fruit tones touched with sweet spice; nicely rounded. **Nebbiolo** NEW ★ Very pale, almost rosé-hued **03**, vague strawberry flavours, harsh tannins masking the sweet berry fruit. **Dry Muscat** ★★★ WO W-Cape, Wolseley fruit. **04** pretty honeysuckle & passionfruit bouquet, soft & sweet-smelling, unexpectedly but pleasantly bone-dry, zesty. — *DH*

Big Five Collection see African Terroir
Big Six see Bellingham, Old Bridge Wines

Bilton Wines

Stellenbosch ▪ 1stB 1998 ▪ Tasting & sales Mon-Fri 8.30-4.30 Sat 10.30-4 (Oct-Apr) ▪ Fee R5 ▪ Closed public holidays ▪ Teas, coffees & soft drinks; BYO picnic ▪ Walks ▪ Owner Mark Bilton ▪ Winemaker/viticulturist Adrean Naudé (Jan 1996) ▪ 108 ha (cab, merlot, shiraz, sauvignon) ▪ 4 000 cs 100% red ▪ PO Box 60 Lynedoch 7603 ▪ bilton@cybertrade.co.za ▪ www.biltonwines.co.za © **881·3714** 🖷 881·3721

The last harvest may have been late, but all the wines in Bilton's cellar show good potential, according to Adrean Naudé (who must be raring to emulate his 2003 achievement: IWSC and IWC golds for his Shiraz). Among the new fruits of the harvest are experimental roobernet, mourvèdre and petit verdot, which may find their way into a future blend. Owner Mark Bilton has now reached his objective of 110ha (108, to be exact, though only 20 are in production). An added attraction on this red wine farm on the slopes of the Helderberg is it's Mountain Cottage, a stay-over destination opened last year.

★★★★ **Merlot** Succulent, sophisticated & classy **02**, rich, enveloping plum-pudding aromas; on palate, creamy mulberry fruit with touch spice from 30% new Fr oak. 14% alc. **01** not tasted. **00** succulent, long, deeply flavoured; This, below, from single-vyds; 15-17 mths wooded.

★★★★ **Cabernet Sauvignon** Seductive vanilla-oak opening to **02**, ripe plums & spice, opulent & impressive without real complexity/structure. This, wine from same vintage above/below, get their stars with caveat: drink soon. Fr oak, 50/50 new/2nd fill. **01** not tasted. *Decanter* ★★★★. **00** was buxom yet well contained. ±14.5% alc.

★★★★ **Shiraz** Modern style, voluptuous, lashings creamy vanilla-oak, but **02** enlivened by crackle of acidity & hint of spice/savoury to fruit. 18 mths Fr/Am oak; 14% alc. A showy wine, so golds at IWSC, IWC for **01** not surprising. — *CR*

Birdfield see Klawer
Bisweni see Havana Hills

Blaauwklippen Vineyards

Stellenbosch ▪ Est 1690 ▪ 1stB 1974 ▪ Tasting & sales daily 9-5 ▪ Fee R20 (informal); R25 (tutored) ▪ Closed Dec 25 & Jan 1 ▪ Tours by appt 10-3 ▪ Two restaurants, deli, BYO picnic & many other amenities (see intro) ▪ Owner Mr & Mrs Stephan Schörghuber ▪ Winemaker Rolf Zeitvogel, with Piet Geldenhuys (Oct/Dec 2003) ▪ Viticulturist Kowie Kotze (1987) ▪ 100 ha (cabs s/f, merlot, shiraz, zin) ▪ 600 tons 30 000 cs own label + 180 000ℓ bulk ▪ 70% red 30% white ▪ HACCP certification in progress ▪ PO Box 54 Stellenbosch 7599 ▪ mail@blaauwklippen.com ▪ www.blaauwklippen.com © **880·0133** 🖷 880·0136

'We will strive to maintain the character of "South Africanness" in our wines without too much focus on New World style,' says winemaker Rolf Zeitvogel, newly arrived here after helping start the Capaia winery on the West Coast. To better focus on that goal, Zeitvogel and Piet Geldenhuys, another new recruit, are overseeing the final trimming of the range from an unwieldy 27 wines to just nine. And the vines? 'There are clearly set goals and targets for each block,' says veteran vineyard overseer Kowie Kotze. Extensive changes have resulted in a variety of options for visitors, including a deli, two restaurants, cigar lounge, conference centre, wine shop and enhanced tasting facilities. Unchanged and still deservedly popular is the Blaauwklippen Blending Competition, which celebrated its 21st anniversary last year with sauvignon as its theme.

Vineyard Selection range

★★★★ **Cabernet Sauvignon** ✓ Handsome, muscular cab from own Paradyskloof vyds. **00**, another yr on, developing nicely; shows cigarbox whiff & attractive earthiness to fruit-filled palate; **01** (★★★★) edgier, though maintains cellar's trademark elegance. Lots of interest now & into future. 2 yrs new Fr oak. ±13% alc. WO Stbosch.

★★★☆ **Merlot 01** elegant structure despite corpulent 14.1% alc; judiciously oaked (14 mths new/used); stewed fruit, earthy tobacco aromas; firm, dry, savoury flavours.

★★★★ **Shiraz 01** still available; no showstopper but warm, welcoming; whiff of old leather, fairly rich choc flavours. Dry finish. Yr Fr/Am oak. 14.3% alc. This, Merlot above, to be discontinued once stocks are sold.

★★★★ **Zinfandel** 'Life is Hell without Zinfandel', sentiment conveyed via California bumper sticker, implicit in this 30 yr feature of cellar's persona. Ostentatiously fruity **02** now has honey overtone to crushed mulberry nose/palate; appealing lightness despite high alc (14.5%). Bushvines, yr Fr/Am oak.

★★★★ **Cabriolet** Elegant blend cab f, cab, merlot, components vinified & matured separately; expensive oaking (18 mths, portion new) reflects care taken. **01** retaste firmer, grainier tannins than last yr, fair thread of acid; needs food.

Sauvignon Blanc Last featured in guide was **01**, in 'std' range. **04** returns in form of winner of 2004 B'klippen Blending Competition, unannounced at press time, so unrated. WO Stbosch.

Blaauwklippen range

★★★★ **Barouche Cape Blend** Has origins in 2000 B'klippen Blending Competition, clinched by **00** mix pinotage, shiraz, cab. Continues as pinotage blend, with tweaks & tucks. Current **01** with cab, shiraz, zin; yr new/used oak. Fine complexity, richness; pervasive spiciness & touch of old leather, dried fruit finish.

> **Red Landau** ☺ ★★★ **02** contains an A-T of varieties (no Zin), all eager to please; lightly savoury with grainy, pasta-friendly tannins. Low 12.5% alc. **White Landau** ☺ ★★★ Soft, fruity blend chardonnay, sauvignon, chenin. **03** ripe tones with cinnamon & jasmine accents, full bodied & just off-dry, for comfortable mouthfeel.

Cabernet Sauvignon ★★★ **03** neatly combines New World fruit on nose, Old World dry mineral palate; super varietal expression without over-extraction. 66% in Fr oak. **Shiraz** ★★★ Partly (Fr) wooded **03**, silky sweet-fruit entry bolstered by dash ripe ruby cab; supple vanilla-toned palate with spice suggestion. All WO Coastal unless noted. – *TM*

Black Eagle

Piketberg ▪ Est 2000 ▪ 1stB 2001 ▪ No tasting/tours, but stay-overs available at Libre Guesthouse B&B ▪ Owner Breda van Niekerk ▪ Winemaker André Oberholzer (Oct 2000) ▪ Viticulturist Johan Viljoen (Oct 2000) ▪ 40 ha (shiraz, chenin, colombard) ▪ 45 000ℓ 5% red 95% white ▪ PO Box 61 Saron 6812 ▪ lushof@iafrica.com ✆ (023) 240·0925 ☎ (023) 240·0238

Lushof, near Porterville, is one of still only a few Cape farms which has switched to organic cultivation. Grapes for their own-range are vinified at Porterville Cellar to the standards of the International Federation of Organic Agriculture Movement. To date two 03 Reserves: Chenin Blanc and Colombard; the 2004 harvest sold off in bulk.

Black Pearl Wines

Paarl ▪ Est 1998 ▪ 1stB 2001 ▪ Tasting, sales & tours just about anytime but please phone ahead (no credit cards) ▪ Closed Dec 25 ▪ Facilities for children ▪ Walks ▪ Conservation area ▪ Owner Lance Nash ▪ Winemakers Nash family ▪ Viticulturist Mary-Lou Nash Sullivan ▪ 8 ha (cab, shiraz) ▪ ±1 800 cs 100% red ▪ PO Box 609 Suider-Paarl 7624 ▪ info@blackpearlwines.com ▪ www.blackpearlwines.com ✆ 863·2900/083·395·6999/ 083·297·9796

There's wine flowing in the veins of the Nash family down on Rhenosterkop Farm. Son-in-law Phil Sullivan is sommelier at Cybercellar but, like the rest of the family, involved in Black Pearl winemaking. In fact, he planted all their vines, with the help of wife Mary-Lou Nash Sullivan, who is winemaker-in-chief. Theirs is a tradition of less is more: 'We're minimalists,' says owner Lance Nash, and their philosophy yielded good results in 2004: 'Superb grapes; concentrated, with fruit and character.' The Black Pearl range has been extended by a new shiraz-cab blend, and the Nashes are considering export, noting in particular the growth of the Asian market. Tasting is at more or less any time (but be sure to phone ahead), and adding charm to the view is a flock of alpacas.

★★★★ **Cabernet Sauvignon-Shiraz** NEW Fruit-driven Aussie-styled **03** with intense ripe berry flavours, big 14.5% alc, ultra smooth. Shiraz (55%) dominates with spices, leather. 13 mths oak; Probably not for long haul: best over next 3 yrs.

★★★★ **Shiraz** Retasted **02** with mocha, raspberry, coconut. Lighter than showy **03** (★★★★), with forward, big aromas/flavours on offer. Needs yr/2 to develop potential of spicy red fruit. Both 14.5% alc. 13 mths Fr oak, 60% new.

★★★☆ **Cabernet Sauvignon 03** step-up on pvs, with perfumed cassis notes, good concentration. 14.5% alc. 13 mths oak, 60% new. **02** (★★★) attractive, but lighter, touch more austere; mineral element to blackcurrant. — *NP*

Black Rock see The Winery
Blijhof see Kosie Möller Wines

Bloemendal Estate

Durbanville ▪ Est 1902 ▪ 1stB 1987 ▪ Tasting & sales Mon-Fri 9-5 Sat 9-4 Sun 11-3 ▪ Closed Dec 25 ▪ Deli/oyster bar ▪ Full conference facilities ▪ Farm produce for sale ▪ Owner Bloemendal Trust ▪ Winemaker Jackie Coetzee ▪ Viti consultant Johan Pienaar ▪ 140 ha (cab, merlot, shiraz, sauvignon) ▪ 5 000 cs own label 73% red 25% white 2% rosé ▪ PO Box 466 Durbanville 7551 ▪ bloemendal@isoft.co.za ©/🖃 976·2682

Jackie Coetzee counts going grey as his biggest personal achievement in the past year, and notes the reappearance of an albino guinea fowl on the estate as particularly newsworthy. Typical. The man refuses to take himself seriously and he loathes pretension. Yet he farms some seriously good vineyards (the vast bulk of whose produce is sold off, to Distell/Durbanville Hills, among others), and his own wines show a seriousness which belies his casual demeanor. Daughter Nina is set to follow in dad's winemaking footsteps, it seems. Last crush she made her first cab, aged all of 10. And showed an auspicious sense of timing, as harvest 2004 was one of the best here. 'Strong character and flavour,' says JC, approvingly.

★★★☆ **Cabernet Sauvignon 00** rich cordial-like concentration, deep-pile velvet texture, light brush of dry tannin on finish. Looser weave, ready, should last ±3 yrs. 14.2% alc. **99** more firmly built, concentrated filling. Should last usual 5-7 yrs. Equal tank/open-vat fermentation. These yr Fr oak, 30% new.

★★★★ **Merlot 01** ripe damson fruit, whiff coriander spice; palate more savoury, still some tannic tautness, whereas **00** (★★★★) was big, soft-centred; sweet fruit backed by firm, elegant tannins. These 14%+ alc. Yr Fr barrels, 30% new.

★★★★ **Shiraz** Back to deep impenetrable blackness, ripeness in **02**; black plum & smoked beef aromas/flavours. Has absorbed oak with ease; massive build, ultra-soft acidity, bordering on flabby. The original Big Easy, will collect many fans. 14.4% alc. **01** lighter textured. Oak 30/70 new Am/used Fr. Traditional open *kuip* fermentation.

★★★★ **Sauvignon Blanc Suider Terras** Named for mature s-facing vyd, beneficiary of bracing sea breezes, 30 yr old bushvines. Latest **04** (sample) has cool-climate pungency, directness. Huge whiff green fig, lemongrass & gooseberry, elegantly built, rapier clean acidity. 13.5% alc. Much in demand.

★★★★ **Semillon** Interesting counterpoint to sauvignon above: **04** (sample) more weight, less flamboyance; spiced lemon, hint apricot in friendly, welcoming version. Silky texture, rounded profile, helped by brush oak (third new). Watch 14.6% alc.

★★★★ **Blosend Rooi** Barrel-fermented dry rosé (or 'Blushing Red', as name translates). **03** was merlot, shiraz blend, ditto **04** (sample), though this version not up to par: quirky greengage, sour plum aromas/flavours, sweetish finish (★).

Brut NV ★★ Fans will be glad to see return of this frisky bubble, light textured & still youthfully fresh. From chardonnay, 9 mths lees before disgorging. **Natural Sweet** ★★★ Golden-hued semillon/sauvignon melange. **03** intriguing whiffs dried apricot, warm hay & caramel; luscious sweetness with some fresher sappy notes. — *IvH*

Blouberg see Graça

Bloupunt Wines

Montagu (see Little Karoo map) ▪ *Est/1stB 1997* ▪ *Tasting & sales Mon-Fri 9-5 Sat 9-4* ▪ *Tours by appt* ▪ *Fully-equipped self-catering cottage* ▪ *Farm produce* ▪ *Owner Phil Hoffman* ▪ *Winemaker/viticulturist Paul Hoffman* ▪ *3 ha (chard)* ▪ *4 000 cs 10% red 90% white* ▪ *12 Long Street Montagu 6720* ▪ *bloupunt@lando.co.za* ▪ *www.bloupuntwines.co.za* Ⓒ/⌨ *(023)* **614·2385**

The Hoffmans, father Phil and son Paul, are earmarking certain vineyards in the area where they hope to buy high-quality grapes for future harvests (they've had to uproot and replace some of their own blocks). Only limited quantities of their two Chardonnays (wooded and unoaked) and Merlot have been made, but the cellar should be up to capacity this year. The current releases, not tasted for this ed, are all 02s.

Blue Bay see Groot Eiland

Blueberry Hill

Franschhoek ▪ *Est/1stB 1998* ▪ *Visits by appt* ▪ *2 self-catering cottages* ▪ *Owners Blueberry Hill Trust (Brian & Lindy Heyman)* ▪ *Vini/viti advisers Nigel McNaught & Paul Wallace (1998/2000)* ▪ *0.6 ha* ▪ *350-400 cs 100% red* ▪ *PO Box 580 Franschhoek 7690* ▪ *bhwine@iafrica.com* Ⓒ **876·3362** ⌨ 876·2114

What's the benchmark for *garagiste* status? If a small cellar is one of the criteria, Brian & Lindy Heyman now have it – a 20-barrel space (their 2004 harvest, off their tiny block of merlot, gave them 15 barriques). Their mission is to 'take the boring out of merlot' by producing a 'rich, racy wine with layers of flavours'. The advantage of being small, they say, is that the grapes are meticulously looked after and can be sorted for quality on the vine.

Merlot ★★★★ Auspicious **03** has mouthwatering plummy/choc-minty flavours, clean oak backing (yr new barrels, 20% Am, positively slurped up by these young vines), long firm finish. Really attractive breezy tone – no striving for effect. Watch this space. – *DH*

Blue Crane Vineyards

Tulbagh (see map) ▪ *Est 2001* ▪ *1stB 2004* ▪ *Visitors welcome but phone ahead* ▪ *Owners Henk & Anita Jordaan* ▪ *Winemaker/viticulturist Henk Jordaan, advised by Vinpro & suppliers* ▪ *6 ha (cab, merlot, shiraz, sauvignon)* ▪ *2 000 cs 75% red 25% white* ▪ *PO Box 306 Tulbagh 6820* ▪ *bluecrane@icon.co.za* ▪ *www.bluecrane.co.za* Ⓒ *(023) 230·0823* ⌨ *(023) 230·0825*

After much deliberation, Johannesburg corporate refugees Henk and Anita Jordaan settled for Tulbagh (their first love) in 2001. An undeveloped tract in the centre of the valley looked promising, and they signed on the dotted line (clinchers included well-structured Glenrosa soils, a good spread of south, west and north aspects – and 5-star shopping less than 90 minutes away). A pair of nesting blue cranes suggested the brand name – acquired from trademark holder Distell through 'a lawyer with a very nice bedside manner'. Six hectares of cab, merlot, shiraz and sauvignon and a 50-ton starter cellar later, their first harvest was crushed in 2004. The Jordaans consult, study and read prodigiously to stay abreast of what's new and happening. 'We can do things impossible or unaffordable in large cellars.' Not tasted, but available this year, are three Blue Crane wines – Cab, Merlot and Shiraz – and a Cab and Sauvignon under the Jagger's Peak label.

Blue Creek Wines

Stellenbosch ▪ *Est 1995* ▪ *1stB 1996* ▪ *Visits by appt* ▪ *Owner/winemaker Piet Smal* ▪ *Viti consultant Johan Smith (1996)* ▪ *7.5 ha (cab, merlot, pinotage)* ▪ *1 000 cs own label 100% red* ▪ *26 Piet Retief Str Stellenbosch 7600* ▪ *blue_creek@email.com* Ⓒ **887·6938** ⌨ 886·5462

Here's the best Cab you've never heard of. Grown in the still relatively unexplored Blaauwklippen Valley outside Stellenbosch by Piet Smal, a local dentist who moonlights as a winemaker. He keeps a resolutely low profile but makes oeno-magic 'with 1 ttle help from my friends'. His 01 was one of only two Cabs awarded four stars in *Wine* magazine's 2004 Cab tasting (it trumped many better-known brands in the process). Just one of many nods and gongs. His secret? Good viticultural practice ('Fine wine comes out of the vineyard') and low yields. A recent expansion in the cellar, with a bigger and better harvest in mind, saw the installation of new tanks.

★★★★ Cabernet Sauvignon ✓ 02 (★★★★★) classy cab with heady bouquet of curry leaf, mint & five-spice. Opulent cassis fruit easily matches 16 mths Fr oak & 14% alc. Depth & structure for cellaring. Dense, chewy yet pliable **01** with satisfyingly dry finish. From vyds in Stbosch reputed 'Golden Triangle'.

Pinotage ★★★ Sells out too quickly for sampling! Last noted was foursquare **00**. — *CvZ*

Blue Grove Hill see Capaia
Blue Ridge see Villiera
Blue Rock see Fairview
Blue White see Old Vines

Blyde Wines

Paarl ▪ Est/1stB 2000 ▪ Tasting & sales at I Love Wine (see Wine shops section) ▪ Tours by appt ▪ Owner/winemaker Lieb Loots ▪ 60 cs 90% red 10% white ▪ ISO 9000 certified ▪ PO Box 3231 Paarl 7620 ▪ lajanc@iafrica.com ▪ www.blyde.com ⓒ 083·270·5706 🖷 872·8799

Harvest 2004 went 'boringly well' for northern Cape crop farmer Lieb Loots (a welcome contrast to the feedback we got from many hard-pressed winemakers). Loots makes his wines at shared cellar premises on Main Street in Paarl, and his admirable philosophy is 'not to bottle any wines that I wouldn't enjoy myself'. Prices are fixed according to quality, 'not for an early retirement'. His Bordeaux-style blend stands out among the predominantly single-varietal bottlings made by the growing number of Cape garagistes.

★★★★ Bona Dea Hand-made cab, merlot, shiraz blend, grapes from Stbosch/Dbnvlle, 14 mths Fr oak, third new for **02**, similar proportions as pvs (40/32/28); still lots of resinous wood on nose; big, concentrated stewed fruit palate with gamey hint; 14.5% alc; **01** retasted, sweet vanilla tone with volatile touch. — *TM*

Blydskap see Baarsma

Bodega

Paarl ▪ Closed to public ▪ PO Box 590 Kraaifontein 7569 ⓒ 988·2929 🖷 988·3527
Range in abeyance till the next vintage.

Boekenhoutskloof

Franschhoek ▪ Tasting by appt ▪ Sales Mon-Fri 9-5 ▪ Owner Boekenhoutskloof Investments (Pty) Ltd ▪ Winemakers Marc Kent & Rudiger Gretschel, with Heinrich Tait ▪ Viticulturist Pieter Siebrits ▪ PO Box 433 Franschhoek 7690 ▪ boeken@mweb.co.za ⓒ 876·3320 🖷 876·3793

The Syrah is back among the guide's five-star selections — an extraordinary fifth such award for this classy cellar. Marc Kent is smiling, and so is Rudiger Gretschel, loving the change from big-volume Nederburg (assistant winemaker till 2002) to boutique Boekenhoutskloof — 'good people, good wine!'. Though no longer so 'boutiquey' at 80 000-plus cases a year. Which has Kent increasingly involved in management & marketing, motivating cellarhand Heinie Tait's promotion to assistant winemaker, and allowing Kent to indulge his innovative explorations and acquisitions (his was one of SA's first sorting tables, now de rigeur; the latest is a computer-controlled hydraulic basket press spotted in Bordeaux). Vinous innovations include an experimental viognier-grenache blanc-clairette blanche blend quietly incubating in barrel; and the Rosé below, hooking into the growing popularity of pinks.

★★★★☆ **Cabernet Sauvignon** Like following wine, timeless style; traditional structure capped with poised ripeness. **02** highly buffed cassis/cedar clarity; mouthful dark-berried claret tension balanced by ripe tannin grip/frame. Needs further yr/2; possibly peaking sooner than expansive, sweet-fruited **01**; balanced, better integrated than more obviously tannic **00** (★★★★★). From single Frhoek hillside vyd; usually promises good decade's development. 27 mths new Fr oak (mostly extra-thin-stave barrels), unfiltered. 14%+ alc.

★★★★★ **Syrah** Sensitive vintage appreciation, consistency, understanding of site character all benefits of Marc K's long-term association with old Wllngtn vyd. **02** (★★★★★) in usual full-blooded style. Brooding, dark berries, meaty intensity; dense mouthcoating richness with focus, freshness from delicious savoury acid core. Individuality heightened by traditional vinification: native yeasts, only used Fr oak, 27 mths. Warmer area classic with 8–10 yr potential. **01** *Wine* ★★★★★, elegant; mellifluous flavours/tannins, great concentration. Scant 600 cs; allocated on a per-bottle basis. Alcs 14%+.

★★★★★ **Semillon** ✓ Individual, reliable in style/ability to mature with gorgeous nutty/waxy viscosity. **03** familiar lanolin/sweet-oak fragrance; beautifully sleek, touch less sumptuous than usual, more citrus zip but with great flavour/texture crescendo, length; augurs well for 5–6 yr improvement. **02** smooth, sumptuous. From Frhoek bushvines; fermented/aged new Fr casks; malo.

★★★★★ **Noble Late Harvest** Intensely vinous, botrytis-brushed **02** dessert from semillon, Creamy honeyed viscosity, contrasted by breathtakingly fresh conclusion. Uncloying, despite massive 240g/ℓ sugar, low 9% alc. Fermented/14 mths new Fr oak. 375ml. Not re-assessed. **03** not ready for tasting.

★★★★ **The Chocolate Block 03** (★★★★★) hedonist's delight; Marc K's penchant for demonstrative wines realised in this multi-dimensional sensory experience; resonating lilies, spice fragrance with plenty dark, creamy choc. Creamy sleek concentration too, but richness contrasted, lightened by bright red fruits, peppery lift. Burly **02** balanced harmony for current/med-term drinking. Shiraz-based with cab, grenache, cinsaut, dab viognier. 15 mths Fr oak, some new. 14.8% alc.

The Wolftrap ☺ ★★★ Often-disregarded cinsaut telling presence in **03**; blend including cab, pinotage, ruby cab, grenache & syrah. Full-bodied; smooth, light texture highlights fragrant spice, wild, red fruit juiciness. *Vin* out of the *ordinaire*. Named after trap set by early settlers for non-existent Frhoek wolf. Fr oak. 14.4% alc. **Wolftrap Rosé** 〔NEW〕 ☺ ★★★ **04** loads of eye/flavour appeal on syrah/cinsaut/ grenache (70/21/9) blend. Sparky wild strawberry, spice concentration piled into rounded, fresh body. Dry.

Porcupine Ridge range

★★★☆ **Cabernet Sauvignon** ✓ Sleek, medium-bodied **03**; attractive cassis/red-berried purity; lively mineral core; well-formed for current enjoyment, can hold yr/2. Inc 14% dab malbec 'to lift fruit'. 25% 9 mths in used Fr oak. Mbury, Stbosch, Frhoek fruit.

★★★★ **Syrah** ✓ Sleek, composed demeanour of **03** in contrast to more boisterous, gutsy **02**. Velvety smooth; similar gamey, dark spice, savoury attractions as big brother Syrah above, delivered in rounder, readier style. Probably best until mid-05. Mainly Mbury, with Stbosch, Wllngtn/home vyds (as for Merlot). Partly oaked. ±14% alc.

★★★★ **Merlot** ✓ **03** juicy, bright-fruited mouthful; hint oak for extra interest; sappy fine tannins. Lunch-time or summer-style red. 13.9% alc. Fr oaked 9 mths.

Sauvignon Blanc ★★★ **04** quieter, lighter than pvs; nettly, tropical whispers; clean; dry. 11.8% alc. — *AL*

Boland Kelder

Paarl ▪ Est 1947 ▪ 1stB 1948 ▪ Tasting & sales Mon-Fri 8-5 Sat 8.30-1 ▪ Closed Easter Fri/ Sun, Dec 25/26 & Jan 1 ▪ Tours by appt ▪ Underground cellar for functions & gatherings *(max 45 people)* ▪ *Events programme during Dec/Jan; phone for details* ▪ *Tourgroups* ▪ *Owners 96 producing shareholders* ▪ *Cellarmaster Altus le Roux (Sep 1984)* ▪ *Winemakers Naudé Bruwer & Bernard Smuts (Dec 1996/Nov 1999), with Jurgen Siebrits & JG Auret (Dec 2001/Dec 2002)* ▪ *Viticulturist Jurie Germishuys (Jul 1998)* ▪ *2 400 ha (cab, merlot, pinotage, shiraz, chard, chenin, sauvignon)* ▪ *±17 600 tons 50% red 50% white* ▪ *Export brands: Montestell, Lindehof, Grand Roche* ▪ *PO Box 7007 Noorder-Paarl 7623* ▪ *info@ bolandkelder.co.za* ▪ *www.bolandwines.co.za* ⓒ *862·6190* 🖷 862·5370

Boland Kelder chair Jannie le Roux was the prime mover behind Cape Coastal Wines, a new initiative involving five cellars in the Paarl/Wellington area intent on increasing market share, particularly in the US. 'There is no question that SA wines, in terms of price/quality, are among the very best in the world,' JlR explains. 'Yet SA lags far behind Australia, New Zealand and South American countries like Chile and Argentina. We need to catch up.' Cape Coastal Vineyards, also chaired by Le Roux, has been established to provide liquid assets to the marketing body. Meanwhile, back at Boland, a harvest which 'wouldn't start, then wouldn't end' delivered outstanding quality nonetheless. The Reserve range (first featured in our 2003 guide) was unveiled to the public in conjunction with a label upgrade.

Reserve range

★★★★ Cabernet Sauvignon 01 super-ripe dark berries & seriously oak, dense & compact, great concentration of sweet ripe fruit. Tannins soft & ripe to match, rich & mouthcoating like a crème de cassis liqueur, but also some beefy 'Bovril on toast' savouriness. Seamless tannin integration, sleek & well groomed. Oak, 60/40 Am/Fr all new. 24 mths. Deserves cellaring 5-7 yrs.

★★★★ Shiraz Choc truffles, brandy snaps, espresso & smoked beef the start of a long list to describe extraordinary **01**. Individual & beautifully put together, draped in dark velvet fruit with sleek tannins & concentration shown in lengthy dry finish. Natural ferment, then oaked new Am, 20 mths. Not for the faint-hearted.

★★★☆ Chardonnay 03 hints of tropical pineapple & lime with butterscotch & oak. Firm fleshed, fruit balanced by good acidity, but shows a heavy hand with oak. 18 mths, all new Fr.

★★★☆ Sauvignon Blanc 03 big wine, ripe & densely fruity, toned with whole citrus spectrum of lemon, lime, hints of grapefruit, sprinkling ground coriander, somewhat muted by whack of oak. Fermented/aged in barriques, all new Fr, extended lees maturation.

Boland range

★★★☆ Cabernet Sauvignon ✓ Discreetly oaked **03**, attractive cassis & riper mulberry in lower key, subtle & unforced. Densely packed, concentrated; tannins finely balanced to show fruit to advantage. Ready, with 3-4 yrs cellaring potential. 14 mths Am/Fr oak. 14.5% alc.

★★★☆ Pinotage ✓ Juicy, lip-smacking & astonishing value at R27 ex-cellar. **03** (sample) sweet redcurrant pastille & cherry aromas/flavours, dry tannins, touch earthiness on finish adds interest. Yr Fr/Am oak. Watch hefty 14.8% alc.

★★★☆ Shiraz ✓ Back on form in **03,** meaty mocha with distinctive whiff Am oak vanilla. Dense dark-berried fruit, properly dry, savoury beefy flavour, attractive dry tannins. **02** (★★★) had less concentration in difficult vintage; for earlier drinking. Staves 7 mths. 14.5% alc. **00** gold at IWSC 2003.

★★★★ White Muscadel Elegant version always flies out of the cellar. **97** was last tasted; sweet but not sugary (even at 182g/ℓ!) thanks to good freshening acidity.

Sauvignon Blanc ☺ **★★★ 04** full tropical fruit assault on nose, sweet-sour tussle on palate, vibrant lime/passionfruit flavours on long tangy finish. Moderate 13% alc.

Merlot ★★★ 03 delicate leafy black fruit, mulberry leaf (like opening silkworm box!) Lighter textured, herbaceous & fresh, tannins need yr or so to settle. Portion yr Am/Fr oak. 14.5% alc. **01** trophy at Concours Mondial 2003. **Pinotage-Cinsaut ★★★** Surprisingly dry **03**, does not detract from easy-drinking style, well padded with approachable tannins, savoury beef flavours. **Chardonnay ★★ 04** light-textured peachy style with smooth accessibility, refreshing finish. Stave-fermented/aged. ±14% alc. **02** VDG. **Chenin Blanc ★★★ 04** shy, but firm-fleshed & lively, tart Granny Smith apple flavours, less exciting than previous but gulpable, 12.5% alc. **Riesling ★★** From Cape riesling/crouchen. **04** light-textured & bone-dry, whiffs of pear-drop; notable for soft acidity – gentle version & an enduring favourite. **Noble Late Harvest ★★★** Veritas & Michelangelo show favourite. **00** raisin, liquidised apricot richness, long mouthfilling finish. From muscat de F. 11% alc. Mid-2004 still delightful, but peaking. upcoming **01** will be last. **Red Muscadel 04** (sample) provisional **★★★**; raisiny, stalky character to this very sweet dessert, fortified to modest 15.4% alc. Dusty, earthy, baked fruit. **Port ★★★** Latest **03** from shiraz; still youthful but more satisfying, not overly sweet at 115gℓ, pruney fruit with dry tannic grip, dry finish, rather good. 17% alc. 16 mths 3rd fill casks. **Sparkling Brut**, **Doux Sauvignon** discontinued.

Bon Vino range

In 500ml 'Bordeaux lite' bottles; 2ℓ & 5ℓ packs. All NV, bargain priced.

Dry Red ☺ **★★★** Just the thing for quaffing round the braai. Juicy cinsaut, with cab, merlot, softest tannins, dab sugar plumps up profile. 14% alc all but guarantees jollity. **Dry White** ☺ **★★★** Designed for everyday drinking. Crisp, dry & light with tart greenapple flavours, refreshing finish. Mainly chenin, with sauvignon for zing.

Semi-Sweet ★★ Will appeal widely. Charming fruity, grapey character & soft sweetness guarantees easy drinking. Low 11.5% alc. – *lvH*

Bon Cap Organic Winery

Robertson ▪ Est 2001 ▪ 1stB 2002 ▪ Tasting & sales Mon-Fri 8-5 Sat/Sun 9-5 ▪ Fee R10 for groups of 8+ ▪ Closed Dec 25/26 ▪ Tours 10.30 & 3 (groups by appt) ▪ BYO picnic ▪ Guest house (self-catering & B&B by appt) ▪ Farm produce ▪ Facilities for children ▪ Tourgroups ▪ Conferencing ▪ Walks ▪ Owners Roelf & Michelle du Preez/SHZ Winecellar (Pty) Ltd ▪ Winemakers Roelf du Preez & Jacques Conradie (2002/2004) ▪ Viticulturists Roelf du Preez & Henning Retief ▪ 45 ha (cab, pinotage, shiraz) ▪ 300 tons 15 000 cs + 135 000ℓ bulk + 500 cs for clients, incl Woolworths & De Mooie Opstal (Belgium) ▪ 80% red 10% white 10% grapejuice ▪ PO Box 356 Robertson 6705 ▪ boncap@intekom.co.za ▪ www.boncaporganic. co.za © (023) 626·1628 ▤ (023) 626·1895

'Give a grape a choice and it would settle in Robertson,' wrote UK wine critic Malcolm Gluck, alluding to the attention lavished on their vines by the farmers of this area. Organic vinegrowers Roelf and Michelle du Preez certainly have that loving feeling – and an enviable sense of purpose. Dismissive of sceptics who equate 'organic' with 'marketing gimmick', Michelle dP declares: 'Though our vineyards were certified organic four years ago, we'd been farming organically much longer because we don't want to use chemical fertilisers, herbicides or pesticides. On the other hand, we believe organic is no more than an added-value to consumers who feel the same as we do. Quality remains paramount.' In spite of stricter yield control, the petit verdot and viognier crops were up 300% last year. ('Hopefully agents won't want to strangle each other over the viognier anymore,' laughs Roelf dP.) Also in 2004, they added a climate-controlled bottle-ageing area, and launched a new, handsomely packaged range, The Ruins.

Organic range

★★★★ **Cabernet Sauvignon 02** well-tailored proportions; pure cassis top notes, still with some mouth-coating tannin. Again the fruit quality impresses. Balanced 14% alc. Barrel-matured to formula above. WO Eilandia, as are all their wines.

★★★★ **Pinotage** Launched with **02** to wide acclaim (BA Business Class, ABSA Top 10, Veritas, Michelangelo etc). **03** more serious, first impression of immaculate fruit; broad, deeply fruity yet unshowy. 9 mths oak, 80/20, Fr/Am. 13.5%alc. Ready.

★★★★ **Syrah** (Pvsly 'Shiraz') Somewhat restrained character to **03**, fine dark berried fruits, dry tannins not overwhelming, but rather savoury grip. A bit sullen when tasted mid-2004, maybe a phase. 10 mths oak, 80/20, Fr/Am. 14.5% alc.

★★★★ **Viognier** SA's first organic version of this Rhône white grape. **04** (sample) Fr oak-fermented, 3 mths on lees. Similar to **03** with delicate apricot scents, rich texture; lengthened, balanced by dash sugar.

The Ruins range   NEW

★★★★ **Pinotage** ✓ Intended as more affordable version of wines above, with surprisingly upmarket labels. **03** more relaxed & marginally lighter textured than regular version, perhaps more accessible, but the same pristine berry fruit. Alc 13.5%.

> **Cabernet Sauvignon-Merlot** ☺ ★★★ Attractive redcurrant fruit in **03**, softer acid & tannins, nothing to detract from main-action berries, slight sweetness on finish. Staves, 5 mths. Note big alc: 14.4%. — *IvH*

Bon Courage Estate

Robertson ▪ Est 1927 ▪ 1stB 1983 ▪ Tasting & sales Mon-Fri 8-5 Sat 9-3 ▪ Coffee shop Mon-Fri 9-4.30 Sat 9-3 ▪ Closed Easter Fri/Sun, Dec 25 & Jan 1 ▪ Play area for children ▪ Owner/viticulturist André Bruwer ▪ Winemaker Jacques Bruwer (1995) ▪ 150 ha (cab, shiraz, chard, colombard, sauvignon) ▪ 30% red 55% white 10% rosé 5% other ▪ PO Box 589 Robertson 6705 ▪ boncourage@minds.co.za ▪ www.boncourage.co.za ✆ **(023) 626·4178** 🖷 (023) 626·3581

A father-to-son story that so many SA farms tell: André Bruwer bought the Robertson estate in 1927, André fils assumed his role in 1974 (so has just celebrated a 30th anniversary) and son Jacques, who came in as a partner in 1990, took over from his father as winemaker in 1995 (so there's a 10th anniversary there). For the story of the vineyards, look no further than Bon Courage's 'cultivar experience', an exhibition of the different varieties grown. One that did the Bruwers proud recently was muscadel — their 02 and 03 were awarded golds in 2004 by the Muscadel Association. 'The estate is moving towards more single-vineyard wines', says the winemaker, 'with a yield of small bunches and small berries.'

★★★★ **Syrah Inkará** The flagship; shows muscle, polish & attention to detail — cold-soaked, whole berry fermented, partial barrel fermentation in Am oak, finished in Fr. For the long haul. **02** impressive complexity in youth; whiffs cigarbox & Xmas pud; firm, solid flavours, lots of lovely berry fruit, big dry finish; quite a way to go, but all building blocks in place. **01** also in emphatic style — densely constructed, with espresso, dark mulberry flavours, punchy but tractable tannins.

★★★☆ **Cabernet Sauvignon Inkará** Premium, limited release **00**, all-new Fr oak-fermented/matured, was elegantly herbal, showed finely-tuned cassis finish. **02** (★★★★) cut above; more clarety concentration, complexity; elegant whiffs cigarbox & toast; generous blackberry fruit, pliable but active tannins. Yr Fr oak.

★★★☆ **Shiraz 03** sweet smelling plummy fruit, hints vanilla & clove; slightly smoky palate with more clove & some sweetness; drinks well now. Partial malo in barrel, only Fr oak (contrast to Am oak used above), 12 mths. **02** had well-bred plummy fruit, taut but fleshy flavours.

★★★★ **Cabernet Sauvignon-Shiraz** 60/40 blend, 8 mths Fr oaked before blending; **02** warm, spicy Xmas pud nose, hint of pepper; sweet ripe profile without jamminess of confection; good dry finish. 14% alc hardly noticeable.

★★★★ **Chardonnay Prestige Cuvée** Classy, barrel-matured version, 6-8 mths on lees in 2nd/3rd fill Fr oak. **03** (★★★☆) pale lime green; emotive nose of green fruits & cream; soft & silky on palate; elegant despite 14% alc. Just lacks bit of zing, which a hallmark of **02**, with mineral thread of acidity cutting the crème brûlée richness.

★★★★☆ **Cap Classique Jacques Bruére Brut Reserve Blanc de Blanc** NEW Hugely impressive debut with **00**, clearly a standout vintage for the estate; interesting contrast between this chard-only bottle-fermented sparkling & version below; here a restrained steely linearity, heightened by vein of green fruit, spicy lemongrass note adding coolness; palate leavened by delicate lees/biscuit/lemon cream type flavours. Impressive stuff. Base-wine whole bunch pressed in stainless steel.

★★★★ **Cap Classique Jacques Bruére Brut Reserve** This MCC has developed own unique fruity style. Latest NV (00) again more supple than sparse 7.6g/ℓ sugar would suggest; hallmark doughy notes, bright lime & grapefruit aromas & crisp, citrus finish. Plenty of frothy mousse. Whole-bunch-pressed pinot, chardonnay (60/40), 18 mths on 2nd lees. Particularly full-flavoured & expressive this yr, hence higher rating. Drinks well.

★★★★ **Noble Late Harvest** From botrytised riesling, sumptuously sweet (±147g/ℓ sugar), with rapier-like fruit acid to balance. **01**, **02** shared similar dried apricot & peach profile. Standout **04** (★★★★★) is delightfully different; has an ethereal quality on both palate & nose. Peaches & cream texture, hint honeysuckle & jasmine, some terpene oiliness, followed by waves of cleansing acidity for a racy/steely finish. Gorgeous. 9.5% alc.

★★★★ **White Muscadel** Long lineage of concentration, richness; **03** has spicy Turkish Delight bouquet, hints caramel & smoke; broad, rich muscat palate with litchi & honeysuckle, toffee apple nuttiness on finish. Muscadel Association gold. Deliciously spirity at 16% alc, slightly higher than **02**, which offered a barrage of bright peach & passionfruit, intense, rich sweetness.

Cabernet Sauvignon ★★★ **03** straightforward but juicy early drinking style; lighter-weight than pvs, not as much structure. **Pinotage** ★★★ Nothing since **01**, which more refined, longer-lived than pvs. **Gewürztraminer** ★★☆ Last tasted was **02** with signature talcum aroma & citrus-rind in finish. **Sauvignon Blanc** ★★★ Shy **04** nose; glimpses crushed nettle & dusty capsicum; everything happens on palate, including attractive minerally bite. **Chardonnay** ★★☆ Green-flecked **04**; shy & fairly lean; lemon-lime flavours, light body, inoffensive. **Colombard** ★★★ Seldom disappoints; **04** spicy guava & crushed leaf tones – rivetting – lots of lemon lime flavours, lovely bright acidity. **Riesling** ★★★ Lightly perfumed off-dry from crouchen. **04** attractive floral notes & honey, botrytis-like tang; more personality than most. **Semillon** NEW ★★★☆ Herbaceous & waxy intro to **04**, lightish but packed with flavour, grapefruit & lime notes, apple hints; sweet-fruited top to tail. **Colombard-Chardonnay** ★★★ Zesty, flintily dry blend not retasted; last was **03**. **Gewürztraminer Special Late Harvest** ★★★★ **04** glows orange-gold; gorgeous, quintessential bouquet of petals, elegant & ethereal; wonderful concentration of passion-fruit flavour, hint botrytis, long creamy finish; full-sweet (±54g/ℓ sugar) but impeccably clean; moderate 12% alc. **Weisser Riesling Natural Sweet** ★★★★ None since **02**, golden, delicious mouthful. **Blush Vin Doux** ★★ Just-pink NV bubbly from pinot/muscadel not tasted. **Vintage Port** ★★★ None since **00**, from tinta. **Three Rivers Ruby Cabernet-Pinotage**, **Chardonnay** & **Chenin Blanc** untasted. – *TM* –

Bonfoi Estate

Stellenbosch ▪ *Est 1699* ▪ *1stB 1974* ▪ *Tasting & sales Mon-Fri 9-5 Sat 10-2.30* ▪ *Fee R10, refunded with purchase* ▪ *Closed public holidays* ▪ *BYO picnic* ▪ *Walks* ▪ *Conservation area* ▪ *Owner/winemaker/viticulturist Johannes van der Westhuizen* ▪ *98 ha (cabs s/f, merlot, pinotage, shiraz, chard, chenin, sauvignon)* ▪ *700 tons 3 000 cs own label 60% red 40% white* ▪ *PO Box 9 Vlottenburg 7604* ▪ *bonfoi@mweb.co.za* ▪ *www.bonfoiwines.co.za* ℂ *881·3774* 🖷 *881·3807*

Making a difference, Johannes van der Westhuizen has up-sized his workforce, instead of shrinking it like most other folk. The reason? 'To have more labour available at critical times. It's also important to train people oneself.' He tried for better balance in 2004, given that varieties like sauvignon and cab didn't easily deliver full-bodied wine (though their fruitiness was 'outstanding'). Try walking through the estate, part of the Bottelary Conservancy, up to the Bottelary Walk which winds along the hills; take a picnic with you.

★★★★ **Cabernet Sauvignon** Steady line of growth from old-Cape-style **97** to modern, ripe-fruited **01**. Attractive cassis with cinnamon-spice oak backing to lively rounded palate; clean-cut, well-balanced flavours. Yr Fr oak. 13.4% alc. Latest **02** seems slightly richer but analysis virtually identical, house style very consistent.

★★★★ **Ouverture** Beautifully crafted & elegant blend, selection of best barrels vinified/matured separately. **02** (sample) 45/30/25 cab s/merlot/shiraz; latter fairly insistent, still very Bdx-like. Smooth seamless blend, yr barrique for components, plus 6 mths for blend. **01** was cab, merlot, shiraz (55/24/21), on taste Bdx varieties dominate in persistent claret fruit (cherries/red berries); tannic grip loosening.

★★★★ **Shiraz 02** spicy, aromatic style with smoke, briar & fynbos in bouquet, ripe plums on palate; already had some complexity in youth. Retasted, shows development potential realised, unfolding stylishly. Yr Fr/Am oak (75/25). ±13.8% alc.

★★★☆ **Chardonnay** Charming **03** has fresh yellow peach fruit, subtly supported by vanilla oak; soft, silky texture, longish finish — nothing overdone, nothing out of place. Fermented in barrel, 50/50 new/2nd fill, all Fr.

Merlot ★★★ Ripe plums/berries & bright acidity on **02**, appealing & unpretentious. 10 mths Fr oak. ±15% alc. **Sauvignon Blanc** ★★★ **03** delicately scented with gooseberry & hints tropical fruit, light-textured, softish acidity, clean dry finish. Pleasant; drink this summer. 13% alc. — *IvH*

Bonne Esperance see KWV International

Bonne Nouvelle see Remhoogte

Bonnievale Cellar

Robertson ▪ Est 1964 ▪ Tasting & sales Mon-Sat 8-5 Sun & public holidays 10-1 ▪ Closed Easter Fri-Mon, Dec 25/26 & Jan 1 ▪ Tours by appt ▪ Conferencing ▪ Owners 72 members ▪ Manager/winemaker Henk Wentzel, with Gerhard Swart & Wilson Madlathu (Aug 1999, Dec 2002/2003) ▪ Viti consultant Briaan Stipp ▪ 800 ha (cab, merlot, pinotage, ruby cab, shiraz, chard, chenin, colombard, sauvignon, semillon) ▪ 10 000 tons 20 000 cs own label + 5m litres bulk 40% red 60% white ▪ PO Box 206 Bonnievale 6730 ▪ office@bonnievalecellar.co.za ▪ www.bonnievalecellar.co.za ⓒ (023) 616-2795 🖷 (023) 616-2137

Despite an inauspicious start (some fruit rotted on the vines) Henk Wentzel calls 2004 'a year to be remembered for good, well-ripened reds', which, for the first time, went through fully automated fermentation tanks. It was also the year the winery, its members now up to 72, celebrated its 40th anniversary. A bundle of appropriate gifts preceded the occasion — Bonnievale was named winner of the Robertson Block Competition for the 2nd year running; its wines had a first-time listing on SAA; and Michelangelo judges presented the cellar with a gold medal. Interestingly, Wentzel sees a marketing opportunity in rosé: 'It's growing worldwide.' Another Wentzel observation worth noting: 'National weather-station data shows Bonnievale is one of the coolest wine districts in SA.'

Vertex Reserve range

NEW

Shiraz Excellent fruit concentration on nose/palate; **03** similar character to Reserve but more intense, perfumed; touches lavender & coconut; lovely fruit-sweet tone; acidity freshens the big alc (14.5%), combines with tannin for mouthfeel, grip. Provisional ★★★★.
Chardonnay ★★★★ Tasted pre-bottling; **03** (sample) opens with scents of peaches & toasty oak; vanilla fairly prominent on taste, cut by citrus tang in finish. Genteel despite 14% alc. Partly new oak fermented.

Bonnievale range

★★★★ **Red Jerepigo** Idiosyncratic NV fortified dessert with contrasting flavours/aromas of tomato sauce & maraschino cherry. 17% alc.

TBWA/HUNT/LASCARIS/DURBAN LO01899

BECAUSE . . .
YOU HAVE GREAT TASTE!

Medieval drinking vessel

TRADITIONAL VALUES

The Riedel glass. A product of generations of innovation. A far cry from the copper drinking vessels of old, these hand-blown glasses are shaped to focus on the flavours, textures and aromas of a particular cultivar and are designed to enhance appreciation of the wine. It is in this spirit that we at RMB will develop solutions to suit your particular needs.

Now that's worth raising a glass to.

*Modern hand-blown
Riedel glass*

INNOVATIVE IDEAS

RAND MERCHANT BANK
——— A division of FirstRand Bank Limited ———

TRADITIONAL VALUES. INNOVATIVE IDEAS.

Vaughan Johnson

What's the measure of wine-retailing success? In a relatively small market like SA, well over 2 million customers over 20 years is pretty good going. But then **Vaughan Johnson** has the touch. First in Johannesburg, latterly at his store on the V&A Waterfront in Cape Town, he reels in crowds with a contagious mix of bonhomie, erudition and no-nonsense value for money.

Hamilton Russell Vineyards

While officialdom encouraged growers to plant vines in the Kalahari desert, visionary winegrower **Tim Hamilton Russell** established the Cape's coolest, most southerly vineyards in the Hemel-en-Aarde Valley near Hermanus exactly 30 years ago. This guide was among the first to hail his 'imaginative pioneering' project. THR and son **Anthony** have been vindicated many times over, including, appropriately enough, a double five-star rating in this edition, for their Chardonnay and Pinot Noir.

So you'd like to acquire some wine?

Which estate?

ISN'T IT TIME YOU TALKED TO A BANK THAT SHARES YOUR PASSION FOR THE WINE INDUSTRY?

NEDBANK
CORPORATE

Since 1997 Nedbank has had a specialised business unit focusing on the wine industry. Our key staff are specialists in this field, and are therefore the ideal financial partners for your business. We also participate regularly in wine trade related events to facilitate contact between importers and exporters.

 Proudly South African

The Jupiter Drawing Room (South Africa)/15389 Nedbank Limited Reg No 1951/000009/06

Business Banking

So, if you're an estate owner, exporter or a supplier to the wine industry, we can provide the right solutions. Be it export advice or constructing a financial package for your needs. For more information e-mail John Barnardt at barnardtj@nedcor.com. You'll find we're the bank most wine industry experts prefer.

Used the world over, SupremeCorq synthetic closures virtually eliminates leakage, evaporation and off-flavours (TCA) associated with tree bark closures. SupremeCorqs can be easily reinserted into the bottle after removal.

With an almost limitless range of colours and printing, SupremeCorqs offer a wide range of branding and promotional possibilities. SupremeCorq is the only synthetic closure company to receive ISO 9001:2000, BRC (British Retail Consortium) and AIB (American Institute of Baking) quality process certifications.

All of which make for a more consistent bottle of wine.

SupremeCorq.
Designed to keep
fine wine fine.

SUPREME**CORQ** ®
Designed to keep fine wine fine.

Suite 151, Private Bag X3018, Strand 7139 South Africa
Tel. +27 (0)21 854 3554 Fax +27 (0)21 854 7573
paulv@supremecorq.com | liesll@supremecorq.com
www.supremecorq.com.

ISO9001:2000
FM68163

SMILE
POWER

IN JUST
ONE HOUR

A toast ... raise your glasses. Now BriteSmile gives you even more reason to celebrate as we can remove years of staining on your teeth in just over an hour. Our blue light and gentle whitening gel have been clinically proven to whiten your teeth with as much as 9.3 shades on average. This in-office procedure, currently number one in the USA, is performed by selected dentists in South Africa.

Call: 0861 93 93 93
www.britesmile.co.za

BRITE✳SMILE
SOUTHERN AFRICA

LIQUOR CITY
THE LIQUOR BOYS

Most ultra-modern the world!

- For the widest variety of competitively priced, quality products under one roof.
- For an upmarket experience in ultra-modern surroundings in a convenient location.
- For the pleasure of regular tastings and promotions, hosted by an attentive, down-to-earth management team.

liquor stores in

WINE OF ORIGIN COASTAL

- Step into a liquor boutique run by the largest independent liquor group in the country!

BRANCHES: Bassonia (011) 432-0457; Bloemfontein (051) 448-6222; Brackengate (011) 900-4493 Broadacres (011) 465-3795; Cleos (011) 916-2358; Cornwall (012) 345-5198; Fourways (011) 465-6910 Garsfontein (012) 993-5042; Geduld (011) 811-5869; Glen Acres (011) 391-7819; Glen Nerine (011) 658-1706 Highlands (012) 6643424; Lambton (011) 827-4566; Lonehill (011) 467-5468; Montana (012) 548-7780 Moreleta (012) 993-0201; Nelspruit (013) 752-2034; Princess Crossing (011) 768-6813; Ruimsig (011) 958-2453 Rustenburg Square (014) 594-2531; Rooihuiskraal (012) 656-8835; Towers (011) 823-5221 Waverley (012) 332-0535; Westwood (011) 894-6567.

Jabulani Ntshangase

Walking the walk where others are content to talk the talk, empowerer **Jabulani Ntshangase** over the past decade has shepherded ten aspiring young black winemakers through Stellenbosch University – that's one for each year since democracy, he proudly reminds us. Snapped with the oeno-godfather at a wine farm near to the campus are protégées **Philisiwe Shange**, **Bawinile Luthuli** and **Marlon Marinus**.

A Fairview feast ... available at our farm and fine retailers countrywide

FAIRVIEW

ROYDON ~ 1ST PRIZE (PASTEURISED CAMEMBERT CLASS), 2003 WORLD CHEESE AWARDS • **LA BERYL** ~ 1ST PRIZE (PONT L'EVEQUE/LIVAROT/REBLACHON CLASS), 2003 WORLD CHEESE AWARDS • **CREAM CHEESE HONEY AND DUKKAH** ~ 3RD PRIZE (SOFT COWS MILK CHEESE WITH ADDITIVES CLASS), 2003 WORLD CHEESE AWARDS • **CAMEMBERT** ~ 1ST PRIZE (CAMEMBERT/BRIE CLASS), 2004 NATIONAL DAIRY CHAMPIONSHIPS • **BLEU EN BLANC** ~ 1ST PRIZE (CAMEMBERT/BRIE - WITH ADDED FOODSTUFFS CLASS), QUALITÉ WINNER, 2004 SA NATIONAL DAIRY CHAMPIONSHIPS • **ROYDON, LA BERYL AND CHEVIN PLAIN** ~ 1ST PRIZE (CHEESEMAKERS CLASS), 2004 SA NATIONAL DAIRY CHAMPIONSHIPS

CONTACT DETAILS: TEL: (021) 863 2450 • EMAIL: cheese@fairview.co.za • WEBSITE: www.fairview.co.za

where else can you
buy virtually all your
south african wine...

and have it delivered to your
door anywhere on the planet?

cyber cellar

www.cybercellar.co.za

info@cybercellar.co.za • phone+27 83 257 6353

Shiraz ☺ ★★★ Flavourful & attractive **03** (sample), ripe plum & prune intro, whiffs sweet spice & pepper, full, round & fruity. **Cabernet Sauvignon Rosé** NEW ☺ ★★★ Ripe red berry lead-in to **04**, redcurrant touch, smooth-tasting rather than sweet. **Sauvignon Blanc** ☺ ★★★ **04** aromatic, lively & firm but easy; tropical fruit tone, lemon-zest finish; super in its youth. **Chenin Blanc** ☺ NEW ★★☆ **04** hint of guava on nose; lemonade flavours with citrus-zest twist; light bodied refreshment. **CCC** ☺ ★★★ Acronym for colombard, chenin, chardonnay; **04** zinging freshness is the hallmark, plus attractive mix of bright tropical & deciduous flavours; best young. **Sauvignon Blanc Brut** ☺ ★★★ Carbonated sparkling showing delightful contrast of mature sauvignon notes & fresh feisty mousse; *Wine* best value selection. NV. **Late Harvest** ☺ NEW ★★★ **04** from chenin; tropical fruit tones & slight hint of peach & pear; super acid balance for light & fresh effect, not at all stodgy.

Cabernet Sauvignon Reserve ★★★★ Seriously made **02**, new Fr oak, 9 mths, New-World-style; retasted, still thickly padded with spicy berry fruit, big whack of oak & chunky tannins need further cellaring. **Shiraz Reserve** ★★★★ Attention-grabbing **02**, new-oak-matured (Fr/Am casks); retasted, shows dark berries with Karoo bush & pepper, sweet spice & toasty oak; firm but ripe tannins. **Cabernet Sauvignon-Merlot** ★★★ Lightly oaked 60/40 blend; **03** has minty touch, floral background to sweet fruit flavours, smooth & drinkable now with potential to develop. **Cinsaut-Cabernet Sauvignon** NEW ★★★ Red plum & strawberry attractions, hint of ripe cherry; full, round & soft. **04** satisfying everyday drink. 55/45 blend. **Kelkierooi** ★★☆ Lightish strawberry-toned melange of cinsaut, cab & ruby cab, unwooded. Lightly chill in summer. 500ml. NV. **Chardonnay** ★★☆ **03** retasted, still quaffably fresh with distinct Granny Smith apple flavour. **Kelkiewit** ★★ Keep-em-guessing blend in a 500ml bottle. Last tasted was **03**, equal chenin/colombard with tropical fruit tones. **Pik 'n Wyntjie** ★★ Late Harvest-style NV from colombard & chenin. Delicate tropical fruit nose, barely sweet taste. — DH

Boplaas Wine Cellar

Calitzdorp (see Little Karoo map) ▪ Est 1880 ▪ 1stB 1982 ▪ Tasting & sales Mon-Fri 8-5 Sat 9-3 ▪ Fee R15 p/p for tourgroups ▪ Closed Easter Fri/Sun & Dec 25 ▪ Tours by appt ▪ Meals by appt during school holidays ▪ Gifts ▪ Owner Carel Nel ▪ Winemakers Carel Nel & Alwyn Liebenberg (Jan 2004) ▪ Viti consultant Willem Botha ▪ 70 ha (cab, merlot, pinotage, shiraz, touriga, chard, sauvignon) ▪ 35 000 cs 50% red 45% white 5% blanc de noir ▪ PO Box 156 Calitzdorp 6660 ▪ boplaas@mweb.co.za ▪ www.boplaas.co.za © **(044) 213·3326** ☏ *(044) 213·3750*

Alwyn Liebenberg, newly appointed as winemaker on this Calitzdorp farm, should have a first vintage to remember: 'It was a very good harvest, specifically for port,' comments cellarmaster/owner Carel Nel. Liebenberg comes with excellent credentials: he worked at Quinta da Pacheca in Portugal as seasonal winemaker from 2000, and made his first Vintage Port there. He also comes to Boplaas with a jewellery-making partner: his wife, Beulah, has crafted work for the likes of Christian Dior and Givenchy. Another newcomer to the team is Roxanne, Carel's daughter, armed with a marketing qualification. New is a tasting room for (pre-booked) parties of up to 20, in the refurbished underground cellar.

Reserve range

★★★★ **Cabernet Sauvignon 02**, first since **99**, balanced, flavourful & juicy; tasted again for this ed, still very youthful, packed with cassis intensity. 13.8% alc.

★★★★ **Pinotage** Complexity, balance, suppleness are hallmarks; **02** (★★★★) well & ripely fruited with plums & black cherries, though alc (14.9%) tad fiery. **01** had appealing banana-custard tones, creamy texture, ripe tannins for 3-4 yrs.

★★★☆ **Shiraz 02**, spicy & rich, some choc blended in with the red berries. 13.9% alc. Yr on, still youthful, sweet-spicy tone with huge fruit concentration. All above ex-Stbosch vyds.

Kuip & Klei 【NEW】 **03** (sample) fascinating & different blend touriga (giving a herby top-note), cab & merlot; layered red fruits, elegant, works really well — not massively alcoholic either (13.5%). Wood (50% new Fr) still prominent mid-2004 but not overpowering. Promising, could rate ★★★★.

Boplaas range

★★★★ **Muscadel** ✓ Velvety fortified white dessert, which develops with distinction; Last was **03**, slightly syrupy raisin richness, fairly muted nose.

★★★★ **Muscadel Reserve** Carel N aiming for new style with lower fortification, though we feel **04** (sample) needs bit more alcoholic grunt fortification to cut the seriously syrupy richness; beautiful jasmine & honeysuckle bouquet. **02** (untasted) gold at SA Muscadel Association 2004 taste-off.

★★★★☆ **Red Muscadel Vintner's Reserve** Olive-rimmed beauty; **75** (not a misprint) decadently smooth & soft caramelised palate; complex, hints of oil & resin, even a meaty whiff; lifted dried-fruit finish. Delicious.

★★★★★ **Cape Vintage Reserve Port** Distinctive & ageworthy fortified dessert, made only in exceptional yrs. Confirms Carel N's mastery, richly elegant **02** joins **99, 91** & **86** in the guide's top echelon. Suffused with gorgeous fynbos fragrance; superb structure, refinement, focus, with no compromise to house's approachable style. *Wine*'s 2004 Port of Yr. **01** (★★★★★) also had that haunting heather aroma, beautifully modulated richness. Like **99**, boosted by mature touriga vines (12 yrs) & ungrafted ±30-yr-old tinta (blend also includes dash souzão). Sugar, alc & acid (roughly 95g/ℓ, 19%, 5.5g/ℓ) geared for edgier, gripper style with elegance. Exciting long-term potential. Oak/fortification as below; No **00**.

★★★★★ **Cape Vintage Reserve Port CWG** Auction bottling, selection of best barrels, tiny quantities, even more sumptuous. **01** a powerhouse with extraordinary potential. **02** (★★★★★) despite macerated plums/brandied fruitcake richness, has surprising elegance & verve, which was Nel's intention; this modelled on classic Portuguese styling, even to use of 500ℓ port 'pipes' (18–24 mths) to finish wine. Perfectly balanced, succulent dark fruit flavours, luxuriously long finish. Touriga, tinta barocca, souzão; fortified with brandy spirit.

★★★★ **Cape Tawny Port** ✓ SA benchmark for style, festooned with awards (including joint best tawny at 2004 FCTWS). Tinta & touriga, wood-matured 10 yrs, freshened before bottling with dash younger wine. This technique very evident in latest (NV) bottling, which has a lively grapiness on nose; palate more conventionally tea-leafy. Lovely limpid hues; vibrant, silky. 18.6% alc.

Sweet Sparkling ☺ ★★★ Zesty, light, sweetly grapey bubbles designed for uncomplicated pleasure. From hanepoot & colombard (60/40) **NV**.

Cabernet Sauvignon ★★★ **02** light-textured/bodied with clean ripe fruit; yr on, still comfortable, undemanding, ready. DG on local bottled show 2003. **Merlot** ★★★ Fruit-driven style; **03** forthcoming cherry freshness, juice; effortlessly quaffable. **Pinotage** ★★★ From 20 yr old vines, **03** presents banana/cherry-stone bouquet; more juice, interest than pvs at similar modest alc (13%). **Shiraz** ★★★★ **02** improved on foursquare pvs; uncorked for this ed, shows a pleasant meaty, smoky veneer, drinks well. **Touriga Nacional** ★★★★ ✓ Still one of very few varietal bottlings; **03** reprises fynbos/herb character of pvs; nice & chewy, has personality, body & balance. **Tinta Barocca** ★★★ **02**, yr on, softer, more accessible yet doesn't show huge concentration. ±13.5% alc. **Dry Red** ★★ NV. Creative medley of two port varieties & shiraz; appealing wild scrub/gamey tints to black fruit; palate somewhat lacking in vivacity. Above reds all unoaked. **Blanc de Noir** ★★ Semi-sweet **04** deeply coloured, closer to rosé in appearance/tone; pleasant, but lacks fruity zing of pvs. 12% alc. **Chardonnay** ★★☆ Unwooded **03** now shows as restrained, with shortish sherbety flavours. **Sauvignon Blanc** ★★★ **04** subdued, undemanding lemon-drop-toned quaffer. **Classic Dry White** ★★☆ **04** equal portions chardonnay sauvignon; appley fruit-salad nose, forthcoming, lightish. **Late Harvest** ★★★ Hanepoot/colombard equal blend; aromatic **04** with fruit pastille tones, clean finish, well made. **Pinot Noir Brut** ★★☆ Pale salmon-hued sparkling; **04** lightish & lively mousse, raspberry/strawberry aromas, red-fruit palate.

Red Dessert ★★★ Last tasted NV was mix tinta/muscadel, fortified to 17.2%; very sweet & raisiny. **Hanepoot** ★★★★ ✓ **04** golden, velvety fortified dessert; muted aroma but palate is essence of sultana; vivacious, lightish bodied, balanced. ±17% alc. **Cape Vintage Port** ★★★★ ✓ Produced annually from tinta, touriga, souzão (50/35/15), ageing/ fortification as per Rsv above; 'correct' lower sugar. Latest **02** hugely concentrated creamy berry fruit, plush, rich. 18.3% alc. *Wine* ★★★★. **Cape Ruby Port** ★★★★ ✓ SA's best-selling NV ruby, always in drier Douro style. Souzão joins tinta (60%), touriga (25%) in latest, again wickedly drinkable. Plum pud nose broadening into X-mas pud palate. Scrumptious. ±18.5% alc. **Late Bottled Vintage Option Port** ★★★★ ✓ Garnet-hued **93** has tea-leaves, stewed fruit & cream on nose, spicily opulent plum palate; deliciously harmonious & balanced. Tinta, touriga, aged 4½ yrs in Portugese oak.18.5% alc. **Cape White Port** ★★★ Latest (NV) more subdued than pvs but riper, fleshier, more obviously fruity (thus broadening its appeal?). 17.2% alc. – *CR*

Boschendal Wines

Franschhoek ▪ Est 1685 ▪ 1stB 1976 ▪ Tasting & sales daily 8.30-4.30 ▪ Fee R12 for 5 wines ▪ Closed Easter Fri, May 1, Jun 16 & Dec 25 ▪ Tours 10.30 & 11.30 by appt ▪ Restaurants & picnics (see Eat-out section) ▪ Tourgroups ▪ Gifts ▪ Conservation area ▪ Museum visits 9.30- 5 ▪ Owner (see intro) ▪ Winemakers JC Bekker & James Farquharson (Oct 1996/Jan 2004), with Lionel Leibbrandt, Schalk van der Merwe & Francois Conradie (Dec 1999/Jul 2003/Nov 2001) ▪ Viticulturist Spekkies van Breda (1995) ▪ ±300 ha (cab, merlot, shiraz, chard, sauvignon) ▪ 3 300 tons 230 000 cs 50% red 33% white 14% rosé 3% sparkling ▪ ISO 9001 & 14001 certified ▪ Pvt Bag X1 Groot Drakenstein 7680 ▪ stockc@amfarms.co.za ▪ www.boschendal.com © 870·4200 🖷 874·1531

The sense that life has been on hold on this magnificent property was blown away with the news, at the end of 2003, that Anglo-American Farms had sold Boschendal for R323m to a consortium including a 30% BEE partner, headed up by Clive Venning. The wine and hospitality operation, under new MD Franco Barocas, runs in tandem with a property development unit which, he stresses, will not affect the eating and drinking side of things. New marketing/export manager Julian Coulter (from Ireland via Harvard) will promote the efforts of the wine team, expanded at the beginning of 2004 by the arrival of winemaker James Farquharson from Reyneke Wines. A marketing campaign will target the US particularly (sauvignon a key focus). Senior winemaker JC Bekker and his cellar men will retain the Le Pavillon range (but without its Boschendal label) and, at the other end of the spectrum, will develop a four-wine premier range, made in a dedicated cellar for a rollout starting in 2007. 'We've always tried and tested and tasted, bottling 40 cases of this and 70 of that,' explains JCB, 'now we'll have a commercial home for what we rate as exceptional.' On the hospitality *werf*, the restaurant will be revamped and modernised, and Le Pique-Nique will be restyled with an upmarket version spread across newly grassed lawns; the historical cottages (sensitively) converted into lifestyle shops; and (good thinking) a second wine-tasting venue opened for picnickers.

★★★★★ **Grand Reserve** Classically crafted & ageworthy flagship from cask selections, in-creased cab f component to 45% in deep-coloured **00** (with 40/15 cab, merlot). Made for long haul, now fragrantly opening up, with velvet fruit-sweetness, sup-ported by sensitive oaking – mix new, 2nd fill Fr. 14.5% alc. **01** broadly similar stats, also grandly serious, but perhaps a little easier-going. Lovely bright, savoury fruit, firm tannic backbone; also needs time to show its best – not easy in youth.

★★★★ **Cabernet Sauvignon Reserve** Elegantly styled maiden **00** had spicy leafiness with cassis fragrance, well-balanced palate, delicate but with firm grip & persis-tence. Darkly rich **01** burlier, but still youthfully tight mid-2004, with tobacco notes, hints of lurking fruit – few yrs required to show more attractions, longer maturation best. Intelligently restrained mix new/older barrels on these. 14% alc.

★★★★ **Cabernet Sauvignon** Welcomed back with **00** after 20 yr absence, good drinking while waiting on Reserve. Firm, big **01** now very appealing; fresh, sweetly lingering cassis fruit, but will keep good few yrs. Mix new/older oak. 14.2% alc.

★★★★ **Merlot 01** was powerful, yet not without elegance, offering leafy edge to attractive plum, choc. Ripe-scented **02** (★★★★) called 'Reserve', but less attractive now – formidable 15% alc surrounding sweet fruitcake, mocha flavours, big tannins with a touch bitterness. Yr oak, 30% new.

★★★★★ **Syrah** Formerly less Frenchly known as Shiraz, yet New Worldish in its forcefulness. Retasted **01** (★★★★) with ripe, smoky bouquet & plenty of savoury red berries, now starting to harmonise with tannic structure & influence of yr in mix new & older Fr oak. Heady 15% alc gives powerful glow to finish. **00** offered pepper, wild scrub joined by fresh, sappy plums.

★★★☆ **Shiraz** 🆕 Grapes from a vyd overlooking False Bay, with dash viognier in **02**. Ripe spicy baked plum aromas leading to soft palate which tightens for firm dry finish. Tasty fruit; integration of disparate elements may come with yr/2 in bottle. Yr Fr oak. 14% alc.

★★★☆ **Lanoy** Big volume blend named after 17th century part-owner Nicolas de Lanoy. **01**, much like **00**, cab-based with merlot (28%), shiraz (12). Beguiling nose, friendly but straightforward firm palate, with sweet ripe fruit. Yr Fr oak, 25% new.

★★★★ **Jean le Long Cabernet Franc** Variety's characteristic fragrance on still-youthful **01**, with cedar & earthy leafiness. Satisfying, lingering & deep flavours rather shouldered aside by dry tannins, partly from 16 mths all-new Fr oak. Mere 65 cs.

★★★★ **Chardonnay Reserve** Spicy oatmeal notes on big, modern but not over-brash **03**, from single, low-yielding home vyd. Balances massive 15% alc with fruit power, rich texture, fresh acidity. Partly native yeast-fermented; 11 mths Fr oak, half new. More serious & satisfying than was exuberantly flavourful sweetish **02** (★★★☆).

★★★☆ **Chardonnay 04** rounded out with a little sugar attractively balancing citrus-sour fruit in neatly elegant package. Modest oak influence (60% barrel fermented) adds touch of complexity. 14% alc.

★★★★ **Jean le Long Sauvignon Blanc** Delicious **03** maturing with fine subdued pungency on silky, well-balanced & flavourful palate, succulent acidity harmonising 5g/ℓ sugar, all finishing with long, rich appeal. 13.5% alc. MIWA, Veritas double golds. Sample **04** similar, with grass & gooseberries, lovely fresh balance, power.

★★★★ **Sauvignon Blanc** Forward aromas/flavours grassiness plus tropical fruit on fresh, pleasantly balanced **04** (★★★★), from Stbosch, Dbnvlle grapes. Possibly just closed up mid-2004 – should anyway benefit from 6 mths+ in bottle. **03** was opulent on release, tropicality of flavour tinged with green.

★★★★ **Jean le Long Semillon** First of the cellar's single-vyd labels, launched **85**, named after property's Huguenot founder. Retasted **00** now mature; richly (almost decadently) flavoured, with lanolin, lemon notes, but still fresh & lively, with big 15% alc adding to creamy texture. Well integrated all-new oak, 50/50 Fr/Am.

★★★☆ **Pinot Noir-Chardonnay** Satisfyingly different flavours from this SA pioneering 'bubbly without bubbles'; no skin contact so only pure white juice from blend. Delicious, rich, fresh & dry **04**, with customary notes of peach, strawberry, earth. 20% barrel fermented; 14.4% alc.

★★★★ **Brut** Supple, yeasty, vintaged MCC from pinot (60% in **99**), chardonnay. Biscuit/ brioche bouquet presages almost decadently rich but well-balanced palate offering strawberry, ripe apple notes, with sweet touch from 13g/ℓ sugar. Our mid-2004 bottle disgorged Jan 2003 (date on label). 2002 MCC Challenge runner up.

Blanc de Noir ☺ ★★★ Gleaming pale salmon-coloured **04**, from 5 smart red varieties, has notes of strawberry, boiled sweets. Attractively off-dry; 13% alc. **Chenin Blanc** ★★★ **04** off-dry, pleasantly rich, with thatch & beeswax notes, succulent acid & too-big 14.5% alc. **Grand Vin Blanc** ★★★ Grassy & tropical fruit sauvignon, 8% chardonnay adding lime notes to **04**. Greenly fresh & bright, softened with a little sugar. 13.5% alc. **Le Bouquet** ★★★ Floral, grapey perfumes billowing from lightish, flavourful & off-dry **04** blend of aromatic whites. **Viognier** Last was maiden barrel-fermented **02** ★★★, rather subdued & lean. **Blanc de Blanc** ★★★ Cheerful sauvignon, chenin, chardonnay blend packed with fresh, bright fruit flavours in **04**; just dry, with clean lemon-drop finish.

Le Pavillon range

★★★★ **Le Grand Pavillon** Cap Classique brut NV from 70/30% chardonnay/pinot (though back label says white varieties only). Reliable continuity of style – spiced baked apple & yeasty notes on lightly elegant dryness. 8g/ℓ sugar; 12.5% alc.

> **Rouge** ☺ ★★★ **03** pleasingly blends cab, merlot, shiraz; boiled sweet & ripe baked aromas/flavours in soft but well-formed package; 14% alc. **Blanc** ☺ ★★★ **04** a quietly fruity blend of happily consorting all-sorts, with attractive sweet-sour tension, well-balanced 14% alc.

Discontinued: **Riesling, Sauvignon Blanc-Semillon.** – *TJ*

Boschenmeer see Oaklands Wine Exports

Boschkloof Wines

Stellenbosch ▪ Est/1stB 1996 ▪ Tasting & sales by appt Mon-Fri 8-6 (sales 8-5) Sat 8-1 ▪ Tours by appt only ▪ Owners Reenen Furter & Jacques Borman ▪ Winemaker Jacques Borman ▪ Viti-culturist Reenen Furter ▪ 19 ha (cab, merlot, shiraz) ▪ 120 tons ▪ 8 000 cs 89% red 11% white ▪ PO Box 1340 Stellenbosch 7599 ▪ boschkloof@adept.co.za ▪ www.boschkloof.co.za ✆ 881·3293 📠 881·3032

Being involved full-time in making his own wine (with father-in-law Reenen Furter) is the realisation of a dream for Jacques Borman, who believes that 'wine must be made with an obsessive passion for the product'. A winemaker with 23 years' experience – at La Motte and on his own account after hours and on high days and holidays, he pronounces the 2004 shiraz 'truly something exceptional; among the best I've made'. In general, he reckons, winemakers with the nerves and patience for the 2004 harvest will have very good wines in their cellars. Borman and Furter look east for new outlets and to Russia; in established markets, shiraz is in demand so SA can, with good-quality shiraz, make a competitive showing.

★★★★ **Syrah** Considerable power within svelte frame. **02** brushes off difficult harvest with laser concentration to spicy, hot-choc fruit. Interwoven tannins will need 3-5 yrs to open up flavour riches. Veritas-lauded **01** (★★★★★) modern & delicious. Half each wild & Rhône yeast ferment, oak now 13 mths Fr, 25% new. 14.6% alc.

★★★★ **Boschkloof Reserve** Special selection cab & merlot, make-up varies from yr to yr. Initially quiet **00** (78/22) allows glimpses of potential, but still a sleeper. Powdery tannins hem in black berry fruits – should mellow into something special in 2-4 yrs. **99** (87/13) rich, deeply concentrated. Now 20 mths Fr oak, 80% new. 14.5% alc.

★★★★ **Cabernet Sauvignon-Merlot** ✓ Stylish Fr oak-matured blend, easier – not lesser – than Reserve. **02** (70/30 blend) proffers tarry gleam to polished vanilla-choc, plum flesh. Firm & most satisfying finish. 65/35 components of **01** have integrated black berries, floral/spicy tints into supple texture. 14 mths oak, 20% new. 14.5% alc.

★★★☆ **Chardonnay** Serious example, now more accessible with less oak, more citrus fruit in its sinewy richness. **03** leads with lemon tang, hint of butterscotch, rapier freshness in attractive dry finish. 30% new Fr oak ±7 mths. 14.2% alc.

Cabernet Sauvignon ★★★★ Measured elegance seamed into fruit/structure of **00**, (retasted, like below) developing beautiful cassis notes in minty/herby fabric. Tightly wound, needs few more years. 14 mths Fr oak. 14.4% alc. **Merlot** ★★★★ Similar restraint, but louder choc-nut flavours in **00**. Components focused in still-youthful palate; plums, violets & minerals need 2-4 yrs more to flow smoothly. 14 mths Fr oak, 15% new. 13.7% alc. – *DS*

Boschrivier Cellar

Stanford ▪ Est 1997 ▪ 1stB 2002 ▪ Closed to public ▪ Owner NJT de Villiers ▪ Viti consultant Mike Dobrovic, with Clinton le Sueur (both Jan 2002) ▪ Viticulturist Johan van der Merwe ▪ 14 ha (cab, shiraz) ▪ 367 cs 100% red ▪ PO Box 809 Caledon 7230 ▪ njtdevill@mweb.co.za ▪ www.boschrivier.co.za ©/📠 *(028) 341·0630*

In the vanguard of first-time wine ventures between Stanford and Caledon is pediatrician Theo de Villiers. In 1997 he inherited two wheat/onion farms off the Akkedisberg Pass (farming here dates back to the 18th century and included must-wine production in the early 1900s). A long-held dream to make wine, combined with a soil expert's 'OK', inspired De Villiers to start planting reds in 1998. The first few crops of shiraz and cab went to Newton Johnson before Mulderbosch winemakers Mike Dobrovic and Clinton le Sueur agreed to vinify small parcels to his specs from 2002. Johan van der Merwe is ensconced as farm manager, and a cellar in Caledon is on the cards. While Merlot has joined the mix, negotiations are underway for exports to Japan. It's green for go.

★★★★ **Shiraz** 🆕 **02**'s retiring wool-oil nose leads to expansive, expressive huckleberry fruit tinged with cassia, roast spice. Soft easy tannins already approachable; generous drinkability in youth. 18 mths Fr oak, half new. 13.6% alc. — *DS*

Boschveld see Baarsma

Bosman's Hill see Saxenburg

Botha Wine Cellar

Rawsonville (see Worcester map) ▪ Est 1949 ▪ 1stB 1974 ▪ Tasting & sales Mon-Fri 7.30-5. 30 Sat 9-1 ▪ Closed Easter Fri/Sun, Dec 25 & Jan 1 ▪ Tours by appt ▪ BYO picnic ▪ Facilities for children ▪ Tourgroups ▪ Conservation area ▪ Owners 71 members ▪ Manager/cellarmaster JC 'Dassie' Smith (Nov 1996) ▪ Winemakers Johan Linde & Michiel Visser (Nov 1996/Nov 1999), with Pierre Hugo & Jacobus Brink ▪ Viticulturist Francois Nel (Nov 2000) ▪ 1 775 ha ▪ 31 000 tons 30% red 70% white ▪ PO Box 30 Botha 6857 ▪ bothawyn@mweb. co.za © *(023) 355·1740/498* 📠 *(023) 355·1615*

Given a 7.30am opening hour, among the earliest in the winelands, wine tourists can start their tasting day here with time to spare (tourgroups and picnickers are now provided for). There's a new Vinotique to browse through; also new, in people terms, is assistant winemaker number two, Jacobus Brink. More signs that this winery's not standing still: the white wine cellar has been given a total upgrade and the red cellar expanded.

Dassie's Reserve range

Chenin Blanc ☺ ★★★ **04** (sample) aromatically subdued but well fruited, lively & light.

Cabernet Sauvignon ★★★ **02** genteel nose with whiffs currant jam & tobacco; dry powdery tannins, obvious wood, lacks polish. 14% alc. Fr barriques, as are all these reds. **Merlot** ★★★ Some complexity on nose of **02**, but vanilla oak dominates palate, ends with firm acidic bite. 14.5% alc. **Pinotage** ★★★★ ✓ Oak/acid better handled here; **02** plum jam & cinnamon spice tones complemented by wood, spicy dry finish, good fresh finish. **Shiraz** ★★★★ ✓ **02** attractive peppery red-berry nose, mocha from oak, classy & not overly large even at 14.8% alc. **Chardonnay** ★★ **04** (sample) starts auspiciously with fresh apple & pear whiffs, turns slightly coarse & phenolic in palate. **Colombard** ★★★★ ✓ **04** (sample) one of their best; appealing & forthcoming guava & fynbos, juicy tropical fruit palate bolstered by well-hidden 10g/ℓ sugar. Delicious. **Sauvignon Blanc** ★★★★ ✓ Crushed nettles & mown lawn welcome you to **04** (sample), herby & flinty notes to palate, attractively taut & austere. **Special Late Harvest** ★★★ Last tasted was lightish **02**, with tropical fruit flavours & light bottle-age.

Standard range

★★★☆ **Red Jerepigo 01** had a youthful purple glow, mirroring palate's lively flavours. **02 (★★★)** dark ruby/plum glints; dried prunes, tar & touch leather in bouquet; full-sweet, redolent of treacle & fruit cordial. 16% alc.

★★★☆ **Ruby Port 99** was the last tasted; spirity & warming, with dryish finish.

★★★☆ **Late Bottled Vintage ✓ 98** full-bodied, 'correct' style despite non-traditional varieties (equal pinotage, shiraz, ruby cab). Meaty, developed nose, dried-fruit character; characterful & appealing. Matured 300ℓ Fr oak.

Following reds unwooded. **Cabernet Sauvignon ★★★** Sweet blackcurrant aromas in **04** (sample); punchy, but tannins well managed, in harmony with fruit. **Merlot ★★☆ 04** (sample) vibrant mulberry jam nose, contrasting palate tight & grainy, slightly under-ripe. **Pinotage ★★★ 04** (sample) beaujolais style fruit-bomb made of mulberries. **Shiraz ★★★ 02** was improvement on pvs; interesting herbs & fynbos bouquet; smooth palate, dry finishing. **04** sample too unformed to rate. 14.2% alc. **Dassie's Rood ★★★** Swiggable braai companion from mainly cinsaut, dollops cab & ruby cab; **03** shows Mediterranean-style lightness, elegance, balance. **Blanc de Blanc ★★ 03** bone-dry equal mix colombard, chenin, crouchen, needs good plate of spicy prawns. **Special Late Harvest ★★ 04** (sample) honeyed & very sweet chenin & hanepoot, with light barley sugar softness. **Chardonnay Brut ★★★** Refreshing dry carbonated sparkling with busy, creamy bubbles. Latest similar flavours to Demi-Sec. Both NV. **Chardonnay Demi-sec ★★★** Appealing, not over-sweet sparkling with masses of prickly bubbles. Latest unusually full flavoured for this style, notes of melon & ginger. **Hanepoot Jerepigo ★★★★ ✓ 02** fortified dessert bursts with jasmine & honeysuckle aromas/flavours — very essence of muscat; hugely sweet & raisiny. Gorgeous. All WO Wrcstr/Brde Rvr Vlly. — *TM*

Bottelary Hills Wines

Est/1stB 2003 ▪ Tasting, sales & tours see Bellevue, Goede Hoop, Groenland, Kaapzicht & Mooiplaas ▪ Owners Bottelary Hills Wines (Pty) Ltd ▪ 70% red 30% white ▪ PO Box 42 Koelenhof 7605 ▪ kaapzicht@mweb.co.za ▪ www.bottelaryhills.co.za ⓒ 906·1620/ 903·6286/865·2055 🖷 906·1622/906·1553

Six wineries (Kaapzicht, Bellevue, Goede Hoop, Mooiplaas, Groenland and Sterhuis) in Stellenbosch's Bottelary Hills are the drivers behind the premium Bottelary Hills range and the second label M23 (the road runs through it). Individual 'estate' labels remain, but these offerings, blended by Kaapzicht's Danie Steytler and Goede Hoop's Pieter Bestbier from contributions by participating wineries, are intended to help establish the Bottelary Wine Route as a distinctive 'wine of origin' area where 'the terroir is reflected in the wines'. On the list are the Bottelary Hills Cab-Pinotage and Shiraz; and the M23 Cab-Merlot, Rhapsody (cinsaut, cab, merlot), Sauvignon and Limerick (chenin, sauvignon).

Bouchard Finlayson   🍷👤♿

Hemel-en-Aarde Valley (see Walker Bay map) ▪ Est 1989 ▪ 1stB 1991 ▪ Tasting & sales Mon-Fri 9-5 Sat 9.30-12.30 ▪ Fee R20 for groups of 8+ ▪ Closed public holidays ▪ Owner Bouchard Finlayson (Pty) Ltd ▪ Winemaker/viticulturist Peter Finlayson ▪ 17 ha (pinot, nebbiolo, sangiovese, chard, sauvignon) ▪ 180 tons 12 000 cs 20% red 80% white ▪ PO Box 303 Hermanus 7200 ▪ info@bouchardfinlayson.co.za ▪ www.bouchardfinlayson.co.za ⓒ (028) 312·3515 🖷 (028) 312·2317

First a broken tin-roofed office in an old cow stable. Then a respectable office complex with modest tasting room and lounge. Now architect-designed 'super-luxury visitor accommodation under thatch'. Pleased though man of the earth Peter Finlayson is about the upward mobility of this Hemel-en-Aarde spread's facilities, it's always been about the wine. His first decade here was spent establishing vineyards; the second, a range of wines of classic refinement and elegance — his Burgundian-inspired Pinots and Chardonnays — and a daringly different style — his sangiovese-based blend, which he says is firmly structured but lighter bodied, and making its mark in a market dominated by deeply extracted reds. Vintage 2004? Particularly for pinot 'perhaps the most promising since 2001' (a five-star in last year's guide). The Czech Republic and Russia are new on his client list; but (happily) nearly 70% of his wines stay here.

★★★★★ **Galpin Peak Pinot Noir** A leading Cape example, characterised by grip & substance: 'mouthfeel'. Classic tautness recently moderated by riper – & equally classic pinot – red berry fruit. Burgundy remains the spiritual focus here. Own vyds, yield concentrated 1kg grapes/vine. Sample **03** usual textured fruit within creamy frame. **02** brooding black cherry woven into richer, juicier, less oaky lattice. More elegant than muscular **01**, **00**. Now only ±40% new oak, 10 mths.

★★★★★ **Tête de Cuvée Galpin Peak Pinot Noir** Cellarmaster's barrel selection in best yrs, more strenuously oaked (75% new Burgundian barrels, 14 mths). Terrific **01** (★★★★★) redolent of truffles, forest berries; velvet texture, super-fine lacy tannins. Garlands from IWC, JCMA. This & **00** not tasted for this ed.

★★★★ **Hannibal** Cape's first sangiovese-led blend, with pinot & 'Mediterranean partners' – nebbiolo, mourvèdre, barbera & now syrah. Deceptively substantial power with finesse. Sample **03** muscular black fruits in firm (not hard) tannin web. **02** tarry forest-floor fruits well ordered in gentle structure, likely ready earlier than brambly **01**. 13.5% alc. ±14 mths oak, quarter new.

★★★★ **Missionvale Chardonnay** The white flagship, given everything – within usual restraint. **03** gleaming crocus, rich composition lanolin fruit & clean oak in classical frame. Unflashy, replete with finesse. Sample **04** structured for promise. **02** 90 pts WS. Own grapes, 100% barrel-fermented/matured 5 mths, 30% new; full malo.

★★★★ **Kaaimansgat Chardonnay** ('Crocodile's Lair') Grapes from cool Villiersdorp vyds classically handled. **03** in the groove; gravelly tones to lemon fruits, structure hints at richness, never gauche – carries 14% alc well. **02** broader, marzipan touches to super juicy length. Part oak-fermented, ±8 mths wood.

★★★★ **Sans Barrique Chardonnay** Unoaked, less complicated than above, but spotlights clean, fresh fruit. Ages well: **03** softened, filled out into a beauty – lemon zest cuts quince pith; chalky tail. Sample **04** delineates limey fruit, refreshing – shorter lees contact (6 mths; was 8). No malo. 14.5% alc.

★★★☆ **Sauvignon Blanc** Formerly measured & demure – 'always crisp, never outspoken' – next **04** in louder, riper style; proffers pungent herbaceous whiffs, riveting flavour cut by rapier dry finish. 13% alc.

Blanc de Mer ★★★★ Vintaged **03** gears up quality; riesling, gewürz take over lead from unusual kerner in pvs (NV), pinot blanc & chardonnay add flesh. Stony flint to perfume, satisfying dry length yearns for shellfish. 13.5% alc. **04** not finished at press time. – *DS*

▓ *Boundary Valley* see Cape Wine Cellars

Bouwland

*Stellenbosch ▪ Est 1996 ▪ 1stB 1997 ▪ Tasting & sales at Beyerskloof ▪ Owners Bouwland Deelnemings Trust & Beyerskloof ▪ Winemaker Beyers Truter, with Anri Truter (1997/2004) ▪ Viti consultant Johan Pienaar (2003) ▪ 40 ha (cab, merlot, pinotage) ▪ 350 tons 30 000 cs 90% red 10% white ▪ PO Box 62 Koelenhof 7605 ▪ bouwland@adept.co.za © **865·2135** 🖷 865·2683*

With the simultaneous launch of their new packaging and first white wine, the 60 trustees of this farmworker-owned winery are stepping out with increasing confidence and 'leaning less' on their mentors and partners, Beyerskloof (though leading light Beyers Truter still assists with winemaking and training). Their front label reads: 'Building a dream takes more than faith, hope and courage; it requires the true spirit of man to shine through in the simple act of taking another's hand.' Meanwhile marketer Veronica Campher can hardly get over her delight at representing the winery on the international stage – at London's International Wine & Sprit Fair – for the first time last year.

★★★☆ **Cabernet Sauvignon-Merlot** ✓ Great value for such engaging ripe aromas/flavours. **02** (as usual 70/30% blend) above all eminently drinkable in its decent, good-humoured fruity savouriness & satisfying balance. No hurry to drink up — this also a fairly serious proposition. Lightly & effectively oaked; 14% alc.

Chenin Blanc 𝗡𝗘𝗪 ☺ ★★★ Pleasantly, forwardly but not overly fruity **03** has notes of honey, dried grass, pear-drop. Freshly flavoursome & balanced for easy drinking. — *TJ*

Bovlei Winery

🍷 ⊚⊚ ♿

Wellington ▪ Est 1907 ▪ Tasting & sales Mon-Fri 8.30–1; 2–5 Sat 8.30–12.30 Non-religious public holidays 9.30–4.30 ▪ Tours by appt ▪ Own-brand olive & grapeseed products ▪ Owners 45 members ▪ Cellarmaster Marius Erasmus ▪ Winemakers Hendrik de Villiers & Albertus Louw (Dec 1996/1998) ▪ Viti consultant Dawie le Roux ▪ 560 ha (cab, merlot, shiraz, chard) ▪ 120 000 cs own labels + 920k ℓ bulk ▪ 40% red 60% white ▪ PO Box 82 Wellington 7654 ▪ lizl@ bovlei.co.za ▪ www.bovlei.co.za ⓒ 873·1567 / 864·1283 🖷 864·1483

This recently revamped winery, already a significant bulk exporter, has joined the Cape Coastal Wines partnership with Wellington, Wamakersvallei, Riebeek and Wellington cellars, and looks set to become an even bigger force offshore. Locally, it has teamed up with marketing and distribution concern, Vinimark, to heighten its SA profile. Personnel changes see Frank Meaker, ex-Blaauwklippen, join as production manager; and Hendrik de Villiers as winemaking partner to well-salted Albertus Louw. Revealing that they are developing a new quality strategy from the vineyard to the bottle, the team declare that 'the road ahead will be to add more value and build brand awareness locally and abroad.'

Reserve range

Merlot ★★★★ **02** big, brawny wine but perhaps more structuring tannins & alc (14.3% alc) now than flesh; give time for ripe plum/mulberry fruit to develop. 14 mths Fr casks. Stylish packaging feature of both ranges. **Shiraz** ★★★★ **02** step up on regular version (as are all these); lots to mull over: plums, mint, clove, vanilla, choc, cinnamon! Should get even more interesting over 3–4 yrs. New Fr oak 14 mths, 14% alc. **Cabernet Sauvignon-Merlot** ★★★★ **02** classic claret tones with floral hint, clean oak backing; ripe fruity tannins, nice long finish augur well; cellar few yrs to realise potential. 14% alc. **Chardonnay** ★★★ ✓ From the New World barrel-fermented chard style-manual: peaches & cream, lashings vanilla/butterscotch. Attractive, vibrant, OTT. Enjoy **03** over the next yr/2. 14.6% alc. **Sauvignon Blanc** ★★★ Team Bovlei pulled out all stops to capture freshness, zing; **03** rivetting spread tinned asparagus, tropical fruit & greenpepper; clean zesty finish. Enjoy in sprightly youth.

Bovlei range

Grand Rouge ☺ ★★★ Bdx blend cab f/merlot bearing red berries & choc; **02** soft & effortlessly drinkable. **Chenin Blanc** ☺ ★★★ **04** light in body but big on taste; guava & passionfruit, bright lemony dry finish. Following NVs available in 3/5ℓ casks & 500ml 'Wellington Dumpies': **Vin Rouge** ☺ ★★ Crisp, jolly, flavourful jumble of ruby cab, cinsaut, pinotage partnership. **Vin Blanc** ☺ ★★ Well-made, lightish, tropical-toned dry quick-quaff from chenin, colombard.

Cabernet Sauvignon ★★★ **02** honest, well-made cab. Warmly & effusive berry flavours & balanced oaking. **Pinotage** ★★★ Classic mulberries & plums on **03**, still quite firm, probably better in yr/2; ex-dryland bushvines. **Shiraz** ★★★ From s-w facing vyd on Groenberg slopes. Barrique ageing shows in spice & toast on **01**, hint red berry, soft tannins, good everyday red. **Chardonnay 03** proffers light tropical tones with honeyed notes; attractive, but not for further keeping. **Sauvignon Blanc** ★★★ Uncomplicated, lightish **03** with generous tropical tones, crisp dry finish. **Bukettraube** ★★ Honeysuckle scents on light, bright, smooth rather than sweet **03**. **Port** ★★ Ruby-style NV offers fresh ripe-plum flavour, as expected from ruby cab (50%, with cab f, roobernet & grenache); traditional low fortification (15.3%). — *DH*

BoweJoubert Vineyards & Winery

Stellenbosch ▪ 1stB 2000 ▪ Visits by appt ▪ Self-catering guest houses ▪ Conference facility for max 100 ▪ Functions & weddings for max 150 ▪ Owners Alphonso Bowe, Andrew Hilliard & Jannie Joubert ▪ Winemaker Jannie Joubert, advised by Mark Carmichael-Green ▪ Viticulturist Lukas Joubert ▪ 80 ha (cab, merlot, chard, sauvignon) ▪ 600 tons 20 000 cs own label 50/50 red/white ▪ Export brands: Oak Lane & Veelverjaaght ▪ PO Box 1114 Stellenbosch 7599 info@bowejoubert.com ▪ www.bowejoubert.com © 881·3103 ▤ 881·3377

Set among these Polkadraai vineyards are self-catering guesthouses and a centre which can accommodate a sizeable conference or a 150-guest wedding or function. Wine-buying visitors please note: tastings are now by appointment only.

Cabernet Sauvignon ★★★ Two vintages currently in stock, both retasted: **01** firm tannins evident but powdery rather than grainy, hint fennel on finish. **02** slightly lighter hued, elegant but perhaps less complex, earthy hints, brambly fruit, also firm tannins. ±13.8% alc; 14 mths Fr oak, some new. **Merlot ★★★★** Duo available: **01** showing complexity — tobacco, cigarbox & leafy notes; ripe fruit, soft choc palate, eager to please. **02** mulberry-juice aromas; supple, again the choc tone. Drinks well. Both retasted, oak as above. **Chardonnay ★★★ 02** revisited: flavourful, creamy but shows signs of benevolent oxidation, needs to be drunk. Barrel-fermented/6 mths Fr/Am, 70/30, some new. ±14% alc. **Sauvignon Blanc ★★★ 03** was last tasted & noted as coolly elegant.— *TM*

▨ *Bradgate see Jordan*
  Brahms see Domaine Brahms
  Brampton see Rustenberg

Brandvlei Cellar

Worcester ▪ Est 1955 ▪ 1stB 1956 ▪ Tasting & sales Mon-Thu 7.30-12.30; 1.30-5.30 (doors close 4.30 on Fri) ▪ Closed public holidays ▪ Tours & group tastings by appt ▪ BYO picnic ▪ Owners 32 members ▪ Manager/winemaker Jean le Roux, with Jandré Human & Tertius Jonck ▪ Viticulturist Pierre Snyman (Aug 2000) ▪ 1 400 ha (13 varieties r/w) ▪ 10 000 cs own label 20% red 75% white 10% jerepiko ▪ PO Box 595 Worcester 6849 ▪ brandvlei@ cybertrade.co.za ▪ www.brandvlei.co.za www.bcwines.co.za ©/▤ (023) 340·4215/ 4108 ▤ (023) 340·4332

This co-operative cellar celebrates its half century with a brand new look and a fresh identity for their wines. These will now be labelled 'BC Wines' instead of Brandvlei. Apparently too many people confused the winery with the the close-by Brandvlei Dam or, less alluringly, the Brandvlei Prison. The attractive new label design represents the highest point of the mountain nearby, known as Jonaskop, and the hole in it suggests the 'eye' of the hot water spring which feeds the dam.

BC range

Ruby Cabernet-Merlot ☺ **★★★** Always a happy marriage, 60/40 ratio, lightly wooded. **03** fully stocked with ripe plum flavour, floral scents, muted toasty touch. **Chenin Blanc** ☺ **★★★** Fresh, charming **04**, sweet tropical fruit tones with hint of fresh flowers; smooth, easy, frisky lemon finish. **Sauvignon Blanc** ☺ **★★★** Picked early for racy freshness & lowish alc (12.5%). **04** notes of fresh cut-grass, guava/pineapple too, all repeat in well-rounded mouth with zingy apple-toned finish.

Chardonnay ★★★ 04 lightly oaked (with chips), sweet fruit tastily melded with butterscotch & vanilla. **Bacchanté ★★★** Appealing semi-sweet white from chenin, few drops hanepoot; **04** wafting sweet tropical fruit nose, gentle palate, easy to drink. 12.5% alc. **Sec Sparkling** Not tasted. **Hanepoot Jerepiko ★★★★ 03** tangy citrus nose with honeysuckle top-note; sweetness & fairly high alc (17%) well controlled. Pour over crushed ice for delicious aperitif.— *DH*

Bredell see JP Bredell

Breeland Winery

*Rawsonville • Closed to public • PO Box 109 Rawsonville 6845 • mlalee@xpoint.co.za ©/
📠 (023) 344·3137*

Family-owned operation producing mainly bulk wine, though limited quantities of 04 Chardonnay Wooded, Chenin and Semillon are available under the Lee & Jones label.

Brenthurst Winery

*Paarl • Est 1993 • 1stB 1994 • Open to public only by special appt • Owner/winemaker José
Jordaan, with viti consultant Johan Wiese (1991) & other advisers • 5 ha (cabs s/f, merlot,
petit v) • 50-70 tons • PO Box 6091 Paarl 7622 © 863·1154/1375 📠 424·5666*

This winery, owned by advocate José Jordaan, may be small, but it certainly has a focused philosophy. 'Our intention is to produce only one wine per season — a top-class Bordeaux-style red,' he says. 'In exceptional vintages a reserve or barrel selected wine may also be produced in limited quantities.' He plans to keep the concern as small and specialised as it is, turning out no more than 5 000 cases a year.

BRL Hardy see Stellenbosch Vineyards
Broken Rock see Arlington, Riebeek Cellars
Broken Stone see Slaley
Broodryk see Bovlei
Bugatti's see De Compagnie

Buitenverwachting

*Constantia • Est 1796 • 1stB 1985 • Tasting & sales Mon-Fri 9-5 Sat 9-1 • Closed public holidays • Tours by appt • Buitenverwachting Restaurant Mon-Sat © 794·3522. Summer
only: Café Petite for light lunches (tel as above) & picnic baskets by appt © 083·257·6083
• Teddy Bear Fair May 1; Valentine's Day Picnic • Conferences • Owners Richard &
Sieglinde (Christine) Mueller, Lars Maack • Winemaker Hermann Kirschbaum (Dec 1992)
• Vineyards Peter Reynolds (Jun 1997), advised by Johan Pienaar • 120 ha (cabs s/f, merlot, pinot, chard, sauvignon, riesling) • 1 300 tons 90 000 cs 18% red 80% white 1% rosé
1% sparkling • PO Box 281 Constantia 7848 • info@buitenverwachting.com • www.
buitenverwachting.com © 794·5190 📠 794·1351*

The gentle, fun-loving folk of this happy winery were devastated by the death in a 2004 diving accident of winemaker Jacques Moelans. Extremely talented, with a great flair with wine, he was being groomed to succeed cellarmaster Hermann Kirschbaum upon retirement. Moelans was to spend a Sancerre harvest studying cool-climate sauvignon, one of this winery's specialities (it was rated top 2004 sauvignon producer by German publication *Alles Über Wein*). Looking back, Moelans was there to share the team's delight at a listing as one of the world's 50 great producers by *Wine Spectator* in early 2004. Looking ahead, the vineyards have come full cycle with early 1980s blocks being replanted and the next 20 years being all about fine-tuning.

★★★★★ **Christine** For over a decade, one of the more serious SA Bdx blends, cab-based, with cab f, merlot, malbec (from **98**). Now 'modernising', with riper fruit, bigger alcs, all-new Fr oak 18 mths, but still forcefully structured, classically oriented. Typically well-knit **99** has lighter texture than most, with vegetal edge. **00** bigger, deeper, riper & sweeter fruited, developing well & only now starting to reveal its authoritative, richly firm best — with long future ahead of it. 14.5% alc.

★★★★ **Merlot** Refined **99** first release in 4 yrs. Un-showy, elegant **00** revealing plenty of spicy, plummy charm on retasting. Powerful 14.5% alc, yet harmonious & very drinkable. Well-integrated wood (18 mths Fr oak), fine tannins.

★★★★ **Cabernet Sauvignon** Another serious-minded wine. Like above, missed since **95**. Approachable but firm, well-balanced **99** followed by bigger **00** (14.5% alc), also darker, deeper, riper, with cedar & blackcurrant dominating savoury balance. 18 mths oak well integrated. *Wine* ★★★★☆.

★★★★ **Meifort** ✓ Second-best blend of most of farm's reds – but Kirschbaum doesn't play the dumbing-down game: always well-balanced, firmly structured. Retasted **00** now drinking well (though still yr/2 to go), with plentiful red fruit, dry savoury finish.

★★★★ **Sauvignon Blanc** Bottled version not tasted since **02**. Sample **04** promises bold flavours, fine acidity pointing up greenfruit undercurrent to tropical fruit notes. Dry; 13.2% alc. A selection of this, unnamed as we went to press, also unbottled, very promising: more focused, ripely concentrated, highlighting passionfruit element.

★★★★ **Chardonnay** Intense spice, lime, toast aromas/flavours on **03**, well balanced, with juicy acidity & silky texture. 13.7% alc. Two thirds fermented/11 mths oak. Less concentrated fruit in **02** (★★★☆) more oak-driven.

★★★☆ **Rhine Riesling** Crisply balanced, nearly dry **03** lightly flavoured with peach, apple; lightly structured too: 11.2% alc, 5.4g/ℓ sugar making for elegantly easy drinking over the next few yrs.

★★★☆ **Buiten Blanc** Big-volume but decent-quality blend sauvignon (80%), chenin, riesling. Previewed **04** (likely ★★★) a touch drier & less charming than usual, with wet-wool note to tropical-fruited, well-balanced pleasantness. WO W-Cape.

★★★☆ **Gewürztraminer** 🆕 Bottled in tall Alsace-type *flûte*. Characteristic spicy, rose-petal fragrance, flavours on **03**, but more elegant than many, with serious but gently balanced palate. Unusually, 7 mths oak – this beautifully integrated. 13.2% alc; almost-dry 5.2g/ℓ sugar. Perfect partner for spicy food.

★★★☆ **Brut MCC** NV not tasted for this ed. Pvs pinot/chardonnay blend drily rich, with fragrant notes of brioche, spice. Characterful & lively. 11.5% alc.

★★★☆ **Natural Sweet** Softly balanced **00** from Dbnvlle sauvignon. Follow-up **02** from own riesling offers pineapple, honey, nuts & terpene notes in a fine balance that's lightly sweet, lovely to sip. 90g/ℓ sugar; 12% alc; unobtrusively wooded.

★★★★ **Rhine Riesling Noble Late Harvest** Beautiful pale gold **02** tasted last yr, with aromas of honey, pineapple, peach. Lightly, seductively delicious, with filigree acidity. Fermented, 6 mths in oak. Will develop complexity over half decade or so.

Pinot Noir No follow-up yet to earthy, chunkily acidic **01** (★★★). **Blanc de Noir** ★★★ The noirs in the dry, lightly strawberry-toned **03** being merlot, cab, cab f. Fragrant, flavoursome, fresh – & very appealing. – *TJ*

BunduStar see Vin-X-Port
Bushbuck Ridge see Long Mountain
Bushman's Creek see Kosie Möller Wines
Bush Vine see Cloof

Buthelezi Wines

Cape Town ▪ Est/1stB 2002 ▪ Closed to public ▪ Owner/winemaker Khulekani Laurence Buthelezi ▪ ±450 cs 100% red ▪ PO Box 12481 Mill Street Cape Town 8010 ▪ buthelezi@ winery.co.za ℂ 461·9590 📠 465·0342

Laurence Buthelezi's fascination with wine started in church. The magical transition from fresh grapes to the communion wine he sipped enthralled him. Many years later an opportunity to work with his brother Nelson, at Ashanti, allowed this quietly spoken, determined young man to unlock this childhood mystery. His mentor, Jean-Vincent Ridon of Signal Hill, where he now works as assistant winemaker, also encouraged LB to make his own wine. Eager to learn, his first working stint in Beaune was sponsored by SAWIT. He's about to return to Burgundy for a theory session at the Elsenburg equivalent, CFPPA, followed by a month of prac. 'My wine', he asserts, 'must reflect my identity.' His Tutuka Shiraz, with label featuring an Zulu warrior in full regalia, certainly does.

Tutuka Syrah ★★★ Individual & personality-packed; for adherents of aromatic, muscular shiraz; **02** gamey whiffs; dense, dark palate with powerful very dry finish. Yr Fr oak, 20% new. ± 14% alc. WO W-Cape. — *JB*

BWC Wines

*Paarl ▪ Est/1stB 1997 ▪ Tasting by appt ▪ Owners Cathy Marshall, Jeff Jolly, Greg Mitchell & Peter Oxenham ▪ Winemaker Cathy Marshall (1997) ▪ 25 tons ▪ 2 000 cs + 350 cs for Woolworths ▪ 85% red 15% fortified ▪ 18 Kiewiet Street Stellenbosch 7600 ▪ wine@barefoot.co.za ▪ www. bwcwines.co.za ⓒ/🖅 **887·9910***

Winemaker Cathy Marshall and her partners traditionally throw a harvest foot-stomp party, and 2004 was no exception. (Benignly) trampled underfoot was a quantity of sauvignon, the first white in this historically red-grape portfolio and a source of great delight to its creators. 'The wine is a treat. We may look at a wooded white soon.' Marshall needed all her winemaking skills to master a difficult harvest, especially pinot and sauvignon. In addition to her duties here, Marshall advises several Paarl and Franschhoek wineries. On a more philosophical note, she feels it's time for SA to look at its own strengths rather than borrowing too much from France, Australia or California. 'We need to come up with a truly SA focus. There is still too much fragmentation in our psyche that seriously needs to be addressed,' she asserts.

★★★★ **Syrah** (pvs Shiraz) Like pinot, **03** more elegant than pvs blockbuster, despite higher 14.5% alc. Liberal smoky meat, spice, red fruits concentration; malleable yet compact mouthfeel; full savoury length. Should grow, gain complexity to ±2009/11. Fr oak 11 mths. **02** dark, brooding; vibrant tannins. Needs & deserves time. 13. 7% alc. Same Paarl vyd as Ridgeback.

★★★★ **Pinot Noir** New fruit source, vintage conditions give delicate, multi-faceted **03**. Medium body, supple, lacy texture emphasise black cherry, underlying gamey charms; soupçon toasty oak too. Smoothly approachable, can develop to 2005/07. Vyds Stbosch, Elgin, Darling. 13% alc. **02** (ex-Stbosch) bigger, denser; also gorgeous fragrance, mouthfeel. 11 mths Burgundy casks.

★★★★ **Sauvignon Blanc** 🆕 ✓ **04** fulsome first-timer. Eager, outgoing tropical, figgy nose; fruit anchored by broad, leesy weight; good presence, ripe persistence. Grapes organically grown (though not certified so), from Reyneke, Stbosch.

Myriad ★★★ Part-fermented, brandy-fortified pinot/merlot, handmade (& 60 pairs feet!). **02** less difficult to drink than categorise. Sweet plum pudding nose, flavours, gentle glow in tail. Discontinued: **Farrago**. — *AL*

Cabrière Estate

*Franschhoek ▪ Est 1982 ▪ 1stB 1984 ▪ Tasting Mon-Fri 9-4 Sun 12-4 (high season only) ▪ Conducted tastings Mon-Fri 11 & 3 ▪ Fee R25/30 ▪ Achim vA's Sat tasting/tour 11 ▪ Tours Sat 11 only; group tours Mon-Fri by appt ▪ Sales Mon-Fri 9-5 Sat 10.30-2 ▪ Closed Easter Fri/Mon, Dec 25 & Jan 1; phone ahead on other public holidays ▪ Haute Cabrière Cellar Restaurant (see Eat-out section) ▪ Tourgroups ▪ Conferencing for groups of fewer than 60 ▪ Owner Clos Cabrière ▪ Winegrower Achim von Arnim (1984) ▪ Viticulturist Sakkie Lourens (May 2002) ▪ 25 ha (pinot, chardonnay) ▪ 40 000 cs 12% red 40% white 48% MCC ▪ PO Box 245 Franschhoek 7690 ▪ cabriere@iafrica.com ▪ www.cabriere.co.za ⓒ **876·2630** 🖅 876·3390*

This estate's slogan — Sun, Soil, Vine, Man — sounds like a mantra, and it is. The former are supplied by the Franschhoek Valley; 'Man' is the inimitable Achim von Arnim, who recognised the valley's potential for MCC sparkling wines (though some would say this has as much to do with his character as that of the valley). He was the first local winemaker to produce a sparkling wine in the traditional method (while at Boschendal in the 1980s), and the first to produce a non-sparkling chardonnay/pinot blend, still a top-seller. After a dry winter, the challenge last year was to monitor vineyards individually for signs of moisture stress while managing a cellar extension. That done, AvA now has the space to extend the bottle-maturation of his bubblies, particularly the Cuvée Reserve, which requires a full 60 months; also new are an auditorium and tasting facilities.

Arnim Sauvignon Rouge ☺ ★★★ Cheeky NV blend unoaked cab & sauvignon blanc (60/40) ex-Bonnievale. Moderate 13% alc, cherry nose, hints of earth, rounded finish.

Haute Cabrière range

★★★★ **Pinot Noir** Made from Burgundian clones, densely planted, gently handled, ±10 mths Fr oaked. **02** generous cherry/clove nose; juicy but fairly aggressive palate, possibly from 35% new wood. Adventurous gourmands may have paired pvs releases with yellowtail, but this will overpower all but oxtail, avers AvA. 14% alc. In spite of its power, less demanding than tannic, austere **01**.

★★★☆ **Chardonnay-Pinot Noir** Innovative blend from juice not used for the bubblies. Well-rounded food-friendly white; **04** (51/49 blend) with citrus zest aromas, dash sugar (6g/ℓ) extends & fills out the palate. Easy 12.5% alc. Bunch-pressed & unoaked.

Pierre Jourdan range

Mostly traditionally made MCCs from chardonnay and/or pinot, named for estate's French Huguenot founder. NV unless noted; alcs ±12%.

★★★★ **Cuvée Reserve** Estate's priciest, now that 'Aurum' version, flecked with 24-carat gold, sold out. Latest from 98 vintage; apple compôte & honey aromas; mellow palate refreshed by limey acidity & excellent mousse. 60/40 chardonnay, pinot from first fraction (500ℓ) of press juice. Unoaked; richness, complexity from 5 yrs+ on lees (disgorged on demand). Only from cellar or in the restaurant.

★★★★ **Cuvée Belle Rose** Latest salmon-pink blush proffers persistent mousse, damp-forest floor notes brightened by lively strawberry fruit. Cleansing acidity, dry finish despite 6g/ℓ sugar. Has structure & depth for cellaring. From pinot, unoaked & bunch-pressed, ex-estate & Frhoek Valley. Vintage 02.

★★★★ **Blanc de Blancs** Sea-breeze aromas & racy acidity in the latest release; delicate smokiness imparted by partial wooding of the base wine (5-6 mths Fr barrels), complemented by creaminess from bottle-age 3 yrs sur lie. 5g/ℓ sugar. Will gain richness with cellaring. Bunch-pressed chardonnay, grown in soils consistently producing best fruit for MCC, says AvA.

★★★☆ **Brut** ★★★☆ ✓ Estate's best seller, marketed in three bottle sizes. Peach & apple tones; sleek, lingering finish; decidedly brut at mere 4.5g/ℓ sugar. Bunch-pressed chardonnay/pinot, 60/40 blend, fruit ex-estate & Frhoek.

★★★☆ **Brut Sauvage** A 'savagely' dry wine, rather unnerving for those used to background bubblies. Same blend as Brut but longer bottle-aged (36 mths) & close as possible to zero residual sugar for 'oyster dry' palate.

★★★★ **Ratafia** Jerepigo-style aperitif from Frhoek fruit, fortified with estate's brandy to 20% alc. Teasing sweetness (115g/ℓ sugar) lifted by warming spirit. AvA suggests foie gras as accompaniment.

Tranquille ★★★ Only non-sparkler in range. Delicate blush hues, lush texture with mineral thread will handle full-flavoured foods. From bunch-pressed pinot, chardonnay (55/45), some *première taille* juice (from near end of pressing time) added for intensity. Light 11.5% alc. — *CvZ*

Calitzdorp Cellar

Calitzdorp (see Little Karoo map) ▪ Est 1928 ▪ 1stB 1977 ▪ Tasting & sales Mon-Fri 8-1; 2-5 Sat 8-12 ▪ Closed Easter Fri & Dec 25 ▪ Tours by appt ▪ Tourgroups ▪ BYO picnic ▪ Farm produce ▪ Owners 60 members ▪ Winemaker Alwyn Burger (Nov 1990) ▪ Viti consultant Willem Botha ▪ 160 ha (13 varieties, r/w) ▪ 3 000 cs 60% red 30% white ▪ PO Box 193 Calitzdorp 6660 ⓒ/🖷 **(044) 213·3301**

A favourite port of call during the Calitzdorp Festival, when flocks of visitors (almost as numerous as the ostriches that provide another tourist attraction) come to sample and buy and jollify. Just 3 000 cases go under the co-operative's own-label, a tiny proportion compared with the 2.4 million litres made for clients. The range, not tasted for this edition, has included Merlot, Blanc de Noir, Chardonnay, Chenin Blanc, Natural Sweet, Golden Jerepigo, White Muscadel and a trio of ports: Vintage, LBV and Ruby.

Camberley Wines

Stellenbosch ▪ Est 1990 ▪ 1stB 1996 ▪ Tasting & sales Mon-Sat 9-5 Sun & public holidays by appt ▪ Fee R5 ▪ Closed Dec 25 & Jan 1 ▪ Tours by appt ▪ B&B guest cottage ▪ Owners John & Gaël Nel ▪ Winemaker John Nel, with Grant Baxter ▪ 7 ha (cabs s/f, merlot, shiraz) ▪ ±35 tons 2 500 cs 100% red ▪ PO Box 6120 Uniedal 7612 ▪ john@camberley.co.za ▪ www.camberley. co.za ⓒ/▤ 885-1176

'A bit of a boring year, I'm afraid,' says 'owner, chief cook and bottle-washer' Johnny Nel apologetically. Not true – first of all, wife Gaël is the chief cook (gourmet class, in fact), and secondly, things have been happening on the Nels' 7ha patch of Helshoogte Pass. Midway through 2004 Grant Baxter came to Camberley from Avontuur's salesroom as GM and aspirant viticulturist. A new sorting table was moved into the production line, and in the vineyards there was a planting of 600 petit verdot vines. Looking abroad, the Nels record 'brilliant' growth of their German and Swiss markets; Japan, mainland China and Hong Kong, they believe, are the areas they should tackle for future growth.

★★★★ **Cabernet Sauvignon-Merlot** Great charm & elegance, sweet red fruit supported by fine, firm tannin, savoury acidity. Well oaked (±14 mths Fr/Russian/Am, much new). **02** impressive complexity, cigarbox, roasted fennel, dark fruit, all married to ripe tannins. Silky, accessible, although easy 5+ yrs still. 71/39 blend. 13.5% alc. Also in 500ml. Retasted **01** (★★★★★) has flavour complexity – violets, Parma ham savouriness interplay with fruit – & thoroughbred lines, excellent balance.

★★★★★ **Shiraz** Latest **03** classically styled, with elegance & verve. Herbaceous, minty tones, merest savoury hint, in juicy, wild-berry fruit. Expensive oaking contributes vanilla, sweet spice, amenable tannins, & subtle strength, framework for long, gentle development. One to watch, still has plenty to give. 14 mths Fr/Am oak, 80/20. 40% new. 14.3% alc. Big, complex **02** also for 5-8 yrs development.

★★★★★ **Philosopher's Stone** NEW The mythical stone that could change base metals – shiraz (75%) & merlot – into gold. Or at least powerful, impressive wine! Shiraz at centre with savoury spectrum: white pepper, underbrush, dark fruit; succulence, creamy richness from merlot. Resist 6+ yrs. 22 mths 2nd fill Fr. 14.4% alc.

★★★★ **Merlot** No **03**: all went to blends. **02** was well built, soft & mellow, with supple grip from seasoned oak (14 mths). 14.2% alc. Unfined/unfiltered.

★★★★ **Cabernet Franc-Merlot** NEW **02** 80/20 blend with raspberries, green walnuts, touch mint, dusted with cedar. Lithe, supple tannins; pervading minerality on palate, finish. Now & for 4+ yrs. 14 mths mainly Fr oak, 25% new. 14.9% alc.

★★★★★ **Pinotage 03** Impresses, from inky colour to sweeping mulberry, black plums, & firm ripe tannins. Structure, fruit concentration copes with whopping 15.5% alc. Hungarian/Am/Fr oak, 75% new. Infanticide now – keep 10+yrs. No **02** to let vines recover from fire damage. – *CR*

Cameradi Wines

Wellington ▪ Est 1998 ▪ 1stB 2000 ▪ Closed to public ▪ Owners Stelvest cc (Pieter Laubscher, Niel Smith, Nic Swingler, Hendrik du Preez & Casper Lategan) ▪ Winemaker Casper Lategan (Jan 1999) ▪ 8 tons 600 cs 100% red ▪ 48 Bain Str Wellington 7655 ▪ lsw@iafrica.com ⓒ 873·1225/082·323·2244 ▤ 873·4910

This comradely wine venture, started by five former university pals, continues hand-crafting very small quantities of reds. They did not bottle any of their 2002 production, but are back in business with the 2003 vintage, of which only 260 cases were made. The wine-mates declare themselves 'very satisfied' with the results.

Cabernet Sauvignon ★★★ Strapping **03** with, mid-2004, daunting tannins & oak fla-vours which dominate pungent green pepper/mulberry fruit. Needs 2+ yrs. **Shiraz** ★★★ **03** impenetrably dark & deep; packed with black pepper, fennel & lily aromas, vanilla fla-vours; tarry oak finish. Allow time (±3 yrs) for integration, rounding out. Samples tasted, ratings provisional. — *CvZ*

Capaia Wines

*Tygerberg ▪ Est 1997 ▪ 1stB 2003 ▪ Visits by appt ▪ Owners Alexander & Ingrid von Essen, Tibor Gál ▪ Winemaker Tibor Gál ▪ Viticulturist Mattie Bothma (Jan 2004) ▪ 55 ha (cabs s/f, merlot, petit v, sauvignon) ▪ 90 tons 4 000 cs 90% red 10% white ▪ PO Box 25 Philadelphia 7304 ▪ info@capaia.co.za ▪ www.capaia.co.za © **972·1081** 🖷 972·1894*

Herewith the first releases from an extraordinary winery in the new Philadelphia appella-tion: Capaia ('Cape' + 'aia', meaning 'a lot of'). The players: top German wine merchant Baron Alexander von Essen; his architect wife Ingrid; Hungarian oenologist Tibor Gál (maker of the famed super-Tuscan, Ornellaia; his son, incidentally, begins oenological studies in Stellenbosch this year); Kiwi soil specialist Daniel Schuster; Italian wine family scion Lodovico Antinori; local eminence Jan Coetzee, of Paradyskloof; winemaker-in-resi-dence Tertius Naudé (ex-Neil Ellis); agronomist Mattie Bothma (tending 1 200 Morgenster-sourced olive trees); and an ingenious cellar featuring a 'ski lift' for pam-pered grapes and one of the world's largest arrays of oak fermenters. How this multi-national collage fits together is best explained by the voluble and charming Baron von A himself. Suffice to say Capaia is the flagship, Blue Grove Hill the earlier-drinking range and the winery, dramatically perched on a hill, is a must-see.

★★★★★ **Capaia** Dark-fruited, sombrely handsome & suave **03** still very young, evidencing 16 mths new Fr oak (after fermentation in big wooden casks), but ripe, concen-trated flavours are lurking. Supple & beautifully structured, fine acidity, meltingly smooth tannins. Massive 14.5% alc not immediately obvious. Deserves min 5 yrs unbroached. (Is this, incidentally, the Cape's heaviest, most wrist-breaking bottle?)

Blue Grove Hill range

★★★★ **Cabernet Sauvignon-Merlot** Ripe, cheerful aromas lead to solidly textured but subtly formed palate on **03**, with savoury-sweet fruit, & finish warmed by 14.5% alc. Well integrated 9 mths new/2nd fill Fr oak.

Sauvignon Blanc ★★★ **03** blends Stbosch/Dbnvlle grapes, clearly picked early to give lightly elegant (12% alc) acid-drop crispness, with notably green but not too aggressive flavours. Half fermented in large wood casks, half in steel. — *TJ*

Cape Africa see Cape First

Cape Bay

Established range of easy drinkers from Newton Johnson now joined by a slightly more upmarket pair. Lack of pretension remains the hallmark though — these are made to drink.

Admiralty House range

Cabernet Sauvignon-Shiraz ★★★★ Aromatic **02** has roast meat, plums & pepper in bouquet, mocha on palate; at 14.5% alc, full bodied but retains some elegance. **Sauvi-gnon Blanc** ★★★ More refined & minerally than version below, more 'European'; **04** includes dash semillon for body/complexity; zinging grapefruit acidity through to finish.

Cabernet Sauvignon-Merlot ☺ ★★★ Miniature Bdx blend, complete with splash petit v, ready for any eventuality; **04** blackcurrant whiffs with fennel; tangy/zesty mouthful, good food-partner. **Pinotage** ☺ ★★★ Plump & sleek **04** with textbook mulberry whiffs & more offbeat tarry touch; bright & softly fruity. **Mellow Red** ☺ ★★★ Quaffably smooth cinsaut-led blend, unwooded, good solo or with food; **04** dusty dried-cherry aromas; slightly savoury flavours. **Chardonnay** ☺ ★★★ **04** unwooded for fruity pleasure; creamy sweet melon aromas, lively ripe apple flavours. **Chenin Blanc** ☺ ★★★ **04** has dusty pear-drops on nose, supple, gently dry, slips down easily. **Sauvignon Blanc** ☺ ★★★ Delicious anytime dry white; **04** contrasting capsicum & sweet-fruit aromas, firm, light bodied but flavourful.

Bouquet Blanc ★★ Fleeting whiffs honeysuckle, crushed nettle & dried herbs in **04**; soft, lightish, juicy off-dry white from mainly colombard & two muscats. — *TM*

Cape Boar see Doolhof Estate

Cape Chamonix

Franschhoek ▪ *Est 1991* ▪ *1stB 1992* ▪ *Tasting & sales daily 9.30–4* ▪ *Fee R10* ▪ *La Maison de Chamonix Restaurant* ▪ *Fully equipped self-catering cottages* ▪ *Tours by appt* ▪ *Gifts* ▪ *Tourgroups by appt* ▪ *Farm-distilled schnapps & spring water* ▪ *Owners Chris & Sonja Hellinger* ▪ *Winemaker Gottfried Mocke (Sep 2001), with Inus van der Westhuizen (Jan 2002)* ▪ *Viticulturist Rodney Kitching, with Gottfried Mocke* ▪ *50 ha (cabs s/f, merlot, pinot, chard, chenin, sauvignon)* ▪ *200 tons 15 000 cs 60% red 36% white 4% MCC* ▪ *PO Box 28 Franschhoek 7690* ▪ *marketing@chamonix.co.za office@chamonix.co.za* ▪ *www. chamonix.co.za* ℂ **876-2494** 🖷 *876·3237*

'An exciting vintage,' enthuses winemaker Gottfried Mocke. 'The wines will definitely be elegant but complex.' His oh-so-elegant Chardonnay Reserve continues on its award-winning way, with a gold for the 02 at the Chardonnay-du-Monde competition. International acclaim, too, for the Pinot 01, also considered a golden wine by judges of the Mondial du Pinot Noir staged in Switzerland. Traditional methods rule here – no irrigation or acidification and native-yeast ferments for some wines. And conversion to organic is proceeding – organic fertiliser is de rigeur and herbicides are on their way out.

★★★★ **Pinot Noir** Traditional open-topped barrel fermentation/finishing, 16 mths oak, 50% new Fr. **02** attractive meaty aromas, generous gamey flavours with austere mineral edge, chalk-textured finish. **01** also savoury, with hints cherry-stone & forest floor flavours. Still youthful, should gain complexity with time.

★★★★ **Chardonnay Reserve** Winery's cellarworthy flagship, internationally applauded. New-oak fermentation/ageing, malo, impart rich, slightly minerally oatmeal aromas to outstanding, beautifully polished **02** (★★★★★), citrus/tropical flavours; textured finish with seamless oak. **01** offered loads of buttery, caramel-toffee flavours, lime/grapefruit acidity & zest.

★★★★ **Chardonnay** Has ability to age with distinction. **02** should mature especially well: gently oaked to showcase impressive mineral nose; focused, chalky, chablis-style palate. **01** also less overtly oaky than pvs; firmly structured, with flavours of lime-crème brulée. ±13 mths Fr oak, ±80% new.

★★★★ **Méthode Cap Classique Brut** From chardonnay, 3 yrs on fine lees. **01** fresh citrus nose with creamy character; lovely yeasty persistence. Will evolve over several yrs, so worth stashing some away. **00** extra-brut with mere 5g/ℓ sugar; restrained, with rapier elegance on long finish.

★★★★ **Méthode Cap Classique Reserve** Occasional special release of the standard version, longer lees-aged. So far only **99**, with intense leesy/spicy tone.

★★★★ **Troika** Tightly-drawn claret style of this blend cabs s/f, merlot, unveiled with maiden **00** (★★★★). **01** needed time to integrate when previewed last yr. **02** (sample) has a serious, cool-climate feel, taut & restrained with great elegance.

Wood (24 mths Fr oak, 100% new) already harmonious, auguring well for development.

★★★★ **Sauvignon Blanc Reserve** Individual steely style, fermented/aged in seasoned oak; retains firm seam of acidity despite partial malo. **02** one of the best of this genre in Cape; **03** similarly intense, persistent; profusion of secondary flavours (savoury & tropical); racy mineral texture makes terrific food partner.

Chamonix Blanc ☺ ★★★ **04** blend chenin, semillon, sauvignon – dash chardonnay for body; 10% wooded. Unpretentious, bone dry & eminently quaffable.

Cabernet Sauvignon 99, **Merlot 01/02** and **Pinotage 02** not ready for tasting. **Rouge** ★★★ Juicy, light, food-friendly *vin de table*. NV mix of 01/02 cab, merlot, pinotage. **Sauvignon Blanc** ★★★★ **04** (sample) fresh whack of sauvignon on nose; well balanced palate with passionfruit flavour, crisp chalky texture. 3 mths on fine lees before bottling. **Blanc de Noir Natural Sweet** ★★★ Convivial tipple for those sweet of tooth. **04** pale salmon-pink hue, crushed strawberry whiffs, juicy finish; moderate 12% alc. – *RK*

Cape Circle see Vin-X-Port

Cape Classics

Stellenbosch ▪ Est 1991 ▪ 1stB 1995 ▪ Closed to public ▪ Owners Gary & André Shearer ▪ Winemaker Mzokhona Mvemve (Jan 2002), advised by Bruwer Raats ▪ 70 000 cs own label 45% red 55% white ▪ PO Box 5421 Cape Town 8000 ▪ info@capeclassics.com ▪ www.capeclassics.com ℃ 881·3810 ▤ 881·3814

There were ululations and celebrations when Cape Classics' Indaba brand turned 10 last year, alongside a nation rejoicing in a decade of democracy. An important part of the festivities was a refinement of the brand. This included a narrowing of the base of producers and grower-partners to a top-of-the-crop handful, and a new label design and packaging. Winemaker Mzokhona Mvemve, first recipient of the Indaba scholarship (2nd graduate Allison Adams currently broadening her horizons at Wines of South Africa's Stellenbosch offices), paid an inaugural visit to the US where he met some of CC's biggest clients. These include Cost Plus World Market (three Indaba selections are part of their national portfolio), the Darden restaurant group and Walt Disney World. Mvemve also met Mac McDonald of Vision Cellars, one of California's few African-American winemakers.

Indaba range

★★★★ **Shiraz** Still the standout; appealing & generous, varietally correct with smooth tannins. Pvs **02** had anise on nose, vanilla hint from Fr oak influence. **04** (★★★★) dusty brambly fruit, peppery hint; well-formed red berry/plum palate. 14.8% alc.

Merlot ★★★ Vibrant, plump **04**, mulberries & damp thatch, smoky note; juicy flavours, low tannins. **Pinotage** ★★★★ Ebullient **04** has typical pinotage estery mulberries on nose; supple & juicy fruit, slightly sweet tail. Fruit ex-Tlbgh. ±14% alc. **Chardonnay** ★★★ **04** inviting baked apple & custard notes; pump, soft melon palate, slightly sweet creamy exit. 14.3% alc. **Chenin Blanc** ★★★ **04** not oaked; waxy aromas; full, creamy, sweet-fruited palate. **Sauvignon Blanc** ★★★ Flinty, light, not unattractively austere **04**, notes of rhubarb & crushed nettles. Above mostly tasted as samples, ratings provisional; all WO W-Cape. – *TM*

Cape Coastal Wines see Cape Wine Cellars
Cape Fest see Oranjerivier

Cape First Wines

Stellenbosch ▪ Est 2003 ▪ 1stB 2004 ▪ Visits by appt ▪ Owners Cape Five Export, Barry Kok, Johan le Hanie & Christo Versfeld ▪ Winemakers Johan le Hanie & Christo Versfeld (both

2004) ▪ *30 000 cs own label* ▪ *40% red 60% white* ▪ *PO Box 3294 Somerset West 7129* ▪
barrykok@capefive.com ▪ *www.capefirstwines.co.za* © *850·4640* 🖷 *852·8862*

The company name might be unfamiliar, but chances are you know at least two of the
personalities here through the wines they've made for top SA cellars: Christo Versfeld
and Johan le Hanie, both widely experienced, and now in a partnership with leading
SA fruit exporter, Cape Five Export, and co-shareholder Barry Kok. Drawing on their wine
know-how, they're creating 'a balanced portfolio of wines' (both high-volume and boutique) to market locally and overseas, using CFE's reach and muscle. Cellar space is
leased from Blue Creek, though an in-house facility is already on the drawing board.
They've found a ready market in China, and are exploring several other avenues, including
Russia and India. A tasting room has been opened at their premises in Somerset West,
and they welcome visitors by appointment.

Makana range

Pinot Noir ★★ Chunky **03** from Rbtsn fruit. Earthy notes, with black cherry, rhubarb, &
mineral finish. 9 mths Fr oak (40% new). 14% alc. WO W-Cape. **Cabernet Sauvignon-
Merlot-Cabernet Franc** ★☆ Herbaceous, red berry fruit hints on **03** 60/20/20 blend, followed by mouth-puckering tannins, austere finish. From Stbosch. **Chardonnay** ★★★☆ Elegantly unshowy **04** barrel sample (so rating provisional) with tropical aromas,
grapefruit/lime flavours, creamy texture from Fr oak (60% new); good length. 13.8% alc.
Frhoek grapes. **Sauvignon Blanc** ★★★ **04** tropical notes pineapple, passionfruit, leading
to honeysuckle mid-palate, sweetish finish (6.5g/ℓ sugar). Ex-Dbnvlle. Above WO
Coastal unless noted.

Three Anchor Bay range

Cabernet Sauvignon-Merlot ☺ ★★★ **04** sample promises attractive, fresh drinking,
with savoury berry notes & soft tannins. 14% alc hidden by abundant fruit. Light oaking.

Chenin Blanc-Chardonnay ★★★★ ✓ Lime & apricot aromas on delicious 60/40 blend
04, succulent, elegant flavours, crisply lingering finish. Moderate 12.8% adds to food-
friendly qualities. This, range below, WO W-Cape.

Hill Station range

Shiraz-Pinotage ☺ ★★★ **03** spicy, brambly whiffs, sumptuous texture, revealing
pinotage most at end with a varnishy note. Tannins softened by slight sweetness (6g/ℓ
sugar). Oaked with staves in tank.

Chenin Blanc-Chardonnay ★★★★ ✓ **04** Blend as above. Similar lime-honeysuckle aromas, crisp elegant palate, persistent finish. — *MF*

Cape Grace

Stellenbosch ▪ *Est/1stB 2004* ▪ *Closed to public* ▪ *Owners Thierry's Wine Services & African Pride Wines* ▪ *Vini consultant Mike Graham* ▪ *100 000 cs + 50 000 for clients, incl
Somerfield (UK)* ▪ *50% red 45% white* ▪ *PO Box 1376 Stellenbosch 7599* ▪ *info@
capegracewines.co.za* ▪ *www.capegracewines.co.za* ©/🖷 *855·5639*

Listings with retailing heavyweights ASDA, Waitrose and Tesco a mere six months after
start-up at the end of 2003 have convinced the owners of this easy-drinking range —
Thierry's Wine Services, represented here by Lucy Warner, and African Pride Wines, part-
owned by experienced winemaker Mike Graham — that they're on the right track. Cape
Grace has been developed in response to growing demand for SA wines in the UK market
— continental Europe and the US will be targeted in due course. 'With the new vintage
coming on line we're looking forward to building on our success,' says Warner.

Most of these tasted as samples; ratings provisional. Unwooded, alcs 12–13.5% unless
noted. **Cabernet Franc** ★★★☆ Elegant; should develop nicely. **02** has notes of black plum

& dried leaves; firmish, concentrated; expensive whiffs of lead pencil, from maturation 16 mths in 2nd/3rd fill barrels. Stbosch grapes. **Merlot** ★★★★ ✓ Effortlessly drinkable **03**, ripe, plum jam whiffs; big, soft, jammy choc flavours, more sweetness in the slippery finish (3.5g/ℓ sugar). **Cabernet Sauvignon-Merlot** ★★★ Modern styling with complexity; **03** plump, juicy, supple, full-bodied; hints of stewed plums, earth & forest floors. **Pinotage-Shiraz** ★★★ **03** plum/mulberry notes, hint of latter grape's woodsmoke; sweetish plum-jam flavours – pinotage asserting itself on palate. **Chardonnay** ★★★ 10% new-oak-fermented shows subtly as hazelnut/butterscotch tint to **04**'s pear flavours. An easy drinker, should appeal widely. **Chardonnay-Semillon** ★★★ Varieties in equal measure impart vibrant & zesty mouthfeel in **04**, with delicate hints pear & quince. **Sauvignon Blanc-Chenin Blanc** ★★★☆ **04** sappy lemon-lime nose, hint marzipan; forthcoming; dry refreshing limy finish. 50/50 light-bodied blend. All WO W-Cape unless noted. — *TM*

Cape Grove see Origin Wine
Cape Haven see Pulpit Rock
Capell's Court see Linton Park
Cape Maclear see African Pride
Cape Mist see Thorntree
Cape Mouton see Mouton House of Wines

Capenheimer

SA's original perlé wine (launched 1962), based on the Italian Lambrusco style. Latest (NV) ★★ has fresh-cut pear aromas; frothy, light & gently sweet palate. By Distell. — *CR*

Cape One see Origin Wine
Cape Original see Origin Wine

Cape Point Vineyards

Cape Point ▪ Est 1996 ▪ 1stB 2000 ▪ Visits by appt ▪ Owner Sybrand van der Spuy ▪ Winemaker Duncan Savage (Dec 2002) ▪ Viti adviser Kevin Watt ▪ 32 ha (cab, pinot, shiraz, chard, sauvignon, semillon) ▪ 100 tons 7 000 cs 20% red 80% white ▪ PO Box 100 Noordhoek 7985 ▪ info@cape-point.com ▪ www.capepointvineyards.co.za © 785·7660 ▭ 785·7662

Previously a white-wine-only cellar, sea-fronting Cape Point can now boast a 20% red production (with 40% a long-term objective). The maiden reds were harvested from the Red Hill vineyard, on the border of the Cape Point Nature Reserve – that's living up to the name! 'It was a wonderful experience to ferment the first grapes from an area never before planted with vineyards,' exults Duncan Savage. On the white-wine front, he's looking forward to expand the range of styles of sauvignon from the terroir, which is well-suited for this cool-climate-favouring variety. A crush with celebrated French sauvignon exponent Didier Dagueneau, on the cards as the guide went to press, should give the talented young winemaker plenty of good (wild?) ideas. On a regretful note – ebullient viticulturist Rosa Kruger has left the team.

Isliedh ⬛ (Pronounced Islay, named for Sybrand vdS's granddaughter) **03** sauvignon, 75% fermented/matured older Fr oak. Unfinished sample firmly built, dry, will need beyond early-2005 release to open. Min ★★★★.

★★★★☆ **Chardonnay** Barrel-fermented/matured in well-structured style. No **02**; all diverted to Scarborough label. Pvs **01** was rich, concentrated. ±2 yrs potential.

★★★★★ **Sauvignon Blanc** ✓ Always intricate & polished. Duncan S's stylistic sights on slow-maturing Loire benchmarks. Long lees enrichment means late release. **03** suave, expressive yet unevolved flavours energised to remarkable length by fine, tense acid. Carries 14% alc with cool ease. Possible peak 2006/07. **04** (sample) potentially most complex/long-lived yet; greater breadth, minerally concentration. All with dash barrel-fermented wine, 7-10% semillon for richness, structure.

★★★★ **Semillon** Distinctive yet unshowy; wild herb, cool citrus & honey mineral thumbprint at new levels of complexity in **03** (★★★★★), with 15% sauvignon. Sleek, compact; silky texture enriched by barely discernible 30% from barrel. Seductive now, potential to at least 2007. Balanced 13.5% alc. **02** charming if slighter, earlier peak.

★★★★ **Semillon Noble Late Harvest 01** With soupçons sauvignon, muscat, chardonnay, developing gorgeous marmalade bouquet, richly textured with mellow, slightly toasty tail. Verve for 2/3 yrs. 123g/ℓ sugar; fermented/aged yr new Fr oak.

Scarborough range

★★★☆ **Chardonnay** Attractive **02** benefits from portion of premium version. Expansive smoky, spice aromas; supple, fresh, elegantly Fr oaked, 40% new. 13% alc.

★★★☆ **Sauvignon Blanc** Approachable, distinctive **03**; rich, with contrasting pure, subtle flavours, pebbly minerality. Good 2 yrs to go. 14% alc. Sample **04** more concentrated. — *AL*

Cape Promise see International Wine Services
Cape Roan see Doolhof Estate
Cape Rock see Overhex
Cape Salute see Coppoolse Finlayson
Cape Table see Riebeek Cellars
Cape Tradition see Origin Wine
Cape View see Kaapzicht

Cape Vineyards

Rawsonville ▪ Est 1994 ▪ 1stB 1996 ▪ Closed to public ▪ Owners 7 shareholders ▪ 15 000 cs + 8.5m litres bulk ▪ 70% red 30% white ▪ Ranges for customers: Pearl Springs (UK/Japan); Andrew Bain Reserve, Jantara (both UK) ▪ ISO 9001/2000 certified ▪ PO Box 106 Rawsonville 6845 ▪ admin@cape-vineyards.com; vicgentis@cape-vineyards.com ▪ www. cape-vineyards.com © (023) 349·1585/1466 ⊠ (023) 349·1592

Export marketing arm of five co-operative wineries and two estates on the Breedekloof (Rawsonville) Wine Route, Cape Vineyards last year raised their glasses at the news they'd met the stringent requirements of the ISO 9001 quality management system. The formerly all-female team is now headed by Victor Gentis (Henriëtte Jacobs pursuing a business opportunity in Paarl), with Aussie Mark Nairn bringing his roving-winemaker touch to 'fingerprinting' the wines to customer specs. Previously from Stellenbosch and with 20 years in the wine industry, Gentis is positive about his leap of faith over the mountains, though one of the coolest growing seasons in 20 years saw the 2004 vintage starting a fortnight later than usual.

Andrew Bain Reserve range   [NEW]

For UK market. **Pinotage** ★★★ Open-textured **03** includes dollop ruby cab; juicy; slightly savoury dry tannins; Fr/Am oak chips supply toasty backdrop. **Chardonnay** ★★★ Vibrant & quaffable **04**, youthful citrus/melon tones enhanced by deft oaking; enjoy young.

Andrew Bain range

Cabernet Sauvignon-Merlot ★★★☆ **02** expansively fruited, sufficiently mellow to drink now; long finish augurs well for development over 2-3 yrs. 80/20 blend, Fr oak staved. 14. 3% alc. Following WO W-Cape: **Chardonnay** ★★★☆ Briefly oaked **02** has improved; well rounded, full flavoured, drinks easily. **Chenin Blanc** ★★★ **04** not ready for tasting. Second look at **02**, fresh & sprightly; bright acidity, touch complexity from bottle-age.

Jantara range

For UK market. **Shiraz** ★★★ Chunky **03** gets extra juice, flavour, from shot ruby cab; generous red berry palate, fairly big but gentle tannins. **Sauvignon Blanc** ★★★ Lightish **03** features conventional gooseberry/capsicum tones plus unusual peachy whiff (from dollop semillon?); bright, zesty finish.

Rawson's range

Pinotage ☺ ★★★ Unwooded for upfront fruitiness; **02** oozes ripe plums from balanced, full-bodied frame (note high alc:14.2%). Delightful drink. **Ruby Cabernet-Merlot** ☺ ★★★ 50/50 mix, briefly oaked; **02** plum & choc flavours with ruby cab's pleasant stalky edge, long sweet-fruited finish. Enjoy soon while at peak.

Shiraz ★★★☆ Unwooded **02** has variety's signature smokiness, smooth red berry palate with enough soft tannins to carrying few more yrs. 14.4% alc. **Chardonnay** ★★ Contains splash colombard in **03**, fetching tropical nose, palate well rounded if somewhat quick. All above WO Brde Rvr Vlly unless noted. — DH

Cape Wine Cellars

Wellington ▪ Est 1994 ▪ Closed to public ▪ Owners: see intro below ▪ Winemakers Jeff Wedgwood & Tinus Broodryk ▪ 250·000 cs 40% red 60% white ▪ Export brands: Boundary Valley, Morning Mist, Goede Kap & Grootgenoegen ▪ PO Box 386 Wellington 7654 ▪ strauss@lantic.net bromar@mweb.co.za ▪ www.capewinecellars.co.za ©️ 873·0230 🖷 873·6909

A joint venture in the Paarl-Wellington area, Cape Wine Cellars is now wholly owned by Cape Coastal Wines, formed in 2004 to sell SA wines abroad. Cape Coastal's initial target market is North America, and an office will be set up in the States this year. 'Once we know exactly which style of wines the market requires, the five cellars in the group (Wellington, Wamakersvlei, Bovlei, Riebeek and Boland) will be able to produce wines to meet those needs,' explains CCW chair Johann Pieterse. Meanwhile CWC's Kleinbosch brand, previously for export only, is now marketed locally, chiefly through supermarkets.

Kleinbosch range

Cabernet Sauvignon ★★★ **03** attractive warm-country jammy/meaty nose; dry savoury finish. Varietally true, well handled. Fr oak staves. **Merlot** ★★★ Powerful stewed plum & leather aromas in **03**; tight, grainy, sour-plum palate. ±14% alc. Unwooded, as is... **Pinotage** ★★★ **02** slightly meaty nose, quite lean & short, jammy. **Shiraz** ★★★ **02** fairly rich dark plum colour/aroma; deftly oaked to highlight c hunky choc/blackberry flavours. 14.4% alc. **Chardonnay** ★★★ Lemon cream biscuit aroma greets you in **03**, touch muscat; full bodied; creamy citrus finale. Fr oak staves. All WO W-Cape. — TM

Cape Winemakers Guild (CWG)

Chair: Christopher Keet ▪ General Manager: Kate Messina ©️ 883·8625 🖷 883·8626 ▪ info@capewinemakersguild.com ▪ www.capewinemakersguild.com

Independent, invitation-only association, founded in 1982 to promote winemaking excellence among its members. Since 1985, the CWG holds a highly-regarded annual public auction. The current members are: Beyers Truter, Beyerskloof; Marc Kent, Boekenhoutskloof; Carel Nel, Boplaas; Peter Finlayson, Bouchard Finlayson; Christopher Keet, Cordoba; David Trafford, De Trafford; Etienne le Riche, Etienne le Riche Wines; Bruce Jack, Flagstone Winery; David Finlayson, Glen Carlou; Jeremy Walker, Grangehurst; Charles Hopkins, Graham Beck Coastal; Pieter Ferreira, Graham Beck Robertson; Kevin Grant, Kevin Grant Wines; Carl Schultz, Hartenberg; Anton Bredell, JP Bredell Wines; Gary Jordan, Jordan Winery; Jean Daneel, Jean Daneel Wines; Danie Steytler, Kaapzicht; Francois Naudé, L'Avenir; Philip Costandius, Lourensford; Neil Ellis, Neil Ellis Wines; Braam van Velden, Overgaauw; Ross Gower, Ross Gower Wines; Teddy Hall, Rudera; Louis Strydom, Rust en Vrede; Johan Malan, Simonsig; Abrie Bruwer, Springfield; Gyles Webb, Thelema; André van Rensburg, Vergelegen; Jeff Grier, Villiera; Nicky Versfeld, Vinfruco; Jan Coetzee, Vriesenhof; Norma Ratcliffe, Warwick; Kevin Arnold, Waterford.

Cardouw see Citrusdal Cellars

Carisbrooke Wines

Stellenbosch ▪ Est 1989 ▪ 1stB 1996 ▪ Tasting & sales Mon-Fri 9.30-2 (all day & Sat 9-12 during Dec/Jan) ▪ Closed Easter Fri-Mon, Dec 24/25 & Jan 1 ▪ Owner/winemaker Willem Pretorius ▪ Viti/vini consultant Kowie du Toit (Jan 1997) ▪ 6 ha (cab, shiraz) ▪ 40 tons 1 500 cs own label 100% red ▪ PO Box 25 Vlottenburg 7604 ▪ wjpret@mweb.co.za ©/☏ 881·3798

New on this pretty Stellenboschkloof farm is a small conference facility which can accommodate up to 20 delegates. There's nothing new, however, when it comes to Willem Pretorius's philosophy. He believes the farm workers should share in the income from certain areas of the property, in the form of a bonus equal to 70% of their annual salary. His Cab 00, well-starred last year, is now on sale at the farm's recently-inaugurated tasting room.

★★★★☆ **Cabernet Sauvignon** Modern but classically inclined cab. We last tasted the **00**, well-padded with sweet, soft fruit, elegantly oaked. Also previewed **01** & noted it as promising. From own single vyd. ±13% alc.

'Red Blend' NEW Yet to be named seamless union of cab (80%) shiraz, dollop merlot; barrelled 2 yrs. Preview **01** impresses: lovely spicy blackcurrant aromas, very ripe fruit, New-World ambience with restraint (moderate 13.5% alc). Probable ★★★★. — *TM*

Carl Everson see Opstal

Carneby Liggle

Export brand made under auspices of Siyabonga's Graham Knox, now discontinued.

Carnival

The Spar chain of convenience stores' boxed wines, available in 1/5ℓ packs. See also Country Cellars and Spar.

Classic Red ☺ ★★ Lightish fruit-juicy crowd pleaser from ruby cab & pinotage. Lightly chill in summer. **Grand Cru** ☺ ★★★ No-frills easy drinker from chenin; smoothly dry & surprisingly flavoursome.

Rosé ★ Blush-coloured, barely vinous semi-sweet from chenin, coloured by pinotage. 7.5% alc. **Stein** ★★ Unpretentious semi-sweet with guava & tropical fruit tones, from colombard & chenin. **Late Harvest** ★★ Similar to Stein, but fuller, sweeter, honeyed. From chenin. All above NV; around alc 12.5% unless noted. — *DH*

Casa do Mar see Ruitersvlei
Casa Portuguesa see Paarl Wine
Cathedral Cellar see KWV International

Cederberg Private Cellar

Cederberg (see Olifants River map) ▪ Est/1stB 1977 ▪ Tasting, sales & tours Mon-Sat 8-12.30; 2-5 Public holidays 9-12;4-6 ▪ Fee R10 ▪ Closed Easter Fri/Sun/Mon & Dec 16/25 ▪ BYO picnic ▪ Fully equipped self-catering cottages ▪ Walks/hikes ▪ Mountain biking ▪ Owners Nieuwoudt family ▪ Winemaker David Nieuwoudt, with Jan Taylor (1997/1998) ▪ Viticulturist Ernst Nieuwoudt ▪ 52 ha (cab, shiraz, chenin, sauvignon) ▪ 12 000 cs 60% red 40% white ▪ PO Box 84 Clanwilliam 8135 ▪ info@cederbergwine.com ▪ www.cederbergwine.com © (027) 482·2827 ☏ (027) 482·1188

Asked about his winemaking philosophy, David Nieuwoud is disarmingly dismissive: 'To produce wine in such an incredible environment you don't need a philosophy. I just love what I do.' At more than 1 000m above sea level, in a valley in the spectacularly rugged Cederberg mountain wilderness area between Citrusdal and Clanwilliam, his vineyards are some of the highest and most picturesque in the Cape. The cooler climate and rocky soils appear ideal for late-ripening varieties. Last year he decided to focus on grapes most suited to these conditions, planting another 10ha of chenin, sauvignon and shiraz, and simultaneously increasing his red wine processing capacity to 100 tons. A good thing too, for what the modest winemaker doesn't mention is the acclaim heaped on his 02 Shiraz. If, as Nieuwoud says, he's 'still trying to figure out how to make shiraz', the future looks promising indeed.

★★★★☆ **V Generations** Stylish commemoration of Nieuwoudt family's tenancy of this high-flying wilderness area. Cab from 20 yr old vyd. **01** (not re-tasted) subtler, more mulberry-spicy fruit & less bold than **00** FCTWS gold, *Wine* ★★★★. Both with intriguing marzipan/nutty scents; solid tannins. New oak 14 mths. No **02**.

★★★★ **Cabernet Sauvignon** Classy, modern; great fruit purity, confidently firm with plenty ripe give. **03** focused cassis, black berry freshness, appropriate cedary spice whiffs; sleek, though youthfully edgy, tight. Needs yr to settle/fill out; potential ±2009–11. **02** full & showy. 14 mths Fr oak, 60% new; malo in barrel; 14% alc.

★★★★ **Shiraz 02** only second vintage from this single, young vyd wowed judges on FCTWS (Shiraz, Best Red trophies) & Shiraz Challenge (★★★★★). Rich, elegant; more toffee, sweet supple fruit than classic shiraz pepperiness. **03** just post-bottling needs to settle, fill out; indicates similar fruit/oak elegance; fine red fruit/lilies top notes, richer base incorporating toasty-meaty effects from portion completing malo in barrel; supple tannins. 14 mths, 70/30 Fr/Am oak, 60% new. ± 14.5% alc.

★★★★ **Sauvignon Blanc** Bracing varietal clarity (minerals, flint, figs) on **04** characterises these high-altitude sauvignons. Vigorously fresh; rich mouthfeel, powerful length, benefits of ripe fruit intensity rather than high alc (this a moderate 13%).

★★★★ **V Generations Chenin Blanc** White flagship from low-yielding vyd well into second decade. **02** intense peach, flower, blossom scents with oak-spice aromas in youth; rich oak/fruit mix on palate, fresh acid in finish. **03** sample similar; great balance/contrast fruit richness with clean, savoury acid. Needs yr/2 to harmonise, reveal more detailed complexity. Fr barrel-fermented/matured 10 mths, half new.

Cederberger ☺ ★★★ Superior red *vin ordinaire*; **03** bright, juicy blend, merlot, pinotage, ruby cab focused by rounded tannin; light oaking extra interest. **Chenin Blanc Unwooded** ☺ ★★★ Straight chenin at its youthful, fruity best. **04** varietal delicacy set off by bright, juicy acids, clean up-beat finish. **03** VDG. **Bukettraube** ☺ ★★★ Semi-sweet — but more peppery, muscat piquancy than sweetness. **04** great balance; enough unshowy poise to partner lightly spiced dishes or as aperitif. 13.5% alc.

Discontinued: **Pinotage** (now channelled into Cederberger); **Chardonnay**; **Chenin Blanc Barrel Fermented**. —*AL*

Cellar Hand see Cloof

Cellar Cask

Well-established budget range; first in SA, in 1979, with a bag-in-box. Soft, light (±11.5% alc) fruitiness are keynotes. All NV, by Distell.

Select Johannisberger Red ★★ Fresh-tasting & juicy Natural Sweet (48g/ℓ sugar) with maraschino cherry tones. **Select Johannisberger Rosé** ★★ Fruit pastille bouquet, fairly full body if slightly cloying, whereas ... **Johannisberger Select White** ★★★ Has vibrancy as well as flavour & some girth; Natural Sweet-style easy-drinker with melon whiffs. Above in 750ml screwcaps; following in 5/2ℓ packs: **Premier Claret** ★★ Rustic four-way blend; plum/prune aromas & earthy, dry, slightly minerally palate. **Premier Grand Cru** ★★ No-frills glugger from chenin, colombard (50/50); lemon-drop freshness & austerity in line with style. **Premier Semi-Sweet** ★★ Fresh-smelling nose of hay & apple; soft, accessible; tastes off-dry rather than semi-sweet. Varieties as for PGC. **Premier Late Harvest** ★★ Sweeter version of Semi-Sweet; latest boxing has glacé pineapple & pear on nose/palate, appealing fruity freshness. All WO W-Cape. —*CR*

Cellar Door see Villiera
Cellar Selection see Kleine Zalze

Cellar-Vie Wines `NEW`

Est/1stB 2004 ▪ Closed to public ▪ Owners Hendri Nagel, Adam Simcock & Karl Watkin ▪ Vini consultant Bartho Eksteen ▪ 245 cs 100% red ▪ PO Box 10136 Edleen 1625 ▪ hermit-age@absamail.co.za © 083·713·9256 ≞ (011) 975·4482

Frequent flier Hendri Nagel, a partner in this new negociant company, began his journey into wine in the 1980s, when fellow SAA crew member Mike Selborne, who'd studied viticulture at Elsenburg, started taking him to wine farms. Still hugely passionate, Gauteng-based Nagel doesn't let remoteness from the winelands get in his way. With help from wine mate Paul Benadé, former owner of Lievland, he's made and marketed a Chardonnay and a Syrah. Now, with British investors Adam Simcock and Karl Watkin, he's enlisted Hermanus winemaker Bartho Eksteen to vinify a red blend to their specs. (Artwork on the front label by wildlife artist Keith Joubert.) In another role – selecting judges for the SAA tasting panel each year – Nagel rubs shoulders with some of the world's top winemakers, including John Duval, one-time crafter of the fabled Grange.

Commitment ★★★★ Bordeaux-style red led by cab (54%), plus four other grapes; **03** dense, dark hues; rich summer pudding nose with spicy wood; mouthfilling ripe red fruit flavours; nicely integrated; long & juicy finish. Sample tasted. 15 mths Fr oak, small portion new. – *JB*

▪ *Chacma's Bark* see African Pride
Chamonix see Cape Chamonix
Chapmans Chance see Kosie Möller Wines
Chapman's Peak see Cape Classics

Chateau Libertas

Admirably consistent & affordable cab-dominated (60%) red, celebrating 60 consecutive vintages with latest **02** ★★★; sloshes cinsaut, merlot, shiraz (20/15/5), partly oak-staved; alc 13.6%. Has a European feel; plums & minerals on nose; firm, markedly dry & food friendly; aromatic fynbos farewell. WO Coastal. By Distell. – *CR*

▪ *Chiwara* see Daschbosch

Christo Wiese Portfolio

Owner Christo Wiese ▪ Winemakers Wynand Hamman (Lanzerac) & Philip Costandius (Lourensford) ▪ Contact Marius Burger/Mark Lester ▪ PO Box 16 Somerset West 7129 ▪ cwp@lourensford.co.za © 847·1661 ≞ 847·0894

This is the umbrella for big-businessman Christo Wiese's extensive wine interests, which include Stellenbosch farms Lanzerac and Lourensford, and branded ranges Five Heirs and Eden Crest, all now listed separately.

▪ *Churchaven* see The Winery

Cilandia `NEW`

Robertson ▪ Est 2002 ▪ 1stB 2003 ▪ Visits by appt ▪ Owners AA Cilliers Jnr & AA Cilliers ▪ Winemaker Albie Cilliers ▪ Viticulturist Abraham Cilliers ▪ 60 ha (cab, cinsaut, pinotage, roobernet, shiraz, chard, chenin) ▪ 700 tons 1 200 cs own label 100% red ▪ PO Box 504 Robertson 6705 ▪ Cilandia@telkomsa.net ©/≞ (023) 626·5209

So the wheel turns: from grandfather Abraham Albertus Cilliers, who made his own wine in Eilandia farm's old cellar, to father AA 'Boetie' Cilliers who joined a co-op as a grape supplier, to third-generation AA 'Albie' Cilliers, intent on restoring winemaking pride to the family spread. Sister Nadia, a Stellenbosch University oenology graduate with seasonings in the US, Australia and locally at Hartenberg and Hamilton Russell, waits in the wings. Her brother hopes to entice her home with a new cellar – Cilandia's maiden Shiraz and Cab were vinified elsewhere. A venerable 1963 block of pinotage promises future excitement. Cilandia, the own-label, comes from selected fruit off 60 hectares — the rest is sold. Cilliers shares a passion for shiraz with Hartenberg's Carl Schultz, whom he lauds for his 'discipline, dedication and honest opinions'. So the wheel will turn.... perhaps to Albie's son, the fourth-generation 'AA'.

Cabernet Sauvignon ★★★☆ Sample **02**, pleasingly, subtly structured; cloaked in stylish dark cassis-scented fruit, similarly fresh acid, tannins carefully managed to ensure early-ish drinkability, say 2 yrs. Will easily hold for 4–5. Yr Fr/Am oak, 50% new. 14.3% alc. **Shiraz ★★★★** Maiden **02** equally impressive; whiffs of dark choc, prune & leather; richly endowed, ripe tannins & some noticeable acid all add up to lengthy life ahead. Promising debut, especially given lacklustre 02 vintage. 14.4% alc. Yr oak, all Fr, 40% new. — *CR*

Cilliers Cellars see Stellendrift
Cilmor see see African Terroir

Cinzano

With the discontinuation of the pink Tiziano, this popular low-alcohol range of semi-sweet sparklers now features only the Asti-inspired **Spumante** (**★★**), from selected muscat varieties. Latest version somewhat out of character: shy, simple, light apple & barley sugar flavours. 10% alc. Carbonated NV from African Wines & Spirits. — *TM*

Citrusdal Cellars

Citrusdal (see Swartland map) ▪ Est 1957 ▪ 1stB 1958 ▪ Tasting & sales Mon-Fri 8-5 Sat 9-12. 30 (sales also at retail outlet in Citrusdal village Mon-Fri 9-7 Sat 8-1) ▪ Closed all public holidays except Easter Sat ▪ Tours by appt ▪ Picnic baskets by appt during Dec holiday, or BYO anytime ▪ Citrusdal Cellars Guest House ▪ Tourgroups ▪ Conferencing ▪ 4×4 trail ▪ Owners 80 members ▪ Winemakers Johan Delport & Pieter Carstens (Dec 2000/Nov 2003) ▪ Viticulturist Bartho van der Westhuizen (Dec 2003) ▪ 1 200 ha (grenache, pinotage, chenin) ▪ 7 000 tons 20 000 cs own label + 5m litres bulk + 20 000 cs for clients ▪ 50% red 40% white 5% rosé 5% dessert ▪ Export brand: Danckaert ▪ PO Box 41 Citrusdal 7340 ▪ citrusdalcellars@yebo.co.za ▪ www.citrusdalcellars.co.za ✆ (022) 921·2233 🖷 (022) 921·3937

In spite of a 2004 harvest reduced by one-fifth due to drought, this cellar remains a hive of activity. A new viticulturist, Bartho van der Westhuizen, now nurses the vines, and a new management system promotes better alignment between source vineyards and ultimate selling prices. The area appears particularly well suited to southern French varieties (80% of SA's grenache vineyards are here), so 2004 saw additional plantings of cinsaut, grenache and shiraz. Perhaps the most exciting development is the accreditation of five growers by the Fair Trade Labelling Organisation. Citrusdal is the first co-op in the world to achieve this, and it means the working and living conditions of the workers meet the requirements of a stringent 'ethical audit'. Here's to drinking with a clear conscience.

Cardouw range

★★★☆ Cabernet Sauvignon Reserve 1st from their Piekenklf vyds (certified as such). Interesting & substantial **00**, mid-2004 still shows structure, generosity, chewy ripe tannins. Could be cellared another 2-3 yrs. 13.9% alc. **Cabernet Sauvignon ★★** Light-bodied **99** should be enjoyed soon, with food. **Grenache ★★★** Among 1st varietal bottlings in SA (WO Piekenklf). Well structured **03** (sample), with bright red-fruit tones, touch of spice too. Could take light chilling in summer. Yr Fr/Am (80/20) oak. 14% alc. **Pinotage ★★ 02** shows touch of ester, slight green edge, fairly strong tannic finish. **President's Red** For Irish market, only in 187ml; same wine as Classique Rouge below. **Chardonnay ★★ 03** balanced, so barrel-fermentation/maturation (Fr, 8 mths) doesn't overpower. Green peach flavour, with some crispness. 14% alc. WO Cdrberg. **Chardonnay Reserve NEW ★★★** Ex Cdrberg/Piekenklf vyds, blended after yr in new Fr oak; **03** (sample) more rounded than above version; good dry finish; vanilla & some peach.14% alc. **Chenin Blanc ★★ 03**'s fruit is very ripe but buoyed by racy acidity; dainty bosc pear flavours. **Blanc Fumé NEW ★★** Lightish & very subtly oaked sauvignon;

03 shows muted apple/pear tastes, lively acidity. WO Piekenklf. This range named after the local Cardouw Pass ('Narrow Road' in Khoisan language). WO W-Cape unless noted.

Ivory Creek range

Cabernet Sauvignon ★★☆ **02** retasted, shows some porty whiffs, dried plum tones on palate; suggest drink soon. **Pinotage** ★★★ Wide-girthed **02** holding up well; plump red berry palate, pleasantly dry tannic finish. 14.4% alc. 7 mths Fr oak. **Merlot** NEW ★★ **03** light-hued but full-bodied dry red; slight green tinge & strongish tannin grip. 14% alc. 6 mths Fr oak. WO Piekenklf. **Shiraz** ★★ **02** still available; shows a dry leaf character, fair amount of tannin though big alc (15.8%) not as evident. **Royal Rouge** ★★★ Now only for Dutch market. Quaffable unwooded **03** mix cinsaut, merlot, tinta, ruby cab, with latter's spicy aroma jumping from glass. **Chardonnay** ★★ **03** unwooded, crisply refreshing, twist of lime imparts extra liveliness. **Chenin Blanc** ★★★ **04** racy bone-dry white; crisp apple & pear aromas/flavours; WO Ctrsdal Mntn (first ever wine with this appellation). **Sauvignon Blanc** ★★ **04** (sample) night harvested for freshness, zing, which achieved; some gooseberry on nose/palate, otherwise straightforward. WO Piekenklf. **Royal Blanc** ★★☆ 4-way blend for Dutch market. **04** (sample) lightish, pleasant; gentle liveliness on deciduous fruit palate. WO W-Cape unless noted. **Semillon** discontinued.

Goue Vallei range

> **Classique Rouge** ☺ ★★★ House's best-seller. Drink-now fruity quartet of reds; **03** still lively though more rounded than last yr; slightly earthy & savoury; unwooded. Also in 3ℓ bag-in-box. **Vin Doux** ☺ ★★★ Lovely bouncy bubbles with honeysuckle fragrance, uncloyingly sweet. NV/uncertified.

Following WO W-Cape unless noted. **Cabernet Sauvignon** ★★★ **02** attractively oaked (6 mths, 70% Fr) to highlight generous cassis flavour, gentle tannins. 14.2% alc. **Pinotage** ★★★☆ ✓ **02** rich, minerally red-berry aromas/flavours with mild oak-char; weighty & firm. 8 mths oak, mainly Fr. **Chianti** ★★ 100% cinsaut. Latest bottling has light red berries on nose, suggestion of bitterness on finish. NV/uncertified. **Classique Rosé** ★★ Lightish, semi-dry **04** again from pinotage, with cherry fragrance; ends fairly crisply. Only for Dutch/German markets. **Chardonnay** ★★ **04** pleasingly light textured; apple/peach flavours & smoky aftertaste from 50% fermentation with Fr oak chips (rest unwooded). **Chenin Blanc** ★★ Quaffable **04** forthcoming guava & pear tones, smoothly dry. **Sauvignon Blanc** ★★ **04** (sample) perky dry white, crisp grassy aromas/flavours, lively dry finish. **Blanc de Blanc** ★★★ **04** charming & lightish chenin-based blend, dashes chard, gewürz, with delicate guava & apple aromas. Also in 3ℓ bag-in-box. **Classique Blanc** ★★ **04** lightish-textured, muted guava & apple whiffs (our sample recently bottled), dry finish. Export only. **Bukettraube** ★★ **03** selected by WOM; our samples showed apple & peach ripeness but also curious chemical tone. **Late Vintage** ★★ Semi-sweet back in line-up as 3ℓ bag-in-box; candied fruit flavours, hints spice/mint — try with glazed chicken or Thai curry. NV/uncertified. **Brut Pinot Gris** ★★★ Vivacious, refreshing dry sparkling with dried-herb & citrus tones, earthy hint. Ex-Piekenklf vyds (certified as such). Another WOM selection, though most now flies to Madagascar. Locally replaced by... **Brut** ★★★ Chardonnay & clairette; stylish dry foam with appetising fresh baked bread tone. NV/uncertified.

Following fortifieds all NV/uncertified: **Sacramental Wine** ★★ For the Roman Catholic Church; aromatic blend pale dry sherry, muscadel & colombard. Like liquid pudding, with vanilla overtone. 14.8% alc. **Red Jerepiko** ★★★ Exotic & interesting dessert from pinotage, with distinctly warming malt & treacle flavours. 19.5% alc. *Wine* Best Value pick. **Hanepoot Jerepiko** ★★★ Wickedly smooth & sweet; mid-2004 wonderful grapey nose; herbal palate with hints mint & buchu. 17.8% alc. **White Muscadel** ★★★☆ ✓ Another *Wine* Value selection; almost a dessert in itself, complete with ripe mango, pineapple & apricot flavours; silky smooth (partly due to low 15% fortification). **Ruby** ★★ From shiraz, straightforwardly sweet, dry for style (86g/ℓ sugar). **Shiraz** and **Blanc de Noir** discontinued.

Zaximus range

Export brand for UK & Italy. **Red ★★** Bright & lively equal cinsaut/merlot concoction; pleasant party wine; ends with a light smack of tannin. **Dry White ★★** Latest is from crouchen; soft appley flavours, balanced acidity, undemanding. Both NV/uncertified.

Sonnigdal range

NV range in 2 & 5ℓ boxes now discontinued – *JN*

Clairvaux Private Cellar

Robertson ▪ Est 2000 ▪ 1stB 2001 ▪ Tasting & sales Mon-Fri 8-5 Sat & public holidays 9-12.30 ▪ Closed Easter Fri-Mon, Dec 25/26 & Jan 1 ▪ Tours by appt ▪ BYO picnic ▪ Owners Wouter de Wet Snr & Jnr ▪ Winemaker Pieter van Aarde (Jan 2004) ▪ Viti consultant Briaan Stipp ▪ 100 ha (cab, malbec, merlot, pinotage, petit v, shiraz, chard, colombard, muscadel, sauvignon) ▪ 3 100 tons ▪ PO Box 179 Robertson 6705 ▪ clairvaux@lando.co.za ▪ www.wine.co.za © **(023) 626·3842** 🖷 (023) 626·1925

Recently arrived from Swartland Winery, Pieter van Aarde has taken over farm management and winemaking duties from long-time incumbent Kobus van der Merwe. In spite of fears that disease would grip the vineyards because of slow ripening, Clairvaux emerged from the 2004 in fine health, with reds attaining 'good colour and a nice ripe flavour'.

Cabernet Sauvignon ★★★ 02 sample seems nervy, slightly lean with hint of eucalyptus. 9 mths Fr oak. **Shiraz ★★★** Combo staves/barrels, all Am, 9 mths, for **04**; wood doesn't compete with sweet ripe plummy fruit, tobacco-fragrant farewell. **Sandberg Purple ★★★ 02** food-friendly equal blend pinotage, ruby cab, merlot, briefly staved; fynbos/mulberry whiffs & dry herby finish. ±14% alc. **Rosé ★★ 03**, from colombard, pinotage, better balanced than pvs, not as sweet, quite juicy. Low 10% alc. **Chardonnay ★★ 04** sample less successful this yr; oak staving rather overt; firm, dry, slightly coarse finish. **Sauvignon Blanc ★★★** Plain but tasty picnic wine. **04** (sample) shy pear-drop/candyfloss aromas; dry; medium-bodied. **Chardonnay-Colombar ★★★** Friendly dry white; **04** (sample) spicy nose & crunchy green fruit palate; suggest drink promptly. 12.5% alc. **Madonna's Kisses ★★★★ ✓ 02** full-sweet white muscadel jerepigo with fiery gold glints in **02**, huge Turkish Delight nose; very rich, sweet & spicy but uncloying; silky potpourri-scented finish. 16% alc. **Port ★ 01** Fireside fortifier from ruby cab, with the variety's leafy character; lacks grip; vanilla-toned finish from ±3 yrs oak. – *TM* –

▪ *Clemence Creek* see Mooiuitsig

Cloof

Darling ▪ Est 1997 ▪ 1stB 1998 ▪ Tasting & sales Mon-Thu 10-4 Fri 10-3 Sat by appt ▪ Closed Easter Fri/Sun, Dec 25/26, Jan 1 ▪ Occasional gourmet BBQ events – pre-bookings only ▪ Owner Cloof Wine Estate (Pty) Ltd ▪ Winemaker Christopher van Dieren (Jan 2002) ▪ Viticulturist Hardie van den Heever (1998) ▪ 166 ha (cabs s/f, cinsaut, merlot, pinotage, shiraz, chard, chenin) ▪ 600 tons 90 000 cs 88% red 5% white 7% rosé ▪ PO Box 269 Darling 7345 ▪ info@cloof.co.za ▪ www.cloof.co.za © **(022) 492·2839** 🖷 (022) 492·3261

Adversity is character building, which is why these unirrigated bushvines on the slopes of the Dassenberg are big on personality. And have serious attitude – their roots go up to 8m deep in search of moisture, making them less sensitive to drought. 'There are easier ways of making wine,' comments winemaker Christopher van Dieren of this extreme site, where harvest starts as early as the first week of January. Unlike the previous vintage, which yielded blockbusters, cooler 2004 saw the crops mature at lower alcohols, resulting in a 'finer, more elegant' structure in some of the wines. A 50% increase in barrels (all French) allowed increased production of shiraz and cab – they bought in grapes from 3 other farms in Darling, which will give them 'fantastic building blocks' when making up their blends.

Crucible range
Shiraz Tank sample **03** has perfumed nose, meaty hints. Subtle oak balanced with fruit, only just-dry 4.9g/ℓ sugar gives pleasant sweetness; remarkable elegance given 15.7% alc. 15 mths new Fr oak. On track for ★★★★ when bottled.

Cloof range
★★★★ **Pinotage** From single bushvine vyd established 1976. No **01**, but **02**'s banana & spice tones, candyfloss aftertaste recall **00**; toothcoating tannins need plenty of time. 15 mths Fr oak. Beware huge 15.5% alc. Swiss gold. **03** tank sample (with 'mere' 14.3% alc) has attractive sugar crystal bite, pleasant mulberry notes.

Cabernet Sauvignon-Cabernet Franc-Merlot Change of varietal emphasis from cab f-led **02** (★★★) Bdx blend. 2 cabs each nearly 40% in previewed 'statement wine' **03**: herbal nose, dark choc; good grippy balance despite 15% alc. 14 mths Fr oak, most new. Likely ★★★★. Discontinued from this range: **Cabernet Sauvignon, Chenin Blanc, Cellar Hands' Blend**.

Bushvine range
★★★★ **Cabernet Sauvignon-Shiraz** Retasted 80/20 blend **02** with red/black berry array in control, nice balance, good length.15 mths Fr oak. 14.5% alc. Like Bushvine below, last appearance in this range.

★★★☆ **Bushvine** Fruity & friendly **02**, blend pinotage, cab, cinsaut (44/33/23) last ed showed ripe fruit, generous tannins, toasty finish; promised to develop well.

★★★☆ **Pinotage** NEW Great concentration of pinotage flavours (banana, mulberry) with some acetone hints on **03**. 14.2% alc. 13 mths older Fr oak.

Cabernet Sauvignon NEW **03** tank sample too young to rate: some sweet berry aromas/ flavours lurking, but all needs time to integrate. 15.3% alc. 13 mths older Fr oak.

Dusty Road range
★★★★ **Chardonnay Unwooded** ✓ Fresh, flavoursome **04** over-delivers on price point. Notes of green apple, chalk. Moderate 13.2% alc, but hefty 7g/ℓ sugar (makes it officially off-dry), adds greatly to richness.
Cabernet Sauvignon ★★★★ **03** Bdx dustiness with a pleasant fruit sweetness & mineral austerity. Good balance. 14.3% alc. **Cabernet Sauvignon-Shiraz** ★★★ Smoky nose, austere character, **03** with some stone fruit flavours from 80% cab, pepper from shiraz. Massive 14.9% alc; just-dry 4.1g/ℓ sugar. **Cabernet Sauvignon-Pinotage-Shiraz** ★★★☆ Nutty nose on pleasantly sweet **03** 40/40/20 blend. 14.5% alc. This range reds unwooded, to keep fruity charm. **Pinotage** ★★★ Shy nose on **03**, some spice & loganberry aromas/flavours. Easy-drinking (despite 14.5% alc), just-dry expression of the grape. **Rosé** ★★★☆ Good partridge-eye colour, full ripe berry flavours from cinsaut, shiraz, pinotage. **04** works! As does touch sugar & friendly 12.7% alc. **Chenin** ★★★ Light (11.5% alc) fruity 'lifestyle' **04** with tropical fruit & a touch of sharpness to offset a little sugar.

Groene Cloof range discontinued: **Pinotage, Rosé, Chenin Blanc**. — NP

Clos Malverne

Stellenbosch ▪ Est/1stB 1988 ▪ Tasting & sales Mon-Fri 10-4.30 Sat 10-1 ▪ Fee R13 ▪ Closed Christian public holidays & Jan 1 ▪ Tours by appt ▪ BYO picnic ▪ Owners Seymour & Sophia Pritchard ▪ Winemaker/viticulturist Isak 'Ippie' Smit (Nov 1997) ▪ 25 ha (cab, merlot, pinotage, shiraz, sauvignon) ▪ 350 tons 24 000 cs 90% red 10% white ▪ Export brands: Shepherd's Creek & Kleinrivier ▪ PO Box 187 Stellenbosch 7599 ▪ closma@mweb.co.za ▪ www.closmalverne.co.za www.capeblend.co.za ✆ 865-2022 🖷 865-2518

'We had a hell of a time developing this winery. We funded everything through sales of wine', says Seymour Pritchard, who remembers having so little infrastructure that they moistened hessian 'socks' to cool the tanks. How times have changed. They're well established now, well reputed, and looking to fine-tune their performance. Says winemaker IP Smit: 'To slightly reduce alcohols and heighten elegance, we're harvesting a bit earlier.' Confessing to 'a love-hate relationship with varietal pinotage', they're unreservedly keen on pinotage blends and maintain these have a 'huge future'. The new well-priced Merlot-Pinotage should convert many a customer to their cause. No such persuasion needed for the Sauvignon: they'd have to double production to meet the demand. New plantings, as well as aerial grafting should take the heat off.

★★★★ **Auret Cape Blend** Standard-bearer of this cellar — cab, pinotage, merlot blend, normally around 60/25/15. As other reds here, basket-pressed, fermented in traditional open-topped *kuipe*. Latest **01** magisterial — firm & unyielding for the present. Glimpses of cassis, plum & mint hint at things to come. Should peak around 2010. **00** leaner, more grainy, with upfront merlot mintiness. Yr Fr/Am oak, 14% alc.

★★★★★ **Auret Cape Blend Limited Release 01** features SAYWS-winning cab (60%) & merlot, plus best pinotage (25%) in cellar. Definite notch up; forthcoming cigarbox & currant; dense, compact flavours of ripe plums, dark choc, fennel. Yr best Fr barriques adds veneer of opulence. 14% alc. Mid-2004 shows discreet, understated power; lots of life ahead.

★★★★ **Pinotage Reserve** Showy, deep-flavoured barrel selection bristles with awards. **01** continues impressive line, bold yet seamlessly elegant. Longer stay in oak (yr, 70/30 Fr/Am) than bottling below adds some sweetness, silkiness, yet retaste mid-2004 shows it still in grip of tannin; suggest cellaring another 2-3 yrs. 14% alc.

★★★☆ **Pinotage 01** offers ripe mulberries & hints of vanilla oak. Tannins still a bit gruff, 4-6 mths Fr & Am oak adds body & spice. 14% alc. Cellar 3-4 yrs.

★★★☆ **Cabernet Sauvignon** Very correct **01** endowed with classic cassis fruit padding around cab's firmer tannic & minerally core. Unshowy, needs time in glass to open & reveal its charms. Properly dry, 14% alc. **00** (★★★★) was classically fine claret — taut & dry. Old/new-clone mix suits medium-oaking style. Yr Fr/Am oak.

★★★☆ **Shiraz 01** savoury, almost earthy style, showing sweetish tannins & meaty, mulberry jam flavours. Am oak component (50/50 with Fr, yr) adds spice. 14% alc. Mid-2004 still needs yr/2.

★★★★ **Cabernet Sauvignon-Merlot Limited Release 01** once-off showcase for 60/40 blend which won Jan Smuts Trophy at SAYWS 2001; held back for further bottle maturation. Not retasted.

★★★★ **Cabernet Sauvignon-Shiraz** Latest **02** shows same seamless integration as **01**; shiraz's amiable nature offsets cab's more austere notes in 70/30 blend. Brambly whiffs framed by peppery, smoky aromas; offers fruit-sweetness & food-friendly dry finish in one. **01** 60/40 marriage. These 4-6 mths in Fr/Am wood.

★★★★ **Cabernet Sauvignon-Pinotage Cape Blend** Latest **01** in same 65/35 mould as pvs, continues to validate Seymour P's claims for pinotage as worthy partner in his blends. Cab's cassis complements pinotage's mulberry notes, gentle Fr oak (yr) adding classical savoury finish. Revisited mid-2004 unfolding splendidly, sleek & suave, almost ready. **00** sold out before we could taste. MIWA gold for **99**.

★★★☆ **Cabernet Sauvignon-Merlot** Major shift in blend for **03** (★★★), much more cab (80%), firmer but also quieter, main action on palate; cassis abounds, rather more classic & perhaps less interesting than revved-up pinotage blends above. 14% alc. **02** 54/46 partnership with minerally backbone.

Devonet Merlot-Pinotage 🆕 ☺ ★★★ **03** intended as entry-level 'Cape blend'; bright warm plummy fruit, terrific rounded profile, juicy & delicious. 4 mths Fr & Am oak, 14% alc. **Shepherds Creek Classic Red** ☺ ★★★ Robust all-sorts blend led by cab, pinotage. High-quality fruit, braaied chop-impervious tannins. Note 14% alc. NV.

Shepherds Creek Chardonnay ★★★ Luscious peaches & cream **03**, curvaceous, soft acidity & nice hint of fragrant oak. This, Classic Red, WO W-Cape. Sauvignon Blanc From home-grown & neighbouring grapes; **04** zesty, lively, dry; gooseberry & grass with sweeter passionfruit notes, fragrant & very correct. Lowish 12.5% alc. — *IvH*

Clouds Vineyards

Stellenbosch ▪ Est 2002 ▪ 1stB 2003 ▪ Visits by appt ▪ Lunches/dinners for small groups by appt ▪ 4 luxury self-catering cottages (meals by appt) ▪ Owners Bernard & Petro Immelman ▪ Vini consultants Gyles Webb & Rudi Schultz ▪ Viticulturist Matthew Castle ▪ 2.5 ha (sauvignon) ▪ 750 cs 100% white ▪ PO Box 540 Stellenbosch 7599 ▪ info@cloudsvineyards.co.za ▪ www.cloudsguesthouse.com © **885·1819** 885·2829

Watching diners enjoy his Sauvignon at local restaurants is as thrilling as sipping his own chilled glass, Bernard Immelman says. The wine is made to his and wife Petro's specs at nearby Thelema. 2004 was a record crop, so there should be a bit more to splash around. Alongside their boutique wine, the Immelmans are developing Clouds into a select holiday destination offering 'great wine, great accommodation and, eventually, great food'.

Sauvignon Blanc ★★★ **04** uncluttered tropical, figgy nose/flavours; easy-going balance; early, straightforward drinking. 13.5% alc. —*AL*

Clovelly Wines

Stellenbosch ▪ Est/1stB 2000 ▪ Visits by appt ▪ Owners Jacques Fourie, Mineke Toerien-Fourie & Deon Toerien ▪ Winemaker Jacques Fourie (Sep 2000) ▪ 3 ha (cab) ▪ 6 tons 2 600 cs 70% red 30% white ▪ Postnet Suite 215 Private Bag X5061 Stellenbosch 7599 ▪ wines@absamail.co.za clovellywines@hotmail.com winesbyjf@hotmail.com © **082·853·7190** 865·2511/865·2600

2004 will go down in wine lore, opines Jacques Fourie, as one that seemed never-ending. The end result, for him, was very good quality, especially of the reds, which included a first batch of shiraz. The red tape required to see an own-cellar up and working in Devon Valley hasn't quite been cut, but he and his partners, wife Mineke Toerien-Fourie and father-in-law Deon Toerien, are holding thumbs. Meanwhile, orders are coming in nicely, thanks to Colleen Thompson, appointed to handle the marketing from Johannesburg; and from clients in the US, Canada and Singapore. If only, J-F sighs, SA were marketed more vigorously as a wine brand.

★★★★ **Cabernet Sauvignon 00**, revisited for this ed, shows no sign of dotage; if anything, tighter & chewier than last yr; cloves & pepper whiffs, dense fruit with dark-choc tinge, good grip. 14.5% alc. **02** (★★★ & WO Stbosch) similar nose; lighter, slightly grainy, less structured. 13 mths oak, some new.

Triangle ★★★ Name refers to trio of partners in this venture; could be either single variety or three-way blend; current NV is the latter: cab, merlot, cinsaut; intriguing savoury aromas of pepper & tomato, sweet fruit, smoky aftertaste. Elegant & interesting. **Chardonnay** ★★★★ **02** retaste: still-fresh, looking good; rich grapefruit & slight herbal whiffs; lush, lots of fruit, nice touch of toasty oak. WO W-Cape unless noted.—*TM*

Cloverfield Private Cellar

Robertson ▪ Est ca 1920 ▪ 1stB 2002 ▪ Tasting & sales Mon-Fri 9-5 Sat 10-2 ▪ Closed Easter Fri-Sun, Dec 25 & Jan 1 ▪ Owner Pieter Marais ▪ Winemaker Cobus Marais (Jan 2002) ▪ Viticulturist Pieter Marais ▪ 120 ha (cinsaut, merlot, petit v, shiraz, chard, chenin, sauvignon, semillon) ▪ ±1 700 tons ±2 000 cs own label 40% red 60% white ▪ PO Box 429 Robertson 6705 ▪ info@cloverfield.co.za © **(023) 626·4118/3** (023) 626·3203

At their spread 'Die Vlakte' in Robertson, sandwiched between Springfield and Bon Courage, Pieter and Liz Marais had an excellent 2004 harvest. Which is good news for the customers who buy most of their production, as well as for their young own-label, Cloverfield, named after one of the three farms which form their property. You can try the wines at their new tasting locale or, if you're not visiting the area anytime soon, son Henry M, back from the UK, has taken over marketing and intends to bring their 'affordable top quality wines' to an outlet near you.

★★★★ **Winemaker's Selection Shiraz** ✓ Maiden **02** still in stock: lovely mix of red fruits, bit of pepper, woodsmoke & toast, gamey hint too — fine complexity; good dry entry, zesty sour-plum exit. Fr oak vats/staves, 9 mths.

★★★★ **Winemaker's Selection Chardonnay** ✓ Cellar's first bottled wine, from a single vyd, fermented/aged on Fr oak. **02**, retasted for this ed, striking brioche & burnt match aromas; grapefruit palate opens sweet, finishes dry, voluptuous buttery peach/grapefruit flavours between. Sexy, upfront number. Unintimidating 14.7% alc. MIWA gold 2003.

Four Clover Selection

★★★★ **Sauvignon Blanc** Tasted newly bottled, **04** apparently unscathed: powerful nose of grapefruit zest which carries into zingy citrus-zest palate, with twist of nettles. **Chardonnay Unwooded** ★★★ **04** (sample) prominent bouquet of sweet melon & peach; sweet impression from massive 15% alc, but nicely balanced. — *TM*

Cogmans Kloof see Zandvliet
Cogmans River see Zandvliet

Cold Duck (5th Avenue)

Gently sweet, low alc (8%) carbonated sparkler from Distell. It signature: heady pineapple scents from Ferdinand de Lesseps grapes (50%, with pinotage, chenin); latest (NV) ★★★ lots of frothy flavour, sweetness in character with easy charm. — *CR*

Coleraine Wines

Paarl • Est 1998 • 1stB 1999 • Visits by appt; tasting/sales also at I Love Wine (see Wine shops section) • BYO picnic • Walks • Owners C & HK Kerr • Winemaker/viticulturist Clive Kerr • 30 ha (cab, cinsaut, merlot, mourvèdre, petit v, ruby cab, shiraz, chard, sauvignon, viognier) • 4-5 000 cs own label 100% red • PO Box 579 Suider-Paarl 7624 • info@ coleraine.co.za • www.coleraine.co.za ©/☎ 863·3443

Last year saw Clive Kerr making inroads into the newly-hot US market when his Cab, Shiraz and Merlot earned big points with probably the world's most influential wine critic, Robert Parker Jnr. It's taken Kerr some time to work out the specific softer, fuller flavour the US palate prefers but as Kerr puts it, 'receive a good Parker rating and you're a rock star'. Kerr was very pleased with last year's long ripening season, with his red varieties promising good quality. Plans to upgrade the tasting area on the farm, reported last edition, are on hold but you can sample and purchase Coleraine wines along with a bevy of like-minded local producers from the new 'I Love Wine' lifestyle centre on Paarl's Main Road (Mon-Sat 9-4).

★★★★ **Syrah (Culraithin)** (Formerly 'Shiraz') Inspired, densely fruited **02** (★★★★☆): nutmeg, cassia, coriander aromas hint at ample mulberry fruit shored up by clean oak & immense tannins, all of which manage opulent 16% alc — just! Though massively ripe, more complex than generous but not fat **01**; harmonious turn of pepper, raspberry & coconut; tannins well-integrated, plush 14.5% alc. VDG. Softer than **00**. 8-15 mths Fr oak, 20-25% new. Latest for the long haul — 2008 onwards.

★★★★ **Merlot (Culraithin)** Further year expands delight, allure of maiden **01**: enticing whiffs of violets, tangy notes to chewy mulberry core; tannins ensure longevity. Yr seasoned oak prelude to 10 mths in new Fr. 14.5% alc.

★★★★ **Cabernet Sauvignon (Culraithin)** Ripe-fruited **02** (★★★★) flaunts spicy cassis, damson depth, savoury hints with dense lacy tannins; fine finish restrains 15% alc. Yr Fr barriqus, 20% new. Riper, more intense than muted, dustily austere **00**.

Cabernet Sauvignon-Merlot (Culraithin) ★★★ 60/40 blend coming off the boil; **99** revisited mid-04 retains taut tether to its rhubarb notes, herbal edge; yr oak, 40% new Fr. 13.5% alc. **Fire Engine Red** ★★☆ **00** easy-drinking merlot, ruby cab, cinsaut blend, lightly oaked. 13.5% alc. — *DS*

Condé see Stark-Condé
Confluence see Douglas Winery, Landzicht

Conspirare

Stellenbosch ▪ Est/1stB 2002 ▪ Closed to public ▪ Owners HB Dowling/LRD Trust ▪ Winemaker Henry Dowling ▪ Viticulturist Francois de Villiers ▪ 24 ha (cab s/f, merlot, shiraz, chenin) ▪ 140 tons 425 cs own label 100% red ▪ PO Box 1210 Stellenbosch 7599 ▪ dowls@mweb.co.za ✆ 855·0722 🖷 855·0706

After trying his hand at winemaking for home use, Henry Dowling decided to 'go for it' and, with the encouragement of his wife, dusky-voiced singer Lesley Rae Dowling, made a decidedly auspicious debut in 2002. A Helderberg fruit farmer, he's always enjoyed a lively dialogue with winemakers and now loves all facets of the art.

★★★★ **Conspirare** Last tasted was elegant **02**, sweet-fruited blend cabs s/f, merlot, with hints of blackcurrant, pencil-shavings; discreetly confident, satisfying. Early drinking, but should develop ±5 yrs. 16 mths Fr oak, third new. 14% alc. Follow-up **03** untasted; blend not finalised at press time.— *TJ*

Constantia Uitsig

Constantia ▪ Est 1988 ▪ 1stB 1993 ▪ Tasting & sales Mon-Fri 9-5 Sat & Sun 10-4 ▪ Closed Easter Fri, Dec 25/26, Jan 1 ▪ Constantia-Uitsig & La Colombe restaurants (see Eat-Out section); Spaanschemat River Café for light meals 8-5 ▪ Constantia Uitsig Country Hotel (see Stay-over section) ▪ Gift/wine shop ▪ Conference facilities ▪ Owners David & Marlene McCay ▪ Vini/viti consultants André Rousseau & John Loubser (Mar 1998/2001) ▪ 32 ha (cab, merlot, chard, sauvignon, semillon) ▪ ±200 tons ±12 000 cs 30% red 70% white ▪ PO Box 402 Constantia 7848 ▪ wine@icon.co.za ▪ www.uitsig.co.za ✆ 794·1810 🖷 794·1812

World-class hotel and eateries; one of the country's few privately owned cricket ovals; the 'schoolhouse' wine shop; vineyards in Constantia's cool-climate heartland; some very fine wines. With all this on offer, this property maintains (by choice?) a low profile, integral to its oodles of charm. Sharing cellar space at Steenberg continues to work well. Perfectionist viticulturist (winemaker too since 2003) André Rousseau chases ripe fruit and the essence of the area's terroir. A mooted worldwide white wine shortage suits C-U's 70% white profile: 'We have never changed plantings based on trends.' (They are, however, establishing cab franc — currently bought in — for their red blend.) New are soil neutron probes, night harvesting (2.30-10am) and (a trend they are in the vanguard of) screwcaps on all their white wines.

★★★★ **Cabernet Sauvignon-Merlot** First of this re-vamped label, **00** elegantly understated; attractive plummy/red berry fruit in well-knit harmonious 50/50 blend, with savoury acidity & good length. **01** adds 15% cab f (ex-Steenberg); similar profile but a littler fuller, more characterful & complete; still rather oaky. Both 2 yrs Fr oak, 50% new; 14% alc; should develop over good few yrs.

★★★★★ **Chardonnay Reserve 03** full, rich & deep, subtly alluding to citrus, honey, butterscotch, with mineral thread; beautifully balanced, coping well with massive 14.5% alc, with supportive oak (fermented, aged 11 mths, 80% new). Less, but more obvious, new oak (30%) on slighter, less concentrated **02** (★★★★).

★★★★★ **Semillon Reserve** Always serious & rather grand. Retasted **02** (Diners Club winner) shows need for some bottle maturation: from shy immaturity has gained depth, harmony & poise, with nutty, lanolin- & citrus-tinged richness, powerful driving finish. Youthful **03** promises similar development, lemongrass burgeoning on creamy palate, fine acidity — 3.75g/ℓ sugar not apparent. 14.4% alc. These fermented/11 mths in 2nd/3rd fill Fr oak.

★★★★ **Semillon-Sauvignon Blanc** Maiden **03** flagship blend now revealing semillon as dominant partner (72%; fermented/6 mths older oak; sauvignon in steel). Still developing, with nutty, biscuitty notes, incipient complexity, creamy texture. Good acid not quite disguising 5g/ℓ sugar. 6 000 bottles, all screwcapped — as are all these whites.

★★★★ **Sauvignon Blanc 03** blossomed flavourfully with time in bottle — as do all the Uitsig whites; tingling acid largely checks 5.5g/ℓ sugar. Similar passionfruit, lemongrass on elegantly intense **04** (★★★★), with finely balanced richness & thrilling acidity. Moderate 13% alc.

★★★★ **Chardonnay Unwooded** Delightful, fresh, pure-fruited **03** with lemon-cream notes; powerful but well balanced; bone dry but gracefully full & round. **04** (★★★★) even more so. These on lees 2-3 mths; ± 14% alc. — *TJ*

Co-operative Group see International Wine Services

Coppoolse Finlayson Winery

Stellenbosch • Est 1991 • 1stB 1994 • Visits by appt only • Owners Rob Coppoolse, Walter Finlayson & Viv Grater • Winemakers Adele Dunbar & Danielle du Toit (Aug 1998, Apr 2002) • Viti consultant Johan Pienaar (2001) • 850 000 cs + 150 000 own label 70% red 30% white • Ranges for customers: Kaaps Geskenk, Kaapse Pracht, Songloed & Nuwe Wynplaas • ISO 9001:2000, HACCP & BRC certified • PO Box 4028 Old Oak 7537 • wine@sentinel.co.za • www.cfwines.co.za ℂ **982·6175** 🖷 982·6296

'Our business got smarter in response to the strong rand,' says Rob Coppoolse. 'To heighten customer buy-in, we're getting our clients involved in the choice of final products.' Is the tactic working? Well, consider this: their three bottling plants now work round the clock to meet international orders for more than 1m cases. A new listing with retailing giant Marks & Spencer will keep the filling lines rolling, as will a recently bagged first major listing for Kaya in Holland, where sales across their brands have grown 25% in recent months. They're also looking to expand their presence in Scandinavia. In another 'smart' move, they appointed HwCg as UK agents for the Kaya brand — now divided into Traditional (Nandi and Shaka), Discovery (blends) and Cape Vineyards (single varieties) ranges.

Kaya Traditional range

Wine for this, ranges below, bought from selected W Cape cellars & blended.

Shaka ☺ ★★★ **03** a 3-way blend, mainly cinsaut & pinotage, dash cab f, juicy & rounded.

Nandi ★★☆ **04** pleasant, lightly tropical fruit dry white with crisp fresh finish.

Kaya Cape Vineyards Level range

 NEW

Chardonnay ☺ ★★☆ **04** (sample) toasty touch to tropical fruit, nicely put together.

Merlot ★★★ Textbook varietal characters of plums, damson & violets; sweet milk choc tastes, smooth, juicy; big ripe tannins augur well for development. **Pinotage** ★★★ Ripe plum & banana whiffs, deft touch oak, rounded ripe tannins; youthfully exuberant & drinkable. **Shiraz** ★★★★ Bright purple hues; nose of blackberries & pepper; toasty, well rounded palate; shows some structure & heft. **Sauvignon Blanc** ★★★ **04** hint of capsicum-spice amid the amenable tropical fruit, lightish, easy drinking. All **04**s, tasted as samples, ratings provisional.

Kaaps Genoegen range

Cinsaut-Pinotage ☺ ★★★ **03** ripe fruited with strawberry & plum on nose/palate, nice & mellow — no rough edges to complicate the pleasure.

Chenin Blanc-Chardonnay ★★ **03**, yr on, still surprisingly fresh & fruity, mellow tropical tones for uncomplicated standalone sipping. This range & all below only for export.

Kaaps Geskenk range

> **Cinsaut-Pinotage** ☺ ★★★ **03** succulent ripe fruit; aromas/flavours of strawberry & plum, appealingly mellow no-frills every drink. **Rosé** ☺ ★★★ **04** punnet of strawberries & cherries, mouthfilling fruity flavours, bone-dry but friendly finish. From pinotage.

Dry Steen ★★ Mildly fruity **03** with tropical fruit touch, light-bodied, finishes clean & dry.

Kaapse Vreugd range
Dry Red ★★★ Similar to Cinsaut-Pinotage under Kaaps Geskenk. **Dry White** ★★ **04** brisk, bony-dry quick-quaff with muted tropical tones. Modest 12.6% alc.

Songloed range

> **Merlot** ☺ ★★★ **03** plums & choc in equal volume, light oak background, distinct tannin, drinkable now with another yr/2 in store. **Dry Steen** ☺ ★★★ Fresh & fruity **04**, attractive tropical nose, bright in the mouth; quaffably light bodied (12.6% alc).

Shiraz ★★★ **03** spiced red fruit, slight savoury touch, pliable tannins; already a hint of bottle-maturity, so for early consumption. The Sentinel range listed separately. — DH

Cordoba Winery

Stellenbosch (see Helderberg map) ▪ Est 1982 ▪ 1stB 1994 ▪ Tasting only by appt Mon-Fri 8. 30-5 ▪ Sales Mon-Fri 8.30-5 ▪ Closed public holidays ▪ Tours by appt ▪ Owner Jannie Jooste ▪ Winemaker/viticulturist Christopher Keet (Oct 1993) ▪ 31 ha (cabs s/f, merlot, shiraz, chard) ▪ 100 tons 7 000 cs 90% red 10% white ▪ PO Box 5609 Helderberg 7135 ▪ mail@ cordobawines.co.za ▪ www.cordobawines.co.za © 855-3744 🖷 *855-1690*

How's this for a glimpse of what it takes to establish a great vineyard? After planting about 10ha of cab franc, shiraz, cab in 2003, Chris Keet (the quintessential vinegrower — he likes to get his hands dirty) spent 2004 training each vine neatly into the form it will maintain 'for the next 25 years at least'. This means attending to 30 000 individual vines weekly for four months. Of course Keet's commitment is legendary, probably because he believes in the primacy of site-specific wines, reflecting the vineyard's identity and individuality — important in a competitive arena selling to increasingly discerning locals (Cordoba limits exports). 2004 wines show great aroma/colour concentration with a 97-style elegance, Keet says.

★★★★★ **Crescendo** Never obvious or showy, few Cape wines demand patience like this classically oriented example does; few likely to better reward many yrs of it. Always based on cab f, matured in new Fr oak, but blend varies. Complex & delightful **00** (★★★★★) had 32% merlot. **01** (more cab f-dominated at 78%) showed subtle voluptuousness, though balanced, seriously structured as ever. Spicy **02** (70% cab f, 20% merlot, 10% cab s) will eventually emerge from gaunt, sulky youth dominated by wood & big dry tannins — fruit is there under well-fleshed musculature. (If impatient now, decant well in advance.) Unusually (for Keet) high 14.5% alc gives finish warmth, detracting a little from customary elegance.

★★★★ **Merlot** This always one of Cape's more serious, focused. Refined, refreshing & persistent **01** (★★★★★) had characteristic roast coffee/dark choc notes over cherries & minty-leafy element. Slightly more severe **02**, particularly, a challenge for those who like merlot lush, overtly charming. Fragrant, savoury & well structured, this deserves attention, time, decanting, & food. 17 mths Fr oak, 20% new; 14% alc.

★★★★ **Chardonnay** Oak-fermented/matured (9 mths, 30% new) **03** suave, fresh, eminently drinkable — helped by easy 13% alc. Rounded but elegant, offering lime-marmalade and vanilla notes. No **02** — grapes not up to Cordoba standard.

Merlot-Cabernet Sauvignon NEW ★★★ Pleasing spicy-minty notes with plummy flavours. Typically dry, firm acid/tannin structure, but fruit lightish over these strong bones. 17 mths Fr oak, 20% new; 13.5% alc. **Shiraz** ★★★ Last of this occasional label was delicate, slightly green **01**. **Mount Claire Mountain Red** ★★★ **01** cab-merlot with dollop shiraz is soft, easily pleasant, unpretentious, but made without condescension. Lightly oaked; modest alc. Drink soon. — *TJ*

Count Agusta see Agusta

Country Cellars

These are the Spar chain of convenience stores' cork-closed wines. See under Carnival for the boxed range, and under Spar for news and contact details.

Country Cellars range

Cabernet Sauvignon ☺ ★★ Attractive, fruity **02**, smoothly rounded & soft, already fairly mature, so don't hold back — enjoy! **Merlot** ☺ ★★★ **03** ripe plum & bit of choc on a floral background, enlivened by clean tannins; serve lightly chilled in summer. **Chardonnay** ☺ ★★★ **04** (sample) peaches & cream character, deft oaky touch, rounded, fresh finish. To be enjoyed young. **Sauvignon Blanc** ☺ ★★★ **04** (sample) quaffable combination of soft fruit & brisk acid; gooseberries & guava tones ripely present.

Claret 03 blend ruby cab, shiraz not ready for tasting.

Non-vintage range

Rosé ☺ ★★★ Ripe-fruit flavours heightened & balanced by zingy acidity; chenin with tinting by pinotage. **Dry White** ☺ ★★★ Light-bodied glugger from chenin; tropical fruit salad tones, softly dry, lively. **Blanc de Blanc** ☺ ★★★ From colombard; round & fruity guava flavour, slightly sweet. **Late Harvest** ☺ ★★★ Latest version offers ripe guava tones, balanced sweetness, uncomplicated enjoyable quaffing. From chenin.

All NV, featuring new, more serious-looking packaging; alc around 12.5% unless noted. **Classic Red** ★★★ Best-selling wine in this stable. Outdoorish *vin ordinaire* from ruby cab (80%), pinotage, briefly wooded; latest bottling shows a pleasant tint of age, rounded dark berry fruit, touch oak, juicy tannins for easy drinking. **Caresse** ★ Low-alc (±7%) blanc de noir-style semi-sweet from chenin, pinotage; 1 000 ml. Current bottling is sweet & fruity, & shows a bit of age. **Light** ★ Light & bright to look at, but well developed on taste; still reasonably crisp though. Low alc (7.5%). **Stein** ★ Usually plain & simple but easy, lightish. Latest version from colombard & chenin untasted. — *DH*

Cowlin Wines

Paarl ▪ Est 2001 ▪ Tasting & sales Tue-Sun 10-4 Sat (winter only) 10-4 ▪ Fee R10 ▪ Dec-Mar deli/picnic lunches; May-Nov (Sat only) soups, breads & cheeses ▪ Closed Easter Fri, Dec 25, Jan 1 ▪ Tours by appt ▪ Facilities for children ▪ Farm produce ▪ Small tourgroups ▪ Walks ▪ Owners Cowlin & Malherbe families ▪ Vini consultant Hardy Laubser, with Rodney Zimba (2002/2003) ▪ Viti consultant Gideon Malherbe ▪ 17 ha (cab, merlot, shiraz, mourvèdre, chard, viognier) ▪ 130 tons 3 500 cs 90% red 10% white ▪ PO Box 174 Simondium 7670 ▪ cowlinwines@iafrica.com ▪ www.cowlinwines.co.za ✆ 874·3844 🖷 874·2948

With the doors open to the public for the first time, this friendly family farm in Simondium is picnic-ready (fill your basket from a deli selection featuring local cheeses and smoked trout). Sit on the verandah, under the trees or on the lawn overlooking a dam (into which a new cellar-water treatment plant dispenses water 'clean enough to drink'). Grapes took their time ripening last harvest; some straggled into the cellar a whole month later than usual. A new sorting table made light work of removing green grapes, leaves and stems.

★★★★ **Shiraz** NEW The new kingpin here; **02** exhibits good varietal character — hints pepper, smoked meat, lively red berry fruit — generous but accommodating tannins; all in an elegant, not overblown package. 13.5% alc. 6 mths oak, casks/staves.

★★★★ **Cabernet Sauvignon 00** (★★★) held back for maturation, so appears after **01**; meaty eucalyptus/herbal notes; firm tannins, fairly lean finish. **01** had a red-berry lead-in; full-flavoured but chewy, needs few yrs for tannins to settle.

★★★★ **Noble Hill** Stylish (wine & packaging) cab-driven blend with merlot; **00** sweetly fruited with red-berry nose, full rounded palate, well-managed tannins. No **01**. **02** 50/50 mix, generously oaked & showing it in grainy texture, very youthful still, touch savoury, needs yr/2 to settle. Paarl/Stbosch fruit.

Merlot ★★★★ **02** not a distinctive merlot, but a nice, plump juicy red; ripe manageable tannins. Yr Fr oak, none new. WO W-Cape, as is... **Cabernet Sauvignon-Petit Verdot** ★★★★ **01** forceful, slightly earthy 65/35 blend, holding up well; still deep hues; cigarbox whiffs from portion new Fr oak. Different. 14% alc. **Jack's Jug** NEW ★★★ Juicy, lively dry red with spicy stewed plum nose/palate; **03** appealingly rustic; 50/50 blend cab, merlot, 6 mths.staved. **Semillon-Chardonnay** NEW ★★★ 70/30 blend, 15 mths 2nd/3rd fill Fr oak; NV, brioche & lees whiffs, hint baked apple which reappears in creamy palate. For current enjoyment. All WO Coastal unless noted. — *TM*

Craighall

Popular range of early/easy drinkers, budget priced, from African Wines & Spirits.

Cabernet Sauvignon-Merlot ★★★ Comfortable standalone drink or food partner; **03** gaining bottle-age dried-fruit, gamey tones; pleasantly astringent dark cherry flavours. 66/33 mix. 13.6% alc. WO Rbtsn, as is... **Chardonnay-Chenin Blanc** ★★★ 51/49 blend; soft, fruity, med-bodied **03**, with melon & cut-grass flavours; holding up well, whereas... **Sauvignon Blanc** ★★ **03** somewhat tired mid-04; modest grapefruit aromas/flavours. 12% alc. WO W-Cape. Follow-up **04** untasted. — *TM*

Credo see Vinfruco

Crows Nest

Paarl ▪ Est/1stB 2003 ▪ Tasting & sales by appt ▪ Tours Mon-Sat 9-5 ▪ BYO picnic ▪ Farm produce ▪ Facilities for children ▪ Tourgroups ▪ Owners Marcel & Deidre de Reuck ▪ Winemaker Marcel de Reuck ▪ Viti consultant Paul Wallace (Aug 2003) ▪ 11 ha (cab, mourvèdre, shiraz, chard, viognier) ▪ 48 tons 4 000 cs 85% red 15% white ▪ PO Box 2571 Paarl 7620 ▪ dereuck@mweb.co.za ☎ 869·8712 🖷 869·8714

'Sometimes you wonder what you've let yourself in for,' sigh Marcel and Deidre de Reuck. 'Then you get a good result in a blind tasting and wonder why you never joined this silly, loving, passionate industry many years ago.' Being a boutique winery, they have to do everything themselves. Latest DIY installations include a new tasting centre. A wine producer's task is for more than simply to market wine, the de Reucks say. 'We believe we're selling happiness and pleasure.'

Marcel de Reuck range

★★★★ **Cabernet Sauvignon** NEW **03** succulent blackcurrant notes, dense tannins, elegant despite opulent textures.

★★★★ **Shiraz** NEW Attractive **02**'s super-ripe raspberry marzipan aromas, coconut whiffs, soft easy textures belie 14% alc. Barrel matured, 20% new, mostly Fr.

★★★★ **Cabernet Sauvignon-Merlot** (Last ed simply 'Marcel de Reuck') Retasted **02** with cassis/mulberry notes; ample tannins — mouth-puckering; now become somewhat austere & drying, with 14% alc showing.

Crows Nest range

Two **03** red blends. **La Karnel** ★★ Soft, vinous, insubstantial, food friendly. **Torres Claude** ★★ Unsupple with chunky dry tannins, 14% alc, like above. All above Dbnvlle fruit, but WO Coastal. — *MF*

Crucible see Cloof

Culemborg

This big-volume range of easy-drinkers (822 000 cases) is for export only; made by DGB. Most retasted for this ed; reds lightly seasoned with Fr oak chips. All WO W-Cape. **Cabernet Sauvignon ★★★ 03** maintains faster pace set by pvs; classic aromas/flavours of cassis, fennel & tobacco; dry but soft dusty tannins, easy drinking. **Merlot ★★★☆** Real red-velvet-curtain character in **02**; mouth-friendly, delectably soft, eager to please — now & for the next 2/3 yrs. 14.2% alc. **Pinotage ★★★ 03** subdued but quintessential mulberry aromas/flavours; soft, sweet jammy finish. **Cinsault ★★★** Warm, sweet almost jammy **03**, warmth reprised spicily on palate with plum pud flavours, grainy & savoury tannins. **Rosé ★★★ 04** strawberries & hints dried fruit; succulent, tangy fruit-cordial flavours, semi-dry & gluggable. **Chardonnay ★★★** Quaffable commercial style. **03** creamy notes of nuts & toffee, full melon/peach flavours, sweet finish, cream again in aftertaste. **Chenin Blanc ★★★** Sweet smelling **04**, fresh fruit salad aromas; bright juicy fruit, well balanced by zesty acidity. **Sauvignon Blanc ★★ 03** green-apple-toned palate; more muted than last yr, losing freshness. — *TM*

Culraithin see Coleraine

Dalla Cia Wine & Spirit Company [NEW]

Stellenbosch ▪ Est 2004 ▪ Closed to public ▪ Owner Giorgio dalla Cia ▪ 7 000 cs 11 Papegaai St Stellenbosch 7600 ▪ gdallacia@iafrica.com ▪ www.dallacia.com ℗/🖥 ☎ 843·3462

Giorgio Dalla Cia, after bowing out as Meerlust cellarmaster for a quarter-century, now has more time to devote to the top-class grappa he's been making with son George since 1996. It's a fragrant family tradition which began in Friuli, Italy over 70 years ago, and will continue in the present stilling house at Meerlust until new premises are found. The Dalla Cia wine range launched while at Meerlust will not only continue but expand, with a new Bordeaux-style red being readied for launch as the guide went to press. The wines are made Dalla Cia-style, without kowtowing to the market or to fashion. 'That would simply castrate their potential.'

Chardonnay ★★★ 03 fruitier style; lemons, limes with hint complementary toasty oak. Juicy, flavoursome mouthful with some leesy weight; rather obvious tail-end sweetness only detraction. 5% barrel-fermented/matured 9 mths. 14% alc. **Sauvignon Blanc ★★★** Dab honeyed bottle age interesting extra to **03**'s gently-paced minerally, tropical flavours. Cool, clean, dry; unobtrusive partner to wide range summer dishes. — *AL*

Danckaert see Citrusdal Cellars
Danford's see Klein Constantia
Danie de Wet see De Wetshof

Darling Cellars

Groenekloof (see Swartland map) ▪ Est/1stB 1996 ▪ Tasting & sales Mon-Thu 8-5 Fri 8-4 Sat 9-12 ▪ Fee R5 ▪ Closed Easter Fri/Sun, Dec 25 & Jan 1 ▪ BYO picnic ▪ Tours by appt ▪ Owners ±20 shareholders ▪ Cellarmaster Abé Beukes (Dec 1997) ▪ Winemakers Johan Nesenberend (reds, Dec 1996) & Albé Truter (whites, Dec 2003) ▪ Viti consultant Gawie Kriel (Sep 2001) ▪ 1 300 ha (cab, merlot, pinotage, shiraz, cinsaut, chard, chenin, sauvignon) ▪ 6 450 tons 120 000 cs own labels + 150 000 cs for clients, incl Kaapse Pracht & Woolworths ▪ 65% red 33% white 2% rosé ▪ BRC certified ▪ PO Box 114 Darling 7345 ▪ jsheppard@darlingcellars.co.za mnel@darlingcellars.co.za ▪ www.darlingcellars.co.za ℗ (022) 492·2276 🖷 (022) 492·2647

'This was one vintage where experience really counted,' says cellarmaster Abé Beukes of 2004. 'At one point there were seven different varieties in the cellar to be vinified simultaneously, as a result of some earlier varieties ripening later, and vice versa.' Helping to make light of the heavy going was experienced ex-Spruitdrift winemaker Albé Truter, who had joined just before the crush. All ended well, and the harvest on the whole shows good flavour concentration and moderate alcohol. Music to the ears of marketers locally and in the more than 12 countries they export to. Travellers on the new Darling wine route should call here for carefully made, well priced wines. Tip: winemaking colleagues are known to make special detours for Abé B's Black Granite Shiraz. 'They tell me they buy it by the case to drink at home.'

Onyx range

★★★★★ **Kroon** Cellar's flagship, an unusual blend shiraz, pinotage, grenache & cinsaut, fermented en famille & matured in small oak. **02** tweaks formula slightly: no Am oak, slightly less pinotage, fractionally more shiraz for final 50/40/5/5 ratio; yr barrelled, 80% new. Wood already well meshed mid-2004; aromas slightly muted but they cover wide spectrum (pepper, roast meat, dark plum); huge alc (15.2%) no detraction. **01** (45/45/5/5) had 10% Am oak; tighter, less approachable on release.

★★★★ **Cabernet Sauvignon** In a lesser vintage, **02** fares well. Plump, even bouncy ripe blackberry fruit, cedar whiff from 70% new Fr oak (up from 60% for last-tasted **00**); finish is slightly drier than expected, so careful monitoring suggested when cellaring. 14.4% alc. From ±10-yr-old dryland bushvines. **01** not made.

★★★★ **Pinotage** These are good adverts for the more extrovert, fruitier pinotage style. **02**, though enormous (15.4% alc), is balanced, not overripe. Classic mulberry tones end with spicy flourish. **01** was a fruit-bomb; ripe mulberry succulence sloshed with sweet vanilla. 14.4% alc. Yr oak, ±80/20 Fr/Am, ±40% new.

★★★★ **Shiraz** Generally more elegant than version below; **02** quietish on nose; palate livelier; peppery black fruit, well rounded, supple, sweetish finish (partly from big alc: 14.9%). **01** chunkier than pvs, showed real Swartland brawn in structure, concentration). Only Fr oak for this premium label; 50% new, ±yr.

★★★★ **Sauvignon Blanc 04** blend of two best vyds; riper, less herbal than version below (at 13%, not high in alc either); tropical tones; full peachy palate with citrus finish. WO Darling. **03** was robust & flavourful with invigorating acidity.

★★★★★ **Noble Late Harvest** We have noted how improbable **02** botrytised chenin seems on paper, given daunting sweetness (240g/ℓ RS). Retasted, it remains a revelation: smoother, richer than pvsly; viscous palate with concentrated tropical fruit, slight terpene hint; potently sweet, but alive with tangy fruit-acid (9.5g/ℓ) it races across the palate. 11.5% alc. Aged 5-9 mths Fr barrels, none new. **Barrel Selection** 🆕 Also (**02**), a choice of the 2 best casks, 14 mths older wood; drier (120g/ℓ), firmer, more elegant, less voluptuous; botrytis' darker tones more evident among the candied fruit flavours. All in this range WO Groenekloof unless noted.

DC range

★★★★ **Black Granite Shiraz ✓ 03** richly coloured, opulent & complex; Karoo bush whiffs; full bodied/flavoured & balanced, supple. **02** recalled sweet plum/mineral tone of pvs, slightly more distinct tannins. Combo staves, casks. ±14% alc.

Terra Hutton Cabernet Sauvignon ★★★★ Vinified for approachability, with few yrs in reserve. **02** blackcurrant aromas with mint & fennel; lively berry palate, grainy but supple tannins; sweet finish (4g/ℓ sugar). Yr older Fr oak. 14.2% alc. **Six Tonner Merlot** ★★★★ Widely appealing version of this variety; **03** open-textured & tasty; lively leaf & cassis aromas; soft, dark plum flavours. 8 mths older Fr barrels. Alc as above. **Old Block Pinotage** ★★★★ 35 yr old vyd delivers the goods; **02** sweet opening to vibrant, youthful plummy palate; gamey/meaty notes; powerful (15.7% alc) but well structured; should mature well. **Quercus Gold Chardonnay** ★★★ Lightish (12% alc), early picked & fairly straightforward; **04** apricot & sweet melon with hint butterscotch from well-handled oak chips. **Bush Vine Sauvignon Blanc** ★★★★ **04** back up to speed after dip pvs vintage; pleasing green tone, herbaceous, hint of lemongrass; lime/flint textures, coolly refreshing. Early picked (12% alc) dryland bushvines. This, ranges below, WO Coastal.

Zantsi Natural Sweet range

Rosé ★★★ Light-bodied sweetie from buket & cab, with coral pink hues, delicate strawberries & cream aromas, up-beat finish. More flavour/structure than... **White** ★★ 100% buket; shy, dusty nose; sweet-sour flavour. Both NV (03), ±9% alc.

Flamingo Bay range

Cinsaut-Cabernet Sauvignon ☺ ★★★ **04** sappy, easy 80/20 blend with spicy stewed plum notes, hint cinnamon, slightly savoury tail. **Lagoon Rosé** ☺ ★★★ Appropriately flamingo-pink easy-drinker; **04** changes from blend to straight pinotage, & from sweetish to dry; shy red-berry aromas, appealing strawberry-toned palate.

Chenin Blanc-Sauvignon Blanc ★★★ 'Sipper' rather than 'quaffer' this year: **04** bit sharp; shy herbal aromas, light body, dry limey flavours. – TM

Daschbosch Wine Cellar

Goudini (see Worcester map) ▪ Est 1956 ▪ 1stB 1965 ▪ Tasting & sales Mon-Fri 8-5 ▪ Tours by appt ▪ Closed public holidays ▪ BYO picnic ▪ Facilities for children ▪ Tourgroups ▪ Walks ▪ Conference facilities ▪ Owners 32 shareholders ▪ Winemakers Gerrit van Zyl & Johan Lötz (Jun 2000/ Jun 2004), with Wilhelm le Roux (Sep 2002) ▪ Viticulturist Gerrit van Zyl (Jun 2000) ▪ 860 ha (15 varieties, r/w) ▪ 14 700 tons 3 500 cs own label 50% red 40% white 10% fortified ▪ Ranges for customers: Welgevonde (Nthrlnds/Belgium); Louwshoek (Nthrlnds); Elephant Trail, Chiwara, Safeway & Kumala (UK) ▪ BRC certification in progress ▪ PO Box 174 Rawsonville 6845 ▪ cellar@daschbosch.co.za ▪ www.daschbosch.co.za ✆ **(023) 349·1110** 🖷 (023) 349·1980*

Now boasting a modern tasting area, Daschbosch can accommodate groups of up to 80 at any one time. Also new is a state-of-the-art white grape processing facility, advantageous given that a 65:35 white to red ratio is the production team's target. New to the team is Johan Lötz, ex-Deetlefs, who joined winemaker Reino Kruger in mid-2004. Daschbosch makes 11m litres of wine for clients, notably the Kumala range for Western Wines, which has found favour in Britain. Looking to reinforce its position as a supplier to the UK market, the winery is seeking British Retail Consortium accreditation

★★★★ **Ruby Cabernet** Well-made & -presented oaked example (±yr staves); ripely padded **01** ageing well; variety's grassy whiffs quite forward, juicy tannins, pleasurably drinkable now & for next yr/2. 14.5% alc.

★★★★ **Nectar de Provision** ✓ Cellar's long-time signature. First local version of Cognac's classic aperitif, Pineau des Charentes; colombard, fortified with 5/3 yr old brandy, yr barrelled post-fortification. Ages well & interestingly. Recent releases finer, more sophisticated than pvs; latest NV opens with orange & choc-mint flavours, hint vanilla; long, elegant, soothing finish. Has potential to develop into ★★★★ over 4-5 yrs if properly cellared. 16.5% alc.

Latest bottlings of **Pinotage** & **Merlot** not tasted. **Cabernet Sauvignon-Cabernet Franc** NEW ★★★ 60/40 mixture no apparent oaking; muted aromas of mint & ripe plum; well rounded, drinkable. 14% alc. **Chardonnay** ★★★ Light-toned everyday white; **03** retasted, shows a fairly prominent vanilla-butterscotch tone, bottle-age character more subtle now but probably not for much longer – drink soon. **Sauvignon Blanc** ★★★★ **03** has become rounder & more interesting with yr in bottle; fresh, clean acidity will make lively drinking this summer. **Louwshoek-Voorsorg Hanepoot** ★★★ Traditional fortified dessert not retasted; last we noted **99** was very sweet yet finished clean. 17% alc. – DH

> *David Frost Wines* see Frost Vineyards
> *DC Wines* see Darling Cellars
> *Decent Red* see Barrydale

De Compagnie

Wellington ▪ Est/1stB 2002 ▪ Tasting & tours by appt ▪ Fee R10 ▪ Sales Mon-Fri 8-4.30 or by appt ▪ Meals for groups of 2-30 by appt ▪ Owners 2 shareholders ▪ Vini consultant Anna-Mareè Mostert-Uys (Aug 2002), with Matewis Thabo (Jun 2003) ▪ Viti consultant Johan Wiese (Oct 2002) ▪ 16 ha (cabs/f, merlot, pinotage, shiraz, chard, chenin) ▪ 85 tons 1 000 cs own label 70% red 30% potstill brandy ▪ Range for customers: Bugatti's ▪ PO Box 395 Wellington 7654 ▪ mail@decompagnie.co.za ▪ www.decompagnie.co.za © 864·1241 ☎ 864·3620

If you close your eyes in the stillness of this Wellington *werf* you may well imagine you hear the creak of ox-wagons as they made their way over the mountains at the start of the Great Trek. Afrikaans author Riana Scheepers and husband Johann Laubser, CEO of Dominion Wine, are the present owners, and they've gone to enormous lengths to re-store the old homestead, with its shady verandah and *rietdak* (Malay master builders in-sisted on sleeping outside after they encountered a ghost, thought to be Anna Lategan, the widow who farmed here in the late 1700s). In addition to their own wine, made with Anna-Mareè Mostert-Uys, the Laubsers own the smallest registered still in the country (ca 1849). They plan to release a 10 year old potstill brandy to coincide with the farm's 300th anniversary this year.

★★★☆ **Privaatkeur** This Bdx-style blend (50/50 cab/merlot) & straight Cab below have settled since tasted last yr & lost their showy exuberance, show more of the **02** vintage character, tannins revealed through sour cherry/raspberry fruit; 6 mths Fr-oaked, none new; 12.5% alc. Suggest drink this & Cab soonish; **03** (sample) features dash cab f (8%), bigger wine (14% alc), deeply flavoured.

★★★☆ **Cabernet Sauvignon 02**, yr on, shows good touch bottle-age to warm fruit, & slight herbaceous edge not pvsly apparent, 13% alc. Oak as above. **03** (preview) more complexity, lots of strong, ripe tannins.

Chardonnay NEW **04** (unrated sample) clean acidic grip to rounded peach/passionfruit flavours; hint sweet spice though unwooded. — *DH*

Debutante see Jacaranda
De Denne see Du Preez Estate

De Doorns Winery

*Worcester ▪ Est 1968 ▪ Tasting & sales Mon-Fri 8-5 Sat 8-12 ▪ Winemaker/manager Danie Koen, with Neil Strydom ▪ PO Box 129 De Doorns 6875 ▪ ddwk@mweb.co.za ©/☎ **(023) 356·2835** ☎ (023) 356·2101*

This co-op in the scenic Hex River Valley has a friendly, welcoming face in the form of a Cape Dutch 'wine house' near the N1 highway, open on weekdays and Saturday morn-ings. Regulars on the wine list are a Cab, Roodehof Dry Red, Chardonnay, Chenin, Colombar, Late Harvest, Red Muscadel, Hanepoot and Demi-sec Sparkling, none tasted.

Deetlefs Estate

Rawsonville (see Worcester map) ▪ Est 1822 ▪ Tasting, sales & tours Mon-Fri 8-5 Sat 10-4 ▪ Closed Easter Fri, Dec 25 & Jan 1 ▪ Picnic baskets by appt or BYO ▪ Traditional 'lapa' enter-tainment area for functions ▪ Owner Kobus Deetlefs ▪ Winemaker Willie Stofberg (Aug 2004) ▪ Viticulturist Coenie van Dijk (Sep 2003) ▪ 100 ha (cab, malbec, merlot, pinotage, shiraz, chard, chenin, sauvignon, semillon) ▪ 40% red 50% white 5% rosé 5% fortified ▪ BRC certification in progress ▪ PO Box 36 Rawsonville 6845 ▪ sales@deetlefs.com ▪ www. deetlefs.com © (023) 349·1260 ☎ (023) 349·1951

Restructuring at this Rawsonville estate, in the family since 1822, has seen substantial growth over the past decade. This is manifest in the newly formed Deetlefs Group, which includes a fully equipped, independent laboratory; bottling and labelling line; processing cellar; temperature-controlled warehousing; and what is believed to be the only com-plete biological wastewater treatment plant at a winery in SA (the resultant water clean enough to irrigate the vineyard). The entrepreneurial winegrower at the centre of this mini conglomerate, Kobus Deetlefs, always has a surprise up his vinous sleeve, be it the first MCC from these parts or a fortified muscat dessert, a quarter-century in the making.

★★★☆ **Merlot 02** lifted floral aromas, moderate alc (13%), controlled sweet-fruit profile all add up to satisfying light-textured mouthful; gentle tannins for instant accessibility.

★★★☆ **Sauvignon Blanc** Ex their vyd nearest Du Toitskloof Mountains, shaded from pm sun; **04** bursts with ripe fig & tropical fruit, welcoming, easy to drink.

★★★★ **Brut Cap Classique** First MCC from this part of the Breede River Valley; **00** limited release of 900 bottles, expensively packaged; vigorous & youthful; attractively light & brisk; mainly chardonnay, with interesting top-notes contributed by dashes semillon & riesling; base-wines 8-9 mths oaked, ±30 mths on lees.

★★★★ **Muscat d'Alexandrie** Superb old muscat, a rarity, to be released only every 25 yrs. **74** shows caramel, butterscotch, treacle bouquet; rich unctuous palate (though not over-sweet) with contrasting coffee & molasses flavours, balanced by firm acidity; slips away to seemingly endless dry finish. Individual, exotic, to drink by the thimbleful at end of a fine dinner. 14.7% alc.

Pinotage ★★★☆ **03**, yr on, rounded & supple now; finishes with morello cherry tang. **Shiraz** ★★★ Winemakers' goal of elegance achieved with 50% barrel-fermented **02**, red fruit & pepper tones, pronounced but accommodating tannins. **Chardonnay 04** (sample), as pvsly, part-barrel-matured (±40%, 20% through malo), so ripe tropical fruit dominates slight butteriness; upbeat citrus bite. Likely ★★★★ on release. **Chenin Blanc** ★★★☆ Full-bodied unwooded style, extended *sur lie* maturation for creamier mouthfeel. **03** pleasingly rounded, with melon/pineapple hints; preview of **04**, full of Granny Smith apple zing. **Semillon** ★★★☆ Subtle oak support (only 35% barrelled, 20% through malo), which presents as fleeting smoky touch to **02**'s bright limy taste, ends with dried-fruit uplift. **03** not ready for tasting. **Weisser Riesling** ★★★ Off-dry **03** was the last tasted; soft, fruity flavours. WO Brde Rvr Vlley.

Stonecross range

Pinotage ★★★ Cherry-toned **04** undoubtedly pinotage, grape's firm tannins impart a certain tautness; need yr/2 to soften, settle. **Merlot-Pinotage** ★★★ **04** (sample) attractively chewy mix cherries & juicy tannins, braai-friendly but could also be cellared. **Rosé** ★★ Dry version. Last tasted was lightish & lively **03**. **Chenin Blanc-Chardonnay** ★★★ **04** delicious, soft peachy curves, plump profile, easy but good underlying fruit, attractive touch fruit-sweetness. 80/20 blend. **Sauvignon Blanc-Semillon** ★★★ **04** appealing dry aperitif-style 60/40 blend with refreshing lemon-lime flavours. All WO W-Cape. — *DH*

De Heuvel Estate see Bianco

De Hoopen

Napier • 1stB 2001 • Tasting & sales at Vindigo Wine & Décor Co Mon-Fri 9.30-5.30 Sat 9. 30-4.30 • Closed Easter Fri & Dec 25 • Gifts, art & collectibles • Owners Nick Yell & Joe Toweel • 108 Sarel Cilliers Street Napier 7270 © (028) 423·3069

This is the in-house range of Vindigo Wine & Décor Co, the wine shop and collectibles gallery in Napier owned by Joe Toweel and Nick Yell. The characterful Shiraz Barrel Reserve, made to their specs by Luddite's Niels Verburg, not retasted, is still available.

Dekker's Valley see Mellasat

De Krans

Calitzdorp (see Little Karoo map) • Est 1964 • 1stB 1977 • Tasting & sales Mon-Fri 8-5 Sat 9-3 • Tasting fee for groups R10 pp • Closed Easter Fri/Sun, Dec 25 • Tours by appt • Vintners platters 12-2 Wed & Sat during Feb (pick your own hanepoot grapes) • BYO picnic • Olive oil sold • Tourgroups • Self-guided vineyard walks year round • Owners/winemakers Boets & Stroebel Nel (1982, 1988) • Viti consultant Willem Botha (2001) • 42 ha (cab, pinotage, tempranillo &

port varieties, chard, chenin & muscats) ▪ *500 tons* ▪ *20–25 000 cs 50% red 10% white 3% rosé 37% fortifieds* ▪ *PO Box 28 Calitzdorp 6660* ▪ *diekrans@mweb.co.za* ▪ *www.dekrans.co. za* ⓒ *(044) 213·3314/64* 📠 *(044) 213·3562*

Their forte is top-class desserts, but brothers Boets and Stroebel Nel are striking out in a new direction with their latest release, Red Stone. It is an unfortified dry red, made with the same varieties used to fashion their widely acclaimed ports. Inspiration springs partly from port's traditional home in Portugal, the Douro Valley, lately making some impressive table wines from the native red varieties. Besides the blend, the Nels have a trio of stand-alone port-grape bottlings, Touriga, Tempranillo (known as tinta roriz in Portugal) and another tinta — Barocca. All are available for sampling at the tasting room below the dramatic mountain which gives Red Stone its name. Cooler-than-normal 2004 may turn out to be a repeat of the exceptional 1997, the Nel brothers venture; the table-reds 'look good', though the jury's still out. The verdict for port is in, however: an unequivocal *mooi*!

★★★☆ **Red Stone Reserve** 🆕 **03** flagship red blend touriga (70%), cab; named for the area's red stone hills & aiming to express its terroir. A gentle giant, with eucalyptus & mixed berry aromas, cassis & dark fruit palate. Alc 13.5%. Substantial tannins, hints Cdorp dust. Depth & structure for cellaring. 10 mths Fr oak, 50% new.

★★★☆ **Tempranillo** ✓ Plaudits to the Nels for bottling less familiar varieties. **03** deeper than pvs thanks to splash cab. Seductive vanilla nose gently mutes subtle clove & cardamom whiffs. Signature sour cherry on palate with silky tannins. 6 mths oak, 25% Am. 13.5% alc. From relatively young vines.

★★★☆ **Touriga Nacional** ✓ Maiden **00** was another SA first. **03** appealing Xmas cake nose expected from this stalwart port variety. Savoury palate with solid tannins matched by exuberant plum fruit. Drink or cellar 3–4yrs. 5 mths wood; alc 14%.

★★★★ **White Muscadel Jerepigo** ✓ **03** at 195g/ℓ, continues trend to drier style (**02** 210g/ℓ, pvs sweeter still). Picked before too many grapes could raisin to preserve spicy muscat aromas; hints candied peaches & pears. Ideal on ice as aperitif or, sans the rocks, with blue-veined cheese. Drink now and over 10 yrs. 15.5% alc.

★★★★ **White Muscadel Reserve** ✓ **03** from 18 yr old muscat de F. Exquisite rose-petal, nut & lychee melange with warming alc; understandably popular in northern Europe. Sugar & alc (160g/ℓ, 15.5%) both a bit lower than **02** — sweet, but fresh acid to balance.

★★★★★ **Vintage Reserve Port** Great presence from classic port varieties, 'declared' only in outstanding vintages. Tinta & touriga increasingly important in blend (85%+) with souzão 10%, tinta r. Fortified with unmatured spirit; 16 mths 4 000ℓ vats. **02** Peter Schulz 2004 award winner; softer tannins, opulent black fruit make this more approachable in infancy than **01**, but has structure for decade-plus. Slightly less sugar than pvs (90g/ℓ vs 95), more alc (20% vs 19.5). **01** classically, generously built, dense. VDG, 91 pts *WS*. No **00**.

★★★★ **Cape Vintage Port** ✓ One of SA's soundest. **02** from tinta b, touriga, souzão, tinta r (55/35/10). Spicy aromas of red boiled sweets & citrus, also exotic whiff pomegranate. Delicious & drinkable early (flies with Air Namibia) though best matured min 2-3 yrs. Integrated 19% alc. Fruitcake, ripe plums in beautifully compact **01**. These 12-15 mths old 500ℓ oak.

★★★★ **Cape Tawny Port** ✓ Sexy fireside warmer; latest mostly tinta b with touriga, tinta r, cinsaut; avg age of wines 8 yrs, freshened with dash younger touriga port. Attractive old-bronze colour dazzles in new 'frosted' bottle. Rich, with dark toffee & caramel bouquet; weighty & sweet (104g/ℓ sugar). NV. WO W-Cape (others all own grapes). Also in 375ml.

★★★★ **Cape Ruby Port** ✓ Latest (NV) continues lively, youthful style. Mulled wine character with citrus tang & layered Indian spice finish. Blend tinta, touriga, souzão (50/45/5), 18.5% alc, 95g/ℓ sugar. Yr 500ℓ casks. Also in 250ml screwcaps.

Chenin Blanc ☺ ★★★ 2 mths on lees add texture to watery white, lightish, bone-dry **04**, with lemon-blossom scents. **Chardonnay** ☺ ★★★ Unwooded **04** offers toasted nut, almond pith & elegant citrus, with rounded mouthfeel from 3 mths on lees.

Cabernet Sauvignon ★★★ Very approachable **03** step up from pvs; sweet vanilla/clove nose, approachable tannins (only 4 mths oak) & ripe cassis palate. **Pinotage** ★★★ **03** continues the upward quality trend. Mulberry & strawberry infused with cinnamon. Forgiving tannins but not-so-forgiving alc (14%) for quaffing. **Tinta Barocca** ★★★ Easy-drinking, light-flavoured, savoury unoaked **03**, peppery fruit, bramble flavours with dusty tannins, refreshing finish. **Merlot-Pinotage** NEW ★★★ **03** 60/40 unwooded blend, nudging 4g/ℓ sugar. Sweet plum nose from merlot, slight bitter grip from pinotage. Sweet & sour cherry flavours. Welcome addition to the picnic basket. **Rosé** ★★★ **03** a super glassful. Unoaked, melding various red grapes. Bubblegum flavours may suggest easy quaffing but note 13.5% alc. **Spumanté** ★★ Semi-sweet fizz, usually with some honeyed richness. NV not tasted for this ed. **Golden Harvest** ★★★ Latest 'bottled sunshine' proffers honeysuckle & lemon; tastes far less sweet than 40g/ℓ sugar would suggest. 13.5% alc. Great winter tipple. Best young. NV. **Heritage Collection White Jerepigo** ★★★ **01** from lightly botrytised gewürz. Label features Honey Badger; profits go to nature conservation education. Golden-hued, with 'ocean rock pool', dried apples & pears on nose; flavours of glacé sultanas. **White Port** ★★ Latest NV from chenin more oxidative than some recent releases, with macadamia nut & kerosene notes. Steely grip. Try as an alternative aperitif to sherry. 19.5% alc. – *CvZ*

Delaire Winery 🍴❍👁👌

Stellenbosch ▪ Est 1982 ▪ 1stB 1986 ▪ Tasting & sales Mon-Fri 9-5 Sat/ Sun 10-5 ▪ Fee R10 + R12 glass deposit ▪ Closed Easter Fri, Dec 25/26 & Jan 1 ▪ Tours by appt ▪ Gifts ▪ Owner Laurence Graff ▪ Winemaker Gunter Schultz (Jan 2004) ▪ Viticulturist Benjamin Booysen (Oct 2002) ▪ ±19 ha (cabs s/f, merlot, petit v, chard, sauvignon) ▪ 95 tons 7 500 cs 60% red 40% white ▪ PO Box 3058 Stellenbosch 7602 ▪ delaire@iafrica.com ▪ www.delairewinery.co.za ©
885·1756 🖷 885·1270

New Year's Day 2004 heralded a clean sweep at this view-rich winery perched above Stellenbosch. New owner Laurence Graff, a London 'rock star' (think diamonds) bought the farm; Gunter Schultz, he of three Schultz winemaking brothers (Carl at Hartenberg, Rudi at Thelema) arrived from Waterford; and plans were put in place for a new look to the property – a new cellar for vintage 2006 (which is when the first petit verdot deliver), a new restaurant and a new tasting area. En passant, plantings of cab, sauvignon, chardonnay, merlot and a bit of shiraz continue, and the installation of irrigation nears completion. The new winemaker is lyrical about his first Delaire harvest, which yielded 'an exceptional cab franc vintage' and 'well above average' quality for all other cultivars.

★★★★★ **Botmaskop** A statement, only in yrs 'when conditions are excellent for red wine'; 100% cab, made 'one-third Old World-style & two-thirds New'. Small quantities (130-150 cs), big mouthfuls — packed with savoury spice, blackcurrants, dry tannins in releases to date; to date **98**, **00**, now **02**, gorgeous; soft & silky, by no means a blockbuster (only 13% alc), elegant, drinking really well already, balanced fruit & oak. 70% new oak, Fr/Am/Russian (±80%, 10, 5), 18 mths. After peak above farm, with view of False & Table Bays.

★★★★ **Merlot** Massive, premium-priced, showcase wine, bottled only in top yrs. From cool, high vyd, easterly aspect, only few hrs daily sun in height of summer. Nothing since **00**, with slight savoury, organic whiffs. Limited (±250 cs) production.

★★★★ **Cabernet Sauvignon-Merlot** All-purpose ready-on-release red, most yrs in ±60:40 varietal ratio; tannins eased by sweet-berry succulence. Embroidered by Am, Fr, Russian oaks as above. Higher % cab (85) in **01** good strong cassis nose with slight earthy seasoning, pleasing dry firmness. Showing hardly any age mid-2004; food-friendly, as always. Pvs **00** showed some incipient mushroom tones.

★★★★ **Chardonnay Barrique** Oaked version pvsly in broad, weighty butterscotch-cara-
mel style, esp up to **00**, whereafter crisper fruit grip, leavened with usual spectrum
barrel flavours. **04** harks back to old style: no unoaked portion (all fermented/9
mths Fr barrels), soft, sweet, easy if unclassic 6g/ℓ sugar. Peach & cream whiffs,
burnt match hints, well-defined apple & melon flavours. Sample should maintain
pedigree of pvs.

★★★☆ **Chardonnay Unwooded** 'Inox' in pvs ed. Unoaked style strives for unadorned
fruit impact; from separate vyds yielding spectrum of flavours (Granny Smith apple, ripe Golden Delicious, quince etc). **04** (sample) shy nettle/herb aromas;
green melon/apple flavours; nicely put together; whistle-clean.

★★★☆ **Sauvignon Blanc Barrel-Matured** Last we tasted **02**, food wine with oak flavours joining gooseberry & grapefruit on palate.

★★★★ **Sauvignon Blanc** ✓ From selected mountain vyds picked at varying degrees of
ripeness to cover whole flavour spectrum. **03** had rich tropical flavour plumped out
with grain sugar (5g/ℓ), mouthfilling alc (14%). No such adornment for **04** (sample),
understated but multi-faceted: pear/capsicum whiffs; flinty, mineral backbone; nice
touch of guava; crisply dry. very attractive & probably best in flush of youth.

'Delaire' 🆕 (To be renamed) Slated to replace Cab-Merlot, features those grapes plus
cab f (50/38/12) in impressively black **03**; absolute buckets of pure blackcurrant fruit,
very compact & chunky, fair lacing of oak on palate in our pre-fining sample, but should
settle down & realise its ★★★★ promise. Oak as for B Kop, 12 mths. — *TM*

▪ *De Leuwen Jagt* see Seidelberg

Delheim

*Stellenbosch ▪ 1stB 1972 ▪ Tasting & sales Mon-Fri 9-5 Sat 9-3.30 Sun 10.30-3.30 (Oct-Apr) ▪
Fee R15 ▪ Tours Mon-Fri 10.30 & 2.30 Sat 10.30 ▪ Closed Easter Fri/Sun, Dec 25 & Jan 1 ▪
Delheim Restaurant; also cheese platters ▪ Tourgroups ▪ Gifts ▪ Farm produce ▪ Winemakers
Brenda van Niekerk & Karen Mouton (2003) ▪ Viticulturist/cellarmaster Victor Sperling (Aug
1993) ▪ 150 ha (15 varieties, r/w) ▪ 60 000 cs 70% red 28% white 2% rosé ▪ PO Box 10
Koelenhof 7605 ▪ delheim@delheim.com ▪ www.delheim.com ℂ 888·4600 🖷 888·4601*

Delheim is another to report a difficult 2004 due to uneven ripening, with a consequently
smaller yield. But Victor Sperling, son of irrepressible owner Spatz, who put Delheim on
the map, says winemaker Brenda van Niekerk is more than satisfied with the quality. Sister Nora Sperling-Thiel (marketing/sales) has also had a busy year, hosting an international 'cross-over' tasting with two other family-owned wineries: Johanninger in
Germany and Canadian cellar Malivoire. As a result of a decade-long association with
Malivoire winemaker Ann Sperling (the shared surname, though it drew them together, is
coincidental), Ann has collaborated with the Delheim team to produce a new Sperling &
Sperling Rosé for release in Canada. This year Van Niekerk launches her first Malbec.

Vera Cruz Estate range

★★★★★ **Shiraz** Modern styling, with darkly gorgeous velvet over firm structure — impressive since maiden **98** (★★★★★), IWSC gold. **00** attractively fragrant, well-structured & savoury. VDG. **01** retasted mid-2004 shows lovely sweet fruit slowly
absorbing oak; still need to wait for max pleasure. 91 pts *WS*. Oak: Fr, Hungary, Am
(20%); 50% new. Both 14.5% alc.

Delheim range

★★★★ **Grand Reserve** Enduring success for this trail blazing flagship; sometimes
blended, latterly 100% cab; latest **01** with 2% merlot. Classy cassis, tea-leaf & cinnamon bouquet; darkly handsome fruit cosseted in fine oak, with house's signature
approachable tannins, classic dry finish. 14% alc. **00** with a big dry tannic structure
These ±18 mths Fr oak, 40% new. 13.7% alc.

★★★☆ **Cabernet Sauvignon 02** also shows evidence of difficult vintage, but underlying class obvious. Intense blackcurrant cordial, hints tar & toast, fruit slightly

muted, tannins cleverly worked to approachability, finish tad awkward. Yr Fr oak, 25% new. 13.5% alc. **01** rather austere & dominated by woody tannin.

★★★★ **Merlot** ✓ Attractive cassis, whiffs cool mint & cedar. Restrained, neat build, mulberry ripeness, soft tannins in **02**, made with regard to merlot's more delicate tannic structure. Sample **03** similarly soft fruited, less tannic. These supportively oaked, ±yr Fr; 13.5% alc.

★★★☆ **Pinotage** Self-conscious version — no varietal extrovertness. Rather, a pleasant red from difficult **02** harvest (★★★). Dry, earthy, hints of plum, tannins manageable, tangy finish with slight bitterness, also showing on **01**. Yr 70/30 Fr/Am oak.

★★★★ **Shiraz 02** aromas of the spice souk — nutmeg, crushed coriander, sweet cinnamon — with supple dark-berried fruits. Sleek, well groomed & eager to please, longish dry finish. Such a charmer. Sample **03**, shade more intense, similarly handsome. Both ±yr oak, mostly Fr, 14% alc.

★★★☆ **Chardonnay 03** bright, polished lemon-scented fruit, graceful curves but not overweight, balanced; showcases fine grapes. For those who like their chards lightly oaked. 20% only, Fr oak, 7 mths. **02** (★★★) offered light citrusy flavours.

★★★☆ **Chardonnay sur Lie** More weighty than above, flavours resonate in lower key. **03** rich, ripe citrus given good whack of oak, not yet fully integrated, some lifting acidity but could do with dab more. These 9 mths Fr oak, ±40% new. **02** (★★★) was dominated by oak. These need yr before opening.

★★★★ **Edelspatz Noble Late Harvest 03** fabulously scented fruit cornucopia spilling Seville orange, minty pineapple, apricot & honey. Richly sweet but in manageable modern proportions (120g/ℓ). Delicious lingering finish seems never-ending. 12% alc. Unoaked, from Rhine Riesling. Pvs was **02** (★★★☆), with shortish finish.

Pinotage Rosé ★★☆ Almost dry **04**, jujube like flavours, high toned & estery. Firm acidity, 9% muscat for added interest. **Sauvignon Blanc** ★★★ **04** solid dry white, modest sauvignon character, crying out for food. Citrus flavours, echoes of gooseberry, zippy acid. 13.5% alc. **Spatzendreck Late Harvest** ★★★ **04** all chenin, wafting pineapple, grapefruit; attractive fresh sweetness. A winner this yr. **Cap Classique Brut 03** not tasted. **Chenin Blanc-Sauvignon Blanc** NEW in **03**, has converted to Heerenwijn.

Dry Red ☺ ★★★ Trusty all sorts red, led by cab & pinotage in **03**. Properly dry, meaty, savoury flavours. Staves/Fr oak, 8 mths. Quaffable 12.5% alc. **Heerenwijn** ☺ ★★★ Deserves a permanent berth as super-quaffer. Bracing & brisk as a sea-dip, **04** notch up for more fruit, better concentration in new blend sauvignon/chenin. Riper, too at 13.5% alc. Bone-dry. **Gewürztraminer** ☺ ★★★★ **04** more Turkish Delight than rosepetal, semi-sweet at 25g/ℓ sugar, beautifully balanced by zingy acidity. Lovely. — *IvH*

Dellrust Wines

Stellenbosch (see Helderberg map) ▪ Est/1stB 1998 ▪ Tasting & sales Mon-Fri 8-5 Sat by appt (phone office or 082·771·3090) ▪ Closed public holidays ▪ Tours on request ▪ Play area for children ▪ Owner Albert Bredell ▪ Winemakers Albert Bredell & Arno Cloete ▪ Viticulturist Francois Hanekom (Jul 2003) ▪ 97 ha (11 varieties, r/w) ▪ 800 tons 6 000 cs own label 75% red 25% white ▪ PO Box 5666 Helderberg 7135 ▪ dellrust@mweb.co.za ▪ www.dellrust.co.za ℂ 842·2752/842·2457 🖷 842·2456

A frustrating and very drawn-out harvest proved worth the wait, rewarding winemaker Arno Cloete with concentrated wines and deep, intense colours in the reds. Other than a thunderstorm which kicked out the electricity mid-pumpover, things are moving along peacefully, Cloete reports, 'though new plantings of cab, merlot and petit verdot are sure to change all of that in the near future'. The farm has been mapped according to soil type, and data thus gleaned is helping new viticulturist Francois Hanekom, who previously tended table grapes in Piketberg, decide which rootstock and varieties should be planted.

★★★★ **Three Vines** Cellar's flagship, harmonious blend merlot, pinotage, shiraz; selected blocks vinified & blended pre-maturation in small Fr oak, ±14 mths. Still-available

01 (★★★★) approaching peak; shiraz now uppermost on nose with hint cigarbox; still well-fruited, elegant. **03** 40/30/30 ratio; darker, chunkier; plummy; hint toast/lead-pencil (from 5% Am barrels?). 14% alc. **02** skipped.

★★★★ **Tinta Barocca-Cinsaut** Current **02** repeats pvs 50/50 formula; appealing spicy nose with hint cloves; supple, juicy flavours of choc-coated blackcurrants. Staves/barrels, 8 mths. 14.5% alc. **03** (sample) seems lighter textured/structured.

★★★★ **Cape Vintage** First release **00**, retasted, gentle plum jam whiffs; soft, silky palate, not a lot of grip. 18 mths Fr oak. 500ml. No **01**. Next **02** (barrel sample) very different: livelier fruit, bigger structure; unusual hedgerow tone with hint coconut; slightly bigger alc (19.5%). Total 24 mths Fr casks. 88/12 tinta, touriga.

Merlot 02 (sample) plumper, richer than pvs, none of the herbal character; youthful still, ample ripe fruit to match the tannins. Potential ★★★. 13 mths Fr oak, further yr bottle age. 13.5% alc. **Pinotage** ★★★ **02** more elegant & drinkable than pvs; ripe mulberry fruitiness to the fore. 14 mths Fr oak. 14.6% alc. **Shiraz** NEW **03** barrel sample clearly enthusiastically oaked: vanilla blanket over quite taut sour-plum flavour; earthy/meaty extras. New wood, 40% Am, yr. Likely ★★★★. **Jerepigo** ★★★★ ✓ Different & interesting NV (02), from botrytised chenin, 16% alc. Gaining complex dried peach/apricot aromas; lovely richness, silkiness to palate. — *TM*

De Meye Wines

Stellenbosch ▪ Est/1stB 1998 ▪ Tasting & sales Mon-Fri 9.30-5 Sat 9.30-2 ▪ Closed Easter Fri, Dec 25/26 ▪ Tours by appt ▪ Home-grown lavender, lavender essential oil & olive oil ▪ Owner JWW Myburgh ▪ Winemaker Marcus Milner (Sep 1999), with Aby Bodlani (Sep 2000) ▪ Viticulturist Philip Myburgh ▪ 60 ha (cab, shiraz, pinotage, chard) ▪ 13 000 cs 90% red 10% white ▪ PO Box 20 Muldersvlei 7607 ▪ demeye@cybertrade.co.za ▪ www.demeye.co.za ✆ 884·4131 ▤ 884·4154

A favourite with the powerful of politics and the big of business who dine at The Bombay Club in Washington DC is De Meye Chardonnay, served by the glass. Such a favourite that when stocks ran low, Philip Myburgh and Marcus Milner, viti and vini men respectively, had an urgent request from management: could they air-freight several cases with a dash of speed, to tide them over until the next shipment arrived? Myburgh and Milner are optimistic they'll satisfy customers with vintage 2004: 'If everything goes right in the cellar, it's going to be memorable.' Visitors note: there's now olive oil on sale at the farm.

★★★★ **Trutina** Second-vintage **01** drinking well, & still getting places, mixing generous warm fruit & classic structure, like **00**. Rich, powerful (13.6% alc) cab-shiraz blend — no variety dominant, with the mineral quality shared by all these characterful reds. Big, ripe but refined tannins, savoury acidity, well-judged oak (2 yrs Fr, 40% new): the Latin name (justified) means 'balance'. Sample **02**, dominated by cab (85% of blend), in youth showing more grainy tannins, touch less fruit depth, freshness.

★★★★ **Cabernet Sauvignon** Firm, savoury **01** has good varietal character, bright fruit, some earthy notes. 16 mths Fr oak, 20% new. 14% alc. **02** (★★★) less powerful (13.5% alc), lighter texture, not as charming, but classic; unfiltered.

★★★★ **Shiraz** SAA-selected **01**'s fragrant, sweet-fruited nose leads to well structured palate, with subtle fruitiness & note of mineral complexity; deliciously approachable but understated. Similar warmly attractive character on **02** (★★★★ ✓), but fuller, deeper, with lovely fruit. 17 mths Fr oak; unfiltered.

★★★★ **Chardonnay** ✓ **03** developing beautifully: powerful, balanced structure carries big flavours (spice, nuts, orange-peel) to lengthy, confident finish. Fr oak (50% new) contributes attractively without domineering. Barrel sample of **04** also full, richly textured — perhaps softer, rounder. — *TJ*

De Mooie Opstal see Bon Cap

De Morgenzon

Stellenbosch ▪ Owners Wendy & Hylton Appelbaum ▪ Manager Anton Ferreira ▪ Viti consultant Kevin Watt (Sep 2003) ▪ PO Box 1388 Stellenbosch 7599 ▪ demorgenzon@absamail. co.za ✆ **881·3030** 🖷 881·3773

Formerly the home of L'Emigré/Nutwood Grove wines, this prime property on the highest slopes of the Stellenboschkloof is being overhauled by new owners Hylton and Wendy Appelbaum. After detailed terrain analysis, 50ha of a 'fruit salad' of varieties (including hárslevelü and 'suspect' zinfandel) is being replanted to classics (5ha of very old chenin remain). Viticulturist Kevin Watt and farm manager Anton Ferreira follow eco-friendly principles, including bio-diverse habitats, alien vegetation eradication (reviving a long-dry spring) and fynbos restoration. Says Appelbaum: 'Great wine inevitably expresses the earth in which it grows.' Their 'great wine'? A combination of New World fruit and Old World elegance, expressive of the site. Their yet-to-be-appointed winemaker 'should share this vision'. A new winery will arise from building renovations.

Denneboom

Paarl ▪ 1stB 2003 ▪ Closed to public ▪ Owner Daniel de Waal ▪ Winemaker/viticulturist Hannes Aucamp ▪ 35 ha (cab, pinotage, shiraz) ▪ 300 tons 100 cs 100% red ▪ PO Box 2087 Windmeul 7630 ▪ hannesaucamp@mweb.co.za ✆/🖷 **869·8073**

The latest seat on the bench of emerging red wine producers along Perdeberg Mountain has been taken by Denneboom. Hannes Aucamp, with a long-held passion for wine (he's a contemporary of Johan Malan, sharing early working years in Simonsig's vineyards), persuaded owner Neil de Waal (uncle of Scali's Willie) to replace his table grapes in 1997. After three vats of 2003 reds (for himself and friends), he went 'commercial' in 2004. Inspired by the performance, and his love of shiraz, he's planting some viognier to add perfume, as in the Rhône's Côte-Rôtie. Vinification is low-key, largely outdoors, with loaned cellar equipment and an building 'barely big enough for four barrels'. He's hoping for a proper cellar at some stage, but all in good time….

★★★★ **Shiraz** Soft, sweet vanilla spice pervades **03**; beneath the heady incense-like perfume, a chunky, extracted wine with massive 15% alc. Fans of wood will love it now; classcists can only hope time brings harmony & balance. Certainly no shortage of character. 25% new Am oak, rest 2nd fill Fr. WO Voor-Pberg. *— TM*

 De Sonnenberg see Premium Cape Wines, Rooiberg
Destiny see Mont Destin

Détendu Wines

Paarl ▪ Est 1995 ▪ 1stB 2001 ▪ Visits by appt ▪ Owner Western Investments Company ▪ Winemaker Anthony Smook, with Francois Louw (Jan 2001/2003) ▪ Viti consultant Johan Wiese (2002) ▪ 33 ha (cab, merlot, pinotage, shiraz, chard, chenin, colombard) ▪ 300 tons 1 500 cs own label 90% red 10% white ▪ PO Box 2917 Paarl 7620 ▪ detendu@sybaweb.coza gkr@iafrica.com ✆ **863·3282** 🖷 863·2480

'The 2004 harvest once again confirmed our belief that the Voor Paardeberg area shows great shiraz and chardonnay potential,' comments owner-company director Garry Roberts, declaring general satisfaction with the way things went in what was the second time round for Détendu's rejuvenated cellar. 'It flowed and worked like a charm.' He can't stress strongly enough the importance of hand-sorting the grapes and pre-cooling before pressing to achieve 'quality, quality, quality'.

Pinotage ★★ Latest (03) not ready for tasting; we last tasted **01** easy-drinker, with softish tannins. **Shiraz** ★★★★ **02** notes of smoky cherries, hints cloves & anise; approachable sweet berry flavours & tannins, oak (18 mths Fr, 30% new) more in tune with fruit than pvs. **Merlot-Cabernet Sauvignon** ★★★ Switches to merlot-led in **02**, with 40% cab (pvs release also featured pinotage); good oaking (18 mths Fr, 25% new), pliable tannins, long fruit-filled finish; should develop over 2–3 yrs. **Chardonnay** ★★★ **03** mouthfeel livened with crisp citrus, pleasant oak char hint on finish; well balanced wooding (50% matured in new Fr oak, 6 mths). WO W-Cape.—*DH*

De Toren Private Cellar

Stellenbosch ▪ Est 1996 ▪ 1stB 1999 ▪ Visits by appt ▪ Fee R180, waived on purchase ▪ Owner Edenhall Trust ▪ Winemaker Albie Koch (Aug 1998) ▪ Viticulturist Ernest Manuel (Mar 2003), advised by Johan Pienaar ▪ 20 ha (cabs s/f, malbec, merlot, petit v) ▪ 47000 cs 100% red ▪ PO Box 48 Vlottenburg 7604 ▪ info@de-toren.com ▪ www.de-toren.com © 881·3119 📠 881·3335

Assemblage of this Stellenbosch winery's flagship blend, Fusion V, is a democratic process, with comment not only accepted but actively canvassed from experts as well as less experienced palates. One such mixed group recently tasted the blend components (percentages vary each year), and all but a few fundis failed to identify the merlot — so they promptly re-named it 'Confusion V'. There's no such misunderstanding in the wider wine world, though, and specialists and the public are in agreement about the quality of this wine. In one of many local and international accolades bestowed last year, the 01 was voted Best Red by visitors to the Johannesburg WineX show. The Fusion brand has gained such currency and cachet, the winery behind it is often overlooked. Owners Emil and Sonette den Dulk named it 'De Toren' after a tower-like structure which forms the centerpiece of an ingenious gravity-flow system, designed to make every cellar process, including bottling, as gentle on the wines as possible.

★★★★★ **Fusion V** One of the leading Cape blends, always a full house of Bdx red grapes (cab, malbec, merlot, cab f, petit v), their proportions varying with the vintage; **02** (60/14/14/8/4) tight, restrained, herbal nose gives way to more expressive, well-crafted palate. Chewy but ripe, quite approachable. Mainly Fr oak, 50% new. **01** elegant expression of great, ripe red-wine yr; components (57/14/14/11/4) truly fused into greater whole while retaining clear, commanding cab influence. 91 pts *WS*; *Wine* ★★★★★. **00** *Decanter* ★★★★. These worth cellaring decade min.

★★★★ **Diversity** Each release carries Greek letter of alphabet. Thus maiden **00** (★★★) is 'Alpha', straight cab, satisfying if fairly simple. **01** 'Beta', varieties as per Fusion; much classier, more classic; **02** 'Gamma', same varieties; light, stalky, Chinon-like character complete with attractive herbal influences. Fresh, taut acidity, but ripe, with potential to evolve. Yr Fr/Am oak, 2nd/3rd fill. Own, Elim fruit.—*RK*

De Trafford Wines

Stellenbosch ▪ Est/1stB 1992 ▪ Tasting, sales & tours Fri & Sat 10-1 ▪ Owners David & Rita Trafford ▪ Winemaker David Trafford ▪ 5 ha (cabs s/f, merlot, pinot, shiraz) ▪ 70 tons 3 000 cs 75% red 25% white ▪ PO Box 495 Stellenbosch 7599 ▪ info@detrafford.co.za ▪ www. detrafford.co.za ©/📠 880·1611

'Somewhere between the "branded hell" of Australian wine and the quagmire of Europe's DOC-type systems, SA should carve a niche with wines that speak of place.' That's eloquent, contemplative David Trafford speaking. Emphasising *au naturel* vineyard management/vinification techniques, he's doing just that. Only De Trafford (and Vergelegen) had four participants among the Cape's (61) best wines selected for a bi-hemispheric SA/UK *Wine* (now *Wine International*) panel tasting last year. Rated tops were David T's Vin de Paille and Elevation 393 (the Cab and Shiraz also shone, rating ★★★★★). *Wine International*'s Charles Metcalfe's comment: 'Every wine was a jewel: serious, balanced, intense. Pity there's so little to go around.' Trafford was equally excited by *Wine Spectator*'s 94-point rave about his Shiraz (highest rating to date for an SA wine). The 03 version, still in barrel, is looking 'the best yet', and the 04 promises to be 'something special'.

De Trafford range

★★★★ **Cabernet Sauvignon** Aristocratic Cape cab. Barrel sample **03** promises ★★★★★: opulent colour, intense cassis fruit stitched into grassy cab structure. **02** shows 'green walnut', leafy scents; more austere than charming **01** (★★★★). Low-yield Stbosch vyds, ±22 mths oak, portion Am. As for cellar mates: natural yeasts, minimal handling; 'no enzymes, acid, wood chips or flavourants added'. ±14% alc.

★★★★ **Merlot** Beautifully crafted plum & mulberry fruits shaped by careful wooding (40% new, mostly Fr, 18 mths), lifted by splash cabs s/f, seamed with elegance. Even carries ±15% alc without clamour. **03** (sample) spotlights bright fruit, most promising. **02** evidences leafy/spicy lift encountered in tangy **01**.

★★★★★ **Shiraz** Always fine & characterful. Preview **03** evinces thrilling white pepper/spice intensity within tailored tannic structure, good prospects for extra complexity over time. **02** dark spice/roast meat nuances add to focus. Reduced Am oak since **01** imparts more elegance, sleekness. 94 pts *WS*. 18 mths oak, half new (35% Fr). Regular 15+% alc here camouflaged by fruit richness, fresh acid spine. 200 cs.

★★★★ **Pinot Noir** Sample **03** throws off recent racking (only one – always minimal intervention here) to suggest ★★★★ promise: shiny black cherry fruit embroidered into firm yet delicate texture, lingering tail. 20% new oak. **02** more flamboyant, fleshy; raspberry/cherry flash highlighted by low acid, melded tannins. Mix Burgundian (±80%) & older BK5 clones. 20 mths wood. Mere 56 cs.

★★★★ **Elevation 393** Allusion to height above sea level of David T's home. Selection best cab, merlot, shiraz, cab f; final ratio for (retasted) **01** is 38/25/25/12. Intense fruit still nestled within oak (mostly new Fr, 21 mths). Echoing tail signals longevity (especially ±400 magnums). Elevated alc (15.5%) part of persona. 120 cs. No **02**.

★★★★ **Chenin Blanc** Two new-wave chenins, same label except for small-print WO demarcation. **Stbosch** version from venerable Hldrberg vyds: sample **04** in the groove; rich, succulent fruit groomed into impressive gravel-toned mouthful by supportive, integrated oak. Fine, lengthy finish. **03** concentrated, structured for longevity; deft seam fruit acid freshens mineral complexity. 90 pts *WS*. Fermented/ 8 mths Fr/Am oak, 20% new; native yeasts; partial malo; unfiltered. **Walker Bay** rendition from new Stanford limestone vyd. **03** more chalky; stony ring to upholstered rather than opulent fruit. Similar handling, less (10%) new oak. ±14% alc.

★★★★★ **Straw Wine** ('Vin De Paille' in pvs ed) Passion & commitment taken to the edge with this elixir coaxed from 'air-dried' chenin grapes. **03** in cask mid-2004, its shimmering golden patina signals intent: incredibly rich, full & complex, yet elegant. Stronger (13% alc vs 10), drier (202g/ℓ sugar vs well-concealed 269) than **02**, product of ridiculously low yield – ambrosial drops: honeycomb riffed with roasted almonds, gorgeous fleshy palate needs & deserves patience. 220 cs x 375ml. Mostly new oak, 50% Am, 19 mths. Unfiltered, not cold-stabilised.

Keermont range

On hold pending redevelopment by owners of the property that supplied grapes. Last were **Cabernet Sauvignon**; **Chenin Blanc** & **Shiraz**. – *DS*

Devonair

Stellenbosch ▪ Visits by appointment ▪ Owner Leon de Wit ▪ PO Box 1264 Stellenbosch 7599 ▪ leondw@channel.co.za © 082·552·2881/082·572·1216

This small Devon Vale property was being sold to Gauteng businessman Leon de Wit as the guide went to bed. Previous releases of the Cabernet, from the vineyard on the property, were made by Kaapzicht's Danie Steytler.

Devon Hill Winery

Stellenbosch ▪ Est 1996 ▪ 1stB 1997 ▪ Tasting & sales Mon-Fri 10-4 Sat by appt ▪ Fee R10 ▪ Closed public holidays ▪ Tours by appt ▪ Olive oil ▪ Walks ▪ Winemaker/viticulturist Erhard Roux (May 2002) ▪ 50 ha (cabs s/f, merlot, pinotage, shiraz, sauvignon) ▪ ±300 tons 80% red 20% white ▪ PO Box 541 Stellenbosch 7599 ▪ info@devonhill.co.za ▪ www.devonhill.co.za © 865·2453 ▤ 865·2444

Now winemaker on this 50ha stretch a cool 270m above sea-level, Erhard Roux is thankful for cellarmaster Theo Brink's guidance (Brink has now re-retired, after temporarily shelving his fishing gear to take on this assignment). After a two-year 'running-in' period, Roux has been involved in 'detail, detail, detail', but fortunately he had Theo B to teach him how to handle stress. For visitors, it's goodbye to stress in the Devon Hill tasting room: perched on the slopes high above Devon Valley, its view arcs from Cape Hangklip to the Franschhoek Mountains. Focus in the cellar is now on the premier Devon Hill range; the second-tier Devon View wines have been dropped and replaced with a single red blend, expectantly named Four Stars.

★★★★ **Blue Bird** Cellar's flagship selection. Current **01** blend merlot, pinotage, cab (73/17/10) has happiness bird delivering fresh blueberry fruit aromas, flavours on cleanly elegant palate. 13.8% alc. Yr Am/Fr oak. **00** pinotage-led, cab f, merlot.

★★★☆ **Cabernet 02** retasted mid-2004, as are all these. Cassis, mint-sauced meat — classic cab in popular, commercial style, though seriously wooded: yr new Fr. Moderate 12.8% alc. VDG.

★★★☆ **Four Stars** 'Made to enjoy', says winemaker of maiden **02**. Yes: flavoursome, fruity, easy-drinking pleasure, light-textured. Blend pinotage, merlot, shiraz, cab (40/30/15/15). Yr oak, none new.

★★★☆ **Shiraz** Earthy presence on nicely mouthfilling first-vintage **02**, with notes of tobacco, leather. 13.5% alc. Yr oak, third new.

★★★☆ **Sauvignon Blanc** Still current **03** needs drinking up soon. Reductive style with tropical fruit flavour profile. 13.5% alc. No **04** – all sold off.

Pinotage ★★ 'Nail varnish' tone now dominates palate of **02**, with bitter element too. Yr Fr oak. 13.7% alc. Far cry from **01** (★★★★), MIWA 2002 gold. **Merlot** ★★★★ Loads of ripe red fruit on **02**, very smooth, sweetish, negligible tannins, ready for drinking. 14.1% alc; yr older Fr oak, none new. Discontinued: **Devon View Pinotage** & **Cabernet Sauvignon**. – NP

Devon View see Devon Hill above

DeWaal Wines

Stellenbosch ▪ Est 1682 ▪ 1stB 1972 ▪ Tasting & sales Mon-Fri 9-4.30 (Oct-Apr) Mon-Fri 10-12.30; 2-4.30 (May-Sep) Sat 10-4.30 year round ▪ Fee R10 ▪ Closed Easter Fri/Sun, Dec 25/26 & Jan 1 ▪ Owners De Waal brothers ▪ Winemakers/viticulturists Chris de Waal & Daniël de Waal (whites/reds, Jan 1976/1989) ▪ Marketing Pieter de Waal ▪ 120 ha (pinotage, shiraz, sauvignon) ▪ 800 tons 20 000 cs 50% red 50% white ▪ PO Box 15 Vlottenburg 7604 ▪ info@uiterwyk.co.za ▪ www.uiterwyk.co.za Ⓒ 881·3711 ▤ 881·3776

Last year we mentioned red-wine maker Daniël de Waal's 'tinkerings' tended to have exceptional results. Example: 50-plus year old vines on their family-owned Uiterwyk estate nurtured to produce Top of the Hill, one of the Cape's top pinotages. And his experiments with fermenting certain reds in oak barrels (as opposed to the more conventional stainless steel) to promote earlier and more complete fruit-oak integration. Now DdW is investigating the beneficial effects of decreasing the gap between the vines. Experience elsewhere suggests that closely planted vines are less vigorous and tend to produce more concentrated and intensely flavoured fruit. Says older brother Pieter, MD: 'We are now planting our vineyards in narrow rows. This way we increase the density of the vines to about 5000 per hectare. With production per vine reduced; quality is upped even further.' Of the 2004 harvest, he advises: 'Look out for our pinotage, shiraz and viognier.' (The latter is the domain of white-wine maker, third brother Chris.) With the bottling of their 2002 DeWaal Estate Wine, they celebrate the 10th anniversary of one of SA's first premium pinotage-based 'Cape blends'.

★★★★★ **Top of the Hill Pinotage** One of the more elegant & serious (yet gorgeous) expressions of this grape, from small bushvine vyd over 50 yrs old. No **98** or **99**, but **00**, then **01** worth the wait: brilliant deep colour, silky tannins, depth & length of fruit, unified to promise harmonious development. Modest 13% alc, 15+ mths new Fr oak. **01** made Daniël de W Diners Club Winemaker of the Year (2003). Still youthful **02**, with prominent spicy toasty wood notes, follows in good form, with deep sa-vouriness, ripe tannin underpinning solid fruit. 60% new Fr oak. Pinotage Top Ten.

★★★★☆ **Pinotage** Maiden **01** made clear that this, from small-cropping ±40 yr old vines, a label to rival illustrious partner for quality. **02** only a touch less intense, with happily refined rusticity, rich mulberry fruit, savoury acidity & firm, dense tannin. 60% new Fr oak well in evidence mid-2004. 14% alc. Allow few yrs of maturation.

★★★★☆ **Cape Blend** (formerly 'Estate Wine') Not the genre's pioneer, but maiden **93** was first of the 90s wave of blends with pinotage – this one a serious-minded, darkly el-egant version. **00** had cab s/f, merlot, characteristically well structured, textured. No **01**. **02** (★★★★) with 30% each shiraz & merlot reflects less fruit-generous vin-tage, but is graceful, well & firmly balanced, with appealing bright red berry fla-vours. 60% new Fr oak. Should keep well ±5 more yrs.

★★★★☆ **Shiraz** Single-vyd release of maiden **01** was graceful & powerful, beautifully struc-tured. 14% alc. 60% new Fr oak adding to toasty-smoky notes. Tank sample **02** makes similar promises, with powerful but restrained characterfulness, sweet fruit, rich ripe tannins.

★★★★ **Merlot 00** Brightly fruited but restrained **00** followed (no **01** made) by lighter-feel-ing **02** (★★★★), with modest plummy, leaf-edged nose, elegantly structured, drink-ing well now. Balanced, integrated 40% new oak. 13.5% alc.

★★★★ **Cabernet Sauvignon** Migrated from Uiterwyk range. Pleasantly savoury bright-fruited **02**, with splash of merlot, has big structure not fully occupied by fruit. Showing much evidence of 60% new Fr oak maturation. 14% alc. Few yrs to go.

★★★★ **Viognier** First Stbosch version of this white Rhône variety, unwooded till **03**, where 15% new Fr oak well contained in peach/apricot/rose aromas, flavours. Aromatic **04** also forceful, a touch uncompromising, but richly textured & lively; probably best yet. 13.5% alc.

★★★★ **Sauvignon Blanc** Steely, grassy & intense **03** marked move to the senior range. **04** (★★★★) adds depth, fresh tropical fruit lusciousness to serious structure. Gratifying, dry lingering finish. Balanced 13% alc.

Standard Uiterwyk range

★★★★ **Pinotage** Least exalted of estate's trio of pinotages but not humble or frivolous: just more easy-going, fruity, from younger vines, less oaking. Delightful, fresh & bright **02** (★★★★) fits pattern well; well integrated 40% new Fr oak; 13.5% alc. **01** saw bright berry fruit successfully combined with rustic warmth.

★★★★ **Shiraz** Last tasted was serious, well-structured & velvet-textured **00**, fermenta-tion on viognier lees adding perfume to spice, plum & toasty-oakiness. Firm tannin, savoury acidity harmonising with fruit & oak (40% new Fr). ±13% alc.

Merlot ★★★ **00** spicy, dusty plum notes, pleasingly balanced; probably peaking now. 13.5% al; Fr oak, 37% new. Discontinued: **Cabernet Franc**.

Uiterwyk Young Vines range

Red ★★★ Low-key & friendly, but in house's refined style: modestly fruity **00** blend (mer-lot, cab, pinotage) for drinking soon. 13% alc. **White** ★★★ **04** easy-going dry & crisp blend chenin, sauvignon. – *TJ*

De Wet Co-op Winery

Worcester ▪ Est 1946 ▪ Tasting & sales Mon-Fri 8-5 ▪ Fee 50c/wine ▪ Closed public holidays ▪ BYO picnic baskets ▪ Conferencing ▪ Owners 60 members ▪ Winemaker/manager Piet le Roux (1995) & Hugo Conradie (2003) ▪ Viti consultant Newald Marais (Jan 2003) ▪ ±1 000 ha (chard, chenin) ▪ 19 000 tons 20% red 80% white ▪ PO Box 16 De Wet 6853 ▪ dewetwynkelder@mweb.co.za ▪ www.worcesterwinelands.co.za ✆ (023) 341·2710 🖷 (023) 341·2762

The 60 members of this Worcester co-op aren't complaining about the 2004 harvest: it was a record, yielding 19 000 tons from the 1 000ha under vine (the average has been 16

000). The winery is a 50% shareholder in FirstCape, the 5th largest exporter of bottled wine to the UK. New releases include a Colombard-Chardonnay blend, Rosé and Shiraz-Pinotage blend; looking prettier is the Pettilant Fronté, in a new bottle with a spruced-up label (and continuing approval of the SA Heart Foundation). There are now conference facilities on-site, and visitors are welcome to bring picnic lunches.

★★★★ **Red Muscadel** ✓ **01** version of this fortified dessert was very clean & light tripping. Current **02** (★★★★), retasted, luscious tropical whiffs & hint freesia, full & round, delicious; could be cellared further. Low 15.7% alc.

Shiraz-Pinotage 🆕 ☺ ★★★ **03** plums & spice, easy, juicy; has some short-term cellaring potential; unwooded. **Dry Red** ☺ ★★★ Formula varies from yr to yr, **03** is a Bdx blend, cab f & petit v; red fruited, with delicate brush oak. Unusually big 14% alc. **Rosé** ☺ ★★ Attractive **03** from shiraz; red berry nose, semi-sweet in analysis but not cloying, easy. **Cape Riesling** ☺ ★★ **03** still swiggable & light but needs drinking soon. **Petillant Fronté Light** ☺ ★★★ Slightly spritzy, extra-low alc white (±8%) endorsed by the Heart Foundation. 100% muscat de F, fragrantly smooth & sweet. NV.

Chardonnay ★ Wooded **02** shows little more than oaky whiffs & honeyed notes; better in youth. **Sauvignon Blanc** ★★ **04** lighter, less satisfying than pvs, not much varietal zing. **Colombard-Chardonnay** ★★ **03**'s light tropical tones overwhelmed by honeyed bottle-age. **Bouquet Blanc** ★★ Scented, lightish off-dry white, **03** from fernão pirez, colombard & gewürz; slight honeyed note creeping in, drink soon. **Special Late Harvest** ★★ 100% gewürz; **04** spicy floral nose, balanced off-dry taste. Pleasantly light 11% alc. **Port** ★★★★ **02** traditional-style fortified with extra character, interest imparted by rare-in-Cape variety pontac; lots of complexity on nose (including tomato sauce!), balanced fruit & alc (17.4%); could develop interestingly. — *DH*

De Wetshof Estate

*Robertson ▪ Est 1949 ▪ 1stB 1972 ▪ Tasting & sales Mon-Fri 8.30-4.30 Sat 9.30-12.30 ▪ Closed Dec 25/26, Jan 1 & Easter Fri/Mon ▪ Tours by appt ▪ Owner Danie de Wet ▪ Winemaker Danie de Wet (1973), with Mervin Williams (2001) ▪ Viticulturist George Thom (1996), advised by Phil Freese & Francois Viljoen (both 1997) ▪ 180 ha (cab, merlot, pinot, chard, sauvignon, semillon, riesling) ▪ 10% red 90% white ▪ ISO 9001, BRC & HACCP certification in progress ▪ PO Box 31 Robertson 6705 ▪ info@dewetshof.com ▪ www.dewetshof.com ✆ **(023) 615·1853** 🖷 (023) 615·1915*

Last year's challenging weather patterns had this team monitoring shifts closely. All that scrutiny resulted in a smaller crop but one with 'stunning wines', says Danie de Wet, owner and winemaker. De Wet is a pioneer of chardonnay in SA (and member of the prestigious Confrerie des Chevalier du Tastevin, in recognition of his efforts with this grape over more than three decades), but he has another Burgundian amour, pinot noir. Theirs is a frictionless ménage à trois. De Wet says: 'I've learned from this grape. It's helped me improve my chardonnay vineyards because, just as the pinot noir shows itself, letting you know exactly how it feels when it's not happy, the chardonnay does the reverse: it hides its stresses and soldiers on.' A formidable marketing network, with De Wet's wife Lesca at its centre, reaches 18 countries.

★★★★ **Bateleur Chardonnay** Estate's flagship, always a personal Danie dW barrel selection — finesse, complexity the aims. **03** doesn't falter. Beyond immediate orange zest/yellow cling peach appeal, class shows: deft oaking (Fr barrique fermented/matured 11 mths) provides toasty nut flavours, sinewy structure, but doesn't overwhelm; racy acidity lifts palate, gives length. One to age, 4+ yrs. 14.6% alc. **02** was taut but packed with citrus.

★★★★ **Chardonnay D'Honneur** Oaky style also features generous ripe fruit. **03** has cellar's trademark peach-laden character, woven with roasted nuts, lemon peel. Ripe, accessible, tasty, but finishing crisply. Oak as above, 10 mths. 14.4% alc. **02** also had a more open, looser weave than the Bateleur.

★★★★ **Finesse Chardonnay** Lightly oaked version of the trio barrel-fermented char-donnays; named **Lesca** for export. **03** more friendly than pvs: enough lightly toasted citrus/peach flavours & freshening acidity for solo enjoyment or food partnership. Nicely balanced. 13.4% alc. VG. Also in 375ml.

★★★★ **Bon Vallon** Unwooded version, first of this style in SA. **04** shows what good quality grapes can do: tropical fruit salad, ripe, luscious, so generously propor-tioned that flavour, silky mouthfeel remain long after the glass is finished. 14.3% alc. Also in 375ml.

★★★★ **Blanc Fumé** Lightly wooded sauvignon with bone-dry finish; good match with seafood. **04** lemon, lime with leafy/green edginess, smoothed by gentle biscuit overlay. Oaking doesn't mask varietal identity. Friendly 11.6% alc.

★★★★ **Rhine Riesling** ✓ Well-regarded example in good yrs allows ageing over 5-7 yrs (some find preferable to drinking young). **02** retasted shows no age: wafting floral bouquet, exotic fruits, delicate & refined. Acidity balanced by touch sugar (8g/ℓ), finishes dry. 12.2% alc. **02** was bone-dry; featured delicate lime-touched elderflower fruit, excellent acid balance.

★★★★★ **Edeloes** Gorgeous, full-blown botrytis dessert from riesling. Multitude of gongs for stunning **98**; topped by triumphant **00** (★★★★★). Former sweeter, softer, more unctuous; **00** honeyed, lovely balance between opulent sweetness & firm, clean acid. Both ageing magnificently.

Blanc De Wet ☺ ★★★ **04** equal partners sauvignon/semillon working well together: reductive winemaking captures juicy gooseberry/guava flavours, zinging citrus fresh-ness which awakens tastebuds. 12.2% alc.

Sauvignon Blanc ★★★ **04** more varietal definition than pvs: green fig intro, herbaceous, nettly; lovely racy, tangy-lime flavours, finish. Good food partner. 12% alc.

Danie de Wet range

★★★★ **Cabernet Sauvignon Naissance** Creditable results from young vines. **02** showing classic plum, cassis profile, liberal spicing. Elegantly structured; firm tannins need bit more time to integrate, soften; all right ingredients to age 4+ yrs. Malo/maturation in seasoned small Fr oak. 13.4 % alc. **01** was first.

★★★★ **Nature in Concert Pinot Noir 03** (sample) follows in generous oak steps of maiden **02**; toasty vanilla-spiced aromas vie for attention with raspberry/straw-berry fruit, whiffs forest floor. Palate reveals supple, amenable tannins, silky-smooth texture, for deliciously satisfying experience. Oak as above. 14.7% alc.

★★★★ **Limestone Hill Chardonnay** Scented unwooded version; very ripe, terrific, bold. Style seems established, & **04** delivers: succulent lime/peach-flavoured ex-perience, long zest finish. 13.3% alc. **03** sold out before we could taste. **02** big, fat, juicy.

★★★★ **Call of the African Eagle 02** retasted mid-2004 holding well. Lime, lemongrass piquancy gives lift to broad tropical/peach flavours, rounded texture. Fr barrique-fermented, briefly aged. 13.9% alc. **02** similar to L-H version but big-ger, less challenging.

★★★★ **Danie de Wet Cape Muscadel** ✓ Excellent new-wave Cape fortified: smartly packaged & refined. **00** seems not to age; aroma & flavours indivisible – barley sugar, grapefruit, marmalade, jasmine; lovely sweet/sour tussle, uncloying mouthfeel. Low 15.3% alc. 500ml.

Chardonnay Sur Lie ★★★ New to the guide but already two double-golds at Veritas, for **02**, **03**; unwooded, 3 months on lees ('longer than on shop shelves,' says Lesca dW). **04** really vivid freshly- grated lemon & -sliced peach perfumes/flavours; softly rounded, for early drinking rather than keeping, but tasty, satisfying. 13,7% alc. – CR

De WetsBerg see Excelsior
Deza see Oaklands Wine Exporters

De Zoete Inval Estate

Paarl ▪ Est 1878 ▪ 1stB 1976 ▪ Tasting & sales Sat 9-5 Mon-Fri by appt (see also intro) ▪ Closed Christian holidays ▪ BYO picnic ▪ Tours by appt ▪ Owner AR Frater Trust ▪ Winemaker/viticulturist John Robert Frater (1999/2004) ▪ 20 ha (cab, petit v, port varieties, shiraz, chard, sauvignon) ▪ 100 tons 5 000 cs own label 50% red 50% white ▪ PO Box 591 Suider-Paarl 7624 ▪ dezoeteinval@wine.co.za ▪ www.dezoeteinval.co.za ℡ 863·2375 🖷 863·2817

The Fraters in 2004 launched a range of fruity reds under a second label, Eskdale, after the Lowlands home of their ancestor Robert John Frater. Long term, however, namesake and fifth-generation winemaker Robert John Frater says, the plan is to trim the range to a flagship white and red, plus a pair of easy-drinkers. All will be 'individualistic wines made with minimal intervention', in line with their long-held philosophy. Recently married, RJF's favourite after-cellar-hours activity is making trial blends around the braai with 'whatever wines everybody brought along'. Visit their tasting room or try the wines at the new venue on Paarl's Main Street, I Love Wine. See Wine shops section for details.

Cabernet Sauvignon ★★ 01 still the current release; potpourri nose with tobacco & cherry; dry, light bodied, somewhat lacking ripeness & fruit; drink up. Yr 1st fill Fr oak. **Cabernet Sauvignon-Shiraz** NEW ★★★ Almost porty nose of prunes & plums, savoury touch; chunky/chewy wine (15.2% alc), quite rustic yet not unappealing. NV. **Grand Rouge** ★★ Individual blend cab & port grapes, yr wooded, 3rd fill Fr; light (11% alc) with hints coconut & tea-leaves, sour plum palate. **Rosé** ★★★ Quirkily made from sauvignon & port varieties; 03, yr on, orangey coral hue, faint strawberry & cream aroma, tastes just off-dry. 13% alc. **Chardonnay** ★★★ 03 retasted, reveals some complexity; European 'burnt match' character, dry, attractively austere on finish. **Sauvignon Blanc** ★★ 04 very pale; slight talcum powder nose; clean, dry, med-bodied with stern limy finish. **Yvette** ★★ From sauvignon, 'made in complicated off-dry style' says winemaker; NV (03) faint floral notes; soft, supple appley flavours. 13.4% alc. **Late Harvest** ★★★ From sauvignon. Last was 03, with supple, light fruit salad tastes. **Cape Vintage** ★★ 01 acquiring mature tawny tint; dusty dried fruit on nose, soft, silky, attractively dry. fortified to low 16.8% alc; 26 mths 500ℓ casks.

Eskdale range

All 03, aged ±10 mths in Fr oak. **Merlot** ★★★ Shows house's slight savoury edge in combo with stewed fruit, obvious acidity, grainy tannins; clearly a food style. 14.7% alc. **Pinotage** ★★★ Bluegum aromas, bouncy mulberry flavours, lighter-bodied (13.5% alc) than rest of range; creamy oak (10% Am) on finish. **Shiraz** ★★★ Roast meat & smoky edge to the dry, firm, full-bodied palate; dry tannins, sweet-sour note on finish. — *TM*

DGB

Wellington ▪ Est 1942 ▪ Closed to public ▪ Owners DGB management, Brait Capital Partners & Kangra ▪ Winemakers/viticulturists: see Bellingham ▪ PO Box 79 Groot Draken-stein 7680 ▪ exports@dgb.co.za ▪ www.dgb.co.za ℡ 874·1011 🖷 874·1690

Well-established merchant house with a wide portfolio of own-brand table wines, ports and sherries. See separate listings for Bellingham, Culemborg, Douglas Green, Heerenhof, Millstream, Oude Kaap, Text and The Saints.

Die Breedekloof see Viljoensdrift
Die Krans see De Krans

Diemersdal Estate

Durbanville ▪ Est 1698 ▪ 1stB 1990 ▪ Tasting & sales Mon-Fri 9-4 Sat 9-3 ▪ Closed Easter Fri/Sun, Dec 25 & Jan 1 ▪ Tours by appt ▪ BYO picnic ▪ Walks ▪ Owner Tienie Louw ▪ Winemaker Johan Kruger (Sep 2004) ▪ Viticulturist Div van Niekerk (1980) ▪ 172 ha (cab, merlot, pinotage, shiraz, chard, sauvignon) ▪ 1 730 tons 15 000 cs own label 85% red 15% white ▪ PO Box 27 Durbanville 7551 ▪ wines@diemersdal.co.za ℡ 976·3361 🖷 976·1810

'We're very excited about the new blood,' messages Joanita Louw from the historic Louw farm on the slopes of the Dorstberg. The new blood she's enthusing about is Johan Kruger, previously winemaker at much-vaunted Jordan, who has his own label – Sterhuis – which had a creditable debut in 2002. New stock notwithstanding, this is 'an old hands-on family business and that's the way we're going to stay,' insists owner Tienie Louw. He's just as determined that there's unique intrinsic value in the word 'estate': 'Estate wines,' he avers, somewhat controversially, 'are currently the only guarantee of terroir character.' An old connection is that enjoyed with African Terroir – Diemersdal is one of four cellars contributing to this multinational Swiss negociant business.

★★★★ **Shiraz** ✓ Modern accessible style with a nod to the classic & tradition; **01** had a deceptively soft entry, generous build & firm dry finish. **02** fynbos & scrub intro; smoky black fruit flavours with hint leather; fairly shy nose; harmonious mouthful, fruit carries through to spicy & dry conclusion. 14.5% alc.

★★★★ **Private Collection** ✓ Red blend, make-up varies with vintage. **01** (★★★☆) was cabs s/f & merlot (70/10/20), with cab's flavours & aromas uppermost, merlot adding flesh. **02** again cab-dominated, with 29% shiraz; similar aromas to staight Cab above; blackcurrant & bouillon, eucalyptus hint; attractively plump, ripe, plummy fruit. Yr oaked. 14.3% alc.

★★★★ **Cabernet Sauvignon 01** was well judged, with attractive mulberry fruit, touches cool cedar, good ripe tannins. Vintage-induced dip in **02** (★★★★), gamey, slightly earthy/meaty aromas; firm, full-bodied; dried fruit character & hint eucalyptus; slightly jammy finish.

★★★☆ **Pinotage** Charm & grace rather than the variety's more usual power. **01** had a subtle vanilla oak & sweet strawberry bouquet, red-berried fruits, subtle tannic farewell. **02** spicy vanilla nose with mulberry whiffs; quite a mouthful – slightly sweet & jammy but finishes dry. 14.4% alc.

★★★★ **Chardonnay 03** (★★★☆) not over-oaked, or overdone in any way, but fruit less bright, satisfying than **02**. Subtle oak aromas, smooth citrus tone, soft charm. **04** (unrated preview) baked apple aromas; blowsy & soft, slightly sweetish palate, crème brulée finish. Barrel fermented/aged 3 mths.

Matys ★★★ Pronounced Mah-*tace*, lightly wooded blend pinotage, shiraz, merlot (51/39/10). **03** leafy whiffs, notes cigarbox & dark plums; big plum flavours; slightly rustic but appealing. 14% alc. **Sauvignon Blanc** ★★★ **04** (sample) floral & sweet bouquet of guava, peach & nettle; soft & juicy, medium bodied & dry, well pitched acidity. – *TM*

Diemersdal Wines see Diemersdal Estate, African Terroir

Diemersfontein Wines

Wellington ▪ Est/1stB 2001 ▪ Tasting & sales daily 10-5 ▪ Fee R15 ▪ Closed Dec 25 ▪ Tours by appt ▪ Seasons at Diemersfontein Restaurant (see Eat-out section) ▪ Guest house with 17 rooms ▪ Farm produce ▪ Conferencing ▪ Walks ▪ Mountain biking ▪ Owners David & Susan Sonnenberg ▪ Winemaker Bertus Fourie, with Francois Roode (Nov 2000/Sep 2003) ▪ Viticulturist Simon Springthorpe (Mar 2001) ▪ 55 ha (cab, merlot, mourvèdre, petit v, pinotage, shiraz, viognier) ▪ 380 tons 15 000 cs + 3 000 cs for Woolworths ▪ 95% red 4% white 1% rosé ▪ PO Box 41 Wellington 7654 ▪ wine@diemersfontein.co.za ▪ www. diemersfontein.co.za ✆ 864·5050 🖷 864·2095

After just four vintages, Bertus Fourie's wines are justifying the rejuvenation of this 18th-century former fruit farm into a new Wellington showpiece. 'One of the greatest harvests ever, if you managed to overcome *parskoors* (panic picking),' Fourie says of 2004. 'Wonderful flavours, complex phenolic profiles', especially on his showpiece pinotage. Then again, 'pinotage in Wellington always has a good year'. He's been busy: the 2003 harvest in France; a maiden viognier and port-style wine; two red collaborations with Woolworths; a wedding (to Siyabonga winemaker Corlea van Wyk). And – cute – a puppy named Pontac. New assistant Francois Roode will help prepare for full compliance with international quality accreditations, in line with their pragmatic belief that 'a beautiful cellar means nothing'.

Carpe Diem range

★★★★☆ **Pinotage** Previewed **03** looks set to continue assertive presence at FCTWS after trophies for pvs two vintages. Same luscious mulberry/loganberry style, with measured ripe tannins, balanced 14% alc keeping teeming flesh, 3.1g/ℓ sugar in check. Improves on **02**, now showing slight acetone notes but retaining impressive concentration. **01** also retasted, a variety benchmark: excellent structure & balance, brilliant fruit, great appeal, length. 60% new oak, mix Fr/Am.

★★★★ **Merlot 03** sample shows fine olive-toned character, plums & poise, in house style of delivering smouldering herbal warmth to tightly arrayed palate. 14% alc. ±18 mths oak. **02** berries in dusty, earthy sternness.

★★★☆ **Shiraz** Sample **03** (★★★) milky notes; heavy fruit, some vegetal notes & hot 14.5% alc; lacks seductiveness of **02** (tasted mid-03): pepper, leather notes; fully-fleshed but hard tannin core. These ±18 mths oak, 14.5% alc.

Cabernet Sauvignon 03 sample possible ★★★★ ; restrained fruity nose, some perfume, pleasant sweetness, red berry rather than usual cassis flavour profile, 14% alc. 70/30 Fr/Am oak, 60% new.

Diemersfontein range

★★★★ **Pinotage 04** tank sample (likely ★★★) packed with notes of mocha, burnt matches, bananas with a pleasing sweetness from super-ripe fruit and 13% alc. Will have its admirers, like Starbucks-special **03**, whose coffee & mocha galore won MIWA gold. These ±13.8% alc.

★★★☆ **Cabernet Sauvignon** Standout **01** had more depth than retasted **02** (★★★), slightly green, but classic cab cassis emerging from austerity & tea leaves.

★★★★ **Merlot** Ripe red plums & freshness hide **03**'s 14.7% alc. Riper than **02**, with choc richness emerging through tannins, braced by herbal tints. 14% alc. Half kept in tank, half in new Fr oak.

★★★☆ **Shiraz 03** tank sample promises ★★★★ . Attractive sweetness on nose, floral palate, with herbal notes. Raises game of **02** with khaki bush/thyme/spice aromas, tannins giving touch hardness to finish. Same whopping 14.5% alcs. Matured new Fr/Am oak.

★★★☆ **Maiden's Prayer** 🆕 **03** merlot, cab, shiraz, pinotage blend, fruit-driven & designed for early drinking. Red fruit, violet aromas lead to firm-tannined palate – a little hard at end. Tank-matured. 14.5% alc.

★★★★ **Heaven's Eye** 🆕 Tannins as tight & sleek as James Bond's tuxedo. Cabs s/f, petit v & shiraz on **03** all supply monster dark ripe fruit, cloves, choc – & midi-monster 14.5% alc. Components matured mainly Fr oak, 10 mths. Keep up to 10 yrs.

★★★★ **Summer's Lease** 🆕 **03** shiraz-dominated (77%), with pinotage, dollop mourvèdre. Meaty, tight, explosive fruit, pleasant sweetness from 14.5% alc. Mix Fr/Am oak, 10 mths. Should develop, keep ±6 yrs yet. – *NP*

Die Tweede Droom see Groot Parys

Dieu Donné Vineyards

Franschhoek ▪ Est 1984 ▪ 1stB 1986 ▪ Tasting & sales Mon-Fri 9-4 Sat/Sun 10.30-4 ▪ Fee R10 ▪ Closed Dec 25/26 & Jan 1 ▪ Cheese platters & picnics in summer; food & wine tastings in winter; all by appt ▪ Tours by appt ▪ Tourgroups ▪ Owner Robert Maingard ▪ Winemaker Stephan du Toit (May 1996) ▪ Viticulturist Hennie du Toit (Apr 1988) ▪ 40 ha (cab, merlot, pinotage, shiraz, chard, sauvignon) ▪ ±280 tons 16 500 cs 60% red 35% white 3% rosé 2% MCC ▪ PO Box 94 Franschhoek 7690 ▪ info@dieudonnevineyards.com ▪ www.dieudonnevineyards.com ℂ 876-2493 📠 876-2102

From his vantage point on the high reaches of Franschhoek Mountain, winemaker Stephan du Toit's view is that 'to keep up with the dynamic SA wine industry, your philosophy is continually re-shaped'. One constant for this Cape Wine Master is the wish to make a Noble Late Harvest, which he finally fulfilled in the noble-rot-conducive conditions which prevailed last year. (It will be his first botrytis wine since 97.) Inducements to visit the winery include summer picnics and cheese platters on the grass decks. In winter, food and wine pairings are held beside a roaring fire. Whatever the season, the views are among the best in the Cape.

Cabernet Sauvignon ★★ 00 light red fruit with slight stalky edge & house's tight tannins. 18 mths Fr oak. **Cabernet Sauvignon Reserve ★★★ 99** similar qualities/oaking to above, mid-2004 still powerfully tannic. Other palates find considerable merit in this wine's qualities: gold at Concours Mondial 2003, UK *Decanter* ★★★★. **Merlot ★★** Current **01** has herbal/stalky nose/palate. 16 mths Fr oak. 14.3% alc. Follow-up **02** being blended as guide went to press. **Pinotage ★★★** Sweet-fruited **01** holds its 15% alc well; improves on old-Cape tone of **01** (which won gold at Concours M 03). **Shiraz ★★★** Individualistic styling which, again, in **01** struck gold at Concours M 03. Latest **02** unusual stalky/earthy nose & burly 15.5% alc, which shows on fiery finish. Yr Fr oak. **Cabernet Sauvignon-Merlot ★★☆** Current release is **98**, 85/15 blend with cab's trenchant tones; mid-2004 shows tertiary aromas yet still youthful raspberry fruit on palate. 18 mths Fr oak. **Rosé ★★☆** From two sauvignons, one red (cab-), other white (-blanc); **04** sees some chardonnay slip into the tank; loaded with fruit, raspberry tang balances the sweetness. **Chardonnay Wooded ★★★★ 03** light, delicate style with attractive citrus freshness; fine oak treatment results in appealing oatmeal whiffs. **Chardonnay Unwooded ★★★** Clean, well-made **04**; *sur lie* 6 mths for touch creaminess, complexity. **Sauvignon Blanc ★★★ 04** bright sauvignon fruit with green figs in a lower-alc, dry but not austere style. Drink before the next vintage. **Maingard Brut MCC** The new **00** not ready for tasting.—*RK*

Die Vlakte see Cloverfield
Disa see Porterville Cellars

Dispore Kamma Wines

Caledon ▪ Est/1stB 2002 ▪ Visits by appt ▪ Owners Philip Mostert & Hannes Coetzee ▪ Winemaker Philip Mostert, with Hannes Coetzee (Jan/Jun 2002) ▪ Viti consultant Willie de Waal ▪ ±100 cs 100% red ▪ PO Box 272 Caledon 7230 ▪ philmos@mweb.co.za Ⓒ (028) 214·1057 (a/h) / 083·448·1670 🖷 (028) 214·1077

Syrah is *garagiste* Philip Mostert's passion, and it shows. His first vintage, Mostert understatedly notes, was 'well received', but it is the 03 that has him really fired up. He believes SA syrah could become the best in the world, and he's intent on making a contribution to the cause through his winemaking philosophy, based on 'optimal ripeness, minimum manipulation, no filtration and adroit use of quality wood'. All of which makes him sound more like a winemaking pro than the country doctor he is. The Khoisan name for Caledon, where Mostert practices, is also the name of his brand.

★★★★ Syrah Immediate critical success for this hand-crafted wine: MIWA Grand Gold, Swiss garagiste trophy, *Wine* ★★★★ for maiden **02**. Follow-up **03** (★★★★) shows none of the porty notes we previewed last ed; just succulent, fragrant, spicy ripe fruit, whiffs cinnamon & vanilla, choc flavour, firm but supple tannins. Brawny 14.6% alc entirely consistent with character. Ultra-ripe Paarl fruit, 12-14 mths 2nd-fill Am oak, unfiltered. Loads of potential.—*DH*

Distell

Stellenbosch ▪ PO Box 184 Stellenbosch 7599 ▪ www.distell.co.za Ⓒ 809·7000

SA's largest wine company was recording a 20% increase in international sales of its brands at last season's start. Though local sales took a slight dip, the stars in the varied portfolio more than made up for it. Like the JC le Roux bubblies (sales up by 25%), the sentimental stalwart Chateau Libertas (2.4m bottles annually), new-look Nederburg's burgeoning figures, Plaisir de Merle's climbing case-count. Then there are the jointly owned Lusan properties (Le Bonheur, Uitkyk, Stellenzicht, Alto and Neethlingshof). Renowned viticultural academic/consultant Eben Archer is on board full-time now to bring out the best of these 'potentially outstanding' vineyards. Meanwhile, back at HQ, chief winemaker Linley Schultz and 'extension winemaker' Albertus van der Merwe continue work on fresh, fruity mid-to-lower-priced wines in global quantities (like the multi-packaged Two Oceans, recording scintillating sales in Scandinavia of, among others, the 3ℓ bag-in-a-box). And at the Adam Tas cellar, Michael Bucholz (reds) and Louw Engelbrecht (whites) give a modern edge to traditional names like Tassenberg and Zonnebloem. On the black economic empowerment front, Distell's Papkuilsfontein/Tukulu West Coast vineyard venture is coming up roses… and garnering show awards.

Note: Distell brands are listed separately in the guide. See entries for 5th Avenue Cold Duck, Allesverloren, Alto, Autumn Harvest, Capenheimer, Cellar Cask, Chateau Libertas, Drostdy-Hof, Durbanville Hills, Fleur du Cap, Graça, Grand Mousseux, Grünberger, Hill & Dale, Jacobsdal, JC le Roux, Kellerprinz, Kupferberger Auslese, Le Bonheur, Libertas, Monis, Nederburg, Neethlingshof, Oom Tas, Obikwa, Oracle, Overmeer, Plaisir de Merle, Sable View, Sedgwick's, Ship Sherry, Stellenzicht, Table Mountain, Tassenberg, Taverna, Theuniskraal, Tukulu, Two Oceans, Uitkyk, Virginia and Zonnebloem.

A rejuvenated facet of Distell's operations is the Vinoteque Wine Bank, marketing fine wines on a pre-release basis with the option of having purchases stored in perfect cellar conditions. www. vinoteque.co.za ▪ info@vinoteque.co.za ✆ **809·8283** 🖷 883·9533

🔲 *Dolphin Bay* see Kosie Möller Wines

Domaine Brahms Wineries

Paarl ▪ Est 1998 ▪ 1stB 1999 ▪ Tasting & sales Mon-Fri 9.30-5 Sat & public holidays by appt (closed Easter Fri-Mon, Jun 16, Sep 24, Dec 25/26 & Jan 1) ▪ Fee R5/wine ▪ Tours anytime by appt ▪ Owners Braam & Gesie Lategan ▪ Winemaker/viticulturist Gesie Lategan, with Petri Morkel (1998/2004) ▪ 15 ha (cab, merlot, pinotage, shiraz) ▪ 100% red ▪ Range for customer: Rose Garden ▪ PO Box 2136 Windmeul 7630 ▪ brahms@iafrica.com ✆ (021) 869·8555/ 8590 🖷 869·8555

Gesie Lategan — 2003's Western Cape Farmer and Female Farmer (Export) of the Year — is not one to rest on her laurels, but even her indomitable spirit was somewhat dampened by last year's unpredictable weather and difficult crush. 'It was crazy. And to top it all my husband was ill during the entire harvest, so I had to make wine via my cell phone.' As someone who is not that comfortable with the descriptor wine 'maker' (Lategan believes that nature takes all the credit, and sees her role merely as nurturer) she is intrigued by what 2004 will finally produce. Meanwhile 10-year-old son Jacques recently proved he has a nose for business — and Cab. Assisted by his mother, arguably SA's youngest winemaker produced 700 bottles, raising a tidy R10 000 for his school.

★★★★　**Shiraz** Classically styled & elegant, with spice rather than fruit dominating. **02** bayleaf, white pepper, gamey hints; fine textures. Developing similarly to **01**, which more herbal notes, but also greener tannins, less persistent flavours which marred succession from standout **00**, now showing smoky notes, nutmeg & coriander. All from low-yielding vyds (±6 t/ha); Fr oak, 15-20% new.

★★★★　**Pinotage** 🆕 Warm, plummy & sweet — very essence of pinotage in **03**. Clever manipulation of tannins (whole berry fermentation, punch-downs twice daily, 26 days on skins) translates into velvet-like feel & texture, early accessibility. Impressive debut. 9 mths oak Fr used, alc a sizeable 14.6%.

★★★☆　**Cabernet Sauvignon** Tasted as Judex Cab last ed, has migrated to Brahms label. **03** very correct & recognisable from cassis & cedar notes, medium bodied despite 14.4% alc, austere dry finish. Barrel selection after 9 mths oak, used Fr.

Judex Provisional Judgement ★★★ Earthy blend pinotage, merlot, ruby cab, shiraz (39/30/28/3); **02** shows attractive berry, herbal & oaky tones. 14% alc. **Chenin Blanc** ★★★ Ripe marzipan & nut aromas in **03**, opens out to show firm-fleshed peachy fruit, good concentration, could do with a tad more acidity for lift & excitement. Matured 9 mths, used Fr. 13.2% alc. **The Verdict Chenin Blanc** discontinued. — *IvH*

Domaines Paradyskloof see Paradyskloof

Dombeya Vineyards

Stellenbosch ▪ Est 2002 ▪ 1stB 2003 ▪ Tasting & sales Mon-Sat 10-4 ▪ Closed Easter Fri/ Sun, Dec 25/26 & Jan 1 ▪ Vineyard Kitchen tea-garden & restaurant ▪ Gifts ▪ Owner Dombeya Vineyards (Pty) Ltd ▪ 15 ha (cab, merlot, shiraz, chard, sauvignon) ▪ 70% red 30% white ▪ PO Box 12766 Die Board 7613 ℂ 881·3490 🖷 881·3491

The aim is to produce only top wines, which is why these newcomers are taking it one step at a time. They used only 20% of the crop for the first (2003) vintage, releasing a small quantity of whites while their reds, the major focus in the future, undergo maturation. Next step is a new cellar, due to open this year. They'll look at exports only in 2006, says owner Robert Sainsbury, when the cellar goes into full production. So many producers are entering an oversubscribed market, and the challenges facing a new label are daunting. Yet given the vineyard's enviable location in Stellenbosch's 'Golden Triangle', the outlook is encouraging. Lovers of hand-crafted goods note: the farm is also home to Dombeya Yarns, offering an internationally known selection of wool, cotton and mohair products, all created on-site.

Chardonnay ★★★★ A very soft & gentle chard, showing early complexity; **03** nose of melon, apple & crème brûlée; yielding 'malolactic' palate, appley tone carries through with hint vanilla; full bodied (14% alc). 6 mths 2nd fill Fr oak. **Sauvignon Blanc ★★★** Building some complexity in bottle; **03** grapefruit whiffs & slight nuttiness; full, firm flavours; dry zesty finish. Fine fruit expression; good sign for the future. — *TM*

Domein Doornkraal

Little Karoo ▪ Est 1890 ▪ 1stB 1973 ▪ Tasting & sales Mon-Fri 9-5 Sat 8-1 ▪ Fee R15 for groups of 8+ ▪ Closed Easter Fri/Sun, Dec 25/26 & Jan 1 ▪ Tours by appt ▪ Jemima's Restaurant, Baron van Rheede Str, Oudtshoorn ℂ (044) 272·0808 ▪ Farm produce ▪ Tourgroups ▪ Gifts ▪ Owners Swepie & Piet le Roux ▪ Winemakers Swepie & Piet le Roux, with Junel Konstabel (2003) ▪ Viticulturist Piet le Roux ▪ 35 ha ▪ 200 tons 1 500 cs own label 50% white 50% red ▪ PO Box 14 De Rust 6650 ▪ doornkraal@xsinet.co.za ▪ www.doornkraal. co.za ℂ (044) 241·2156 (farm) (044) 251·6715 (tasting room) 🖷 (044) 241·2548

Witty and unpretentious as their wines, the Le Rouxs are. As challenges facing the SA industry, they list (among others) 'non-wine drinkers'. Their solution? 'We drink more and pray, or vice versa.' They're more upbeat about the 2004 harvest: 'smaller but excellent quality' with surprising flavour on colombard, chardonnay and cab, thanks to strict crop control. Father-and-son duo Swepie and Piet hold the fort while daughter Maria polishes her winemaking skills at Backsberg and in Bordeaux. Says her proud brother: 'I miss her terribly. She's a wonderful source of inspiration and new ideas.'

★★★★ Pinta ✓ Luscious jerepiko-style dessert from pinotage, tinta; lately dash touriga too (necessitating name change?); damson jam aromas, prune flavours; harmonious; fresh dry finish. VDG. 30/50/20 ratio; alc slightly higher than pvs (17%). NV.

★★★★ Ten Year Old Tawny Port Among handful of SA vintaged tawnies; old-fashioned but delicious. **92** vibrant amber hues; coffee/crème caramel melange with twists cedarwood, tobacco; concentrated but leavened by beautifully balanced sweetness. Pinotage, tinta; ±18% alc. VDG. Premium priced: R150 ex-tasting room.

Cabernet Sauvignon ★★★ 02 ripe cassis aromas; focused & quite rich; quick finish but pleasant enough. **Merlot ★★** Awards? 'Not likely,' quip Le Rs good-naturedly of quirky, sweet & simple **03**, fermented with native yeasts. **Kannaland ★★** Latest a vintaged (**03**) mix merlot (70%) & cab, dollop pinotage, unwooded; savoury aromas, lightish red berry flavours. **Tickled Pink ★★** Light (12% alc), friskily foamy blanc de noir sparkler; intense ripe grapey aromas; sweet but very fresh finish; packaged with shocking pink home-grown ostrich feather. **Jerepigo** ★★★ Comfortable & warming NV fortified from muscat de F; subdued, almost minerally nose, rich raisiny flavours with hints pipe-tobacco. 18% alc. Also available but not tasted: **Kuierwyn** (dry & Natural Sweet), **Ruby/White Port**.

'Military' range

NV fortified desserts. **Majoor** Idiosyncratic white jerepiko from chenin, with cold-tea flavours & jasmine bouquet; unrated. 16% alc. 'Great Martini mixer,' avers Piet le R, 'or pour over crushed ice with twist lemon – bliss!' **Kaptein** & **Luitenant** not assessed (both AWOL at time of tasting). — *JB*

Dominion Wine Company

Stellenbosch ▪ Est/1stB 2002 ▪ Closed to public ▪ Winemaker Lelanie Germishuys (2004) ▪ 12 000 cs own label 50% red 49% white 1% rosé ▪ Export brands: Kaapslig, Welgedacht, Keteka ▪ Postnet Suite 280 Private Bag X29 Somerset West 7129 ▪ info@ dominionwineco.co.za ▪ www.dominionwineco.co.za ⓒ 883·8879 🖷 883·8782

This creator and builder of brands (Domaine Brahms and Riverstone among them) was delighted to welcome ex-Winecorp winemaker Lelanie Germishuys on board their 'virtual' winery. 'She's already made a difference to the wines,' says Johann Laubser, so no doubt they're expecting many happy returns of the recent Wine of the Month Club tasting in which their Rolling Hills Chardonnay trumped 50 other contenders. Though feeling the effects of the strong rand, they're suceeding in building volumes. The goal remains to deliver high quality wines and excellent service, says new marketing and sales assistant Renette van der Merwe.

★★★★ **Syrah Milestone Limited Release 01** elegantly modern; forward but unflamboyant bramble/choc fruit within trim, firm structure. **02** retasted, shy red berry aromas, hint of smoked meat; fairly taut palate with slight sour-plum twist; subtly oaked (yr Fr). 13.5% alc.

Rosé de Syrah ★★★ **03** pungent aromatic strawberry nose, some herbal whiffs, bone-dry flavours; mouthfilling & characterful style, versatile. **Dominion Merlot** ★★★★ **03** quite complex notes of plum, game & leaves; dark choc flavours still bound by tight tannins; give 2-3 yrs to open up. From a singe vyd in Paarl. 14.8% alc. **Dominion Shiraz** ★★★★ Strikingly deep **03**; stewed plums & pepper aromas; leathery tobacco flavours; elegant, slightly grainy texture still but good now with richer food or could be cellared 2/3 yrs. 14% alc. Lightly oaked. **Dominion Cabernet Sauvignon-Merlot** ★★★ **03** 51/49 blend, both varieties equally active; notes of mulberries & cream on nose, tobacco hint; medium body, mocha & choc flavour. Pleasant middle-of-the-road red, finishes slightly sweet. Yr Fr oak. **Dominion Rolling Hills Chardonnay** ★★★★ ✓ **03** green-gold glints, hint butterscotch, lots of obvious sweet oak; creamy soft dry finish. Big flavoursome wine, will be liked by lovers of woodier styles. 14.3% alc. 7 mths Fr oak. **Chardonnay 'Milestone' Limited Release** ★★★★ ✓ **03** less oak-powered than above version; fruit salad & peach tones; lightly toasty caramel finish. Yr 1st/2nd fill barrels. **Sauvignon Blanc** ★★★ **04** (sample) shy herby aromas, lightish & very dry with hint of grapefruit rind. **Sauvignon Blanc Brut** ★★★ Pale yellow-gold; aromatic pear-drop nose, hints honeysuckle, medium body, refreshingly active mousse; bone-dry conclusion. 11.5% alc. NV (03).

Sugar Bush Ridge range

Cabernet Sauvignon-Merlot 03 (sample) complex with whiffs cedarwood, smoke; fair weight & concentration; possible ★★★★. **02** (retaste ★★★) gamey, slightly vegetal notes, medium-bodied, not nearly as much fruit. 20% new Fr oak, 24 mths. **Sauvignon Blanc** ★★★ **03** shows a light attractive honeyed tone, very dry, grapefruity, fairly structured & taut. A good food style.

Kaapslig range

Naglig ★★★ Cinsaut, ruby cabernet mix (60/40), unoaked; **04** ruby c making its presence felt in cassis/thatch whiffs; dry, savoury, mid-weight palate with cherry-stone twist. **Daglig** ★★★ Harmonious **04** chenin, chardonnay blend (60/40), sweet peach aroma, quite full & dry, some quince flavour on the finish. **Merlot Kingsview**, **Chenin Blanc 'Longkloof'** & **Sauvignon Blanc 'Kingsview'** discontinued. The wines sourced widely, so various WOs. — *CR/TM*

Doolhof Estate

Wellington ▪ Est 1996 ▪ 1stB 2001 ▪ Visits by appt ▪ Conferencing ▪ Walks ▪ 4x4 trail ▪ Mountain biking ▪ Owners Kerrison family ▪ Winemaker Therese Swart (Aug 2004) ▪ Vineyard manager Hendrik Laubscher (Aug 1996) ▪ ±35 ha (cabs s/f, malbec, merlot, petit v, pinotage, shiraz, chard, sauvignon) ▪ 220 tons 10 800 cs ▪ PO Box 975 Wellington 7654 ▪ wine@doolhof.com ▪ www.doolhof.com ▪ © 873·6911 ☏ 864·2321

Developments have been happening apace at Doolhof since the Kerrison family purchased the farm in 2003. The new cellar is due for completion this year, Therese Swart is the newly appointed winemaker (Hendrik Laubscher still oversees viticulture) and David Kerrison their man in marketing. Producing predominantly noble red varieties (under a Signatures of Doolhof label — the old Maze Valley brand no longer used) alongside two blends (Cape Roan and Cape Boar), Swart believes that the global surplus of wine has put pressure on growers to increase quality. As a result Doolhof is pitching itself firmly at the top end of the market. Picturesquely situated between Groenberg and Bainskloof, Doolhof benefits from cooler conditions, Swart says, with up to two hours less direct sunlight and a constant breeze throughout the summer. 2004 was a particularly cool season, resulting in intense fruitiness from the grapes — all hand-picked and -sorted.

Both **03**s, unoaked. **Cape Boar** ★★★★ Blend led by cab, with shiraz, merlot (50/30/20); attractive red-fruit nose, earthy & gamey touches, palate-coating mulberry flavours; powerful stewed fruit character, sweetish finish. 14.7% alc. **Cape Roan** ★★★★ Shiraz leads the charge (70/20/10); similar character, slightly more pepper; bigger — massive! — alc (15%) but more control, less overt sweetness. Flashy wines both.

Signatures of Doolhof range

These **04**s mostly tasted as early samples, so unrated. None oaked, though wooded versions of the each of the reds are in the pipeline. **Shiraz** Youthfully gawky; ripe, ebullient mulberry fruit, full body. **Cabernet Sauvignon** Also extremely youthful; tastes for all the world like cassis juice. **Merlot** Still with fermentation yeast aromas, appealing plum/mulberry fruit. **Pinotage** Mulberry & banana aromas, bit drier than the others, very juicy. **Unwooded Chardonnay** ★★★ 04 a real crowd-pleaser: scented nose of passionfruit & pear; perceptible sweetness (technically off-dry at 5.5g/ℓ RS), hauled into line by fairly tart sherbety acidity. — TM

Dormershire

Stellenbosch ▪ Est 1996 ▪ 1stB 2001 ▪ Closed to public ▪ Owner SPF Family Trust ▪ Winemaker Sunette Frost (reds), with consultants Ronell Wiid (whites) & Hilko Hegewisch (reds) ▪ Viti consultant Johan Pienaar (Jan 2001, Feb 2000) ▪ 7 ha (cab, shiraz, sauvignon) ▪ 2 500 cs 80% red 20% white ▪ PO Box 491 Bellville 7535 ▪ frostyr@iafrica.com © 903·1784 ☏ 945·1174

For Sunette Frost, co-owner with her husband, Paul, 2004 was a year to remember. With the help of consultant Hilko Hegewisch, who came on board late in 2003, she made her first red wines — first to be vinified on the home farm in a new 100-ton cellar. (The whites are still being made on a neighbouring farm by Hazendal cellar chief Ronell Wiid.) It's also the year in which the first bottled red — the Shiraz 02 — went on sale. The Gauteng market is a focus locally, and the Frosts have an eye on the export arena, particularly the East.

Sauvignon Blanc ☺ ★★★ More authority in **03**, whiffs ozone & flint to herbal, lime flavours, firm lingering finish. Pleasingly moderate alc (13%); food friendly, too.

Cabernet Sauvignon 03 (barrel sample) classically constructed, class immediately apparent despite youth, provisional rating ★★★★. Taut, ripe dark-berried fruits, still under influence of good oak; 13 mths, all Fr, 15% new. **Shiraz** ★★★ **02** has settled well into bottle, warm plummy fruit with distinctive smoke/leather, tannins not too stern. Serious oak (15 mths Fr, 20% new). **03** preview a notch up; softer tannins, easier to drink. — IvH

Dornier Wines

⸰ *Stellenbosch ▪ 1stB 2002 ▪ Tasting & sales Mon-Fri 9-4.30 Sat 9-3 ▪ Fee R20 ▪ Closed Easter Fri-Mon, Dec 25/26, Jan 1 ▪ Tours by appt ▪ Tourgroups ▪ Self-catering cottage ▪ Owner Christoph Dornier ▪ Winemaker Ian Naudé (Jan 2001) ▪ Viticulturist Lucas de Kock (1996) ▪ ±67 ha (cabs s/f, merlot, chenin, sauvignon, semillon) ▪ 10 000 cs 85% red 15% white ▪ PO Box 7518 Stellenbosch 7599 ▪ info@dornierwines.co.za ▪ www.dornierwines. co.za ℂ 880-0557 🖷 880-1499*

The clean, curving lines of Swiss-based painter Christoph Dornier's minimalist cellar – its reflection in an adjacent ornamental lake forms the shape of a giant fish – is spawning a small range of wines which combine Old World elegance with New World exuberance. This juxtaposition is echoed in the contrast between the modern cellar and the restored Cape Dutch manor on home-farm Keerweder which, with three other properties, forms the Dornier domaine. Winemaker Ian Naudé, perched in 'the eye of the fish', has facilities to vinify the vineyard blocks separately, creating a varied palette from which to assemble his blends. The first of these, a white and two reds, were launched last year (future red versions could feature malbec and petit verdot). For travellers, there's an opportunity to reserve the farm's guest cottage and hang up your 'gone fishing' sign.

★★★★ **Donatus** Pencil shaving-like complexity appears in rich, restrained **02**, blend cab, merlot, shiraz, cab f (35/30/25/10), 18 mths new Fr oak (shiraz new Am). Modern, with lifted fruit; gently textured. Shiraz shows on nose, but defers to a Bdx-like structure on palate. Approachable now, but will evolve beautifully over next 5 yrs. Flew 1st Class Lufthansa. Commendable maiden release in difficult vintage.

★★★★ **Donatus White 03** clever & challenging blend chenin & semillon, dash sauvignon for freshness, complexity (58/28/16). Aromatic peach-toned nose reminiscent of viognier, but in fact from the chenin. Poised, focused, seamlessly oaked palate with structure, length, minerality. Can only add to growing reputation of blended Cape whites. 30% fermented in new Fr oak.

Cabernet Sauvignon-Merlot NEW ★★★ **02** 60/40 blend, oak as above. Rich, silky, high toned, with sweetness/ripeness on palate. Well-handled oak. Best young. — *RK*

Douglas Green

Wellington ▪ Est/1stB 1938 ▪ Closed to public ▪ Owner DGB ▪ Cellarmaster (blending cellar) Gerhard Carstens, with Liesl Carstens-Herbst (2003) ▪ Oenologist Jaco Potgieter (2000) ▪ Vini advisor John Worontschak ▪ Viti advisers VinPro (May 2000) ▪ 6 000 tons 580 000 cs 50% red 50% white ▪ ISO 9002 & HACCP certified ▪ PO Box 246 Wellington 7654 ▪ douglasgreen@ dgb.co.za ▪ www.douglasgreen.co.za ℂ 864-5300 🖷 864-1287

It's big: brand owner DGB makes more than half-a-million cases under the 67-year-old Douglas Green label. And growing: production of the two Faces of Africa blends jumped from 5 000 to 130 000 cartons in three short years. Looking for expansion, DGB has identified Scandinavia and new markets such as India and China. The range is growing too – recent new products are a Shiraz and Chenin, which 'looks particularly promising', according to peripatetic oenologist Jaco Potgieter, fondly known as 'Skim' (Phantom). The reds have 'a very positive quality' thanks to their being pressed at lower sugar levels because of a combination of harvest conditions.

★★★☆ **Cabernet Sauvignon** ✓ Understated but generous dry red usually in drink-now mode, though **03** (★★★) shows unexpectedly dry tannins pleading time to fill out & soften, & for lead-pencil & mineral tones to develop.

★★★★ **Merlot** ✓ **02** returned to gushy-fruity styling of **00**, with oodles of plums & mulberries shouting to be noticed. Latest **03** again multi-fruited, lovely red berry nose, well constructed; balanced & integrated oak (Fr staves, 3 mths).

★★★☆ **St Augustine** ✓ Favourite SA red since the 1940s; now mainly cab & merlot — equal 43% with shiraz in **02**, warm & generous plummy aroma; smooth, good & juicy. 14.4% alc. **01** built its fruit & charry oak around solid core of minerals.

Pinotage ★★★★ **02** tasted as sample last ed has realised its potential; ripe rhubarb & black fruit aromas; forward, rich, almost sweetly ripe fruit; could be cellared 3-4 yrs. **Shiraz** ★★★ **03** tasty commercial style with typical smoky/meaty whiffs, soft, accessible, lots of vanilla from 3 mths on Am/Fr staves. 14.2% alc. **Chardonnay** ★★★ **04** melon & light buttered-toast whiffs; soft & easy but quite quick. 14.5% alc. **Sauvignon Blanc** ★★★ **04** crunchy acidity, appley fruit salad tones, not as flavourful/sparkly as pvs. 12.4% alc. **Cape Ruby Port** ★★★★ Latest NV version not tasted; last we noted an LBV (rather than Ruby) style, fragrant & warming; a real winter snuggler. Both ranges WO W-Cape.

Faces of Africa range

Cinsaut-Pinotage ★★ Wood a bigger presence in **04** than pvs, cherry fruit-pastille palate fairly firm in 50/50 blend, ends furrily. 14.3% alc. **Colombar-Chardonnay** ★★★ Light-textured **04** tenders bright lemon-drop flavours, refreshing crisp acidity. — *CR*

Douglas Winery

Northern Cape ▪ Est 1968 ▪ 1stB 1977 ▪ Tasting & sales Mon-Fri 8-5 ▪ Fee R5 ▪ Closed public holidays ▪ Tours by appt ▪ BYO picnic ▪ Gifts ▪ Owners 45 shareholders ▪ Winemaker WH 'Pou' le Roux (Jan 1978), with Danie Kershoff (Jun 1994) ▪ Viticulturist Wrensch Roux (Jun 2003) ▪ 360 ha (cab, merlot, shiraz, chard, chenin, colombard, gewürz) ▪ 6 000 cs own label 19% red 43% white 8% rosé 30% dessert ▪ PO Box 47 Douglas 8730 ▪ wynkelder@gwk.co.za ▪ www.gwk.co.za ✆ (053) 298·8314 🖷 (053) 298·1845

A killer of a black frost in the Orange River Valley in October 2003 spared this cellar near Kimberley — fortunately the vines had not started budding. Hence, no drop in tonnage and a bountiful 4m litres from the 2004 harvest. The 45 members took a further step towards an upgrade in quality with the appointment, mid-2003, of Wrensch Roux as viticulturist; a more recent follow-on was the installation of new fermentation and holding tanks.

Avoca certified range

Only the **Gewürztraminer** currently available; not tasted (not for want of trying, we might add — Pieter Louw & co sent multiple batches of samples down from Kimberley, at least one of which was destroyed in transit. A consolation ★★★★★ for trying).

Avoca Classic range

Red ☺ ★★★ Uncomplicated lightish fruity tipple with jammy mulberry & red-fruit flavours, hint of tannin. 60% cab, rest shiraz.

Available but not tasted this ed: **Rosé**, **White** (dry) & **Gold** (semi-sweet); all NV.

Avoca fortified range

The following are NV. **Red Muscadel** ★★ Pale rosé hue belies extroverted bouquet of muscat & grapeseed; sweet spirity flavours. 16.5% alc. **Red Jerepigo** ★★★ Unusual & varied flavour combo of muscat, liquorice, tar & molasses; light-toned & balanced. Alc as above. **Ruby Port** ★★ Normally from ruby cab, lightish for style, so latest unusually spiritous at 19% alc; clean if straightforward red fruit flavours; coffee-tinged farewell. **Sweet Hanepoot** available but untasted.

Confluence range

Shiraz-Cabernet Sauvignon ★★ 60/40 mix with briary red fruit aromas; soft, juicy, medium bodied; lightly oaked. **Chenin Blanc-Colombard** ★★ Clean but quiet & four-square 65/35 blend; light bodied. Both **03**s. Available but not tasted: **Classic Red/White**.

Provin range

Available but not tasted: in 2/5ℓ bag-in-boxes: **Dry Red**, **Grand Cru**, **Stein**, **Special Harvest** & **Late Harvest**. Also **Vin Doux Sparkling**. — *JB*

Drakensig Wines

Paarl ▪ Est 1999 ▪ 1stB 2000 ▪ Tasting & sales Mon-Fri 9-5 Sat 9-1; low season by appt ▪ Closed Easter Sun, Dec 25/26 & Jan 1 ▪ Home-grown olive oil for sale ▪ Conference facilities for groups of 5-10 ▪ Owner/winemaker/viticulturist Marais Viljoen ▪ 13 ha (cab, pinotage, shiraz) ▪ 4 000 cs 80% red 20% white ▪ HACCP implementation in progress ▪ PO Box 22 Simondium 7670 ▪ drakensig@mweb.co.za © 874·3881 ☎ 874·3882

A gold for his Cab Reserve at Veritas 2003 underlined the 'value' aspect of owner/winemaker Marais Viljoen's value-for-money philosophy (now sold out, it was retailing at R55). The Shiraz Reserve also did well, taking a silver. Late as it was, the 2004 harvest delivered good grapes, in his opinion, so there's no lack of choice for buy-in.

Marais Viljoen Reserve range

★★★★ **Cabernet Sauvignon** Last was the **01**, notch better than standard version.
★★★★ **Shiraz** ✓ Sophisticated & stylish **02**, fruitcake aromas/flavours, drier, more structured than version below. 14 mths Am/Fr barrels, 50% new. Fruit ex-Mbury.
Pinotage ★★ **01** statement wine, big & unsubtle; porty character, hints prune & smoked meat, gamey palate-coating flavours. 14.5% alc.

Standard range

Shiraz ★★★ Retasted **02** smoky mocha whiffs & bramble fruit; sappy redcurrants on palate; easy drinking despite high 14.5% alc. **Cabernet Sauvignon** ★★★ **02** tasted anew, smoky redcurrant whiffs, soft choc flavours, full body; holding & should do so few yrs. Alc 14.5%; 11 mths Fr oak. **Pinotage** ★★ **02**, yr on, rustic, sweet & jammy; tones of mulberry jam & salami; Am/Fr oak 11 mths, 30% new. **Sauvignon Blanc** ★★★ Last tasted was **03**, more restrained than pvs. All WO Coastal.— *TM*

Drostdy Wine Cellar

Tulbagh ▪ Est 1964 ▪ Tasting & wine sales at De Oude Drostdy Mon-Fri 10-5 Sat 10-2 ▪ Owner Distell ▪ PO Box 9 Tulbagh 6820 ▪ www.drostdywines.co.za © (023) 230·0203 ☎ (023) 230·0510

De Oude Drostdy, Tulbagh's old magistracy, built in 1804 and now a national monument, is the spiritual home of Drostdy-Hof wines. The range, intended to be fruity and accessible early, is exported to Scandinavia and other parts of Europe.

Drostdy-Hof range

Claret Select ☺ ★★★ Lightish vat-matured blend tinta, pinotage & cab; latest (NV) surprisingly rich Xmas pudding tones but finishes pleasantly dry, with food-cordial firmness. **Adelpracht** ☺ ★★★ Smooth, tangy SLH from chenin, lovely confectioner's shop scents on **03**; surprisingly rich for just 11.7% alc.

Cabernet Sauvignon ★★★ **02** shows a hint of cab's austerity; minty tinge to lightish palate; firm finish; cellar 2/3 yrs or drink now with food. Fr barrels/staves, 9 mths. **Merlot** ★★★★ Still a standout red in range; yr Fr oak, new, 2nd & 3rd fill; **03** more savoury than pvs but elegant & satisfying, with good dry finish. 14% alc. **Pinotage** ★★★ Unlike burly pvs, **03** light coloured/textured & fresh, for early drinking; soft caramel custard tone from Fr oak staves, 9 mths. 13.9%. **Ruby Cabernet** ★★ **03** shows none of the eager fruitiness of most SA ruby cabs; dense, chunky & dry with furry tannins needing time. **Shiraz** ★★★ **03** more juicy than pvs; smoked meat & gamey notes should go well with savoury foods. Fr/Am staves 9 mths. **Cape Red** ★★★ Smooth & flavourful **03** more 'serious' than pvs, not just a gulper; plumminess enlivened by rhubarb & fynbos; blend cab, pinotage, ruby cab (40/30/30), small portion oaked. **Rosé** [NEW] ★★★ **03** melange of carignan, cinsaut, pinotage & pinot; bone-dry gravelly richness imparts a distinctly European feel. **Chardonnay** ★★★ **03** effusive aromas of biscuits & tropical fruit; oak (chips) a definite but not overwhelming presence; pleasantly light 12.8% alc. **Sauvignon Blanc** ★★★ **04** riper tasting than pvs (figs & granadilla rather than 'green' fruit); still light textured, crisp & refreshing.

Extra Light ★★ Big-selling, low-alc (9.5%), steely-dry NV dieter's friend; latest (**04**) from barely-ripe chenin, colombard. **Steen/Chenin Blanc** ★★★ **04** early picked & showing it in grassy, hay-like bouquet; nicely textured, refreshingly crisp & lightish. **Premier Grand Cru** ★★★ Latest NV offers more of everything than austere pvs; dominated by pungently herbaceous sauvignon, one of 4 varieties in light, bone-dry blend. **Stein Select** ★★ Gentle, easy-drinking semi-sweet from quartet of varieties incl palomino, with honeyed tropical aromas. **Late Harvest** ★★ Soft, gently sweet NV from chenin; latest fruity & generous on nose though palate's less giving. Above mainly WO Coastal. Some also available in 340ml, 2ℓ and 5ℓ packs.

African Sky range

Untasted export wines: **Cabernet Sauvignon**, **Shiraz-Pinotage** NEW, **Cirrus** (mainly pinotage, with cab, merlot, cab & cinsaut), **Crux** (chiefly cab, splash ruby cab), **Rosé** (pinot & cab), **Cape Red** NEW, **Cumulus** (chenin), **Chenin Blanc-Chardonnay** NEW, **Cape White** (chenin), **Sauvignon Blanc** & **Celeste** (sauvignon, semillon). — *CR*

Dry Creek see Du Preez Estate
Due South see Kosie Möller Wines
Dumisani see Winecorp
Duncan's Creek see Rickety Bridge
Du Plessis see Havana Hills

Du Preez Estate

Goudini (see Worcester map) ▪ Est 1995 ▪ 1stB 1998 ▪ Tasting & sales Mon-Fri 9-5 ▪ Closed Easter Fri-Mon, Dec 16/25/26 & Jan 1 ▪ Tours by appt ▪ BYO picnic ▪ Facilities for children ▪ Tourgroups ▪ Owners Du Preez family ▪ Winemaker Hennie du Preez Jnr (1995), with Sias du Toit (2003) ▪ Viticulturist Jean du Preez (Dec 1996) ▪ 300 ha (cab, merlot, petit v, chard, chenin, sauvignon) 56% red 40% white 2% rosé 2% sparkling ▪ Export brands: Rockfields, Dry Creek, Route 101, De Denne ▪ Ranges for customers: Lion Rock & Red Shed (UK) ▪ PO Box 12 Rawsonville 6845 ▪ dupreezestate@intekom.co.za ✆ (023) 349·1995 🖷 (023) 349·1923

When Polla's Red, a rank outsider from this Rawsonville estate took the trophy best for non-Bordeaux red blend at the FCTWS in 2002 it caused quite a commotion. But when the Merlot Reserve was judged best in its class at the same show two years later, it simply confirmed they were running true to form. With the challenge 'to produce such quality that the current surplus doesn't touch you', Hennie du Preez remains steadfast when it comes to realistic pricing. BYO picnics to enjoy on the estate are another affordable option for day-trippers to this area, which is fast gaining ground.

★★★★ **Hendrik Lodewyk Petit Verdot** NEW Hardly a youth, but **01** very youthful still, deserves time. Flowery nose of violets & lavender; ripe-berry taste; palate expansive (14% alc) but livened by fruity acid. Serious wooding (30 mths small oak) for clean spicy effect, uncluttered with vanilla. NE. 14% alc. One of still small handful of standalone bottlings of grape in SA. Promising.

★★★★ **Merlot Reserve** Easily recognisable by its spicy, high-toned pungency; edgy style, zingy but ripe; **01** FCTWS trophy clincher maturing nicely; fermented with oak chips, then barrelled 18 mths, some Am. Richly coloured; pulpy plums/mulberries & choc touched with suggestion of bottle-age decadence. Lots more to give.

★★★★ **Shiraz 01** attractive & bright, plums spiked with smoky bacon; full flavoured elegance in **02**, ripe red berries, pepper & spice sprinkle; active but suave tannins, supportive oak (as for Merlot). Off a single-vyd.

★★★★ **Polla's Red** Individual & fragrant blend of pinotage, shiraz, ruby cab, petit v. Loads of satisfying spicy flavour. **00** FCTWS trophy winner. Retasted **01**, ageing interestingly as anticipated; coffee-choc palate with charry/smoky touch, good ripe tannins. Oak/alc as for Merlot.

★★★★ **Hanepoot** Invariably smooth jerepigo-style dessert. Last we tasted was the **03**.

Chardonnay ★★★ 04 unwooded portion blended with barrelled fraction for lower oak profile. Big (14% alc) but gentle, polished. **Sauvignon Blanc** ★★★ Lightish, early-picked & crisp but not shrill 04, floral bouquet with pineapple/green pepper hint.

Rockfields range

Red Stone ★★★☆ 02 spicy red-berried blend merlot, shiraz, ruby cab, petit v; characterful & stylish yet easy; part barrels/staves. **Chenin Blanc** NEW ★★ 04 (sample) gentle tropical fruit aromas, fresh, tangy flavours. **Sauvignon Blanc** ★★★ 04 (work in progress) tropical fruit & the same light, zingy character as pvs. 11.5% alc.

Dry Creek range

Red ★★★ 04 abundant ripe red berry fruit with floral touch, all tweaked for unproblematic quaffing. **White** ★★★ Pleasing jumble of 04 chenin, colombard, sauvignon; softly rounded, effortless. Last two ranges NE. — *DH*

� *Du Preez Wine* see Migration, Leidersburg

Durbanville Hills

Durbanville ▪ Est 1998 ▪ 1stB 1999 ▪
Tasting & sales Mon-Fri 9-4.30 Sat & pub hols 9.30-2.30 Sun 11-3 ▪ Fee R15 ▪ Tours Mon-Fri 11 & 3 Fee R20 ▪ Closed Easter Fri/Sun, Dec 25/26 & Jan 1 ▪ @ The Hills Restaurant (see Eat-out section) ▪ Farm produce ▪ Facilities for children ▪ Tourgroups ▪ Gifts ▪ Conferencing ▪ Walks ▪ Owners Distell, 8 farmers & workers' trust ▪ Winemakers Martin Moore & Riaan Oosthuizen, with Günther Kellerman (Nov/Dec 1998, Nov 2003) ▪ Viti consultant Johan Pienaar ▪ 770 ha (cabs/f, merlot, pinotage, shiraz, chard, sauvignon, semillon) ▪ 4 440 tons 140 000 cs own label 40% red 60% white ▪ 70% red 30% white ▪ ISO 9000 certified; ISO 14000 in progress ▪ PO Box 3276 Durbanville 7551 ▪ info@durbanvillehills.co.za ▪ www.durbanvillehills.co.za
℃ *558·1300* 🖷 *559·8169*

'What you get is what you make — unless you stuff it up in the cellar', says Martin Moore. The south-east wind which hits the eponymous hills and spills into the valley is cold during harvest. So much so, 'it blows you off your feet — the staff work with jerseys on'. Moore, who is devoted to sauvignon, believes bigger can be better: they've seen sales of their varietal sauvignons jump from 5 000 cases to 50 000, and the quality, Moore asserts, has improved. (A recent vertical tasting, starting with the Biesjes Craal 99 and ending with components from specific blocks underlined his point.) With 'a huge amount of the flavour sitting in it', lees is treated like gold in the cellar. The restaurant, with its newly enlarged kitchen, is a great place to partner wine with food and views of Table Bay. If you're lucky Moore will be there to amuse you with his own take on pairing people with wine and food.

'Single Vineyard' range

★★★★★ **Caapmans Cabernet Sauvignon-Merlot** Impressive debut 99, only vintage to date; shows influence that cab commands — more structure, discipline, than Merlot, ripe mulberry-scented fruit, balsamic notes of fine oak. Suggest cellar another 1-2 yrs, will keep 5-7 at least. 2 vyds; 2 yrs new Fr oak. 13.8% alc. MIWA gold.

★★★★ **Luipaardsberg Merlot Reserve** To date the extraordinary, showy 99; strong choc/peppermint crisp edge to black cherry fruit (flavours carefully protected during passage through cellar); big savoury palate — all delivered with almost treacly intensity. Single vyd on Klein Roosboom farm; 2 yrs new Fr oak. 13. VDG.

★★★★★ **Biesjes Craal Sauvignon Blanc** Only produced when weather conditions cool enough. From very steep south-facing vyd. 04 (sample) quivering intensity: piercing green character (asparagus, capsicum, fresh herbs); racy acidity & mouth-tingling freshness. Impressive elegance & verve, evoking comparison with the Loire. 11.5% alc. Pvs was 01, which refuted widely held view that sauvignon should be consumed in first yr. 2 producers, selected blocks, 'not just cool — almost cold'.

Rhinofields range

★★★☆ **Merlot 00** retasted mid-2004, unfolding after slow start. Black choc, hints mint, heather, underlying brambleberries. Palate more forthcoming, appealing elegance, accessibility. Ready, but will age gracefully 5+ yrs. Yr Fr oaked, 75% new.

★★★★★ **Chardonnay** From selected vyds, each imparting particular character. Delicious **03** wonderful sashay between lemongrass, lime/orange zest, & peach-tropical aromatics, confirming complexity & class. Flavours more toasty, with citrus undertones, but smoothly ripe, good length. Combo tank/barrel fermented/matured, new Burgundian oak. Good 3+ yr ageing potential. 13.4% alc. No **02**. More oak, weight (from older vines) in delicious **01**, several notches above pvs. MIWA gold.

★★★★ **Sauvignon Blanc** Fruit from 2 producers, selected vyds. **04** riding on gooseberry core, shows distinctive Dbnville 'wet heath' pungency, plenty green aromatics. Prepares you for racy acidity, crisply clean finish. Nothing unripe or lean, just intense, tightly packed, zinging freshness. 12.7% alc. **03**, was riper, less aggressive but thrilling. **02** vigorous; distinctive aromatics of cool Dbnville fruit.

Premium range

★★★☆ **Cabernet Sauvignon** As rest of range, intended for earlier drinking. **01** retasted mid-2004, retains dark-fruited appeal, supple tannins, friendly approach, yet underlying structure will support few yrs cellaring. Exciting **99** (★★★★) introduction followed by less 'serious' **00**, for earlier drinking. Substantial 10 000 cs.

★★★★ **Merlot** More than merely charming. **01** yr on, tannins more integrated, accessible; drinking beautifully. Opulent creamy plum-choc fruit main attraction, seduces. Oak as above. 13.2% alc.

★★★★ **Pinotage** The goal – 'very friendly, accessible wine'. **02** doesn't put foot wrong: vanilla spicing adds extra dimension to lush plummy fruit; rounded body, supple tannins meet quality-drinking criteria. Oak as above. 14.6% alc. **01** arguably the nicest of the Premium range that yr. **00** extrovert & interestingly wild.

★★★★ **Shiraz** Latest **01** delicious & ready; good aromatics (wild berries, black pepper, woodsmoke, underbrush); fleshy, amenable tannins, freshening acidity. Yr Fr/Am barriques, combo new/used. 14% alc. **00** quiet on nose, but revved up on taste.

★★★★ **Sauvignon Blanc** ✓ Their entry-level, high-volume (±26 000 cs) sauvignon, in 'tamer', more popular style. Reductively vinified **04** (sample) returns to form. Zinging gooseberry/passionfruit concentration, lip-smacking freshness. Tangy, juicy, delicious. 12.7% alc. **03** (★★★) was friendly but quiet.

Chardonnay ★★★ **03** fruit main focus: forthcoming peach-tropical aromas, lightly oaked for extra flavour, interest, boosted structure. Essentially friendly, easy-drinking style. Qtr blend oaked (new Fr). 13.3% alc. **Semillon-Sauvignon Blanc** discontinued.– *CR*

▪ *Dusty Road* see Cloof

Du Toitskloof Winery

*Rawsonville (see Worcester map) ▪ Est 1962 ▪ 1stB 1970 ▪ Tasting & sales – Winery: Mon-Fri 8-5 Sat 9-12.30 Wine Shop: Mon-Fri 9-5.30 Sat 10-5 Sun 11-4 ▪ Closed Easter Fri/Mon, Apr 27, Sep 24, Dec 16/25/26, Jan 1 ▪ BYO picnic ▪ Tours by appt ▪ Formal tasting for groups max 40 ▪ Owners 17 members ▪ Winemakers Philip Jordaan & Shawn Thomson (May 1983/Oct 1999), with Derrick Cupido & Christo Basson (1993/Jan 2002) ▪ Viti consultant Schalk du Toit (1997) ▪ 750 ha ▪ 13 500 tons 30% red 70% white ▪ PO Box 55 Rawsonville 6845 ▪ dutoitcellar@intekom.co.za ▪ www.dutoitskloof.com ✆ **(023) 349·1601** 🖷 (023) 349·1581*

Du Toitskloof is synonymous with good value, so it is reassuring that this consistent cellar hasn't hiked its prices though it was won numerous awards (including two *Wine* Best Value Cellar citations). Winemaker here for 21 years, Philip Jordaan's philosophy is unvarying: 'easy-drinking wines, from whites to reds to desserts, at affordable prices'. For a laid-back and (that word again) affordable outing, bring your own picnic, taste the wines, choose a bottle and soak up the scenery. The nearby wine shop at Du Toitskloof Lodge, with rock pools backdropped by mountain peaks, is another outspan option.

★★★★ Shiraz 01 gonged by SAA, MIWA judges; **02** (**★★★**) smoky plums, true to type, oak slightly planky & apart mid-2004; perhaps just needs time. This, varietal reds below, ±8 mths Fr oak.

★★★★ Noble Late Harvest ✓ Botrytised dessert from muscat & chenin; to date the debut **99**, SAYWS champ.

★★★★ Red Muscadel ✓ Among the Cape's top fortified muscats: opulent, elegant, wonderful in effusive youth (esp lightly chilled), graceful in maturity. **02** pleasing complexity — mocha & tobacco on bouquet, dried fruit & potpourri on palate. ±230g/ℓ sugar; 16.5% alc. Off single bushvine block 10 yrs old.

★★★★★ Hanepoot Jerepigo ✓ Gorgeous & delicious fortified dessert; pvs pair of vintages (**99**, **00**) absolute crackers; retasted **01** (**★★★★**) not quite as rivetting, especially on palate, which too silky, easy-drinking — lacks grunt. 15.5% alc.

★★★★ Cape Ruby ✓ Latest **03** inaugurates switch from old Cape, pinotage based to a more modern style featuring 'correct' Portuguese varieties tinta, souzão, touriga in equal measure; inviting stewed plum whiffs, raisin hint; rich, supple, dryish & smooth, molasses hint on finish. 18% alc; yr small oak.

Merlot ☺ **★★★** Gains extra juiciness from partial carbonic maceration; **02** bold (14% alc) & forthcoming; red fruit aromas, dry savoury palate with slightly grainy food-inclined tannins. **Pinotage-Ruby Cabernet** ☺ **★★★** Plump, soft **03** has ruby c's damp thatch aroma, pinotage's slightly sweet finish. 50/50 blend, 4 mths new Fr Oak. Appears as **Dry Red** under 500ml screwcap NV. **Blanc de Noir** ☺ **★★★** 04 smoky stewed plum aromas, bone-dry tastes, elegant sappy red-fruit character, refreshing. From cinsaut. **Sauvignon Blanc** ☺ **★★★** Uncomplicated good-value quaffer. **04** quiet whiffs of nettle & guava; comes alive on palate with apple & limes, brisk finish. **Blanc de Blanc** ☺ **★★★** Softly dry, effortless chenin, semillon blend; 500ml screwcap, NV. Attractive herbal/leesy nose, gentle apple finish. **Special Late Harvest** ☺ **★★★** Light-bodied semi-sweet muscat d'A. **04** tints of apple & pear, whiff jasmine, poised sweetness, soft passionfruit flavours. **Sparkling Brut** ☺ **★★★** Lightish & busy bubbles with smoothly dry crisp finish. Carbonated NV from chard, sauvignon & muscadel.

Cabernet Sauvignon ★★★ 02 sweetish plummy fruit, savoury dry finish with powdery but good tannins, drinkable & well made. **Pinotage ★★★ 02** subdued on nose, lightish coloured/textured, dominated by wood. *Wine* best value selection. **Chardonnay ★★★ 04** barely oak-brushed to showcase delicate lemon-rind hints; quite austere finish, needs a saucy fish. **Chenin Blanc ★★ 04** ultra-shy apple & pear whiffs; clean & correct, simple green melon flavours, low 11.5% alc. **Bukettraube ★★★ 04** surprisingly full-flavoured for variety, fruit salad tone, well-balanced sweetness. **Riesling ★★** Unusually characterful for crouchen; **04** herby whiffs; dry & pleasantly austere, 'European' hint of almonds, ideal for spicy grilled calamari. **Late Vintage ★★★** Fruitily sweet & light NV from chenin & muscat d'A. 500ml screwcap. Latest has perfumes of jasmine & spice, supple fruit salad & melon flavours. All WO Worcester. — *TM*

D'Vine see Swartland Wine Cellar
Dwyka Hills see New Cape Wines
Eagle's Cliff see New Cape Wines

EagleVlei

Stellenbosch ▪ Est/1stB 1997 ▪ Closed to public ▪ Tasting & sales for trade by appt ▪ Owners Steve & Jean Weir, André & Tessa van Helsdingen ▪ Winemaker André van Helsdingen ▪ Viticulturist Henry Fisk, advised by Paul Wallace ▪ 11 ha (cab, merlot, pinotage) ▪ 40 tons 3 000 cs 100% red ▪ PO Box 969 Stellenbosch 7599 ▪ avanhels@adept.co.za ▪ www. eaglevlei.co.za ©/🖷 (021) 880·1846

Many growers suffered a late harvest last year, yet all the varieties on this Muldersvlei property came in on exactly the same date as in 2003. 'We were very happy with the degree of ripeness', says André van Helsdingen. 'The grapes appeared full of fruit. Generally, as good as 2003.' Recognising that marketing is the main challenge for a small winery such as this, focusing on top-end reds, UK partners Steve and Jean Weir are stepping up their efforts to raise awareness among British consumers. A recent 4-star rating for their Cab in UK *Decanter* should up their profile a notch or two.

★★★★ **Cabernet Sauvignon** Cassis-perfumed **02** (with splash merlot) now brazening its youthful charm. Gushing sweet fruit, but good ripe tannin support. Pure cab **03** more subtly savoury, also delicious, with plentiful berry flavours, balanced smooth strong tannins, lingering finish. 14% alc. Open-vat ferment (as all these), yr Fr oak.

★★★☆ **Pinotage** Deep velvet-plush hue presages friendly but firm approach. Softly fruity **02** (retasted) has sweet-sour element, ripe tannin core, supportive wooding (yr, 20% Am); 14.5% alc. More exuberant **03** drier, less powerful 13.5%; first offers boiled sweet & disconcerting rubber notes, then lushly ripe flavours.

★★★☆ **Merlot** 〔NEW〕 Welcoming fruity, choc-coated aromas on **03**. Flavoursome, with soft ultra-ripeness clinging to firm tannic core, yet a slightly green note too. Well integrated oak influence from yr Fr barrels. 14.5% alc. — *TJ*

Eden Crest

Part of the Christo Wiese Portfolio (see entry), this blended range takes its name from its 'fertile garden origins' in the Stellenbosch area.

Cape Blend 〔NEW〕 ★★★ Tasty, early-drinking **03** merlot, pinotage, cab blend (55/33/12), with dominant partners supplying appealing red berry fruit focus, & cab contributing more to structure. Lightly oaked. 14.2% alc. **Shiraz-Merlot** 〔NEW〕 ★★★ Sweet, ripe fruit on 58/42 blend **03** — strawberries, mulberries, with cedar/savoury toastiness from light oaking. Enjoy in youthful freshness. 14,3% alc. **Chardonnay-Chenin Blanc** ★★★ Maiden **03** enhanced with sauvignon, touch oak, in 55/24/21 blend. Summer fruits character, with enough freshness to ensure good food partnership. 13% alc. — *CR*

 *Edenhof* see Schalkenbosch ·

Eikehof Wines

*Franschhoek ▪ Visits by appt ▪ Owner/winemaker/viticulturist Francois Malherbe ▪ 43 ha (cab, merlot, shiraz, sauvignon) ▪ 70 tons 4 000 cs 60% red 40% white ▪ PO Box 222 Franschhoek 7690 ▪ eikehof@mweb.co.za ▪ www.zeplins.com/winelands/franschhoek/ eikehof/startup.htm ©/✉ **876·2469***

Francois Malherbe's roots stretch back to the arrival of the French Huguenots in Franschhoek more than 300 years ago. He's custodian of a family tradition of winemaking and century-old semillon bushvines. A trio of reds has more recently made their home here too. Further afield, this outdoorsman can often be found on the West Coast or in Namibia pursuing his other passions, diving and hunting.

★★★★ **Cabernet Sauvignon** ✓ Dense, showy wine, always with big, chunky tannins needing time. Medium-bodied **02** well layered with ripe berry fruit; fairly evident oak should harmonise over the next 3-4 yrs. ±5 mths oak (same for all the reds). **01** fuller, will drink earlier than pvs; **00** spicily astringent on release.

Merlot ★★★ Med-bodied **02** returned to earlier-approachable mode; mid-2004 offers choc & plum flavours, forward soft tannins. 12.5% alc. **Shiraz** ★★★ Yr in bottle has softened **02**; smoky touches, long finish concludes with sweet-fruity touch. **Chardonnay** ★★★ Bunch-pressed & cask-fermented. **03** now quieter; slight citrus hint; alc fairly prominent — suggest drink up. **Bush Vine Semillon** ★★★ Features ancient low-cropped bushvines, bunch-pressed, fermented/aged 5 mths Fr/Am casks. **03** light-toned; bouquet of lime & lemon with lees nuance on palate. **Sauvignon Blanc** discontinued. — *DH*

Eikendal Vineyards

Stellenbosch (see Helderberg map) ▪ *Est 1981* ▪ *1stB 1984* ▪ *Tasting & sales — Sep-May: Mon-Fri 9-4.30 Sat/Sun 10.30-3; Jun-Aug: Mon-Fri 10.30-3* ▪ *Fee R10 (5 wines)* ▪ *Tours 10 & 3* ▪ *Closed Easter Fri -Mon, Jun 16, Aug 9, Dec 25/26 & Jan 1* ▪ *Cape-style buffet & Sat/Sun picnics (Oct-May); cheese fondue Fri evenings (Jun-Aug); BYO picnic* ▪ *Eikendal Lodge Guest House/B&B ⓒ 855·3617* ▪ *Facilities for children* ▪ *Tourgroups* ▪ *Small conferences* ▪ *Walks* ▪ *Winemaker Henry Kotze (Sep 2004)* ▪ *Viti consultant Johan Pienaar (Sep 2001)* ▪ *±65 ha (cabs s/f, merlot, shiraz, chard, chenin, sauvignon, semillon)* ▪ *±500 tons ±35 000 cs 65% red 35% white* ▪ *PO Box 2261 Stellenbosch 7601* ▪ *info@eikendal.co.za* ▪ *www.eikendal.com ⓒ 855·1422 🖷 855·1027*

'Some call it global warming, we call it harvest havoc', grumbled the new crew here after a tricky season in which varying sugar levels, often within the same row, caused severe headaches. Though labour intensive, 2004 delivered a bumper crop. Good news for incoming winemaker Henry Kotze (who's worked with oenological heavyweights Neil Ellis and André van Rensburg), and Grant Newton and Chris Saager, local and international marketers respectively. Newton and Saager are intent on not merely raising Eikendal's historically low profile but making it a household name. Early signs suggest they're willing to take a gamble. Noticing that previously out-of-vogue chardonnay is rebounding in Europe, they've decided to launch a lightly wooded version here. More predictably, they're looking to make a splash with blocks of in-demand shiraz coming into production. And, to slake the thirst for wines by the glass in restaurants and wine bars, they've turning out more of their popular 'composer range', Verdi, Rossini and Puccini.

★★★★ **Cabernet Sauvignon Reserve** Made in best yrs from selected fruit, barrels; balances house's firm-structured seriousness with ripe fruit. **00** developing well mid-2004, but serious wooding (20 mths new Fr) & big dense tannins still need few yrs to harmonise with sweet fruit, good acidity. 14% alc. Pvs **99** more austere. 150 cs.

★★★★☆ **Cabernet Sauvignon** Conservatively styled, honest & rather sombre cab. Firmly vinous **00** still has rum-&-raisin sweetness on nose, with cedar, spice. Youthful **01**'s savoury freshness, deep fruit a little lighter, more outgoing; should soften, but probably always tannic. Solid 14.5% alc; 16 mths oak.

★★★★ **Merlot 02**, retasted, offers choc-mint, spice, plum; savoury padding around firm centre. 13% alc; 14 mths Fr oak. Lighter, less concentrated & earlier maturing than darkly handsome, well-textured, deep-fruited **03** (judging by barrel sample).

★★★★☆ **Cabernet Franc** Maiden **02** retasted: fragrantly spicy, loads of dark berries, light ripe tannins. Still developing. 12 mths oak; 13.5% alc. **03** (tasted from barrel) looks even more promising — perhaps ★★★★ — with its delicious fresh ripe fruit, good concentration & structure.

★★★★☆ **Shiraz** Vibrant **02** big-hearted, well-constructed; lots of toasty oak from 16 mths in barrel, but sweetly savoury, some wild dried-herb notes. Massive 15% alc. Sample softly sweet **03** suggests over-ripeness: less fresh, lively. Likely ★★★.

★★★★☆ **Classique** Deep-hued **01** (★★★★) blends cab, merlot, cab f (60/30/10 — much same as **00**). Youthfully dominated by tobacco/cedar/spice from 20 mths new Fr oak, but ripely round, with sweet fruit wrapping firm, dry tannic core. Savoury, generous, ultra-big — non-classique 15% alc! Deserves few yrs more in bottle.

★★★★ **Rossini** ✓ Lightly oaked blend merlot cabs s & f, shiraz. **01** (★★★★) with some elegant lightness, now ready for drinking (though no hurry). Fruitcake scents/flavours, hints of rosemary, savoury & firm. **00** more intense, muscled.

★★★★ **Chardonnay** Chest of awards over past decade, given new lift in spicy, vanilla-toasty **03** — slightly excessive but appealing evidence of fermentation/9 mths new Fr oak. Richly textured; fine citrus fruit. 14% alc, like promising **04** (tasted ex-barrel), also full-flavoured, rich. Track record for good development over 3-5 yrs.

★★★★☆ **Semillon** Maiden **03** developing attractive bouquet lanolin, lemon, honeyed nuttiness. Rather elegant, crisp balance but also full, rich. Previewed **04** happily looks like giving more of the same. These fermented/6 mths in wood; 13.5% alc

★★★★ **Sauvignon Blanc** ✓ Consistent, reliable, restrained. **04** tank sample suggests repeat of racy **03**'s gooseberry notes, grassy, good structure. Lingering greenly fruity finish. 13.5% alc.

★★★☆ **Puccini Special Late Harvest** ✓ Longstanding chenin favourite charming as ever in **04**, reprising **03**'s dried/fresh apricot ladled into sunny fruit salad of honeyed flavours. Zippy acid, moderate 12.5% alc gives light freshness. 12.5% alc.

> **Sparkling Brut** ☺ ★★★ Latest NV bubbly from sauvignon, chardonnay most attractive: lively baked apple freshness, soft & full-flavoured.

Chenin Blanc ★★★ Lightly oaked **04** (preview sample) promises peach & melon pleasure, green-fruit undertones; round, smoothly textured. **Janina Chardonnay** ★★★ Maiden **03**, only touch oak, now very appealing in its crisp, well-balanced limy zestiness. 14% alc. **Verdi** ★★ Duet of sauvignon/chardonnay pleasantly crisp & dry, unexceptional; 13.5% alc. — *TJ*

Eikestad see Vinfruco
Elandsberg see Viljoensdrift

El Dorado Wines

*Paarl ▪ Est 1999 ▪ 1stB 2001 ▪ Closed to public ▪ Owner Proteus Trust ▪ Winemaker/viticulturist Shannon Booth (1999) ▪ 1 ha ▪ 4 tons 300 cs 100% red ▪ PO Box 2042 Windmeul 7630 ▪ tmurray@iafrica.com ▪ www.eldorado.co.za ©/🖷 **869·8830***

'Place of Gold' is an apt name for this Paarl farm, run by the Booth and Murray families. Their Midas touch has seen expansion from export proteas to thoroughbred racehorses and now wine. Micro in scale, their vineyard is planted with cab, merlot and a soupçon of shiraz (inspired by neighbours Domaine Brahms). Shannon Booth is both viticulturist and winemaker. What started as a fun venture for private consumption proved so bounteous, it prompted sales to retailer Wine Concepts in Cape Town and export to the UK. Family remains firmly in focus, with wines named after the children: the 02 is Aquila; Annabela, Kei and Byrne will follow.

Aquila ★★★ Attractive cab/merlot (80/20) blend with whiff of mocha, mulberry & intriguing balsamic notes of damp fynbos. Full bodied & rich **02**, slowly unfurls to reveal tangy fruit, backed by still-firmish tannins, dry finish. Praiseworthy first effort, less acid would have ensured higher rating (7.4g/ℓ). **03**, previewed pre-blending hints at better balance. All ±yr Fr oak, third new. — *IvH*

Elements see Hartswater
Elephant Trail see Daschbosch

Elgin Vintners

*Elgin ▪ Est 2003 ▪ 1stB 2004 ▪ Tasting & sales Mon-Fri 9-5 by appt ▪ Closed public holidays ▪ Owners James Rawbone-Viljoen, Derek Corder, Alastair Moodie, Max Hahn, Rob Semple, Cornel Spies & Ross Gower ▪ Winemaker Ross Gower ▪ Viti adviser Paul Wallace ▪ 26 ha (merlot, sauvignon) ▪ 15 tons 450 cs ▪ PO Box 121 Elgin 7180 ▪ rossgower@worldonline. co.za pam@icon.co.za © **844·0197/859·2610** 🖷 844·0197/859·4478*

Their motto is: 'We started off with a bang', referring to the thunderous noise made when the press shot through the roof of ex-Klein Constantia winemaker Ross Gower's newly-built cellar. He's one of the vintners, of whom there are six more, all Elgin farmers who felt that diversification into wine might help them forget about the fickleness of the apple and pear markets. Since start-up mid-2003 they've produced the Sauvignon below and a Merlot, still in barrel at press time. 'But watch this space, as there are numerous other surprises in the ground,' they advise. Although, admitting they're a thirsty bunch, the magnificent seven are concerned they might not have any wine for market.

Sauvignon Blanc NEW Sample **04**'s expressive flinty fruit tempered by tropical tones, heather/scrub interest, focused by layered cool-climate structure. Rich leesy breadth softens the lance, copes with 13.9% alc. Potential ★★★★ when finished, could gain extra complexity with 1-2 yrs rest in cellar. — *DS*

Elixir see African Terroir
Emerald Glen see Stellekaya
Engelbrecht-Els see Ernie Els
Enon see Zandvliet
Equus see Zandvliet
Erica Vineyards see Raka

Ernie Els Wines

Stellenbosch ▪ Est 1999 ▪ 1stB 2000 ▪ Tasting & sales Mon-Fri 9-5 Sat: May-Sep 9-3 Oct-Apr 9-4 ▪ Closed Easter Fri, Dec 16/25 & Jan 1 ▪ Gifts ▪ Owners Ernie Els & Jean Engelbrecht ▪ Winemaker Louis Strydom (2000) ▪ Viti consultant Paul Wallace (2004) ▪ 50 ha (cab, merlot) ▪ 1 200 cs 100% red ▪ PO Box 7595 Stellenbosch 7599 ▪ info@ernieelswines.com ▪ www. ernieelswines.com ✆ 881·3588 📠 881·3688

From playing the international golf circuit to buying a wine farm, the 'Big Easy' takes it all in his swing. With namesake wine established and showing outstanding form (including a 93-point rating in US *Wine Spectator*), the next round for Ernie Els was finding a vinous home. Where better than in the same neighbourhood as his wine-partner, Jean Engelbrecht of Rust en Vrede? The Webersburg property — a four-wood and a wedge down the road from R&V — is a perfect fit. 'We have been using grapes from Webersburg for some time,' explains Jean E. A barrel cellar and tasting room are already in place, and a vinification facility is being added for the 2005 crush. The intention is to plant another 5ha of cab, merlot and petit verdot, and boost production to 6 000 cases.

★★★★★ **Ernie Els** In its third yr, this Bdx blend already a leader in the field; skilfully put together to reflect best of each vintage. Latest **02** with quieter confidence than plush **01** *Wine* ★★★★★, 93 pts *WS*; taut, bold **00** (★★★★). Insinuating, brooding youngster, of some cerebral complexity; not over-heavy, but with dark-fruited richness of length, balanced freshness; still checked by fine tannins, classy oak. Needs yr/2 before broaching (or decant well in advance); possible 7-9 yr maturation. 61% cab, 24% merlot with equal parts cab f, malbec, petit v. 20 mths new Fr barrels. Smnsberg, Hldrberg fruit. 14.5% alc.

Engelbrecht-Els Proprietor's blend NEW **03** quintet as above, plus effective input from 21% shiraz; more immediately expressive yet still seriously styled; ex-barrel shows pure berry fruits layered on velvety texture. Looks a promising ★★★★ . — *AL*

Ernst & Co NEW

Stellenbosch ▪ Est/1stB 2004 ▪ Closed to public ▪ Owners Ernst & Gwenda Gouws ▪ Winemaker Ernst Gouws ▪ 12 ha (chenin, sauvignon) ▪ 5 000 cs 50% red 50% white ▪ Export brands: Timbili & Imbizo ▪ PO Box 7450 Stellenbosch 7599 ▪ info@ggwines.co.za ✆ 886·6965 📠 886·6975

For the Gouws family, 2004 was a Rubicon year: Ernst, marking his silver anniversary as a winemaker, sold his share in Hoopenburg and set up Ernst & Co, the company being his family, all of whom will be involved in the business. Wife Gwenda handles marketing and finances, daughter Inke is a wine marketer, her sister Ezanne a budding viticulturist and Ernst Jnr wants to follow in his father's footsteps. The company's based in Stellenbosch, with purchase of land pending as this guide went to press. Harvest 2004 was crushed at Koelenhof. Ernst G is responsible for a new Ernst & Co range, comprising two whites and two reds (a Cape blend a possibility for the future), as well as for the export labels Imbizo and Timbili. He acknowledges the difficulties of launching a new brand into a competitive market but reckons his experience and established contacts give him an edge.

Merlot ★★★☆ **02** shy cassis peeking out, ripe blackberried charm, not overdone, still under influence of oak, savoury & dry, no tough tannins. Yr oak, all Fr, 14.5% alc. Needs yr/ 2. **Shiraz** ★★★☆ Neat, compact wine opening out now, properly dry. Black cherry touched with vanilla in **01**, oak supportive; dry tannic grip on finish. 14% alc. Yr Fr oak. **Chardonnay** ★★★ **03** light & lemony with touches of butterscotch from oak & lees contact. Low 12% alc for carefree quaffing. **Sauvignon Blanc** ★★★ **04** shows fresh mown grass, green apple aromas/flavours, brisk as a sea breeze. Easy 12% alc for summer tippling; grapes ex-Wllngton, WO Coastal. Timbili & Imbizo export wines not tasted.—*IvH*

Eshkol Kosher Winery

Wellington ▪ Est/1stB 2003 ▪ Tasting & sales Mon-Fri 10-7 ▪ Fee R15 ▪ Closed Jewish holidays ▪ Tours by appt ▪ Cheese platters by appt; also meals at Onverwacht Restaurant ▪ Tourgroups ▪ Owner ERIE Trading ▪ Winemakers Shalom Epstein & Hein Hesebeck (2003/ 2004), with Ruani Visser (Apr 2003) ▪ Viticulturist Hein Hesebeck ▪ 15 ha (merlot, pinotage, ruby cab, shiraz, chenin) ▪ 10·000 cs 90% red 10% white ▪ PO Box 151 Wellington 7654 ▪ eshkol@ezinet.co.za ▪ www.eshkol.co.za © 864·3356 ☏ 873·0871

Competing against a huge field of conventionally made wines, this boutique kosher winery's Cab took a gold at the Los Angeles Tasters Guild International competition; a further seal of approval was a decision by the leading US kosher wine specialist Abarbanel to add Eshkol to its list. Newly appointed, widely-seasoned cellarmaster Hein Hesebeck produced three new wines in 2004 (a year he describes as 'a nightmare for the grower but a real feast for the winemaker'). The Israeli-born owners are putting down SA roots: executive director Shalom Epstein has bought half of Domaine Brahms farm near Paarl and is now living there; marketing man Ori Ilan has settled in Wellington. Eshkol is officially on the Wellington Wine Route, and a tasting room (closed Saturdays and Jewish holidays, of course) is now open to visitors.

Note that the following wines are literally 'cooked' during flash-pasteurisation, a process which militates against finesse & fruit — something to consider when comparing with conventionally vinified examples. **Pinotage** ★★ Fresh berry nose, good varietal definition & character, **04** not overwhelmed by wood (50/50 Fr/Am). **Chardonnay** ★★ **04** (sample) fermented on 100% Am oak, hence pervasive toasty tone; crisp, lemony, light-bodied palate. **Chenin Blanc** ★★ Off 28 yr old bushvines, fermented on oak, mainly Am; **04** soft & easy with hints of melon. All WO Paarl. Wines featured in pvs ed not retasted: **Cabernet Sauvignon, Merlot, Shiraz, Classic Dry Red & Premier Chenin Blanc.**—*CR*

Eventide see Mischa

Excelsior Estate

*Robertson ▪ Est 1859 ▪ 1stB 1997 ▪ Closed to public ▪ Owners/viticulturists Stephen & Freddie de Wet ▪ Winemaker Johan Stemmet (Nov 2003) ▪ 270 ha ▪ 3 500 tons (60 000 cs own label) 67% red 33% white ▪ Exported as Stonehurst & De WetsBerg ▪ HACCP certified ▪ PO Box 17 Ashton 6715 ▪ info@excelsior.co.za ▪ www.excelsior.co.za © **(023) 615·1980** ☏ (023) 615·2019*

The fifth generation of De Wets are involving themselves in this extensive family business: Peter, son of co-owner Freddie, mainly in viticulture, quality control and marketing, and Jamie, son of the other owner, Stephen, in aspects of production as well as sales and marketing. Excelsior's wallet-friendly formula is widely recognised (the Cab has two SA *Wine* magazine Best Value awards and the Paddock Shiraz has featured in the UK *Independent Review*'s Top 10 Value Wines), and it's clear the cousins understand what it's all about. 'You can't make a good wine from a low base,' says Jamie dW. 'We monitor everything with great care.' For cognoscenti, the De Wets and new winemaker Johan Stemmet (ex-Ruitersvlei) offer the Reserve Cab, the 2002 vintage of which was recently released. 'It will also over-deliver,' JdW promises.

★★★☆ **Cabernet Sauvignon Reserve** ✓ Modern style, well formed, offering generous but not overstated flavour, oak, alc (14–14.5%). **02** tasted post-bottling shows juicy black fruit, rounded approachability, potential to go 3-5 yrs. **01** (★★★★) had similar early-accessible charms with the vintage's sturdier structure. 18 mths oak, Fr/Am.

★★★★ **Cabernet Sauvignon** ✓ Always eager to please — and it does; **03** has an abundance of blackberry fruit, very well wielded oak, juicy tannins. **02** billowed cinnamon & fruitcake. 8-9 mths oak (as are reds below). ±14.5% alc.

Sauvignon Blanc ☺ ★★★ Affordable, satisfying everyday tipple. **04** repeats successful formula of tropical breadth & cool crispness. 13.5% alc.

Merlot ★★★★ **03** a step up; already shows some complexity, soft round tannins, succulent flavour. Alc less daunting at 14% alc. **Paddock Shiraz** ★★★★ Unsubtle but attractive **03**, bouquet a gamut of berries, coffee, choc, herbs & scrub; sappy, fruity palate; fairly unyielding 'tarry' finish the only detraction. 14.5% alc. **Chardonnay** ★★★ Delicious, lightly wooded **03** ingratiates with peach, lime & vanilla aromas, sweet tropical flavour, clean citrus finish. Best enjoyed young. 14.5 alc. — DH

Excelsious Wines

Vredendal (see Olifants River map) ▪ Est 1997 ▪ 1stB 1998 ▪ Tasting & sales Mon-Fri 8-12; 2-5 Sat 9-11 ▪ Fee R10 ▪ Closed Easter Fri-Mon, Dec 25 & Jan 1 ▪ Owners Stoumann & Sons ▪ Winemaker Napoleon Stoumann ▪ Viticulturist Gideon Stoumann ▪ 112 ha (cab, merlot, shiraz, chard) ▪ ±1 900 tons ±300 cs own label 96% red 2% white 2% rosé ▪ PO Box 307 Vredendal 8160 ▪ stoutmans@kingsley.co.za ©/🖻 (027) 213-2323

Excelsious, owned by brothers Gideon and Napoleon Stoumann, may be the smallest winery in the Olifants River Valley (it produced a mere 3 000 bottles last year), but quantity is not what winemaker Napoleon S is after. Excited by what he sees as a new trend for lighter, easy-drinking styles, he believes this emerging region is capable of delivering the goods with shiraz and merlot (the latter bottled here for the first time last year, along with a maiden sauvignon). Like all Excelsious wines, the new wines will be marketed under the Stoumanns label to avoid confusion with Robertson's Excelsior. Napoleon S is a firm believer in the growth that tourism offers, and to this end has extended his tasting hours to include Saturdays.

Faces of Africa see Douglas Green
Fairbridge see Paarl Wine

Fairseat Cellars

Cape Town ▪ Closed to public ▪ Owner Dick Davidson ▪ PO Box 53058 Kenilworth 7745 ▪ fairseat@mweb.co.za © 797-1951

Negociant and Cape Wine Master Dick Davidson sources wines locally for export to Europe, chiefly buyers' own brands (BOBs) for the German market. Current production (untasted) includes the Fairseat Cellars Ruby Cab; Mountainside Cab, Merlot and Chardonnay; and Ruiters Red and White, all 03.

Fair Valley Workers Association

Paarl ▪ Est 1997 ▪ 1stB 1999 ▪ Tasting & sales at Fairview (see entry) ▪ Owners Fair Valley Community ▪ Winemaker Awie Adolph (Feb 1997) ▪ 18 ha ▪ ±50 000ℓ for own label 50/50 red/white ▪ PO Box 583 Suider-Paarl 7624 ▪ marlene@fairview.co.za © 863-2450 🖻 863-2591

US With buyers from the US, Japan and Europe also weighing in, Fair Valley chair Tommy Fortuin and his team simply can't keep up — an enviable position in today's competitive market. Fortuin & co purchase their Sauvignon and Pinotage from Fairview and Perdeberg for bottling under their own label. Profits are reinvested into the business, with a percentage going towards housing F-V workers — spanking new 3-bedroomed homes, of which 8 have been built. With 32 more to go, Fortuin ('Fortune') better live up to his name....

Pinotage ★★ Compared with modern, gluggable pvs, latest **03** to us somewhat less amicable & generous; firm acidity, big alc (14.3%) but not too much flesh; **Chenin Blanc 04** untasted. **Sauvignon Blanc ★★ 03** again fairly neutral & estery. All WO Coastal. — *RK*

Fairview 🍷 ◉◎ ὤ

*Paarl ▪ Est 1693 ▪ 1stB 1974 ▪ Tasting & sales Mon-Fri 8.30-5 Sat 8.30-1 ▪ Fee R10 ▪ Closed Easter Fri, Dec 25, Jan 1 ▪ Groups by appt ▪ Also tasting & sales of Fairview cheese ▪ Owner Charles Back ▪ Winemakers Charles Back & Anthony de Jager (Dec 1996), with Erlank Erasmus (Jan 2001) ▪ Viticulturist Johan Botha, advised by Andrew Teubes & Thys Greeff ▪ 300 ha (cab, barbera, malbec, merlot, mourvèdre, nebbiolo, pinotage, shiraz, sauvignon, viognier) ▪ 1 800 tons 80% red 15% white 5% rosé ▪ Export brands: Blue Rock & Tower ▪ ISO 9001:2001 & HACCP certified ▪ PO Box 583 Suider-Paarl 7624 ▪ info@fairview.co.za ▪ www.fairview.co.za www.fairviewwine.com www.goatsdoroam.com © **863·2450** 🖷 863·2591*

'Going back in winemaking is the way forward', maintains Charles Back, marching, as ever, to his own tune and wasting no time putting into practice what he preaches. Hence the installation of assorted new equipment based on old winemaking methods, including basket presses, sorting tables and a wooden fermenter. Showing promise are unusual varieties, mostly old vines dry-farmed in Malmesbury, such as sangiovese, barbera, grenache and petite sirah. To the uninitiated, Fairview's extensive winelist may seem like a supermarket shelf, trying to cover all bases. In fact, each wine comes from small quantities of selected fruit, carefully made. Consider how many are written up in red below, and highly scored by the likes of US *Wine Spectator*. (Speaking of which: the US, Far East and Sweden are rated 'huge growth opportunities' by the prescient Back.) 'Menu' changes are driven by Back's philosophy of winemaking: 'If you work from a wine recipe book… toss it! Every year each vineyard and vintage changes. If you're not consistent, that's OK. So long as it's better.'

Red Seal range

★★★★ **Caldera** 🆕 Punters who eagerly awaited this long whispered-about Rhône-style blend need hold their breath no longer. But they will have to look sharp to get their hands on some — a mere 8 barrels made, from selected Swtlnd vyds of grenache, mourvèdre & shiraz. Those lucky enough to lay in a supply will want to break out the cork & drink it all in. But no. Having sampled the maiden (non-vintaged) release, we'd urge patience: the wine isn't ready. Multi-vintage blend, grenache in lead (47/29/24); lightish, earthy, some would say rustic; pepper & spice extras; fresh acidity & taut tannins cry out for bottle-ageing. Will be worth the wait. WO Swtlnd.

★★★★ **Pegleg Carignan** Features some of the oldest carignan in SA; bushvines accidently found whilst looking for old-vine pinotage. **02** more open than pvs; plenty of flesh, flavour. ±8 mths oak. **03** sampled from barrel seems lower-keyed, slightly leaner than pvs, with firm acidity. 14% alc.

★★★★☆ **Primo Pinotage** Massively flavourful & aromatic; off bushvines on eponymous Agter-Paarl farm. Entered the top league with striking & assured **00** (★★★★★), IWSC gold medallist; **02** had bitter-cherry tones, clearly expressed. Current **03** shows solid stewed aromas, rich dense fruit needing time to soften. 14 mths 2nd/3rd fill Fr/Am oak; malo in barrel. 15.1% alc.

★★★★ **Cyril Back Shiraz** Spotlights two parcels of Fairview vines planted in late 70s by Charles B's late father, a shiraz pioneer. Big, powerful & slow starting. Those qualities epitomised by **02**, slightly unformed mid-2004, restrained, with brisk acidity, demanding further bottle-maturation. 14 mths Am/Fr casks, partial malo in cask. 14.5% alc. **01** displayed similar signs of future elegance & potential. 90 pts *WS*.

★★★★☆ **Solitude Shiraz** A sense of place pervades this wine, made from 8-10 yr old vines in single dryland Pdberg vyd. Debut **01** deep, focused, layered with expressive fruit. Great potential. **02** retasted, shows bright shiraz fruit; complex, forward yet elegant with good texture; well-handled oak (14 mths Fr/Am; 50% new). 14.5% alc.

★★★★☆ **Beacon Block Shiraz** From naturally low-vigour vyd in Koelenhof, 10 yrs old. Luxuriously oaked (16 mths new Fr), refined **01** had gorgeous mineral & spice-laden palate, exceptionally fine structure. **02** as impressive, but mid-2004 still restrained, brooding; elegant despite soaring 15.5% alc. 93 pts *WS*.

★★★★ **Jakkalsfontein Shiraz** Mature bushvines in single vyd on western slopes of the Pdberg. **02**, youthful, firm & restrained on release, but with great potential for complexity. 92 pts *WS*, gold at Concours Mondial 2004. 14.8% alc. WO Swtlnd.

★★★★ **Akkerbos Chardonnay** Allusion to the numerous oaks shading Fairview. Own grapes given full Burgundian oak treatment — fermented/*sur lie* 10-14 mths; full malo in barriques (Fr, of course). **02** showed delicate wooding, creamy texture with mineral persistence. **03** slightly more overtly oaky, silk textured, fresh & limy with similar attractive minerality. 14% alc. WO Coastal.

★★★★☆ **Oom Pagal Semillon** Remains a standout in a category increasingly filled with fine examples. Exudes sophistication & class. Move towards older oak — for more refinement — apparent in latest **03**, 2nd/3rd fill barrels. Wonderfully clean, healthy fruit, focused, with firm mineral acidity. Cask-fermented/matured 7 mths. 14.8% alc. **02** was also brilliantly structured & persistent; barely perceptible oak.

Fairview range

★★★★ **Shiraz** ✓ This winery's signature & Cape benchmark since **74**. **02** returns to open, approachable mode of **00**; **02** polished in older oak for a more Old World quality (15.3% alc notwithstanding). **01** was tighter on release. ±14 mths mostly Fr oak. Clonal cocktail from home, Pdberg vyds.

★★★☆ **Zinfandel** Consistently good & true to variety. **03** has rosehip tea-like aromas with cinnamon & spice. More restrained than **02**, with sweet-sour combo of ripe fruit & firm acid. Usually hovers around 15% alc.

★★★★ **Agostinelli** [NEW] Italianate blend of barbera, sangiovese, primitivo (aka zinfandel), nebbiolo. A first for Fairview. From young vineyards, grapes barrel-fermented in 'neutral' oak for fruitier profile. **03** full, open, earthy nose; bright fruit. Light & quaffable; food-friendly, too, thanks to brisk acidity & grippy tannins. Gold at Concours Mondial 2004.

★★★★ **Sauvignon Blanc** From unirrigated Swtlnd bushvines with some Dbnvlle fruit. **04** has green fig tone, with welcome low (12%) alc. Occupies the more vegetal end of spectrum, as did **03**, with crisp capsicum nose & minerality, and semillon-enriched **02**, packed with zingy fruit.

★★★★ **Semillon** Last tasted was polished **02**, which raised the bar.

★★★★ **Viognier** Hailed since inception as among the finest New World examples of this mercurial Rhône white, **04** (sample) continues to underplay oak, rely more on fresher, less 'oily' character while retaining good varietal definition. 50% fermented/aged Fr barrels, 15% new. 14.8% alc.

★★★★☆ **La Beryl Blanc** Massively concentrated but enlivened by rapier acidity. Ripe chenin, grapes air-dried on straw mats. Gorgeous **03** pure & delicate with complex flavour array of apples, pears, toffee apple and crème caramel. Only 5 barrels made. ±14% alc. **02** had intriguing peach & quince bouquet, great persistence.

Cabernet Sauvignon ★★★ **02** pale, light & inoffensive. WO Paarl. **Malbec** ★★★ **03** first crop of Stbosch fruit with Swtlnd filler; pleasant, light-textured; should gain concentration as vines mature. **Pinotage** ★★★ **03** earthy, but with distinct varietal character; taut food-craving acidity. **'SMV'** ★★★ Shiraz & mourvèdre with viognier spicing, crushed together & aged ±14 mths in Fr/Am oak; **03** creamy fruitcake aromas, touch leaner on palate; needs bit of time to harmonise. **Chardonnay** ★★★ **03** fresher than pvs; shows clean citrus & slightly mineral tone on palate. Bunch-pressed, fermented/aged 6 mths Fr/Am oak, some new. **Sweet Shiraz** ★★★ Fairview's fortified winter warmers tend to change variety every year. Pvs Pinotage succeeded by this, ripe, sweet & spicy Shiraz which holds 17% alc well. Yr older oak. This range WO Coastal unless noted. Goats do Roam listed separately.— *RK*

False Bay Winery & Waterkloof Vineyards

Est/1stB 2000 ▪ Closed to public ▪ Owner Boutinot UK ▪ Winemakers Werner Engelbrecht & Paul Boutinot (2004/2000) ▪ Viti consultant Johan Pienaar, with Werner Engelbrecht ▪ 40 ha (cabs s/f, grenache, merlot, mourvèdre, petit v, shiraz, chard, sauvignon) ▪ *350 000 cs 50% red 42% white 8% rosé* ▪ *Export brands: Hoop Huis, Paarl Heights, Post Stones & Vals Baai/False Bay* ▪ *PO Box 899 Wellington 7654* ▪ *ceo@boutinotsa.co.za admin@ boutinotsa.co.za* © ***873·2418*** 🖷 *873·7580*

The addition to the title signifies False Bay Winery's acquisition, in 2003, of Waterkloof farm on the Schaapenberg hills in the Helderberg. A follow-on will be the moving of operations from the winery's present Wellington base to Somerset West. Next step will be the building, on Waterkloof, of a 600-ton winery and extension of the present 40-ha vineyard. Previously, FBW (subsidiary of the UK-held Boutinot group) was an all-export company but will sell into the local market from later this year, when it launches its Waterkloof range of whites. First will be a Chardonnay and Sauvignon; reds will follow in 2007. Also available this year will be two False Bay Reserves, Shiraz and Chardonnay, from a different fruit source. Newly-arrived winemaker Werner Engelbrecht (ex-Vinfruco and Avondale) will head up the Waterkloof venture and supervise vinification of FBW's bigger brands.

▪ *Famous Butcher's Grill* see Deetlefs
Fantail see Morgenhof

Fat Bastard

Tongue-in-jowl international label created by European wine-partners Thierry Boudinaud and Guy Anderson. Now made in serious quantities (500 000+ cartons) and distributed in Europe, America and the Far East. The SA versions, featuring a cartoon hippo on the front-label, are from Robertson Winery.

Shiraz ★★★★ Lumbering wine lives up to its name. **03** ripe bramble fruit, aromatic, touches meat, clove & anise, supple tannins, big alc (14%). **Chardonnay** ★★★★ Much nicer than name suggests, & not so podgy either. **04** ripe & tropical; waddles on to rich, vanilla-toned finish. Partially oak-fermented.—*DH*

▪ *Fat Ladies* see Winecorp
Fernkloof see Cape Wine Exports

Fierté Wines

Worcester ▪ *Est 1950* ▪ *1stB 2001* ▪ *Tasting by appt* ▪ *Sales Mon-Fri 8.30-5* ▪ *Attractions/amenities: see intro* ▪ *Owners TCB Wines, The Goudyn Farm & Fierte Wines* ▪ *Winemaker/viticulturist TC Botha Jnr* ▪ *95 ha (merlot, ruby cab, shiraz, chard, chenin, colombard, sauvignon, semillon, riesling)* ▪ *±600 tons 15 000 cs + 300 000ℓ bulk 60% red 40% white* ▪ *PO Box 300 Rawsonville 6845* ▪ *fiertewines@mweb.co.za michelle@fierte-organicwines.com* © ***(023) 349·1748/ 082·443·7873*** 🖷 *(023) 349·1325*

The Botha family farm Goudyn, supplier to Goudini co-op (founded by grandfather TC in 1948), has been transformed into a slick export business. Just under half of their crop, including organic cab franc, malbec, petit verdot and 40-year-old chenin (for whose separate vinification Ken Forrester provided inspiration) is bottled and shipped to the UK and the US. An opening into China seemed a possibility at press time. TC Jnr (after-hours manager of the Springbok tug-of-war team) is mindful of the importance of vine health, low yields and quality oak. Wife Michelle (daughter of a former Springbok tug-of-war team manager) pores over the marketing strategies. Clearly a family that pulls together.

Chenin Blanc ☺ ★★★ Bright aroma of melon on **03**, palate shows clever & appealing balance of zippy acidity, apple fruit & gentle sweetness.

Double Cabernet ★★ Eucalyptus & dried herbs fairly prominent on **01** nose, hint of smoke; concentrated cassis flavour with sour twist; 50/50 blend cab s, ruby cab. All reds 8 mths 2nd fill oak, Fr, except for... **Organic Shiraz** ★★★★ **02** lively Ribena/blackcurrant aromas, hint vanilla from Am oak; soft, juicy & plump, slick of fruit sweetness in tail. **Rouge Classique** ★★★★ Bdx blend (cabs s/f, merlot, petit v, malbec) off vyds in conversation to organic.**02**

animated plum pudding nose with hint tobacco; plump & fruity; savoury dry finish; well oaked for overt but controlled New-World style. **Sauvignon Blanc** ★★★ Medium bodied **03**, bone-dry with demure hints of lemongrass. **Organic Classic White** ★★★ **03** shy green melon & apple notes; herbal hint; apple & fruit, steely acidity. Chiefly colombard (58%), with chard & sauvignon. All WO W-Cape. — *TM*

Fired Earth see Villiera
Firefly see Stellar Winery

FirstCape Vineyards

Closed to public ▪ *Est 2002* ▪ *Owners De Wet Co-op Winery, Goudini Wines, Newton Johnson family & Brand Phoenix* ▪ *60% red 40% white* ▪ *PO Box 868 Somerset West 7129* ▪ *info@firstcape.co.za* ▪ *www.firstcape.com* © **850·0160/1** 🖷 850·0155

'It's been a rocket ride!' says MD Bevan Newton Johnson of this joint-venture brand's stratospheric growth. In just three years, it has become the fastest-selling SA brand in the UK and the fifth-largest bottled wine exported to that country. No wonder Johnson feels 'a bit like the first tourist in space'. His brother Gordon makes the wines in conjunction with partner wineries Goudini and De Wet, to specs developed with Surrey-based Brand Phoenix and Johnson père, Dave. Pinotage features in all the reds, and the range aims to provide 'consistent, excellent quality' in the affordable £3.99 to £4.99 bracket.

Pinotage NEW ☺ ★★★ **03** juicy, elegant version with pinot-like cherry tone; hint of sweetness makes it slip down easily. Note: 14% alc. **Shiraz-Pinotage** ☺ ★★★ **04** supple red-fruited mouthful, soft & youthfully delicious, chillable in summer. **Chardonnay-Semillon** ☺ ★★★ Easy-going 53/47 blend, **04** shows vintage's shy aromas but palate's its usual bouncy self; zesty apple flavours, good dry flinty finish. — *TM*

Fish Eagle see Le Grand 1881

Five Heirs

This brand, part of the Christo Wiese Portfolio (see entry), takes its name from the Wiese family, heirs to the cultural riches of Lanzerac and Lourensford, their wine farms in the Jonkershoek and Lourens River valleys. The grapes are grown and the wines vinified on the two properties before selection and blending.

★★★★ **Cabernet Franc** Serious enough, but friendly & unintimidating. Yr on, **01** more open, better integrated. Trademark green walnuts, supported by red berry, cherry fruit profile. Lively, medium-weight palate, with firm backbone from 15 mths Fr oak. Good for 4-5 yrs yet. 14.5% alc. No **02**s for this range.

★★★★ **Merlot** Tasty, fruit-driven: has 'drink me' written all over it. **03** (★★★) lighter tone, simpler than **01**. Inviting red berries, gentle toastiness from light oaking. 14% alc.

★★★★ **Pinotage** Stylistic change for **03**: fresher, but simpler, with vibrant fruit purity & juicy, lively appeal. Touch oak. Oh-so-easy — enjoy at youthful best. 14.5% alc.

★★★★ **Cabernet Sauvignon** NEW **03** grassy/herbaceous top-note, cherries, red berries; no hard edges, lively, friendly & well-balanced, using oak in support role, allowing fruit to shine through. Ready, but could age ±3 yrs. 14% alc.

★★★★ **Shiraz** NEW **03** requisite plum compôte fruit profile, with light oaking adding smoky touch, definition. Juicily ripe, delicious drinking now, but has few years ageing potential. 14% alc.

Rosé ★★★ Uncomplicated al fresco lunch companion. Revisited **03** shows fruit pastille tones more mellow, palate rounder. Tasty, appealing, but drink soon. 13.2% alc. **Chardonnay** ★★★ **03** lime & orange peel flavours now integrated with oak; uncomplicated, light-bodied, for youthful drinking. Partial oak fermentation. 13.5% alc. **Chenin Blanc** ★★★ **04** pear-drop, hay & melon typicity, softly rounded, with refreshing finish. Nicely quaffable, though note 13.8% alc. **Sauvignon Blanc** ★★★ Light-textured quaffer for early drinking. **04** captures English meadow, nettles/herbaceous character; crisp finish. — *CR*

Five Senses see Overhex

Flagstone Winery

Somerset West ▪ Est 1998 ▪ 1stB 1999 ▪ Tasting & sales Tue-Sun 10-6 ▪ Fee R50 redeemable with any purchase ▪ Tours by appt ▪ Owners Jack family ▪ Winemakers Bruce Jack, Wilhelm Coetzee, Marlize Beyers, Elize Wessels & Gerald Kakijana ▪ Viticulturist Bruce Jack ▪ 90 ha under management ▪ 400-600 tons 40-70 000 cs (varying % reds/whites) ▪ PO Box 3636 Somerset West 7129 ▪ admin@flagstonewinery.co.za sales@flagstonewinery.co.za ▪ www.flagstonewines.com © 852·5052 ✉ 852·5085

Bruce Jack is taking flying winemaking to new lows. It's an 11-hour road trip to reach the late-ripening vineyards of Guillaume Swiegers in the Langkloof, so the tireless Jack flies there during crush, using bucolic George Airport as gateway. Which often means circling for up to an hour in thick mist before spying a gap and plunging down, vertiginously, onto the runway. Gut-wrenching stuff. 'But hey, when the grapes are calling, you have to follow.' And follow he does: pinotage and shiraz from the Swartberg, cab from Elim and Constantia, cab franc from the Robertson foothills (a new joint venture with grower Angela de Frater bottled under the Mary le Bow label), to name a few. They've planted experimental vineyards on their farm near Napier in the Overberg highlands, including tannat, tempranillo and several port varieties. New projects include a brand called Fish Hoek; and a blended white, using the Two Roads chardonnay vineyard as cornerstone. BK5 Pinot Noir will be made from organically grown grapes, and sister Fiona Jack made and launched her own wine, named Fiona, last year. Despite a gruelling schedule, Jack finds time to ponder: 'Wine should do a small, simple thing — it should add joy to life'.

★★★★ **Bowwood Cabernet Sauvignon & Merlot** Promise of something special in sample **03** 87/13 blend: bold juicy mulberry fruits bursting through overt oak spice; quality key is the ripe, sweet tannins. **02** similarly full & warm-hearted, loaded with plums, pinch of herbs; brooding minerality needs time to yield. 14% alc; wild yeasts; 18 mths mostly Am oak. Partnership with the Johnsens in Pdberg.

★★★★ **Mary Le Bon** NEW Another cellar first — no Am oak! Cab, shiraz, merlot (63/25/12) cold-soaked for 2 wks, then Fr barrels, third new. Elegantly restrained **03**. Clean wood frames ripe blackcurrant fruits, spicy interest in lingering tail. Approachable, but should unfurl over 3 yrs. 13.7% alc. Result of cooperation with the Fraters, Rbtson.

These a joint venture with employees committed 'beyond the monotonous security of a monthly salary'. **Cellar Hand Chenin Blanc** NEW ★★★ **04** offers tropical, pulpy guava flavours, gently firmed by reductive palate, refreshingly moderate 12% alc. **Cellar Hand The Backchat Blend** ★★★ Mix 8 varieties, mostly cab, shiraz, merlot. **02** has developed toned berry fruits mingled with silky-soft tannins. Composed grip, delicious. 13.5% alc.

The Berrio range

★★★★ **Cabernet Sauvignon** This, below, joint venture with Francis Pratt, 'grower of magical grapes near Elim'. **01** Cool-climate rendition of cab, velvety, with lilting cedar; deep & soft; restrained oaking. 13.5% alc. Not retasted for this ed. No **02**.

★★★★ **Sauvignon Blanc** Deliciously measured stone character, neither opulent nor austere. Sample **04** smooth and velvety even in youth, super fruit concentration, fine finish. **03** captivated UK writer Matthew Jukes ('glacially cool'): green-pepper notes in defined herbal grip, outstanding flavour intensity. Food friendly. 14% alc.

Foundation range

★★★★ **Longitude** ✓ Beautifully orchestrated fruit ensemble; shows excellent vinosity. Latest **02** cab-dominated in analysis, juicy shiraz to fore in flavour. Spicy red berry richness in gentle, unaggressive structure. Easy now, will unfold until 2006. **00** mainly shiraz, pinotage, merlot; sumptuous berries; dense tannins. 14% alc.

★★★★ Dragon Tree Not for classicists perhaps, but Cape individuality in complex blend cab, pinotage, cab f (63/34/3). Revisited **01** shows soft, warm red berries & dates in flavour cacophony, under the baton of oak. Persuasive rather than insistent. 13.5% alc.

★★★★ Shiraz [NEW] **02** a brooding monster lurking in cellar, awaiting release — & a name. Hotland (Swtlnd, Wrcstr, Tlbgh) fruit hints at spice, but trussed up in oak, ripe tannin; 15% alc. Whether the fruit is big enough for the chassis, time will tell.

★★★☆ The Music Room Cabernet Sauvignon 'Best attempt yet' declares Jack of latest offering of this food-friendly red. **02** (★★★★) from Tulbagh, Elim vyds: densely pigmented, juicy bramble fruit, tangy flesh to oak-char warmth, retains taper in sea of flavours. **01** attractive savoury notes, firm finish. 14% alc. Decanter ★★★★ for **00**.

★★★☆ Writer's Block Pinotage Bottelary grapes, under 'what is right for the wine' screwcap; emphatic **02** (★★★★) needs containment! Opulent pears-in-wine sweet fruit filled out further with date, shimmering mocha, even bacon tints. Dense tannins need time to evolve. **01** supple, harmonious. 14% alc.

★★★☆ BK5 Pinot Noir BK5 clone's propensity for organic notes holds sway in current **03** (★★★): vegetal, boiled fruit characters flirt with palate before retiring. Lighter (12.5% alc), drier than bold **01**. 11 mths Am, Fr wood, 30% new.

★★★★★ The Poetry Collection Pinot Noir Sophisticated, where above is artisanal. **00** shapely punnet of strawberries & raspberries, supple tannins, well-woven oak. 14% alc. This & sold-out **01** not tasted for this ed. No **02**.

★★★☆ Free Run Sauvignon Blanc Natural handling of small parcels of Swartberg, Elim free-run juice. **04** belts out floral aromas, tropical appley palate balanced by flinty edge. More restrained than stable mates. **02** IWC gold.

★★★★ Heywood House Barrel Fermented Sauvignon Blanc Sophisticatedly handled old 'weerstasie' clone, named for music teacher Elsie Fraser Munn ('taught thousands from Ghana to Grahamstown'). **02** glistening golden sheen, creamy spiced oak softens sauvignon spikes. No **03**. Wild yeast-fermented/10 mths. oak. 14% alc.

★★★★ Two Roads Chardonnay Elegant **02**, tropical fruit, butterscotch whiffs; rich mid-palate. Native yeast-fermented; full malo. Not retasted for this ed. No **03**.

★★★☆ The Last Word Port [NEW] One would expect nothing less from Team Flagstone: exotica such as tannat jostle with mourvèdre, sangiovese & friends in an eclectic take on the higher alc/lower sugar genre. **02** loaded with ripe plums, coffee/mocha & cigar smoke, beautiful dry finish. 18.2% alc; 56g/ℓ sugar.

Semaphore ☺ **★★★** A refreshingly dry rosé to bring a smile to any face. **04** pinotage dominated, soupçon cab f & sauvignon blanc: copper-pink, cherry/berry aromas, enough grip in mouth for food — from picnics to silver-service salmon.

'Noon Gun' **★★★** Aromatic miscellany of 6 white grapes, winner at The Houston Livestock & Rodeo Show! **04** well-weighted tropical fruit, spice tints, crisp tail. At table or solo.

Strata Series
'Experimental, once-off & seriously adventurous' wines.

★★★★ Cape Blend ('Unnamed Blend' in pvs ed.) **02** improbably soft & silky fusion shiraz, pinotage & merlot; sweet-fruited, lavender & pepper pervade the assembly. Revisited mid-2004, shows linear elegance; a foil for cellar's other mouthfuls. 14% alc.

★★★★ The Glass Carriage Chenin Blanc Fragile fruit mostly unscathed from 10 mths mostly Am oak, in emphatic **02**: tropical melon swaddled in vanilla, creamy spice. Big, round palate, 14.5% alc.

Other once-offs, not retasted for this ed.

★★★★ Ruby in the Dust A singular take on ruby cab; **02** eschews variety's aromatic pungency; just pulpy ripe fruit. Am oak's vanilla & spice, voluptuous 15% alc.

★★★☆ **Heartbreak Grape Pinot Noir** In fact, this **01** less envelope-pushing than pinots above. Strawberries/redcurrants on nose, nice tart fruity bite; firm dusty finish.

The Shindig Shiraz ★★★ **00** less extrovert than name implies: leathery & slight gamey notes; youngberry fruit; sinewy tannins. 13% alc. **In Cahoots Merlot-Pinotage** ★★★. **01** 79/21 blend — mellow mineral core, sweet fruit, spicy textures. 13.5% alc. — *DS*

▓ *Flamingo Bay* see Darling Cellars
Fleermuisklip see Lutzville

Fleur du Cap

*Stellenbosch ▪ 1stB 1968 ▪ Tasting & sales at Bergkelder ▪ Owner Distell ▪ Senior winemakers Kobus Gerber (whites) & Thinus Krüger (reds), with Tariro Masayiti & Jaco van der Walt ▪ Viticulturist Bennie Liebenberg ▪ 18 000 tons 200 000 cs 60% red 40% white ▪ Enquiries: Jackie Thirion jhthirion@distell.co.za ▪ www.fleurducap.co.za ✆ **809·7000** 📠 883·2603*

They operate from a building vaguely reminiscent of a bunker, but there's nothing cloistered about this winemaking squad. They work with partner growers in most of the high-profile areas and some pretty obscure places too. On the seaward side of remote Lutzville on the West Coast, on a kink in the Olifants River, viticulturist Bennie Liebenberg has found a marine-conditioned sauvignon block to gladden the heart of any cool-climate-wine aficionado. White wine makers Kobus Gerber and Zimbabwe-born Tariro Masayiti are also dipping into the vaunted Elim vineyards near Cape Aghulas to add some sea-breeze bite to their sauvignons. Red specialists Thinus Krüger and Jaco van der Walt continue to impress, especially with their Unfiltered range. Fans of their excellent 96 Chenin NLH will be pleased to know there's a follow-up, and it's worth the 7-year wait.

Unfiltered Collection

★★★★ **Cabernet Sauvignon** From a Bottlry vyd. **01** very ripe fruit, more dried-prune than red plum, leathery quality verging on porty. Huge concentration, full-bodied & rich (14.9% alc), tannins unravelling stylishly. Difficult vintage **02** (★★★☆) less ripe, more elegant, ripe mulberry fruit still in tannin grip, too-high acidity. 16 mths Fr oak, all new. These need 5-8 yrs.

★★★★ **Merlot** ✓ Current **01** shows huge concentration of fruit, a real feat to ease into bottle! Ripe cassis & damson fruit, lead-pencil whiffs, spicy tannins. Would rate higher but for noticeable acid on finish. **02** (★★★★) terrific cassis fruit, but acid still higher. These from single vyd, Bottlry; 18 mths oak, all new Fr.

★★★★ **Pinotage-Rooibernet** In abeyance. Last was strapping, firm-fleshed **01**.

★★★★★ **Chardonnay 03** (★★★★) rather more New World in pvs, ripe flavours lavishly applied, without classic restraint of lime citrus on **01** & **02**. Spiced peach, with dollop toffee, oak not yet fully integrated mid-2004, slight sweetness to finish. Fermented/aged 9 mths Fr/Am (80/20) oak, 30% malo. 14.2% alc.

★★★★★ **Sauvignon Blanc** ✓ Statuesque beauties reflecting thoughtful teamwork down the line. **04** with ripe gooseberry & tropical lime, passionfruit invitation; gorgeous sweet-sour interplay, vibrant acidity. Mouthwatering flavours from bolder tropical spectrum. Not overripe at 13.6% alc. Stbosch, Darling vyds.

★★★★★ **Sauvignon Blanc Limited Release** (formerly 'Reserve') Interesting counterpoint to above — **04** more finely drawn, less overtly tropical though higher (14.5%) alc. Intense ripe fig, passionfruit aromas/flavours, applied with lighter brushstrokes but no loss of intensity. From promising new vyd near Gansbaai, says Kobus G.

★★★★ **Semillon** Graceful **03** with Seville orange marmalade, subtle oak, & not a trace of the variety's usual lanolin. Fleshy but firm, balanced by good lively acidity; developing creaminess. Fermented/6 mths 40% new oak, 30/10 Fr/Am. 14.1% alc. No **02**.

★★★★ **Viognier-Chardonnay-Sauvignon Blanc-Semillon** ('White Blend' last ed.) Equal parts to **03** blend, as in maiden **02**. Elegant rather than bold, with citrus & flower perfume, tangy citrus flavours, firm acid & fresh finish. Seems less weighty, more vigorous than whites above, no less flavour. Fermented/matured separately, 9 mths Fr oak, some new. 14.3% alc.

Standard range

★★★★ **Cabernet Sauvignon** Longest-lived of reds so held back extra year, a bonus to consumers. Latest **01** (★★★★) packed with signature cool cedar & cassis fruit, classically structured with firmish dry tannins – will benefit from another yr. Long cassis-flavoured finish. 18 mths oak, one third new Fr.

★★★★ **Merlot** Strong label in this range, newest **02** no exception. Mulberry-scented with sprig mint; fleshy berry-infused palate, attractive dry tannins, good-ish finish. Ready, will easily keep 5 years, says Coenie S. 18 mths oak, 60% new.

★★★★ **Pinotage 02** (★★★) ripe & plummy, but a casualty of lesser vintage. Slightly sweet prune-like flavours with dry earthy finish. 14.9% alc. Contrasts with stylish **01** with sweet redcurrant fruit. 15 mths Fr oak, none new. 14.3% alc.

★★★★ **Shiraz 02** mulberry ripeness, hint liquorice & leather, nicely proportioned with smooth approachable tannins, well balanced & not over-extracted. Ready, should keep 2-3 yrs. From selected Stbosch vineyards. Fr/Am oak 18 mths, 30% new.

★★★★ **Chardonnay** Is label winding down so as not to detract from Unfiltered version? Workmanlike **03** (★★★) some attractive lime-scented fruit, oak unobtrusive (6 mths, 30% new Fr); made to please many & varied tastes. 13.7% alc.

★★★★ **Chenin Blanc 03**'s oak subtle & supportive, takes time to be absorbed, now hitting its stride. Baked apple, quince, camomile, minerally – all one expects from classic chenin. Lively, with years ahead. 14.7% alc. Nudging higher rating rung. Preview **04** (sample) quieter, soft spicy flavours, still embryonic.

★★★★ **Sauvignon Blanc** ✓ Latest **04** has loads of green capsicum & intriguing touch gunflint; bone-dry & assertive: a real show-off! Biggish at 13.7% alc. No mean feat to consistently produce to this standard in large volumes.

★★★★ **Noble Late Harvest 03** with fragrant glacé apricot, pineapple, honey & rivetting botrytis. Beautifully poised, sweetness & acid in harmony, lengthy finish. From riesling, unwooded; 125g/ℓ sugar. Previewed **04** less obviously arresting, but perhaps even finer; pineapple & mint, & less sweetness at 107g/ℓ.

Natural Light ★★★ Low ±10% alc especially suitable for lunchtime tippling. **04** green apple, crisp, finely etched acidity, hint sugar almost not noticeable. – *IvH*

Footprint see African Pride
Forellen see Lanzerac
Forge Mill see Franschhoek Vineyards
Forrester see Ken Forrester
Fortress Hill see Fort Simon

Fort Simon Estate

Stellenbosch ▪ Est/1stB 1998 ▪ Tasting & sales Mon-Fri 9.30-5 Sat 10-2 Public holidays 10-4 ▪ Fee R1/wine ▪ Closed Easter Fri/Sun, Dec 25/26 & Jan 1 ▪ Tours by appt ▪ Meals & locale for after-hours receptions/conferences (max 40 guests) by appt ▪ Walks ▪ Owners Renier & Petrus Uys ▪ Winemaker Marinus Bredell (Jun 1997) ▪ Viticulturist Renier Uys ▪ ±78 ha (cabs s/f, malbec, merlot, pinotage, shiraz, chard, chenin, crouchen, sauvignon, viognier) ▪ 280 tons 20 000 cs own label 50% red 50% white ▪ PO Box 43 Sanlamhof 7532 ▪ fortsimon@telkomsa.net ▪ www.fortsimon.co.za ⓒ/📧 906-0304

Marketing moves merchandise. Owners Renier and Petrus Uys can vouch for that: sales show that their new marketing arm, Interactive Wines, has brought the Fort Simon brand closer to the consumer. Increased demand has put pressure on production, so new tanks went into the cellar in 2004. It was a good season, says winemaker Marinus Bredell: 'The reds were among the best we've ever made.' Judges at the French Vinalies Internationales 2004 competition will be impressed – they liked his Shiraz 01 enough to award it the only gold medal received by an SA wine.

★★★★ **Cabernet Sauvignon** NEW After years as maker of fine white wines, Marinus Bredell now eager to take on reds. Maiden **01** understated, compact; ripe cassis, touches capsicum & cedar, medium-weight with soft silky tannins. 18 mths Fr/Am oak. 13.4% alc.

★★★★ **Merlot 01** cassis & choc beckon, palate with savoury dryness & fresh acidity; neat, compact, lighter textured. 13.2% alc. **00**, retasted mid-2004, choc-plum of yesteryear giving way to savoury complexity; highlights estate's signature drinkability. 18 mths oak vs 9 for pvs; 25% Am, 2nd/3rd fill.

★★★★ **Chardonnay** ✓ In elegant, understated house style, **03** lime marmalade, whiff vanilla, not overripe at 13% alc. Leaner, attenuated build yet ultra-long finish. Fermented/aged 9 mths new Fr barriques. **02** ripe, plump flavours, balanced & fruity, oak supportive.

★★★★ **Chenin Blanc Barrel Fermented** ✓ Bredell's experience with wood shows: lightest hand for delicate chenin. Latest **03** quieter when retasted mid-2004 (not unusual in 2nd yr); dried pear aroma; poised, vigorous untrammelled fruit with lively acidity, resonating finish. Standout **02** (★★★★★) had a silky palate, very long finish. Both dry, ±14% alc. These will easily last 5-7 yrs. Fermented/aged 4 mths, new Am oak. **Chenin Blanc Barrel Fermented Reserve** Limited release of above wine, sold at Nederburg Auction Pre-release.

Pinotage ★★★ **00** shyer than last yr, but mouthwatering sweet fruit, nice touch tangy acid, well-judged tannins on finish; satisfying glassful. 15 mths Fr/Am oak. **Shiraz 02** ★★★ Cool herbaceous character, slender build, quite austere. Alc 12.9%. Yr small-oak, 30% Am. **Anna Simon Merlot-Pinotage** ★★★ **01** interesting savoury, ground coffee aromas/flavours, tell-tale touch pinotage sweetness in finish. Staves/barrels 8-10 mths. 13.3% alc. **Chenin Blanc** NEW ★★★ Lightly wooded **03** delicate, poised; vibrant tone thanks to firm fruit & finely etched acidity. **Restelle** ★★★★ ✓ Resuscitated label; **03** blend sauvignon, chard, chenin (60/30/10), sauvignon dominant taste-wise. Curvaceous, tangy acid & lingering finish. 13.2% alc. Unoaked. **Sauvignon Blanc** ★★★★ **03** good figgy, nettly aromas/flavours with some riper tropical notes. Revisited mid-2004, still vigorous but calmer. 13.5% alc. **Sauvignon Blanc Barrel Fermented** ★★★ **03** fermented & aged 4 mths Eur oak. Wood prominent, has tamed wilder edges of sauvignon, plumped up profile of otherwise slender style, adds creaminess, some weight. This, Chenin Barrel Fermented, will become alternating releases.

Fortress Hill range   NEW

Second label, not available at estate, all labelled 'Reserve'. **Merlot 00** ★★ Rustic red, meaty-rich, still some abrasive tannins. **Pinotage** ★★ Lightly oaked **02**, ripe & plummy; softer than regular, approachable tannins, savoury twist to tail. 30 yr old vines, since uprooted. **Sauvignon Blanc** ★★★ Whiff passionfruit, greengage in **03**; easy-drinking version plumped with touch sugar.

Chenin Blanc ☺ ★★★ Gorgeous ripe melon, spice on rich but lively **03**. Vibrantly fruity. Terrific tipple (but note 14% alc). **Merlot-Pinotage** ☺ ★★★ **01** seamless blend shows yet again how comfortably these two live together; plump rounded profile, amiable easy red, smooth tannins for early accessibility. Lightly oaked. — *IvH*

Four Clover Selection see Cloverfield

Fraai Uitzicht 1798

Robertson ▪ Sales at reception/restaurant during opening hours (see Eat-out section) ▪ Closed Easter Fri/Sun, Dec 25 & Jan 1 ▪ Tours strictly by appt ▪ For amenities & activities, see Stay-over section & intro below ▪ Owners Axel Spanholtz & Mario Motti ▪ Winemakers/ viticulturists Axel Spanholtz & Mario Motti, advised by local experts ▪ 10 ha (cab, merlot, shiraz) ▪ 500 cs 100% red ▪ PO Box 97 Robertson 6705 ▪ info@fraaiuitzicht.com ▪ www. fraaiuitzicht.com ©/✉ (023) 626·6156

Axel Spanholtz and Mario Motti work tirelessly to provide culinary and leisure pleasure on their picturesque red-wine farm, which boasts the oldest cellar in the Robertson district. The quality of their guest house was underlined recently in an AA Accommodation Awards competition; when it comes to rating chef Motti's food there's no contest. But there's a philanthropic aspect here too — the most recent project invites guests to 'adopt' a local child, subsidising tuition, school uniforms and a daily meal supplement.

★★★★ **Merlot 02** (★★★) still quite austere, greengage & mulberry notes, herbal hints. **01** fatter with sweet smoky notes, sumptuous refined mid-palate. Both retasted. — *MF*

Franschhoek Cellars see Franschhoek Vineyards

Franschhoek Vineyards

Franschhoek ▪ Est 1945 ▪ 1stB ca 1975 ▪ Tasting & sales Mon-Fri 9.30-5 Sat 10-4 Sun 10.30-3 ▪ Fee R10 ▪ Closed Easter Fri & Dec 25 ▪ La Cotte Restaurant (booking advised) ▪ Facilities for children ▪ AV presentation for groups ▪ Owners 120 shareholders ▪ Winemaker Stephan Smit (Aug 2002), with Jolene Calitz (Nov 2002) ▪ Viticulturist Annette van der Merwe (Aug 2003) ▪ 2 800 tons 47 000 cs own label 45% red 55% white ▪ Ranges for customers: Millberg, Keates Drift (UK) ▪ ISO 14000 certification in progress. PO Box 52 Franschhoek 7690 ▪ info@ franschhoek-vineyards.com ✆ 876·2086 🖷 876·3440

The 'little cellar that could' is still purposefully chugging up the hill. Viticulturist Annette vd Merwe is now onboard full-time to help the growers manage their vineyards and, at crush, coordinate receipt of batches of fruit, ranging in size from over 200 tons to a few hundred kilograms. Young winemakers Stephan Smit and Jolene Calitz have access to the experienced ears and hands Jacques Borman (La Motte, Boschkloof), and are spreading their wings a bit with a new Reserve range. The inaugural Merlot, made in 2002, to be joined by a Shiraz and a Semillon. Despite limited resources, they have a 'structured barrelling programme' for vinifying and maturing these small batches in barriques. Engine driver Daan Coetzee is hugely chuffed with their selection as supplier for Woolworths' House White and Red. Is there anything they can't do?

Franschhoek Cellars range

Chardonnay ☺ ★★★ **04** tropical fruit nose; tangy citrus palate with vanilla lick, upbeat finish. Partly wooded. **Chenin Blanc** ☺ ★★★ Notes of guava & pineapple introduce **04**, floral touch, tropical fruit salad flavours, zesty. To enjoy solo or with light meals, label suggests. **Sauvignon Blanc** ☺ ★★★ **04** attractive tropical fruit on nose, slightest hint of cut grass, softly dry & fruity.

Cabernet Sauvignon ★★★ **03** greeting of red & black berries with vanilla; big ripe tannins, firm finish; includes dashes cab f & shiraz. **Merlot** ★★★★ **03** ripe plummy tones & easy tannins, hints coffee & lavender, charry oak (±8 mths Fr barrels) in tune with fruit; accessible & could develop over 2/3 yrs. **Merlot Reserve** 🆕 ★★★★ **02** handsomely packaged addition to the stable, massive (16% alc!) but behaved; expansive mulberry & prune flavours, good charry wood backing, lively tannins, though tad fiery on finish from the alc. 17 mths Fr oak, 30% new. **Pinotage** ★★★ **03** leads with plums & mulberries, then charry oak & obvious but undaunting tannins, firm minerally/estery aftertaste. **Shiraz** 🆕 ★★★★ Bright purple hues on **03**, youthful, inviting; fruit-driven style with elegance; generous pliable tannin; legs to carry a few yrs. 14.2% alc.

La Cotte range

Semi-Sweet ☺ ★★★ Blend hanepoot, chenin (70/30) in **04**, attractive tropical tone; fresh guava & pineapple flavours buoyed by sweetness.

Grand Rouge ★★★ **02** aromas of strawberry & plum; charry backing from oak-staving; full flavour, light tannic grip. **Sauvignon Blanc** ★★★ **04** greenpepper & cut grass in bouquet, lightish apple-fresh finish. **Blanc de Blanc** ★★★ **04** fruity & floral nose, hints of guava; fresh, crisp palate, to be enjoyed young. **Port** ★★ LBV style, from pinotage, 40 mths Fr oak, 19% alc. **00** plum & prune on nose, slight estery whiff; full & round; fairly lightly flavoured compared to the 19% alc. **Chardonnay Brut, Sauvignon Blanc Brut and Demi Sec** discontinued.

Forge Mill range

Pinotage ★★★ **03** (sample) prune & mulberry whiffs, subtle minty touch, firm tannins. **Shiraz** ★★★ **03** traditional style with smoky/leathery whiffs, dark berry fruits, supple tannins. 14.2% alc; combo chips/staves. **Cinsaut-Cabernet Sauvignon** ★★★ Last was **02**, refreshing tangy red-fruited blend. **Chardonnay** NEW ★★★ **04** notes of ripe peaches, passionfruit & pineapple; vanilla-tinged sweet fruit on palate; easy drinking. Fr/Am oak staves. **Bush Vine Chenin Blanc** ★★ **04** light but ripe guava tone, fresh fruity lift on finish, airy vibrant texture. **Sauvignon Blanc** ★★ Latest version not tasted; **03** was lightish, with nettle & pear tones. **Semillon** discontinued.

Anvil range

Red ★★★ Merlot/pinotage mix (80/20), **03** gushes mulberries & prune, light oak touch (8 mths staved), juicy tannins. **Rosé** ★★★ **04** appealing red-berry nose, bright & breezy, rounded dry finish; from pinotage. **White** ★★★ **03** five-way blend with pleasant fruity nose, smooth flavours of lemonade & fruit salad, crisp finish. All screwcap. — *DH*

Fredericksburg see Rupert & Rothschild Vignerons

Fredine le Roux Wines

Est/1stB 2004 ▪ Tastings/sales at Goedvertrouw ▪ Owners Josias and Fredine le Roux ▪ Winemaker Fredine le Roux ▪ 240 cs 60% red 40% white ▪ PO Box 338 Caledon 7230 ▪ Josiasfredin@mweb.co.za © *(028) 284·9026/083·274·9606* ▢ *(028) 284·9029*

Ex-Le Grand Estate winemaker Fredine le Roux's feet didn't touch ground last harvest. She not only sourced and pressed grapes for her first releases, but also helped a frantic Elreda Pillmann of Goedvertouw host a large group of BMW motorcycle buffs (Le Roux got use of the Pillmann cellar in return). Owning no vineyards, Le Roux sources fruit from selected vineyards. With demand outstripping supply, this wasn't easy, but Le Roux feels she achieved her goals. Bottling her own Chenin was a heady experience, even for someone who wanted to be an astronaut, and still studies the influence of the moon on vines and wines. The Grenache in the blend below was a gift from family friends, off a 50 year old vineyard her father used to play in.

Chenin Blanc ★★★ Marked by sinewy elegance; sample **04** has kiwi & passionfruit on nose, fairly prominent oak but enough vivacious lemon fruit to carry it. 13% alc. Grapes from Barton Farm, W Bay. Following **04** reds too young to rate but showing considerable potential; both destined for 5-8 mths Fr oak maturation: **Cabernet Sauvignon** distinguished by ultra-ripe but gorgeous cassis/plum fruit, beautiful mineral touch; makings of an exciting wine. **Grenache-Cabernet Sauvignon** oozes ripe, juicy, berry fruit. — *DH*

Freedom Hill see Klompzicht
Friends see Lutzville
Frog Hill see Anura

Frost Vineyards

Paarl ▪ Est 1994 ▪ 1stB 1997 ▪ Visits by appt ▪ Owners David & Michel Frost ▪ Winemaker Mark van Buuren, with Freddie Theunissen (Jan 2003/2002) ▪ Viticulturist Michel Frost (1994) ▪ ±24 ha (five Bdx reds, shiraz) ▪ ±100 tons ±7 500 cs 100% red ▪ PO Box 7358 Noorder-Paarl 7623 ▪ frostms@global.co.za ▪ www.frostwine.com © *869·8339* ▢ *869·8732*

Mark van Buuren says he felt a bit like a cat on a hot tin roof during his first harvest here in 2003. (The winery is owed by international pro-golfer David Frost and his brother Michel.) But MvB landed on his feet in 2004 and tackled the crush 'with a lot more focus and

direction'. Besides 'good cab and lovely merlot', first crops of shiraz, petit verdot and mal-
bec 'prove we're well-suited'. Growing the local market is a goal (golf fans: there's a fu-
tures-style 'Passport' option offering exclusive access to David F and to the wines). And,
MvB chirps, 'there are many other exciting places like the Comores, Hawaii etc where we
MUST GO and market our wines'. In your dreams, kid. Travel he did, though: to Ch Le Bon
Pasteur, home-base of the Frosts' wine guru Michel Rolland, for a mid-2003 crush.

★★★★ **Cabernet Sauvignon Reserve 00,** as usual with dash merlot. Intense plum/
blackberry flavours & finely grained tannins offer super ageing potential. Retasted,
oak (22 mths Fr) still overshadows fruit. Needs time to harmonise.

★★★★ **Cabernet Sauvignon 02** (★★★) raspberry & mint promise future complexity on a
yet closed nose. Powdery tannins & big alc (15%) fight for dominance over ripe
blackcurrant flavours. Cellaring should give fruit the upper hand. 18 mths 42% new
Fr oak. **01** remains dense, supercharged with cassis fruit & pencil shavings. Velvet
tannins & slightly lower alc (14.5%) taper slowly to persistent finish.

★★★★ **Par Excellence** NEW **02** cab-dominated Bdx blend, aptly named given co-owner
David F's success on the fairway. Excellence in flavour department too, deep,
slightly decadent choc-truffle tones; so keenly balanced, nearly 15.5% alc goes unnoticed; has structure & intensity to improve with cellaring. 18 mths new Fr oak.

★★★☆ **Merlot Reserve** Massive **00** ripe plum, prune flavours & fiery 15.5% alc make
this a bottle to share rather than drink alone. Generous tannins from 20 mths Fr
oak (30% new) & sweet jammy finish.

★★★☆ **Merlot 02** (★★★) savoury, high-toned monster packs tremendous fruit & alc (15.
4%) on the finish. Expect mellowing with time in bottle — but not overnight. Retasted **01** full-bodied, ripe & malt-like with tannins unsoftened by year's cellaring.

★★★★ **Chardonnay 02** offers restrained lemon cream aromas despite aroma-enhancing
barrel maturation & frequent lees stirring. Balanced, with cleansing acidity & dry,
lemony finish. More elegant than Rubenesque **01,** with buttered toast & lime fleshiness. Like white below, fruit ex-Asara (Stbosch).

★★★☆ **Sauvignon Blanc 02** Still fresh, hints coriander & green nettles, well held together by nervy lime acidity. **03** more rounded (higher 13% alc), but fresh acid.
Passionfruit & tropical nose; reductive handling gives characteristic herbaceous
hints.

Blanc de Noir discontinued. — *CvZ*

Fryer's Cove Vineyards

*Bamboes Bay • Est 1999 • 1stB 2002 • Closed to public • Owners Jan Ponk Trust, JH
Laubscher Family Trust & Wynand Hamman • Winemaker Wynand Hamman (Apr 1999) •
Viticulturist Jan van Zyl (Apr 1999) • 6 ha (cab, merlot, pinot, sauvignon) • 25 tons 1 500 cs
66% red 34% white • PO Box 213 Doringbaai 8151 • janponk@kingsley.co.za © (027)
213·2312/082·800·7367/082·550·8749* ☎ *(027) 213·2212*

Winemaker Wynand Hamman and viticulturist brother-in-law Jan 'Ponk' van Zyl are justifiably proud of the interest ocean-kissed Fryer's Cove has generated in what they describe as 'the stepchild' of the SA wine industry — the Olifants River region. Their first
release was a Sauvignon; due to increasing demand (03 was particularly well received)
Hamman and van Zyl planted another hectare. They also experimented with pinot on a
small scale, and, despite the extreme conditions (the vineyards literally a stone's throw
from the frigid Atlantic) the results look promising. Last year also saw the release of the
first Cab-Merlot blend, named Richard Fryer in honour of the first Bamboes Bay farmer,
buried nearby.

★★★★☆ **Sauvignon Blanc** Layered depth, subtlety, beyond the immediately appealing
gooseberry aromas in **04** (sample): summer meadow, grapefruit, 'oyster shell'; flavours are pure sauvignon, arresting just-picked freshness, lingering finish. Very
classy. **03** polished, cool feel; streets ahead of maiden **02** (★★★).

Merlot ★★★ **02** yr on, shows more perfume: violets, creamy-ripe cherry/plum fruit, gentle spicing. Attractive light-textured drinkability. Malo/matured new/used Fr oak, 13

mths. 13% alc. **Cabernet Sauvignon ★★★ 02** developing nicely: cassis, scrub tones more integrated, juicy-fruited elegance, supple tannins drinking well. Alc/oak as above. Grapes for this, pvs wine, now diverted into… **Richard Fryer ★★★★ NEW** Harmonious **03** (unrated sample) cab/merlot blend (51/49) capturing red berry fruit purity, plus extra dimensions both varieties can bring; whiffs creamy choc, herbs (including mint). Elegant savoury finish. Barrels as above, 14 mths. One to watch. — *CR*

■ *Foundation Series* see Flagstone

Gallop Hill

Paarl ▪ Est 2001 ▪ 1stB 2002 ▪ Visits by appt ▪ Attractions/amenities: see intro ▪ Owners Dijonne du Preez & Jim Deane ▪ Vini consultants Olive Nel & Anthony Hamilton Russell ▪ Viti consultant Kobus Mosterd ▪ 20 ha (cab, shiraz) ▪ ±240 tons 2 500 100% red ▪ PO Box 7539 Stellenbosch 7599 ▪ info@gallophill.co.za ▪ www.gallophill.co.za ℂ 869·8956 🖷 869·8133

This elegant Paarl spread has been a thoroughbred stud farm for generations. Current owners Dijonne du Preez and Jim Deane developed 20ha of virgin soils into vineyard. Their red blend, First Chukka, to date has been available mainly to the polo-playing fraternity and has been so sought-after, customers have been placing advance orders. A reflection, no doubt, of both intrinsic quality and the cachet of the winemaking advisors associated with the project: Hamilton Russell Vineyards' Anthony HR and wife Olive. Now the owners are opening their exclusive domain to the wine-public by appointment. Enticements, if any are needed, include five-star accommodation and spa, a mountain reserve and, by special arrangement, 'exquisite' lunches and tastings with the winemaker in the farmhouse. A runaway success in the making?

★★★★ **The First Chukka 02** big beefy red with roast/toast aromas, intense baked prune fruit hardly ruffled by any tannin, but it's there, ripe to match fruit & seamlessly integrated. High alc at 14.5% adds sweet notes & slight burn to finish. Perfect for winding down after a few chukkas in winter. Blend shiraz, pinotage, cab 75/15/10, 3rd fill barrels 13–14 mths. Ready, will keep for 2–3 yrs. — *IvH*

■ *Garob* see Kango

Gecko Ridge

Owner Pernod-Ricard SA ▪ Winemaker/viticulturist Eben Rademeyer (Jun 2004) ▪▪ 50% red 49% white 1% MCC ▪ PO Box 1324 Stellenbosch 7599 ▪ davies@prsa.co.za ℂ 880·8800 🖷 880·8860

Consumer-friendly range launched in 1998, featuring bright, attractive packaging. **Cabernet Sauvignon Reserve ★★★ 02** not retasted; we last noted it as offering uncomplicated red-berried drinkability. **Chardonnay Reserve ★★★ 03** minerals & grapefruit pith on nose, some creamy lees, gently & supportively wooded. Both WO Brde Rvr Vlly. — *JB*

■ *Genesis* see Stellenbosch Vineyards

Gerhard Britz Wines

Walker Bay ▪ Est 2002 ▪ 1stB 2003 ▪ Visits by appt ▪ Owner Gerhard Britz ▪ Vini consultant Bartho Eksteen, with Gerhard Britz ▪ 10 tons 650 cs ▪ 78% red 22% white ▪ 13 Swartdam Rd, No 8, Hermanus 7200 ▪ Gerhardbritz@yahoo.com ℂ (028) 314·0797 🖷 (028) 314·0005

When computer systems consultant Gerhard Britz bottled his first own-label wine the moment was everything he imagined it would be, matched only by the pride he felt when this maiden Semillon was later featured as Editor's Choice in *Good Taste* magazine. Last year Britz bottled his first Bordeaux blend, and he hopes it will evoke a similar response. He spends much of his time in the US, developing a system to assist students manage their education. While Britz's bottles wing their way over the seas, this is one system he hopes to import to SA.

Coalesce Multi-regional Bdx quintet (cabs s/f, malbec, merlot, petit v), matured in Fr/ Am small-oak. **03** sampled pre-bottling, ripe almost stewed character; chewy, with fruit-cake richness. Provisional ★★★★. ±14% alc. **Semillon Unfiltered ★★★★ 03** from W Bay fruit, Fr-barrique-fermented/aged, some new. Yr on, delicious lemon-cream biscuit aromas, brisk citrus-zest flavours; oak well-meshed; good food style. — *CR*

Gilga Wines

Stellenbosch ▪ Est/1stB 1998 ▪ Closed to public ▪ Owner/winemaker/viticulturist Chris Joubert ▪ 700 cs 100% red ▪ PO Box 3 Vlottenburg 7604 ▪ chris.joubert@gilga.com ▪ www.gilga.com ✆ 881·3475 🖷 881·3248

A 'one-man show' is how Chris Joubert describes his winery. As 'a South African syrah specialist', he identifies single vineyards remarkable for their quality and individuality, buys in the grapes and then, in leased space and using the least possible intervention, makes 'terroir-specific world-class' syrah. Owner/winemaker Joubert dons the viticultur-ist's hat on a couple of hectares of his own.

★★★★★ **Gˢ** ('Gilga Super') NEW A wine to stop you in your tracks. Micro-selection of cellar's best, lavished with 18 mths new Fr oak, packaged in fetching squat, black-labelled bottle – just 300 of them, all at a premium price, only in Switzerland. **02** inky black, dense violet fruit, in massive structure. Likely to be trumpeting in 2010. 15.3% alc.

★★★★ **Syrah** Hand-crafted wine, deep-fruited, forged by new Fr oak into statement of note. Exciting sample **03** gentian tincture, mulberry fruits, stylish structure, prom-ise long-haul pleasure (20 yrs, suggests CJ). 13.8% alc. Emphatic **02** retasted: io-dine tints to roasted spice in mammoth trellis of minerally, well-sprung tannin, burly (15.2%) alc. 8 mths new, then 10 mths 2nd fill wood.

★★★★ **G-Syrah** Heady Provençal pepper, spice & all things nice infuse barrel sample of gently ripened **03**, with fruit swaddled in woollen tannins. Promise of ★★★★ when complete.13.5% alc. **02** bigger boned, more brazen (14.8% alc), with long crushed-bayleaf finish. Complex oaking regimen, ± 20% new Am. — *DS*

Glen Carlou Vineyards

Paarl ▪ Est 1984 ▪ 1stB 1988 ▪ Tasting & sales Mon-Fri 8.45-4.45 Sat 9-12.30 ▪ Fee R10 ▪ Closed Easter Fri/Sun, Dec 25/26 & Jan 1 Phone ahead on other public holidays ▪ Tours by appt ▪ Tasting/sale of home-made cheese (other attractions see intro) ▪ Owners The Hess Group (Switzerland) ▪ Winemaker David Finlayson, with Arco Laarman (1994/2000) ▪ Viticul-turist Marius Cloete (2000), with Richard Camera ▪ 70 ha ▪ 450 tons 45 000 cs 60% white 40% red ▪ PO Box 23 Klapmuts 7625 ▪ welcome@glencarlou.co.za ▪ www.glencarlou.co.za ✆ 875·5528 🖷 875·5314

Swiss shareholder Hess Group, owner of wineries in California, Australia and Argentina, has bought the Finlaysons' share of the winery they established 20 vintages ago. A major upgrade, including an art galley exhibiting some of international tycoon Donald Hess' pri-vate collection, is planned for 2005/6. Paterfamilias Walter F intends enjoying retired life – fly-fishing (mention New Zealand and see the smile), checking on his dairy herd (wife Jill also retired – their champion cheeses now made/marketed by a licensor) and helping daughter Carolyn and husband, Swiss winemaker Jean-Claude Martin, establish a wine farm in the Hemel-en-Aarde Valley. Son David F, down to earth but savvy, continues chas-ing the goal of consistency and 'maintaining a decent quality-to-volume ratio'. He be-lieves 'only the best and/or mega-rich will be around in 2-3 years. Why? We in SA often miss the big picture. We have to learn to adapt and be ready for challenging times, not sit crying into our *moerkoffie* when the rand is a charging rhino.'

★★★★ **Pinot Noir 03** more than makes up for difficult **02** (★★★) with perfectly ripe, se-ductive raspberry/cherry fruit profile, silky texture, pinot's classic elegance & charm. Harmonious oaking (11 Fr, only 15% new). 14.5% alc. Hard to resist, but will reward 4+ yrs cellaring. **02** showed good pinot expression, but stalky & firm acid on finish. **01** was supported by ripe tannin, savoury acid, well-judged oak.

★★★★ **Syrah** Re-branded 'Shiraz' nods to Rhône in name, composition & character: now features soupçons mourvèdre, viognier. Continues to pick up accolades around the globe. **03** (★★★★★) explores savoury spectrum: interleaved tones of woodsmoke, clove, black pepper, espresso & dark fruit. Deep, complex, intriguing, individual. Already approachable, but expensive oaking laid foundation for longer haul, 6+ yrs. 15 mths equal Fr/Am, 60% new. 14.5% alc. **02** 90 pts *WS*.

★★★☆ **Zinfandel** Last tasted was **01**, packed tight with ripe flavours, big dry tannins & enormous 15.5% alc. For CWG auction.

★★★★ **Grand Classique** Historically, flagship red of range. **02** (★★★★★) step up; classic 5 Bdx varieties, but as with **01**, cab, merlot dominate. Intense cedar-spiced cassis, cherries, with herbal, minty hints. Juicy, ripe, lots of vitality & interest; lithe deep-veined tannins from expert oaking (2 yrs Fr barriques, half new, rest château sourced). Already delicious, but has 10+ yr ageing potential. 14.8% alc. **01** reticent reserved mid-2003, taut tannins & firm acid, somewhat unknit.

★★★★ **Chardonnay** Latest **03** keeps house style: rich butter-biscuit, vibrant citrus & tropical fruit aromas, followed by lemon-sharpened taut minerality on palate. Still tightly knit, a keeper, cellar 4+ yrs. 10 mths barriques, mainly Fr, mixed cooperage. 14.5% alc. **02** tad more commercial in style; **01** richly textured.

★★★★★ **Chardonnay Reserve** Intense, rich & serious, under CWG Auction label for past 10 yrs. Last tasted was **02** textured, concentrated with vein of minerality.

★★★★ **Chardonnay Reserve 'Black Label'** For export to UK/US only. Duo of vintages tasted: **03** (★★★★★) from single-vyd; lemon zest, underlying creamy tropical tones, but still in youthful prime, fruit tightly reined. Has concentration, length, classic biscuity richness & sinewy structure. 14% alc. **02** showy; pervasive butterscotch integration of citrus/toasty oak, very New World, impressive. Lemon/lime tangy freshness rescues it from going over the top. 13.5% alc. Both natural-yeast fermented. Concentration, oaking (yr new Fr) give 5+ yrs ageing ability.

Tortoise Hill White NEW ☺ ★★★ Unpretentious varying blend. **04** equal partnership chard, semillon, lightly oaked. Pear drop tones, appealing lemon/lime palate freshness, body plumped up by touch sugar. 13% alc.

Tortoise Hill Red ★★★ For easy-drinking wine, gets surprising care. **03** blend mainly cab plus zin, shiraz, touriga, merlot, aged in seasoned Fr/Am 15 mths. Fresh-picked red berries, supple tannins, no hard edges to interfere with enjoyment. 14.5% alc. **Devereux** Occasional label; from chenin, last was **00** ★★★☆. **Daniella** & **Cape Vintage** discontinued. — *CR*

▨ *Glenhurst* see Quoin Rock

Glenview Wines

Cape Town ▪ Est/1stB 1998 ▪ Closed to public ▪ Owner Robin Marks ▪ Vini consultant Hein Hesebeck ▪ 7 000 cs 50% red 50% white ▪ PO Box 32234 Camps Bay 8040 ▪ bayexport@ kingsley.co.za ▪ www.glenview.co.za ✆ 438·1080 🖷 438·3167

Vintner and veteran surfer Robin Marks continues to attract fans with his low prices and good quality wines. 'Not enough South Africans drink wine,' he laments, but he believes one category which has the potential to help raise per capita consumption a notch is chenin, as the general trend is towards lower-acid, easier-drinking styles. Like his, in fact.

Merlot ★★★ Fairly compact **03**, food-friendly range of flavours — mocha, bitter-choc, savoury; approachable tannins. 6 mths oak. **Chenin Blanc** ★★ Soft & accessible **04** bears boiled sweet aromas, gentle melon/hay flavours, mild alc. Both WO Paarl. — *CR*

GlenWood Vineyards

Franschhoek ▪ Est/1stB 2000 ▪ Tasting & sales Mon-Fri 9-1 Sat/Sun (Sep-Apr only) 11-3 Public holidays by appt ▪ Fee R10 ▪ Tours daily 11 ▪ BYO picnic ▪ Walks ▪ Owner Alastair G Wood ▪ Winemaker/viticulturist DP Burger (May 1992), advised by Cathy Marshall ▪ 21.5 ha (chard, sauvignon, semillon) ▪ ±150 tons 2 000 cs own label 30% red 70% white ▪ PO Box 204 Franschhoek 7690 ▪ glenwood@adept.co.za ▪ www.glenwoodvineyards. co.za © 876·2044 ▤ 876·3338

This brand is gaining awareness locally (and venturing into the export market), reports winemaker/viticulturist DP Burger, which means more visitors are keen to try and changes have to be made. Among them the appointment of Ashley Clayton as tasting room assistant. Another newcomer is Nicky Jacobs, assistant manager, whose CV includes basic cellar training at Elsenburg. His first harvest in Franschhoek came late and light. '2004 was made for the winemaker with the patience of an angel', sighs Burger, who spent the Easter weekend in the cellar instead of on a boat, behind a rod. Recognition is growing that GlenWood is a budding beauty: the Reserve Chardonnay was awarded a gold medal at the Swiss Awards soon after it was recommended to Wine 500 Club members.

★★★★ **Shiraz** Elegantly mouthfilling **02** was a rung above pvs; anise whiffs & peppery ripe plum flavour; follow-up **03** (★★★) from own vyds, foursquare, earthy; needs time to harmonise. 11 mths 2nd fill Fr/Am oak; 70% new. 14.5% alc.

★★★★ **Chardonnay Vignerons Reserve** Pvs versions of their oak-matured Chard variously listed as 'Barrel Fermented' or 'Wooded'; **03** tops them all; seriously & expertly oaked for vibrant citrus freshness, with structure. Natural yeasts, 11 mths new Fr oak. Only detraction is touch alc (14.5%) on finish. Swiss gold, *Wine* ★★★★.

Sauvignon Blanc ★★★★ **04** watery colour, but nothing dilute about zingy coriander aromas/flavours; attractive twist bitter grapefruit-pith to finish. Grapes picked at 3am, kept under cover of dry ice to conserve freshness, says DP Burger. **Semillon Barrel Fermented** & **Semillon Unwooded** sold out. **Semillon-Sauvignon Blanc** ★★★★ ✓ Youthful & mouthfilling **04**, sampled soon after bottling show no sign of shock: powerful nose, hints melon & apricot, attractively herbal, bone-dry lime flavours. 65/35 blend, unoaked, semillon bunch-pressed. Moderate 13% alc. — *RK/TM*

▨ *Goat Roti* see Fairview

Goats do Roam Wine Company

Paarl ▪ Est/1stB 1998 ▪ 86% red 10% white 4% Rosé ▪ See Fairview for details

Fairview's Charles Back has herded the Goats do Roam range into its own business paddock and added the Goat Roti and Goats Do Roam In Villages brands to the irreverent original. Stand-alone status is merited: it's the biggest SA brand in the US, where consumers have taken to the quaint moniker ('legend' has it that some of the Paarl home-farm's goats broke free and strayed into the vineyards, where they nosed out the ripest grapes for nibbling) as much as to the quality and quaffability of the wines. The reds are combos of half-dozen or so varieties, with viognier and grenache blanc adding piquancy to the white.

★★★★ **Goat Roti** Shiraz plus seasoning of white grape viognier — calculated to deliver the spicy tones of the northern Rhône. Which it does, again, in **03**. Youthful, fresh, with lifted fruit. Fairly generous & open, but would benefit from keeping to allow brisk acidity to settle. 14.5% alc. **02** was concentrated, with good potential. 91 pts *WS*. 12-14 mths Fr/Am oak, none new.

★★★★ **Goats do Roam in Villages Red** ⬛ Serious 'Cape blend' with a flippant moniker. **03** homogenous, well assembled shiraz (30%), pinotage & mourvèdre, plus thimble viognier for spicy top-note. Fr/Am oak, none new. 14.7% alc.

★★★☆ **Goats do Roam Rosé** Non-serious but authentic Mediterranean-style rosé. **04** dry, earthy with attractive austere edge. Contrast with **03**, which crackled with perky summer fruit. Widely sourced grapes. 14.3% alc.

★★★★ Goats do Roam in Villages White Innovative blend of Stbosch sauvignon & chardonnay, with dry-farmed clairette (Swtlnd) & grenache blanc (Piekenklf); unwooded, *sur lie* 6 mths. **03** broad, well harmonised aromas; textured palate with persistent fresh acidity. 14.2% alc.

Goats do Roam Red ★★★ Côtes-du-Rhône-style red featuring Mediterranean varieties herded by shiraz; pinotage adds local dimension. **03** ripe red fruits & clean tannic grip; refreshingly, doesn't rely on wood. 14.2% alc. **Goats do Roam White ★★★★** White Rhône lookalike, featuring trio grenache blanc, clairette & crouchen with dash semillon in **03**, with appealing dry austerity. For early drinking. All WO W-Cape/Coastal. — *RK*

Goede Hoop Estate

Stellenbosch ▪ *Est 1928* ▪ *1stB 1974* ▪ *Tasting, sales & tours Mon-Thu 10-5 Fri 10-3* ▪ *Closed public holidays* ▪ *Tours, meals & refreshments by appt* ▪ *BYO picnic* ▪ *Conferencing for 10 people max* ▪ *Owner Pieter Bestbier* ▪ *Winemaker Carel Hugo (Dec 2002)* ▪ *Viticulturist Johan de Beer (Apr 2000)* ▪ *80 ha (cab, carignan, malbec, merlot, pinotage, shiraz, chenin, sauvignon)* ▪ *11 000 cs* + *90-100 000ℓ bulk 91% red 9% white* ▪ *PO Box 25 Kuils River 7579* ▪ *goede@adept.co.za* ▪ *www.goedehoop.co.za* ✆ **903·6286** 🖷 *906·1553*

A refreshingly honest appraisal of the 2004 harvest from winemaker Carel Hugo. He reports that vines, struggling through a dry winter and summer heatwave, produced both lower yield and quality (the exception being shiraz, which is developing a lovely intensity). But there was, as always, still reason to celebrate: the Cab excelled again at the Michelangelo awards, viticulturist Johan de Beer tied the knot, and a new sauvignon block, planted last year, is expected to produce great results. With the malbec swinging into production this season and a renewed focus on marketing there can be little doubt that the 'Good Hope' will continue to be realised.

★★★★ Cabernet Sauvignon ✓ Currently selling **99** shows developed sweet-spicy Xmas cake aromas over leafy, cassis notes. Older oak (2nd/3rd fill Fr, 18 mths) avoids swamping fruit, yet adds classic cigarbox notes, tones the dry finish. Still has time to go. **00** nose more open, aromas of plum pudding; concentrated creamy rich fruit, balanced tannin, fine structure for ageing.

★★★☆ Shiraz 01 shyer than pvs, savoury, showing some black pepper notes & elegant, med-bodied redcurrant fruit. 18 mths 2nd/3rd fill barrels lends softness, spice to finish. Next-up **02** interesting combo black fruit & white pepper, some savoury spicing; quite chewy/youthful, needs time; classy, has good credentials.

★★★★ Merlot-Cabernet Sauvignon ✓ Current **00** is a 60/40 blend, showing spice & complexity; soft ripe-plum flavours with mocha & choc; restrained wooding makes for plush style. Follow-up **01** charming & delicious; juicy, ripe, already accessible with plenty to give. 19 mths 2nd/3rd fill barrels.

★★★☆ Pinotage ✓ **01** is the current release; mulberry jam notes, sweetness on palate; smoked meat/gamey complexity, elegant oaking (8 mths 2nd/3rd fill Fr); same regime for next-up **02**, somewhat leaner, vegetal, with savoury undertone, prominent but ripe tannin.

★★★★ Pinotage Private Collection ✓ Limited release; last tasted was **01**, which exhibited a classical, almost Burgundian tone.

Domaine **★★★** Spicy cab/carignan blend (53/47), 'lightly styled for everyday use' says winemaker; **02** red currants & cherries, open/accessible weave, savoury & peppery fruit, firm dry finish. Dryland vyds; unwooded. **Chardonnay ★★★☆** Quite a powerful wood presence in **03**, 10 mths new Fr barriques, 30% malo; lots of butterscotch & toast, but good limy fruit backing too, extended finish, rounded mouthfeel, richness. ±14% alc.

Sauvignon Blanc ★★★★ ✓ Tasted newly bottled last ed, still-available **03** now more generous, expressive: nettles & crisp salad greens on nose, appley flavours, refreshing, zesty finish. Blend of 4 different blocks; 10 months *sur lie*. — *CR*

Goede Kap see Cape Wine Cellars
Goede Moed see Baarsma

Goedgenoegen see Baarsma

Goedvertrouw Estate

Bot River (see Walker Bay map) ▪ *Est 1990* ▪ *1stB 1991* ▪ *Visits by appt* ▪ *Home-cooked meals & accommodation by appt* ▪ *Play area for children* ▪ *Farm produce* ▪ *Small conferences* ▪ *Conservation area* ▪ *Small art gallery* ▪ *Owner/winemaker/viticulturist Elreda Pillmann* ▪ *8 ha (cab, pinot, chard, sauvignon)* ▪ *70% red 30% white* ▪ *PO Box 37 Bot River 7185* ▪ *Josiasfredin@mweb.co.za* ©/℡ **(028) 284·9769**

If Arthur Pillmann — predisposed to rebuild vintage BMWs on the kitchen table — were still alive he would be beaming with pride. Not only has his widow, Elreda, now in her 60s, seamlessly picked up where he left off as winemaker, last year she successfully hosted all of 1500 (!) BMW motorcyclists during harvest! She did have help, though, in Fredine le Roux, previously winemaker at Le Grand Estate in Robertson. In turn, Le Roux used the Goedvertrouw cellar to make her first own-wines, also available from the Goedvertrouw tasting room. Tannie Elreda and Fredine have found they share the same passion — for life and for wine. Theirs is a combo that's working 'even better than carrots and peas'.

★★★★ **Cabernet Sauvignon** Native yeast-fermented (as are its stablemates), matured ±yr in seasoned Fr oak. Last was **03**, which we tasted as a sample, marvellous deep colour; dense ripe cassis fruit swathed in grainy tannins. **04** not ready.

Sauvignon Blanc Individual style, more 'white wine' than 'sauvignon'; **03** (★★★) was last tasted. **Pinot Noir** ★★★ Idiosyncratic, fragrant & very dry; acquires game/truffle overtones with age. **03**, sampled pre-bottling, strapping, slightly rustic, with generous red flavour & earthy undertone, enough fruit to develop with interest. 14.5% alc. **Chardonnay** Last sampled was **01** (★★★). Will reappear next yr as MCC. **Pardoemps** [NEW] ★★★ Individual concoction of **03** pinot, pinotage, cab (50/25/25); rich nose of ripe plums & strawberries, eucalyptus whiff; oak dominant mid-2004, shows promise of development. Quirky name a favourite word of Arthur P's. — *DH*

Goedverwacht Estate

Robertson (see map) ▪ *1stB 1994* ▪ *Tasting & sales Mon-Fri 8.30-4.30 Sat 10-2* ▪ *Closed Easter Fri/Sun, Dec 25, Jan 1* ▪ *Tours by appt* ▪ *Snacks served with wine tasting; also BYO picnic* ▪ *Owner Jan du Toit & Sons (Pty) Ltd* ▪ *Winemaker Jan du Toit* ▪ *Viticulturist Pieter Venter (Dec 2002), advised by Francois Viljoen* ▪ *110 ha (cab, merlot, shiraz, chard, colombard, sauvignon)* ▪ *1 500 tons 40 000 cs own label 43% red 50% white 7% rosé* ▪ *Exported as Soek die Geluk, Pier 42, Thys Drift & Ama Ulibo* ▪ *PO Box 128 Bonnievale 6730* ▪ *goedverwachtestate@lando.co.za* ▪ *www.goedverwacht.co.za* © **(023) 616·3430** ℡ (023) 616·2073

'If you pay enough attention to your vineyards and spend enough time in them,' Jan du Toit believes, 'the vines will tell when their grapes are ready to pick.' Spoken like a true man of the soil, which Jan dT is: he's been farming this riverfront for the past 20 years, exactly half under the banner of Goedverwacht Estate. In that time he and marketer wife Marian have seen demand jump from 250 to 40 000 cases. While their unfailingly appealing Colombard put them on the map, their other whites offer remarkable value and their reds are garnering increasing attention too. Investment — latterly in a barrel hall, new barriques and additional small-batch vinification plant — continues unabated. Antecedent Gabriël dT, who named the property 'Soek die Geluk', firmly believing he'd find happiness here, would doubtless have approved.

★★★★ **Cabernet Sauvignon-Merlot** ✓ Current release is **02**, 60/40 blend, yr Fr/Am oak, some new. Retaste reveals gathering complexity & mature roundness; still ripely cushioned with berry fruit, floral touch & hint coffee, big juicy tannins, minerally touch to tail; 14.9% alc hardly perceptible. Will develop further.

★★★★ **Crane White Colombard** ✓ One of the best & most reliable; features mouthwatering fruit, brisk acidity & uncompromising dryness. **04** sappy tropical fruit with guava hint, lovely freshness. Enjoy in its youth.

Shiraz Rosé ☺ ★★★ Flavourful, smoothly dry **04**, whiffs of ripe cherries & greenpepper; red berry flavours. Serve well chilled. **Great Expectations Chardonnay** ☺ ★★★ Wooded, but you'd hardly know. **04** guavas & peaches uppermost in bouquet, slight citrus touch & clean vanilla, round & fruity.

Crane Red Merlot ★★★★ One of the elusive *soft* Cape merlots. Yr 2nd fill Fr oak for **04**, blended with 15% of **03**; bouquet of plums, prunes & oak-char; sweet choc-cherry flavours; should improve further over 2-3 yrs. 14% alc. **Acre of Stone Shiraz** NEW ★★★★ Ex-young vyd on cooler, lightly south-sloping site; **03** very well filled out with dark sweet fruit & toasty oak; notable persistence. Elegant rather than a blockbuster style despite high 14.7% alc. Good start, augurs well for future. **The Good Earth Sauvignon Blanc** ★★★ From riverside vyd, 12 yrs old; **04** guava bouquet with snips green-grass; tropical fruit palate; drink soon to capture its zinging freshness. — *DH*

■ *Goeie Tye* see Rooiberg

Golden Alibama

No-frills NV (★★) white by Distell; now discontinued.

■ *Golden Kaan* see KWV International
   Gordon's Bay see Zidela

Goudini Wines

Rawsonville ▪ Est 1948 ▪ Tasting & sales Mon-Fri 8-5 Sat 9.30-12.30 ▪ Closed Easter Fri-Mon, Dec 25/26, Jan 1 ▪ Coffee shop ▪ Conferencing ▪ Gifts ▪ Owners 40 members ▪ Winemakers Hennie Hugo & Dominique Waso (Dec 1984/Oct 2001), with Ruaan Terblanche (Nov 2001) ▪ Viti advisor Hendrik Myburgh (Nov 2001) ▪ 1 040 ha (merlot, ruby cab, shiraz, chard, chenin, semillon) ▪ 20 000 tons 33 000 cs own label 45% red 45% white 10% rosé ▪ Ranges for customers: Safiki (UK), Hummelhof (Germany) ▪ PO Box 132 Rawsonville 6845 ▪ winesales@goudiniwine.co.za ▪ www.goudiniwine.co.za © (023) 349·1090 ✆ (023) 349·1988

'The biggest challenge for any co-op is to offer both value for money and excellent quality,' says manager and viti adviser Hendrik Myburgh. In response, Goudini has streamlined its range and is concentrating on a core of wines, including a new Premium collection. Last year the cellar was among the first in SA to introduce Pera thermoflash technology, to extract more colour and friendly tannins in reds. This involves briefly heating the grape must to 85°C in a vacuum, causing the cells in the berry-skins to burst. Affordability remains a key focus, hence the introduction of a red partner to the popular Umfiki white. The 'wine house' now has a coffee shop where visitors can enjoy refreshments in a peaceful vineyard setting.

Premium range

NEW

Pinotage ★★★ **03** plummy, mellow & tasty casual quaffer. Small portion oaked, 2nd fill Fr barrels. 14.6% alc. **Shiraz** ★★★ **03** spicy red berry character; lively but smooth with smoky tannins, touch maturity showing though life for another yr/2. Partly oaked, 75% Am. **Ruby Cabernet-Merlot** ★★★ Oak-brushed **02**, 60/40 blend oozing ripe plums & liquorice, pervasive gentle fruity tone which needs to be enjoyed fairly soon. **Blanc de Noir** ★★ Partridge-eye-pink **03**; faint red berry nose, whiff candyfloss; honeyed, smooth, still enjoyable but drink soon. 10% alc. **Special Late Harvest** ★★ **03** full tropical aromas, flavours tapering off now, must drink. From chenin. 11% alc. Next will be labelled Natural Sweet. **Muscat d'Alexandrie** ★★★★ Delicious **02** still fresh & velvety; concentrated muscat & raisin aromas; honeysuckle, lemon & lime flavours; not for keeping. 17% alc.

Goudini range

Ruby Cabernet Reserve ★★★☆ **02** tasty spread of ripe plum, thatch & herbs; rounded mouthfeel, some good bottle-age showing. Ready. Yr 1st-3rd fill oak, 10% Am. **Chardonnay Barrel Fermented** ★★ **03** appears to be ageing rapidly, though still a pleasant drink. 100% new oak, 15% Am, 4 mths. **Unwooded Chardonnay** ★★ **04** ripe peach & pineapple flavours; bit plodding: could do with more acidity to enliven the big alc (14.3%), sugar (±5g/ℓ). **Chenin Blanc** ★★ **04** off-dry charmer with tropical fruit/guava tones, soft & rounded; one to drink soon. **Sauvignon Blanc** ★★★ **04** ripe mix of guava & ripe gooseberry, bright, fresh, pleasant & drinkable. **Brut Sparkling** ★★★ Carbonated sparkling from sauvignon; sweet apple-scented nose; contrastingly racy 'brut' palate; good appetiser; 'will cheer up any party,' says **03** label. **Port** ★★★ **01** with traditional low fortification (18%) shows some good bottle-maturity as well as further development potential.

Umfiki range

Pinotage-Cinsaut ☺ ★★★ **03** delightful quaffer; chock full of strawberries & plums, suggestion of tannin. Glides down effortlessly.

Clairette Blanche-Colombar ★★ Slight tropical tone, touch of acidity, easy, pleasant glassful. NV. Also in 3ℓ. — *DH*

Goudveld Winery

Free State ▪ Tasting & sales Mon-Fri 8-6 Sat by appt ▪ Tours on request ▪ Conferences & receptions for 100-120 guests ▪ Owner Jan Alers ▪ Winemaker/viticulturist Merkil Alers (1985) ▪ 15 ha ▪ 120 tons 1 000 cs own label ▪ PO Box 1091 Welkom 9460 Ⓒ/☎ (057) 352-8650
The Alers family have taken the for-sale sign off the gate and, though they no longer reside on the property, are keeping the cellar and their wine business going on a reduced scale. They're still very happy to receive visitors (you're welcome to bring something to grill on the braai) and of course to show off their wines. Made, as always, in the light, refreshing style that goes down well in their warm climate. The streamlined range now features a Cabernet, Pinot, Ruby Cab, Sweet Colombard and two Ports, 3 and 5 years old.

Goue Vallei see Citrusdal Cellars

Graça

Vinho Verde-inspired lightly spritzy swiggers, the original white version still among SA's top-selling cork-closed wines. By Distell; exported as Blouberg.

Graça ☺ ★★★ Cleverly made semi-dry crowd-pleaser, anytime-light (12% alc); grassy freshness from sauvignon (60%, with semillon, crouchen), tangy fruit-filled palate.

Rosé ★★★ Slightly sweeter, less zippy version; lowish alc as above (±11%). Latest with maraschino cherry aromas. These NVs also in 375 ml; both WO W-Cape. — *CR*

Graceland Vineyards

Stellenbosch (see Stellenbosch map) ▪ Est 1997 ▪ 1stB 1998 ▪ Visits by appt only ▪ Fee R30 ▪ Closed public holidays ▪ Two-bedroom B&B with many amenities & views ▪ Owners Paul & Susan McNaughton ▪ Winemaker/viticulturist Susan McNaughton (2001) ▪ 10 ha (cab, merlot, shiraz) ▪ 55 tons 4 000 cs 100% red ▪ PO Box 7066 Stellenbosch 7599 ▪ graceland@iafrica. com ▪ www.gracelandvineyards.com Ⓒ 881-3121 (admin) 881-3394 (cellar) ☎ 881-3341
Packaged in purple tissue and boxed in wood, Graceland's new flagship wine was enthusiastically received by the market, so much so that the 600-case launch was a sell-out. Labelled Three Graces, it was described as 'seamless' by those who snapped it up. The McNaughtons new 'Beehive' vineyard has produced a honey of a maiden crop — 'excellent cabernet sauvignon fruit', enthuses winemaker Susan M. She and husband Paul

believe they should 'take the fruit, the sun and all the wonderful flavours of the vineyard and put them in the bottle with as little interference as possible'. Their other guiding philosophy is: 'Drink more wine; it makes you more philosophical'.

★★★★ **Cabernet Sauvignon** Traditionally made cab, vinified in open *kuipe* (as are all these), 16 mths Fr oak, ±35% new. **02** (★★★) mirrors difficult vintage: light, leafy, minty nose; dry, firm palate. 14% alc. **01** was riper yet classically styled; balanced structure for ±5 yrs ageing. **00** showed commendable finesse in big, ripe yr.

★★★☆ **Merlot** These usually soundly oaked (±16 mths Fr, ±30% new), though **02** shows some charry wood on fairly sinewy palate; herbaceous whiffs. 14% alc. Unlike approachable, Veritas/Juliet Cullinan-gonged **01**.

★★★☆ **Shiraz 02** (★★★), with soupçon merlot, cab, reveals some ripeness on palate but still very tight, introverted on nose too; may evolve with time. 25% new oak, mainly Am, 14 mths. 13.5% alc. VG. Classic & appealing **01** reflected cellar's trademark structural elegance.

Three Graces NEW ★★★ **02** sees above varieties as a cab-led blend (50/25/25). Light, restrained on nose; palate still tight, grippy. Good focus & structure but needs time to develop. 20 mths oak. 14% alc. — *RK*

Graham Beck Wines 🍷

Franschhoek/Robertson ▪ Est 1983 ▪ 1stB 1991 ▪ Tasting & sales Mon-Fri 9-5 Sat 10-4 ▪ Closed Easter Fri/Sun, Dec 25/26 & Jan 1 ▪ Tours by appt ▪ Owner Graham Beck ▪ Viticulturist Leon Dippenaar (Aug 2000) ▪ 55% red 25% white 20% MCC ▪ market@grahambeckwines.co.za ▪ www.grahambeckwines.co.za ▪ ISO 14001 certified ▪ Robertson cellar: Cellarmaster Pieter Ferreira, with Jacques Conradie (Aug 1990/Nov 2001) ▪ 182 ha (cab, merlot, pinot, shiraz, chard) ▪ 1 400 tons ▪ PO Box 724 Robertson 6705 ✆ (023) 626·1214 🖷 (023) 626·5164 ▪ Coastal Cellar (Franschhoek): Cellarmaster Charles Hopkins (1998) ▪ 192 ha (cabs s/f, merlot, petit v, pinotage, shiraz, sauvignon, viognier) ▪ 1 200 tons ▪ PO Box 134 Franschhoek 7690 ▪ ✆ 874·1258 🖷 874·1712

It's called synergy: one brand (Graham Beck, now more smartly attired after a packing revamp) made by two wineries (Robertson, Franschhoek) maintaining distinct but complementary identities. The winemakers: compact, bespectacled Pieter Ferreira in his zany, multi-coloured Robertson cellar (home of their classy MCCs); tall, laid-back Charles Hopkins in the elegant, sophisticated Franschhoek winery (finally, open for tasting/sales). They share a poet-philosopher's soul, but let's stay technical. Both report a 'bumper' 2004 harvest (34%-plus tonnage increases each). In Robertson it was young vines fruiting (cellar standout shiraz looking good); in Franschhoek, grapes from new 'up-and-coming' areas (including Plattekloof). Ferreira talks of biological, environmentally friendly pest/disease controls, and first use of destalkers in the vineyard to deliver clean fruit to the cellar. Hopkins rates 2004 one of the best vintages of the past decade. Greater lees contact on his sauvignon added richness; whole bunch fermentation in small quantities promises something extra in his wines. An impressive export portfolio lists an impressive 19 countries, including exotics like Vietnam and Laos. The big challenge? 'Producing the right style of wine for the American market.'

★★★★★ **The William** Named for Beck's grandson. Cabs s/f, pinotage (40/30/30), vinified separately at the Rbtsn & Frhoek cellars prior to blending. **01** opulent, deep, fruit-rich, yet trademark elegant structure of cellar's top wines. Black plums, hints forest floor, savoury spice; respected, not overwhelmed, by deft oaking. Has long life ahead. **02** (★★★★) less impressive, ripe: herbaceous leanings, with pinotage dominant. Shows meat extract, berries, black cherries, rhubarb; strong vanilla ex-oak. Sinewy tannins need time to meld, soften, will support wine as it develops into the future. These yr oak: Fr (cabs)/Am (pinotage). 14% alc. **00** Lufthansa 1st class.

★★★★ **Cornerstone Cabernet Sauvignon** From Firgrove 'coffee stone' (decomposed granite). No **01**. **02** deep, complex blackcurrants, cedar, dried herbs. Balanced & elegant, with svelte structure, well judged oaking (15 mths, mainly new Fr), giving framework for 8+ yr development. 14% alc. **00** also deserved further maturation.

★★★★ **Cabernet Sauvignon** Serious & classic styling. Retasted **01** pulpy blackcurrant intro, still youthful, scarcely allowing other nuances (cedary, herbaceous) to peep through. Elegant, firm ripe tannins give platform for future. 14 mths oak, 50% new. 14% alc. WO Coastal (as are two reds above).

★★★★ **The Old Road Pinotage** From 1963-planted, low-yielding Frhoek vines. Retasted **01**, with 5% cab, developing beautifully. Remarkable fruit intensity: piquant wild berries, cherries, with mocha spicing, plenty of richness, depth. Built for longer haul, sturdy but ripe tannins promise 8+ yrs. Yr new Fr/Am oak. 14% alc.

★★★★ **Pinotage** Sunshiny, unambiguous pinotage. **03** (★★★) simpler than rich **02**. Vanilla-spiced rhubarb, red berry intro; softly rounded, accessible & easy, for earlier drinking, despite 13 mths Am oak, third new. 14% alc. From Frhoek, as is above.

★★★★★ **The Ridge Syrah** Internationally acclaimed single-vyd (Rbtsn) wine. **02**, last glimpsed ex-cask, has piercing mulberry fruit core, with mocha/woodsmoke spicing. A lesson in elegance, finesse, & harmonious tannins: iron fist in velvet glove. Has 7+ yr future. 14 mths 70/30 Fr/Am oak, 60% new. 14.2% alc. **01** generous savoury fruit in elegant finish. Hugely concentrated **00** IWC gold, shiraz trophy.

★★★★ **The Joshua** (Sampled last ed as 'Shiraz-Viognier'). Adopts Beck's second name. Cellar flagship, with price to match. 7% viognier in maiden **02** adds fragrance, peachy pith to focused shiraz fruit. (Varieties crushed, fermented together.) 15% alc. 9% infusion in finer **03**, not to soften but to bring perfume, more complexity, à la Côte Rôtie. Very ripe (enormous 15.5% alc) sour cherry, roasted spice flavours. Yr Fr/Am barrels, 60/40. Will develop 6+ yrs, but already drinking well. WO Frhoek.

★★★★ **Shiraz 03** shows wild berries, classic smoky spice tones, with seamlessly integrated fruit & tannin. Tiny portions tannat, mourvèdre, viognier for added complexity. 13 mths mostly Am oak. 15% alc. Can age 3-4 yrs, but very tempting now. **02** had roast-spice intensity, accommodating tannins, 15% alc. WO Coastal.

★★★★ **Railroad Red 03** offers, as intended, spicy shiraz aromas in gentle cab frame. Harmonious, lightly oaked 60/40 blend, fruit-rich & flavourful, with lively drinkability. 13.5% alc. WO Coastal.

★★★★ **Chardonnay** Elegant fruit & sympathetic wooding the norm. **03** doesn't disappoint: softly rounded, biscuit & peach tones harmonise, finish with palate-rejuvenating citrus zest. Fermented/8 mths Fr oak, third new. 13.5% alc. WO Rbtsn.

★★★★ **Brut Rosé** Latest (NV) has appealing raspberry, warm brioche character, structural delicacy & finesse. Pinot/chard 70/30, grapes crushed together, 30 mths on lees. 12.5% alc. Pvs, similar blend, was vintaged **00**, 11.8% alc. WO W-Cape.

★★★★ **Blanc de Blancs** Brut MCC from chardonnay, amongst Cape's classiest. **99** (★★★★★) raises bar with impressive concentration, vibrant freshness, characterful nuances rich biscuit, citrus-peel. Creamy mousse & long full-flavoured finish. 50% of bunch-pressed grapes fermented in oak; ±4 yrs on lees. Delicious. 12.5% alc. *Decanter* list best 20 SA wines. **98** CWT gold. WO Rbtsn, as is Brut below.

★★★★ **Brut** Stylish NV MCC for many the winery's hallmark. Lively, with chardonnay's lemony freshness, gentle yeasty overlay from 2 yrs on lees. Pinot (46%) plumps up body, lends flavour. 20-25% 'reserve' wine added for consistency.

★★★★ **Rhona Muscadel** Fortified white muscadel ex-Rbtsn, made & packaged with panache. Retasted **99** glorious, perfumed orange marmalade character, still youthful. Spirity bite adds definition to rich sweetness (150g/ℓ sugar). 17.5% alc. 500ml.

Pinno ☺ ★★★ **03** shows trademark pulpy, rhubarb/wild berry character of unwooded pinotage. Gulpably light-textured, juicy & very user-friendly. A chillable red. 14% alc.
Pinno Rosé ☺ NEW ★★★ **04** has pinotage in flirtatious mode: cranberry/winegum aromas, juicily friendly palate-lengthening touch sugar (but tastes dry). Looks good too. 13% alc. **Waterside** (Pvsly added 'White') ☺ ★★★ **04** plump, peachy, smooth-textured & tasty blend chardonnay with some colombard. 13% alc.

Merlot ★★★ Blend of wines vinified at both cellars. **03** restrained, with cool berry & herbaceous tones, beefed up by white pepper, cedar ex-oak. Elegantly structured, with chewy tannins needing time to soften, meld. 14% alc. **Sauvignon Blanc ★★★★** Good varietal character on **04**, with 9% semillon adding weight, texture. Ripe & figgy, with just enough green edginess to spark interest, be food-friendly. Moderate 12.5% alc. WO Coastal, as is Viognier below. **Viognier ★★★★ 04** sample shows early promise of spicy, peach pip & floral bouquet aromas, silky texture, long mouthfilling finish. Deftly oaked (50%, rest in tank), to allow unique fruit character to shine through. 14% alc. — *CR*

Grande Provence see Agusta

Grand Mousseux

Since 1929, a range of affordable, dependable, all-occasions sparklers. By Distell.

Vin Sec ★★ Latest version tastes sweeter than pvs; Golden Delicious apple flavours, soft perfumed froth. Equal clairette/chenin confection, as is... **Vin Doux ★★★** New bottling more characterful than Sec; tropical fruit & honeyed sweetness refreshed by bustling bubbles. **Spumante** discontinued. All carbonated, NV, WO W-Cape. — *CR*

Grand Roche see Boland Kelder

Grangehurst Winery

Stellenbosch (see Helderberg map) ▪ 1stB 1992 ▪ Tasting & sales Mon-Fri 9-4 Sat & public holidays 'take a chance' 9-4 ▪ Self-catering guest cottage ▪ Owner/winemaker Jeremy Walker (1992) ▪ Viti consultant Thys Greeff ▪ 13 ha (cab, merlot, mourvèdre, petit v, pinotage, shiraz) ▪ 50-60 tons ±3 500 cs 100% red ▪ PO Box 206 Stellenbosch 7599 ▪ winery@grangehurst.co.za ▪ www.grangehurst.co.za © 855·3625 ▤ 855·2143

Jeremy Walker is really looking forward to this harvest, the start of the second phase in Grangehurst's history: crushing the first grapes from Sunset Vineyard. This 13 ha of own prime red Stellenbosch terroir includes shiraz, mourvèdre and petit verdot, grapes not previously in the Walker repertoire. At full production in 2008, Sunset should provide half of Grangehurst's goal of 140 tons, and possibly contribute to Walker's immediate aim of further improving the image and quality of his Nikela red blend (a significant proportion of pinotage reflects his support of the variety's contribution to a Cape Blend). Constant tweaking — typical of this explorative mind — includes a new sorting table 'to remove diseased/unripe grapes and MOG (Material Other than Grapes) pre-crushing'. All in aid of better expression of fruit, and slightly earlier-approachable wines. 'Accessibility will not be overdone, however, as we do not intend to release our wines until they are at least 3 years old. We want them to be capable of improving for at least 8 years from the vintage.'

★★★★★ **Nikela** 'Tribute', in Xhosa, to Jeremy Walker's late parents. Blend cab (50+%), pinotage, merlot, from 4 Stbosch areas. Deep-coloured, engaging **00** (38% pinotage) drinking well, red berries over ripely firm tannins. 14% alc. Should keep happily 5+ yrs yet. (Consumers of these enjoy big advantage in their comparatively late release.) Tasted once more, **99** (★★★★), with 32% pinotage, also bright sweet red fruit, solid tannins, but showing now as less substantial, though will give pleasurable drinking for few yrs. These ±2 yrs oak, including some Am.

★★★★★ **Cabernet Sauvignon-Merlot 00** still youthful, but authoritative & satisfying, sombrely rich fruit well balanced with grippy tannins, savoury acid, big 14.2% alc. No hurry to drink. 27 mths oak (mostly Fr) finely integrated. 80% cab, as is retasted **99**. This now maturing well & elegantly, with sweet blackcurrant fruit, though lesser concentration. 13.8% alc. Grapes for these mostly ex Hldrberg, Firgrove.

★★★★ **Pinotage** Serious-minded, restrained version, with splash cab; grapes from own, Hldrberg, Firgrove vyds. As with all these, fermented in open *kuipe*. Pleasing soft sweet fruit of **00** layered on big dry tannins; greater harmony will hopefully come. 14% alc; 14 mths oak, quarter Am. No **99. 98** elegant with good grip & soft fine tannins. As with all above wines, also available in magnums.

★★★★ **CWG Auction Reserve Cabernet Sauvignon** Since **95**, the only outlet for Walker's Cab. Oak still dominates firm, supple **01**, masking the fruit which undoubtedly there. Like **00**, ripe & balanced with well-focused acidity, wanting few yrs to reveal its best. 14% alc (00 had 14.5%); ± 22 mths Fr oak, 80% new.

★★★★ **CWG Auction Blend** First since **99**, the **01** a happy ménage à trois of cab, pinotage, shiraz (49/37/14). Deep-coloured, youthful, fruit excitingly forward on nose leading to freshly, well & elegantly structured mouthful. Plenty of flavour, & of savoury ripe tannins. Like all Walker's wines, genuinely dry. Serious wine for long term. 26 mths oak, 69% new, some Am.

★★★★ **Chairman's Reserve Cabernet Sauvignon 00** Fine, handsome bottling mostly for a private organisation; Hldrberg vyds. Attractively fresh bouquet blackcurrant, touched with spicy cedar. Well structured, balanced, wearing 14.5% alc quite gracefully. 27 mths Fr/Am (75/25) wood. Also magnums. 5+ years to go. — TJ

Green Field see Origin Wine
Green Wine see Ladismith
Griekwaland West Co-op see Douglas
Groblershoop see Oranjerivier Wine Cellars
Groene Cloof see Cloof
Groenekloof see Darling Cellars, Neil Ellis, Vinfruco, Woolworths

Groenland

Stellenbosch ▪ Est 1932 ▪ 1stB 1997 ▪ Tasting & sales Mon-Fri 10-4 Sat & public holidays 10-1 ▪ Fee for large groups ▪ Closed Easter Fri/Sun, Dec 25, Jan 1 ▪ Meals for 20-60 by appt; also BYO picnics ▪ Tours by appt ▪ Conference & reception facilities ▪ Owner Kosie Steenkamp ▪ Winemaker Kosie Steenkamp, with Piet & Marié Steenkamp (1975/2001/ 2003) ▪ Viticulturists Kosie & Piet Steenkamp ▪ 152 ha (cab, merlot, pinotage, shiraz, chard, chenin, sauvignon) ▪ 1 050 tons 3 600 cs + 54 000l 100% red ▪ PO Box 4 Kuils River 7579 ▪ steenkamp@groenland.co.za ▪ www.groenland.co.za © 903·8203 🖷 903·0250 Wishing to be more hands-on, the Steenkamp family are assuming key responsibilities from their long-time joint venture partners, KWV. They're determined, however, to maintain a high standard and (fans will be pleased) the signature Groenland style. Daughter Marié, a qualified winemaker also involved in sales and marketing, winemaker Kosie, assisted by son Piet, declare: 'If the wines aren't good enough, we'll take them off the market.' The farm is a 'Green Land' in name and in deed, with colourful rose gardens, a tasting room folded into a converted reservoir and an entertainment venue (open for bookings of 20-60 people) where wife Heléne serves up country cuisine.

★★★★ **Cabernet Sauvignon 00** (★★★), retasted, brick-red rim, nose fairly evolved; some meaty hints; lighter than follow-up **02**, densely fruited but minerally, unshowy yet attractive.

★★★★ **Shiraz** New World in fruit/wood-approach. **01** well-oaked (yr Am, half new), ripe tannins for immediate enjoyment, with ability to age. **02** (★★★) opaque plum colour; vibrant ribena fruit; overtly fruity, good Am wood backing (yr, 1st/2nd fill) yet just a shade less complex, interesting.

★★★★ **Antoinette Marié 01** a 60/40 cab/shiraz blend, neither holding back; retasted, shows as ultra-ripe, with slight leafy edge acting as a toner; Merlot joins in **02** for a 51/40/9 composition; cab dominates on paper & taste; sweet fruited, again a slight herbaceous whiff, understated wood, dry tight finish. Yr 1st/2nd fill oak.

Groot Constantia Estate

Constantia ▪ Est 1685 ▪ 1stB 1688 ▪ Tasting & sales daily 9-6 (Dec-Apr) 9-5 (May-Nov) ▪ Fee R25 , R30 (tasting & tour) ▪ Closed Easter Fri, Dec 25 & Jan 1 ▪ Tours on hour, every hour 10-4 (summer); 10, 11 & 3 (winter); or by appt. Also new 'theme' tours/tastings (see intro) ▪ Simon's at Groot Constantia Restaurant © 794·1143 (see intro); also BYO picnic ▪ Tourgroups ▪ Gift shop ▪ Conferencing ▪ Walks ▪ Museum ▪ Managed by Groot Constantia ('Section 21' co) ▪ Winemaker Boela Gerber (Jan 2001), with Therese Swart (Jan 2002) ▪ Viticulturists Callie Bröcker & Boela Gerber, advised by Johan Pienaar (1996) ▪ ±90 ha (12 varieties, r/w) ▪ 600 tons 42 000 cs 60% red 40% white ▪ *Export brands: Nova Constantia & Hoop op Constantia* ▪ *Private Bag X1 Constantia 7848* ▪ *cellar@grootconstantia.co.za* ▪ *www.grootconstantia.co.za* ▪ ✆ *794·5128* 📠 *794·1999*

'It really put the winemaker's patience to the test,' says Boela Gerber of vintage 2004. The waiting game had its rewards, however, with 'amazing complexity' on the reds, sauvignon and chardonnay. The winery has seen big changes in the interests of more red fermentation space, 'to allow longer skin contact on the reds for better extraction and integration'. Big changes, too, in the leisure area – a new restaurant, Simon's at Groot Constantia, offers lunches (al fresco or indoors) and dinner, as well as breakfast over the weekends (but do your own picnic thing if you prefer). More visitor entertainment is provided by a DVD system now operating in the tasting room and the Bertrams Cellar. Group evening tastings are conducted in the Manor House by staff dressed in period costume.

Gouverneurs range

★★★★ **Gouverneurs Reserve** Modern-style Bdx blend – 65/35 cab/merlot in **01**. Cedar, vanilla, mocha overlay to blackcurrants, red berries. Well-knit blend muscular tannins, balanced acidity, promises fine development over 5-7 yrs. 14.1% alc. 18 mths new Fr barrels impart obvious oak tone, in youth at least. Unfiltered, as are most of the premium reds.

★★★★ **Gouverneurs Merlot** Opaque **01**, cassis & spicy oak on nose. Lithe & graceful, rich warm fruit, savoury, ripely soft tannins. Big 14.5% alc. Last year's worries about excessive wood unfounded when tasted yr on – absorbed with ease. 18 mths Fr. Diners Club Winemaker of the Year award 2002. CWT gold 2003.

★★★★ **Gouverneurs Shiraz 02** dark-berried allure with depth & resonance, given luxurious oaking, but fruit density will ensure full integration. Picked riper at 14.1% alc (vs 13.6% for regular), fruit-sweet, spicy; clever tannins allow for earlier accessibility. 18 mths Fr, all new. **01** sweet, spicy fruit, lingering finish. Worth ageing 3-6 yrs.

★★★★ **Gouverneurs Reserve Chardonnay** Latest **03** rather quiet on nose, though palate more generous; ripe citrus, touch toasty wood, creamy length. 10 mths Fr oak, 70% new. **02** exuberant & rich, but overwhelmed by toasty wood.

Groot Constantia range

★★★★ **Cabernet Sauvignon** Mulberry ripeness on **02**, oak well tucked away, shows the variety's firmer tannins, but here worked to accessible levels. **01** pleasingly big-bodied, firmly constructed. 13-15 mths in barrel, high proportion new. Cellar 3-6 yrs, otherwise only ready for the impatient.

★★★★ **Merlot** Ripe choc mint immediate impression, follows through onto **02** palate, deceptively easy: this no pushover, fine dry tannins come back on finish. Thoughtful winemaking showcases grape's ample charms. Yr Fr oak, 60% new.

★★★★ **Shiraz** Black cherry fruit invitation in **02**, though still quite closed, rich & ripe, crammed with blackberries, cherries, oak very subtle. **01** more emphatic at same stage, more accessible, but also more obvious oak. Yr oak mostly Fr, 40% new.

★★★★ **Pinotage** Latest **02** with warm plummy fruit, telltale sweetness of the variety, full-bodied & fleshy, leaning towards cinsaut parent. Soft, ultra-ripe tannins, unobtrusive. Ready. Watch alc at 14.5%. Yr oak, mostly Fr, 60% new.

★★★★ **Sauvignon Blanc** Never aggressive, but shows distinctiveness. **04** deceptively slender, but decently ripe at 13.7% alc; taut, swingeingly dry, lip-smacking, textbook sauvignon at its exuberant best. **03** similarly elegant & fine.

★★★★ **Semillon-Sauvignon Blanc** NEW Individual & stylish, unoaked **03** 60/40 blend, nuances of tropical fruit & signature lanolin of semillon, still youthful, bone-dry & creamy. Wine for grown-ups. Preview of **04** (sample) more tropical, more focused; winemaker onto a winner here.

★★★★ **Weisser Riesling 03** last vintage to be made, bids farewell with a flourish. Semi-sweet, heavily botrytised, pineapple & mint aromas/flavours, rich & unctuous with firm acidity (10g/ℓ), should age beautifully. Alc 14.4%.

★★★★ **Cap Classique** Last tasted was an NV (00); rich style, not quite bone-dry.

★★★★ **Cape Ruby Port 02** unclassically a vintaged ruby, more like an LBV in style. Sweetish & definitely moreish; caramel & toffee flavours, ready to drink. Tinta/touriga. 18.9% alc.

Merlot-Shiraz ★★★ Generous & approachable, fruity choc mint flavours, **02** well structured; yr older wood. **Constantia Rood** ★★★ Cab/merlot with pinotage, early drinking & crowd pleasing style, soft, fruity, yet showcases classy fruit in latest **02**; yr older wood; 13.5% alc. **Blanc de Noir** ★★ Palest shell pink **04** (sample), off-dry & soft. Soft fruit pastille flavours, from cab & merlot. **Chardonnay** ★★★ Ripe citrus, modest oak in juicy **03**, fleshy but lively. **04** (sample) similarly structured, but more tropical. **Bouquet Blanc** ★★★ Latest **04** off-dry rather than sweet, seductive rose-petal/incense perfumes. Lightish, from morio muscat. **Constantia Blanc** discontinued. — *IvH*

▪ *Grootdrink* see Oranjerivier Wine Cellars

Groot Eiland Winery

Goudini (see Worcester map) ▪ Est 1962 ▪ 1stB 1980 ▪ Tasting & sales Mon-Fri 8-5 ▪ Closed public holidays ▪ Tours by appt ▪ Meals by appt or BYO picnic ▪ Gifts ▪ Owners 30 members ▪ Winemakers Erik Schlünz & Albertus Louw (2000/2003), with Lyndi Kotzé & Johan Möller (both 2003) ▪ Viti consultant Johan Möller (2003) ▪ 1 000 ha (cab, merlot, pinotage, shiraz, chard, chenin, colombard, sauvignon) ▪ 50 000 cs own label 30% red 50% white 20% rosé ▪ PO Box 93 Rawsonville 6845 ▪ grooteiland@lando.co.za ▪ www.grooteiland.co.za ℗ **(023) 349-1140** 🖷 (023) 349-1801

A bravo for the product followed honours for the man (manager/winemaker Erik Schlünz was named winemaker of the year for the Worcester area in 2003) when the chardonnay 03 was awarded a Veritas gold. History awards the winery a silver — the Groot Eiland Co-op bottled its first wine 25 years ago. There were considerable changes as the anniversary approached — Albertus Louw as winemaker, and Lyndi Kotzé and Johan Möller as assistants joined the winemaking team, and a new red cellar provided them with more space. Next is a marketing drive both locally and abroad to promote the Groot Eiland brand (recently given a new label) and the new trio in the Meander range (Fruity Red, Fruity White and Crisp Dry).

Cabernet Sauvignon ★★★ Sweet spice, lavender, greenpepper, whiff bluegum — all in bouquet of **03**, aromas transfer to palate with earthy hint, pleasing roundness. **Merlot** ★★★ Cherry-choc nose with floral hint echoes on **03** palate, supple fruit-sweetness well tempered by tannin. **Pinotage** ★★★ Soft, malleable **03**, sweet red berry nose & hint vanilla. **Shiraz** ★★★ Well-expressed, ripe black/red berry mix with smoky oak backing, **03** fullish bodied, lengthy savoury finish. **Rosé** ★★★ Semi- (not too-) sweet **04** offers pretty strawberry & candyfloss aromas, balanced refreshment. **Chardonnay** ★★★ **04**'s lovely ripe peach & orange fragrance marred by over-wooded palate, vanilla dominating everything. 14.2% alc. **Sauvignon Blanc** ★★★ **04** attractive combo of ripe fig, grass & lemon, rounded yet lively, enjoy in its youth. **Honigtraube** ★★ Light-bodied **03**, very retiring nose, peaches & pineapples in mouth, easy drinking semi-sweet. **Hanepoot Jerepigo** ★★★★ Still-youthful **02**, honeysuckle, dried apricots & raisins all delightfully present on nose & in silk-smooth palate.16.8% alc.

Meander range

Fruity Red ★★★ Yes, it's fruity; **02** red berries, full, generous; nice earthy touch too; enjoy while youthfully fresh. **Crisp Dry** ★★★ Suitably crisp & dry **04**, with tropical fruit tones, apple zest finish. **Fruity White** ★★ Sweeter version of above; nicely balanced **04**. — *DH*

Groote Post Vineyards

Darling (see Swartland map) ▪ 1stB 1999 ▪ Tasting & sales Mon-Fri 9-5 Sat 9-2.30 ▪ Closed Easter Fri-Mon, Dec 25 & Jan 1 ▪ Fee R10 for groups of 10+ ▪ Groote Post Restaurant (see Eat-out section) or BYO picnic ▪ Tours by appt ▪ Facilities for children ▪ Tourgroups (max 40 people) ▪ Farm produce ▪ Conferencing ▪ Walks ▪ Conservation area ▪ Mountain biking ▪

Owners Peter & Nicholas Pentz ▪ Winemaker Lukas Wentzel (Nov 2000) ▪ Jannie de Clerk, advised by Johan Pienaar (1999) ▪ 100 ha (cab, merlot, pinot, shiraz, chard, chenin, sauvignon) ▪ 430 tons 26 000 cs 40% red 60% white ▪ PO Box 103 Darling 7345 ▪ gpwines@wcaccess.co.za ▪ www.grootpost.com ⓒ (022) 492·2825 🖷 (022) 492·2693

At the end of a long dusty road, a postcard-perfect West Coast *werf*, with an up-and-coming winery housed in a Dutch East India Company fort. Winemaker Lukas Wentzel, after a protracted harvest, announced 2004 a vintage to remember: 'Our red vines came of age; the fruit shows much more complexity and depth.' Future excitement is promised by promising new blocks of sauvignon. Supplementary irrigation, used for the first time in 2004, aids the winemaker's goal of 'balance from vineyard to bottle.' Co-owner Nick Pentz says more is being done to bring visitors to the farm. Game and wildflower tours are laid on, and the award-winning Hilda's Kitchen, run by Prue Leith-trained Debbie McLaughlin, is drawing a lengthening stream of diners through its 18th-century doors.

★★★★ **Chardonnay** ✓ Delicious **03** continues impressive trend with intensity, vigour. Shot through with pungent lemon/lime, crushed nuts; palate richness tempered by food-friendly acidity. Deftly oaked; 8 mths *sur lie* maturation, adds weight, flavour, creates harmonious whole. FCTWS gold. **02** complex & inviting; fleshy with loads of juicy fruit. Bunch-pressed. **01** (★★★★) had slightly less definition, vibrancy.

The Old Man's Blend ☺ ★★★ Anytime wine to 'drink on the stoep with your old man'. **02** mainly merlot, touch pinot, cab s; toasty vanilla & juicy cherry/mulberry fruit happily co-exist; ripe but firm tannins. Half blend oaked, yr seasoned barrels.

Merlot ★★★★ **02** seductive berry-choc perfume, whiffs creamy spice; ripe dark-fruited flavours framed by firm tannins. Potential to age 3/4 yrs, but already drinking well. 13 mths Fr oak. 14.5% alc. Young vines. **Shiraz** ★★★★ **02** succulent cherries/black plums, tantalising smoky notes, roasted fennel. Creamy fruit cloaks tannins, amenable but more than able to handle 4+ yrs ageing. Yr equal Fr/Am oak. 14.5% alc. Also in 375ml, 1.5ℓ. **Cabernet Sauvignon-Merlot** NEW ★★★ **02** though cab dominates (70%), both grapes are in play: freshly picked berries, touch mint, light dusting cedar. Vibrant, fleshy, to enjoy at youthful best, though there's structure for some ageing. 13 mths Fr oak. 14% alc. **Chenin Blanc** ★★★ Easy drinking style. **03**, yr on, melon character taken on slight honeyed tone. Juicy palate drinking well. Unoaked, bone- dry. 13% alc. Above WO Coastal, following Darling: **Pinot Noir** ★★★★ **03** charms with piquant red berry, forest floor typicity, juicy, lively palate. Elegantly structured, enough oak backbone (10 mths used Fr) to age ±3 yrs. 13.5% alc. Off ocean-facing vyd, 490m above sea level. **Chardonnay Unwooded** ★★★ **04** greets with freshly sliced peaches, dash lemon; continue onto palate, tasty, varietally true. 14% alc. **Sauvignon Blanc** ★★★ **04** appealing Cape gooseberry, summer fruit salad fragrance/flavours, with expected refreshing lift on finish. Friendly, soft textured. 13.5% alc. **03** MIWA gold. — *CR*

▓ *Groot Geluk* see Vinfruco
Grootgenoegen see Cape Wine Cellars

Groot Parys

Paarl ▪ Est 1699 ▪ 1stB 2003 ▪ Closed to public ▪ Owners Eric Verhaak & Peter & Mariëtte Ras ▪ Vini consultant Naudé Bruwer ▪ Viti consultant Gawie Kriel ▪ 64 ha (ruby cab, chard, chenin, colombard, hanepoot, sauvignon, semillon) ▪ 900 tons ±1 500 cs ▪ Export brand: Die Tweede Droom ▪ PO Box 82 Huguenot 7645 ▪ grootparys@wam.co.za ▪ www.grootparys.co.za ⓒ🖷 872·7140

Good news for this historic property is that a re-direction of nearby Jan van Riebeeck Drive will remove the busy thoroughfare from the immediate vicinity, galvanising the owners to go ahead with a 32-home development to help finance the restoration of the 'stunning but rundown' original Groot Parys homestead. The trio are also pretty pleased with their own-label wines: a second-vintage Chenin and maiden Chardonnay, intentionally made in a light, fresh style by Boland's Naudé Bruwer. 'It really helps improve wine quality if your vineyard practices are up to standard', notes Mariëtte Ras, listing new farm manager Hein Basson as another positive development.

Die Tweede Droom range
Chardonnay Unwooded NEW ★★★★ Intense pinned pineapple aroma & hint camomile; clean tropical flavours, ripe & enjoyable; **04** shows more intensity, character than most. **Chenin Blanc** ★★★★ **04** archetypical Paarl chenin: lifted ripe-tropical nose with guava uppermost, good concentration, long finish, balanced. Both tasted as samples. — *JB*

Grünberger

Originally developed for the Bergkelder, now part of Distell, by German oenologist Alfred Baumgartner, hence the Frankish 'bocksbeutel' bottles for the non-spritzy wines. All are off-dry or semi-sweet, and quaffably light.

> **Rosenlese** ☺ ★★★ Sauvignon, splash ruby cab supplies the coral hue; **04** fruit pastille flavours & appealing sweet-sour cranberry tang. **Freudenlese** ☺ ★★★ Latest **04** also mainly sauvignon, with gewürz/muscadel for perfume; zesty, lots of life, grip & flavour. Both Natural Sweet; varieties mentioned on the label.

Stein ★★ **03** chenin, riesling, gewürz mix, now with perfectly pleasant honeyed bottle-age, round melon flavours, fresh finish. **Spritziger** ★★★ Lightly petillant poolside sipper; delicate **03** still crisp, refreshing if fairly ordinary. Screwcap. All WO W-Cape. — *CR*

Grundheim Wines

Oudtshoorn (see Little Karoo map) ▪ Est/1stB 1995 ▪ Tasting & sales Mon-Fri 8-5 Sat 9-1 ▪ Fee R10 for groups of 10+ ▪ Closed Easter Sun, Dec 25 & Jan 1 ▪ Owner Danie Grundling ▪ Winemaker Dys Grundling (1997) ▪ 25 ha (cinsaut, tinta, touriga, ruby cab, r/w muscadel, colombard, hanepoot, palomino) ▪ 360 tons 10 000ℓ for own labels 100% fortified ▪ PO Box 400 Oudtshoorn 6620 ▪ grundheim@absamail.co.za ©/🖷 (044) 272-6927

Grundheim celebrates its 10th anniversary this year, though many of the vines on the farm are much older: some muscadels and cinsaut are veritable geriatrics at 50-60 years. Most of the grapes are made into fortified muscadels and jerepigos, but owner Danie Grundling, a master distiller, recently produced an unusual kosher wine spirit, possibly the only one made in SA. This to join amusingly named favourites like Danie se Withond (the eponymous bull terrier charmingly featured en famille on the front-label). In the maturation cellar there's been a switch to oak barrels for the ageing of the sweet wines.

Red Muscat ★★★ Subtitled 'Muscat de Frontignan'. **95** lovely tawny hues; aromas of Karoo bush & raisins, soft caramel texture. ±17% alc. **Red Jerepigo** ★★★★ ✓ Silky & characterful fireside warmer crammed with damson & dark choc, whiffs mint. NV. 17% alc. Ruby cab & tinta. **White Muscadel** ★★★ Attractive **98** redolent of spice, herbs & grapefruit; palate more straightforwardly sweet, with barley-sugar flavours. **Golden Jerepigo** ★★★★ ✓ White muscadel in full sunshine mode; wafts of spice & raisins; packed with flavour. NV. **Cape Ruby** ★★★ Rich & sweet with sniff of mint, distinctly warming. Also available, not tasted: **Classic Red, Chenin Blanc, Late Harvest** & **Cape Vintage**. — *DH*

▮ *Guardian* see Lost Horizons

Guardian Peak

Stellenbosch ▪ Est/1stB 1998 ▪ Closed to public ▪ Owner Rust & Vrede Estate ▪ Winemaker Louis Strydom, with Ettienne Malan (1998/2002) ▪ Viti consultant Paul Wallace (1999) ▪ 35 000 cs own label ▪ 100% red ▪ PO Box 473 Stellenbosch 7599 ▪ info@guardianpeak.com ▪ www.guardianpeak.com © 881-3148 🖷 881-3000

Shiraz is the star for winemakers Louis Strydom and Ettienne Malan at this reds-only operation, following a New World style. The star shone especially bright last harvest: 'Good berry and ripe fruit flavours', comments marketer Duncan Woods, 'and good tannins'. The range is one of those frequently singled out by wine retailers as remarkable for its value and quality.

★★★★ **Syrah-Mourvèdre-Grenache** Rhône-style blend made mark with first, distinctive **01**; VDG; FCTWS 2003 gold. **02** satisfyingly savoury, fleshy; rounded tannins for current drinking, further 2-3 yrs. Preview promising **03** equal syrah/mourvèdre, 10% unoaked grenache (ex-Ctrsdal), very ripe, reverberating flavours — rare roast beef, blood, iron notes; richly textured; robust but supple. 14.5% alc. Fr/Am oak, some new, 13 mths.

★★★★ **Frontier** ✓ 'Cabernet Sauvignon-Shiraz-Merlot' in last ed. Sample classy **03** (possible ★★★★); finely nuanced mocha, soft dark berry. Rich, intense with elegant, tapered length. Cab, shiraz, merlot (43/42/15); partly oaked. 13.9% alc. Dbnvlle; Elgin; Klawer; Stbosch vyds. **02** structured; drinks well.

★★★★ **Merlot** ✓ **03** striking dark clarity; vibrant tannin/oak support to pure plum/mulberry juiciness; good now & yr/2. 9 mths oak. Ex-Stbosch/Klawer. 14% alc.

★★★★ **Shiraz** ✓ **03** expressive, ripe fusion meat/spice/smoke; broad generous flavours satisfyingly controlled by freshness, grip; subtle oaking. Enjoyable without being over-complicated. Yr used Fr/Am oak. Klawer; Dbnvlle vyds. 14.5% alc — *AL*

Gusto Wines

Stellenbosch ▪ Est 2001 ▪ 1stB 2002 ▪ Tasting by appt ▪ Owners PG Slabbert & Nicolette de Kock ▪ Winemaker Nicolette de Kock ▪ Viticulturist PG Slabbert ▪ 500 cs 30% red 70% white ▪ PO Box 6045 Uniedal 7612 ▪ gustowines@hotmail.com ✆ 082·807·4447 🖷 883·8965

There's no stopping a girl with gusto. Certainly not Nicolette de Kock, who has Italian-Afrikaner roots. Her close friend and wine-partner PG Slabbert, by day winemaker and manager of Stellenbosch Hills, has had to scale back his involvement with this after-hours venture (though he still advises). So NdK has stepped forward and, in spite her own demanding career (CE of the Stellenbosch Wine Routes and chair of the SA Wine Routes Forum), made the 2004 wines. 'Wine to me is passion,' says she, echoing Robert Mondavi. 'And making my own gives me immeasurable pleasure.'

★★★★ **Destino** Unshowy maiden **01**, tasty merlot/cab blend ex-Stbosch, developing well on retasting, still room to go. Vegetal & earthy tints to warm red berries; savoury fresh acidity, unassertively firm tannins. 16 mths Fr oak, 70% new, not too obvious; 13.5% alc.

★★★★ **Sauvignon Blanc** ✓ Cool grass & warm tropical fruits, limey green core noted last ed on balanced, friendly but not frivolous or too overt **03**. Previewed **04**, also Stbosch grapes, exuberantly flavourful, promising well. 14% alc. — *TJ*

Hagelsberg see Middelvlei
Hakuna Matata see Remhoogte

Hamilton Russell Vineyards

Hemel-en-Aarde Valley (see Walker Bay map) ▪ Est 1975 ▪ 1stB 1981 ▪ Tasting & sales Mon-Fri 9-5 Sat 9-1 ▪ Also tasting/sales of estate cheese & olive oil ▪ Closed Easter Fri/Sun, Dec 25/26 & Jan 1 ▪ Tours by appt ▪ BYO picnic by appt ▪ Conservation area ▪ Owner Anthony Hamilton Russell ▪ Winemaker Hannes Storm (2004) ▪ Viticulturist Noeil Vorster (April 2002) ▪ 52 ha (pinot, chard) ▪ 150 tons 13 500 cs 40% red 60% white ▪ PO Box 158 Hermanus 7200 ▪ hrv@ hermanus.co.za ✆ (028) 312·3595 🖷 (028) 312·1797

How fitting to celebrate 30 years of winemaking with five stars in this guide for your duo of internationally acclaimed wines. Let's recall Johannesburg-based adman Tim Hamilton Russell's pioneering of the Hemel-en-Aarde Valley's virgin viticultural territory, via world-class Cape-Burgundies, back in 1975. For 15 years he challenged a conservative, over-regulated, parochial industry, becoming an international player long before Cape wine went global. Succeeding his father as HRV's caretaker in the early 1990, Anthony

HR donned the same mantle (in a more progressive, competitive, free-thinking environment). But more tellingly, he early verbalised his father's idea of wines showing 'individuality and expression of origin', the mantra that has become de rigeur in local cellars. Recently though, the son has adopted his own cause, becoming a champion of SA's pinotage. Synonymous with his Southern Right venture, it's being groomed for a star role in a what promises to be a seminal Cape red. Bastenburg — the maiden 2001 is pure pinotage — 'will earn a place on its own' (apart from HRV and SR) soon. Its maker, HRV cellar helmsman for 10 years, Kevin Grant, has left this new challenge in the capable hands of former assistant Hannes Storm.

★★★★★ **Pinot Noir 03** (★★★★★) similar to **97** as a vintage, but with longest ever hangtime. Full, well defined & better focused than pvs. Classy mineral tone; obvious wood, but integrated; excellent structure & balance. Would benefit from cellaring. At 2 800 cs, an all-time production low. 50% new Fr oak. **02** reticent on release, retasted mid-2004, light but sound pinot fruit, elegant. Reflects weakness of vintage, but still very creditable. Extraordinary **01** world class, with perfume seldom seen outside Burgundy. Standout **00** stunningly scented, remarkably complex. Since **99**, only Dijon clones (777, 115, 113 and 667 — all pvs 'champagne' BK5).

★★★★★ **Chardonnay** Marks 21st vintage having been rated Best SA White Wine with a Track Record by panel of SA experts in *Grape* magazine poll. **03** a very smart wine. Noticeable oak, but with integrated, toasty, silky qualities. Delicately complex; lovely structure & a stony minerality, ringing freshness. 100% barrel-fermented; 43% new oak, rest 2nd/3rd fill. **02** (★★★★★) Old World feel; delicate aromas & refined, splendid wood integration, gentle creaminess & well focused finish. Terrific **01**, expressive mineral-and-toast bouquet & fine thread. — *RK*

Hartenberg Estate

Stellenbosch ▪ *1stB 1978* ▪ *Tasting & sales Mon-Fri 9-5 Sat 9-3* ▪ *Nominal tasting fee for groups, refunded with purchase* ▪ *Closed Easter Fri/Sun, Dec 25 & Jan 1* ▪ *Vintners lunches (al fresco, weather permitting) Mon-Sat 12-2 (picnic platters in summer; soup & vetkoek in winter); booking advisable* ▪ *Owner Hartenberg Holdings* ▪ *Winemaker Carl Schultz, with Jaco van der Merwe (Jun 1993/Jan 2001)* ▪ *Viticulturist Frans Snyman (1996)* ▪ *95 ha (cab, merlot, pinotage, shiraz, chard, riesling, sauvignon)* ▪ *500 tons 42 000 cs 72% red 26% white 2% rosé* ▪ *PO Box 69 Koelenhof 7605* ▪ *info@hartenbergestate.com* ▪ *www.hartenbergestate.com* ©
865·2541 🖷 865·2153

Broadening its horizons, the Hartenberg team's been on the move. Cellar assistant Patrick Ngamane, beneficiary of the Patrick Grubb Scholarship, spent the 2003 French vintage at Château d'Angludet in the Médoc; assistant winemaker Jaco van der Merwe had three months with acclaimed Californian merlot specialists Duckhorn Vineyards; and winemaker Carl Schultz went from a technical conference in Melbourne to an international shiraz producers' huddle in the Barossa (compatriots Charles Back and Kevin Arnold also invited). On the home front, tasting-room duo Sonnette Rabe and Margie Kroesen made two barrels of wine in 2004, doing everything themselves from picking to punch-down. And there was play as well as work: Schultz kayaked the length of the Fish River Canyon (while in flood) and participated in the first descent, through the Swartberg, of the Gamka River, while viticulturist and Bisley shottist Frans Snyman was awarded national colours. And the wine? The wine's fine, thank you, partly due to their conviction that 'the magic has to happen in the vineyard. There are no tricks. It's a matter of hands-on common sense'.

★★★★ **Cabernet Sauvignon** Classic cassis/mulberry intensity in **02**, cedar tones, some fennel & coriander spicing. Elegant, juicy, lively, everything in harmony. Misleadingly friendly — oaking has longer-term intentions. 19 mths Fr, half new. 13.8% alc. **01** classy, statement wine; tightly knit, yrs to go. SAA red wine trophy. Subtler cassis in notably ripe **00**, with thicker texture. These built to last 7+ yrs.

★★★★ **Merlot** Much garlanded version, firmly built but fruit filled. **02** rich plum, dark choc depths, creamy spice. Sleekly muscular; although the tannins are ripe, this is a keeper, 6+ yrs. Malo/matured Fr barrels 15 mths, half new. 13.6% alc. **01** was hard to resist but would reward keeping 5+ yrs. VDG.

★★★★ **Pinotage** Particular attention & research from cellar to create richly flavoured non-traditional style. Young vines (first crop **01**), but focus already showing some results in **02**. Piquant, dark-fruited rhubarb pie flavours, slightly gamey. 15.2% alc easily assimilated. Palate smoothly accessible, balanced, yet with underlying structure for 4+ yrs cellaring. Mainly Fr barrels, 50% new, 17 mths.

★★★★★ **Shiraz** Serious but unshowy, with spicy earthiness adding character, justifying Schultz's favouritism here. **02** back to house style. More restrained than pvs but no less impressive: complex layers roast veg, prosciutto, smoky spice; seductively creamy fruit appears on palate. Svelte structure, but iron fist in velvet glove, with good 6+ yr potential. Fr oak for malo/maturation 60% new, 16 mths. 13.6% alc. **01** a taste sensation; gold at CWT.

★★★★★ **CWG Auction Reserve Gravel Hill Shiraz** From single vyd with gravelly red soil ('Poorest on the property, producing our best wine' according to Schultz). **02** as impressive as **01** but more savoury. Intensely perfumed, nuances of violets, white pepper, wild scrub, all interacting with dark fruit base. Fruit shines through on palate, svelte tannins provide framework. Has refinement & class. Oak as for **01**, wondrously perfumed; succulent, lithe, structure to age but utterly delicious now. 16 mths Fr barriques, 60% new. Both 14.5% alc.

★★★★ **Zinfandel** ✓ One of Cape's more idiosyncratic offerings. **00** final vintage, 18 yr old vyd now ripped out. 'Best yet' opines Schultz; opulent richness supports claim. Multi-faceted: dried herbs, savoury prunes, vie for attention with maraschino cherries/wild berries; all held together with sturdy framework of 19 mths Am barrique treatment. 15.5% alc not obvious, masked by fruit. One to savour. **99** also burst with flavour, billowed spice.

★★★★ **Cabernet Sauvignon-Merlot 03** not ready for tasting. Last was **95**, 60/40 blend.

★★★★ **Cabernet Sauvignon-Shiraz** Revisited **02** shows unabated roasted spice, shiraz brambleberry fruit focus, herbal notes from cab (59/41). Integrated tannins, lively, smooth, very drinkable. 80/20 Fr/Am oak, yr. 13.5% alc.

★★★★ **Chardonnay Reserve** From premium vyd blocks, only in best vintages. Next will be **03**, not ready for tasting.

★★★★ **Chardonnay** Bold, concentrated style. **03** layers peach, hazelnuts & wood spice, freshened by limy edginess. Silky, voluptuous body, richly flavoured. Fermented/matured 8 mths new Fr barriques, soupçon Am. Hard to resist, but will age well ±3 yrs. 14% alc. **02** bold, striking; peach/English toffee aromas, lip-smacking lemon/lime flavour intensity. **01** first to be all barrel-fermented, all-new oak 15 mths.

★★★★ **Zinfandel Natural Sweet** NEW ✓ Stylish, different, delicious one-off; vyd now gone, but given last chance after abysmal 2001 crop; 40% botrytised **02** is result. Fruit intensity stops you in your tracks: tangy apricots, orange rind, honeycomb. Red fruit only apparent on palate, with dry, edgy savouriness, crisp acidity, amazing finish of tannin. Good future, 6+yrs. 42g/ℓ sugar, 9.9g/ℓ acid, 15.1% alc. 500ml.

Chatillon ☺ ★★★ Easy-drinking characterful white. **03** lighter toned than pvs; mainly sauvignon, semillon. Peardrop tones, pepped up by leafy freshness of sauvignon.

Sauvignon Blanc ★★★★ Piquant Cape gooseberries, sliced pears assail senses in **04** but palate main attraction: richly fruity, supple, rounded texture; a great drinking wine, solo or with food. 13.9% alc. **Weisser Riesling** ★★★★ Semi-sweet, friendly rather than racy version of this great variety. **04** very aromatic, tangerine rind perfume leaps out of glass. Softly rounded, flavourful, enough juicy freshness to make it easy. 13.5% alc. **Bin 9** Untasted NV dry red; only ex-estate & Gauteng restaurant, Luca's. **Bin 3** made occasionally. **Pontac** & **L'Estreux** discontinued.—*CR*

Hartswater Wine Cellar

Northern Cape ▪ Tasting & sales Mon-Fri 8.30-5 Sat tasting by appt ▪ Sales also from outlet in Hartswater town; orders delivered to liquor stores in Northern Cape (350km radius), Free State & Pretoria ▪ Tours by appt ▪ Fully licensed restaurant with braai ▪ Conference facilities ▪ Owner Senwes ▪ Winemaker Roelof Maree (1978) ▪ 5 000 tons ▪ PO Box 2335 Hartswater 8570 ▪ wynkelder@senwes.co.za ⓒ (053) 474·0700 🖷 (053) 474·0975

This Northern Cape winery, far away from the traditional Cape Dutch gables and green valleys of the coastal areas, continues to produce surprisingly good value for money. The Hartswater team are involved in an empowerment project with the 11 members of the Schmidtsdrift Claimants' Trust, who recently acquired a winefarm. 'This group of farmers is hugely excited about their vineyard, and quite a bit of expansion is planned in conjunction with the winery,' says cellarmaster Roelof Maree. As for consumer preferences, Maree is convinced Hartswater is on the right track with its lighter style of winemaking. 'It's just right for the SA wine-drinking public.'

Elements range

Earth ☺ ★★★ Dry red with herby (rather than earthy) hint to its red fruits, soft bite of tannin. Pinotage, shiraz, cab. **Fire** ☺ ★★★ Natural Sweet rosé from chenin, pinotage, with slight orange glint, strawberries & cream aromas, crisp finish. Serve well chilled.

Wind ★★ Off-dry chenin-based white with peach blossom aroma; light, juicy, with refreshing lemon acidity. **Rain** ★ Natural Sweet white from chenin, colombard, with soft, somewhat diluted fruit-salad flavours. All above light-bodied, low-alc wines (9.5-12.5%); 'drink now' urges winemaker. NV.

Hinterland range

Chenin Blanc ☺ ★★★ Natural Sweet-style **03** with shy talcum powder nose, ripe fruit salad flavours; very nice zesty acidity.

Ruby Cabernet ★★ **03** has a smoky, almost gunpowder-like aroma with leafy notes & racy — perhaps unbalanced — acidity; demands rich food. **Cabernet Sauvignon**, **Chardonnay**, **Red Jeropigo** & **Port** available but not tasted; neither were **Overvaal Grand Cru**, **Late Harvest**, **Special Late Harvest** (in 3ℓ bag-in-boxes), **Doux Sparkling**. None above wooded. — *TM*

Haut Espoir

Franschhoek ▪ Est 1999 ▪ 1stB 2004 ▪ Tastings & tours by appt; sales Mon-Fri 9-4 (phone ahead) ▪ Owners Ian & Anne Armstrong ▪ Winemaker/viticulturist Nikey van Zyl (Oct 2003), advised by Cathy Marshall & Paul Wallace ▪ 12 ha (cab, merlot, petit v, shiraz) ▪ 40 tons 2 000 cs 70% red 30% white ▪ PO Box 681 Franschhoek 7690 ▪ wine@hautespoir.co.za ▪ www.hautespoir.com ⓒ 876·4000 🖷 876·4038

After four years of intense work, the Armstrong family (Ian and Anne recently joined by their son Rob in a management/marketing capacity) are finally enjoying the fruits of their 'High Hope'. The first harvest of cab and shiraz went without a hitch, and the grapes show great promise. Their spacious new cellar was completed and equipped, and winemaker Nikey van Zyl (advised by Cathy Marshall) was oozing with confidence as he prepped the new tanks and barrels. In 2004 three whites — a Chardonnay Reserve, Sauvignon and Semillon — were made alongside a Syrah and Cab (none tasted for this edition). Though the range will be predominantly red in future, Armstrong is especially delighted with the Chardonnay.

Havana Hills

Tygerberg ▪ Est 1999 ▪ 1stB 2000 ▪ Visits by appt ▪ Owner Kobus du Plessis ▪ Winemaker Nico Vermeulen (Jun 1999) with Joseph Gertse (Jan 2000) ▪ Viticulturist Rudi Benn (2001) ▪ 58 ha (cabs s/f, merlot, mourvèdre, shiraz, pinot, chard, sauvignon) ▪ 120 tons 20

000 cs 85% red 15% white ▪ Export brands: Lime Road 1481 & Virgin Earth ▪ Postnet Suite 57, Pvt Bag X18, Milnerton 7435 ▪ sales@havanahills.co.za © **972·1110** 📠 972·1105

Harvest 2004 was a milestone for this winery in the new Philadelphia ward, cooled by breezes off the Atlantic Ocean. For the first time, all grapes for the Du Plessis and Havana Hills ranges were cropped off their own vineyards. Having made their reputation with red wine, they're placing more emphasis on white. A dedicated white-wine cellar was in the last stages of completion as the guide went to press. Its design uses gravity to move wines and musts from vessel to vessel — there will be nary a pump in sight. In a related move, they planted 8ha of sauvignon. A small block of shiraz was also rooted, reminding that reds continue to rule the roost here — and rake in the competition hardware: owner Kobus du Plessis is delighted that the Du Plessis Reserve Cab-Merlot nabbed the trophy for best Bordeaux blend at the 2004 FCTWS. Adding a Burgundian touch is their first Pinot, maturing in the hold....

★★★★ **Virgin Earth** 🆕 Unique product of grapes grown in Langeberg foothills in the Karoo, fermented in open vats, never pumped. **03**, intriguing cool spearmint nose, with elegant, linear structure braced with similarly cool, svelte fruit. Offers promise, as vyds mature. Cab & merlot (43/37) joined by shiraz, malbec & petit v; yr oak, 30% new.

Du Plessis Reserve range

★★★★★ **Du Plessis** Pvsly 'Cabernet Sauvignon-Merlot'. 55/36 blend, with 9% cab f, carrying own warm West Coast fingerprint. **02** (★★★★) arresting cedar, coffee aromas; balanced, richly textured if less concentrated than deep **01**, FCTWS trophy. **00** (★★★★★) the standout. These all Fr oak-matured, 30% new, 15 mths. ±14% alc.

★★★★ **Cabernet Sauvignon 02** in sappy mode, reviewed mid-2004: aromatic walnut nose now allowing blackcurrant fruit to bloom, juiced berries hang on nicely integrated palate, dry finish. Sufficient substance to grow over 3/4 yrs. **01** classic cab profile; refined power, rich core. **00** *Decanter* ★★★★. Fr oak, 15 mths, 30% new.

★★★★ **Merlot** Power with elegance in **02**, revisited for this ed: structured core encircled by ripe choc-berry/plum flesh, vigorous grip to medium texture in long, bone-dry tail. **01** extremely rich; luscious. 14.3% alc. 15 mths Fr oak-matured, 30% new.

★★★★ **Shiraz** Nuanced & refined, despite regular, hearty 14%-plus alc. Revisited **02**'s plum entrée to a censer of thrilling milled-pepper spice followed by meaty richness built into solid but unaggressive frame. Satisfying dry, savoury length. Oaking settled into Fr/Am 85/15, 30% Fr new, 15 mths. **01** elegant, more minerally, tight.

Havana Hills range

★★★★☆ **Lime Road 1481** Pvsly 'Havana 10'. **02** mainly shiraz, cab (46/39), with fruity lift from merlot. Mid-2004: cherry fullness to fresh spicy/red berry aromatics; supple, grassy tension in savoury finish. 14 mths Fr/Am oak, 30% new.

★★★★ **Sauvignon Blanc 04** in aromatic form, fleshy tropical/gooseberry richness splinted by racy, cut-grass edge. Subtle, without varietal bang, a compatible food partner. **03** quieter; textured, balanced natural verve. Grapes ex-farm & Dbnvlle. 13% alc.

Chardonnay ★★★ **03** individual peachy character to full body, oak (60% wooded, 40% new) well integrated. 14% alc. Discontinued: **Cabernet Sauvignon**, **Merlot**, **Shiraz**.

Bisweni range

In abeyance pending brand redevelopment: not retasted for this ed.

★★★★ **Cabernet Sauvignon** Polished, charismatic, for long haul. **01** (★★★★★) beautifully proportioned; dry finish lends 'claret' lightness to solid 14.5% alc. Fr oak (40% new, 14 mths). Swtlnd/Dbnvlle vyds.

★★★★★ **Merlot 01** opulent, showy; almost a meal in itself. 14.5% alc; oak as above.

Khanya range

Meaning 'shine', range made for specific European export clients, not reviewed for this ed. Last tasted were **Cabernet Sauvignon-Merlot 01**, **Shiraz-Cabernet Sauvignon 01** & **Sauvignon Blanc 03**; all ★★★★. *– DS*

Hazendal

Stellenbosch ▪ Est 1699 ▪ 1stB ca 1950 ▪ Tasting & sales Mon-Fri 8.30-4.30 Sat/Sun 9-3 ▪ Fee R5; R10 incl tour ▪ Tours Mon-Fri 11 & 3 ▪ Closed Easter Fri, Dec 25 & Jan 1 ▪ Hermitage Restaurant (see Eat-out section) ▪ Museum of Russian art & culture ▪ Gifts ▪ Conferencing ▪ 4×4 trail by appt ▪ Owner Mark Voloshin ▪ Vini/viti consultants Ronell Wiid & Schalk du Toit (Jan 1998/ 2000) ▪ 68 ha (cab, merlot, shiraz, chenin, sauvignon) ▪ 400 tons 25 000 cs own label 40% red 60% white ▪ PO Box 336 Stellenbosch 7599 ▪ info@hazendal.co.za ▪ www.hazendal.co.za ℂ 903·5112 ▤ 903·0057

'Very tricky, this 2004 vintage,' frets winemaker Ronell Wiid. 'Weather-wise, it was changing all the time. Probably a bit like a woman — couldn't make up its mind. Oops, this *is* a woman speaking!' Wiid constantly changed her mind about harvest dates (just like a woman?). So much so, the merlot was selectively picked thrice over. Clouding the picture was the mooted sale of the property, bought in 1994 by Russian entrepreneur, Mark Voloshin. 'Never a dull moment at Hazendal,' notes Wiid, wryly. In the end, they did what one should in such circumstances: they threw a party to mark the 10th anniversary of the deeds-signing. Beluga and vodka flowed. Which must have tipped the scales: soon after, the estate was off the market. 'The Russians are staying! Yippee!' whoops Wiid.

★★★★ **Shiraz-Cabernet Sauvignon** ✓ Ripe **00** led by shiraz (51%); striking deep colour; early juicy succulence quietening down to drier savoury appeal, still some gruff tannins when retasted mid-2004, 'maybe it's my winemaking style', remarks Wiid. Only Fr oak (30% new), whereas **98**, Diners Club award-winner, also mostly shiraz, portion Am oak. No **01**; **02** unready at press time.

★★★★ **Shiraz** NEW ✓ Discreet & classically toned behind the flamboyant orange label; **01** beautifully crafted from ripe fruit — gamey, plummy, spicy with touches choc & smoked beef. Boldly but elegantly constructed. Partly fermented in Fr oak, yr, 30% new. 13.5% alc. Worth cellaring 3-5 yrs.

★★★★ **Merlot** Each year a notch up on previous as vines mature, now nudges 4 stars. Latest **02** 'surprisingly rich for disappointing vintage' says Wiid. Fragrant oak with cassis & choc aromas/flavours, velvety mouthfeel, ready. Yr oak, all Fr, upped to 30% new. **01** has a berried mocha sheen to soft, yielding tannins.

★★★★ **Chenin Blanc Wood Matured** Latest **03** firmer, more taut than Bushvine below, whiffs toasted nuts, green tea & apple. Natural fermentation in oak, 10 mths Fr, none new. 14% alc. **02** (★★★) soft, easy mouthful with nutty oak tone.

★★★★ **Sauvignon Blanc 04** (sample) boldly scented & flavoured; wafting melon/grass flavours, biggish build, generously fruity, good concentration seen in long finish; structured for food. **03** developing cat-pee & asparagus notes, similarly proportioned & flavoured to the younger version. Both 13.5% alc.

★★★★ **'Straw Wine'** NEW Still to be named. **03** with dried apricot & fruitcake bouquet; palate rich & unctuous, crammed with dried fruits lightened by fresher citrus — orange & mandarin. 'Had lots of fun making it.'

★★★★ **White Nights Cap Classique** Tribute to the 'Beliye Nochi' — midsummer nights of St Petersburg, so far north it never becomes properly dark. **00** chardonnay/ pinot (60/40) blend, nearly 4 yrs on lees, latest batch disgorged June 2004. Fresh, lively, light-textured & toned, dances prettily. Very dry at 5g/ℓ sugar.

Pinotage ★★★★ Small quantity (500 cs), exclusive to UK market. **02** Paarl/Walker Bay fruit; WO W-Cape; creamy damson, deep roasted-spice spiked with choc. Brush oak from barrel maturation. **Blanc de Noir** ★★★ Gulpable **04** (sample) brilliant, almost luminous salmon-pink. Dryish fruit pastille aromas/flavours, soft & easy. Light 12% alc. **Chardonnay** ★★★ **03** in lower key, soft rounded fruit, fleshy, oak in background. Fermented/aged in barriques, 30% new Fr, mainly natural yeast.

Bushvine Chenin Blanc ☺ ★★★ Intensity of low-yielding bushvines crammed into ripe **03**; evolving beautifully; full bodied, apricot liveliness & touches of toastiness. A revelation for those who believe must drink chenin in first year. Will easily last 2-3 yrs.

Kleine Hazen range

★★★★ **Reserve Red** 'No oak, lots of fruit,' says Wiid of cab, shiraz, merlot ensemble that's ready on release. Newest **02** (★★★) more classic thanks to higher proportion cab, nice tannic grip. **01** had loads of smoky berries. WO W-Cape.

Konynwijn ★★ **03** fruity semi-sweet chenin, mostly for own restaurant. — *IvH*

Heaven-On-Earth see Stellar Winery

Heerenhof

This popular, budget-priced 5ℓ boxed range from DGB now discontinued.

Hegewisch Wines

Est 2000 ▪ 1stB 2002 ▪ Closed to public ▪ Owner/winemaker Hilko Hegewisch ▪ Viticulturist Francois van Schoor ▪ 60 ha (merlot, pinotage, shiraz, chard) ▪ 800 tons 300 cs own label 40% red 60% white ▪ 22 Van Coppenhagen Str Rozendal Stellenbosch 7600 ▪ hegewisch@xsinet.co.za ℂ 887·9544 🖷 883·2310

Qualified chef and experienced winemaker Hilko Hegewisch and his wife Andrea run their own wine and food business, advising clients as far-flung as Sapporo in Japan. They also make wine for their own account in a rented cellar in Robertson.

★★★★ **Cabernet Sauvignon-Merlot** 🆕 **03** cab-dominated nose of cassis & cigarbox; medium-full bodied, well-made & balanced with firmly ripe tannin, food-friendly acidity; could age a few yrs. 55/45 assemblage, Allier oak matured. 13.5% alc.

★★★★ **Chardonnay 03** bigger wine than pvs (14.3% alc) yet harmonious, agreeable; creamy cling-peach aromas & hint of citrus; well flavoured. **02** lovely concentration but also restraint, elegance.±9 mths oak, 25% new. Both WO Rbtsn. — *JB*

Heinrick Muller see Keerweder
Helderberg Winery see Stellenbosch Vineyards

Helderkruin Wine Cellar

Stellenbosch ▪ Est 1997 ▪ 1stB 1998 ▪ Tasting & sales Mon-Thu 9- 5 Fri 9-4 Sat 9-1 ▪ Closed public holidays ▪ Tours during tasting hours ▪ Catered functions for groups of 30-120; also BYO picnic ▪ Owner Niel du Toit ▪ Winemaker Koos Bosman, with Bosman Bonthuis (Nov 1997/Jan 2003) ▪ Viticulturist Pietie Goosen (1980) ▪ 100 ha (cab, merlot, pinotage, shiraz) ▪ 1 000 tons 10 000 cs 70% red 30% white ▪ PO Box 91 Stellenbosch 7599 ▪ helkruin@iafrica.com ℂ 881·3899 🖷 881·3898

After a rather trying 2003 vintage, during which winemaker Koos Bosman suffered from tick-bite fever and kidney stones, the new vintage passed relatively peacefully, apart from a pressure surge in the press, which sent its lid rocketing right through the roof. Life is seldom boring in a cellar. 'I want to produce wines that are so user-friendly, you finish a bottle and decide you really have to order another,' says Bosman. 'Wines with huge flavours and aromas may win awards and competitions, but they're not for everyday enjoyment.'

Ben du Toit range

★★★★ **Pinotage** Remains the cellar's kingpin until the new blend below makes its debut. Savoury **02**, mid-2004 shows some good mature qualities & enough ripe plum fruit-stuffing to go another few yrs.

Ben du Toit 🆕 Unrated preview of the new flagship promises well; cab-led blend (52%) with petit v (25), merlot; **02** reverberating sweet-violet fragrance; cherries & black berries, spice from 16 mths new oak; whiff eucalyptus in the parting. **Merlot** ★★★ Well-constructed **02** shows some bottle-age whiffs; also an attractive ripe-fruit tone, hints coffee & choc; still something in reserve. 14 mths new oak, same as for... **Shiraz** ★★★ **02** dense, chewy, needing more time. 12% alc.

Helderkruin range

Cabernet Sauvignon ★★★ **00** ready now; easy soft tannins, mellow red fruit, touch bottle-maturity all pleasantly harmonised. 16 mths Fr oak. **Merlot** ★★★ **01** has undergone the usual 18 mths Fr/Am oaking, now needs time to settle; good plummy fruit lurks, waiting to unfold. **Pinotage** ★★★ The new vintage – **01** – still redolent of barrel maturation character (20% new wood), time required for oak, muscular tannins to settle, meld. Sample tasted. **Shiraz** ★★★ **01** (sample) Strident tannins currently conceal **01**'s sweet jammy fruit; further bottle-maturation needed. 14.5% alc. **Chardonnay** ★★★ Oak-fermented but not -aged; **04** (sample) ripe peaches & citrus touches, distinct vanilla on palate but also well-weighted sweet fruit. 14.3% alc. **Sauvignon Blanc** ★★★ **04** (sample) continues quicker pace of pvs; greenpepper & exotic orange-rind whiff, clean & fresh; for early enjoyment.

Yellow Cellar range

Dry Red ★★★ Straightforward, light-textured cab/merlot blend, unwooded; **99** has a fresh berry nose, better flavour than pvs, low 12.4% alc. **Dry White** ★✩ Chenin, **03** with tropical fruit aromas, slight honeyed patina, firm dry finish. — *DH*

Helgerson see La Bri

Helshoogte Vineyards

Stellenbosch ▪ Est 2000 ▪ 1stB 2003 ▪ Visits by appt ▪ Owner Sebastiaan Klaassen ▪ Winemaker Sebastiaan Klaassen, with Miles Mossop (both 2003) ▪ Viti adviser Aidan Morton (2002) ▪ 7 ha (cabs s/f, merlot) ▪ 600-1000 cs 100% red ▪ PO Box 449 Stellenbosch 7599 ▪ helshoogte@mweb.co.za ▪ www.helshoogte.co.za © 885·2334 ▦ 885·2714

Dutch couple Sebastiaan Klaassen and Anna Poll fell in love with the Cape on a kite-surfing holiday, found a young vineyard up the Helshoogte Pass, and never went home. Now he makes wine, under tutelage of Miles Mossop from nearby Tokara, who takes in some of the fruit from these young Simonsberg vines; she does charity work (R10 of each bottle of the Helshoogte Bordeaux-style blend goes to local community childrens' projects); and their two blond pre-schoolers gallivant around the vineyards. An old shed converted into a quaint, colourful hands-on winery nestles among the trees. Malbec, petit verdot has joined three classic Bordeaux reds; sauvignon, semillon are planned for high-lying parts.

Isa Dark choc, smoked beef, dark cherry in dense ripe blend of merlot, cabs s & f: 60/25/5 (barrel sample). **03** ripe fruit now undergoing firm disciplining in oak. Class already apparent. Provisional ★★★★. 14.5% alc. — *IvH*

Hemelzicht

Walker Bay ▪ Est 1998 ▪ 1stB 2003 ▪ Tasting & sales Mon-Fri 8.30-5 Sat 8.30-1 at 19 Long Street Hermanus ▪ Closed public holidays ▪ Owner Louis Saaiman ▪ Winemaker Hannes Storm (2003) ▪ 16 ha (cab, malbec, shiraz, chard, sauvignon) ▪ 800 cs 100% white ▪ PO Box 469 Onrusrivier 7201 ©/▦ (028) 313·2215 (cellar) © (028) 312·3512 (a/h)

'Winemaking is really quite a simple business,' says Louis Saaiman, echoing Baroness Philippine de Rothschild of Ch Mouton Rothschild, 'only the first 200 years are difficult.' Undaunted, relative winegrowing novice Saaiman is upbeat about his second harvest, not least because the holistic approach advocated by vineyard guru Eben Archer (who helped identify the exact location for specific varieties) is already bearing fruit: Hemelzicht chardonnay, shiraz and cab grapes were sold as soon as they were picked; Saaiman's sauvignon is also showing great promise. But the real test comes this year, when most blocks swing into full production....

★★★★ **Chardonnay** Steely, minerally **03** gains extra flavour & interest from 10% oak-fermented portion. Revisited, shows refined cool-climate tone, fleeting glimpses toast & butterscotch, fine line of citrus fruit. Understated; could age nicely.

★★★★ **Sauvignon Blanc** Night-harvested **03** ageing attractively in bottle; hints grape-fruit, lemon rind; full bodied, balanced, whistle-clean finish. **04** also bright-fruited, 'cool'; crushed nettle, gooseberry, capsicum array & rather nice honey-suckle touch; 5g/ℓ sugar gives user-friendly plushness. – *TM*

Hemisphere see Lost Horizons
Hendri Nagel see Cellar-Vie

Hendrik Boom

Feel-good range (portion of profit goes to Help Aids Kids of Africa, a privately run support group) recognising the vinous contribution of Hendrik Boom, founder of the Cape's first vineyard. See Jonkheer for contact names and numbers.

Red ☺ ★★★ Easy **01** glassful with gamey fruitcake whiffs, fullish body, soft dry sa-voury finish. Equal portions 5 red grapes; *Wine* best value selection in 2004. 1 000ml .

White ★★★ To date a smooth & relaxed **01**, not retasted. – *TM*

Hercules Paragon see Simonsvlei

Hermanus Heritage Collection

This in-house range of Hermanus retail outlet Wine Village has been replaced by a Shiraz under the Wine Village label. See that entry and the Specialist wine shops section.

Herold Wines

Outeniqua (see Little Karoo map) ▪ *Est 1999* ▪ *1stB 2003* ▪ *Visits by appt* ▪ *Walks* ▪ *Conservation area* ▪ *Owner Mark Chandler* ▪ *Winemakers Ernst & Hannes Storm (Oct 2003)* ▪ *Viticulturist Vivian Harpur (1999)* ▪ *6 ha (pinot, sauvignon)* ▪ *2.3 tons 100 cs 100% red* ▪ *PO Box 10 Herold 6610* ▪ *heroldwines@mweb.co.za* ℂ *072·833·8223* 🖶 *(044) 873·4212*

Spearheading the development of the new cool-climate Outeniqua ward is Mark Chan-dler, a Gauteng-based winelover and frustrated farmer looking for a retirement hobby. His Cradock Farm, formerly SAB-owned hopsland, carries (besides hazelnuts and blueber-ries) 6ha of pinot and sauvignon. Clinging to a site 450-600m up Cradock Peak, the high-est point in the Outeniqua range, these vines qualify for the label 'extreme'. Radical, too, are marauding baboons, fruit-eating birds and billows of downy mildew. All of which Chandler's George-based sister, Vivien Harpur, and six novice vineyard workers managed to overcome in 2003, to supply contracted winemakers Hannes Storm and brother Ernst (full-timing at Hamilton Russell and in California, respectively) with enough pinot for a maiden vintage. They repeated their feat in 2004. Avowed naturalists, they're resigned to electric fencing and netting to save future harvests, which will include experimental char-donnay, merlot, shiraz and cab. The toughest will take eventual plantings to 12ha.

★★★★ **Pinot Noir** Beautiful jewel-bright hue on **03**, obviously carefully made, with re-spect for demanding variety. Forest floor, organic aromas but clean, not funky. Shy strawberry fruit & smooth silky, curvaceous palate with sensual appeal, like pinot should. Impressive debut, watch this label. 13.5% alc. – *IvH*

Heron Ridge

Stellenbosch (see Helderberg map) ▪ *Est 1997* ▪ *1stB 2001* ▪ *Visits by appt* ▪ *Fee R10 p/p for groups* ▪ *Closed public holidays* ▪ *Owners Pete & Jane Orpen* ▪ *Winemaker Pete Orpen* ▪ *Viti consultant Paul Wallace (Mar 1999)* ▪ *4 ha (cab, shiraz)* ▪ *30 tons 1 800–2 000 cs 100% red* ▪ *PO Box 5181 Helderberg 7135* ▪ *orps@xsinet.co.za* ℂ *842·2591* 🖶 *842·2501*

After the busyness of previous years preparing for their maiden 2003 Shiraz, Pete and Jane Orpen exude a sense of contentment in their second life as wine farmers. 2004 vin-tage's slightly uneven growth left their calm unruffled – they merely picked the unripe berries off the bunches on the vines. Their nerve held though the two-week harvest delay, and their reward was 'fruit with the same depth as last year'. Keen to let their wine 'just do its own thing', they elected not to filter but to apply only a light egg-white fining, and live with the resultant (perfectly harmless) sediment.

★★★★ **Shiraz 04** sample already offering sumptuous raspberry marzipan notes; very ripe though big alcohol not dominating; rich, finely textured, with lovely concentration. Smoky, gun flint notes on **03**, & dense compressed tannins. Though apparent, the oak (yr 30% new; 70% Fr, remainder Am) not overwhelming. Unfiltered. 14.5% alc. Elegant unshowy **02** had light 'sapling' whiffs, though fully ripe (15.2% alc). — *MF*

Hidden Valley Wines

Stellenbosch ▪ Est/1stB 1995 ▪ Closed to public (sales by appt) ▪ Owners David & Marguerite Hidden ▪ Winemakers Jeremy Walker & Niels Verburg (1994/2004) ▪ Viticulturist Johan 'Grobbie' Grobbelaar (Feb 1999) ▪ 34 ha (cab, merlot, pinotage, shiraz) ▪ 154 tons 2 700 cs 100% red ▪ PO Box 12577 Die Boord 7613 ▪ info@hiddenvalleywines.com ▪ www. hiddenvalleywines.com © 855·0296 ▤ 855·0297

A brace of winemakers makes for a singular pinotage? Owners Dave and Marguerite Hidden think so: they're delighted to have multi-tentacled Niels Verburg (Beaumont, Luddite, Iona) join long-time winemaker chum Jeremy Walker (Grangehurst) on their team from harvest 2004. Their vision is to blend Walker-made pinotage with pinotage from Hidden-owned vineyards in Devon Valley and the Helderberg, vinified by Verburg at Iona cellar in Elgin. The results, the Hiddens believe, 'will be really stunning'. Walker continues to make the cab and merlot while Verburg adds his touch to shiraz. With new vineyards coming on-stream, Hidden Valley finds itself at a crossroads, presented with global challenges of declining production and demand in some markets, and calls from new consumers and upped production of New World grapes. Undaunted, the pro-organic Hiddens are putting together strategies such as extending their range both up and down the price scale.

★★★★ **Pinotage** From a 30+ yr old Devon Valley vyd. Revisited **01** beginning to show its true form. Dark fruit, ripe & concentrated, well spiced with mocha, pepper tones; smoky, savoury palate. Youthful but amenable tannins. Still unfolding, many yrs of life ahead. 11 mths Fr/Am (78/22) oak. 14.6% alc. **00** also needed time.

★★★★ **CWG Auction Reserve Pinotage** Last was serious, succulent **01**, with 13% cab.

★★★★ **Cabernet Sauvignon** Fruit from Firgrove/Hldrberg sites. Traditional vinification, including small open fermenters, basket press. **00** revisited mid-2004 showing well: creamy plum/blackcurrant core, with layers cedar, aromatic spice, subtle herbaceous edge. Has elegance, style, ripe but firm tannin & a long development future. 24 mths barrique oaking, mainly Fr, portion Am, Russian. 14.3% alc. — *CR*

High Constantia

Constantia ▪ Est 1683 ▪ 1stB 2000 ▪ Tasting, sales, tours 8–5 ▪ Fee R25 ▪ Closed Dec 25 & Jan 1 ▪ Owner David van Niekerk ▪ Winemakers David van Niekerk & Roger Arendse ▪ 9. 5 ha (cabs s/f, merlot, pinot, chard, sauvignon) ▪ 40 tons 3 400 cs own label ▪ 91% red 3. 5% rosé 5% MCC ▪ Range for customer: Sherwood-Berriman (UK) ▪ Puck's Glen Groot Constantia Rd Constantia 7800 ▪ david@highconstantia.co.za © 794·7171 ▤ 794·7999

Vintage 2004 was good to High Constantia. 'I'm extremely happy with the results of a very healthy crop,' confirms David van Niekerk. Concentrating mainly on reds (though there's some young sauvignon waiting in the wings), he's added a hectare more cab and merlot to his vine holdings dotted around the Constantiaberg. The vintage was similarly kind to his classic, classy MCC, delivering 'the best fruit to date' from mature (13-year) chardonnay and pinot. Total production has doubled to around 3 400 cases, with still-meagre yet sought-after pickings distributed among seven countries (plus SA). As for the steady spate of new wineries, this financial adviser is all for competition to improve quality on the world market.

★★★★ **Sebastiaan** A blend of cabs s & f as elegant & understated as its packaging. Last yr **01** showed ★★★★★ class. Leaf, berries, spice & blackcurrant notes all to be found. Fine tannins, sweet savouriness, 13.6% alc, yr Fr oak in excellent balance with fruit. Less earthy than maiden **00** where creamy, denser, more mineral notes abound.

★★★★ **Cabernet Sauvignon** Leafy earthiness on **01** (last tasted 2003), blackcurrant on austere palate. Good tannin support, dry finish. 13% alc. Yr new/2nd-fill Fr oak.

★★★★ **Cabernet Franc** Classically styled **01** (★★★★) showed prominent herbal notes & fragrant leafiness over cedar & sweet red berries, tasted 2003. Sombrely elegant & harmonious; Fr oak; 13.7% alc. Finer, more intense than gamey **00**.

★★★★ **Clos André MCC** Beautifully, elegantly packaged, like all these. Fine maiden effort was NV, but follow-up vintaged **03** (★★★★★) even better (our sample disgorged Jan 2004, says back label). Full, rich style but bone-dry, delicate, with lovely spicy brioche notes on nose, long flavours. From 70/30 chardonnay/pinot grown on s-facing Constia slopes. 11.7% alc.

Rosé ★★★ **03** mostly bled-off cab f, 8% from MCC press-wine; still interesting & delightful; earthy, raspberry fragrance; just about dry; 13.7%. No **04**. **Chardonnay** discontinued. — *TJ*

High Gables see Klein Constantia

Hildenbrand Estate

Wellington ▪ Est 1998 ▪ 1stB 1999 ▪ Tasting & sales daily 10-4 ▪ Closed Easter Fri-Sun, Dec 25, Dec 31, Jan 1 ▪ Tasting fee R25 ▪ Tours by appt ▪ Hildenbrand Restaurant (closed Tue) ▪ Klein Rhebokskloof Country & Guest House ▪ Farm-grown olives & olive oil ▪ Owner/viticulturist Reni Hildenbrand ▪ Winemaker Reni Hildenbrand, with Matthew Orton (Jun 2004) ▪ 18 ha (cab, malbec, shiraz, chard, chenin, semillon) ▪ 4 800 cs own label 50/50 red/white ▪ PO Box 270 Wellington 7655 ▪ info@wine-estate-hildenbrand.co.za ▪ www.wine-estate-hildenbrand.co. za ✆ 873·4115 🖷 0866·700·147

Where does she get the energy? Besides running a country guest house and restaurant, making wine and pressing a select range of olive oils, Reni Hildenbrand also writes (a book, *Olives & Oils in South Africa*) and educates (she helped launch the first olive oil course at the Cape Wine Academy). Given her chock-a-block schedule, it's no surprise she appointed a winemaking assistant, Matthew Orton, in June last year. Both are excited about the 2004 harvest, especially the semillon which 'has wonderful depth and balance, and is sure to pick up a few accolades'.

★★★★ **Cabernet Sauvignon Barrique** Latest **01** with classic cassis attractions, fragrant with classy oak, dry tannins not inelegant. Oak Fr third new, 13 mths. **00** developed nuances of violets & damp-earth, 'warm' tar-like tones.

★★★★ **Shiraz** Revisited **02**, shows potential being fulfilled, needs 2-3 yrs more, unfolding slowly, gracefully. Well-flavoured & structured aromatic style; whiffs Marmite-on-toast, pepper, scrub — the whole spectrum covered from a generously fruited, elegantly tannined bed of redcurrants & cherries. 14.7% alc.

★★★★ **Chardonnay Barrique** **01** deliciously austere; mineral edge to grapefruit & lime palate, slightly relieved by butterscotch suggestion. Revisited, shows developing attractive toasty nuances. Delicious. **03** sold out.

★★★★ **Cabernet Sauvignon Unwooded** ★★★ **01** a notch up from pvs; good berry fruit, tannins soft & approachable, dry earthy finish. A pleasing 12.5% alc.

Rosé ☺ ★★★ Arresting psychedelic pink! Off-dry **04** vibrant fruit, crushed raspberry flavours, some fruit pastilles, juicy & tangy, delicious. From shiraz.

Malbec 🆕 Barrel sample **04**, blueberry, brambleberry introduction to ripe stalky fruit, blackberry cordial-like intensity, followed by earthy, dry finish. Minute quantities, ex-estate only; bigger quantities promised for next yr. Provisional ★★★★. **Chardonnay Unwooded** ★★★ Ageing without any loss of flavour or style. **02** lemongrass whiffs in a fresh herbal bouquet; seamless carry-though into refreshing palate. 14% alc. **03** sold out. **Chenin Blanc** ★★★ **02** honeysuckle perfume; full-flavoured buttery melon palate; big & fat; soft acidity, needs light-textured food to give it life, maturing well. 14% alc. **03** sold out. **Semillon** ★★★ Latest **04** more focus/flavour, delicious, could do with a dab more acidity for higher rating. — *IvH*

Hilko Hegewisch see Hegewisch Wines

Hill & Dale

Owner Lusan Holdings • info@hillanddale.co.za • www.hillanddale.co.za
Ready-on-release range featuring fruit from selected Stellenbosch vineyards, vinified by Guy Webber at Stellenzicht (see entry for details of tasting/sales). All WO Stbosch.

- ★★★★ **Cabernet Sauvignon-Shiraz** 50/32 blend with dollop fattening merlot, big but not bothersome alc (15%). **02** still on the list; now with smoke & pepper overtones, dry finish showing some oak (Fr/Am) — we'd drink reasonably soon.
- ★★★★ **Pinotage 03** has homey charm of pvs; lots of vanilla & rich fruitcake flavour, dry finish without any hard edges.
- ★★★★ **Stellenbosch Red** Still-available **99**, attractive red-fruit-led combo merlot, shiraz, cabs s/f, malbec; nicely welded together & holding up well. Dry minerally palate invites plate of good food. Mix Fr, Am, Russian oak, ±17 mths. 13.8% alc.

Dry Rosé Merlot ★★ **03** bouquet now has a savoury edge with hint smoked meat, restrained palate, very dry finish. 14.8% alc. **Chardonnay** ★★★ **03** retasted, fairly restrained lemony tones, dry tail; appealing, probably at peak now. Fr/Am oak fermented. 13.8% alc. **Sauvignon Blanc** ★★★★ ✓ **04** copybook sauvignon; pungent blast of asparagus & herbs, vivid green flavour; slighter than pvs (12% alc) but big on character. — *CR*

Hillcrest Estate

Durbanville • Est/1stB 2002 • Tasting & sales Tue-Sun 10-6 • Closed Easter Fri-Mon, Dec 25 & Jan 1 • Restaurant for lunches during tasting hours (& pvt evening functions by appt) • Tours by appt • Owners PD Inglis, R Haw & G du Toit • Winemaker Graeme Read (Jan 2003) • Viticulturist G du Toit • 25 ha (cab, merlot, shiraz, chard, sauvignon) • 32 tons • ±3 000 cs 45% red 55% white • Private Bag X3 Durbanville 7551 • mail@haw-inglis.co.za © 976·1110/975·2346 ≜ 976·8802

Graeme Read's dream of a micro-cellar took flight with his very first vintage, the Sauvignon and Bordeaux-style red garnering flattering reviews in this guide and elsewhere. Further encouraged (if that were possible — his enthusiasm levels were way off the scale to start with), ultra-meticulous Read is establishing cabernet franc, petit verdot and malbec. Befitting the success of the wines, this hillside property now features a tasting room, entertainment patio and restaurant (lunch & private functions only) with exceptional views of Table Bay. The cellar has also been extended, revamped and re-equipped to handle up to 50 tons; allowing Read to exercise his creativity and winemaking passion with even more PhD precision and control.

- ★★★★ **Merlot-Cabernet Sauvignon** Graeme R believes farm best suited to merlot-dominated blend, so **03**'s 54/46 reverses varietal order of maiden **02**. Style too metamorphosed. **03** welcoming, warmly ripe mulberry/plum scents, comfortably plump though firmly-structured body, readied by sweet fruit filling, v different from **02**'s more austere profile; compact, slender palate, terse tannins.
- ★★★★ **Sauvignon Blanc** Maiden **03** applauded by consumers, but GR feels it could have done with more mouthfeel. So fruit fine-tuning in **04**; sample reveals generous tropical richness with hint of Dbnvle's vivid 'wildness', weightier feel. Less attention-grabbing than pvs, will take longer to get into stride. 13.6% alc. **03** developed sooner than expected. Mellowing, honeyed tone; probably best over next yr.

Chardonnay ★★★ Attractively pronounced peach, citrus blossom/zest on **04** sample; imperceptible oaking, fresh acid spine anchors fruit to pleasurable length. Possible ★★★★.

Fruitier than more obviously oak-influenced **03** now with some honeyed development; best enjoyed soon while light peachy/creamy distinction lasts. — *AL*

Hill Station see Cape First
Hinterland see Hartswater
Homtini see Anthony de Jager Wines

Hippo Creek

Value-for-money brand exclusive to Picardi Rebel Liquors (see entry).

Sauvignon Blanc ☺ ★★★ Continues livelier tone of pvs; **04** (sample) perfumed guava nose with hint capsicum, juicy combo limes & pear-drops, light, quaffable.

Cabernet Sauvignon ★★★ Nothing since **99**, described as a carnivore's wine. **Merlot** ★★★★ Most serious of these; **01** attractively bottled-aged, hints leather & smoked meat; peaking, must uncork. **02** (★★★) quieter, more simple stewed plum tones, vegetal hint, but could mature as well as pvs. ±Yr Fr oak. 14% alc. **Pinotage** ★★★ **01** friendly, swiggable unwooded red; retasted, showing an orange rim & some pinot-like forest floor hints, slight earthiness. **Chardonnay** ★★★ **03** unready for tasting; **02** was noted as low-keyed but attractive. All WO W-Cape. — *TM*

Hoopenburg Wines

Stellenbosch ▪ *Est 1992* ▪ *1stB 1994* ▪ *Tasting & sales Mon-Fri 9-4.30 Sat & public holidays 9.30-1* ▪ *Fee R10 refunded with purchace of 6+ btls* ▪ *Closed Easter Fri-Mon & Dec 25/26* ▪ *BYO picnic* ▪ *Tours by appt* ▪ *Owner Gregor Schmitz* ▪ *Winemaker Neil Hawkins, with Kajo Malek (Jan 2005/Feb 2004)* ▪ *Viti consultant Paul Wallace* ▪ *40 ha (cab, merlot, pinot, shiraz, chard)* ▪ *270 tons 16 000 cs 75% red 25% white* ▪ *PO Box 1233 Stellenbosch 7599* ▪ *info@hoopenburg.com* ▪ *www.hoopenburg.com* ⓒ **884·4221/2/3** 🖷 884·4904

The winds of change have been blowing at Hoopenburg. Business consultant Gregor Schmitz became sole owner in 2004 (ex-partner Ernst Gouws now has his own, eponymous wine business), and he's swept the place clean. Albert Rossouw is his man in marketing, aided by two newly appointed export coordinators. Neil Hawkins has been appointed winemaker for the 2005 vintage, assisted by Kajo Malek, and Paul Wallace is the new consultant viticulturist. Neil H comes with a rather promising pedigree: his maiden Sauvignon earned 90 points in *Wine Spectator*; his maiden Shiraz a gold at Veritas and silver at the *Decanter* World Wine Awards. Neil H spent the past two years gaining experience in New Zealand, France and Germany, and is ready to put into practice the Schmitz dictum: to produce new-age wines in an Old-World style.

- ★★★★ **Cabernet Sauvignon** Retasted **01**, rich, full-flavoured, deep-piled red berry nose, smoky oak background, mouthfilling, well-formed tannins. **02** (sample) huge, rich wine (15.4% alc), oak showing strongly mid-2004, big tannins will need some time to soften. Yr 3rd fill Fr oak.

- ★★★☆ **Merlot 01** (★★★☆) retasted, nice enough red wine but not a lot of varietal character; **02** (sample) up to par; deeply coloured; textbook plums, coffee & choc in bouquet; sweeter fruit & better balanced tannins.

- ★★★★ **Shiraz 02** (★★★) characteristic spiciness on nose plus some mature bottle-age qualities, noticeable drying tannins; needs to be enjoyed soon; 14 mths 2nd/3rd fill Fr oak. **01** had sweet prune fruit & toughish tannins, needing another 2-3 yrs.

Pinot Noir ★★★ Whiffs charry oak introduce **02**, hints raspberry & rhubarb, lots of tight tannin needing time. 10 mths 2nd/3rd fill Fr oak. **Pinotage** ★★★ **01** characterised by a clean fresh-fruit tone, ripe plums & strawberries uppermost, tannins still firm, give more time. **Chardonnay** ★★★ **03** attractive peaches & cream character, rounded, supportively oaked; fresh, yet slight hint of maturity creeping in, best enjoyed soon. 50/50 new/used Fr oak, 6 mths. **Sauvignon Blanc** ★★★ Lightish **04** (sample) ebullient green grass &

nettle bouquet, zesty, refreshing & not too dry. WO Coastal, all others Stbosch. **Winemaker's Selection Cabernet** & **Merlot**, both **99**s, available, not retasted. — *DH*

Hoop Huis see False Bay Winery

Horse Mountain Wines

Paarl ▪ Est 1997 ▪ 1stB 2001 ▪ Visits by appt Mon-Fri 9-5 Sat 9-1 ▪ BYO picnic ▪ Owner Far Horizons Wine Estate (Pty) Ltd ▪ Winemaker Charles Stassen (Jan 2002) ▪ Viti consultant Paul Wallace (Jan 2000) ▪ 45 ha (cabs s/f, merlot, pinotage, shiraz) ▪ 400 tons 15 000 cs own labels + 65 000ℓ bulk ▪ 80% red 10% white 10% rosé ▪ PO Box 2143 Windmeul 7630 ▪ wine@horsemountainwines.com ▪ www.horsemountainwines.com ✆ 869·8328 ▤ 869·8329

'Screw the cork' instructs a notice on the twist-off caps of the Quagga Ridge wines. 'That'll sort out anyone against this progressive closure,' declares owner Craig Lardner, satisfied that what began as a part-time venture in the new Voor Paardeberg ward is becoming what he wants it to be: an income-earning grower of fine red wine. A trip Down Under brought him up to speed with latest viticultural developments. 'Different vineyards, even within a block, have different trellising systems,' he noted. His current project is to secure international (ISO) quality certification. The 100-ton winery and barrel maturation cellar are now complete, but even these accomplishments couldn't beat the thrill of international recognition for his 2003 Pinotage, a silver at the IWSC.

★★★★ **Pinotage 03** excellent mouthfeel with some perfume, this is pinotage done right & IWC agrees with silver medal. 14% alc. 20% Am oak for added spice. Should develop ±5 years. Good follow-up to pinot-like **02**.

Also 🆕 **04** barrel samples, too unfinished to rate: richly fruited, powerful **Shiraz**; **Michele** Blend cabs s/f, merlot – big 14.5% alc, promising classy fruitiness.

Quagga Ridge range
The following all 🆕 in this reformulated selection.

Red ☺ ★★★ **03** a 50:50 fruity blend merlot, pinotage; friendly despite 14% alc, & a shoo-in for restaurant house red. **White** ☺ ★★★ Light, dry **04** unpretentious quaffer of 60/20/20 sauvignon/semillon/chenin; 13% alc.

Rosé ★★ Dusky rose colour blooming on dry **04**, earthy aromas, flavours. 13% alc. Discontinued: **Merlot-Pinotage**, **Pinotage**, **Merlot**, **White Merlot**. — *NP*

Huguenot Wine Farmers

Wellington ▪ Closed to public ▪ Owner Kosie Botha ▪ Cellarmaster Bill Matthee (1984) ▪ Trade enquiries Gert Brynard ▪ PO Box 275 Wellington 7654 ▪ jcb@mynet.co.za ✆ 864·1293 ▤ 873·2075

Privately owned wholesaling company which blends, markets and distributes a wide range of wines, liqueurs and spirits. The range, not assessed, includes: Cabernet, Pinotage, Smooth Red (cinsaut/pinotage), Premier Grand Cru (chenin/crouchen), Stein (chenin), Late Harvest (chenin), Hanepoot, Red/White Jeripico (red/white muscadel), Invalid Port, Tawny Port, Nagmaalwyn and Old Brown Sherry. And the Zellerhof 5ℓ vats: Stein, Late Harvest and Premier Grand Cru.

Hummelhof see Goudini
Ibis see Schalkenbosch
Idiom see WhaleHaven
Ietsie Anders see Kosie Möller Wines
Imagine see Southern Sky
Imbizo see Ernst & Co
Impala see Citrusdal Cellars

Imvelo see Premium Cape Wines
Indaba see African Terroir, Cape Classics, Excelsior
Indalo see Swartland Wine Cellar
Infiniti see Stellenbosch Vineyards

Inglewood Vintners

Stellenbosch • Est/1stB 2002 • Closed to public • Owners Neil Ellis Wines & Vinfruco • Winemaker Nicky Versfeld (2002) • ±25 000 cs 70% red 30% white • ISO 9001 & HACCP certified • PO Box 12730 Die Boord 7613 • info@vinfruco.co.za • www.vinfruco.co.za © 886·6458 ▭ 886·6589

Now in its third year as a standalone, this Neil Ellis/Vinfruco partnership is bearing fruit, notably in the form of a gold for the Sauvignon at the Canadian Sélections Mondiales 2004. Guiding philosophy is to 'over-deliver on quality'.

Cabernet Sauvignon ★★★ Latest **02** workmanlike, some dark-berried concentration, properly dry. Firmish tannins. Partly oaked (10-12 mths, older casks). **Shiraz ★★★☆ 02** attractive smoked beef & Karoo scrub overtones to dense, ripe fruit, tannins already approachable. **Chardonnay ★★★ 03** in established unwooded, style; citrusy, smoky note could be mistaken for oak, smooth & plump. Has charm. **Sauvignon Blanc ★★★ 03** shy, but good figgy, grassy attack on palate, tangy & dry, still vital. — *IvH*

Ingwe

Stellenbosch (see Helderberg map) • Est 1998 • 1stB 1999 • Visits by appt • Owner Alain Mouieix • Winemaker PJ Geyer (Sep 2001) • Viticulturist Francois Baard (Sep 1999) • 28 ha (own/leased; cabs s/f, malbec, merlot, shiraz, tempranillo, chard, sauvignon) • 110 tons 18 000 cs 95% red 5% white • PO Box 583 Somerset West 7129 • ingwewine@eject.co.za ©/▭ 858·1063

Blends are more interesting than single varieties, states Alain Moueix (unsurprisingly, given he's a Bordeaux château owner/vintner). Thrilled by 2004 (unlike virtually the whole of the Cape, a smooth, timeous harvest — 'things happen differently in Sir Lowry's Pass', explains GM/viticulturist Francois Baard), Moueix immediately rolled up his sleeves and started mixing components. Young winemaker PJ Geyer is an adventurer, too (his first Elsenburg student-wine blew up his mother's fridge), and passionate: Moueix hired him because 'he talked about making wine with sensitivity, not from a recipe'. A new ingredient for Ingwe blends is some excellent cab franc. More merlot is being planted. Sauvignon is doing exceptionally well on the breeze-swept Schaapenberg slopes — expect it to feature in a white blend soon. The range is now available locally.

★★★★ **Ingwe** Poised maiden **02** blend (52% merlot, 48% cab) re-tasted, revealing more class, with an appealing subtle sweetness to smoky damsons, blackberries, some mineral notes; round tannins, good oak integration (18 mths Fr, 60% new); persistent. 13.8% alc.

★★★★ **Amehlo** 'Eye' in Xhosa; cab-dominated (54%) blend with shiraz, merlot, malbec. **02** intensely aromatic — ground coriander, crushed leaves — dense & austere textures, leafy finish. Seductive sweetness has attenuated rougher edges. 18 mths Fr oak, 20% new. Step up on more peppery **01**. Both retasted.

★★★★ **Sauvignon Blanc** Re-tasted **03** classic cat's pee & gooseberry bush notes, with greenpepper, vegetal flavours, beautifully balanced palate. ±13.5% alc.

Chardonnay discontinued. — *NP*

Initial Series see Jean Daneel
Inkawu see Laibach

International Wine Services

Est 1991 • Closed to public • SA GM/winemaker Jonathan Snashall (Jul 2003) • 1m ℓ own label + 3m ℓ ±40% red ±60% white • Ranges for UK customers: Rock Rabbit, Tokolosh,

Somerfield, Co-operative Group, Wine Society • UK office: Punchbowl Park, Cherry Tree Lane, Hemel Hempstead, Hertfordshire, HP2 7EU, UK • PO Box 432 Franschhoek 7690 • iwsinsa4@ new.co.za • www.waverley-group.co.uk ℗/☎ 876·3927

Waverley, the parent company of this big-volume export concern, has merged with The Beer Seller in the UK to become the largest on-trade seller and distributor in Britain (trading as Waverley TBS). The SA-sourced Cape Promise wines, ranging from pocket-friendly blends to more serious Reserves, continue to gain ground and recently entered the list of top 20 brands in the UK. Now also being targeted is Scandinavia.

Cape Promise Reserve range

★★★☆ **Cabernet Sauvignon** Easy, appealing New World style; dollops Ribena fruit, toned in **02** by attractive hint of bottle-age; harmonious, soft choc-mocha palate, savoury wood hint on finish. Yr oak; includes splash shiraz.

★★★★ **Merlot** Stylish but unpretentious wine. Harmonious **01** followed by aromatic **02**, with rich, ripe fruit. **03** (sample) good few rungs above standard version below; solid, chewy but unknit mid-2004, dominated by spicy oak; provisional ★★★★. May integrate with time & match the general rating.

★★★☆ **Chardonnay 03** full-on commercial crowd-pleaser: lashings peaches & cream, toasty oak, plump fruit holds its own, then more richness via crème brûlée finish. 6g/l sugar. 30% barrel-fermented/6 mths aged.

★★★☆ **Private Reserve Noble Late Harvest** 🆕 Muscat/chenin; **03** striking orange-gold colour, appealing passionfruit/peach/apricot fruit array, vague hint citrus. Silky, supple, delicious; touch more acid would have clinched 4-star rating.

Pinotage ★★★☆ **02** more to offer than regular version; underpinned by same mulberry fruit, more grown-up/sophisticated, drier, less bumptious fruit/tannins. **Shiraz** ★★★☆ **02** harmonious, complex nose featuring vanilla spice & white pepper; full silky flavour; pleasing melding of fruit, oak & high alc (14%). Like above reds, yr oaked. **Sauvignon Blanc** 🆕 ★★★☆ Green-tinged **04** from Dbnvlle, with herby/grassy notes; unfruity, almost smoky/fumé bouquet; palate fruitier, zesty, lots of good minerality.

Cape Promise range

Cabernet Sauvignon ★★★ **03** (sample) opaque with plum rim; warm aromas of damp earth; slight edginess should settle by mid-2005. **Merlot** ★★★ Uncomplicated **03**, shy hints dried fruit & eucalyptus; soft jammy sweetness firmed by powdery tannins. **Pinotage** ★★★ **03** (sample) with splash merlot; banana & mulberry confirm pinotage is in charge; sweet palate-coating mulberry fruit, fairly robust but tasty. **Shiraz** ★★★ **03** good varietal nose showing meaty/peppery whiffs; charred mocha wood to spice up the red fruit. All above 6 mths oak. **Cinsaut-Ruby Cabernet** 🆕 ★★★ Deeply dark **04**, dry hillside scrub whiffs, plummy fruit spiked with pepper; well knit; softly & simply delicious. **Merlot-Shiraz** ★★★ **03** warm Xmas pud whiffs, cigarbox hint; lively & harmonious plump fruit, bit of milk choc on finish. 6 mths oak. **Ruby Cabernet-Pinotage** 🆕 ★★★ Duo of fruity varieties abetted by dash of another smoothie, cinsaut (60/20/20); **04** thatchy smells from ruby cab, mulberries from pinotage; plummy in-your-face flavour. 60% oaked, 4 mths. **Merlot Rosé** 🆕 ★★★ Neon pink **04** (sample) features wonderfully juicy palate, bright red-fruit aromas, bone-dry finish. Delightful. **Chardonnay** ★★★ **04** (unfinished sample) pleasant spicy nose, hints vanilla & butterscotch; soft peach & lime flavours. 60% wooded 6 mths. **Chenin Blanc Barrel Fermented** ★★★ Sparingly oaked (70% 6 mths) & showing in fetching vanilla twist to **04**'s guava/passionfruit aromas, creamy apple flavours. Sample tasted. **Chenin Blanc Unoaked** 🆕 ★★★ Creamy ripe baked-apple nose with hints quince & lanolin; touch honey in farewell. **04** (sample) shows some development potential. Fruit ex-Stbosch. ±14% alc. **Sauvignon Blanc** ★★★ Appealing **04** (sample), spicy bouquet of capsicum & grapefruit, softly dry & juicy, generously flavoured. **Chardonnay-Colombard** 🆕 ★★ 55/45 blend; **04** (sample) muted herby nose with lemon zest hints; simple fruity dry flavour. **Dry Muscat** ★★★ Turkish Delight & talcum powder billow from **04** glass; soft fruity tone yet firm, bone-dry flavour; satisfying; easy to quaff. From muscat d'A. Above ranges sourced widely: WOs Stbosch, Dbnvlle, Wrcstr & W-Cape. — *TM*

Intrusa see Overhex

Iona Vineyards

Elgin • Est 1997 • 1stB 2001 • Tasting, sales & tours Mon-Fri 8-5.30 • Closed Easter Fri/Sat/Sun, Dec 25 & Jan 1 • BYO picnic • Self-catering guest house • Walks • Mountain biking • Owner Andrew Gunn • Vini consultant Niels Verburg, with Thapelo Hlasa (both Feb 2004) • Joseph Sebulawa, advised by Kevin Watt (Nov 2001) • 25 ha (cab, merlot, chard, sauvignon, semillon) • 5 000 cs 25% red 75% white • PO Box 527 Grabouw 7160 • gunn@iona.co.za • www.iona.co.za Ⓒ (028) 284·9678/284·9953 ☐ (028) 284·9078

Though 2004 was considered a cool year for most of the Cape, Andrew Gunn's elevated, habitually chilly farm had warmer than usual weather and brought in its harvest a week earlier. Not that it was a problem. In fact, winemaker Niels Verburg could not be more effusive about the quality of the fruit: 'beautifully balanced, perfect analysis' — just what he needed for his debut vintage here (he now makes Gunn's wines and his own Luddite Shiraz in this newly completed cellar). Like others, Verburg believes that a big challenge facing SA wineries is to make wines that truly reflect their site. Not only is that Iona's intention to do just that, but Verburg — aware of international trends — intends to produce wine that is high in flavour but lower in alcohol.

★★★★★ **Sauvignon Blanc 04** sumptuous yet elegant with gooseberry/nettle notes, depth of flavour; well-textured linearity. Five clones across two vyds enhance complexity, as did long ripening season — end-March harvest date. Step up on more herbal, greenpepper-like **03** (★★★★).

★★★★ **Merlot** [NEW] Infusion of 15% cab in **02**. Savoury, green olive notes with plum, coffee whiffs. Slightly austere tannins. Yr Fr oak, 25% new; 13% alc. — *MF*

Itakané see Mouton House of Wines
Ivory Creek see Citrusdal Cellars
Ivy du Toit see Jason's Hill
Izimbali see Eshkol

Jacaranda Estate

Wellington • Est 1993 • 1stB 1994 • Tasting, sales, tours Mon-Fri 10-5 Sat 10-2 • Closed Easter Fri/Sun, Dec 25 • Self-catering/B&B cottage • BYO picnic • Farm-grown/made cheeses, jams & olives • Owners Jan & Trish Tromp • Winemaker/viticulturist Jan Tromp • 2.8 ha (cab, merlot, chenin) • 25 tons 300 cs own label • 75% red 25% white • PO Box 121 Wellington 7654 • jacranda@iafrica.com Ⓒ 864·1235

Things have been happening on the Tromp estate; winemaker Jan recently celebrated his 10th year of winemaking, his 70th birthday and the 40th anniversary of his marriage to Trish, who owns the farm with him. As promised, he's released his 03 Merlot, to 'a good reception'. He mentions that two more bird species have been spotted — what happens beyond the vineyards is as important as what happens to the harvest.

Cabernet Sauvignon ★★ Individual & rustically charming **01** was the last tasted. **Merlot** [NEW] ★★★ Soft & light textured, **03** shows a good tannin structure & deft oaking (Fr staves). **Debutante** ★★★ **01**, yr on, still a lightish but well-fruited cab/merlot blend (75/25) with clean tannins. 67/33 ratio for **03** (sample), fairly subdued, apparently needs time to show its best. Lightly Fr oaked. **Dry Red** ★★★ 'Debutante' under another name (correct labels not available at bottling time so old 'Dry Red' versions used instead); cab-merlot (79/21); **02** nice & soft, combo red & dark fruits, well integrated. 13% alc. **Chenin Blanc** ★★ Fast-forward to **03** (pvs was **99**); unwooded; soft, fruity-dry with pear tones, medium bodied. **Jerepigo** ★★★ Winter-warming **96**, 100% chenin; retasted, honeyed lanolin tone with slight savoury edge; individual & attractive. 18% alc. — *JN*

Jackal's River see Beaumont

Jack & Knox Winecraft

Somerset West ▪ Est/1stB 2001 ▪ Not open to the public ▪ Owners Graham Knox & Bruce Jack ▪ See under Flagstone & Siyabonga

It's energetic Graham Knox again, collaborating with creative fruit-sourcer(er) Bruce Jack (Flagstone Winery). They buzz around the winelands, winkling out exciting/unusual vineyards, capturing the essence of variety, nurturing the young and nursing the old back to life. And bottling under the most descriptive names: Frostline – from 1 000m high, not-quite-snowline Swartberg mountain vineyard); Outsider – 30-year-old 'uittand' block (dead vines leaving 'toothless' gaps); Green on Green (semillon colloquially called 'green grape' here in bygone days). Recent releases received raves from UK critics Malcolm Gluck, Tim Atkin, Anthony Rose and James Lawther. Grist to the mill of creative risk....

★★★★ **Green on Green** Textural rather than bright varietal tones garnered from Wllngtn vyd. **03** subtle beeswax maturity; silky with thread lemony freshness, leading to elegant conclusion. Native yeasts; Am/Fr oak, 30% new; 14.1% alc.

★★★★ **Frostline Riesling** ('Snowline' in pvs ed) Variety's aromatic pepper-lime delicacy in **03**. Fuller style, bone-dry with well-padded fruit richness, if short on riesling zing. Food partner rather than aperitif. From high in Swartberg; splash Elim sauvignon.

★★★★ **The Outsider Shiraz 02** brooding blockbuster. Ultra-ripe waves liquorice, crushed dark spice concentration, noticeable Am oak; tannins bolster chewy viscosity. Begs hearty game dish, further yr/2 calming. 14% alc. Swtlnd, Wrcstr, Tbgh, Bottlry vyds.

Frostline Chardonnay ★★★ ('Snowline' in pvs ed) **03** now shows vanilla, roast hazelnut aromas marching in bright, New World tandem. Slightly dimmer in mouth; smooth body; after-glow of 15% alc advocates early drinking. Barrel-fermented Fr/Am oak, 30% new.

East of Eden Cabernet Sauvignon 02 one-off, never released. – *AL*

▪ *Jackson's of Stanford* see Mauroma

Jacobsdal Estate

Stellenbosch ▪ Est 1916 ▪ 1stB 1974 ▪ Tasting & sales at Bergkelder (see entry) ▪ Owner Dumas Ondernemings (Pty) Ltd ▪ Winemaker/viticulturist Cornelis Dumas, with Hannes Dumas ▪ 100 ha (cab, pinotage, chenin, sauvignon) ▪ 600 tons 7–10 000 cs own label 100% red ▪ PO Box 11 Kuils River 7579 ▪ info@jacobsdal.co.za ▪ www.jacobsdal.co.za ©/ ☎ 905·1360

After planting small blocks of cabernet sauvignon for more than two decades – the estate enjoys (or should that be suffers?) dryland conditions – Cornelis Dumas was able to make his first commercial Cab in 2001. A follow-up 02 is now in barrel and available *en primeur* via the Distell Vinoteque's futures scheme. Dumas' speciality remains pinotage, which he's been making the traditional way since 1966. And he isn't taking his eye off the ball: 'My goal is still to make more classic red wines which age well'.

★★★★ **Pinotage** One of the originals (first made **66**), still made traditionally: 25-35-yr-old dryland bushvines, native yeasts, open fermenters, free-run juice only, 12-18 mths small Fr oak. **01** marks an improvement on pvs two vintages. Remains resolutely artisanal, rustic, but shows very good fruit concentration. Will evolve into something classic. **00** (★★★) maintained pinot-like flavour spectrum of pvs; lowish alc & light tone combine to strict, almost austere effect.

Cabernet Sauvignon Made exactly like the Pinotage, from dryland bushvines 8–20 yrs old. (Interestingly, transferred to barrel only 6-7 mths after harvest – ie in June; only Fr oak used.) Maiden **01** (unrated sample) was a bold but carefully modulated statement of rich fruit & velvet tannin. **02** not tasted. – *RK*

▪ *Jacobus de Wet* see Baarsma

Janéza Private Cellar

*Robertson ▪ Est 2000 ▪ 1stB 2001 ▪ Visits by appt ▪ Fee for tourgroups R5 ▪ Open public holidays by appt ▪ Platters by appt Mon-Fri during opening hours ▪ Owners Jan & Eza Wentzel ▪ Winemaker Jan Wentzel ▪ Viti consultant Briaan Stipp ▪ 18 ha (cab, merlot, shiraz, chard, sauvignon) ▪ 3 000 cs own label 80% red 20% white ▪ PO Box 306 Bonnievale 6730 ▪ jan. eza@lando.co.za ▪ www.janeza.co.za ⓒ **082·978·7020** ☎ (023) 616·2848*

History meets tradition on Jan and Eza Wentzel's stretch outside Bonnievale. The farm's history includes owners from both their families; the winemaking methods they use are traditional: 'We want to make full-bodied, fruity wines from the best grapes, as naturally and with as little influence as possible.' Traditionalists and historians note: the tasting area (like the cellar, attractively converted from stables and cattle pens) is open by appointment only.

★★★★ **Tresuva** 'Three Grapes' in Spanish name are cab (50%), shiraz & merlot from selected blocks, made traditionally, 13-16 mths Fr/Am oak. 14.5% alc. **01** had intense earthy/savoury palate, firm long aftertaste. **02** (★★★) shows vintage's light herbacious tone (despite seemingly ripe 14.5% alc), slightly grainy tannins.

Chardonnay ★★★ **04** shy baked apple & lees aromas, followed by bright fruit-salad flavours; hint of sweetness on finish; unwooded. **Sauvignon Blanc** ★★★ **04** entrée of green herbs & nettles, crisp, steely palate, piercing freshness perhaps a little overdone given the fruit-weight. 12% alc. — *TM*

Jantara see Cape Vineyards
Jardin see Jordan

Jason's Hill Private Cellar

*Slanghoek (see Worcester map) ▪ Est/1stB 2001 ▪ Tasting & sales Mon-Fri 9-5 Sat 10-1 Sun by appt ▪ Fee R10 ▪ Closed Easter Fri, Dec 25 & Jan 1 ▪ Tours at 2 pm during harvest ▪ Cheese platters all day Fri-Sat in summer; Sun & winter by appt ▪ Facilities for children ▪ Farm produce ▪ Conferencing for max 50 ▪ Owner/viticulturist Sakkie du Toit ▪ Winemaker Ivy du Toit (Jan 2001) ▪ 100 ha (13 varieties r/w) ▪ 600 tons 50% red 45% white 5% rosé ▪ Brand for customer: Wolvenbosch (UK) ▪ PO Box 14 Rawsonville 6845 ▪ jasonshill@lando.co.za ▪ www.jasonshill. com ⓒ **(023) 344·3256** ☎ (023) 344·3146*

As a child Ivy du Toit spent all her spare time in the vineyards, so when she asked her father Sakkie to give her a small quantity of shiraz (the family farm supplied Slanghoek co-op), he humoured her, little knowing that he would soon be building her a cellar. Three years later Ivy – aged 23 – won the 2003 Diners Club Young Winemaker of the Year Award, the first woman to do so. With no formal training, Ivy credits feminine intuition for her remarkable skill. But if you add her drive ('my dad always said no-one ever died of hard work') and humility ('the best thing is I'm still young enough to learn much more about everything'), clearly you have a winning formula.

★★★★ **Noble Late Harvest** 🆕 Shimmering golden **03** dessert; 50/50 chenin/muscat d'A. High-toned, fresh honey/nutty fragrance; luscious but not over-heavy, slightly cloying finish. 12.8% alc. 109g/ℓ sugar.

Cabernet Sauvignon ★★★ **01** developing some mocha/mushroom features to dark berried bouquet. Fresher though solid mouthful; oak/fruit/tannins well-integrated for current drinking. 15% alc. **Merlot 01** ★★★ **01** (retasted mid-2004, as were all reds below) ripe, sweet-oak-laced red plums; soft fleshy fruit, balanced tannins. Hint alc glow (14.7%) suggests best open soon. Fr casks, 14 mths. **Pinotage** ★★★ **01** confected oak vanillins leading quiet red-berry notes; smooth, light-textured & less weighty than 14.5% alc would suggest. Best over next yr. 10 mths used Fr oak. **Shiraz** ★★★ **01** subdued gamey/ sweet berry bouquet; sweet oak flavours dominate; alc warmth in tail. Drink up. 20% new Am oak, rest old Fr. 15% alc. **Rosé 04** blend shiraz, pinotage, merlot; dry. 14% alc. Not available for tasting. **Chardonnay** ★★ **03** forward butterscotch, sweet vanilla powdery confection, strongly reprised in tail; uncomplicated, lightweight creaminess. Fermented/

5 mths Fr oak. 13.5% alc. **Sauvignon Blanc ★★★ 03** well-timed peaking to win Diners Club Young Winemaker of Year for Ivy du Toit. Also VDG; MIWA Gold. Retasted, retains some dried grassy perfume; palate less persuasive; lightish, short. **Ivy du Toit White Blend** NEW **★★★ 03** blend equal parts semillon, sauvignon, chardonnay; still youthfully unintegrated. Brisk dried grass, citrus aromas well to fore; sweet oak vanillins prominent on med-bodied palate; good thread balancing acid; may harmonise, gain extra half-star. Fermented/ 8 mths new Fr oak. 12.8% alc. SA Woman Winemaker of Year award.

> **Chenin** ☺ **★★★ 04** invitingly fresh, delicate sweet melon, guava tones, lively medium-bodied sipping; fruitily dry. 12% alc.

Discontinued: **Semillon**, **Jasonté Vin Sec** — *AL*

▪ *Jay Gatsby* see Third World Wines

JC le Roux

Stellenbosch ▪ 1stB 1983 ▪ Tasting & sales Mon-Fri 8.30-4.30 Sat 9-4 Sun (Sep-Apr only) 10-3 ▪ Fee R20 ▪ Tour & AV show Mon-Fri 10, 11.30, 3 Sat 10, 12 Sun (Sep-Apr only) 11, 12 Mid Dec-Jan 10, 11, 12, 2, 3 ▪ Breakfasts & light lunches Tue-Sat 10-3 Sun brunch (Sep-Apr only) 10-1 Booking essential ▪ Closed Easter Fri/Sun, Dec 25, Jan 1 ▪ Tourgroups ▪ Gifts ▪ Conferences ▪ Owner Distell ▪ Winemaker Melanie van der Merwe (1995), with Hentie Germishuys & Wilhelm Pienaar (Oct 2002/April 2004) ▪ Farm manager Willem Laubscher; viticulturist Bennie Liebenberg (both Jan 2000) ▪ 27 ha own vyds ▪ 766 000 cs 20% red 80% white ▪ ISO 9200 certified ▪ PO Box 184 Stellenbosch 7599 ▪ jclr@distell.co.za ▪ www.jcleroux.co.za Ⓒ **865·2590** 🖷 865·2586*

In the decade Melanie van der Merwe has been mistress of this sparkling cellar, she's seen the words of famed champagne widow Lily Bollinger – 'I drink (champagne) when I'm happy and when I'm sad' – begin to gain currency. Melanie vdM explains: 'Bubbly is no longer confined to special occasions. Just as we think nothing of eating out any day of the week, we're perceiving sparkling as an everyday drink.' With this in mind the range adapted to suit most occasions and tastes, though personally MvdM believes it's 'still important to put my signature on every wine made'. The restaurant at the chic *maison* in Devon Valley is under new management and, with numerous other enticements on offer, well worth a visit.

Pongrácz range

★★★★ **Desiderius** Pays homage since **96** to legendary viticulturist Desiderius Pongrácz (pronounce Pon-*grats*) with aristocratic packaging, boutique quantities. Classic 60/40 chardonnay/pinot blend, Stbosch grapes, bunch-pressed. Latest **98** generous mousse, caramel & apple/quince nose & opulent palate from 5+ yrs on lees. **97** was slightly lighter, less complex.

★★★★ **Pongrácz** Applauded brut-style NV sparkler, blend as above. Latest has sherbety sea-spray/'rock pool' bouquet. Shorter time on lees (2 yrs), so not as rich as the above. Bracing acidity, persistent, appley finish.

Méthode Cap Classique range

★★★★ **Scintilla** Dominated by chardonnay (75%), bottle-matured 4½ yrs on lees. Attractive embossed bottle hints at classy contents. Maiden **98** poised & elegant but presenting attractive black fruit flavour & weight. Yr on, more complexity on nose (also some honey & slight funkiness which suggest caution be applied when cellaring) rich, firm palate.

★★★★ **Pinot Noir** ✓ Latest **96** a fine mezzo to Chardonnay's soprano. Black-fruit heft, minerality softened by strawberries-&-cream flavours. Forceful impression bolstered by complexity imparted by 7 yr *sur lie* ageing. Stylish, with lazy bubbles, dry finish (7.8g/ℓ sugar).

★★★★ Pinot Noir Rosé A must-taste for those who (mistakenly) think pink sparklers frivolous. Debut **00** followed by current bottling **96**. Enticing partridge-eye colour,
characteristic pinot earthiness, strawberries & cherries on nose & palate. Weighty,
pleasantly dry (9g/ℓ sugar).

★★★★ La Vallée ✓ From pinot gris, idiosyncratic & popular semi-dry bubbly (33g/ℓ sugar).
Latest **99** takes a while to open up in glass; apple-pie & cream aromas intermingle
with grilled nuts, chamomile, plus honey notes from 4 yrs bottle-age.

★★★☆ Chardonnay All-white sparkler, driest of range (±6g/ℓ sugar), classically long-
matured (5-9 yrs on lees). Latest **97** shows apple compôte richness; round, toffee-apple palate with earthy chalk tones. Developing complexity.

Sparkling range

All carbonated; NV unless noted. **Le Domaine ★★★** Sweet party fizz from sauvignon,
Muscat, chenin, with floral & spicy muscat tones, lively bubbles, low 7.8% alc. **La Chan-
son ★★★** Big-volume ruby-hued sweet sparkler. Low 7.7% alc, with abundant berry fruit
from mix red varieties. Tannins provide contrast, absorb some of the sweetness. **Sauvignon Blanc ★★★** Summer holiday bubbly. Latest **04** with grass & Granny Smith apple
aromas; tastes sweeter than 11g/ℓ sugar suggests. **JC Blue ★★** Aimed at younger market, packaged in jewel-blue bottle with screwcap & easy-sipping straw. Soft, semi-
sweet, fairly explosive bubbles. Floral perfume with touch muscat. 187ml. — *CvZ*

Jean Daneel Wines

*Napier ▪ Est/1stB 1997 ▪ Visits by appt ▪ Owners/winemakers Jean & René Daneel ▪ 3.25 ha ▪
42 tons 3 000 cs 30% red 70% white ▪ PO Box 200 Napier 7270 ▪ jdwines@worldonline.co.za
© (028) 423-3724 🖷 (028) 423-3789*

Having made a name for himself at Buitenverwachting and Morgenhof, Jean Daneel
made the break every winemaker dreams of: he set up his own cellar (in a renovated stable in Franschhoek) in 1997 and started producing under his own name. He likes to buy
grapes from a variety of sources, but with two sons eager to enter the industry, he also
wanted his own vineyard. Out-of-control prices in Franschhoek sent him further afield. He
found a small property in the emerging Napier area and spent 2004 preparing the soil.
Chenin lovers who missed his previous vintages (the bottles seem to fly) will be pleased
that the 2004 harvest provided 'a great yield'; with any luck he'll be ready to release his
first port and sparkling wine this year.

Signature series

★★★☆ Cabernet Sauvignon-Merlot Revisited **01** (★★★★☆) (75/25 blend), showing
brilliant development since last ed. Cassis marzipan layered with slight leafy
notes, dense tannins, restrained, elegant mid-palate flavours, great length. Fruit
evident despite 22 mths new Fr oak, ample development potential — 8 yrs min.
Stbosch fruit. *Decanter* ★★★★. Pvs **02** was robust, dense. WO Coastal — as are all
these except where indicated.

★★★☆ Chenin Blanc Signature After flavoursome, richly multi-layered & oaky **02**, a
leap with magnificent **03** (★★★★★) ✓ to starry placing as Guide's Wine of the
Year. Sumptuous aromas of apricot, pineapple foreshadow honeysuckle, marzipan flavours. These wrapped together with 14% alc & dense textures in superbly
balanced palate; restrained, persistent finish. Dry — no 'enriching' sweetness
needed with this quality, finesse, but complexity & creaminess of mouthfeel enhanced by 7 mths Fr oak, 20%. From low yielding Stbosch vyds.

Initial series

New stunningly attractive, minimalist front-label for wines listed last ed just varietally.

★★★★ Cabernet Sauvignon-Merlot ✓ Revisited maiden **01** (54/46 blend), savoury/
herbal notes. Fine tannins add touch refined austerity, suggest 5 yrs future development. 14.5% alc. 22 mths Fr oak. Frhoek, Stbosch fruit. MIWA gold.

Chenin Blanc-Sauvignon Blanc 03 ★★★ Honeysuckle, herbaceous aromas, then tautly structured palate, elegant despite 14% alc; more restrained successor to **02**, where oak, honeycomb notes enhance complexity. WO Frhoek. — *MF*

John B see Rietvallei
John Faure see Ruitersvlei

Jean le Riche

This popular pair of NV carbonated sparklers from Simonsig now discontinued. Last tasted were: **Vin Sec** ★★ Attractive half-dry blend chenin/colombard. **Vin Doux** ★★ Aromatic, with fruity-sweet grapey palate.

Jonkerskloof `NEW`

Budget-priced quaffing wines in 500ml and 2/5ℓ packs by Robertson Winery for Vinimark. All light in alc (±11% unless mentioned), NV. **Dry Red** ★★ Tasty berry-fruited *vin ordinaire* with low tannins. **Rosé** ★★ Pale, light-textured, softly sweet. **Johannisberger** ★★ Quiet but pleasant fruity off-dry white. 10% alc. **Late Harvest** ★★ Honeyed semi-sweet with gentle tropical tone. — *DH*

Jonkheer

Robertson ▪ Est 1912 ▪ 1stB 1956 ▪ Visits by appt ▪ Closed public holidays ▪ Proclaimed conservation area ▪ 4×4 trail ▪ Owners Nicholas Jonker & sons ▪ Winemakers Erhard Roothman & Dirk Jonker (1970/1992) ▪ Viticulturists Andries Jonker & Gideon van Niekerk (1985/1981) ▪ 185 ha (cab, chard, muscat de F) ▪ 2 500 tons 15 000 cs own label + 1.2m cs for customers, incl Semaya (US & Scandinavia) ▪ 30% red 70% white ▪ PO Box 13 Bonnievale 6730 ▪ info@ jonkheer.co.za ▪ www.jonkheer.co.za ℭ (023) 616·2137/8/9 🖷 (023) 616·3146

The Jonkers are reaping the rewards of their labours. The first phase of the cellar revamp now complete, the new fully automatic punch-down system 'did wonders' for the reds (and their sleep?). They doubled the cooling facilities and tripled-insulated the roof, significantly reducing ambient temperatures and 'preserving whole new flavour dimensions in the whites'. Also tripled is their Family Reserves' representation in top hotels. Then there's the baby in the family, the Dead Frogge Chardonnay, the story behind it first told in last year's guide: 'We had so many requests, it was virtually sold out prior to release,' says a mildly bemused Dirk Jonker. They've planted their first rows of petit verdot: 'We believe it has a home in the Robertson Valley and can't wait to get our hands on the first crop.'

Jonkheer range

★★★★ **Pinotage** Dense & chewy **02** (sample), gamey/porty aromas matched by pleasing palate sweetness; big, booming style. 14% alc. No **01**. **00**, mid-2004, significantly quieter, better-mannered & -balanced. Yr 100% new oak.

★★★★ **Chardonnay Family Reserve** Serious & classically styled, 100% new oak fermented, *sur lie* 8-12 mths, native yeasts. Enveloping richness on **02**, retaste shows thrilling lime-gold colour; concentrated aromas of dried peaches, honey & botrytis; huge, complex, creamy palate, exceptional length. Impressive wine. 14% alc.

★★★★ **Dead Frogge Chardonnay** Name (inspired by remark in a pvs guide) belies a wine of considerable gravity. Selection of best barriques of vintage; full-bodied & overtly oaky. Maiden **02** evinced ripe peaches lashed with toast, toffee & butterscotch; long full-fruited finish. **03** (★★★★) bilows toast & grapefruit marmalade; big & somewhat blowsy, heavily wooded; our sample appears to lack the elegance of pvs release. Must just be in a youthfully gawky phase. 14.2% alc.

★★★★ **Muscatheer Family Reserve Muscat de Frontignan** ✓ Started off in **00** as a new-wave fortified dessert featuring lower alc & sugar (±15%, 114g/ℓ), presented in suitably elegant 500ml bottle. Yet **04** (sample), aptly nicknamed 'Monster', is the anthesis: massively sweet (288g/ℓ) & weighty, high (but rounded) spirit – 17%

alc. **00**, retasted, very different: lightweight, elegant, already far evolved with meaty, slightly sherried character, needs to be drunk.

Cabernet Sauvignon Family Reserve 03 (sample) introverted mid-2004; muted nose with hint of fennel; sweet & juicy palate entry, well-fruited but unevolved; on present form merits ★★★★, but could evolve & improve; Dirk J feels it's the 'best since 1912'. **Cabernet Sauvignon-Merlot 03** (sample) youthful fuchsia rim; wild bramble tones with cedar & cigarbox; ripe, lively palate; chewy wine, full-bodied (14% alc). New World-inclined. Promising ★★★★. **99** (★★★) retaste, shows dried fruit/meat, quite complex but old-style, with soft herbal tones; needs drinking. **Chardonnay** ★★★ Unoaked; **04** (sample) delicate floral/honeysuckle nose; full-flavoured with refreshing limy acidity. **Buccaneer Touriga Nacional** ★★★★ Ruby style port, matured 18 mths in 2nd fill fr oak; **01**, retasted, russet-edged, complex, with hint dusty prune; rum & raisin flavour, lovely spicy touriga fruit. 500ml. 18% alc.

Bakenskop range

★★★★ **Red Muscadel** ✓ Traditional-style fortified dessert; sweet, warming, muscatty. Latest is luscious **04** (sample) herb & tea-leaf aromas; slightly higher-toned, less fruity than White; crème brûlée flavours with hint of dried fruit & touch raisin; marvellous silky texture.

★★★★ **White Muscadel** ✓ Raisiny fortified dessert, beloved of competition judges. **04** (sample) burnished orange-gold colour; on nose, cascade of sweet floral aromas (including orange rind, honeysuckle & dried fruit), full-sweet lucious palate with citrus underlay; slippery, delicious.

Cabernet Sauvignon ★★★ Briefly oaked **03**, retasted, redcurrant jam nose, hint eucalyptus; dry & taut with sour-plum flavours, grainy tannins; needs food. **Merlot** ★★★ **03** medium ruby hue; choc & plum tones; softer, mellower than Cab, partly thanks to 4g/ℓ sugar. **Chardonnay** ★★★ Unwooded **04** (sample) offers pears & marzipan aromas, sweet candy nose, nice melon mouthful with slight creaminess on finish. Latest versions of **Chenin Blanc, Colombard** and **Blanc de Noir** not tasted. **Sauvignon Blanc** ★★★ **04** (sample) notes of dusty nettle; crisp & lean; good minerally texture. **Blanc de Blanc** ★★ **04** (sample) herby green melon aromas, fairly full melon/apple flavours. — *TM*

Joostenberg Wines

Paarl ▪ Est 1999 ▪ Tasting, sales & tours Fri 2-5 Sat 10-2 ▪ Closed Easter Fri/Sun/Mon, Dec 25/26 & Jan 1 ▪ Owner Myburgh Winery (Pty) Ltd ▪ Winemaker Tyrrel Myburgh (Dec 1999) ▪ Viticulturists Anette Myburgh & Steven Pons (Jun 2002) ▪ 33 ha (cab, shiraz, merlot, chenin, viognier) ▪ 200 tons 8 000 cs own label 35% red 50% white 15% dessert ▪ PO Box 82 Elsenburg 7607 ▪ joostenberg@mweb.co.za ▪ www.joostenberg.co.za © 884-4932 ✉ 884-4052

No new plantings 'and not much new in the cellar', admits winemaker Tyrrel Myburgh. What *is* new is firstborn Sebastian (so Anette M is tending the babe as well as the vines), and what's news is the performance of the Noble Late Harvest 03 which took a gold at the most recent International Wine Challenge and a Fairbairn trophy back home (not to mention five stars here). Looking for export possibilities, Tyrrel and brother Philip are investigating several opportunities in the US. 'We are doing everything we can to improve the quality of our wines', adds the vinifier. 'Super-premium-quality SA wines need to be internationally recognised if this country wants to be taken seriously.'

★★★★ **Joostenberg** Serious, rather restrained blend cab/merlot/shiraz (56/33/11) in ripe & spicy **02**; rich fruit over big dry tannins. 14% alc; well balanced 18 mths oak, 25% new. Savoury, delicious but needs few yrs in bottle (should keep 5 more). **01** was politely assertive, persistent blend merlot (60%), cab; showing ripe berry fruits.

★★★★ **Merlot-Shiraz** ✓ Generous offering of plum & minty/leafy dark choc on **02**, 85/15 blend, with fresh acid, robust tannin. Spicy **03** (59/37, plus splashes of cab, touriga & a drop viognier), touch riper, rounder, more generously balanced, but still tight — give yr/2. Both 14% alc; older-wood maturation.

★★★★ **Chenin Blanc Natural Sweet** Last made was **01**, luscious yet elegant, light-textured dessert. Old-oak-fermented/aged 7 mths. 11.5% alc.

★★★★ **Chenin Blanc Noble Late Harvest** ✓ Retasted **02** no longer introverted, but fresh, pure, supple, offering notes of sultana, honey, orange-blossom. **03** (★★★★★) even more delicately powerful, complex, with racier acidic tension to sweeter but fine honeyed richness. Its elegance & depth admired by others too: FCTWS trophy; IWC gold. These native yeast-fermented/aged 8-12 mths older wood.

Chenin Blanc ★★★ Quiet pleasure from lightly elegant **04**, with some thatch & honey hints; dry, crisply green finish. 14% alc. Discontinued: **Cabernet**; **Chardonnay Barrel-Fermented**; **Chardonnay Unwooded**; **Tinta Barocca Cape Vintage**. — *TJ*

Jordan Winery

Stellenbosch ▪ Est 1982 ▪ 1stB 1993 ▪ Tasting & sales Mon-Fri 10-4.30 Sat 9.30-2.30 (Nov-Apr); Mon-Fri 10-4.30 Sat 9.30-12.30 (May-Oct) ▪ Fee R15 refundable with purchase ▪ Group tastings for up to 15 by appt ▪ Closed Easter Fri-Mon, Dec 25 & Jan 1 ▪ Tours by appt only (no public holidays) ▪ BYO picnic ▪ Function room for special occasions ▪ Owners Jordan family ▪ Winemakers Gary & Kathy Jordan ▪ Production Sjaak Nelson (2002) ▪ Viticulturists Ted & Gary Jordan (1982) ▪ 105 ha (cabs s/f, merlot, shiraz, chard, chenin, sauvignon, riesling) ▪ 900 tons 65 000 cs 55/45 red/white ▪ PO Box 12592 Die Boord 7613 ▪ info@jordanwines.com sales@jordanwines.com ▪ www.jordanwines.com ☎ 881·3441 🖷 881·3426

After a short sojourn at this impeccable winery, Johan Kruger departed for Diemersdal, and founding winemakers and co-owners Gary and Kathy Jordan, who'd been hoping to take a well deserved step back, found themselves at the coalface once more, with their long-time production chief Sjaak Nelson. All enjoyed the long, late 2004 harvest, and with 'superb flavours' developing in the barrels, Gary J's only regret was the shortage of cab. A new block, named Sophia's Vineyard, should alleviate the shortfall in the long term. A more immediate issue was the small fleet of excavators which had been wrecked during Sophia's preparation. So unyielding was the granite substrate, the contractors eventually had to resort to dynamite, and for a few days the Stellenboschkloof thundered and shook (naturally, puns about 'explosions of flavour' abounded). Last year also saw the local launch of their good-value Bradgate range, as well as their first Shiraz.

★★★★ **Cabernet Sauvignon** Viticultural attention pays off in better as well as lesser vintages for this premier-league cab. Sensitive vinification also promotes pleasure from lesser **02**; gentle tannins to firm, not smother plum, cassis flesh, promote medium-term drinking. 15% alc. **01** wide, long tannins for tension, longevity. Some minerally tautness from 7% cab f. 14.5% alc. Concours Mondial trophy; VDG. **00** (★★★★★) IWC gold; 19 mths new/used Fr oak. Deserve 4-7 yrs to show best.

★★★★ **Cobblers Hill** Selection commemorates the Jordan cobbler forbears, as 'ultimate expression of an outstanding wine'. Make-up depends on vintage; **02** cab/merlot (85/15) very structured, with more cab austerity, fresh cassis/blackberry focus; bigger, broader feel than plush-textured **01** (52% cab, 24% each merlot/cab f); mouthfilling mocha, plum flesh; dense though fine, soft tannins give grip for long haul. Both ±15% alc. 14% alc, 2 yrs new oak. *WS* 90-rating.

★★★★★ **CWG Jordan Sophia 02** 3-barrel Cobblers Hill, Cab mix, as pvs. Impressively polished dark berry/cedar/wood smoke; youthful cab austerity, resistant tannins shielding sweet-fruited richness. 2 yrs oak. CWG Auction only. 15% alc.

★★★★ **Merlot** One of few achieving impact via quiet presence, not over-extraction/oaking. Stylish, focused **03** beautifully balanced; palate caressing yet fresh, persuasive plum/damson elegance; spicy/savoury extras extend pleasure. **02** stony/mineral charmer, quiet. Oak (yr new/used Fr) supports, juicy fruit carries, 14% alc.

★★★★ **Syrah** NEW **03**'s generous, rounded accessibility reflects west-facing slopes' warmer imprint; rich, supple texture infused with roast meat, dark spices. As with all these reds, low yields of ripe grapes ensure concentration to balance even higher alcs – here ±14%. Mix Fr/Am barrels, 14 mths.

★★★☆ **Chameleon Cabernet Sauvignon-Merlot** Slots between Bradgate & Cobblers Hill; stylistically more in common with former though sterner-framed, more obvious oak, but also ageworthy. **03** cassis/cedary/smoky intensity; medium-bodied, dry; can improve with ±4 yrs. Inc dash cab f. Matured 14 mths Fr oak.

★★★★★ **Nine Yards Chardonnay Reserve** Statement of terroir, from 15 yr old, east-slope vyd. Classically styled in modern vein: richly oaked (yr new Fr); dry; ultra-creamy texture with probing pickled lime/citrus zest clarity; imposing yet with winning charm, elegance. **03** still zestily fresh; should be magnificent in further 5-8 yrs.

★★★★ **Chardonnay** From maiden **93**, some worthwhile award each vintage; **03** Concours Mondial gold, usual penetrating limey/leesy complexity; barrelled creamy richness all delivered with understatement, poised balance. Includes 12% fruit-enhancing tank-fermented wine. Barrel-fermented (Burgundian oak), *sur lie* 9 months. 14% alc.

★★★☆ **Chardonnay Unoaked** 〖NEW〗 Third member of chardonnay trio both stylish & crowd-pleasing. As above, lees enrichment; partial malo. Mature vyds deliver sustained fruit, body. Ripe lime overtones; flexible leesy padding, further accessibility from ±4g/ℓ sugar.

★★★★ **Sauvignon Blanc** ✓ Exhilarating without varietal over-statement. **04** fusion ripe figs, gooseberries fired up by bracing minerality. Pure, richly flavoursome, long. In style of **03** but greater concentration, panache. 13% alc. **02** rated 90 *WS* points.

★★★★ **Blanc Fumé** ✓ Wooded sauvignon, richer, more sophisticated than above. **03** can still grow. Rich 'fumé' complexity from both fruit/barrel, grape's character remains. Sleek, elegant, tropical fruit persistence, lifted by 31% tank-fermented component.

★★★★ **Mellifera Noble Late Harvest 04** unsettled just post-bottling; suggests promising racy mouthful, laced with honey, apricot, peppery zest. Neither heavy nor oversweet; follows **03**'s adaptability in sundowner or nightcap role. From riesling.

★★★★ **Chenin Blanc** Consistent, quietly assertive, good all-rounder at table. **03** firmly structured, with spicy, pear/honey presence, expansive finish. Mellow rather than off-dry (5.5g/ℓ sugar). Barrel/tank-fermented (69/31), 7 mths on lees.

Chameleon Sauvignon Blanc-Chardonnay ★★★☆ Chenin joins regular, reliable partners (44/40/16) in **04** 'for richness'. Weighty mouthfeel; expressive concentrated flavours, bracing fruity freshness add balanced support. **Rhine Riesling** ★★★ Off-dry with spicy-limy distinction. **04** (sample) racy tension to balance 9g/ℓ sugar; fruity persistence.

Bradgate range

'Easy-drinkers' developed for world-wide markets, but also available locally.

Chenin Blanc-Sauvignon Blanc ☺ ★★★ More character than most in crowded category. Expressive floral freshness on previewed **04** 59/41 blend; sauvignon zest extends rounded fruity persistence. 13.5% alc.

Syrah ★★★★ ✓ **03** flourishes convincing spicy, smoky, gamey fragrance; supple, dry, yet palate-friendly & packed with flavour. Delicious. 13.5% alc. Fr/Am oak finish. **Cabernet Sauvignon-Merlot** ★★★★ ✓ Step-up **03** (with 17% shiraz) tasty, fresh mouthful cassis/ smoky persistence. Dry, medium-bodied, compact, buffed for immediate satisfaction. Concours Mondial gold confirms quality. 13.5% alc. — *AL*

Joubert-Tradauw Private Cellar

Tradouw (see Little Karoo map) ▪ Est/1stB 1999 ▪ Tasting & sales Mon-Fri 9-5 Sat 10-2 ▪ Breakfasts, teas & deli lunches Mon-Fri ▪ Tours by appt ▪ Lentelus B&B, facilities for children & many other attractions ▪ Owner Joubert Family Trust ▪ Winemaker/viticulturist Meyer Joubert (1999) ▪ 30 ha (merlot, shiraz, chard) ▪ 2 500 cs own label 70% red 30% white ▪ Range for customer: Unplugged 62 ▪ PO Box 15 Barrydale 6750 ▪ joubert.r62@ lando.co.za ▪ www.joubert-tradauw.co.za © (028) 572·1619 🖷 (028) 572·1315

For Meyer Joubert, the Tradouw Valley is proving to be a place of discovery. It's climatically continental, and his first shiraz bottling shows so much potential he's inclined to think it, and not slow-ripening cab, will be his future focus. He's itching to plant pinot (upon arrival of clean, virus-free material) on a small southerly slope of weathered shale. And move towards biodynamic/organic cultivation. Vintage 2004 was disappointing for cab, outstanding for shiraz and chardonnay, and thrilling for little boys (the birth of Meyer's and Beate's third child). Make this hospitable winery a weekend destination this vintage: wino's, foodies, young and not-so-young, overnighters, hikers, bikers, offroaders — all are made to feel wonderfully welcome.

★★★★ **R62 Cabernet Sauvignon-Merlot** Classically oriented (as all these) blend, 60% cab in **01**. Firmly built but elegant, with savoury spice, tobacco, attractive ripe berry fruit. As was **00**, happily mouthfilling; lightly firm structure & unobtrusive support by yr Fr oak. Should keep good few yrs. Alc 14%. Natural approach: part native-yeast fermentation, no fining/filtration.

★★★★ **Chardonnay** Elegant, silky, thoughtful **02** attractively balanced, with lovely citrus fruit, fresh vibrant acidity & sensitive supportive oaking — barrel fermented/matured, 20% new. 14% alc. **01** was rather lighter-weight.

★★★★ **Syrah** 〈NEW〉 Thoroughly delicious, supple **03** has plenty of spice, smoky red berries; lively & moreish despite big 14.5% alc. Well-judged oak (yr, 80/20 Fr/Am). Unfined/unfiltered. When vines mature in a few yrs, should be something special. — *TJ*

▮ *Journey's End* see Western Wines

JP Bredell Wines

Stellenbosch (see Helderberg map) ▪ *1stB 1991* ▪ *Tasting & sales Mon-Fri 8.30-5* ▪ *Fee R4/ glass* ▪ *Closed public holidays* ▪ *Tours by appt* ▪ *Owner Helderzicht Trust* ▪ *Winemaker Anton Bredell* ▪ *95 ha (cab, merlot, pinotage, shiraz, souzão, tinta, tourigas f/n)* ▪ *7 000 cs own label 80% red 20% port* ▪ *PO Box 5266 Helderberg 7135* ▪ *jpbredellwyne@new.co.za* ✆ *842·2478* 🖷 *842·3124*

Beefy winemaker/owner Anton Bredell makes big wines. So he holds them back a few years, the only sure way to protect the more undisciplined drinkers amongst us from themselves. Case in point is the maiden (00) Cab: originally due for release in 2003, is still considered unready. In its stead comes the 02, which Anton B says is the first he's (only just) prepared to relinquish. Despite some scorching of the berries in early January's heat, harvest 2004 produced the usual intense flavours. While the shiraz and merlot are showing early quality, Anton B assures it is the cab, currently 'the quiet one', which will grab the limelight — in (three? four? ten??) years, of course. In fact, says he, so exceptional is 2004, he's 'declaring' a port vintage. Can we possibly wait?

★★★★ **Merlot** Elegant, fine-boned, delicately scented **00** maturing well, revisited mid-2004; nose unfolding with cedar, violets & smoked meats, supple structure still cossets berry fruit. **01** (★★★★) big (14% alc) & plummy; not retasted for this ed.

★★★★ **Shiraz** Old-World style, yet juicy blackberry fruit bursting out of yr sweet vanilla Am oak, 14.5% alc to boot, **01** gives emphatic riposte with spiced 'cool' linear structure — and no clashing cymbals. Truly measured finish. **00** leather tones, chunkier fruit, bolder despite more moderate 13% alc. Best in exuberant youth.

★★★★ **De Rigueur 00** Unfined, unfiltered, the un- works. Which leaves all the brambly/ woodsmoke flavour jam-packed into latticework of sturdy tannins, sweet plum-jam finish. Blend cab, merlot & shiraz favoured with yr Fr oak. 14% alc.

★★★★ **Cabernet Sauvignon** 〈NEW〉 ✓ Full-blooded **02** deeply coloured/perfumed; wafting cedar scents, with cassis, ripe fruits in soft, easy tannin frame, tangy finish. Nothing simple, just so (too?) easy to engage in youth. 14 mths Fr oak, 30% new. 14.5% alc.

★★★★★ **Cape Vintage Reserve** Benchmark Cape port since first **91**. **98** much-awarded ('won all the medals/trophies on offer!'), shows stunning complexity, enduring length — yet with best to come in 5-10 yrs. Lots of everything: opulent black fruit, minty spice, power & grip. 5% touriga f now joining tinta, touriga, souzão (50/35/

10). 20% alc, 93g/ℓ sugar. Succulent, fine **97** only marginally the lesser; mellowing mid-2004. 20% alc, 86g/ℓ sugar. Both have VDG, FCTWS, JCMA awards.

★★★★ **Late Bottled Vintage** Not-so-serious but still weighty version of above – 'fireplace port', says Bredell; drink while waiting on those. Less structure, complexity, but rich & silky. Next **00** in sync with **99**; fruit-pud flesh in taut palate, herby tail. Tintas b & f/ souzão/touriga; 3 yrs wood; 19% alc; 94g/ℓ sugar. Ready, but, as pvs, no rush.

Discontinued: **Pinotage**; **Cabernet Sauvignon-Merlot**. – *DS*

Judex see Domaine Brahms

Kaapdal see Robertson Wide River

Kaapse Hoop see Vinfruco

Kaapse Pracht see Baarsma, Coppoolse Finlayson, Darling Cellars

Kaapse Vreugd see Coppoolse Finlayson

Kaaps Genoegen see Coppoolse Finlayson

Kaaps Geskenk see Coppoolse Finlayson

Kaapslig see Dominion

Kaapzicht Estate

*Stellenbosch ▪ Est 1969 ▪ 1stB 1984 ▪ Tasting & sales Mon-Fri 9-4.30 Sat & public holidays 9-12 ▪ Fee R10 ▪ Closed Easter Fri-Sun, Dec 25 & Jan 1 ▪ Tours by appt ▪ BYO picnic ▪ Self-catering chalet & separate 'Wingerd Kraal' braai area for ±70 people; conference/entertainment venue ℃ 906·1621 a/h ▪ Farm produce ▪ Conservation area ▪ Owner Steytdal Farm (Pty) Ltd ▪ Winemaker Danie Steytler, with Charl Coetzee (Jan 1979/2003) ▪ Viticulturists George Steytler, Charl Coetzee & Schalk du Toit (Jan 1984; Mar/Jun 2003) ▪ 146 ha (cab, merlot, pinotage, shiraz, chenin, sauvignon) ▪ 1 100 tons 35 000 cs own label 65% red 35% white ▪ PO Box 35 Koelenhof 7605 ▪ kaapzicht@mweb.co.za sales@kaapzicht-wines.com exports@kaapzicht-wines.com ▪ www.kaapzicht-wines.com ℃ **906·1620** ☎ 906·1622*

It was a year of awards and anniversaries for the Steytlers, though typically of these unassuming folk, one would scarcely know it. For Danie and his proudly pinotage blend, Vision, the Pichon Longueville Comtesse de Lalande trophy for best blended red at the London IWSC (Kanonkop and Vergelegen are sometime SA winners). Also a string of further accolades for this and their other wines. Excitingly, he expects similar quality from the 2004 harvest. New cellar aids include two red wine fermenters, giving reds more time on the skins; and doubled cooling capacity, allowing for 24-hour cold soaking for reds and benefitting fermenting whites. There's also a 10-ton Italian press for more reductive white wine making. The anniversaries? 20 years of bottling under the Kaapzicht label (a Weisser Riesling was their first wine), and for viticulturist George, two decades in the vineyards.

Steytler range

★★★★☆ **Vision** 'It's just such a good farm,' says Danie Steytler modestly of his signal achievements with this statement wine. Creative assemblage of ultra-ripe pinotage, cab, merlot; excellent 5-8 yrs+ maturation potential. **01** (★★★★★) another blockbuster but manages elegance, too. Dark, brooding appearance; richly concentrated, massive underlying structure discreetly cloaked in dense dark-berried fruit, wears its oak/alc very well, stately unfolding of tannins. Pinotage up to 40% from pvs ±37%, cab unchanged at 50%. 19 mths, new Fr barriques. 15% alc. Gold at Concours Mondial 2003. Impressive follow-up to **00** with hallmark chewy fruit in balance with weighty oak.

★★★★★ **Pinotage** Since maiden **98**, multiple show winner & pretender to Cape's pinotage crown. **01** (★★★★★) a perfect pinotage; excellent structure with round, ripe tannins; massive build (15.3% alc). 100% new Fr oak, yr. Showpiece for a sometimes maligned grape's best qualities. Ditto **00**, with well-managed tannins, balanced fruit & oak. From ±30-yr-old single-vyd. 2004 IWSC Best Pinotage.

Kaapzicht range

★★★★★ **CWG Auction Reserve Blend** NEW Barrel selection of Vision above. Massively built **01** — magisterial, a wine with undoubted presence. Enormous depth to dark-berried fruit, pinotage from this estate allowed to ripen & soften to velvety richness so achieves a genuinely seamless blend. Less yielding than version above. Sumptuous — for self-congratulatory occasions. 5–8 yrs good life ahead.

★★★★ **Cabernet Sauvignon** Immensely stylish **01** (★★★★★), shows classic restraint, but all the intensity, flavour there — cassis, lead pencil, firm but unobtrusive tannins. Finely judged & sleek, hides 15% alc. with ease. 19 mths Fr oak, 50% new. **00** darker, looser weave, less gravitas, no less pleasure. 14 mths Fr oak, 40% new. Worth ageing 5–8 yrs.

★★★★★ **CWG Cabernet Sauvignon** NEW **01** intense dark mulberry, slight sweetness from ultra ripe fruit, tannins still slightly rough, bodes well for long life. Deep-pile velvet richness, still brooding, sullen, but will open out & be splendid. 19 mths Fr oak, all new. One for the deep part of the cellar.

★★★☆ **Merlot** Intriguing mixed signals in **01** when retasted mid-2004, blackcurrant pastille, dark choc & smoked beef, palate with the softer tannic structure one expects from variety. Excellent fruit, oak slightly heavy-handed; should settle with bottle-ageing. 19 mths Fr, 35% new.

★★★★ **Pinotage** No denying Steytler has a way with pinotage, **01** tamed & turned into handsome number — sleek, suave & individual. Deep colour, dense fruit, tannins loosening mid-2004, slightly sweet finish. Small Fr oak, 2nd fill 15 mths. 14.4% alc. ABSA Top 20 finalist. On par with **00**. Both worth cellaring 2-4 yrs.

★★★★ **Shiraz** Whiffs leather & spice in **01**, still firm but richly fruity, just needs time to loosen. 17 mths Fr oak, 30% new, cleverly freshened with dash unwooded. Two bottlings, one EW, other NE. In style of meaty **00**, intense spice/tobacco tones & substantial palate weight (14.5% alc).

★★★★ **Bin-3** ✓ Balanced, accessible, crammed with dark berries & choc richness in **03**, blend merlot/cab with Steytler's beloved pinotage tucked in for good measure at 7%. Sleek & fat; amiable & just waiting to please. 50/50 staves/Fr barrels 9 mths. **02** similar style, less oak at 6 mths. Cellar 1-3 yrs for extra pleasure.

★★★☆ **Kaapzicht Estate Red** Upwardly mobile cab/shiraz blend (65/35), **03** components successfully submerge identities; rich, muscular, deep flavoured with black mulberry fruit, tannins ready only for resilient palates — better to wait 2-3 yrs. Matured 9 mths Fr staves. 14.6%.

★★★★ **Hanepoot Jerepigo** ✓ Excellent, chilled, for a breakfast in the bush; 100% muscat d'A, with grape's intoxicating perfume in **01**, honey & raisins on palate, thread of mint; should last good 5 yrs. Fairly high 18% alc.

Combination NEW ☺ ★★★ Chenin-led blend with sauvignon, will vary with vintage. **04** bright fruit, lively dry with mouthwatering lemony notes. 13.5% alc. **Cape View Classic Red** ☺ ★★★ **03** a real bargain. Shows sweetness of perfectly ripe fruit. Rich, meaty, classy quaffing. All-sorts red with cinsaut, malo on Fr staves. NB: 14.2% alc.

Chenin Blanc ★★★ **04** a big wine, deep flavoured with stewed quince & spiced apple, vibrant acidity not out of place here — structured to last. **Sauvignon Blanc** ★★★ **04** assertive but not showy, some green fig-leaf aromas/flavours, firm-fleshed & dry. Try with grilled fresh yellowtail. — *lvH*

Kakamas see Oranjerivier Wine Cellars

Kango Winery

Little Karoo ▪ Est 1976 ▪ 1stB 1977 ▪ Tasting & sales Mon-Fri 8-5 Sat 8-4.30 ▪ Tours by appt ▪ Picnic baskets by appt, or BYO ▪ Farm produce ▪ Owners 58 members ▪ Winemaker Flip Smith ▪ Viti consultant Willem Botha (2001) ▪ 295 ha (cab, merlot, pinotage, shiraz, chard, chenin,

colombard, hanepoot, muscadel r/w, sauvignon) ▪ *3 000 tons 18% red 82% white* ▪ *Export label: Adventure* ▪ *PO Box 46 Oudtshoorn 6620* ▪ *flip@kangowines.com* ▪ *www.kangowines. com* © *(044) 272·6065* 🖷 *(044) 279·1038/1339*

Flip Smith had a baptism of fire in 2004, what with a disappointing muscadel harvest, thanks to too much rain (in the Karoo!), and a power failure which disrupted production. He's put in place a different winemaking process, learnt from his father, Dassie, cellarmaster at Botha: 'The wines are made according to the family method,' he says, somewhat cryptically. Among the reds, there are three new wines: a Cab, Shiraz and as yet unchristened blend (none ready for tasting). For visitors as fond of their food as their wine, a fresh produce market sets up on a Saturday.

Mont Noir range

Merlot ★★★☆ 02 still available, still with ripe plums, cherries & choc – all nicely rounded from extra yr in bottle. **Pinotage ★★★** Big, burly **02** well upholstered with ripe plums. **Chardonnay ★★** Honeyed **02** very dry, firm; booming 14.5% alc. **Sauvignon Blanc ★ 03** lightly fruity, simple dry white. All WO W-Cape. **Chenin Blanc** & **Grand Cru** not tasted.

Rijkshof range

★★★★ Red Muscadel Coppery fortified dessert with gorgeous, open bouquet of honeysuckle & sweet spice; well rounded & beautifully mature; balanced sweetness; lightly higher fortification for latest bottling (17.4%). VG.

Red Jerepigo NEW **★★** Mahogany-hued warming drop with attractive sweet-sour tweak; mainly cab, dash chenin. **White Muscadel ★★☆** The new version has a rich golden colour; deep, syrupy, honey-caramel palate with touch of spice. ±17% alc. **Golden Jerepigo ★★★** White muscadel & chenin (50/50); appropriately golden hues; rich aromas; though NEW, already delightfully rounded & mature. **Hanepoot ★★** Latest version, though light on colour/nose, has bit more to offer; floral hints, balanced sweetness. **Ruby Port ★★** From tinta, but nothing like the Portuguese style; sweetly sippable nutty flavours, soft spirity bite. 16.5% alc. **Vintage Port** NEW **★★★★** From tinta, with local traditional-style low alc (17.4%); rich red/black berry bouquet, vanilla throughout (from 18 mths oak); smooth & sweet. WO W-Cape. All above NV. **Sparkling Wine** not tasted.

Garob range

Dry Red ☺ **★★★** Lightish berry-toned trattoria wine from merlot & cab (80/20); latest bottling has juicy, rounded tannins, whiffs fruitcake & bottle-age.

Dry White ★★ Lightish, bone-dry colombard/chenin combo (70/30) with fruity/floral nose & clean acidity. **Late Harvest ★★** Semi-sweet version of above; new bottling (unlike pvs) is bright, fresh & fruity. All NV; also in 2, 3 & 5ℓ packs. **Heerenhof** in 5ℓ pack not tasted; neither were **Vlakteplaas Red/White Muscadel**. *– DH*

Kanonkop Estate

Stellenbosch ▪ Est 1910 ▪ 1stB 1973 ▪ Tasting & sales Mon-Fri 8.30-5 Sat 9-12.30 ▪ Fee R10 ▪ Closed Easter Fri , Dec 25 & Jan 1 ▪ Traditional snoek barbecue only by appt (min 15 people) or BYO picnic ▪ Owners Johann & Paul Krige ▪ Winemaker Abrie Beeslaar (2002), advised by Beyers Truter ▪ Viticulturist Koos du Toit ▪ 100 ha (cabs s/f, merlot, pinotage) ▪ 500 tons ±40 000 cs 100% red ▪ PO Box 19 Elsenburg 7607 ▪ wine@kanonkop.co.za ▪ www.kanonkop.co.za © *884·4656* 🖷 *884·4719*

What response to expect from internationally acknowledged class act Kanonkop when asked about its winemaking philosophy, after decades of producing fine wine? Co-owner Johann Krige replies: 'To increase minimum quality requirements year on year – ask Michael Schumacher.' And what has this champion of the Cape's F1-wine-circuit recently done to tweak its performance? What many other competitors have: refurbished its processing cellar to incorporate hand-sorting tables; and brought on board a dedicated viticulturist (Koos du Toit, freeing winemaker Abrie Beeslaar to concentrate on vinification and elaboration, under the eagle eye of veteran Beyers Truter, now acting as a consultant after 20 years full-time on the estate). Which is to say, Krige & co have nothing out of the ordinary to up their performance. How do they stay ahead of the field then? Terroir? Undoubtedly. Great vineyards? But of course. Winemaker? Youthful, and still fairly new in the seat, but looking good. And? *Technology*. From the industrial heartland of the US. Krige reveals: 'I wore the T-shirt for ages. Now I finally got me a Harley-Davidson.'

★★★★☆ **Paul Sauer** Fine Bdx-style blend, one of few undoubted Cape classics – with recent yrs showing modern touches to classicism. Vinified traditionally, like all these, in open fermenters. **01**'s 64% cab less than usual 80%; with equal amounts cab f & merlot. From first sniff, obvious claims to illustrious lineage: violets, tea-leaf, black berries, presented subtly & superbly. Finely structured & balanced palate, strongly elegant, with succulent acidity & silky tannins, plentiful understated fruit. 26 mths new Fr oak will knit. Few more years will bring harmony, heralding rewarding, lengthy maturity. **00** very ripe but strikingly balanced.

★★★★★ **CWG Auction 'Kanonkop'** This from a selection of best barrels of above, so same basic stats, essentially similar. **01** certainly offers great structural finesse, lovely fruit, but somehow masked now by oaky effects. Time will tell. **00** not tasted.

★★★★ **Cabernet Sauvignon** More conservatively styled than siblings perhaps now are, from 30+ yr old vines. **01**'s spicy, tobacco, berry bouquet/palate cooperate with firm ripe tannins to offer youthfully fine, sternly elegant profile. 14% alc; 2 yrs Fr oak, half new. Needs & deserves good few years to give of its best. **00** was marked by super-ripe blackcurrants, plush tannins, deep earthy redolence in finish.

★★★★☆ **Pinotage** Long respected, serious-minded example, from old bushvines, typically rich, full-bodied, full-flavoured. Vibrant, lingering **02** (★★★★) all this, but berry, cherry fruit too overlaid, at least in youth, by oak (16 mths mostly new Fr), & a forest floor note. Well supported by soft firm tannins & acid. Vintage (+oak?) gives tiny twist of bitterness, acceptable in context. Chunky 14.5% alc. **01**'s bright fruit richly cosseted by balanced structure. Preferably mature min 5 yrs from vintage.

★★★★★ **CWG Auction Pinotage** The **02** (★★★★) barrel selection of above means more emphatic structure, with big dry tannins seemingly mostly from even more obvious oak, behind which all that dense sweet ripe fruit tantalises, hopefully to emerge one day (Truter says 4 yrs more should integrate the wood).

★★★★ **Kadette** ✓ Modestly wooded pinotage-based blend has estate's seriousness moderated by sophisticated rusticity. **02** (with 25% cab, 20% merlot) appeals immediately with bright, wild & spicy aromas, flavours, carried by typically well-balanced confidence; ripe soft tannins & a concluding hint of bitterness that genuinely adds to focus. 14% alc. **01** had cherry/berry fruit knitted to mineral core. — *TJ*

Kanu Wines

Stellenbosch ▪ Est/1stB 1998 ▪ Tasting & sales Oct-Mar: Mon-Fri 10-5 Sat 9-1; Apr-Sep Mon-Fri 10-4.30 Sat closed ▪ Fee R3/wine ▪ Closed public holidays ▪ Gifts ▪ Cheese Bar for farm-style products ▪ Functions venue ℂ 881·3225 functions@kanu.co.za ▪ Permanent art exhibition ▪ Owner Hydro Holdings ▪ Winemaker Richard Kershaw, with Johan Grimbeek & Adéle Swart (Jan 2002/Jun 2003) ▪ Viticulturists Johann Schloms (Jan 1997) & Dawid van Papendorp ▪ 54 ha (cab, ruby cab, shiraz, sauvignon, viognier) ▪ 1 000 tons 50 000 cs own label 50/50 red/white ▪ PO Box 548 Stellenbosch 7599 ▪ info@kanu.co.za ▪ www. kanu.co.za ℂ 881·3808 ▤ 881·3514

Kanu aficionados will be disappointed to learn there will be no Wooded Chenin 03. New cellar master Richard Kershaw felt he needed time to adopt his own approach to what has become Kanu's signature wine. Nevertheless Kanu continues to surprise the most seasoned critics of this underrated variety: after impressing US *Wine Spectator* palates, the oaked Chenin went on to win last year's Chenin Challenge and, having amassed the requisite credentials, was granted inaugural Super status by the Chenin Producers' Association. According to one of the farm's veteran labourers, all those who fall under the spell of Kanu (a mythical bird of promise) will be blessed with a bountiful harvest, and 2004 was no exception. Last year also saw the release of a new version of the easy-drinking

Kanu Red ('improved, but at the same price', notes the affable Kershaw, married to SA-born artist Mariette), as well as the next Noble Late Harvest. Kershaw's Chenin 04, like his Chardonnay, is 100% naturally fermented, to be released around February/March this year.

Limited Release range

★★★★ **Cabernet Sauvignon** No **02**, so last tasted was sensational **01** (★★★★☆) for pvs ed. Masterly composition of juicy bramble, choc-berry richness supported by fine tannins — 14.5% alc unnoticed. 100% new Fr oak, 20 mths.

★★★★ **Merlot** ✓ **02** (sample) beguilingly perfumed: violets, redcurrants, cedar, mint-choc. Elegant structure, with harmonious oak (20 mths Fr, 20% new); accessible, but with much to offer over time. 14% alc. Similar stats for reticent, refined **01**, tasted mid-2003, minty-choc coolness, herby sage warmth, elegant grip to finish.

★★★☆ **Shiraz 02** retasted: creamy plum focus broader, deeper, more layered, with dried herbs, roast veg tones. Smooth; drinking beautifully. Integrated 14 mths Fr oak, half new. With 13% petit v, soupçon cab. 90 pts WS. No **01**. WO W-Cape.

★★★★ **Keystone** ✓ Last tasted was **01**: sensual, ripe Bdx blend cab, 12% merlot, with blackcurrants shrouded by dense structure mid-03, needing years to unfurl. Crackerjack **00** VDG. Koelenhof/own grapes; 22 mths Fr oak, new for cab only.

★★★★ **Chardonnay Limited Release** (Pvsly in Kanu range) Chenins spotlit, but measured elegance of this a fine alternative. **03** has more depth, sophistication than peach-pip first impression suggests: subtle savoury tones, marzipan oak effect, exotic lime edginess. Food-friendly acidity (copes with just-off-dry 5.8g/ℓ sugar) ensures lemony/mineral flavours will hold freshness for some time. Fermented/10 mths new Fr oak. 14.5% alc. Khof fruit.

★★★★ **Chenin Blanc Wooded** 'Statement wine' — and much lauded, including Chenin Challenge triumphs for both **01**, **02**. On latter we noted toasty oak nose, bulging tropical/kumquat fruit, weighty palate bursting with fruit, wood, sweetness (13g/ℓ sugar). ±14% alc. Wine ★★★★★; WS 90 pts. Grapes from Khof bushvines; barrel-fermented/aged 8 mths, Fr oak, 40% new.

★★★☆ **Sauvignon Blanc Limited Release 04** (sample) has appealing varietal fruit purity (though with tiny dollop chenin): gooseberries, nettles, green meadow. Elegantly structured, long zesty finish. Perfect food partner, summer patio fare.

★★★★ **Noble Late Harvest Kia-Ora** Botrytised dessert, appearing when vintage permits. **01** from chenin, dryish 36g/ℓ sugar, 12% alc. Next **03** (★★★★★) blends chenin/hárslevelü (85/15); a powerhouse of richness, concentration: apricots, kumquats, dried peaches, all overlaid by honeycomb/botrytis. Racy acidity (9.8g/ℓ) keeps it fresh, adds tang & appetite appeal to flavours. Very impressive; beautifully balanced, good length. 6 mths new Fr barriques. 13% alc. Classy 375ml package.

Kanu range

★★★☆ **Chenin Blanc** ✓ Perennial charmer multi-awarded (Diners Club, Chenin Challenge, FCTWS, etc). Retasted **03** shows no signs of ageing. Tropical fruit flavours & youthful appley vein; bracing acidity offsets off-dry 6.2g/ℓ sugar. 14.4% alc.

Red ☺ ★★★ Anytime wine, good lightly chilled. Revisited **02** a basket of lightly wooded 5 reds, ruby cab dominating — so full of pulpy, freshly-crushed red berries. The only concession to passage of time is a softening, mellow drinkability. 13.9% alc.

Escape range [NEW]

Chenin Blanc ☺ ★★★ Ripe, intense sample **04** from 24 yr old bushvines: peardrops, guava & apple-rich summer fruit salad. Invigoratingly fresh, vibrant — cries out for food. 13.6% alc. **Sauvignon Blanc** ☺ ★★★ **04** has appealing cool-grown character, nettles, green meadow, grapefruit, without being aggressive, unfriendly. Wonderfully refreshing, finishes with citrus tang. 12.5% alc.

Red ★★★ Designed for early drinking, **02** is juicy, ripe & fruit-driven. Led by ruby cab, with cinsaut, shiraz, pinotage, with fleshy red berry focus. Touch of oak contributes definition. 13.3% alc. **Rosé** ★★★ **03** candyfloss/cerise hue is first attraction, light-toned redcurrant/cranberry fragrance & flavours come next. Softly amenable, plumped up by soupçon sugar. Blend cab s/merlot/shiraz. 13.4% alc. — *CR*

Karmosyn see Terroir Wines

Katbakkies Wine

*Est/1stB 1999 • Tasting & sales by appt • Owner Andries van der Walt • Vini consultant Teddy Hall (2002) • 450 cs 33% red 66% white • PO Box 21675 Kloof Street 8008 • Avdwalt@inds-ct.co.za © **424·6883** 🖷 426·1967*

Andries van der Walt released his first Syrah (the 02) in May 2004, after debuting earlier with a Chenin (he's manager of the Chenin Blanc Association). In the pipeline are the follow-up Syrah 03 and one barrel of Cab which is 'very special, and at this stage just for me'. Teddy Hall of Rudera is his collaborator; both use the excellent Koelenhof servicecellar. AvdW is also collaborating with a neighbour on a newly planted block of petit verdot, which they hope to harvest this year. If the experiment works, the vineyard will be among the highest in the Cape, at 1 100m. The intriguing name? It's that of AvdW's farm in the Swartruggens foothills of the Cederberg, and probably refers to the hollows in the rocks which fill with water after rain and are used by wild felines as 'cat bowls'.

★★★★★ **Syrah** ✓ Excellent debut **02**, though from youngish (7 yrs) vyds, proffering ground pepper, raspberry, cloves; with fine marzipan whiffs. Surprisingly accessible, with sumptuous tannins, the big 14.2% alc well concealed by the dense fruit. Persistent finish. 11 mths Fr oak (20% new); unfiltered. Tiny production: ±150 cs.

★★★☆ **Chenin Blanc** Lime apricot notes apparent on elegant, unshowy **03**; some enrichment from touch sugar (3.5g/ℓ), but dry. Fermented/8 mths Fr oak. Big 14.3% alc. Mere 150 cs. Both WO Stbosch. — *MF*

Kautzenburg

*Stellenbosch • Est 2000 • 1stB 2002 • Closed to public • Owners Peter & Nina Ruch • Winemaker Jeremy Walker (2002) • Viticulturists Peter Ruch, advised by De Waal Koch & Hannes Bredell • 5 ha (pinotage) • ±25 tons ±300 cs 100% red • PO Box 91 Somerset West 7129 ©/🖷 **842·3903***

Swiss expats Peter and Nina Ruch are fairly upbeat about their 2004 Pinotage, finding 'exceptionally fruity flavours on initial maturation'. The young couple – they have a 5 year old son – are still happily ensconced on a 12ha piece of prime land in the Helderberg. Ruch tends the vineyard himself, but calls in Grangehurst's Jeremy Walker to vinify the grapes. Fruit that doesn't go into Kautzenburg bottlings (some of the ±300 cases find a ready market back home) are diverted into the highly rated Pinotages of both Grangehurst and neighbour JP Bredell.

★★★★ **Pinotage 03** unshowy wine from low-yielding bushvine vyd, with elegant clove, nutmeg aromas, high-toned black cherry finish; but soft tannins can't fully conceal 14.6% alc. Massively fruited **02** has brawny, blockbuster 15% alc; 16 mths Fr oak. — *MF*

Kaya see Coppoolse Finlayson
Keates Drift see Franschhoek Vineyards
Keermont see De Trafford

Keerweder

Franschhoek • Est 1692 • 1stB 1994 • Visits by appt • Owner Nick Roditi • Winemaker Marié Smit (Nov 2003) • Viticulturist Danie Lambrechts (1999) • 15 ha (cab, merlot, petit v,

*pinotage, shiraz] ▪ 60 tons 2 700 cs ▪ 100% red ▪ PO Box 300 Franschhoek 7690 ▪ mail-box@keerweder.co.za © **876·3442** 876·3770*

A newcomer to the guide (but by no means new), Keerweder was the first Franschhoek farm given title: it was granted to Heinrick Müller of Basel in 1692. Its 200 hectares (big by the area's standards) lie at the end of the valley, with nowhere to go but up the mountain, hence the name 'Turn Round Again'. What started out as a hobby for owner Nick Roditi a decade ago has turned into a serious business, so he's reclaimed lost land, restored the original Cape Dutch homestead and adjacent buildings, added a winery and cellar, and appointed winemaker Marié Smit, whose local experience was gained at Avondale before she worked a harvest in California. Her reds-only vineyards, she says, 'have got everything going for them – low temperatures to preserve flavours, good viticultural practice, great slopes'. The latest releases, a blend of cab, merlot, shiraz and petit verdot, and a Pinotage were not ready for tasting.

Keimoes see Oranjerivier Wine Cellars

Kellerprinz

High-volume NV glugger from Distell. Now a single **Late Harvest** ★★ Lightish semi-sweet chenin/colombard in 2ℓ jug; muted aromas; restrained tropical palate. – *CR*

Ken Forrester Wines

*Stellenbosch (see Helderberg map) ▪ Est 1993 ▪ 1stB 1994 ▪ Tasting & sales daily 10-5 (farm & 96 Winery Road Restaurant – see Eat-out section) ▪ Closed Easter Fri-Mon, Dec 25/26 & Jan 1 ▪ Cellar tours by appt ▪ Tourgroups ▪ Conferencing ▪ Owners Ken & Teresa Forrester ▪ Vini consultant Martin Meinert, with Henk Marconi (1997/1995) ▪ Viticulturist Shawn Smit (Jan 2001) ▪ 33 ha (grenache, merlot, mourvèdre, shiraz, chenin, sauvignon) ▪ 200 tons 50 000 cs own label + 300 000ℓ for clients ▪ 30% red 70% white ▪ HACCP certified ▪ PO Box 1253 Stellenbosch 7599 ▪ ken@kenforresterwines.com ▪ www.kenforresterwines.com © **855·2374** 855·2373*

Volcanic restaurateur and man-about-vine Ken Forrester says he's had to work like crazy to keep up with an increasingly competitive market, but it's paying off: the brand-new maturation cellar and tasting facility on his Helderberg property is adorned with 'an absolute chunk/bevy/herd' of awards, including six medals from the International Wine Challenge 2003, and a gold (the only one for SA) from the Philadelphia Starwine competition (for his Chenin, now listed on BA's International Business Class). Even more than 2003, last year's harvest tested Forrester's and winemaking business partner Martin Meinert's patience. But both are excited by the 'concentrated fresh juice' of the chenin and the 'superb' grenache. As for new plantings and plans to optimise market trends, Forrester is keeping his cards close to his chest ('Classified for now'). But if you can catch him at 96 Winery Road Restaurant – arguably the most convivial 'tasting locale' in the winelands – you may be able to prise a few secrets from him.

Icon range

★★★★ **Gypsy** Impressive, individual New-World fusion of mostly grenache with shiraz, smattering pinotage; **02** (sample) continues vibrant fruit-driven style: liberally spiced prunes, sour cherry confit, with underbrush nuances. Sleekly muscular & generously oaked (18 mths); finished wine should show more integration, potentially ★★★★★. Vyd/barrel selection, deserving of hefty price tag. Only 800 btls. **01** pinnacle of reds from cellar, whose instant appeal belied complexity.

★★★★ **Forrester/Meinert Chenin Blanc** Designed to 'put Cape chenin indelibly on the map'. We last admired 2nd vintage **02**'s (★★★★★) sweeping canvas of flavours. **00** sold on 2001 CWG Auction as Meinert Scholtzenhof Grand Chenin.

★★★☆ **Sauvignon Blanc** Sleek, suave version, sophistication & complexity aided by dash semillon & barrelled portion (both 10%). **02** still available; prominent honeyed fig aromas backed by full-bodied textured ripeness. 13% alc. Discontinued.

★★★★★ **'T' Noble Late Harvest Chenin Blanc** Mesmerising botrytised dessert, both solo-perfect & food-cordial. No **02**. Last available **01** (★★★★★) dazzling follow-up to FCTWS trophy-winning **00**. The younger wine, mid-03, had 24 mths new Fr oak adding complexity. Richly layered tropical fruits, botrytis, creamy spice notes, palate's lush silkiness & flavour intensity, improbably long finish. But it's the balance that sets it apart: rich yet supple, sweet (134g/ℓ) with a tangy core (9g/ℓ acidity). Native yeast-fermented. 13.5% alc. An experience. FCTWS gold, WS 91 pts.

Ken Forrester range

★★★★ **Shiraz** Moves here from above slot in **02** (sample), classic varietal character, hints savoury spice, woodsmoke, without sacrificing plumy fruit foundation. Balanced, elegant, with amenable ripe tannin & enough freshness for lively, food-friendly finish. First was initially understated **01**, which slowly opened up.

★★★★ **Merlot** Like siblings, shows good varietal character. **03** cassis, mocha & cherry fruitcake, succulent & ripe, yet with lovely structural elegance & vitality. Enough backbone for 5+ yrs cellaring. Yr Fr oak. 14% alc.

★★★★ **Grenache-Syrah** Unusual & piquant 55/45 blend; Grenache from 50 yr old vines, producing just 2 t/ha. **02** transports you to southern Rhône with white pepper, spice-infused redcurrant character, fleshy accessibility. Deftly oaked, 9 mths seasoned Fr, touch Am. 13% alc. **01**, 55/45 blend, seductive silky elegance. Harmonious oak.

★★★★ **Chenin Blanc** ✓ From 30+ yr old Hldrberg bushvines, pruned for low yields. **03** (★★★★★) powerful, impressive; Lush, intense melons & tropical fruit, well judged integrated oak (9 mths Fr), trademark brisk finish. Scrumptious. Will age beautifully 4+ yrs. **02** opulent tropical fruit & whiff botrytis, extra dimension from oak.

★★★★ **Sauvignon Blanc 04** (unfinished sample) epitomises freshness; nettles & Cape gooseberries, quivering with racy vibrancy. Ideal food partner. **03** sleek, fresh, inviting; invigorating acidity ensures food compatibility.

Petit range

Petit Pinotage ☺ ★★★ Juicy unwooded style. **04** (sample) pulpy essence of variety; brambleberries & rhubarb, perky, uncomplicated drinking pleasure. 13.5% alc. **Petit Chenin** ☺ ★★★ 'Keep in the fridge for anytime', suggests Ken F. **04** exuberantly fresh; guavas, crunchy Golden Delicious apples, with loads of appetite appeal. 14% alc. — *CR*

Keteka see Dominion
Keurfontein see Viljoensdrift
Kevin Arnold see Waterford
Khanya see Havana Hills
King Solomon see Eshkol

Klawer Co-operative Winery

Olifants River ▪ Est 1956 ▪ Tasting & sales Mon-Fri 8-5 Sat 9-1 ▪ Fee R5 ▪ Closed public holidays except during wildflower season ▪ BYO picnic ▪ Conferences ▪ Owners 120 members ▪ Winemakers Bob de Villiers, Hermias Hugo & De Wet Hugo (Dec 2000/Dec 2003/Aug 2003)2003), with Roelof van Schalkwyk & Dewald Huisamen (Jan 1999/Nov 2002) ▪ Viticulturist Klaas Coetzee (Jun 2001) ▪ 2 095 ha ±40 000 tons 14% red 85% white 1% rosé ▪ PO Box 8 Klawer 8145 ▪ klawerwyn@kingsley.co.za ▪ www.wine.co.za ℗ (027) 216·1530 🖷 (027) 216·1561

A pair of awards at the local Young Wine Show sealed the recent merger of Klawer with Trawal: the Chardonnay was named white wine of the region, while the cellar claimed the title of top performer overall. More to follow? Well, the winemaking team (boosted to three by the arrival of De Wet Hugo) singles out the ruby cab as 'exceptional' among the

2004 reds, and the chenin and sauvignon as having promise. Responding to the burgeoning demand for export bulk wine, the team is looking for distributors into foreign markets. **Red Muscadel ★★★ 04** (sample) pale coppery pink, harmonious flavour & alc; pleasant spicy touch. 16.5% alc. **White Muscadel ★★** Straightforward muscat tone, **04** (sample) still quite fiery mid-2004, needs time to settle, develop. 16.6% alc. **Hanepoot** 🆕 ★ Sweet, strongly alcoholic (17.5% alc), unsubtle **04** (sample). **Blanc de Noir, Grand Cru** & **Late Harvest** available but not tasted.

Birdfield range

Cabernet Sauvignon 🆕 **★★ 02** notes of red berries & eucalyptus, full palate of red fruit, big oak & dry tannins overwhelm fruit mid-2004; needs plenty of time. **Merlot ★★★ 04** ripe plums with minty note, lively, well rounded, unwooded. 14% alc. **Pinotage ★★ 02** smooth, with oaky touch; still fairly strong tannins & not much pinotage character. 14% alc. **Shiraz** 🆕 **★★★** 30% new Am oak a spicy presence in **03**; touches pepper & anise, evident but supple tannin; should improve further over next 18–24 mths; brawny 15% alc. **Shiraz-Merlot ★★★** Red fruit pervades **02**, touches pepper & lavender; rounded, good fruity persistence; has potential for short-term development. Fr/Am oak. 14.5% alc. **Chardonnay ★★★ 04** reverts to unwooded, huge alc (15%) well hidden amidst the sweet ripe tropical fruit. **Chenin Blanc ★★ 04** light-textured, tropical, with bracing acidity. **Sauvignon Blanc ★★** Less appealing **04**, firm acidity, needs a fatty line fish.—DH

Klawervlei Estate

Stellenbosch ▪ Est 1994 ▪ 1stB 1995 ▪ Tasting & sales Tue-Fri 10-5 Sat 10-2 ▪ Closed Dec 25 & Jan 1 ▪ Tours by appt ▪ Klawervlei Pantry (see below) ▪ Owner Quickstep 584 (Pty) Ltd ▪ Winemaker Christoph Hammel ▪ 20 ha (cab, merlot, chenin) ▪ 100 tons 3 000 cs own label ▪ 70% red 30% white ▪ PO Box 144 Koelenhof 7605 ▪ chrisdejager@mweb.co.za ▪ www.klawervlei.com © 865·2746 ✆ 865·2415

Breathing fresh air into this farm, one of the first in the Cape to grow grapes entirely organically, is well-known Pretoria restaurateur Chris de Jager (Toulouse and Chagall's among his claims to fame). He and wife Anne have teamed up with winemaker Christoph Hammel, who co-owns the Hammel Weingut in Germany's Weinstrasse as well as other vinous interests in Europe, and with retired media executive Werner Luig from Zurich, to buy and revitalise the property. First on the agenda is a new eatery offering meals and gourmet farm produce. The accent is on family, and Chris dJ says 'children are welcome to use use the activity centre or roam about the lawns while their parents play *petanque* and sip wine or *pastis*'.

Klein Avontuur see Avontuur
Klein Begin see New Beginnings, Vinfruco
Kleinbosch see Cape Wine Cellars

Klein Constantia Estate

Constantia ▪ Est 1823 ▪ 1stB 1986 ▪ Tasting & sales Mon-Fri 9-5 Sat 9-1 ▪ Fee R20 for groups ▪ Closed public holidays ▪ Farm produce ▪ Owners Duggie & Lowell Jooste ▪ Winemaker Adam Mason, with Trizanne Pansegrouw & Corina du Toit (Jul 2003/harvest 2004) ▪ Viticulturist Kobus Jordaan (Feb 1981) ▪ 82 ha (cabs s/f, merlot, pinot, shiraz, chard, muscat de F, riesling, sauvignon) ▪ 500 tons 40 000 cs 25% red 75% white ▪ Export brands: High Gables & Danford's ▪ PO Box 375 Constantia 7848 ▪ info@kleinconstantia.com ▪ www.kleinconstantia.com © 794·5188 ✆ 794·2464

Expression of site is paramount, agree Lowell Jooste and Adam Mason, hence an extensive recent digital survey of the entire farm to pinpoint suitable terrains for future vineyards. Co-owner and winemaker were equally amazed to discover that Simon van der Stel, the 17th-century Cape governor who established the estate, 'hit the nail on the head without this level of technology'. Temperature monitors, installed on three sections of their Constantiaberg slopes, confirm they are situated in one of the Cape's 5 coolest wine areas. Implicit affirmation of the benefits of the climate was the superlative showing of two older KC vintages at the 2003 Tri Nations Challenge in Sydney. The 87 Blanc de Blanc and 95 Rhine Riesling took top honours in their respective categories. The 03 release of the latter was also the first KC product bottled under screwcap. 'We regard the move as a resounding success', Jooste says. 'Who knows? Maybe there will be a similar bottling of Sauvignon if the demand is there.'

★★★★ **Cabernet Sauvignon** Cassis, earthy whiffs in austere **00**, & some sweet fruit lurking amongst the dry tannins. 20+ mths new Fr oak; 14.2% alc. Pattern followed in **01**, which a little quieter all round. Should keep few more yrs, & hopefully soften somewhat.

★★★★ **Marlbrook** Ambitious, seriously styled blend of half cab with merlot & dash cab f. **00** has cab severity rounded by softer merlot fruit offering cherry sweetness before dry finish. Cedar notes from new Fr oak 2 yrs; 14.3% alc. **01** less austere, more rounded. These designed to grow over 3+ yrs in bottle.

★★★★ **Pinot Noir** Light-coloured (almost rosé-like) **03** has raspberry, forest-floor bouquet/flavours, with fresh savoury acidity, well integrated oak (yr 50% new Fr). 14% alc. Not for long keeping.

★★★★ **Shiraz** Roasted, ripe, spicy aromas on **01** (★★★) leading to soft, lightish palate, for easy drinking. 13.2% alc. Flavourful, juicy **02** more bracing, with satisfyingly savoury-sweet red fruit. 13.6% alc. 18 mths Am oak, 30% new.

★★★★ **Shiraz Reserve** Last was **01** selection from new barrels of above – more grip, intensity, toasted oak. Soft juicy tannins enfolding sweet red fruit. 12.9% alc.

★★★★ **Chardonnay 03**'s aromas of oatmeal, elegant butterscotch lead to broad, creamy mouthful – soft, with well integrated oak (70% fermented/8 mths in oak, 50% new) & 13.7% alc.

★★★★ **Sauvignon Blanc** Enduring favourite, noted for rewarding ageability in some vintages, with dash semillon for more complexity. Fine, cool-climate character on **03**, well-balanced acidity enlivening passionfruit, fig flavours, with mineral element. Fresh, lingering finish. **04** sample promises more of same, with an excellent separately bottled selection of the best also envisaged.

★★★★ **Rhine Riesling** ✓ Now under screwcap to safeguard aromatic purity. **03** (no **02** released) had deeper richness from 20% botrytised grapes; 13.3% alc, 11g/ℓ sugar. Hints of a regime change in Adam M's inaugural **04**: somewhat drier (though still just perceptibly off-dry), lower alc, ±12%. Aromatic, with tinned pineapple & pepper, delicately fresh & lively. Will develop more complexity with few yrs in bottle – some vintages happily last a decade.

★★★★ **Sauvignon Blanc Noble Late Harvest** Rich, botrytised dessert, intermittently produced. Last was spicy-sweet **98**. Next will be old-gold **02**, tank sample packed with toffee, butterscotch flavours; softly unctuous on firm framework.

★★★★★ **Vin de Constance** Confirming anew the international status its ancestor enjoyed 2 centuries back, & fortunately soon in greater quantities, from new plantings of muscat de F. Frequent ★★★★★ over the yrs. Usually no botrytis element, just healthy ripeness taken to a superb extreme, to give a long-lived, silkily textured wine with fine mineral acidity. Raisiny luxuriance of **99** also evokes dried apricot, marmalade, shot through with thrilling acid; fine lingering farewell. 14.5%; 183g/ℓ sugar. Preview of stunning **00** suggests even more youthful complexity, refined richness. Some 2 yrs in used 500ℓ Fr oak barrels, after ferment/time in tank. – *TJ*

Kleindal see Robertson Wide River Export Company

Klein DasBosch

Stellenbosch ▪ Closed to public ▪ Owner James Wellwood Basson ▪ Viti/vini consultant Jan Coetzee (1997) ▪ Marketing director Nikki Herbst ▪ 5.5 ha ▪ 35 tons 2 000 cs own label 89% red 11% white ▪ PO Box 826 Brackenfell 7561 ▪ wine@kleindasbosch.com ▪ www. kleindasbosch.com ℂ **880·0128** ▤ (021) 880·0999

Range made at Vriesenhof by rugby-and-wine legend Jan Coetzee for his neighbour James 'Whitey' Basson, CEO of retailing empire Shoprite. Current releases include an 02 Merlot and Pinotage, and an 04 Chardonnay. Mostly exported, though some do appear on selected local restaurant lists.

Kleine Draken

Paarl ▪ Est 1983 ▪ 1stB 1988 ▪ Tasting & sales Mon-Fri 8-12.30; 1.30-5 ▪ Closed public holidays & Jewish holy days ▪ Tours strictly by appt ▪ BYO picnic ▪ Owner Cape Gate (Pty) Ltd ▪ Winemaker Neil Schnoor, with Mabusa Nyaniso (Sep/Jul 1999) ▪ Viticulturist Frank Pietersen (1984) ▪ 9 ha (cabs s/f, malbec, merlot, chard, riesling, sauvignon) ▪ 90 tons 10 000 cs own label 50% red 50% white ▪ Brand for customer: Tempel Wines ▪ ISO 9000 certification in progress ▪ PO Box 2674 Paarl 7620 ▪ zandwijk@capegate.co.za ▪ www. kosherwines.co.za © 863-2368 ⌨ 863·1884

'It's our intention to match the quality of non-kosher SA wines,' says former industrial chemist Neil Schnoor, 'and this is fast becoming a reality.' No mean feat when you consider that these kosher wines are flash-pasteurised to meet the strict standards of the Cape Beth Din – a process which is not conducive to the retention of delicate aromas and flavours. Last harvest was not only 10 days later but also far longer than normal, allowing for better cellar management.

★★★☆ **Sauvignon Blanc** ✓ **04** grassy first sniff; full flavoured - good mouthful of ripe gooseberry – refreshing, well-balanced acidity. Amazing achievement given the vinification process.

Cabernet Sauvignon ★★★ **01** still well-structured & -fruited; good dry tannins containing cassis & black berries; improving in bottle, showing complexity. **Pinotage** NEW ★★★ **03** red cherries & red berries, strong tannins & dry finish; like Cab, best cellared further or enjoyed with food. 6 mths Fr oak, some new. **Dry Red** ★★★ **03** lightish-bodied Bdx-style blend of equal portions cab f, merlot, malbec, with generous dark-fruit flavours; unlike other reds, immediately approachable, user-friendly. Fr oak 4-6 mths, 2nd-3rd fill. **Kiddush** ★★ Natural Sweet sacramental wine from cinsaut; we last tasted **01**. **Chardonnay** ★★★ New-oak-fermented **04** soft & easy to drink, good dry finish; melon flavour upfront, touch vanilla oak behind. **Bouquet Blanc** NEW ★★★ Another look at **04** sauvignon; upfront 'fruity' rather than 'aromatic', also very pleasant, semi-dry, light bodied – *TM*

Kleine Hazen see Hazendal
Kleine Parys see Kosie Möller Wines

Kleine Zalze Wines

Stellenbosch ▪ Est 1695 ▪ 1stB 1997 ▪ Tasting & sales Mon-Sat 9-5 Sun 11-4 ▪ Closed Easter Fri, Dec 25 & Jan 1 ▪ Fee R15 ▪ Tours by appt ▪ 'Terroir' Restaurant (see Eat-out section) ▪ Guest cottages & golf lodges ▪ Play area for children ▪ Tourgroups ▪ Conferencing ▪ Owners Kobus Basson & Jan Malan ▪ Winemaker Johan Joubert, with Erika Obermeyer (Nov 2002/Sep 1999) ▪ Viticulturist John Fullard, advised by Schalk du Toit (both 2000) ▪ 60 ha (cab, merlot, shiraz) ▪ ±1 500 tons 80 000 cs 60% red 40% white ▪ PO Box 12837 Die Boord Stellenbosch 7613 quality@kleinezalze.co.za ▪ www.kleinezalze.com © 880·0717 ⌨ 880·0716

The wine and winelands-lifestyle vision behind this Stellenbosch spread is rapidly taking shape, and it's best surveyed from the new function venue suspended above the cellar. There, glass walls afford views into the winemaking hub, over their vineyards and onto the jointly owned De Zalze golf course and residential estate. Cellarmaster Johan Joubert experienced one of his 'best harvests ever' as a result of intense team effort, both in the vineyards (on this and their Groote Zalze farm next door, and on co-owner Jan Malan's Wellington farm) and in the cellar, where practices now include hand-sorting and lengthened skin contact. Their new range, Foot of Africa, is taking steps into newer markets like Scandinavia and America. You can taste the wines in the extended tasting room with its inviting fireplace, then traipse over to Terroir, the new restaurant under the oaks.

Vineyard Selection

★★★★ **Cabernet Sauvignon Barrel Matured 03** (sample) smoky plum aromas, a fruity first impression; palate chewy, extracted, rippling cedarwood & fruit; provisional ★★★★ with potential to add ★ with bottle-ageing. **02** diverted to range below; **01** more elegant, lighter, classical & minerally. 12-15 mths oak, Fr/Am, 30-100% new.

★★★★ **Merlot Barrel Matured 03** (sample) lovely rich, dark colour; mint-choc aroma, slight leafy note & lead pencil; dark plummy palate, cedarwood tinge; slightly grainy dry tannins; **02** diverted to range below; **01** lighter colour, bricking; plum with dried-fruit character & leafy touch; elegant choc fruit, maturing well. 12-18 mths oaked, Fr/Am, 30-100% new. 14% alc.

★★★★ **Pinotage Barrel Matured 03** (sample) vibrant mulberry aromas, whiff cedarwood; dense dark-plum flavours – a palate coater; **02** diverted to Cellar Selection below. **01** (★★★) retaste shows some complexity/maturity on nose; savoury, quite elegant palate, almost peppery. Oak as for Cab.

★★★★ **Shiraz Barrel Matured** Tasting mid-2002 of 3 current vintages: **01** quiet roast meat & smoke notes, sweet fruited, not quite depth of flavour of pvs. Enjoy soon. **02** fynbos & scrub intro, same savoury style as pvs; cigarbox whiff, hint pepper. **03** (★★★★) style change? Pitch black; concentrated prune & cinnamon aromas; massively modern, showy. 12-18 mths Fr/Am oak, 1st-3rd fill. Alcs ±14.5%.

★★★★ **Barrel Fermented Chardonnay** ✓ ±8mths Fr oak, 30% new, 50% malo. **02** marmalade toast aromas with apricot; fat & soft, toffee apple notes on finish, bit blowsy; drink up. MIWA gold. **03** (sample) generous creamy melon & baked apple notes, big, firm, juicy wine; looks promising. 13.7% alc.

★★★★ **Chenin Blanc Barrel Fermented** ✓ 100% oaked, 50% in new Fr barriques – so a serious wine; **04** (unrated progress report) lots of primary pineapple aromas, hints caramel & butterscotch; rich tropical fruit flavours; **03** retaste; full-on dessert chenin: luscious, fragrant with honey & botrytis; appealing. 14% alc.

Cellar Selection

★★★★ **Merlot 01** grew seamless & round while retaining its sweet plummy fruit. **02** (★★★★) shows vintage's somewhat reduced concentration, with leafy, damp earth overtones; fairly vibrant blackcurrant fruit, though, grainy tannins keeping it in check. 14.2% alc. 11 mths older Fr barriques.

★★★★ **Chenin Blanc Bush Vines** ✓ Unwooded version, from warmer s-w facing slopes, technically off-dry (±6.5g/ℓ sugar). Amplitude, richness & potential the hallmarks **03** was a tropical fruit basket lifted by acidity; **04** luscious melon, lanolin & honeysuckle whiffs; rich, sweetly scented jasmine palate; gorgeous; 14.4% alc.

Cabernet Sauvignon ★★★ 02 (sample) retiring redcurrant whiffs; slightly sweet, soft, dusty finish. **01** retaste: shy redcurrant aromas, tart flavours with sweet-sour tinge. 13 mths older Fr oak. ±14% alc. **Pinotage ★★★★ 02** ripe nose of mulberries & earth, plump but not blowsy, juicy; fruit well reined-in, elegant despite 14.4% alc. 60% oaked, yr 3rd/4th fill Fr. **Gamay Noir ★★★ 03** light coloured; light strawberry palate, supple & juicy. **04** unrated preview total contrast: spicy wild fruits, roast meat whiffs; big fruit-cordial palate, sour plum finish. Very different; ex-Wlnton vyds. 14% alc. **Chardonnay ★★★** Unwooded, zippy version usually with big alc. **04** quiet nose, some dusty pear whiffs; pear carries through onto fairly rich palate with hints marzipan, citrus.14.5% alc. **Sauvignon Blanc ★★★★** Invariably sprightly, with long-luncheon-lowish alc. **04** forthcoming aromas of tropical fruit, crushed nettle, fig; full & lively, explosion of ripe lime/grapefruit flavours on palate, zinging fruit acid. Above, below, various WOs including Coastal, W-Cape & Stbosch.

Foot of Africa range

Chenin Blanc-Chardonnay ☺ **★★★ 04** aromatic & floral with sweet aromas; supple & juicy melon/passionfruit flavours. Note high 14% alc.

Pinotage-Shiraz ★★★ **03** subdued on nose; pinotage ascendant in slightly jammy mulberry-toned palate. 14.5% alc. Partly oaked, 11 mths older Fr. — *TM*

Klein Gustrouw Estate

Stellenbosch (See map) ▪ *Est 1817* ▪ *1stB 1993* ▪ *Tasting, sales & tours by appt '24x7' (closed Dec 25/26)* ▪ *Conservation area* ▪ *Owners Chris & Athalie McDonald* ▪ *Winemaker/ viticulturist Chris McDonald* ▪ *16 ha (cab, merlot)* ▪ *21 tons 1 600 cs 100% red* ▪ *PO Box 6064 Stellenbosch 7612* ⓒ/🖃 *(021) 887·4556*

'We just bang on', explains Chris McDonald who, with wife Athalie, owns the spread at the entrance to the Jonkershoek valley, land included in the Jonkershoek Conservancy. Consistency, vintage to vintage, marks their Bordeaux-style red, for which fans in Europe are paying stellar prices: the 00 sells in top London restaurants at £38.50 a bottle and £8. 50 a glass. (How lucky local diners are to enjoy it at R150 a bottle!) The McDonalds link a hands-off philosophy of viticulture with intense involvement in the production process — every bunch on the conveyor passes through Chris's hands and Athalie personally separates 300 eggs to provide whites for fining.

★★★★☆ **Cabernet Sauvignon-Merlot** Complex, finely delineated Bdx-style red. Upcoming May 05 release for **02** (★★★★) showing asphalt nose mid-2004, accessible blackcurrant fruit in lighter style; a yard off super **01**, sumptuous ripe cassis folded into tobacco notes, earthy anchors; great persistence to elegant balance. ±60/40 cab/merlot blend. 12-16 mths oak, third new. 14% alc. — *DS*

Klein Optenhorst

Wellington ▪ *Est/1stB 2001* ▪ *Closed to public* ▪ *150 cs 100% red* ▪ *See Siyabonga*
Another example of vino-preneurship from Graham Knox, whose innovative collaborations with various Wellington growers show — delightfully — what a risky business winegrowing can be. Here he links up with Naas Ferreira, whose ½ha of pinot on the Groenberg slopes 'has the most delicious flavours when looked after — as Naas does — passionately'. Weather vagaries in 2002 caused havoc, resulting in an overripe wine. Freshened up with merlot, it was no longer a pinot and became simply 'Knife's Edge'. Luckily, subsequent vintages have survived intact.

★★★★ **Pinot Noir** Individual SA take on classic grape. **03** recaptures unpretentious allure of **01**; touch more delicacy hinted at in attractive cherry clarity. Pervasive darker cherries with truffle scents/flavours; fullish, oak-firmed, brisk, lithe. Delicious now/ next 2-4 yrs. 11 mths Fr oak. 13% alc. **02** unbottled, diverted to wine below.
Knife's Edge Pinot Noir-Merlot 🆕 ★★★ 'Declassified', quietish **02** pinot, freshened with unoaked plummy merlot in straightforward, smooth quaffer. 12.7% alc. — *AL*

Klein Parys see Groot Parys
Klein Simonsvlei see Niel Joubert
Kleinrivier see Clos Malverne
Klein Tulbagh see Tulbagh Winery

Kleinvallei Winery

Paarl ▪ *Est/1stB 2000* ▪ *Tasting by appt* ▪ *Owners Piet & Sandra van Schaik* ▪ *Vini consultant Jean-Vincent Ridon (2000)* ▪ *10 ha (cab, malbec, merlot, petit v, pinotage, shiraz, chard)* ▪ *17 tons 940 cs 90% red 10% white* ▪ *PO Box 9060 Klein Drakenstein 7628* ▪ *klein vallei@ mweb.co.za* ▪ *www.kleinvallei.co.za* ⓒ *868·3662/082·399·5075* 🖃 *868·3130*

Owners Piet and Sandra van Schaik are keen opera lovers and so pleased with their first red blend, they've decided to call it 'Bel Canto'. In a difficult growing season, when some neighbours struggled to achieve reasonable sugar levels in their grapes, Kleinvallei had no problems ('still not sure why'). Though yields were down, sugars turned out perfect. They produce wines in the 'classic, full-bodied style', rather than follow the modern trend toward fruity, early-drinking wines. As with several other Cape winegrowers, the Van Schaiks see China as the export market with the greatest potential for our wines.

Cabernet Sauvignon ★★★ **01**, re-opened for this ed, typical blackcurrant, cream & toast aromas; slightly leafy & austere, showing bit of acidity; best enjoyed soon. 20 mths Fr, some new. ±14% alc. **Bel Canto** NEW ★★★ Forceful & extracted cab-led blend (62%) with shiraz (23%), merlot; red berry/sour plum flavours, lots of grainy tannins; **02** grapes seem to have been worked hard, give time to settle, knit. 15.5% alc. **Pinotage** ★★★ Idiosyncratic & massive; **03** scales new heights of quirkiness: 16% alc, 9g/ℓ sugar! Opens with intriguing smoky/earthy nose; mulberry-drenched palate, finishes with fat, friendly lick of sweetness. Yr mths Fr oak, some new. Not a little grey creature. **Chardonnay** NEW ★★★ Alluring peach & lemon cream biscuit aromas in **03**; full bodied, persistent; dollop toasty oak from yr in 4th fill Fr casks. — TM

Klippenkop see Kosie Möller Wines

Klompzicht

Paarl ▪ Est 1997 ▪ 1stB 2000 ▪ Tasting & sales Mon-Fri 8-5 ▪ Closed public holidays ▪ BYO picnic ▪ Owner Francois Klomp ▪ Winemakers Hempies du Toit & Mark Carmichael-Green (both Jan 2002) ▪ Viti adviser Paul Wallace (Jan 1998) ▪ ±19 ha (cab, merlot, pinotage, shiraz) ▪ 140 tons 2 000 cs 100% red ▪ Export label: Freedom Hill ▪ Range for customer: Shibula ▪ PO Box 6353 Uniedal 7612 ▪ info@freedomhill.co.za ▪ www.freedomhill.co.za ℂ 084·906·6895 ▤ 882·8207

Francois Klomp's farm on the Wemmershoek Road between Paarl and Franschhoek is now open to the public. There are facilities for tasters and buyers, and picnickers are welcome to bring a lunch to enjoy with their wine. The Klompzicht label has been retired; Klomp is now bottling under the Freedom Hill label, with Shibula-branded wines 'exported' to his lodge in the Waterberg. No real exports are happening: Klomp sees opportunities for growth through local sales to private buyers and the hospitality sector, with marketing a necessary precursor.

Freedom Hill range
★★★★ **Merlot 02** includes dash merlot; plump, soft plum & currant aromas; very ripe style — warm cassis fruit in abundance, wood (2 yrs Fr, 2nd/3rd fill) a pleasing background scent. 14.7% alc.

★★★★ **Shiraz-Cabernet Sauvignon** Hallmark of 50/40 blend (plus splash merlot) is New World ripeness, generosity; **01** fairly extracted but harmonious, well contained. 14. 3% alc; oak as above.

★★★★ **Shiraz 02** features great troughs of Aussie-style fruit, flavour just oozes from glass; oak quite dominant on palate, as is formidable 15.7% alc. 2 yrs Fr small-oak. **03** work-in-progress equally pungent, brash; massed Ribena fruit, meaty whiff, drier on palate, brighter, more lively than pvs (slightly higher acidity); some Am oak used, ditto for **04**, too unformed to rate; seems lighter, different character.

Shibula range
★★★★ **Merlot** Ripe plums as above but with meaty hint in **01**; big, juicy, supple wine; hints oak & cigarbox; fair amount of complexity which should increase with time. 2 yrs 3rd fill Fr barrels. 14.7% alc. These Stbosch, Paarl & Coastal WOs. — TM

Kloofzicht Estate see Alter Ego Wines

Kloovenburg Vineyards

Swartland ▪ Est 1704 ▪ 1stB 1998 ▪ Tasting & sales Mon-Fri 9-4.30 Sat 9-2 ▪ Fee for groups R10 ▪ Closed Christian holidays ▪ Tours during tasting hours by appt ▪ BYO picnic ▪ Farm-grown olive products for tasting/sale ▪ Walks ▪ Conservation area ▪ Owner/winemaker Pieter du Toit ▪ Viti consultant Kobus van Graan (Jun 2000) ▪ 130 ha (cab, merlot, pinotage, shiraz, chard, chenin)

▪ *6 000 cs own label 70% red 30% white* ▪ *PO Box 2 Riebeek-Kasteel 7307* ▪ *kloovenburg@ wcaccess.co.za* ▪ *www.kloovenburg.com* ⓒ *(022) 448·1635* 🖷 *(022) 448·1035*

A visitor, smaller and furrier than most tourists, was discovered in the cellar complex of Pieter and Annalene du Toit's farm: a baby antelope, just three weeks old. (Did Pieter dT marvel at the little animal's good taste? Or wonder whether it preferred the Shiraz, their flagship, or the tasty Chardonnay, or Annalene's tapenade?) After a spell at a rehabilitation centre (not for over-indulgence, we are assured), it was released back onto its Kasteelberg turf. After riding out a February heat wave and twice picking some unevenly ripened blocks, the resulting merlot, shiraz and chardonnay 'all look outstanding'. Good news for new UK agents Bibendum.

★★★★★ **Shiraz** Stand-out elegant, restrained northern-Rhône style. **03** (tasted ex-barrel), dense, peppery, textured, already showing persistence. Bolder than **02** (despite 14.5% alc vs super-ripe 15%). This now showing spicy aromas, sweet brambly fruit, sumptuous textures, balance, restraint & length. Fr / Am oak. **01** now quite peppery, dense fruited. These ±14 mths older Fr/Am wood.

★★★★ **Chardonnay** ✓ Classical, elegantly unflamboyant styling. Preview **04** shows intensity, suppleness, elegance; persistent grapefruit notes. Lower alc (13.9%) than similarly restrained **03**, with fine lime citrus aromas, butterscotch mid-palate; 14. 5% alc concealed by fruit intensity. Fermented/14 mths Fr oak, 30% new.

Cabernet Sauvignon ★★★ Preview of unshowy **03** reflects style of pvs **02**, leafy aromas dominating red berry fruit; sinewy, vinous. 14.5% alc. Fr oak matured. **Merlot** ★★★ **03** sample showing sweeter, riper notes of mulberry, plum. Yr Fr oak, 30% new. More intense than **02** (★★★) herbal hints, fine tannins, sweetish finish. 14.5% alc. *— MF*

Knorhoek Wines

Stellenbosch ▪ *Est 1827* ▪ *1stB 1997* ▪ *Tasting & sales Mon-Sat 9-5* ▪ *Fee R10* ▪ *Closed Dec 25* ▪ *Restaurant/lapa Sep-May 12-4* ▪ *Guest house (B&B) with conference, function, entertainment area* ▪ *Facilities for children* ▪ *Tourgroups* ▪ *Walks* ▪ *Conservation area* ▪ *Owners Hansie & James van Niekerk* ▪ *Winemaker/viticulturist Corius Visser (Jan 2003), with adviser* ▪ *105 ha (cabs s/f, merlot, pinotage, shiraz, chenin, sauvignon)* ▪ *700 tons 10 000 cs own label 70% red 30% white* ▪ *Export label: Two Cubs* ▪ *PO Box 2 Koelenhof 7605* ▪ *office@knorhoek.co.za* ▪ *www.knorhoek.co.za* ⓒ/🖷 *865·2627*

These Simonsberg heights were once a wild place, with predators preying on livestock. Hence the name Knorhoek, 'Place Where Lions Growl'. The Cape Mountain Lion may have disappeared, but leopards are still spotted on the higher reaches and are featured on the front-labels of the bottles. The contents are still made at Kanonkop and matured at Knorhoek, where a full production cellar is being readied. News is the birth of an easy-drinking blended range, Two Cubs. Accommodation in the renovated coach house, entertainment facilities, restaurant and pool make this a popular spot with visitors.

★★★★ **Cabernet Sauvignon** Slightly more new oak (30%, Fr), longer barrelling (16 mths) for **01**, mellowing into elegant deliciousness. Ripe red berries in velvet palate, hint greenpepper & mint; equally fulsome **02** has black berry, cassis & spice at its sweet-fruited centre, embroidered with choc-mint. ±14% alc.

★★★★ **Pinotage** Aiming for a food wine. Uncorking **01** for this ed reveals a bottle-age note adding interest/complexity to slightly earthy mulberry/plum fruit. Yr oak, 40% new. 14% alc. Standout **00** (★★★★) was choc-toned with savoury hints.

Sauvignon Blanc ★★★ Harvested at different ripeness levels for complexity; retasted **03**, alluring mix tropical & gooseberry tones, rounded yet retains some grip. **Chenin Blanc** ★★★ **03** ageing attractively; flavours of ripe fruit salad, passionfruit top-note, semi-dry finish still crisp, satisfying. 14.5% alc. *— DH*

Knysna Cellars

Knysna ▪ *Est 2001* ▪ *1stB 2002* ▪ *Tasting & sales Mon-Fri 8.30-1; 2-5 Sat 8.30-1 (Summer only)* ▪ *Fee R100 for 'vintage tutored tasting' (min 6 wines)* ▪ *Closed Dec 25/26 & Jan 1* ▪

Tourgroups of up to 12 people ▪ Farm-style cheeses ▪ Owner/winemaker Geoff Boomer ▪ Viticulturist Mark van Haldren (Apr 2003) ▪ 590 cs ▪ 12a Watsonia Street Knysna 6570 ▪ gbalstar@pixie.co.za ✆ (044) 382·6164 🖷 (044) 382-6193

In spite of help and advice from some of the Cape's best-known winemakers, Knysna's only grower, Geoff Boomer, is finding wine farming rather more difficult than he imagined. All his vines had to be uprooted when it was discovered the clay soils needed far more preparation than expected. There will be no 2005 harvest, but even this setback has not daunted the feisty Irishman. He's starting from scratch, more determined than ever.

Koelenhof Winery

Stellenbosch ▪ Est 1941 ▪ 1stB 1974 ▪ Tasting & sales Mon-Thu 8.30–1 2–5; Fri 8.30–1 2–4. 30; Sat 9–1 Public holidays 9-1 ▪ Closed Easter Fri, Ascension Day, Dec 25/26 & Jan 1) ▪ BYO picnic (excellent deli nearby) ▪ Play area for children ▪ Conferencing ▪ Owners 75 shareholders ▪ Winemakers Wilhelm de Vries & Martin Stevens (Jan 2001/Oct 2003) ▪ Viticulturist Herman du Preez (Jan 2002) ▪ 11 000 tons 6 000 cs own label ±9m litres bulk 30% red 60% white 2% rosé 8% sparkling/grape juice ▪ HACCP certification in progress ▪ PO Box 1 Koelenhof 7605 ▪ koelwyn@mweb.co.za ✆ 865·2020/1 🖷 865·2796

Herman du Preez, previously a viticultural consultant here, has now joined the permanent staff, bringing with him valuable experience gained at Eersterivier and Bottelary cellars. Andrew de Vries, who stood in as white wine maker for a few years, is now the full-time financial manager of this cellar while Martin Stevens, schooled at Stellenbosch University and polished in Bordeaux and Champagne, among others, takes his place. Other recent changes include the expansion of the tasting area to make it an attractive venue for wedding receptions and conferences.

★★★★ **Merlot** Unveiled with **98**, which ripened attractively; next was standout **99** (★★★★), with extra heft from mostly new Fr oak; **02** (★★★ sample) all new oak, 15 mths. Probably victim of poorer vintage: muted red berry nose; leafy herbal tone carries through into palate, unripe plum flavours.

★★★★ **Cabernet Sauvignon** Has more substance than ±12% alc would imply. **01** richly coloured & textured with dark fruit & ripe tannin. **02** (sample) classically styled, food-friendly; notes of dusty cassis. Wooding as above.

★★★★ **Sauvignon Blanc** ✓ **04** (sample) lively green hues, lemongrass & coriander aromas; full juicy lime flavours, acid well aligned with fruit. Light-bodied.

Koelenhoffer ☺ ★★★ Unpretentious semi-dry white a perennial brisk seller; **04** (sample) from sauvignon, fragrant guava whiffs; chirpy, crisp. **Koelenkeur** ☺ ★★★ Juicy semi-sweet **04** (sample) from bukettraube, with variety's ethereal bouquet of jasmine & muscat. Charming, pretty.

Pinotage ★★★ **02**, sans pvs dollop merlot, given VIP oak treatment (as for next wine); sample not overtly pinotagey; meaty, smoky complexities; firm & dry damson flavours, sprightly fruit, creamed with oak. Attractive. **Shiraz** 🆕 ★★★★ **02** (sample) dark fruits with touches fynbos & dried herbs; seamlessly oaked yr staves/3rd fill barrels. **Cape Blend** 🆕 ★★★ Merlot (55%) plus pinotage & cab, seriously handled (100% new oak, 15 mths). **02** spicy, plummy nose – evidencing pinotage; still grainy tannins, sweet-sour finish. Medium-bodied, with tweak of acid, like all reds in range. 12% alc. **Pinotage Rosé** ★★ **04** (sample) offers appealing beaujolais-style crushed-fruit sappiness, perhaps a touch too sweet, even for fructose fans. **Chardonnay Wooded** & **Chenin Blanc Wooded** 🆕 **04** not ready for tasting **Koelnektar** ★★★ **04** (sample) citrus-spicy semi-sweet gewürz, cream-textured, slips down like nectar. **Sparkling Sec** ★★★ Explosively fizzy, lightish semi-dry sparkling; latest (NV) not ready for tasting, nor was... **Sparkling Rosé** 🆕 NV from pinotage & **Pinoporto** 🆕 LBV port, also from pinotage. – *TM*

Koelfontein

Ceres ▪ Est 1832 ▪ 1stB 2002 ▪ Visits by appt ▪ Owners Handri & Zulch Conradie ▪ Vini consultant Nicolaas Rust (Jan 2002) ▪ Viticulturist Zulch Conradie ▪ 21 ha (cab, merlot, shiraz, chard, colombard) ▪ 222 tons 1 500 cs own label + 130 000ℓ for customers ▪ 50% red 50% white ▪ PO Box 4 Prince Alfred Hamlet 6840 ▪ wine@koelfontein.com © (023) 313·3130 ☎ (023) 313·4898

'We're settling into this game quietly,' says Handri Conradie, co-owner of this Ceres farm with his brother Zulch, 'and want to retain a fairly low profile until we really have something to brag about.' Obviously it's early days: the brothers' first vintage was the 02. But in 2004 a Shiraz ('particularly good') was produced, making a trio of products with the original Merlot and Chardonnay. Winemaker was Dewaldt Heyns, now at Saronsberg in Tulbagh after a successful spell at Avondale.

★★★★ Merlot NEW Showy 02 can hardly fail to impress with its oak-boosted pungency; concentrated stewed plum tone, hints mocha & espresso; vibrant, juicy plum flavours, perhaps a tad jammy; wood (11 mths Fr oak, 40% new) too forceful for fruit mid-2004, time needed for settling down. 14% alc.

★★★★ Chardonnay 03 leesy aromas of grapefruit, toast & burnt match; rich & heavily wooded – overpowering now, but good core of lime fruit waiting to assert itself. Oak-stave-fermented/aged ±10 mths. 14% alc. **02** had lime & butterscotch in rich mid-palate, creamy tropical finish. — *TM*

Kogmans Kloof see Zandvliet
Koningshof see Avondvrede

Koningsrivier Wines

Robertson ▪ Est/1stB 2002 ▪ Visits by appt ▪ Owner SW Colyn ▪ Winemaker Niël Colyn ▪ Viti consultants Anton Laas & Briaan Stipp ▪ 9 ha (cab) ▪ 435 cs 100% red ▪ PO Box 144 Robertson 6705 ▪ nscolyn@yahoo.com © (023) 625·1748/082·588·1262 ☎ (023) 625·1748

Niël Colyn's maiden Cab, the 03, which we tasted last year as a sample destined for further barrelling, went on to do the young winemaker proud, clinching gold at the National Young Wine Show and finishing top of its class in the competition's regional tastings. 'Not shabby,' smiles he, 'for a first attempt.' It certainly isn't, considering the vines were in only their third leaf. Unready for tasting for the previous guide was a non-vintage Merlot-Cab. The young vintner, who syphons off some of the grapes from the 100 family-owned hectares earmarked for Robertson Winery, was readying a follow-up Cab and a new Shiraz, both 04s, as the guide went to bed.

Kosher see Backsberg, Eshkol, Grundheim, Kleine Draken

Kosie Möller Wines

Paarl ▪ Est/1stB 2000 ▪ Tastings & sales: 42 on Main Restaurant & Wine Shop Mon-Sat 10–8; Kleine Parys farm Mon-Fri 8–5 ▪ Closed Easter Fri/Sun, Dec 16/25/26 & Jan 1 ▪ Facilities for children ▪ Tourgroups ▪ Owners Kosie Möller & Duncan Spence ▪ Winemaker Kosie Möller, with Herman Roux ▪ Viticulturist Herman Roux ▪ 52 ha (cab, chard, chenin, semillon, viognier) ▪ 100 000 cs ▪ 50% red 50% white ▪ Export brands: Chapmans Chance, Marimba, Rising River, Withof, Something Else/letsie Anders, Klippendal, Blijhof & ranges below ▪ PO Box 1317 Suider-Paarl 7620 ▪ kmoller@kmw.co.za ▪ www.kosiemollerwines.co.za © 863·1471/872·8527 ☎ 863·1472/872·8527

Winemaking entrepreneur Kosie Möller has linked up with Duncan Spence, a businessman from the Channel Islands with wide business interests including, locally, Rickety Bridge in Franschhoek. The move coincides with an extension of the Kosie Möller Wines range, exported to more than a dozen countries. At Kleine Parys, one of the original Paarl farms, plans to develop a top wine and tourism venue are in the final stages. Seems there's no stopping this former KWV cellarmaster, who's also paired up with local restaurateur Mark Maingard of 42 on Main Street. Möller's wine shop shares the same premises, and a boutique hotel on the site is in the pipeline.

Alphen Hill range

All reds 6 mths Fr/Am oak. **Cabernet Sauvignon** ★★★ 03 fresh red berries & pencil shavings on nose, accessibly smooth ripe tannins, undemanding & ready. ±14% alc. **Merlot** ★★ Going back a vintage to 01; beguiling soft-berry nose, contrasting with big puckering tannins. 14.5% alc. **Pinotage** ★★★ 01, yr on, warmly ripe; spiced berry pudding aroma; lightly fruity palate, very dry finish. Only 3 mths oak. **Shiraz** ★★★ Retasted 02 reveals leathery/organic notes, dark fruit on palate; could do with more persistence. 14.8% alc. **Pinotage-Shiraz** NEW ★★★ Complementary blend showing spiced wild berry tones, generous fruit; 03 just needs yr/2 to soften. **Chardonnay** ★★ 04 smooth & creamy, good citrus flavours undominated by oak (only 15% Fr-barrelled). Much slimmer wine than pvs at 12.2% alc. **Chenin Blanc** ★★★ 04 sample softly quaffable, gentle, lightish melon & hay tones. All ranges WO W-Cape unless noted.

Bushman's Creek range

All reds ±18 mths barrelled. **Cabernet Sauvignon** ★★★ 03 grassy fynbos bouquet carries through into palate, which fairly lightly fruited. Fr/Am oak. 14.5% alc. **Merlot** ★★★ 01 revisited, proffers sleek black choc/plum combo, firm but good tannin backbone, very dry finish. Only Fr oak. 14.5% alc. **Pinotage** ★★★ 01 engaging, effusive bouquet of plums & red berries; firm dry palate with big alc (14%) & not a lot of concentration. 15% Am oak. **Cabernet Sauvignon-Merlot** ★★★★ 02 modern, accessible style. Oak has settled since last tasted, charming & easy, agreeably firm finish. **Chardonnay** ★★★ Chardonnay-du-Monde 2004 gold for 03, prefaced by citrus zest & toasted almonds, tangy lemon flavours showing minimal wood (only 30% barrel-fermented, 40% Am oak).

Kleine Parys Selection

Following all NEW unless noted: **Shiraz** ★★★★ 03 beautiful dense crimson hue, lots of creamy concentration, subtle oak seasoning (60/40 Am/Fr, yr), not over-extracted tannins. Should improve with 3-4 yrs. **Pinotage** ★★★★ 03 trumpets the variety from the glass, rich, ripe-fruit nose, sprightly palate. Nice. 60/40 Am/Fr oak, yr. **Beatrix Selection** ★★★★ Serious oaking: new barrels 2 yrs, Am/Fr (60/40); meaty/spicy blend shiraz (60%), cab, merlot, pinotage; 02 delicious fruitcake flavour, rich & ripe. Contrived & obvious in the nicest way. **Cabernet Sauvignon-Merlot** ★★★★ We last tasted the 02, sleek & juicy in modern mode. **Chardonnay** ★★★ 04 sample new-barrel-fermented, which shows in deepish golden sheen, toasty nose, toasted-nuts palate. **Chenin Blanc** ★★ Crisp, appley; has an attractive coolness about it; sample of 04 tasted. All WO Paarl.

Dolphin Bay range: NEW

All reds 6 mths in Am/Fr oak, varying proportions; some tasted as samples. **Cabernet Sauvignon** ★★ Cassis & plums waft from 03, quite short but amenably structured, no hard edges. 14.5% alc. **Merlot** ★★ Appealing soft red-berry fragrance on 01, but tannins still fairly aggressive. 14% alc. **Pinotage** ★★ 01 forthcoming fruity little number, ripe mulberries in tasty quaffing format. **Shiraz** ★★★ 02 appealing old-leather sniffs, light-toned fruity palate, soft tannins. 14.5% alc. **Pinotage-Ruby Cabernet** ★★★ Juicy 70/30 blend with wild berry, green banana on nose; smooth 04. **Rosé** ★★ Bouquet of fruit pastilles; 04 some gentle red berry tastes; lightish casual quaffing. **Chardonnay** ★★ 04 very gentle oaking, delicate peach flavours, soft & accessible if bit short. **Chenin Blanc** ★★★ Undemanding 04 fruity quaffer, softish & semi-dry.

Due South range   NEW

Pinotage-Shiraz ★★★ Brambleberries & 'cool' fruit aromas preface 03, soft ripe tannin, good flavour & length, deftly put together, ready. Fr/Am oak 6 mths. **Rosé** ★★★ 04 nicely berry fruited, rounded & soft; a friendly picnic companion. **Chenin Blanc-Chardonnay** ★★★ 04 (sample) chenin's melon flavour dominates, chard gives some fatness for easy, dry, flavoursome tippling. — CR

Kranskop

Robertson ▪ Est/1stB 2001 ▪ Tasting & sales Mon-Fri 10-5 Sat 10-2 1st Sun of mth 10-1 ▪ Fee R10 ▪ Closed Easter Sun, Dec 25 & Jan 1 ▪ Tours during tasting hours ▪ BYO picnic or use the braai facilities; also meals by appt ▪ Tourgroups ▪ Facilities for children ▪ Walks ▪ Owner/winemaker/viticulturist Nakkie Smit ▪ 40 ha (cab, merlot, shiraz, chard) ▪ 500 tons 2 500 cs own label 90% red 10% white ▪ PO Box 18 Klaasvoogds 6707 ▪ kranskop@ myisp.co.za ▪ www.kranskopwines.co.za ⓒ/🖷 (023) 626·3200

A 'brother' for their old basket press – also over 100 years old – made lighter work of vinification for traditionalist Nakkie Smit. When it comes to winemaking, he feels that 'your heart must be in it, the consumer must be excited by your product'. (The Wine of the Month tasters, too, got excited, and selected his Shiraz for the Reserve Club.) A swimming pool and trampoline will keep children happily busy at this family-friendly farm while you enjoy a personalised cellar tour, or hit the mountain bike trail or the tasting deck to drink in sensational views. Nearby attractions include the largest outdoor cactus garden in southern Africa and the Fraai Uitzicht restaurant just across the valley.

★★★★ **Cabernet Sauvignon-Merlot** Replaces one-off Cab tasted pvsly. Light-textured **02** with ultra-dry plum fruit enlivened by fresh acidity – a signature note for this cellar. 50/50 blend with gentle dusting Fr oak. The most drinkable/accessible of these, with lighter tannic structure. Barrelled yr, 15% new, all Fr.

★★★★ **Merlot Reserve 02** elegant, youthful – qualities it retained when retasted mid-2004. Dark minerally fruit, savoury & tart from firm acidity, touch earthiness on dry finish. 14.5% alc. Well-judged spicy Fr oak, 100% new, yr.

★★★★ **Shiraz 02**, retasted for this ed, seems ageless; attractive dark choc fruit, savoury & tart, thanks to fresh acidity. Varietal smoke on ultra-dry finish. Subtly oaked 20% new Am, balance Fr older. Alc 14%.

Merlot ★★★ **02** big wine with 14.5% alc shows no sign of ageing when retasted mid-2004; dark berry/choc richness presently challenged by exuberant acid; subtler oak (yr Fr, 30% new), tannins make for good partner with richer meat dishes until ±2006. **Chardonnay** 🆕 ★★★ Full-bodied & firm-fleshed version, attractive chalk/lime fruit tension in barrel-fermented **03**. Distinctly Rbtson. 14.5% alc. All these WO Klaasvoogds.–*IvH*

Krone see Twee Jonge Gezellen

Kumala see Daschbosch, Porterville, Western Wines

Kumkani see Stellenbosch Vineyards

Kupferberger Auslese

Consistent, lightish semi-sweet by Distell. Current (NV) ★★★ clever mix chenin, riesling, sauvignon (60%), latter giving acidic uplift for uncloying tropical-toned drinkability.–*CR*

KWV International

Paarl ▪ Est 1918 ▪ Tasting daily 9-4 ▪ Fee R15 Sales 9-5 ▪ Tours Eng: 10, 10.30 & 14.15; Ger: 10.15 ▪ Coffee shop 9-4 ▪ Tourgroups ▪ Gifts ▪ Owner KWV Group ▪ Winemaker Sterik de Wet (2001), with Thys Loubser & Ian Nieuwoudt (2001) ▪ Viticulturist Chris Albertyn, advised by Cobus van Graan ▪ ±13 000 tons ▪ PO Box 528 Suider-Paarl 7624 ▪ customer@ kwv.co.za ▪ www.kwv-international.com ⓒ 807·3900 🖷 863·2000

Big news in 2004? KWV wines were available in SA for the first time since this winery's founding in 1918. On local shelves are the KWV Reserve range, long-time 'under-the-counter' favourite Roodeberg, and the easy-drinking Roberts' Rock & Pearly Bay blends. With three overseas subsidiaries (in the UK, Germany and US) and 28 markets, KWV aims to be exporting 5m cases this year. Keeping the spigot open is winemaker-in-chief Sterik de Wet, supported by Ian Nieuwoudt and Thys Loubser. Assistants Chris Jansen, Tania Joubert and Nmonde Khubeha (pioneering young black woman winemaker) have been seconded to the new 2 000-ton Robertson production facility. All coped with the 'interesting' season where 'recipes didn't work', exacerbated by fruit sourced across the winelands (including the Paarl mountain-top, single-vineyard Perold, groomed — and priced — to be KWV's 'Penfold's Grange'). As the guide went to press, new chairman Danie de Wet (of De Wetshof repute) and team were negotiating a major black economic empowerment deal — bellweather of the rapidly changing profile of SA wine.

Cathedral Cellar range

★★★★★ **Cabernet Sauvignon** Expensively, carefully made cab, heaped with praise. **01** already showing deep-veined cassis, mint-choc intensity, complex, tantalising nuances peeping through; but needs time for tannins, elegantly layered structure to unfurl, show greatness within. Leave yr/2, drink for 10. New oak 26 mths. 13.5% alc. **00**, elegant, tightly knit, showing class but not yet full potential. *Wine* ★★★★.

★★★★☆ **Merlot** No expense spared in fruit selection or wood treatment. **01** succulent spice-laden cherries, red berries first impression, other nuances unfold in glass; smoky campfire, dark choc, candied violets. Classically styled, lithe structure, with oaking (26 mths Fr seasoned barrels) laying foundation for 4/5 yrs ageing. 13.5% alc. **00** sleeker; tight tannins needed time to soften. VDG. **99** continued standout form of **98**, both with plenty in store.

★★★★ **Pinotage** Much-acclaimed label, here & abroad. Modern, impressive **01**, opulent, dark fruited, creamy banana richness, with dabs roasted spice, woodsmoke. Built to last; ripe but forceful tannins will show better in yr, have good 6+ more ahead. 24-mth oak supercharge downshifted to 18, seasoned barrels only. 14.5% alc. **00** beautifully integrated but a sleeping giant with big future. WO Coastal

★★★★☆ **Shiraz** Lauded/laudable house style, complex, silkily elegant. **01** delivers beautifully: deep scrubland shadings, wild berries, mocha, savoury spice. Most accessible of reds: supple tannins cloaked by lush fruit, deft oaking. 2 yrs seasoned oak, equal Fr/Am. Already delicious, will keep 5+ yrs. 14.5% alc. **00** showed flavour complexity, ripe firm tannins in support mode for structure, ageing potential.

★★★★ **Triptych** Now established as a cab-merlot blend with shiraz; 36/30/34 ratio in **01** (sample); piercing cassis, crushed berry focus, with creamy roasted spice, touch smoked meat; succulently juicy palate & long lingering finish. Lithe tannins from expensive oaking (26 mths new Fr), easily assimilated; framework for 6+ yrs ageing. 15% alc. Impressive **00**'s lithe, muscular structure suggested serious intent. VDG.

★★★★ **Chardonnay** Showy, powerful **03** keeps to house style: nutty oak richness offset by citrus peel intensity. Very moreish to drink, lovely peach-citrus toned silky texture. Fr barrel fermented/matured 8 mths, all new. 14% alc. **02** like pvs, rescued from over-the-top excess deep-veined citrus zestiness. Pvsly shifted (rather attractively) between voluptuousness (**98**, **01**) & citrus-powered zing (**99**, **00**).

★★★★☆ **Sauvignon Blanc 03** (★★★) lacks intensity, length of pvs. Asparagus, nettles & capsicum in both aroma & flavour. 12.5% alc. **02** showed lip-smacking freshness, flavour, length, food-friendly grippy acidity.

KWV range

★★★★☆ **Roodeberg** A Cape institution, the last pair of vintages apparently ending a stylistic see-saw from modern to traditional & back again. **02** same blend as pvs (cab s, shiraz, merlot, smidgen ruby cab), coming together harmoniously in lively, piquant mulberry/cherry package. Dry toasty finish gives definition to fruit-driven style. Admirable quality considering large quantities. Yr small Fr oak, 20% new. 14.5% alc. Also in 1.5ℓ, 3ℓ, 5ℓ.

Cabernet Sauvignon ★★★★ **02** given added complexity by whiffs roasted fennel, smoky spice. Medium-weight, amenable tannins, good length. Like siblings, ready now, could age 2-3 yrs. Yr small Fr oak. 14% alc. **Merlot** ★★★★ Continues in succulent, fleshy style set by pvs. **02**'s oak (as above) supportive, allows silky berry fruit centre stage. Could age few yrs, but drinks well now. 14.5% alc. **Shiraz** ★★★★ Shadings of smoked meat, liberally dosed with pepper, share space with ripe plums, red berries in **02**. Savoury finish, balanced oaking, contribute towards tasty drinkability, ±3 yr ageing potential. Yr small Am barrels. 14.3% alc. **Pinotage** ★★★☆ **02** Impresses with modern styling of wild berries' fresh appeal, smooth-textured palate; lighter-toned, more elegant than pvs. Shows serious side in fine-grained tannins. Yr Fr oak. 14.5% alc. **Cape Blush ★★★** Blanc de noir features 'Blushing Bride' protea on bright, attractive label. **04** (sample) pungent cassis, fruit pastille aromas, lip-smacking juiciness, long flavourful finish. Cinsaut, merlot, touch sugar. **Chardonnay ★★★** Aromas of **04** (sample) still muted, should show better in finished wine. Smoothly accessible, citrus & peach flavours, delicately enfolded by toasty oak, deftly handled. **Steen ★★** Chenin's 'old-Cape' name for this bone-dry version, slightly sterner than sibling below. **04** gentle fruit salad fragrance/flavours, refreshingly dry. For early drinking. 12.8% alc. **Chenin Blanc ★★☆** Melange of summer fruits incl guavas, apples in **04**; crisp acidity balanced by touch sugar, gives tasty quaffability. 12.8% alc. **Chené ★★★** Lightly wooded chenin. Typical melon/guava fruit well partnered by gentle toastiness, finishing with lemon-biscuit tang in **04** (sample). **Sauvignon Blanc ★★☆ 04** a drop in weight, concentration. Varietally-true green fig, summer meadow aromas; enough palate herbaceous freshness to be food-friendly. 12.1% alc. **Cape Riesling ★★** Restrained, mown hay with touch leafy freshness in uncomplicated, softly accessible **04** (sample). **Late Vintage**, **Mousseux Blanc Cuvee Brut** & **Mousseux Blanc Demi-Sec** discontinued.

Reserve range

★★★★   **Cabernet Sauvignon** Impressive fruit purity, concentration, depth: cassis, minted cherries, cedar-infused from new Fr oak (16 mths). **01** well crafted; firm but ripe tannins within elegant structure. Excellent development potential – 6+ yrs.

★★★★   **Merlot** Classic mint-choc & sour cherries, intense, powerful. **01** firmly supported by oak (16 mths used small Fr); tightly knit, leave another yr to show potential, could cellar 5+. 13.5% alc.

★★★★   **Sauvignon Blanc** From single vyd. Quintessential sauvignon in **03** zinging, fresh mode. Nettle, green fig & herbaceous interleaving; bone dry, but good body weight & roundness from 3 mths lees infusion. 12.8% alc. VDG.

★★★☆   **Shiraz** Like siblings, **01** showy New World style. Mulberries, complex shadings white pepper, 'wet heath', all given sweet spice infusion by Am oak (16 mths). Ripe but firm tannins, well structured for ± 4 yrs ageing. 13.5% alc.

★★★☆   **Chardonnay** From single vyd. **03** lemon/orange zest, liberally spread on toast. Tangy, nutty, showy & delicious. 6 mths fermented/matured new Fr oak. 14% alc. Gold at Chardonnay du Monde. This range WO Stbosch.

Robert's Rock range

★★★★   **Chardonnay-Semillon** ✓ Lively, flavoursome. **04** (★★★☆) sample easier, earlier drinking than pvs. Ebullient peach/lemon peel fragrance, flavours, smoothly supple for appealing accessibility. Unwooded 51/49 blend. **03** 60/40 mix, affirmed partnership's compatibility.

Cinsaut-Ruby Cabernet ☺ **★★★ 03** step up on pvs. Freshly crushed red berries, juicy enough to tantalise tastebuds, drink easily. Touch oak (6 mths) adds interest, focus. NB: 14% alc.

Cabernet Sauvignon-Merlot ★★★☆ ✓ Tasty early-drinker. Cab's dominance (54%) shows in **03**'s Fortris pungency, merlot lightens body, refreshes palate. Touch oak. 13.5% alc. **Merlot-Cinsaut ★★★ 03** not ready for tasting. **Pinotage-Pinot Noir ★★★☆** ✓ Idiosyncratic, but works. **03** 60/40 blend. Pinotage to fore in brambleberry/beetroot character, but elegance, fresh vibrancy is pure pinot. Yr's oaking well integrated. 13.5% alc. **Shiraz-Malbec ★★★☆** ✓ Compatible **03** partnership delivers some underbrush, smoky nuances, cherry flavours. Barrel sample nicely balanced; well-judged oak. **Cinsaut-Chenin Blanc ★★★ 04** not ready for tasting. **Chardonnay ★★★ 04** (sample) peach & tropical fruit flavours aid easy, uncomplicated quaffability. Lightly oaked. **Chenin Blanc-Chardonnay 04** (unrated sample) appealing perfume & freshness; peach-lemon, merest hint of oak add character to lively, tasty quaffer. 51/49 blend.

Golden Kaan range [NEW]

All **03** ★★★, alc 13–14%. **Cabernet Sauvignon** Juicily ripe blackcurrant/mulberry fruit dominates lithe, smooth palate. Oaking (9 mths seasoned Fr) only apparent in dry finish, but still friendly, amenable. Can keep for few yrs. **Merlot** Succulent cherries, red berries, with just enough oak contribution (as above) to provide structural framework without interfering with easy drinkability. **Shiraz** True to variety, in fresh, light-toned way. Wild berries, whiffs pepper & underbrush, lively fruit-dominant palate, all contribute to friendly, approachable style. Oaked 9 mths used small Am. **Pinotage** Like rest of range, designed for easy accessibility: creamy berry/rhubarb pie aromas, light-toned fruity drinkability. Fr/Am oaking doesn't intrude. **Chardonnay** Plumply amenable. Smooth-textured peach & nut character, tasty, appealing. Lightly oaked. **Sauvignon Blanc** Shows ripeness, verve: passionfruit, gooseberries in medium-weight structure; limy/tropical tang, zesty finish.

Bonne Esperance range

First-time listing in guide for this established range. **Dry Red** ★★ This, below, in 1ℓ screwcap, sold internationally; in SA only for KWV staff. From cinsaut, ruby cab, smattering pinotage. Softly friendly; juicy ripe berry flavours. 13.5% alc. **Dry White** ★★ Chenin-based. Appley fruit salad, with crisp, light, easy-drinking texture.

Pearly Bay range

Cape Red ☺ ★★★ Flavoursome early-drinking blend cinsaut, ruby cab, dash pinotage; fruit-gum whiffs, juicy cherries, light-hearted. 12.5% alc.

Cape White ★★ Light-bodied everyday dry drink from mainly chenin. Delicate peardrop tones, soft friendly palate. 11.8% alc. Both NV.

KWV Fortified range

★★★★ **Millennium Port 99** 'last bottled KWV port of the old millennium' still available, ageing gracefully; cinsaut/tinta, high alc (19.5%), moderate sugar (110g/ℓ), huge grape-tannin structure for keeping. Unwooded.

★★★★ **Tawny Port** Long ageing (5–8 yrs old-oak) creates a fine tawny style. Latest (NV) continues layered styling but notch higher: tealeaves & English toffee, honeycomb, nutty oak. Full-bodied, almost syrupy texture, with a long aromatic, brandied finish. Gorgeous. Equal tinta/souzão. 19.3% alc. 120g/l sugar.

★★★★ **Vintage Red Muscadel** [NEW] From selected Rbtson vyds; **75** deep amber hue, more than passing resemblance to tawny port in character. Admirable complexity: tea leaves, nutty oiliness, brandy-soaked raisins. Long savoury/sweet finish, plenty life, sophistication. Large oak 8 yrs. 17.3%. 150g/ℓ sugar. Must-have collector's wine at affordable R70 ex-cellar.

★★★★ **White Muscadel** [NEW] Twin of Red, incl packaging. Amber colour alerts you to delights to come. Beyond sultana-essence concentration lies layered complexity: tobacco, English toffee, freshening leafy edginess. Palate reveals ambrosial richness, yet savoury, almost tawny-like. Good ageing potential. Classy, impressive. Unwooded. 17.5% alc.

Red Muscadel ★★★★ Bright, colourful packaging is first attraction, raisiny richness is second. Xmas cake/glacé fruit opulence offset by racy freshness. Eminently drinkable. 8 yrs large oak. 17.5% alc. NV. Just enough spirity tang to balance sweetness, get juices going. **Ruby Port** ★★★ Current NV offers creamy depths, prunes & stewed fruit, with smoothly textured tasty drinkability. 2 yrs large oak. From tinta/souzão. 19.3% alc. All ranges WO W-Cape unless noted. — CR

Laborie Cellar

Paarl ▪ Est 1691 ▪ Tasting & sales daily 9-5 (Nov-Apr) Mon-Fri 9-6 (May-Oct) ▪ Fee R9 (tasting only) R18 (tasting & tour) ▪ Closed Easter Fri & Dec 25 ▪ Tours for groups 10+ by appt ▪ Laborie Restaurant ▪ Owner KWV South Africa ▪ Winemaker Gideon Theron (Oct 1994) ▪ Viticulturist Henri van Reenen (Oct 1998) ▪ 32 ha (cab, merlot, shiraz, chard, sauvignon) ▪ 400 tons 80 000

cs ■ PO Box 528 Suider-Paarl 7624 ■ therongi@kwv.co.za ■ www.kwv-international.com
℃ 807·3390/3196 ☎ 863·1955

At KWV's stately Paarl property, winemaker Gideon Theron continues his quest for quality. Being able to buy in grapes from carefully selected areas, a benefit of no longer being registered an estate, has contributed considerably. An 'interesting' harvest resulted in good colour and balance, with lower alcohols a plus in the red wines (more of which were put through cold maceration, intensifying flavours and softening tannins). The Shiraz, latest in the lineup of single-varietal wines, is a winner with red meat says Theron, who regularly goes on hunting sorties to Namibia and prepares game for friends and family. Try the wines in the chic tasting room or match them with food on the tree-shaded verandah at the restaurant, with its valley views.

★★★★ **Jean Taillefert** The flagship, a boldly New-World shiraz; opulence & cherry/dark-fruited mocha richness are key elements of retasted **01**, as are oodles of vanilla-spice from 13 mths new Am oak. Supple tannins for both drinkability & 4+ yrs ageing. Unfiltered, as is rest of red range. 14.7% alc. 90 pts US *Wine & Spirits* mag.

★★★★ **Cabernet Sauvignon 02** (★★★★) lighter textured than pvs; speaks of restraint, careful handling, from fine layers cassis, violets, cedar, to firm but ripe tannin. Accessible now, drink 3-4 yrs. Yr Fr oak, 20% new. 14.2% alc. **00** VDG; **01** VG.

★★★☆ **Merlot** Beguiling creamy red berries, whiffs spice in **02**. Juicy, has elegant accessibility & life, well-judged ripe tannins. Oak as above. 14.7% alc. **01** has plummy richness, supple tannins, silky accessibility.

★★★☆ **Merlot-Cabernet Sauvignon** 60/40 blend. Latest **02**, as pvs, inviting, succulent berry profile with just enough oak providing framework to hang it on. Character, charm, 3+ yrs potential. Oak as above. 14.4% alc. **01** also fruity, light textured for earlier drinking.

★★★☆ **Chardonnay** Big, bold **03**; candied fruit & hazelnut richness. Despite only partial oaking, gives toasty presence on palate. 13.6% alc. **01** showed similar toast/hazelnut influence. **02** whizzed out of cellar before we could taste.

★★★★ **Blanc de Blanc Brut** ✓ 'Méthode Cap Classique' in pvs ed; renamed to reflect 100% chardonnay composition since **98** (pvs chard/pinot), with plenty of character from ±3 yrs bottle-ageing on lees. Cap Classique Challenge ★★★★. Current **99** showy, impressive. Waves of fresh baked bread richness, citrus peel; creamy mousse, long lingering bone-dry finish. 12.5% alc. Brut sparkling, usually a chardonnay/pinot blend with plenty of character from ±3 yrs bottle-ageing on lees.

★★★★ **Pineau de Laborie** Luxurious (-tasting & -looking) dessert from pinotage, mostly unfermented, matured 18 mths in barrels (none new), fortified with in-house-distilled potstill brandy (also pinotage) to ±17.5% alc. Sugar (±100g/ℓ) tweaked for comfortable solo sipping or with dessert/cheese. **01** doesn't disappoint in impressive run of vintages: opulent, brandied plum pudding flavour, yet enough zip to refresh palate, avoid cloying effect. 375ml. Own grapes (WO Paarl).

Pinotage ★★★★ Latest **02** step up: juicier, has vivid berry fruit, lip-smacking verve & texture. Serious wood (yr small Fr barrels, portion Am) doesn't negate charm. Enjoy now, cellar 3-4 yrs. 14.1% alc. **01**, mid-2004, drinks smoothly. Rhubarb/red berry tones in lithe, approachable structure. **Shiraz** 🆕 ★★★ Delicately fruit-driven **02** with added smoky, spice nuances. Medium-weight, lively, juicy, for early drinking. Unfiltered. Yr small Fr, touch Am. 14.7% alc. **Sauvignon Blanc** ★★★ **03** fig & Cape gooseberry piquancy in medium-weight structure; zesty, refreshing. Acidity toned down from pvs to comfortable 6g/ℓ. 13.2% alc. **Blanc de Noir** ★★★ Made by transfer method, aperitif-style dry sparkler now from mainly pinot, dash other red varieties. Current **00** fresh-picked redcurrants, cherries, with herbaceous notes. Tangy fruit flavours, rounded by honeyed bottle maturity. 12.7% alc. Own grapes; remainder WO Coastal unless noted. — *CR*

La Bri

Franschhoek ■ Tasting & sales Mon-Fri 10-12.30 Oct-Apr or by appt ■ Fee R12 ■ Closed public holidays ■ Owner Robin Hamilton ■ Winemaker Stephan Smit (2003) ■ 18 ha (cabs s/

f, merlot, petit v, shiraz, chard, semillon) ▪ *3 000 cs own label 80% red 20% white* ▪ *Ranges for customers: Helgerson Wines (US), Makro* ▪ *PO Box 180 Franschhoek 7690* ▪ *info@ labri.co.za* ▪ *www.la-bri.co.za* ⓒ *876·2593* 🖷 *876·3197*

Vintage 2004 will have helped along owner Robin Hamilton's expressed desire to devote more of his energy to producing serious reds. It was a good year, according to farm manager Johan Haasbroek, delivering 'elegant, compact red wine'. Taste it right there on the historic Franschhoek farm: a facility has recently been opened, offering intimate, sit-down tastings for no more than 12 at a time.

Reserve range

★★★★ **Cabernet-Merlot Reserve** ✓ Retaste of latest releases prompts higher general rating for these impressive cab-dominated reds. 82/18 blend in **01**, showing good bottle-development mid-2004, carefully wielded oak, supple tannins firming up ripe plum flavours. *Wine* ★★★★. 94% cab in **02**, yet more approachable (factor of the vintage?), more 'New World', stacked with succulent cassis. 14.5% alc, 20 mths Fr oak, third new.

Merlot ★★★☆ Ripe plum flavours, fine almost silky tannins, **02** ends on sweet floral note. Ready & appealing now, probably not for keeping. 20 mths Fr oak, some new.

Limited Release range

No new releases of **Cabernet** (★★★★), **Chardonnay** (★★★) or **Semillon** (★★). – *DH*

◼ *La Cave* see Wamakersvallei
La Cotte see Franschhoek Vineyards

La Couronne Estate

Franschhoek ▪ *Est/1stB 1999* ▪ *Tasting & sales Mon-Fri 10-4 Sat Nov-Apr only by appt* ▪ *Fee R15* ▪ *Tours by appt (R10 p/p)* ▪ *Closed public holidays* ▪ *Picnics (see intro)* ▪ *La Couronne Hotel* ▪ *Facilities for children* ▪ *Tourgroups* ▪ *Owners The Austrian Trust* ▪ *Winemaker Dominic Burke (Jul 2001)* ▪ *Viti consultants Andrew Teubes & Johan Wiese (Jan 1999)* ▪ *26 ha (cabs s/f, merlot, chard, sauvignon)* ▪ *60-90 tons ±8 000 cs 80% red 20% white* ▪ *PO Box 459 Franschhoek 7690* ▪ *info@lacouronne.co.za* ▪ *www.lacouronne.co.za* ⓒ *876·3939/2110* 🖷 *876·4168*

The farm was awarded its ISO 14001 certificate early in 2004. 'It's important,' explains winemaker Dominic Burke, 'because it shows our clients and supporters that we're serious about caring for our natural environment, particularly as a working winery producing wine effluent.' What's also important is that the owners have bought the farm Normandy (between L'Ormarins and Boschendal), so Burke will have those vineyards to produce from. Look out for the estate's new range – 277, after the number of original French Huguenots who settled in the valley – launched late in 2004 with a Sauvignon. Another launch due at year's end was a picnicking spot where visitors can enjoy the estate's magnificent views.

★★★★ **Ménage à Trois** Blend cabs s/f, merlot, separately vinified/matured. **01**, pvsly tasted as work in progress, well fleshed with blackcurrants & mulberries; has elegance, verve as well as juice; firm dry finish; some yrs to go.

★★★★ **Merlot** Has progressively moved away from lighter-toned, lightly oaked style; **01** fully 20 mths wooded, all Fr, 2nd/3rd fill; still fragrantly fresh; red berries, violets & minty nuance; midweight; ready & could be cellared another few yrs.

★★★★ **Chardonnay** Formula changed from partial to full oaking (though only 33% new barrels, 8 mths) with **02** (★★★). Mid-2004 retaste shows muted toasty lemon-butter aromas, light-textured palate. 13.9% alc. **03** unusual meaty whiffs; toasty lemon-lime flavours; has some life, finishes with brisk acidic smack.

★★★★ **Chardonnay Reserve** 100% new oak, 10 mths, for this version; **02** richer, more guts & structure than above; English toffee creaminess on nose, toasty peach flavours; peaking, enjoy over the next 12-18 mths. Alc 13.9%.

Cabernet Sauvignon ★★★ Russet-edged **01** fairly sinewy profile with lead pencil tone; appealing mineral bouquet. 24 mths oak, 50% new. **Rogues Rouge** ★★★ Medium-bodied blend cabs s/f, merlot, 14 mths Fr oak, some new; NV; 13.5% alc. **01** retasted, still has attractive youthful freshness about it; clean dry eucalyptus finish. **Sauvignon Blanc '277'** ★★★ **04** lively passionfruit/green fig aromas, chunky asparagus flavour, tart food-friendly finish. Light 12% alc. **Sauvignon Blanc-Chardonnay** ★★★ Showcases best of both grapes. Lightish **03** slightly honeyed fig aroma; quite rich, rounded ripe-melon flavours, tangy mouth-watering finish. Pvs was chard-dominated **02** (★★), labelled 'Chardonnay-Sauvignon Blanc', now shows its age; suggest drink these soon. – *CR*

Ladismith Co-op Winery

Little Karoo ▪ Est 1939 ▪ 1stB 1988 ▪ Tasting & sales Mon-Fri 8-5 ▪ Closed all public holidays except Easter Sat ▪ BYO picnic ▪ Tours by appt ▪ Conferencing ▪ Owners 75 members ▪ Winemaker Jim de Kok (Jan 2002) ▪ Viti consultant Willem Botha (Jan 2001) ▪ 600 ha (ruby cab, chard) ▪ 8 000 tons 4 200 cs own label + 3.2m litres bulk ▪ PO Box 56 Ladismith 6885 ▪ lkws@telkomsa.net ▪ www.kleinkaroowines.co.za © (028) 551·1042 ≣ (028) 551·1930

This winery in the Little Karoo town is certainly doing all it can to explore new markets. They celebrate their 65th anniversary with the release of a new brand called Lady J Smith, after Juana, Spanish-born wife of 19th century Cape governor Sir Harry, for whom the village is named. The range (untasted) will eventually consist of two whites and a red. On the premises there are now facilities for small conferences, and an area where visitors can enjoy picnic lunches (welcome to BYO).

Unless noted, all appear under the Towerkop label; none of the reds oaked. New versions of **Cabernet Sauvignon**, **Merlot**, **Green Wine Pinotage** & **Shiraz** untasted. **Pinotage** ★★★ **03** revisited, hints of dried fruit, spice & pepper, reoccurring on lightish but pleasant palate. **Ruby Cabernet** ★★★ Showcases warm-climate thatchy fruit; lightish **03** still a fruity easy drinker mid-2004, sweet warm fruit still sippable. **Rosé** ★★★ Retasted semi-sweet NV **03** shows pale blanc-de-noir shade, bright cherry fruit, low ±11% alc. **Chardonnay Wooded** ★★ **03** has lost the vanilla we last tasted, zing's gone too, just modest melon & citrus flavour left. **Chardonnay Unwooded** ★★ **03** lighter quaffable style, undemanding; still has life, gentle melon & pear tone. **Chenin Blanc** ★★ **03** light textured & easy with some guava character, touch of liveliness still. **Colombard** ★★ **03** has lost its bright zesty character, still an acceptable no-frills quaff. **Riesling** ★★ Cape riesling, **03** soft & clean but very little personality. **Sauvignon Blanc** ★★ **03** notes of green pears, soft, undemanding. **Blanc de Blanc** ★★★ Latest version not ready for tasting. **Stein** ★★ Supple, lightish summer drink with soft acidity; latest NV (02) has a very dry finish for this style; from colombard, chenin. **Amalienstein Muscadel** ★★★★ Powerfully scented **02** red fortified dessert with generous flavours of tangerine liqueur, has improved since last tasted; 16.5% alc. **Towersoet** ★★★ Fortified hanepoot with lively muscat aromas; light texture, not sickly sweet. – *JN*

Lady Anne Barnard see African Pride

Laibach Vineyards

Stellenbosch ▪ Est 1994 ▪ 1stB 1997 ▪ Tasting & sales Mon-Fri 9-5 Sat 9-1 (Nov-Apr only) Public holidays 9-1 (closed Easter Fri/Sun, Dec 25 & Jan 1) ▪ Fee R10 refunded on purchase ▪ Tours by appt ▪ Owners Laibach family ▪ Winemakers Stefan Dorst & Francois van Zyl (Jan 1997/Jan 2000) ▪ Viticulturist Michael Malherbe (Jun 1994) ▪ 42 ha (cabs s/f, malbec, merlot, petit v, pinotage, chard) ▪ 300 tons 24 000 cs own label ▪ 600 cs for Woolworths ▪ 70% red 30% white ▪ Export brands Inkawu & Special Selection ▪ PO Box 7109 Stellenbosch 7599 ▪ info@laibach.co.za ▪ www.laibach.co.za © 884·4511 ≣ 884·4848

Francois van Zyl is flooring the accelerator. The chequered flag: 'to achieve something great by 2005, be up there with the big boys'. His 2002 reds (marked by a difficult growing season) were 'frustrating when you know you're driving a 12-cylinder car and only 4.5 cylinders are firing'. But wine spectators can look forward 'something special' with the 2003s. He's sick and tired of saying Laibach is next to Kanonkop. 'Maybe I can get them to say Kanonkop is next to Laibach. The farm's enormous potential just needs fine-tuning and older vines.' A 2004 high point: their first organic wine, The Ladybird (honouring this little insect's return to fight vineyard scourge, the mealybug). Six hectares organically farmed suffered just 2% crop loss in 2002 versus 30% elsewhere.

★★★★ **Friedrich Laibach** Flagship with quality as goal: so no **02**: 'not good enough'. **01** certainly is. Imposing rich fragrance; 82% cab's structural influence evident in tailored, sophisticated palate; 18% merlot. Sweet-fruited, fantail finish. Still way off best. Cab 20 mths oak, 75% new; merlot yr. **00** was 100% cab; *Decanter* ★★★★.

★★★★ **The Dogleg** (formerly Cabernet Sauvignon-Merlot) Named for golfing analogy: Francois vZ noted improvement when tiny percentage petit v, cab f added. **02** nuanced blend, no variety dominating. Flavoursome cedary, plum, mulberry, violets & much else on supportive structure. Pleasurably savoury, fresh. Yr Fr oak, 30% new. 13.5% alc. No **01**. **00** disciplined equal blend. 15 mths Fr oak. 14% alc.

★★★★ **The Ladybird** 🆕 **02** blend named for mealy-bug predator; SGS-certified as organic, first for Stbosch. Plush, riper style than above; merlot's plummy notes leading cabs s/f partners (61/21/18 mix), presently challenged by generous oak. Has guts to resolve imbalance next 3-4 yrs. 25% new Fr oak. 14% alc.

★★★★ **Cabernet Sauvignon** ✓ **02** claret-like fresh cassis, cigar box notes; polished tannins complement ripe fruit. Immensely satisfying without huge complexity. Yr Fr thin-stave barrels, 40% new. 14% alc. No **01** – diverted to Friedrich Laibach.

★★★★ **Merlot 02** cedar-touched mulberry charm; bouncy persistent fruit; roundly dry. Good presence in difficult vintage. Yr Fr oak, 15% new. 14% alc

★★★★★ **Pinotage Unfiltered 01** one-off. Had impressive concentration, mouthfilling with tannins gently firming up finish. 18 mths oak, 85% new. 14.5% alc.

★★★★ **Pinotage** ✓ From **02** (★★★★) sole pinotage flag-bearer. Minimalist tannins, smoothing brush oak highlight straightforward tangy damsons, redcurrants; best over next 2 yrs. Nip bitterness would be negated by suitable hearty dish. 14.5% alc. 80% oaked, 16 mths. **01** ABSA Top Ten; intensely flavoured but not over-extracted.

★★★★ **Chardonnay** Elegantly handled oak (40% new, 5 mths) well-forged with tropical/oatmeal fruit on **03**. Big, not too heavy; malo suppressed for freshness. 14% alc.

★★★★ **Natural Sweet 04** still unsettled shortly after bottling. From chenin. Unusual mix styles: oak-fermented/2 mths, but Germanic low 7.5% alc. Dainty peach/pear-drop nose; poised 140g/ℓ sugar, 9.5g/ℓ acid. Ideal summer aperitif. 375ml.

Chenin Blanc ☺ ★★★ Fresh, full-bodied **04**; gently-paced floral, citrus fruit; drinkability enhanced by clean, dry finish. 14% alc. Stbosch vyds.

Sauvignon Blanc ★★★ Gooseberry/grassy stimulation on sprightly, pure **04**. Medium body adds to general liveliness, appeal. Bone-dry. 12.5% alc. —AL

Lammershoek Winery

*Swartland ▪ Est/1stB 1999 ▪ Tasting, sales & tours Mon-Fri 9-5 Sat/Sun & public holidays by appt ▪ Fee R10 (free if purchase exceeds R150) ▪ Tours Mon-Fri 9-5 by appt ▪ Special house platter (R40 p/p) Mon-Fri 9-5 by appt; or BYO picnic ▪ Walks ▪ Conservation area ▪ Mountain biking ▪ Owners Paul & Anna Kretzel, Stephan family ▪ Winemaker Albert Ahrens (Jun 2002) ▪ Viticulturists Paul Kretzel & Albert Ahrens ▪ 130 ha (12 varieties, r/w) ▪ 100 tons 10 000 cs own label 85% red 15% white ▪ PO Box 597 Malmesbury 7299 ▪ kretzelp@ intekom.co.za ▪ www.lammershoek.co.za ©/🖨 **(022) 482·2835**

Big, spicy reds and rich, expressive whites – there are some mighty wines in the making in these rugged hills, suited as they appear to be to southern French and Spanish varieties. While most of Paul and Anna Kretzel's carefully tended crop previously went to a nearby co-op, they're now selling to independents (skimming off some of the cream for their own label), including neighbour Eben Sadie and several other young winemakers in the know. White blend Roulette Blanc was recently released to partner their Rhône-inspired red. Also new is the Aprilskloof range, a red and white for everyday.

★★★★ **Roulette** ✓ Delicious Swartland answer to southern Rhône appreciated by French judges, with CWT gold. **02** spicy, savoury melding of shiraz, carignan, grenache, viognier; fragrant cedary expansion. Fresh appeal offsets 14.6% alc though still tannic, unevolved. Excellent potential to 2006-07. Mix Fr/Am oak, ±35% new. Unfined, not cold-stabilised, as all in range, so may throw harmless sediment.

★★★★ **Syrah 02** retasted still pretty impenetrable. Embryonic exotic complexity more evident on palate: rare beef, woodsmoke & Eastern spices in long, earthy warmth. Big, but balanced: fruit concentration match for 15.5% alc, 50% new Am oak.

★★★☆ **Pinotage Barrique** ✓ **03** modern, elegant. Sweet raspberry, plum whispers, lifted by cedar. Light-textured; fine vibrant tannins still envelop fresh, ripe fruit. Dry, long. 14% alc. Partially fermented large casks, matured yr Fr barriques, 33% new.

★★★☆ **Tinta Barocca Barrique** ✓ **02** revisited shows appealing cedary/fresh earth bouquet. Finely balanced, supple; sweet-fruited length, well-integrated tannins add to overall drinkability. Matured Fr barriques, 33% new. 30+ yr old vines. 14.6% alc.

★★★★ **Cabernet Sauvignon-Merlot Barrique** ✓ Hearty, warmer-climate style; **02**, full, soft dark berries, vanilla from 18 mths Fr oak, 40% new; dense texture, ample red earth savouriness, sturdy tannins will benefit from yr/2. 60/40 blend.

★★★★ **Roulette Blanc** NEW ✓ Replaces Viognier Barrique. Delightful, intriguing barrel-fermented **03** chenin-dominated blend, with viognier, hárslevelü, chardonnay. Swtlnd generous flavours, body with balanced elegance. Apricot, orange blossom scents; pickled lime fresh overlay to supple, creamy palate. Subtle Fr oak. Potential to 2006-08. 15.5% alc. Home vyds, as is entire range; occasional Coastal WO due to bureaucratic demands.

★★★☆ **Chardonnay Barrique** Fresh **02**; interesting hazelnut richness to dried peach core; poise, balance suggests best enjoyed over next yr/18 mths. Californian clone; bunch-pressed, fermented/aged 8 mths, 30% new Hungarian oak, balance used Fr.

★★★★ **Chenin Blanc Barrique** ✓ Buxom **03** also refined, sophisticated. Youthfully unevolved floral/honey concentration; beautifully balanced with fresh, creamy mouthfeel. Less heavy, drier (2.8 vs 9.7g/ℓ sugar), than seductively New-World **02**. Good potential to 2010. Fermented/matured used Fr barrels. 15.5% alc.

★★★☆ **Straw Wine** Last tasted **03** from air-dried hárslevelü. Peach/apricot notes, touch botrytis. Viscous, soft sweetness. 106g/ℓ sugar. 14.3% alc. Used Fr oak, 6 mths. Beautifully presented in tall, 375ml bottles. **04** not ready for tasting.

Zinfandel Mega-ripe 00 (★★★), with splash tinta last tasted; **04** under consideration. **Cape Ruby Zinfandel** ★★☆ Subtitled 'Sweet Zin'; **01**, ruby-style port, chunky, robust & sweet. **02** not read for tasting. **Pinodoux** NEW ★★★ New guise for pinotage. **03** fermented dry, sweetened with grape-juice to 102g/ℓ, fortified with brandy; yr used Fr oak. Result less exotic than technique. Smooth, rich red fruits, some toffee undertones. Clean, unheavy 16% alc.

Aprilskloof range   NEW

Sauvignon Blanc ★★★★ ✓ **04** bright, tropical, figgy flavours melded with delicious savoury acidity. Satisfying presence, length with moderate 12% alc.

> **Cabernet Sauvignon-Pinotage** ☺ ★★★ Forthcoming rich, dark berry aromas/flavours on **03**. Firm yet accessible; pleasantly dry, medium-bodied.

Discontinued: **Shiraz-Carignan Barrique.** —*AL*

La Motte

Franschhoek ∎ Est 1984 ∎ Tasting & sales Mon-Fri 9-4.30 Sat 10-3 ∎ Fee R10 ∎ Closed Easter Fri/Sun, Dec 25 ∎ For attractions & amenities, see below ∎ Owner Hanneli

Koegelenberg ▪ Winemaker Edmund Terblanche (Dec 2001), with Werner Geldenhuys (Jun 2003) ▪ Viticulturist Pietie le Roux (May 1986) ▪ 108 ha (cabs s/f, merlot, shiraz, chard, sauvignon) ▪ 900 tons 30 000 cs own label 53% red 47% white ▪ Exported as Schoone Gevel ▪ ISO 14001 certified ▪ PO Box 685 Franschhoek 7690 ▪ cellar@la-motte. co.za ▪ www.la-motte.com © 876·3119 ≣ 876·3446

Like most of his peers, winemaker Edmund Terblanche believes wine is made in the vineyard. 'But', he adds, 'it's a mix of nature, science and hard work. Timing's the critical factor throughout, and that comes from practice, repetition, training and experimentation.' He predicts that 2004 will deliver better red wines than whites, especially in the case of merlot and shiraz. Those reds now have their own new cellar which can handle 400 tons a season; extra tables for hand-sorting have also been installed. The historic red wine cellar hosts classical concerts each month (the interests of owner, mezzo-soprano Hanneli Koegelenberg, neé Rupert, are felt here). Other attractions, in a Cape Dutch setting, include a summer (that's December to March) restaurant in the garden and a cosy fire warming winter visitors to the tasting-room.

★★★★ **Shiraz** Admirably enjoyable Cape fixture for many yrs now. Latest **02** entices with redcurrant, roast beef & whiff sweet vanilla; subtly & sensuously caressing fruit, slight savouriness, lingering finish. Ripe at 14.5% but elegant. **00** just about squeezed its ripeness into typical elegance. These partial natural yeast ferment, 21 mths Fr/Am oak, third new.

★★★★ **Shiraz-Viognier** NEW Impressive debut. Made separately to wine above, 90/10 shiraz, viognier. Yr oak, 90/10 Fr/Am 20% new. Sample **03** dense blackberry richness, smoked beef & shy violet an attractive invitation. Crammed with blackberry & cherry fruit, luscious padding around dry, minerally core, fine tannins.

★★★★ **Millennium** In latest **01**, class evident from first sniff — fine oak, cedar, hints tobacco & cassis richness. Gorgeous deep-pile velvet entry, rounded fruit, then savoury bite of oak & dry fruity finish with brush tannin — appeal is both sensual & cerebral. Blend cab s, merlot, cab f 39/39/22. 2 yrs oak, all Fr, 50% new. 14.9% alc.

★★★★ **Cabernet Sauvignon** House style well established; cedar coolness, dark choc richness, touches roast beef in **02**. Pleasantly plump, with dry savoury finish, helped by 21 mths in Fr oak. 14.3% alc. **00** savoury, structured & vinous.

★★★★ **Chardonnay 03** (sample) bursts with spiced peach & lime fruit, silky creamy mouthfeel from 50% natural yeast fermentation, yielding higher glycerols. **02** looking a little plain in comparison, but packed with tangy citrus fruit. These part barrel-fermented, ±yr Fr oak well integrated. Keep 2-3 yrs.

★★★☆ **Sauvignon Blanc** Latest **04** delicious, manages balancing act of 'fresh & lively' with elegance. Bracing thread of zesty, lime acidity offsets smooth texture & tropical notes. 14.1% alc. — *IvH*

Landau du Val

Franschhoek ▪ Tasting by appt ▪ Sales at La Cotte Inn Wine Sales, Franschhoek ▪ Owners Basil & Jane Landau ▪ Winemaker Jean Daneel ▪ Viticulturist Jaco Schwenke ▪ © 082·410·1130 ≣ 876·3369

Celebrating their centenary in 2005, the semillon bushvines on Basil and Jane Landau's farm, La Brie, continue to produce an acclaimed wine. Yield from these venerable vines, carefully nurtured and unirrigated, is limited to three tons per hectare at the most. Winemaker Jean Daneel also produces a 100% sauvignon, again in limited quantities.

★★★★ **Semillon** Big bones, high alcs (14.5%) of recent vintages nudge balance equilibrium, demand fine dining accompaniment. Next **03** from 99 yr old bush vines eking out 3 tons/ha: very concentrated candle wax/sheep's wool fullness to pink grapefruit twist, smooth with late alc fillip. Similar mould to **02**, both show refined, well-delineated fruit. Fr oak-fermented/aged 6 mths, mix new/seasoned.

★★★☆ **Sauvignon Blanc Private Selection 04** not bottled at press-time. **03** well-fleshed with tropical fruit, soft borders, easy-going palate. 13.8% alc. — *DS*

▨ *Landsdowne* see Arlington

Land's End Wines

Elim ▪ *Est 1998* ▪ *1stB 2000* ▪ *Closed to public* ▪ *Viticulturist Tienie`Wentzel (1999)* ▪ *35 ha (cab, merlot, shiraz, sauvignon, semillon)* ▪ *50-70 tons ±3 500 cs 50/50 red/white* ▪ *taster@mweb.co.za* ▪ *PO Box 181 Simondium 7670 Ⓒ/🖷 434·8650*

These are some of SA's most southerly vineyards, situated close to Cape Agulhas and owned by a syndicate of six owners who continue to insist on anonymity. Viticulturist Tienie Wentzel reports that the vines are now well established and well balanced, and beginning to reflect the great winemaking potential of the area. 'Last harvest showed that heatwaves such as experienced at the end of January have no effect here at the coast. The cool afternoon air brings the temperature right down', he says.

★★★★ **Shiraz** Maiden **02** last ed, gentle tannins, rich, softish; youthfully unintegrated. Matured 66% Fr, rest Am oak. **03** (ex-cask) shielded by oak; similar chocolatey red fruits, velvety softness underneath. At 14.8% alc, riper, bigger — unexpected given Elim's cool climes. Possible ★★★★ on release.

★★★★ **Sauvignon Blanc** Unfinished **04** 'best yet', claim the team**.** Cool, sea-freshened grassiness teams up with semillon's lemony purity (10%). Bracing & agile with sound, dry length. Should evolve with finesse. 12.7% alc.

Discontinued: **Semillon**; **Cabernet Sauvignon**.— *AL*

Landskroon Wines

Paarl ▪ *Est 1874* ▪ *1stB 1974* ▪ *Tasting & sales Mon-Fri 8.30-5 Sat 9-1* ▪ *Fee R3 for groups* ▪ *Closed Easter Fri, Dec 25 & Jan 1* ▪ *Tours by appt* ▪ *BYO picnic* ▪ *Self-catering cottage* ▪ *Play area for children* ▪ *Tourgroups* ▪ *Gifts* ▪ *Walks by appt* ▪ *Permanent display of Stone Age artefacts* ▪ *Owners Paul & Hugo de Villiers* ▪ *Winemaker Paul de Villiers, with Fanie Geyser (Jan 1980/Dec 2002)* ▪ *Viticulturist Hugo de Villiers Jnr (1995)* ▪ *270 ha (14 varieties r/w)* ▪ *1 100 tons 86% red 11% white 3% port* ▪ *PO Box 519 Suider-Paarl 7624* ▪ *landskroon@ mweb.co.za* ▪ *www.landskroonwines.com Ⓒ 863·1039 🖷 863·2810*

It's anniversary time for the de Villiers family, fifth-generation owners of this farm on the flanks of Paarl Mountain: a silver for Paul, who has been making wine since 1980, and the celebration of a decade of viticulture for Hugo Jnr. Last season saw new vines — mainly shiraz, cab and merlot — replacing old blocks, as well as the installation of a new bottle-maturation cellar. 'Keep things as simple as possible, and use wood sparingly,' is Paul dV's philosophy, 'so that it doesn't dominate the wine.' He also advocates collaborative marketing to promote SA wines to Far Eastern markets like China and possibly even India.

★★★★ **Paul de Villiers Cabernet Sauvignon** ✓ The flagship, from selected parcels on the home-farm, comprehensively oaked (all-new Fr, ±14 mths), limited quantities (± 600 cs). **00** excellent mulberry, herbal whiffs; flavours similar to version below but more concentrated; retasted for this ed, shy, still closed on nose; hints black fruit; nicely managed tannins, suave wine, give time; **01** more forthcoming, cedar hints; fruit more youthful, dry savoury edge with grainy tannins still.

★★★★ **Cabernet Sauvignon** ✓ A lot of attention given in vyds & cellar shows in excellent fruit concentration, expensive oak. **01** retaste; pleasing greenpepper touch, obvious but good tannins; now mellower, rounded, gaining complexity; augurs well. **02** shows a greater concentration of fruit, smoky whiffs; full, almost robustly flavoured, long full finish; excellent ageing potential. Fr oak ±10 mths, some new.

★★★★ **Shiraz 01** good concentration of fruit, quite serious. Warm, inviting spicy bouquet with flavours to match, good firm dry finish. **02**, retasted, mix of plums & fragrant scrub; almost sweet on palate, spicy touches, very long finish. 10 mths Am barrels. 14% alc.

★★★★ **Paul de Villiers Shiraz** ✓ More concentrated, tougher version of above; partially Am barrel-fermented/aged, remainder Fr-oaked ±16 mths. **00** showed stylish berry fruits, spicy oak, touches varietal woodsmoke. **01** deep, inscrutable on release; mid-

2004 more open; scrubby bouquet with red fruit; supple & juicy, full-bodied. **02** (sample) has more oomph, characteristic scrub on nose, sweet-fruited, lovely long finish. Deserves cellaring. Possible ★★★★★.

★★★☆ **Morio Muscat Jerepico** ✓ Very fresh, intensely sweet with soft acidity, beguiling perfume. Made à la muscadel — fermented briefly, stopped by addition of wine spirit (±18% alc). 04 (sample) billows honeysuckle, full, sweet, with keen spirity lift; possible ★★★★.

★★★★ **Port** ✓ Made from one-third each tintas b/r, souzão; *still* in squat 'quick-quaff' bottle, belying elegant contents. **99** retaste; gamey meaty opening; hints dried fruit & cocoa; soft & silky, not a lot of grip, early drinking style, open textured. **00** (sample) red berries & choc on nose; rounded, noticeable oak on palate. Both ±100g/ℓ sugar, 18% alc.

Cinsaut ☺ ★★★ They do it so well! Delicious & sweet-tempered **03**, retaste: has mellowed tastily; mix of plums, earth & redcurrant; rounded mouthfeel. 14.5% alc. **Blanc de Noir** ☺ ★★★ **04** only pinotage this yr; delicious; hint red berry & candyfloss on nose; caramelised sugar & tropical fruit salad palate, rounded rather than sweet.

Cabernet Franc ★★★ 02 retaste; unexpectedly subdued, not a lot of varietal character. **Merlot** ★★★ 02 has improved, smoothed; plums, violets & choc notes; fairly supple on the palate. **Pinotage** ★★★ 02 plum & banana whiffs; big wine (14% alc) with big tannins; touch earthiness; give yr/2 to soften. **Cabernet Franc-Merlot** ★★★★ Step up in difficult vintage **02**, attractively stalky cab f nose, plummy violet whiffs from merlot; shows some good bottle-development; wood still fairly dominant on palate mid-2002; needs bit of time; good potential. **03** (sample) similar characters, less tannic, rounder, more juicy-fruity. **Cinsaut-Shiraz** ★★★ Popular formula: production now tops 16 000 cs. **03** ripe berry fruit & obvious spiciness, firm & full, attractively chewy. Could be cellared couple of yrs. 14% alc. **Chardonnay** ★★★ Unwooded med-bodied **03**, retasted, hints of peach & pear, show very subtle oaking. **Sauvignon Blanc** ★★☆ **04** faintest tropical hints, light & fruity on palate, almost soft; pleasant dry wine. **Chenin Blanc Dry** ★★ **04** bone-dry, lightish tropical nose, fairly bland. **Chenin Blanc Off-Dry** ★★★ **04** shy nose but palate nicely filled out; quaffable, just off-dry. — DH/TM

Landzicht GWK Wines

Jacobsdal (see Northern Cape & Free State map) ▪ Est 1976 ▪ 1stB ca 1980 ▪ Tasting & sales Mon-Fri 8-1; 2-5 Sat 9-12 ▪ Tasting fee on application ▪ Closed public holidays ▪ Tours by appt ▪ Meals/refreshments by appt, or BYO picnic ▪ Farm produce sold ▪ Play area for children ▪ Tourgroups ▪ Conferences ▪ Owner GWK Ltd ▪ Winemakers Ian Sieg (1984) & Chrisna Botha (Jan 2002) ▪ Viti consultant Wrensch Roux (Jun 2003) ▪ 300 ha (cab, merlot, pinotage, shiraz, chard, chenin, colombard, muscadels) r/w) ▪ ±4 300 tons 40 000 cs own label 20% red 40% white 20% rosé 20% fortified ▪ PO Box 94 Jacobsdal 8710 ▪ landzicht@gwk.co.za © (053) 591·0164 ▤ (053) 591·0145

Ian Sieg, probably SA's most climatically challenged winemaker, has faced off torments of biblical severity in the 20 years he's spent 'uncovering the secrets' of this northerly winegrowing area. Floods, hail, even marauding locusts. Yet against all the odds, last year he took in 'a crop like never seen before: 4 300 tons of well-balanced grapes, no hail and no frost'. What's more, he picturesquely adds, 'so far the babies' nappies smell like talcum powder'. Miraculous harvest over, a new empowerment bottling operation sprang into action, promising to benefit wine quality as well as the community. The range, unavailable for tasting, includes Cabernet Sauvignon, Merlot, Pinotage, Shiraz, Blanc de Blanc, Gewürztraminer, Blümchen (Natural Sweet white), Rosenblümchen (Natural Sweet rosé), Vin Doux, Sweet Hanepoot, Red Jerepigo & Red/White Muscadel.

Langkloof Vineyards see Schoonberg

Langverwacht Cellar

Robertson ▪ Est 1956 ▪ Tasting & sales Mon-Fri 8-12.30; 1.30-5 ▪ Closed public holidays ▪ Tours by appt ▪ Owners 30 members ▪ Manager/winemaker Johan Gerber, with Henry Conradie (Dec 1986, Dec 2003) ▪ Viti consultant Briaan Stipp (2000) ▪ ±600 ha (ruby cab, shiraz, colombard, sauvignon) ▪ ±9 800 tons ±9 000 cs own label 60% red 31% white 9% rosé ▪ PO Box 87 Bonnievale 6730 ▪ langverwacht@lando.co.za ☏ (023) 616·2815 🖨 (023) 616·3059

Five decades ago this year construction began on cellar facilities for this little co-operative between Robertson and Bonnievale, initially christened Boesmansrivier (the name changed after strenuous objections by an eponymous co-op producer of cheese). Interestingly, the structure was designed by Pon van Zyl, 'father' of colombard. Varieties unheard-of in his day, merlot and petit verdot, harvested for the first time in 2004, taking advantage of the dedicated red wine cellar which was recently added.

> **Ruby Cabernet** ☺ ★★★ **03** black plum & thatch aromas; succulent plum/choc flavours with tobacco suggestion; softly dry, with savoury twist. Note: 14% alc.
> **Colombar-Chardonnay** ☺ ★★★ Invariably fruitful partnership here; **04** (sample) lively floral/herby aromas, sappy, light, nettly palate.

Cabernet Sauvignon ★★★ **03**, retasted, stewed currants, hints of lead pencil & bluegum, slightly jammy & green. 5 mths Fr oak. **Shiraz** ★★★★ Briefly Am-staved; **03** strikes all right chords, red fruit & peppery spice; balanced acidity; spicy finish. **Chardonnay** Last tasted as a promising sample was **03**, better structured than pvs, likely ★★★★. **Chenin Blanc** ★★★ Green-tinged **04**, colour mirrored in green melon aromas, very muted; fuller on palate, refreshingly brisk. **Colombard** ★★★ Lots of personality here; **04** whiffs Karoo Bush & herbs to pears & quince fruit. Well flavoured, leaves a fruit-sweet impression in the farewell. — *DH*

Lanzerac Wines

Stellenbosch ▪ Est 1991 ▪ 1stB 1995 ▪ Tasting & sales Mon-Thu 9-4.30; Fri & pub hols 9-4; Sat 10-2; Sun 11-3 ▪ Fee R16 (incl tasting glass) ▪ Tours Mon-Fri & pub hols 11 & 3 ▪ Closed Easter Fri, Dec 25 & Jan 1 ▪ Five-star Lanzerac Hotel for stay-overs; also Governor's Hall Restaurant & Craven Lounge ☏ 887·1132 ▪ Tourgroups ▪ Gifts ▪ Conferencing ☏ 887·1132 ▪ Walks ▪ Winemakers Wynand Hamman (Aug 1993) ▪ Viticulturist Tommie Corbett (Aug 2002) ▪ 50 ha (cabs s/f, malbec, merlot, petit verdot, pinotage, shiraz, chard, sauvignon) ▪ 500 tons 30 000 cs 80% red 20% white ▪ ISO 14000 & HACCP certification in progress ▪ PO Box 6233 Uniedal 7612 ▪ wine@lanzerac.co.za winesales@lanzerac.co.za ▪ www.lanzeracwines.co.za ☏ 886·5641 🖨 887·6998

Christo Wiese's gracious Lanzerac farm has long been associated with pinotage (the 61 vintage SA's first commercial release). But the repertoire has since broadened and is widening further with the unveiling of a maiden Shiraz and the planting of the red blending component, petit verdot. Winemaker Wynand Hamman foresees growth in the UK, US and China markets for Rhône-style wines and cuvées with pinotage, and a new Cape blend, due later this year, should do well there and elsewhere. The varietal Pinotage in the range is now cropped entirely off own vineyards. 2004 was a particularly difficult harvest because of the cold, which delayed ripening. Still, most varieties show 'wonderfully complex and full flavours'. Of special interest to visitors is that the tasting centre is now open on Sundays.

★★★★ **Merlot** Exuberantly classic as usual, stylish **02**'s fruit intensity again spot on: mulberry/blackcurrant, with tantalising whiffs chopped herbs, cedar. Lithe, supple structure, 18 mths Fr oak (30% new) easily accommodated by fruit. Dash cab f adds interest, complexity. 13.5% alc. As with elegant **01** & pvs, no hurry to open.

★★★☆ **Cabernet Sauvignon** Built to last. **00** yr on, intensified berry & spice layers; tannins integrating, but 21 mths oaking (Fr, third new) reflect seriousness of intention, long-term potential: ±10 yrs. 14.3% alc. MIWA gold.

★★★☆ **Classic** Approachable blend of classic Bdx red varieties — merlot (47%) lending charm, accessibility, with cabs s/f & splash malbec. **02** has toasty component in attractive berry compôte, cigarbox character from serious oaking (18 mths Fr, 80% new). Built to last 6+yrs. 14.5% alc. **01** also powerful oak, good fruit.

★★★☆ **Pinotage** Modern styling now for this first pinotage label (**59** vintage), with lithe structure, firm dry tannins. **02** lively mulberry, cherry, & oodles of oak-spice from 14 mths Fr/Am, which also helps ensure 5+ yrs ageing potential. 13.5% alc.

★★★☆ **Shiraz** NEW Stylish, delicious **03**: deep, black fruit, whiffs smoke, savoury spice, underbrush. Judicious oaking (partial for ferment, full for malo; maturation yr Fr, touch Am, third new) allows tasty accessibility without compromising ageing potential. 14.8% alc.

Chardonnay ★★★☆ Bold style, generously oaked. **03** lime-peach aromas & flavours vie with oak's buttered-toast richness, to create satisfyingly mouthfilling experience. Fermented/10 mths Fr barrels, 60% new. 14% alc. **Sauvignon Blanc** ★★★☆ Tangy, flavourful **04** has lemongrass, gooseberry perfume, mouthwatering zestiness, personifying variety's food compatibility. 13% alc. **Forellen Pinot Blanc** ★★ Dry, sleek **02** (not retasted) leafy, lemon freshness. 13.4% alc. *— CR —*

La Petite Ferme

Franschhoek ▪ Est/1stB 1996 ▪ Wines below available in the restaurant or from the cellar 8.30-4 daily ▪ French country-style lunches daily; luxury guest suites (see Eat-out/Stay-over sections) ▪ Gifts ▪ Owners Dendy Young family ▪ Winemaker Mark Dendy Young (Jan 1996) ▪ Vineyard manager John Dendy Young ▪ 8 ha (merlot, shiraz, chard, sauvignon) ▪ 5 000 cs 40% red 60% white ▪ PO Box 55 Franschhoek 7690 ▪ lapetite@iafrica.com © 876·3016 ✆ 876·3624

The Dendy Youngs' winery and vineyard, attached to their country restaurant and guesthouse, now grows up to 80% of its own grapes. Last harvest was 'exceptionally good', comments winemaker Mark DY, especially for sauvignon (they pressed 11 000ℓ and were sold out within 5 months). A dedicated cellar built under the popular new wine bar means they have twice the previous capacity for barrel-fermenting and -ageing their wines. Temperature control ensures steadier fermentation, particularly of their Chardonnay and Semillon. The latter, Mark DY believes, is synonymous with Franschhoek, 'and we need to support those few trying to get good semillon on the map'.

★★★★ **Merlot 02** took a step beyond pvs with great intensity, palate weight & flavourful freshness; Mix F'hoek/Stbosch fruit. **03**, all own grapes, retasted for this ed unexpectedly dry, firm; spicy wood protruding into the damson plum & choc tones. ★★★ on present showing; might simply be in a dip. 20% Am oak.

★★★★ **Chardonnay** Food-friendly, 100% barrel-fermented version; single vyd (among highest in Frhoek) accorded VIP treatment, incl new Fr oak (60%), full malo, partial native-yeast ferment; pvs **01** showed great finesse. **03** retaste: appetising lemon custard tone seamlessly melded with the fruit. Well & carefully made. 'Always a sell-out', says MDY, unsurprisingly.

Cabernet Sauvignon ★★★☆ **03** focused blackcurrant & mint aromas, accented with soft vanilla; clean, well-defined Ribena palate, firm but fine tannin, wood well balanced. From two blocks, winemaker says, one yielding classic qualities, the other more New World. Fr/Am oak. **Pinotage 04** (sample) first since **01**; upfront & juicy, good & ripe; lifted mulberry & black fruit nose, creamy vanilla wood still apart, finishes fresh; should rate ★★★☆ when released. 14 mths Fr oak. At 14.5% alc, the biggest red here. **Shiraz** ★★★☆ **03** well stacked with white pepper & black cherries, smoky bacon aromas; cherry flavours roll onto med-bodied palate with toasty wood; elegant style, dry. 11 mths oak, 20% Am. **Cabernet Sauvignon-Merlot** ★★★☆ No new releases since **02**, with cedar fragrance to bouncy, minty black fruit. **Chardonnay Unwooded** ★★★ **04** fine creamy lemon blossom aromas; lightish, slightly short, floral tones repeating, subtle cling-peach finish.

. **Sauvignon Blanc** ★★★★ Individual & rather tasty; **04** fresh Cape gooseberry aroma, persists onto palate, nice & fresh, extended finish. Usual lowish alc, 12.5%, nicely balanced. **Blanc Fumé** ★★★★ Softer, broader version of above, thanks to small Fr oak-matured portion, usually from pvs vintage. **04** ripe tropical tones, hints papaya & lemon, lightish bodied, wood just a pleasant accent, balanced & attractive. **Semillon** Back with **04** (unrated sample), somewhat unformed mid-2004, sappy wood not yet integrated with fruit; potential to develop into something really nice though; well filled out mid-palate. Part barrelled; 12.5% alc. **Nectar du Val** ★★ None since **02**, fragrant off-dry muscat/sauvignon blend with balancing freshness. **La Petite Sieste** 𝗡𝗘𝗪 ★★★★ Striking & delicious vin de paille-style dessert from semillon (75%), chenin & muscat d'A; **03** nose unfolds with dried apricots & caramel, whiff botrytis; concentrated apricot preserve & caramel flavours; could have done with more acid to balance the 90g/ℓ sugar. 17.5% alc. Barrel-fermented/3½ mths. — *JB*

La Siesta see Signal Hill
Lategan see Bergsig

Lateganskop Winery

Worcester ▪ Est 1969 ▪ 1stB 2004 ▪ Tastings & sales Mon-Fri 8-12.30; 1.30-5 ▪ Tours by appt ▪ Owners 5 members ▪ Winemaker Vlam Fourie, with J Manewick (Aug/Dec 1990) ▪ 238 ha (cab, cinsaut, merlot, pinotage, ruby cab, chenin, colombard, hanepoot, riesling, sauvignon, semillon, viognier) ▪ 650 cs + 2.2m litres bulk ▪ 50% red 50% white ▪ PO Box 44 Breërivier 6858 ▪ lateganskop@mweb.co.za ✆/📠 *(023) 355·1719*

Built by oupa Willie Lategan in 1969 and now owned by five members, all Lategans, this Breedekloof winery celebrated a milestone in 2004: for the first time in its history some wine was bottled instead of being sold off in bulk (250 cases of Sauvignon and 400 of Cab). Winemaker Vlam Fourie believes wine is made in the vineyard (nothing revolutionary about that) but holds the less frequently expressed view that the work begins two years at least before harvest, with careful selection of berries.

Twin's Peak Sauvignon Blanc ★★★ Slight chalky edge to **04**; lightish & fresh, with variety's electric acidity to quench a summer thirst. WO Breede River. — *JB*

L'Auberge du Paysan

Stellenbosch (see Helderberg map) ▪ Est 1995 ▪ 1stB 1998 ▪ Tasting & sales during restaurant hours (see Eat-out section) ▪ Closed Easter Fri-Mon, Dec 25/26, Jan 1 ▪ Art gallery ▪ Owners Frederick Thermann & Michael Kovensky ▪ Winemaker/viticulturist Tjuks Roos, with Ricardo Adams ▪ 3.8 ha (merlot, pinotage) ▪ 14 tons ±1 250 cs 100% red ▪ PO Box 315 Somerset West 7129 ✆/📠 *842·2008*

'Best-balanced wines since 98', recounts Frederick Thermann, Helderberg vintner and co-owner of the French-glossed L'Auberge du Paysan restaurant, of his 2004 vintage. At present the whole crush is pinotage (which experience has taught Thermann to decant well ahead of time so that maximum softness is achieved), but a new small block of merlot is expected to yield from 2006. Also new on the property is Froggies Bistro & Tastevin, a playful variation on the Gallic theme. See the Eat-out section for details.

★★★★ **Pinotage** Trio of recent vintages tasted this ed; **02** pinot side of grape showing: forest floors & sweet fruit, elegantly mouthcoating. **01** gamey & earthy, raspberry toned, promising; both 14% alc. **00** strawberry jam whiffs, softer, obvious bottle-age, tannins turning grainy — suggest drink fairly soon. 13.5%. — *TM*

L'Avenir Estate

Stellenbosch ▪ Est/1stB 1992 ▪ Tasting & sales Mon-Fri 10-5 Sat 10-4 ▪ Fee R10 ▪ Closed Easter Sun, Dec 25 & Jan 1 ▪ Tours by appt ▪ BYO picnic ▪ Luxury 9-bedroom B&B guest lodge ▪ Play area for children ▪ Tourgroups ▪ Farm-grown olives & olive products ▪ Conference facilities ▪ Owner Marc Wiehe ▪ Winemaker Francois Naudé (Jan 1992), with Stephan du Toit ▪ Viticul-

turist Francois Naudé ■ 53 ha *(11 varieties r/w)* ■ 350-370 tons ■ ±24 000 cs 55% red 43% white 2% rosé ■ PO Box 1135 Stellenbosch 7599 ■ *lavenir@adept.co.za* ■ *www.lavenir.co.za* ✆ **889·5001** 📠 889-5258

Francois Naudé – who made his first wine in the kitchen (destalking by hand, with family feet pressed into service) – is one of SA's great DIY success stories. With no formal oenological training (pharmacist in a former life), his wines are heralded by local and international critics alike. The challenging and uneven harvest 2004 managed to do the unthinkable: dampen the eternally upbeat Naudé's spirit. But only temporarily. He is now effusive about the length of the ripening season, which made for fine tannins. Naudé bought a new toy in 2004 – a micro-oxygenation unit – but the real milestone was the entry to the industry of his son and namesake (at Beyerskloof, as brand/export manager). 'Nice to know the supply chain won't be broken when I grow old.'

★★★★ **Cabernet Sauvignon** ✓ **02** exemplifies Naudé's decade-plus experience; reliable, top-class cab even in challenging yr. Perfectly proportioned, oaked, in light, fresh frame; cedar-brushed blackberry fragrance reprised in gently plump filling. Good now; best around 2005-08. Rich, mocha-toned **01**, with dash merlot, reveals meaty/blackberry glimpses behind unyielding tannins. **99** *Decanter* ★★★★. ±14% alc. 18 mths Fr oak, 33% each new/2nd/3rd fill.

★★★★ **Auction Reserve Cabernet Sauvignon** CWG Auction special. **02** (★★★★) strongly influenced by 20 mths new Fr oak maturation; glimpses cassis, gentle 13% fleshy merlot, bit short on concentration, weight to fully absorb oak. Better sooner than seamless, polished **01** with possible 10 yrs potential. 14% alc.

★★★★ **Pinotage** ✓ Few understand, love this sometimes wild local like Naudé. **02** sixth Top Ten selection; **01, 00** IWSC gold. **03** flaunts usual finely-honed Rubenesque proportions. Smartly oaked, mashed soft berries, plums; generous sweet flesh in tight-knit, though ripe tannin frame. 100% bushvines, first since **98**. **02** like **01**, palate-expanding 15% alc matched by flavour. 13 mths Fr oak, 50% new.

★★★★★ **Auction Reserve Pinotage** Pushes showy class envelope to extreme. Imposing **03** unbelievable viscosity, concentration without overt varietal tones; soaks up 100% new Fr oak. 15% alc amazingly balanced with dry, if rich, finish. **02** extends style of **01, 00**: plush; manicured tannins, peacock's tail send-off.

★★★★ **Merlot** So far only elegant maiden **01**. Spans approachability & power. 10-14 mths oak, 40% new. 14% alc.

★★★★ **Chardonnay** Silver for **03** chalks up laudable 7th consecutive Chardonnay-du-Monde medal, including 2 golds. Consistency also in bottle: harmonious toasty/peachy ensemble; buxom but not flabby; buttery, oatmealy opulence promises future mellow savouriness. **02** full but not blowsy; striking length. 10 mths Burgundian-coopered oak; regular lees stirring aids creamy feel.

★★★★ **Chenin Blanc** ✓ One of Cape's first success stories in chenin's renaissance. 'Same as always, portion botrytis, no oak', confirms Naudé of previewed **04**. Invariable inviting immediacy: fragrant, honey-licked melons in fresh mouthful; juiciness intensified by 5.5g/ℓ sugar. Be bowled over now & in 4-5 yrs. **03** mouthful ripe melons, glossed by honey. Gold MIWA & Canadian Sélections Mondiales. 14% alc.

★★★★ **Sauvignon Blanc** ✓ Reliably styled to please wide variety of tastes. **04** invigorating, bouncy mouthful; well-paced tropical figgy clarity to upbeat conclusion. 13.5% alc. Meets Naudé's 'you should always want to reach for a second bottle'.

★★★★ **Vin de Meurveur Noble Late Harvest** Intermittently produced golden dessert, dependant on '*good* botrytis'. Last **00** colombard/crouchen 'more in Sauternes style – barrel-fermented, not too sweet'; opulent, intense flavours. 91g/ℓ.

★★★★ **Cape Vintage (Port) 03** successor to delicious **99** still yr+ from release (possibly ★★★★). Sample ex-cask already ridiculously irresistible, if not classic; luscious choc, prunes; vanilla tones. With cab, but Portuguese specs: 85g/ℓ sugar; 20% alc.

Rosé Maison Dry 🆕 ☺ ★★★ Old-time Cape favourites clairette, cinsaut with cab, pinotage in appealing pearly pink **04**. Gentle summer fruits/flowers in fresh body for al fresco sipping. **Vin d'Erstelle** ☺ ★★★ Proudly unpretentious. Persuasive **04** colombard / riesling/crouchen marriage; spicy fruit salad with juicy kick in tail. 12.5% alc.

Black Label Reserve 🆕 Previewed **03** 'best selection in cellar'; pinotage important, with cabs s/f, merlot (30/30/15/25). Voluptuous, rich dark fruits; big but not heavy; fine, ripe tannins. Amazingly drinkable already. Should rate min ★★★★. Minuscule 170 cs.
L'Ami Simon ★★★ Cab f joins usual merlot/pinotage/cab partners (50/22/19/9 mix) in unpretentious **03**. Gushy spicy, slightly porty nose; lots of chunky, sweet fruit; used Fr oak-smoothed, but honest country red at heart. 14% alc. **Rosé Maison** ★★★ The original, off-dry house pink; **04** from pinotage. Pretty hue, wild red fruits; juicy but sweeter than 9g/ℓ sugar suggests, missing some *joie de vivre*. —AL

░ *Lazy Bay* see Baarsma

Le Bonheur Estate

Stellenbosch ▪ Tasting & sales Mon-Fri 9-5 Sat 10-1 ▪ Fee R10 ▪ Special tastings on request ▪ Light meals by appt ▪ Owner Lusan Holdings ▪ Winemaker Sakkie Kotzé (1993) ▪ 435 tons ±31 000 cs ▪ PO Box 104 Stellenbosch 7599 ▪ info@lebonheur.co.za ▪ www.lebonheur.co.za ✆ 875·5478 🖷 875·5624

Elegant, soft, well-structured wines which age well are Sakkie Kotzé's goal at this historic estate, granted by Lord Charles Somerset in the late 18th century to Jacob de Villiers, descendent of one of the original French Huguenots. Fruit selection and careful handling are the winemaker's mantras. Bunches are hand-picked and -sorted, and only ones which pass 'exacting scrutiny' are fermented. 'The slightest bruise and they fail the test,' Kotzé insists. His reason is simple: 'If some of the best French châteaux take the trouble to select their grapes, so can we.'

★★★★ **Prima** Well-established merlot-led (±75%) blend with cab; recently softer, more approachable; **01** typical Le Bonheur lifted fruit with pure redcurrant aroma/flavour; back on track after less focused, lighter & probably earlier-maturing **00** (★★★★); ±18 mths Fr/Am oak, 50% new. **99** had enough structure for ±5 yrs' ageing.

★★★★ **Cabernet Sauvignon** Offers good flavour at pleasingly modest alcs (13-13.5%); **01** aromatic & forthcoming; red-fruit tones with capsicum edge; finishes dry with firm acidity. **00** lacked complexity of pvs; more delicate, lighter toned.

Chardonnay ★★★ **03** fresh, unchallenging & gently wooded. **Sauvignon Blanc** ★★ **04** vinous rather than varietally true or expressive. —RK

░ *Lee & Jones* see Breeland
░ *Leef op Hoop* see Le Riche
░ *Leeurivier* see Terroir Wines
░ *Leeuwenberg* see Swartland Wine Cellar

Le Grand 1881 Estate

Robertson ▪ Est 1881 ▪ 1stB 1999 ▪ Tasting & sales Mon-Thu 8.30-5 Fri 8.30-5.30 Sat 9-2. 30 ▪ Closed Easter Fri/Sun/Mon, Dec 25/26 & Jan 1 ▪ Tours by appt ▪ Deli & gifts ▪ Owner/ winemaker Albertus de Wet, with Wickus Erasmus (Jan 2001) ▪ Viti consultant Francois Viljoen (Jan 1998) ▪ 250 ha (cab, pinotage, ruby cab, shiraz, chard, colombard, sauvignon) ▪ 3 500 tons 8 000 cs own label 43% red 54% white 3% rosé ▪ PO Box 439 Robertson 6705 ▪ lgc@intekom.co.za ▪ www.lgc.co.za ✆/🖷 (023) 626·1048 (cellar) ✆/🖷 (023) 626·5781 (tasting room)

New winemaker Wickus Erasmus has something to talk about — a Brut MCC, made from chardonnay grapes, on the shelves now. Which illuminates another talking point — the

'Chasseur', an allusion to splendid African Fish Eagle found on this Breede River-fronting property, has been chased from the name of the brand. The non-sparkling Chardonnay 02 sparkled nonetheless at Michelangelo 2003, taking a gold. But it is sauvignon that 'owner Albertus de Wet looks to as best suiting southern African climes and tastes — 'tropical rather than grassy'. His grander ambition is to produce and market wine that will lift the image of this country (and the African continent) in the eyes of the world. Practical steps along that path include the installation of a mechanical punch-down system in the red wine cellar as well as small tanks to improve quality and make better use of good enzymes and yeasts.

★★★★ **Shiraz** Tasty, ready on release & padded with enough fruit for few yrs' cellaring. **01** was mineral-led with firmish tannins. **02** red berried, quite chunky, muscular tannins need yr/2 to relax. Fr oak, 9 mths; balanced 14% alc.

LGC Red ☺ ★★★ **02** retasted, mellowing attractively; succulent red berry, plum & greenpepper mix; juicy rounded tannin; enjoy soon. Equal ruby cab, cab, 8 mths Fr/Am oak. ±14% alc. **Chardonnay** ☺ ★★★ Fermented/*sur lie* 8 mths in new Fr oak, yet wood's a subtle backdrop to bright & lively **03**; appealing ripe peach tones, butterscotch hint. Note: 14.5% alc. **Sauvignon Blanc** ☺ ★★★ **04** gushes ripe tropical flavours; sweet-fruited chirpy finish. Enjoy young. **Sparkling** ☺ ★★★ NV from pinotage bursts with sweet red-berry flavour & excited bubbles. Huge fun.

Cabernet Sauvignon ★★★★ **02** still improving in bottle; sweet berries on nose/palate; big but comfortable tannins should go 2-3 yrs yet. Fr oak, 5 mths. **Pinotage** ★★★ Accommodating & sweet-fruited, briefly Fr oak-matured **03**, very drinkable now; ripe plum aromas, some charry oak, pliable fruity tannins. **Rosé** ★★☆ Pinotage's candied aromas on orange-tinged NV (03), with just enough honeyed development to remain attractive; drink up. **LGC White** ★★★ Colombard/chardonnay (60/40) in **03**, now with lemon & peach tones, fairly substantial & rounded; enjoy within the next yr. 14% alc. **Brut MCC** Not ready for tasting. — *DH*

Leidersburg Wines

Stellenbosch/Paarl ▪ Est 1996 ▪ 1stB 1997 ▪ Visits by appt ▪ Owners Jan du Preez & Brian Craddock ▪ Winemaker/viticulturist Jan du Preez (1996) ▪ 6 ha ▪ 2 000 cs 100% red ▪ PO Box 7210 Stellenbosch 7599 ▪ leidersburgwines@intekom.co.za ☏ 082·856·3560

Historically focused only on Cab, this range has now made way for a small quantity of Sauvignon, which experienced oeno-man Jan du Preez vinified from a well-sited vineyard on the Bottelary Hills, and subjected to extended lees maturation to give extra character and dimension. The result, he declares, is 'very satisfying'. The awarded Cab remains the main event here, though. It's still grown in the house-owned Leidersburg vineyard in Paarl, which is being developed apace and will soon feature its first permanent structure. 'As from early this year, visitors will be welcomed at Leidersburg,' says a delighted JdP.

Cabernet Sauvignon ★★★★ **02** gentle but sustained nose of red fruits & fragrant oak, well rounded; berried palate with herby touch, supple tannins; elegant, enough structure to develop 5-6 yrs. 14% alc. 14 mths oak, 10% new. **Sauvignon Blanc Vintner's Reserve Sur Lie** ★★★★ **03** sweet tropical tones & touch herb; melon & pineapple on palate; brisk & fresh; lively lemon finish with parting whiff wild scrub. 8 mths on lees. — *DH*

Le Manoir de Brendel

Franschhoek ▪ Est/1stB 2003 ▪ Tasting & sales Mon-Sat 8-5 ▪ Fee R10 ▪ Lunches daily 12-4 ▪ Luxury accommodation & other amenities/facilities (see intro) ▪ Owner Christian Brendel ▪ 26 ha (cab, merlot, shiraz, chenin, sauvignon, semillon) ▪ Export brand: Wine 4U ▪ PO Box 579 Franschhoek 7690 ▪ lemanoir@brendel.co.za ▪ www.le-manoir-de-brendel.com ☏ 876·4525 ᠍ 876·4524

At Christian & Maren Brendel's wine farm with a difference, you're encouraged to let your inner sybarite escape by doing 'as little or as much as your soul can muster'. On the property is a 5-star guesthouse, and if you stay over you can loll about at the pool, play tennis, fly-fish or go wandering in the vineyard. You can even get married in the chapel. Or spend your time dining at the restaurant and trying the own-label wines.

Wines currently being sourced as WO Rbtson include **Riesling ★ 02** simple, off-dry, with muted muscat tone. **Sauvignon Blanc ★ 03** and **Chardonnay ★ 03** both simply vinous. **Pinotage ★ 02**, showing some honest varietal expression & charry wood finish, and **Merlot 02** both WO W-Cape. **Cabernet** and **Shiraz** untasted; **Chenin** discontinued. — *RK*

Lemberg Estate

Tulbagh ▪ Tasting, sales & tours Mon-Sat 8-5 Sun 10-5 ▪ Fee R5 ▪ Gourmet lunches & dinners (book 2 days ahead) ▪ Luxury guest cottage (see Stay-over section) ▪ Walks/hikes ▪ Owner/winemaker/viticulturist Klaus Schindler ▪ 4 ha (pinot, pinotage, sauvignon) ▪ 50/50 red/white ▪ PO Box 317 Tulbagh 6820 ▪ schindler@lando.co.za ▪ www.kapstadt.de/ lemberg © (023) 230·0659/083·270·3449 ▯ (023) 230·0661

Klaus Schindler, originally from Freiburg in Germany, and wife Uschi continue to do it their way on their postage-stamp estate. They've trimmed their range to just three wines: a Pinotage, Pinot Noir and a beefier than usual Sauvignon — at 13.5% alc — now closed with a twist-off cap. 'Nothing's really new,' they say, 'except another baby boy, named Patrick. A lovely, sweet child. The first real South African in the family.'

L'Emigré see De Morgenzon

Leopard's Leap

Franschhoek ▪ Est/1stB 2000 ▪ Closed to public ▪ Owner Historic Wines of the Cape ▪ Winemakers Eugene van Zyl, with Dawie Botha (2000/2002) ▪ Viti adviser Francois Viljoen ▪ 600 ha (merlot, shiraz) ▪ ±167 860 cs 70% red 30% white ▪ ISO 1400 certified ▪ PO Box 685 Franschhoek 7690 ▪ ap.marketing@leopardsleap.co.za ▪ www.leopardsleap.co.za © 874·1026 ▯ 874·1361

Big-selling brand (more than 160 000 cases) owned by Historic Wines of the Cape, a fine-wine maturation, labelling and distribution services company established by Franschhoek Valley farms La Motte, L'Ormarins and Fredericksburg. The range is grown in vineyards locally and at Darling and Bot River, and exported mainly to Europe and Canada. 'Easy-drinking, approachable wines' are winemaker Eugene van Zyl's goals. Watch out for exceptional pinotages, shirazes and semillons in 2004, a harvest van Zyl describes as 'challenging with some amazing surprises'.

★★★★ **Sangiovese-Pinotage-Cabernet Sauvignon** NEW Spicy & wild shiraz-like aromas followed by ripe plumminess in attractive & different **03**; tart redcurrant flavours, sweet-fruited suppleness aided by touch sugar. Still tight & unevolved; would benefit further cellaring. 14% alc. Equal blend.

Cabernet Sauvignon-Merlot ★★★ Slightly more cab in **03**, 57/34 blend; still well padded with berry fruit, in house style. Combo staves/micro-oxygenation (ditto all the reds). 13.5% alc. **Pinotage-Shiraz** ★★★ **03**, as pvs, 50/50 blend neatly balancing approachability & structure. Plums & spice, hint toasty oak. 14.5% alc. **Lookout Red** ★★☆ Jumble of 5 varieties (including nebbiolo) in **03**; plums, berries & spice; firmish tannins cushioned by smidgen sugar (3.3g/ℓ). **Sauvignon Blanc** ★★★★ Lively, light & well fruited; enjoy in bloom of youth. **04** gooseberry & ripe fig whiffs, with some greener notes for interest. **Chenin Blanc-Viognier** NEW ★★★ Quaffable **04** loaded with tropical fruit & citrus flavour, plumply round from touch sugar (±4g/ℓ). **Semillon-Chardonnay** ★★☆ Regime-change to unoaked in **04**, equal blend; attractively light & supple with the usual gentle acidity. **Lookout White** ★★★ Sprightly everyday drink under screwcap. Dollop semillon replaces chardonnay in **04** (chenin, colombard remain); tasty lemon-lime tones. All WO W-Cape. — *DH*

Le Pavillon see Boschendal

Le Pommier Fine Wines

Stellenbosch ▪ Est 2002 ▪ Tasting & sales daily 9-6 (summer) 9-5 (winter) ▪ Fee R5/ wine ▪ Le Pommier Restaurant & Country Lodge (see intro for other amenities/attractions) ▪ Tours by appt ▪ Owner Le Pommier Fine Wines (Delarey & Sandie Brugman) ▪ Winemaker Bruwer Raats, with Neil Moorhouse (both 2002) ▪ Viti adviser Kevin Watt (2002) ▪ PO Box 6365 Uniedal 7612 ▪ wine@lepommier.co.za ▪ www.lepommier.co.za ⓒ 885·2070 ☐ 885·1583

Besides country cuisine, there's been a lot cooking at this pumpkin-coloured restaurant and guesthouse on the rejuvenated Zorgvliet property above Stellenbosch. Delarey Brugman and wife Sandie (daughter of Zorgvliet owner Mac van der Merwe) are now the owners of the Le Pommier wine brand, previously marketed (and listed in this guide) under Zorgvliet. The Brugmans, doubly blessed last year by the arrival of identical twin daughters Ilse and Karla, are selling the range through the restaurant and wine shop on the premises. Which makes a trip into this Banhoek area over Helshoogte Pass an even more attractive proposition.

★★★★ **Cabernet Sauvignon 03** big advance on straightforward **02** (★★★). Attractive cassis nose, dark fruit, choc & tobacco, reasonable tannin structure & moderate 13% alc make for elegant wine with good concentration. Yr Fr oak, none new.

Cabernet Franc ★★★☆ ✓ A Bruwer Raats favourite, which he handles sympathetically. **02** vivid leafy, spicy fragrance. Light-textured, bright fruit held by squeeze tannin. 13% alc. Yr Fr oak, none new. **Shiraz** ★★★ Smoky leather nose, spicy choc & plums on **03**, evidencing 16 mths older Fr/Am oak (70/30). **Rosé** ★★★ Spicy, floral, smoothly persistent **03**, shiraz/cab f mix, was last tasted; 13% alc. **Sauvignon Blanc** ★★☆ **04** takes 'cool-climate' profile of pvs vintages bit far; vegetal aromas, fruit subtle to point of being oversimple. 13.2% alc. WO W-Cape. **Semillon** 🆕 ★★ **04** rubbery aromas, flavours with just an edge of honey & a little shy fruit. 13.1% alc. WO Coastal. — *NP*

Le Riche Wines

Stellenbosch ▪ Est 1996 ▪ 1stB 1997 ▪ Tasting & sales Mon-Fri 10-12.30 2-4.30 ▪ Closed public holidays ▪ Self-contained B&B ⓒ 887·8958 ▪ Owner Etienne le Riche ▪ Winemaker Etienne le Riche, with Mark Daniels (1998) ▪ 5 000 cs 100% red ▪ PO Box 6295 Stellenbosch 7612 ▪ lerichewines@adept.co.za ⓒ/☐ 887·0789

'Focus on one thing and do it to the best of your ability', says Etienne le Riche. 'That way you build a following.' And this genial Cab specialist certainly has. Last year he held a vertical tasting of his Reserves, from the inaugural 97 to the 01. The tasters were unanimous and effusive in their praise of his elegant, complex wines. 'Born gorgeous' and 'These are wines I'd like to wear' were some of the comments. Le Riche has also been making wine in the Bergerac area, and a few hundred cases of his French creations are available. It's worth trying to get your hands on some if only to compare the differences wrought by fruit structure and terroir. Despite the accolades, Le Riche remains unassuming. He explains his success away with three simple rules: stay involved, keep up to date and only make changes when they are for the better.

★★★★★ **Cabernet Sauvignon Reserve** E le R marked the 2004 crush with a review of the first five vintages of this island of classical elegance. His favourites? **01** & **97**. Sample **02** well-fruited, carrying extended oaking (now 2 yrs) with ease. **01** still a 'sleeper', concentrated cassis fruit resting under cover of delicate yet authoritative tannins; tapered length. **00** (★★★★★) rich fruit, underpinned by unobtrusive, supple tannin & acid, with characterful finesse. Jonkershoek & Firgrove grapes, traditional open fermentation, then 18-24 mths in mostly new Fr oak. Alc ±13.5%.

★★★★★ **Cabernet Sauvignon** Similarly fine-grained, unflashy, serious & delicious in sculpted style. **01** sees cool bramble fruit peeking out from behind soft tannic curtain; lovely elegance in extended finish. Accessible, but will reward maturing 4-6 yrs. **00**, with splash merlot, developing to potential; soft ripe tannin, deft wood to showcase deep juicy fruit. Stbosch fruit, 18 mths in barrel, mostly older. 13.5% alc.

★★★★ **Cabernet Sauvignon-Merlot** Proof that medium-bodied need never be lesser quality: the easier sibling with which to await big brothers' (above) maturity. Still current **01** has rounded out into choc-berry richness, supple merlot fruit hung on chewy cab scaffold. Rich & firmly structured; soft and drinking well already. Like **00**, 75/25 Stbosch grapes. 13% alc.

Discontinued: **Leef op Hoop Cabernet Sauvignon, Cabernet-Merlot.** – *DS*

Le Roux see Vendôme
Les Pleurs see Avondale

Libertas

For selected export markets, this brand fills a value-priced slot in the Distell portfolio. The wines, untasted, include a Cab, Merlot, Pinotage, Shiraz, Chardonnay & Chenin.

Lievland Estate

Stellenbosch ▪ Est 1982 ▪ Tasting & sales Mon-Fri 9-5 Sat & Sun 10-4 ▪ Fee R10 ▪ Closed Dec 25 ▪ Tours by appt ▪ Meals/picnics (see intro) ▪ Owner Susan Colley ▪ Winemaker Kowie du Toit (Jan 2004) ▪ Viticulturist Bob Hobson (Sep 2003) ▪ 50 ha (cabs s/f, merlot, mourvèdre, roobernet, petit v, riesling, shiraz, viognier) ▪ 250 tons 15 000 cs 50/50 red/ white ▪ PO Box 66 Klapmuts 7625 ▪ lievland@icon.co.za © 875·5226 🖷 875·5213

The first phase of a 5-year plan under new owners John and Susan Colley went smoothly as 1½ ha of mourvèdre and 3 of new-clone shiraz went into the ground and 'have taken fantastically', enthuses viticulturist/manager Bob Hobson. He was joined at the beginning of 2004 by winemaker Kowie du Toit, ex-Vlottenburg/Stellenbosch Hills. For the winemaker and new owners their first Lievland harvest was 'late and very protracted' but apparently of above average quality. Light meals are now available by arrangement – picnic baskets in summer (or bring your own) and 'pot-luck' soup and breads in winter.

The range is being comprehensively restructured & there will be no **01** releases of the following (all ★★★★) in pvs ed: **Syrah, Shiraz, Cabernet Sauvignon, Cabernet Franc, Merlot & DVB** (Bdx-style blend). Bob Hobson advises the wines below will be launched under a 'refreshed label'. **Lievlander 02** untasted. **Chardonnay** ★★ **04** big change for this pvsly unforthcoming label; big charry nose/palate from 4 mths oak staving; wood somewhat apart & overpowering mid-2004; might settle with time. **Sauvignon Blanc** ★★ Returns to line-up after extended break. Lemon-drop & Golden Delicious apple on nose, 'green' palate tone, piercing acidity on **04**. **Weisser Riesling** ★★★ **04** style change, more quaffable than pvs; ethereal pineapple & tropical fruit fragrances/flavours; light, refreshing, off-dry. **Chéandrie** ★★★ Lightish summer drink, now made dry, from chenin & semillon (66/34); **04** herbaceous tone with sherbet nuance, refreshing acidity. '**Natural Sweet**' At press time unsure whether this will get certification as NLH; **04** from riesling very light, unintense; modest floral aromas; peachy flavours with hint quince on unexpectedly dry finish; partly barrel fermented; 12% alc. – *CR*

Lifestyle see Simonsvlei
Lime Road see Havana Hills
Lindehof see Boland Kelder

Linde Vineyards

Tulbagh ▪ Est 1998 ▪ 1stB 2001 ▪ Visits by appt ▪ B&B self-catering ▪ Walks ▪ Owners Olof Gregor & Sylvia Linde ▪ Winemaker Sylvia Linde ▪ Viticulturist Olof Gregor Linde ▪ 14 ha (cab, merlot, shiraz) ▪ 80 tons 100% red ▪ PO Box 146 Tulbagh 6820 ▪ lindevineyards@mweb.co.za © (023) 230·2837 🖷 (023) 230·2836/8

Olof Gregor and Sylvia Linde live parallel lives within the wine universe. They split their time between California and the Cape. Up north, their 6ha cab/merlot vineyard in Geyserville, Alexander Valley (circa 1989) produces 3-4 barrels plus extra (sold to Geyser

Peak Winery). Down south, 14ha in Tulbagh (circa 1998) also provide a handful of barrels, the rest going to KWV. (Their Diggers Home 03 cab-merlot blend was tasted from barrel for this ed but considered too unformed to rate.) Winemaker Sylvia was weaned on her Swedish grandma's dandelion wine; vineyard man Olof comes from the Californian corporate wine world. Inspiration comes from Geyserville's Italian community (everyone makes their own wine). The challenge? Matching Sonoma neighbour Silver Oak Cellar's lofty $70-plus Cab. Rather apt for this intrepid 70-something couple.

Lindhorst Wines

Paarl ▪ Est 1996 ▪ 1stB 2002 ▪ Tasting Mon-Sun 10-5 ▪ Fee R20 (incl tasting & snacks, redeemable against purchase of 12 btls) ▪ Closed Easter Sun, Dec 25 & Jan 1 ▪ Phone for availability of meals/refreshments; or BYO ▪ Accommodation: see intro ▪ Facilities for children ▪ Gifts ▪ Farm produce Owners Mark & Belinda Lindhorst ▪ Vini consultant Cathy Marshall (Nov 2002), with Ernie Wilken ▪ Viti consultant Kevin Watt (Jan 2001) ▪ 18 ha (cab, merlot, pinotage, shiraz) ▪ 60 tons 2 000 cs 100% red ▪ PO Box 1398 Suider-Paarl 7624 ▪ belinda@lindhorstwines.com ▪ www.lindhorstwines.com © 863·0990 🖷 863·3694

Mark Lindhorst, having half-given up his day job, is now spending more time managing this boutique operation and 'smousing' wines. He and wife Belinda were over the moon to have their 02 Shiraz, the newly released maiden vintage, take one of three SA golds at the inaugural 2004 Decanter World Wine Awards. The Pinotage of the same vintage is due for official release: 'It has a lady's touch,' says Belinda, the touch being itinerant winemaker Cathy Marshall's. The tasting facility, recently opened, welcomes German and Swiss visitors in their home languages. Even more attractive is a new two-bed luxury guest cottage on the border of the merlot vineyard, self-catering but catered on request.

★★★★ **Shiraz** Retasted mid-2004, massive (15% alc), opulent **02**, rich textures masking spice, marzipan raspberry notes, intense, flamboyant. 15 mths Fr oak, 87% new. Gold medal at *Decanter* awards. All these WO Coastal.

Statement ★★★ ('Merlot-Shiraz' last ed) Shiraz/merlot **02** blend (70/30) Paarl, Stbosch fruit. Revisited mid-2004 offers plum vanilla, whiffs of nutmeg; palate shows dense tannins, robust 14.6% alc. Fr oak, 15 mths. **Pinotage** ★★★ **03** rustic acetone notes, dense palate, hefty tannins, 13.3% alc, all well integrated. 10 mths mostly Am oak. Super-ripe **02** (14.7% alc) now quite jam-textured, flattening out. — *MF*

Lindiwe Wines [NEW] 🍷

Paarl ▪ 1stB 2003 ▪ Tasting & sales at KWV ▪ Fee R15 ▪ Winemaker Chris Jansen (Oct 2003) ▪ Viticulturists Chris Albertyn & Cobus van Graan ▪ 20 000 cs 50% red 50% white ▪ ISO 9001 certified ▪ Suite 170 PostNet, Pvt Bag X3036, Paarl 7620 ▪ info@lindiwewine.co.za © 949·6013/4 🖷 949·6036

Lindiwe ('The One We Have Been Waiting For') is owned by Reinvest, a BEE company with a 25% shareholding for disadvantaged folk. The wines are made by Chris Jansen at KWV's Vinnova contract cellar, the latter company providing important initial guidance. The grapes are sourced from the Breede River Valley, with the ultimate aim of buying from other empowerment projects. Separating the BEE *indoda* (men) from the *abafana* (boys), says Lindiwe's Vukile Mafilika, is marketing experience. Judging from their already impressive sales coverage (supermarkets, specialist wine shops, upmarket restaurants), we'd say Lindiwe falls in the former's camp. *Inyanisile* (True)!

Cabernet Sauvignon ☺ ★★★ Modestly oaked, with leafy blackcurrant aromas, & an elegant insubstantiality, with some green notes on end, despite 14.2% alc. **Sauvignon Blanc** ☺ ★★★ **03** tropical gooseberry whiffs, pineapple finish, attractively accessible. Easy-going 12.5% alc.

Merlot ★★★★ ✓ **02**, as are all the reds. Pleasing, plummy & ready for drinking; soft savoury notes, lightish feel (despite substantial 14.5% alc), good length. Yr Fr oak. WO

W-Cape, as are all these. **Shiraz** ★★ Light peppery notes & soft raspberry-recalling textures, but an oaky finish. Not much concentration here, despite very solid 14.3% alc. **Pinotage** ★★ Recalls the old days, with its estery, tannic rusticity. 14% alc; lightly wooded. **Chenin Blanc** ★★ Smoky apricot notes on **03**; food-friendliness abetted by briskly crisp, dry finish & lightish 12% alc. **Chardonnay** ★★ Marzipan aromas on oak-fermented (& 3 mth matured) **03**; still dominated by wood – which also helps with creamy texture, as just-dry 4g/ℓ sugar helps the soft finish. 13.5% alc. – *MF*

Linton Park Wines

Wellington ▪ Est 1995 ▪ 1stB 1998 ▪ Tasting & sales Mon-Fri 8-5 by appt ▪ Tours by appt Mon-Fri 9-4; also guided cellar/vineyard tours by appt (incl barrel tasting) ▪ Light lunches/picnics for small groups Mon-Fri 9-4 ▪ Owner Linton Park plc ▪ Winemaker Hennie Huskisson, with Danie Stevens (Jan 2001/Oct 1999) ▪ Viticulturist TBA ▪ 89 ha (cab, merlot, shiraz, chard, sauvignon) ▪ ±750 tons 12 500 cs 80% red 20% white ▪ Export brand: De Groene Heuwel ▪ PO Box 1234 Wellington 7654 ▪ lpwines@mweb.co.za ▪ www.lintonparkwines.co.za © 873·1625 ☐ 873·0851

Last year winemaker Hennie Huskisson released the Linton Park Reserve range and, in keeping with their stated philosophy ('innovate and experiment') also launched Linton Park chocolates. Filled, as those who know their penchant for a touch of sugar could guess, with shiraz. Post-prandial coffee surely will never be the same again, particularly if you opt to join in the new monthly cook-offs held in the old homestead on the home-farm: well-known chefs create a great meal, and serve it with the house's wines. Like so many of his colleagues, Hennie H found the 2004 harvest challenging. The grapes struggled to raise sugar, but the wines are now progressing well, particularly the cab. Hennie H is, as always, a touch disappointed with his Sauvignon, but we think it's rather good this year.

★★★★ **Shiraz** From their 'Summer Hill' vyd, yr Am oaked; **02** revisited: sweet brambly fruit, hints fried flowers & fynbos; softer & lighter than Rsv below. On release, **01** had choc, black cherry & spiced-meat tones, smoky youngberry tastes.

★★★★ **Shiraz Reserve 01** same vyd, different wooding (yr Am, finished off with extra yr Fr) adds to flavour spectrum. Brazen New-World styling with potential longevity. Though crammed with Ribena fruit, this version more structured than above; attractive leathery touch, sweet fruity finish. 14% alc.

★★★☆ **Cabernet Sauvignon 02** retasted, offers bright bramble aromas; plump & juicy fruit with hint cigarbox, attractive New World styling with restraint. Yr new Fr oak. **01** was bigger & more sumptuous.

★★★★ **Cabernet Sauvignon Reserve 01** from same block ('Bush Vine') as above, more extensively barrelled (1 yr new Fr oak, further yr 4th fill). Similar New World styling, spicy oak perhaps more evident; ripe mint-choc character à la Australia yet not a statement wine, fairly easy to drink.

★★★☆ **Merlot** From 'River Garden' vyd; yr Fr oak, none new. **02** (★★★), pvsly tasted as sample, uncorked for this ed shows as light hued; red plum jam nose, light, simple jammy fruit; 14% alc. Not a lot of structure, unlike **01**, which had intense, supple minty flavours & fine tannins.

★★★★★ **Merlot Reserve** Maturation regime similar to Cab Reserve gives added flavour concentration & savoury olive-like tones. **01** retasted, gaining complexity, fuller, more backbone, healthy tannins still. *Wine International* ★★★★★.

★★★★ **Chardonnay** Dense, creamy, elegant & persistent wine from farm's Claire Division vyd; **02** (★★★) retaste, billowing toasty passionfruit, crème brûlée & 'burnt match' aromas; big, opulent & slightly exotic; very low acidity (4.7g/ℓ) otherwise would have rated higher. **01** has rich grapefruit & apricot tones with tobacco whiffs.

★★★★ **Port** Limited release made in a sweet LBV style, 3 yrs aged in 4th fill Fr oak. Any resemblance to authentic Portuguese style ends with high alc (20%): sweet (120g/ℓ), varietally incorrect (ruby cab) – but appealing; ripe raisin/prune nose, hint cinnamon spice; rum & raisin flavour, spirity backbone, fruitcake on finish; NV.

Capell's Court range
Cabernet Sauvignon ★★★ **03** unwooded, straightforward cab flavours edged with slight herbal tone; soft, full bodied, dark choc & mocha flavours; sugar (4.2g/ℓ) masked by grainy tannins, finishes dry. **Merlot** ★★★ **03** sweet Xmas pud nose with earthy notes; plump, fleshy but nicely balanced by grainy mint-choc flavours, poised despite 15% alc. **Shiraz** ★★★★ 'Not your typical shiraz style' say winemakers of this unwooded, early-drinking version, enriched with dollop sugar (6–8g/ℓ); **03** dark juicy/smoky plums, hint of *garrigue*, very soft & jammy, overtly sweet finish. **Chardonnay** ★★★ **04** rich straw-green; spicy whiffs cloves & cinnamon with lees; soft peach/pear flavours; lots of personality; low 12.5% alc. **Sauvignon Blanc** ★★★ **04** fresh green capsicum, hint of guava; crisp apple flavours, dry mineral thread. Modest 13% alc. Both ranges WO Paarl. — *TM*

■ *Liquor Boys* see Oranjerivier
Live-A-Little see Stellar Winery
Live-A-Lot see Stellar Winery
Living World see Oranjerivier

Long Beach Café

Mediterranean-inspired range by Robertson Winery for Vinimark, pitched at SA's 'ever-burgeoning café society'. Attractively presented in latest screwcap bottles.
Rosé NEW **04** not tasted. **Chardonnay** ★★ **03** some biscuit/melon flavours, attractive fleshiness, clean zesty finish. **Sauvignon Blanc** ★★ **04** nice 'dry white' rather than 'sauvignon', some pleasant ripeness. Quaffably light 13% alc. — *DH*

Long Mountain Wine Company

Stellenbosch ▪ Est/1stB 1994 ▪ Closed to public ▪ Owner Pernod-Ricard SA ▪ Winemaker/viticulturist Eben Rademeyer (Jun 2004) ▪ 50% red 49% white 1% MCC ▪ PO Box 1324 Stellenbosch 7599 ▪ Vanda.davies@pernod-ricard-southafrica.com ▪ www.longmountain.co.za ℗ **880·8800** 🖷 *880·8860*
Celebrating 10 years of winegrowing in SA's 10th year of democracy, this Pernod Ricard-owned operation was poised to release a Reserve range, Bushbuck Ridge, at press time. Newcomer Eben Rademeyer has what Long Mountain takes ('tracking the wine from vineyard to cellar'): experience-wise, he earned his winemaking spurs at Rooiberg, and his training is as a viticulturist. He'll be closely involved with a new vineyard programme which allows closer control of grape quality and the style of their Long Mountain and Gecko Ridge wines — 'integrated fruit flavours and a soft tannin structure'.

Ruby Cabernet ☺ ★★★ Appealingly ripe & juicy **03**, vibrant spicy ruby cab nose, bright jammy red fruit, simple but fun to drink. Like all reds below, ±13.5% alc.

Cabernet Sauvignon ★★★ Scaled- but not dumbed-down cab: **03** lifted black fruit on nose/palate, sweet-oak in support, fresh acidity & variety's noticeable tannin. Structure to drink/keep 2/3 yrs. **Pinotage** ★★ Undemanding **03** offers combo dusty red pepper & creamy red berry, generous enough red fruit flavours. **Merlot-Shiraz** ★★★ **03** light-weight, with shy black fruit aromas, appealing new-leather hints; slightly more assertive & dry than its range-mates. **Shiraz-Cabernet Sauvignon** ★★★ Accessible & seamless 55/45 blend; **03** shy meaty hints on nose, more action on palate: ripe gripping tannin & sweet ripe fruit. **Chardonnay** ★★ Invariably a tasty mouthful; **04** tropical melon & mango, medium-full bodied, rewarding. **Chenin Blanc** ★★★ Vinified for fruit-juiciness; **04** typical of the variety: Golden Delicious apple flavour with touches honey & guava, balanced & easy to drink. **Sauvignon Blanc** ★★ **04** (sample) tropical/passionfruit aromas, clean, fresh, well made if somewhat quick; low 12.5% alc. **Semillon-Chardonnay** ★★★ These have some staying power, but best in flush of youth; **03** pleasant honey-bush & melon tones, balanced & still fresh, fair persistence. **Chardonnay-Pinot Noir Brut** NEW ★★★★ Affordable, carefully made MCC offering toasty hazelnut/lemon cream aromas; lively lemon flavour with fine lively bubble. Very nice. 60/40 *cuvée*, base-wine briefly Fr-oaked. NV; WO Rbtsn; all others Brde Rvr Vlly. — *JB*

Long Neck see Simonsvlei

Longridge Winery

Stellenbosch (see Helderberg map) ▪ *Est/1stB 1995* ▪ *Tasting & sales: Mon-Fri 9-5 Sat 9-2 Sep-May, otherwise by appt* © *855·2004* ▪ *Fee R10* ▪ *Closed Easter Sun, Dec 25 & Jan 1* ▪ *Cheese platters & picnic baskets (book day ahead)* ▪ *Owner Winecorp* ▪ *Winemakers/viti-culturists: see Winecorp* ▪ *60 ha* ▪ *23 000 cs 60% red 40% white* ▪ *ISO 9001 certified* ▪ *PO Box 99 Lynedoch 7600* ▪ *annareth@winecorp.co.za* ▪ *www.longridge.co.za* © *881·3690* 🖷 *881·3699*

Well-established, widely acclaimed brand, vinified in the Longridge cellar in the Helderberg foothills and matured at nearby Spier. Bay View is the good-value range. Both available for tasting/purchase at Longridge's tasting room, now open from September to May and offering light lunches by arrangement. See also Winecorp.

★★★★ **Cabernet Sauvignon** Serious & delicious wine to cellar few yrs while taking in the Bay Views below. **02** built on muscular lines, as pvs. Savoury spice, mocha, smoky top-notes add complexity to dark-fruited core; velvety fruit-texture misleads, wine still in early stage of development, deep-veined tannins will slowly unfurl, promising 10+ yrs enjoyment. 14 mths small Fr oak, 60% new. 14.7% alc. **01** cried out for time to show true worth. Concours Mondial gold.

★★★★ **Merlot 02** impresses with vibrancy, choc-mint & mulberry intensity, chewy tannins within sleekly muscular framework. Not a shy bone in its body. Will show better with another yr's cellaring, good for 5+. Fr/Am oak, 14 mths. 14.7% alc. **01** had this wine's signature choc-mint in abundance, alongside creamy plum/red berry flavour appeal. *Wine* ★★★★.

★★★★ **Pinotage** Multi-awarded label, most recently Concours Mondial gold for **02** (★★★★★), a lesson in the variety's ability to impress: creamy dark fruit core, enlivening whiffs of cherries, herbs, roasted spice. Silky fruit, poised tannin, never-ending finish. Beautifully crafted, harmonious, despite hefty 14.9% alc. Fr/Am oak, 70/30, 14 mths. 2003 IWC gold. **01** admirable structure. IWC gold.

★★★★★ **Chardonnay** Consistent & individual barrel-fermented white, showered with awards since first **96**. Current **02** creamy biscuit, honey overlaying peach-cobbler richness. Built on generous lines (touch sugar), with oodles of toasty flavour; appetising. Yr Fr barrel fermented/matured. 14.5% alc. Golds at Concours Mondial, Chardonnay-du-Monde. **01** had the same pedigree lines. Gold medal & runner-up to best wine of show at 2003 Michelangelo.

Bay View range

★★★★ **Cabernet Sauvignon** ✓ **02** similar aromas to pvs, mocha & cassis/dark cherries, but sleeker, smoothly ripe; tannins supportive, allowing fruit to hold centre stage. Seasoned small Fr oak, 11 mths. 14% alc. **01** needed to show its best.

★★★★ **Merlot** ✓ **03** house-style red berry focus, pepped up by whiffs herbs, white pepper. Deftly oaked, 11 mths Fr, adding flavour, structure, without interfering with juicy accessibility. 14% alc.

Shiraz ★★★★ **03** more depth, concentration than pvs. Bold, flavourful, unmistakably New World: black cherry, scrub, roasted spice; firm but ripe tannins, savoury finish. Drink, or keep 3+ yrs. Oak as above. 14.7% alc. **Pinotage** ★★★ Easy drinking but not simple; **03** rhubarb/brambleberry layered with cedar; sound structure, finishing firmly dry, perfect for rich food. Mainly Fr oak, touch Am, 11 mths. 14.7% alc. **Chenin Blanc** ★★★ **04** (sample) bursting out of its seams with exuberant freshness; juicy fresh-cut pears, guavas, long zesty finish. Reductively made. **Sauvignon Blanc** ★★★ Now for export market only. **04** (sample) pear-drop, with gooseberry, passionfruit notes; crisp acidity gives focus to fruit salad flavours, helps food compatibility. 13% alc. This range WO W-Cape/Coastal. — *CR*

L'Ormarins Private Cellar ♟♙⚪☯

Franschhoek ▪ Est 1965 ▪ 1stB 1982 ▪ Tasting & sales Mon-Fri 9-4.30 Sat 10-3 ▪ Fee R20 ▪ Light lunches Mon-Sat Dec-Mar ▪ Closed Easter Fri/Sun, Dec 25 & Jan 1 ▪ Small tourgroups ▪ Owner Johann Rupert ▪ Winemakers Christo Hamerse and Neil Patterson ▪ Viticulturist Pietie le Roux (Oct 2002) ▪ 120 ha (cab, merlot, pinot g, chard, sauvignon) ▪ 1 000 tons 25 000 cs own label 50/50 red/white ▪ ISO 14001 certified ▪ PO Box 435 Franschhoek Valley 7690 ▪ tasting@lormarins.co.za ▪ www.lormarins.com ✆ 874·1026 🖷 874·1361

Johann Rupert is now the sole owner of this Franschhoek property, lovingly transformed during the 1980s into a showpiece by his late younger brother Antonij. Under Johann R's aegis, L'Ormarins is entering a new era. A new 200-ton red wine cellar is being completed, and sophisticated satellite geo-positioning technology brought into play, to aid the matching future vineyard sites to the most suitable variety. Each existing block on the farm is coming under scrutiny, too. The aim is to improve fruit selection and generally fine-tune the management of individual vineyards. 'This gives us better components to work with in the cellar, reflected in the bottle', say winemakers Christo Hamerse and Neil Patterson (Riaan van der Spuy now involved with another rejuvenation, at Meerendal). Flying the Italian flag in this French-toned valley is the Terra del Capo range, brainchild of Antonij R. Both the Pinot Grigio and Sangiovese are available for tasting, along with the newly repackaged L'Ormarins wines, in the tasting area on the property.

★★★★ **Optima** Consistently excellent claret-style red. **02** blend of cab (70%) & merlot only (pvs included cab f); elegant & refined bouquet of ripe cassis & woodsmoke; palate more flagrantly New World: creamy, mouthfilling (14% alc), supple. Delicious; great prospects. Yr Fr oak, 40% new. Standout **00** (★★★★★) had fluid textures; beautifully managed oak, fruitcake richness & complexity. No **01**.

★★★★ **Cabernet Sauvignon 02** classic bouquet of cassis & cigarbox; light textured but ripe & elegant, promising; deserves time. 15 mths Fr oak; 60% new. 14% alc. **01** 91 pts *WS*. No **00**. **99** VDG heralded upturn for this label: more exuberance yet plenty in reserve for good cellaring.

★★★★ **Merlot** Improved recent track record continued with **01**, in 2003 clinching both VDG & gold at Concours Mondial. **02**, in difficult vintage, achieved richness, complexity; well wooded blackcurrant palate with dry cedary finish. Current **03** sweet, youthfully fruity nose with chunky high-toast oak; good concentration & grainy texture; give time. ±15 mths oak, 70% new Fr. ±14.5% alc.

★★★★ **Barrique Select Merlot** 🆕 **02** netted trophy for category at Concours Mondial. All bells & whistles special selection with bright, clean, elegant fruit. Generous & juicy; supple tannins & persistence — all good auguries. 15 mths 70% new Fr oak.

★★★★ **Sauvignon Blanc 03** was unusually assertive for this cellar — burst with flavour, bright acidity; ethereal water-white **04** (sample), dusty sweet pear-drop & candyfloss bouquet, sherbety flavours. Frhoek/Darling fruit.

★★★★ **Sauvignon Blanc Cold Soaked** 🆕 Arresting green fig & capsicum pungency in **03**, following through to complex palate where melded with crunchy asparagus; loads of vim, personality; combo Dbnvlle/Darling fruit, pre-fermentation soak (at 8°C) for 20 hrs to unleash flavour. Limited release of 1 000 cs. SAYWS gold.

Chardonnay ★★★ Not a loud style, medium-weight but satisfying, versatile at table. 30% new-barrel-fermented/11 mths (rest equal 2nd fill & unoaked) in **04**, peach crème brûlée aroma; supple & juicy; soft & elegant (despite 14% alc) with a vein of minerality. **Blanc Fumé** ★★★★ Two-thirds barrel-fermented portion (+4 mths 2nd fill Fr) blended with third unwooded for understated food-cordial suavity. **04** (sample) shy lemongrass & smidgen cinnamon spice on nose; bright, juicy but soft flavours, revitalising twist of acid on finish. **Pinot Grigio** Locally better known in French: pinot gris. **04** (sample) continues higher wow-factor of recent vintages. Fragrant almond & marzipan whiffs, pleasantly dusty/nutty palate, bright finish; likely ★★★★. Commendably informative back-label here & throughout range.

Terra del Capo range

Sangiovese ★★★★ Grows more convincing by the vintage. Authentic 'Italian' feel to **02**, tight nose/palate with rich damson fruit behind; balancing acidity & promising structure; needs both time & food. Yr oak, 75% Fr. 14% alc. **Pinot Grigio** Though partly barrelled, **04** more overtly fruity than version above; zesty & refreshing; appetite-whetting green apple bite on finish. Potential ★★★★. Both ranges WO Coastal. — *RK/TM*

Lost Horizons Premium Wines

Paarl ▪ Est/1stB 1995 ▪ Tasting & sales at Simonsvlei International (see entry) Mon-Fri 8-5 Sat 8.30-4.30 Sun 11-3 ▪ Fee R15 for 5 wines (incl glass) ▪ Closed Easter Fri & Dec 25 ▪ Tours by appt ▪ Owner Norton Sky Cooper ▪ Viti consultant Schalk du Toit (Jun 1999) ▪ ±250 000 cs 50% red 30% white 20% rosé ▪ Export brands: Guardian, Panorama, St Dalfour ▪ ISO 9001:2000, HACCP & BRC certified ▪ PO Box 568 Suider-Paarl 7624 ▪ horizons@global.co.za ▪ www. losthorizons.co.za ℂ 863·3848 ⌨ 863·3850

As an exporter to an array of markets from Kenya to the Caribbean, GM Jacques Jordaan acknowledges the pressure created by the strong rand but believes this should not be a major obstacle: 'If you produce quality wines that are consumer-friendly your product will sell.' And no reason, he adds, that it shouldn't sell as well as product from Australia or Chile. Jordaan is pleased that Simonsvlei, where all his wines are produced, is now ISO- and HACCP-certified, and that it's been recognised by the British Retail Consortium, a global quality-standards watchdog.

Classic Red ☺ ★★★ Unpretentious red; **03** mix ruby cab, pinotage, merlot. Slightly smoky flavours make it a versatile braai partner. **Sauvignon Blanc** ☺ ★★★ Muted on nose but **04**'s ebullient on palate: zingy green flavours, tart sherbety acidity to counter anything rich & fishy. Sample tasted. **Classic White** ☺ ★★ Charming & gentle dry blend chenin, chardonnay; lightish, touches quince & citrus, sweet-melon palate. NV.

Cabernet Sauvignon ★★★ **02** good everyday red, smooth & easy; mouthfilling (14.5% alc) but balanced; not oaked, as are all these. **Merlot** ★★★ Grapes from SwtInd; **02** holding up well (and proving us wrong — last ed we said drink up); meaty/gamey whiffs; full-ripe fruit, soft, suggestion of sweetness on finish. **Cabernet Sauvignon-Merlot** ★★★ Equal blend in **02**, trattoria-friendly as always; retasted; seems shier than last; some leafy strawberry fruit, soft, juicy palate. **Chardonnay** ★★★ **04** (sample) back in perky form with crisp, lemony flavours, juicy, uncomplicated but nice. **Guardian Chenin Blanc** Exclusive to European market; latest version not ready for tasting.

Quantum range

Classic Ruby Red ☺ ★★★ **03** unwooded mix ruby cab, pinotage, merlot. Creaminess on nose/palate, smoky whiffs, thatchy tang from ruby cab; gulpable. **Petillant Rosé** ☺ ★★★ Of its style, still one of SA's top sellers; delicately sparkling, just-not-dry picnic wine; **03** bright coppery salmon pink; candied flavours from dash muscat; very slight prickle lifts the fruit.

Petillant Blanc ★★ Latest version of refreshing, slightly spritzy off-dry untasted.

Hemisphere range

Classic Ruby Red ☺ ★★★ Unostentatious anytime red, unwooded, as are all these; mix ruby cab, pinotage, merlot in **03**, smoky banana nose; soft palate where fruity pinotage dominates. **Petillant Rosé** ☺ ★★★ Delicate spritz tickles the palate in **03**, shimmering coppery hue pleases the eye; ungreedy price delights the pocket. **Sauvignon Blanc** ☺ ★★★ Shy gooseberry nose with hint guava; **04** comes alive on palate: bright, green, sherbety flavours; good lightish quaffing.

Cabernet Sauvignon ★★★ Ripely Ribena-toned **02**, similar but rounder, plusher, better balanced than LH version. **Merlot ★★★ 02** appears slightly fleshlier than the LH version; similar meaty/gamey sniffs; full, ripe, soft fruit. **Cabernet Sauvignon-Merlot ★★★ 02** perfectly pleasant medium-bodied quaffer, fairly laid-back; some soft leafy strawberry fruit. **Chardonnay ★★ 04** (sample) lemon crispness, well juiced, simple but pleasant. All ranges WO W-Cape. — *TM*

Louiesenhof Wines

Stellenbosch ▪ Est/1stB 1992 ▪ Tasting & sales daily 9-5 (summer) Mon-Sat 10-3 (winter) ▪ Fee R10 ▪ Closed Christian holidays ▪ Light picnic meals in summer ▪ Play area for children ▪ Farm produce ▪ Walks ▪ Conservation area ▪ Owner WS Smit Watergang Trust ▪ Winemaker Stefan Smit, advised by Jos le Roux in 2004 ▪ Viti consultant Gawie Kriel (2000) ▪ 120 ha (cab, merlot, pinotage, tinta, chard, chenin, sauvignon) ▪ 800 tons 3 000 cs own label 70% red 28% white 2% rosé ▪ PO Box 2013 Stellenbosch 7601 ▪ lhofwine@iafrica.com ▪ Louiesenhof.co.za Ⓒ 865-2632 🖷 865-2613

'We got very worried because the harvest took so long to start', confides Stefan Smit. However, a few months later he found the 2004 wines more exciting than those of the year before. Chief winemaker for the season was well-seasoned Jos le Roux, working with Avril Robain, who has been on the farm for 10 years and was recently promoted to assistant. The production team's slogan was 'less and better': 'We've decided to shorten our wine list', explains Smit, 'to give more quality to fewer wines'. The same concept applied in the vineyards, where quality blocks were given special attention. New plantings were postponed because of the long dry period preceding winter but 15 hectares of vines were trellised.

> **Pinotage Blanc de Noir ☺ ★★★** ('Rosé Secco' in pvs ed) **03** coral glints, sappy strawberry tones with touch of cream, bone-dry conclusion. Good food style.

Pinotage ★★★ 02 envisaged as a 'lifestyle' wine, selected grapes from cooler slopes for bigger flavour, reveals Stefan S; unwooded; retasted, shows some meaty whiffs. **Tinta Barocca NEW ★★★ 02** Mediterranean-style, food-cordial red; shows house's firm, sinewy aesthetic; pleasing mix red berry & dried fruit on nose; hint choc on finish. Briefly oaked. **Chardonnay Unwooded ★★★ 04** shy pear/green melon on nose; minerally & lean, good foil for seafood. **Sauvignon Blanc ★★★ 04** water-white; lees & dusty bellpepper whiffs; lemongrass hint in dry, lean, flinty palate. **Perroquet Cape Tawny ★★★★** Rustic winter glow-inducer from tinta, off very old vyd; fortified with brandy, aged 5 yrs in barrels; NV; 19% alc; raisin & treacle notes in fairly developed bouquet; savoury touch; dried fruit & nuts on finish with hint orange rind. **Shiraz & Red Muscadel** discontinued. — *TM*

Louisvale Wines

Stellenbosch ▪ Est/1stB 1989 ▪ Tasting & sales Mon-Fri 10-4.30 (sales close at 5) Sat 10-1 Oct-Apr only, else by appt ▪ Fee R10 ▪ Closed Easter Fri-Mon, Dec 25/26 & Jan 1 ▪ Tours by appt ▪ BYO picnic ▪ Owners Michael A Johnston, Hendrik Kotzé, Martin Delaney & Jonathan Pedley ▪ Winemaker Simon Smith (Jul 1997) ▪ Viti consultant Paul Wallace (Nov 2002) ▪ 23 ha (cab, merlot, shiraz, chard) ▪ 200 tons 15 000 cs 20% red 80% white ▪ ISO 9000:2001 certification in progress ▪ PO Box 542 Stellenbosch 7599 ▪ winery@louisvale.com ▪ www.louisvale.com Ⓒ 865-2422 🖷 865-2633

After assessing the market potential and the continuing suitability of its sites, this small Devon Valley winery has elected to refocus on its traditional strength: chardonnay. Aiming to be one of SA's top niche producers, flamboyant Scot Mike Johnston and partners say they will concentrate on three different interpretations of the grape: unwooded, medium- and full-bodied. The Bordeaux-style blend Dominique will be the sole red in the line-up. Louisvale is also transforming itself into one of the most socially-aware wine farms, joining the fight against cancer (R3 from every Chavant Chardonnay sold donated to CANSA), and taking the lead in the valley in terms of education and skills development.

★★★★ **Dominique** ✓ **00** introduces dash cab f to flagship blend of cab, merlot (55/30); retasted, shows luxurious velvet texture to opulent dark-berried fruit, pleasant dryness, should hold min 3-4 yrs. Yr Fr barriques. 14.1% alc. **01** less opulence, more oak discipline & classicism, firm claret grip should loosen in 1-2 yrs. Sample **02** similarly styled, cab f upped to 23% (balance cab/merlot 40/37). Still toughish tannins to well-endowed profile, long way to go, similarly stylish.

★★★★ **Chardonnay** Since maiden **89**, among most consistent in Cape, with track record for good ageing; regular at Nederburg Auction, yet **03** (★★★★) shade less arresting — more obvious oak (though less time in barrel — 6 mths vs 8), austere; standout bouquet still features toast, grilled hazelnuts, ripe citrus. Compact, neat citrus flavours replace ripe peach of **02**, returns to style of earlier vintages.

★★★☆ **Chavant Chardonnay** Back to less obviously oaky style in **03** (★★★), also less aroma & style than **02** & pvs, though similarly handled (4 mths small-oak, 10% new). & peach is out, citrus is in, more zing & zap.

GlenDevon Chardonnay Unwooded ★★★ **04** fresh as the proverbial daisy, floral bouquet with white peach fleshiness, satin texture, combine for easy drinkability. Dash sugar ensures cushioned landing. **Louisvale Cabernet Sauvignon, Merlot** & **Ovation**; **GlenDevon Cabernet Sauvignon, Chenin Blanc** & **Pinotage** discontinued. — *IvH*

Lourensford

Stellenbosch (see Helderberg map) ▪ Est 1999 ▪ 1stB 2003 ▪ Tasting & sales Mon-Fri 8.30-5 Sat 9.30-2 ▪ Fee R15 ▪ Closed Easter Fri, Dec 25 & Jan 1 ▪ Soup lunches Mon-Fri 12-3 Jun-Aug ▪ Tours Mon-Fri 11 & 3 ▪ Conferencing ▪ Winemakers Philip Costandius, Wynand Lategan & Hannes Nel (all Dec 2002) ▪ Viticulturists Barry Humby, Ben de Villiers & Annelie Viljoen ▪ 250 ha (cab, merlot, pinotage, shiraz, sauvignon, viognier) ▪ 1 000 tons 80 000 cs 80% red 20% white ▪ ISO 14000 certification in progress ▪ PO Box 16 Somerset West 7129 ▪ winery@lourensford.co.za ▪ www.lourensford.com ✆ 847·0891 🖷 847·0896

The Lourensford team hit the road running, taking in their maiden harvest before the cellar was completed. A year on, the first vintage is in bottle or barrel, and the R86m cellar in the Helderberg whirring smoothly (it's one of the largest privately held facilities in SA, developed by business magnate Christo Wiese, who also owns Lanzerac). The second harvest (2004) amounted to 1 000 tons and the goal is 5 000. Even on a spread this big, size isn't everything. The farm is divided into smaller units, each with its own manager. Though blessed with every technical innovation money can buy, cellarmaster Philip Costandius' motto is unambiguous and refreshingly traditional: 'fruit is first'.

★★★☆ **Seventeen Hundred** Name alludes to date of property's establishment: blend cab (75%), merlot, soupçon shiraz. Fruit from Faure, in future only from Lourensford, as for others in range. **03** shows bold oaking (yr Fr, half new); first impression of toasty, sweet spice aromas, forceful tannins, all in dark-fruited, savoury construct. 14.6% alc. Still closed; needs time to show true worth — up to 10 yrs' ageing potential.

★★★☆ **Sauvignon Blanc 04** classic-styled asparagus, nettles, fleeting glimpses herb garden, summer fruits. Reductively made to capture zinging, youthful freshness. Finishes bone-dry, just what's needed with food — as is moderate 12.8% alc.

Cabernet Sauvignon Early pre-bottling glimpse of **03** shows lovely aromatic elements, savoury, rich-fruit spectrum, but tannins still busy integrating, will show better in finished wine. Seriously made, like flagship above, with even bigger 14.9% alc. — *CR*

Luddite Wines

Bot River (see Walker Bay map) ▪ *Est/2000* ▪ *Tastings by appt* ▪ *Owners Niels Verburg &*
Hillie Meyer ▪ *Winemaker Niels Verburg* ▪ *Viticulturist Penny Verburg* ▪ *2.5 ha (shiraz)* ▪ *1*
800 cs 100% red ▪ *Export brand: Niels Verburg* ▪ *Ranges for customers: Iona, Barton & Hid-*
den Valley ▪ *PO Box 656 Bot River 7185* ▪ *luddite@telkomsa.net* ℭ *(028) 284·9308*
🖃 *(028) 284·9045*

Niels Verburg is emphatic: 'Wine is made from grapes, yeast and beer!' (It took a good
few crates to entice their city friends to help them harvest the first crop off their own Bot
River vines.) Wife Penny V has been hit by the realisation that this is suddenly a 'real, full-
on business' (they recently went solo after running in tandem with Beaumont, where
Niels V full-timed). Mrs V quickly reassures that along with 3 children, 5 dogs and a couple of chickens they're thriving. And planting another 2ha, and exporting to several countries, including Australia. An Aussie on holiday here so loved their Shiraz, he promptly
opened an agency in Melbourne to import it. Verburg also consults to several wineries including Barton Farm, Iona and Hidden Valley.

★★★★☆ **Shiraz 02** continues its unshowy development with great polish; whiffs of ground
pepper, clove, allspice leading to sumptuously fruited but unflamboyant palate,
with ample grip from fine tannins. Manages to conceal 15.5% alc. Bigger, more
mouth filling than finely spiced **01**, now reined in, silky. From Mbury, Stbosch fruit.
Yr mainly Fr oak, 30% new. — *MF*

Lusan Premium Wines

Stellenbosch ▪ *Closed to public* ▪ *nee@mweb.co.za* ℭ *883·8988* 🖃 *883·8941*
Umbrella organisation for Alto, Hill & Dale, Le Bonheur, Neethlingshof, Stellenzicht and
Uitkyk. Wines from these farms, totalling some 800 ha of prime Stellenbosch vineyards,
marketed by Distell. See individual entries.

Lushof Estate

Stellenbosch (see Helderberg map) ▪ *Est 1997* ▪ *1stB 2000* ▪ *Tasting & sales Mon-Fri 9-5* ▪
Closed public holidays ▪ *Tours by appt* ▪ *Owners Hennie & Linda Steyn* ▪ *Winemaker/viticul-*
turist to be appointed ▪ *10 ha (cab, merlot, shiraz, chard, sauvignon)* ▪ *60 tons 3 000 cs*
60% red 40% white ▪ *PO Box 899 Stellenbosch 7599* ▪ *lushof@icon.co.za* ▪ *www.lushof.*
co.za ℭ *855·3134* 🖃 *855·3623*

Daniel Hudson had been at Lushof only 18 months when the UK-bred winemaker was offered an opportunity to climb some remote glacier in Russia. With a well-developed taste
for adventure, he jumped, leaving assistant Erica van Zyl at the helm. Still, Hudson's brief
tenure coincided with a great season, the cooler temperatures more reminiscent of Bordeaux (where he has also worked) and another slow, late harvest — the best cab picked on
April 28. Hudson nurtured the estate's first release Shiraz and flagship red blend with a totally minimalist approach ('you don't kick the ass out of wines'). While the Shiraz is on the
market, the cuvée is still gathering force under Van Zyl's watchful eye.

★★★★ **Cabernet Sauvignon** Like Merlot below, **02** revisited mid-2004, more demure
than suggested last yr. Dainty, sweet-fruited cassis, leafy notes set off by fine
tannin, now well-absorbed oak (15 mths, 50% new Fr). Softish, tad short; difficult vintage well realised for current drinking. 13.8% alc. Young vines showing
potential.

★★★★ **Merlot** Well-tailored **02** now showing good cohesive decorum; elegant interplay
cedar spice, fresh red plums/cherries; light-textured; tasty savoury acid, well-
controlled tannin support. 13.4% alc. Oak as for Cab.

★★★★ **Shiraz** 🆕 **03** deftly executed to show off best of 3 yr old vines. Deepish carpet
pile texture, balanced natural freshness complement elegantly expressive dark
spice, savoury meaty hints. 14.3% alc. 11 mths Fr/Am oak, 50 % new.

★★★★ **Chardonnay** ✓ Similar barrel-ferment regime (Fr, 50% new) on **03** delivers
toasty/spicy aromatic features of **02**. Full-bodied, smoothly rounded; oak

characters well supported by limy, tropical succulence; geared for current drinking. 14.1% alc.

★★★★ **Sauvignon Blanc ✓ 04** among yr's more subtly expressive. Ripe gooseberries, figs, pears fragrance delivered with pinpoint clarity; reprised in layers on broad, bouncy palate. Juicily clean; very moreish. 13.6% alc. Unfiltered.

As yet unnamed NEW **03 Flagship blend** cab, merlot, shiraz, previewed ex-cask, shows refinement for which Hldrberg noted; sleek, sinewy with sound fresh raspberry, red plum flesh, tender tannin backing to dominant smoky, toasty oak. Fr oak, 80% new. – *AL*

Lutzville Cape Diamond Vineyards

Olifants River ▪ Est 1964 ▪ 1stB 1980 ▪ Tasting & sales Mon-Fri 8-5 Sat 9–12 ▪ Closed public holidays ▪ Tours by appt ▪ Picnic baskets by appt, or BYO ▪ Function/conference venue ▪ Tourgroups ▪ Gifts ▪ Farm produce ▪ Owners 109 shareholders ▪ Winemakers Albie Rust & Emile Schoch (Jan 1999/Dec 2003) ▪ Viticulturists Jaco Lategan & Christiaan Visser (Dec 2002/Dec 2003) ▪ 2 100 ha (cab, merlot, pinotage, ruby cab, shiraz, chard, chenin, colombard, sauvignon) ▪ 47 500 tons (20 000 cs own label) 10% red 87% white 1% rosé 2% fortified/sparkling ▪ PO Box 50 Lutzville 8165 ▪ info@lutzvillevineyards.com ▪ www.lutzvillevineyards.com © **(027) 217·1516** ☏ *(027) 217·1435*

In its 40th year, SA's second-biggest cellar and largest supplier for the top-selling export brand Kumala has updated its identity, and now calls itself 'Lutzville Cape Diamond Vineyards'. The new name, logo and labels are the outward signs of progress, as is the new 'wine garden' in front of the extended tasting facility, billowing with umbrellas above its tables. However, there's plenty happening on the inside too. Veteran winemaker Emile Schoch, after nearly 20 years at Nordale, now heads up an expanded winemaking team. Bottling and labelling are now done on-site, and the pressing process has been modernised to improve quality. Change is being rewarded: Riaan Wiese was named Farmer of the Year – a first for Lutzville growers – and the cellar's Most Westerly Pinotage 02 recently had a Best Value award from SA Wine.

Chardonnay Unwooded ☺ ★★★ **04** baked apple & cream aromas, melon flavours, balanced freshness. From selected grapes; class-winner on local Young Wine Show.

Cabernet Sauvignon ★★★ Retaste of light-bodied **00** reveals herbal camomile nose, hint stewed currant, dry savoury finish, some bottle-age complexity. **Merlot** ★★ **03** lightly oaked; smoky plums & hint of currant; abrasive tannins; big (14% alc) but not concentrated. **Most Westerly Pinotage** ★★★ **02** retasted, typical pinotage: warm stewed mulberry aromas; estery hint, slight gaminess; dry finish. **Ruby Cabernet** ★★★ Last was unnwooded **01**, dry tannins nicely cushioned by fruit. **Shiraz** ★★★ NEW Ripe, sweet **04** (sample), touch jam on nose; plummy/meaty tones, concentrated if uncomplex; soupçon sugar adds cushioning, as does fat 15% alc. **Chardonnay Wooded** ★★ **02** pleasant lightweight quick-quaff not retasted. **Colombar** ★★ Undemanding **03** was last. **Sauvignon Blanc** ★★★ **04** (sample) estery peardrop aromas; slightly dusty/zesty grapefruit flavours; bone-dry. **Semillon** ★★★ **03**, with new-clone dusty capsicum aromas, was the last tasted. **Chenin Blanc Off-Dry** ★★★ **04** subtle green melon aromas; quite full flavoured with melon & apples, semi-dry; well balanced.

Bat's Rock range

Rosé ☺ ★★★ **04** (sample) soft creamy semi-sweet with deep ruby colour; slightly dusty strawberry aromas, balanced red berry flavours; from pinotage & colombard.

Ruby Cabernet ★★★ **03** typical smoky plum with fresh thatch aroma, slight herbal note; soft, silky & plump, warming. **Robyn** ★★ We last tasted **03**, unoaked, with big powdery tannins. **Blanc de Noir** Available, not tasted. **Chenin Blanc** ★★★ **04** (sample) understated lemony aromas, just off-dry, crisp. **Bouquet Blanc** ★★★ Last was semi-sweet **03**

from morio muscat, colombard. **Somersoet** ★★ Literally 'Summer Sweet', from chenin. **03** was the last sampled. **White Muscadel** ★★★ **03** orange marmalade & floral notes; sweet & silky; citrus rind character carries onto palate; delicious; moderate ±15% alc.

Friends range

NVs in 500ml screwcaps. All ★★. **Ruby Sunset** Blend ruby cab, shiraz, merlot; fleshy red-plum nose; firm, dry, finishes bit hard/green. **Misty Morning** Equal mix semillon & colombard, lightish, dry. **Sunny Day** Lightish semi-sweet colombard, hanepoot; slight grape/rose-petal whiffs, soft & supple. All above WO Olifants River or Lutzville. — *TM*

Lyngrove

Stellenbosch (see Helderberg map) ▪ 1stB 2000 ▪ Tasting & sales by appt © 842·2116 ▪ Owner Baarsma's Holdings BV ▪ Winemaker Conrad Vlok, with Stefan Hartman (Sep 2002/Jan 2004) ▪ Vineyard manager Pikkie Grobler ▪ 76 ha (varieties: see intro) ▪ 50 000 cs 80% red 20% white ▪ PO Box 7275 Stellenbosch 7599 ▪ info@lyngrove.co.za ▪ www.lyngrove.co.za © 880·1221 ▤ 880-0851

The past few years have seen Lyngrove, previously just another brand in the Baarsma stable, come into its own. It is now a standalone range, made from selected vineyards on the Lyngrove farm in the Helderberg. About 70ha in production (and create a fine backdrop to the Lyngrove Country House, a 5-star stay-over), with new sauvignon and petit verdot added to the existing blocks of cab, merlot, shiraz, pinotage, pinot, chardonnay and chenin. Conrad Vlok, who joined Baarsma from Delheim in 2002, is the winemaker, assisted by recently appointed Stefan Hartman.

'Premium' range (to be named) [NEW]

★★★★ **Pinotage** Barrique-matured **03** very obviously pinotage but well behaved; lots of fruity flavour in a spicy vanilla-toned package. Delicious. Agreeable lifted finish. Yr Am oak; unfiltered.
Shiraz ★★★★ Quite a mouthful; zero finesse but **03** compensates with loads of interest (roast meat, toasted nuts), extract, alc (14.3%). Yr oak, 80% Am, none new. Dead ringer for an Aussie, whereas… **Cabernet Sauvignon-Merlot** ★★★★ Tends towards a European style. Slight herbal veneer to the clean cassis; medium-bodied; fine, slightly minerally structure. Yr Fr oak. **Chardonnay** ★★★★ Well constructed **03** has a tight limey entry, followed by whiffs marmalade toast & cinnamon; soft butterscotch finish. Yr Fr oak.

Lyngrove Reserve range

These all **02** vintage, WO Coastal. **Pinotage** ★★★★ Classic ripe-picked pinotage: sweet, palate-coating black fruit flavours, traces spicy oak & vanilla adding plusher feel; big (14.5% alc), obvious yet not a blockbuster; yr combo Fr/Am barrels. **Cabernet Sauvignon-Merlot** ★★★ Light-textured 60/40 blend, matured yr in Fr oak; eucalyptus hint on sweetish, Ribena-toned palate. **Shiraz-Pinotage** ★★★★ Interesting & compatible 80/20 partnership; peppery mulberry flavours; dry & fairly reserved, a hint of green oak. 14.5% alc. Oak as for Pinotage. **Chardonnay** ★★★★ Showy wine — looser woven & much more outgoing than when tasted for last ed; full, rich layers of creamy fruit with hint of botrytis. Barrel-fermented/aged in Fr oak.

Lyngrove Collection range

Reds tasted pre-bottling — ratings provisional. Unless stated, aged with Fr oak staves, yr. **Cabernet Sauvignon** ★★★ **03** acceptable but not as immediately pleasing as pvs; blackcurrant jam palate shows as a touch lean, diffuse. **Merlot** ★★★ **03** eucalyptus whiffs precede greenish, fairly tart sour-plum palate. Needs hearty stew or pepper steak. **Pinotage** ★★★ **04** straight-down-the-line pinotage: jammy, sweet, but saved by nice tweak of acidity. 14.2% alc. Am oak. **Shiraz** ★★★ Punchy, vibrant **03**; nose a censer of white pepper & tar; plump plummy palate buoyed by racy acidity. **Chardonnay** ★★★★ Not oaked but not bland either. **03** shows a creamy complexity, long juicy finish with attractively contrasting touches asparagus & peach. **Sauvignon Blanc** ★★★ Well balanced **04**, supple & forthcoming with grapefruit, green nettle & crushed leaf freshness; med-bodied. **Brut** ★★★

Though carbonated, **03** has some of the character, complexity of an MCC; very fine appley bubbles; full, slightly leesy flavour. WO W-Cape. — *TM*

Lynx Wines

Franschhoek ▪ Est/1stB 2002 ▪ Visits by appt ▪ Self-catering cottages ▪ Owner Vista Hermosa (Pty) Ltd ▪ Winemaker Dieter Sellmeyer (2002) ▪ Viti adviser Kevin Watt (Apr 2002) ▪ 11 ha (cabs s/f, merlot, shiraz, viognier) ▪ 500 cs 100% red ▪ PO Box 566 Franschhoek 7690 ▪ winemaker@lynxwines.co.za ▪ www.lynxwines.co.za ℂ 867·0406 📠 *867·0397*

Spanish-born Dieter Sellmeyer admires the modern wines of rugged Priorato (it's said they get wine out of a stone). But he's relishing the lushness of Wemmershoek farm Lusthof, overlooking the Simonsberg. On the property are immaculate vineyards (Kevin Watt advises), citrus orchards, paddocks, stables and a showjumping arena (he's a keen equestrian, surviving concussion and various broken body parts 'I couldn't even blame on winetasting'). A winemaker via a vinicultural product supply business, Sellmeyer works in a small but functional cellar using traditional methods and equipment. Resolutely low-tech, he's planning to introduce concrete fermenters. Packaging is particularly elegant.

★★★★★ **Shiraz 03** a fine debut: sumptuous yet elegantly restrained (though 14.1% alc). Spicy, pepper, cassia notes. Seamlessly integrated palate & lingering finish make for a striking presence. 11 mths oak, third new Am, rest Fr.

★★★★ **Cabernet Sauvignon** Super-ripe **03** (15.1% alc), with opulent blackcurrant aromas, succulent sweet tannins, elegant dry finish. 50% in open fermenter, 50% Fermentabag (an Oz invention). 11 mths Fr oak, 25% new.

★★★★ **Xanache 03** classic Bdx make-up: cab, merlot, cab f (64/22/14). Blackcurrant mulberry notes, sweet herbal spice. In youth, fruit restrained, oak evident (11 mths Fr, 25% new); should integrate with few yrs. 14.5% alc indicates ripeness. — *MF*

▨ *M23 see Bottelary Hills Wines*
Maankloof see Mountain River Wines
Madiba see Bovlei

Maiden Wine Cellars

Gordon's Bay ▪ Est 1995 ▪ 1stB 1999 ▪ Tasting/tours by appt; also tailor-made wine tours (max 6 people) ▪ Managing director Danie Hattingh ▪ 750 cs 100% red ▪ PO Box 185 Gordon's Bay 7151 ▪ www.maidenwines.com ℂ 082·554·9395 📠 *856·5085*

This negociant house historically had clients mainly in the US and Britain, but recently gained a foothold in the Middle East and Malaysia. To follow: China. The partners say they take great care to create blends specifically suited to their target markets, sometimes using wines from several regions to reach exactly the style they feel will be acceptable. Their own range has included a Private Reserve (red blend) and Chardonnay Sur Lie.

Main Street Winery

Paarl ▪ Est/1stB 1999 ▪ Tasting & tours by appt ▪ Owner/winemaker Marais de Villiers ▪ 500 cs 100% red ▪ PO Box 2709 Paarl 7620 ▪ mainstreet@mweb.co.za ℂ/📠 872·3006

With retailing facilities and a liquor licence finally becoming a reality, Marais de Villiers is now looking forward to offer cellar door sales at his small winery on Paarl's Main Street. (The premises are shared with a group of fellow *garagistes*.) While making his own wines, De Villiers is also a mentor to several newcomers and recent entrants to the wine-making game, supplying not only infectious enthusiasm and sage advice but also his inge-nious 'DIY' vinification system. Longer barrel maturation is now a feature here, as quickening sales enable De Villiers to invest in additional oak.

Shiraz 03, from barrel, aromatic & savoury dry red; smoky stewed plum aromas, gamey whiffs; full but well-mannered alc (14%). Possible ★★★★. All reds yr-16 mths 2nd fill Fr oak. **Merlot ★★★ 03** shy & slightly herbal; soft plummy fruit with hint liquorice. 14% alc.

Sauvignon Blanc NEW **04** (sample) bright, zingy but soft, with apple & pear aromas/flavours. Likely ★★★. This, version below, WO Dbnvlle.

Stoep range   NEW

Shiraz ★★★ 02 rather impressive opaque glassful; good peppery bouquet; black plummy palate touch austere on finish. 14.5% alc. **Merlot ★★★** Modern style: upfront smoky/tarry notes, dark choc fruit. Farewell slightly green & grainy. **Pinotage ★★★** With Bovril aroma & hint of prune. **02** shows quite a bit of tannin, so better with food. **Dry Red ★★★** Amiable 4-way blend with hint of ruby cab's thatch; more harmonious, easy-drinking than stablemates. NV. **Sauvignon Blanc ★★★ 04** (sample) lightish & very shy on nose; palate bit livelier, slightly sherbety. Might perk up with time. — *TM*

Major's Hill Winery   NEW

Robertson ▪ 1stB 2002 ▪ Tasting & sales Mon-Fri 9.30-4.30 Sat 10-4 ▪ Closed Apr 27, May 1, Jun 16, Aug 9, Sep 24 & Dec 16/25/26 ▪ Tours by appt ▪ Owners Louw brothers ▪ Winemaker Alkie van der Merwe, with Nico Renoster (both Jan 2003) ▪ Viti consultant Briaan Stipp ▪ 52 ha (cab, merlot, pinotage, shiraz, chard, sauvignon) ▪ 2 500 cs + 120 000ℓ bulk ▪ 60% red 40% white ▪ Range for customer: Martins Red (China) ▪ PO Box 561 Robertson 6705 ▪ info@majorshill.co.za ▪ www.majorshill.co.za ℗ (023) 626·6093 ☎ (023) 626·1043

In 1994, a good year for new beginnings, the Louws decided to sell their family construction business and buy Major's Hill farm, named after maj Kosie Marais, father of the famous Klipdrift brandy. Soon they became frustrated with the co-op system, but elected to postpone a bid for independence until they'd replanted the entire spread and seen the vines mature. Now they're ready to make a splash. Their maiden 03 sold out after only 7 months. Harvest 2004 delivered about 7 tons/ha — again a fairly modest yield, but deliberately so: bunches are hand-picked for 'colour and character, and treated with as much gentleness as a new baby', says winemaker Alkie van der Merwe (brother to Saxenburg's Nico). The offspring to watch is the merlot, AvdM advises. Once restored, the winetasting area will be moved to the original 'Klippies' cellar.

★★★★ **Merlot 03** mocha plum notes still dominated by oak (Yr 70/30 Fr/Am), though fine savoury fruit starting to emerge, offering coconut/raspberry succulence; lengthy finish bodes well for development. 14% alc well hidden by vinous character.

★★★★ **Pinotage** Varietally typical banana/varnish aromas on **03**, graced with some glacé cherry; smoky bouillon flavours, textured oaky finish. 14% alc. Very accessible already. **02** (★★★) more austere, with dense tannins & rather heavy finish. 13.7 alc. These ±yr in wood.

★★★★ **Sauvignon Blanc 04** herbaceous, greenpepper notes, with an austere, quite elegant dry palate; enough firm structure to allow good evolution. 13.5% alc.

Cabernet Sauvignon ★★★ Extra-ripe, soft **03** already showing some development. Caramel, blackcurrant aromas. With such ripeness, big 14.3% alc. Yr Fr (70%)/Am barrels.
Chardonnay Tank sample **04** (★★★★ rating very provisional) from youthful vines, ripe tropical, pineapple aromas. Still oaky from 3 mths in cask. Restrained 13.7% alc, but just dry — 4.2g/ℓ sugar lending round softness to finish. — *MF*

Makana see Cape First

Makro

See Specialist wine shops section for opening hours ▪ Enquiries Carolyn Barton ▪ cbarton@ makro.co.za ▪ www.makro.co.za ℗ (011) 797·0503 ☎ (011) 797·0366

Here's a one-stop wine shop: you'll find all you want, from everyday quaffing to special-occasion collectors' items (this retail giant is a regular big spender at the Nederburg Auction). Wine buyer Carolyn Barton points out that there's plenty on offer in 1.5ℓ bottles, and that best-value-for-money is the watchword when it comes to their in-house brands.

Makro is strong on wine events and promotions. Its goal is to nurture interest where it exists and gently introduce newcomers to the world of wine.

Private Reserve range

★★★★ **La Bri Cabernet Sauvignon Reserve** Winery showing much improved form in recent yrs. **02** well stocked with sweet ripe plums, milk choc hints; sappy oak (30% new Fr, 18 mths) shows on finish. Not for long keeping. 14.5% alc. WO Frhoek.

★★★★★ **Overgaauw Touriga Nacional-Cabernet Sauvignon** ✓ **01**, elegant & characterful 67/33 blend showing its class with extra yr in bottle; heady bouquet of spicy dried herbs, lots of complexity & flavour. Plenty of life ahead. 18 mths oak.

★★★★ **Yellowwood Ridge Cabernet Sauvignon-Merlot** ✓ Made by Vergelegen's André v Rensburg. **01** 58/42 blend, 16 mths Fr barriques. Lovely lucid, claret-like feel (cassis, cigarbox, lead pencils); finely tuned, elegant fruit. WO Stbosch.

★★★★ **Truter's Reserve** From Beyerskloof's Beyers T. Blend of cab & merlot (70/30) in pvs **01**, ripe red-berried wine with softish tannins. Had more to give than current **02** (★★★☆), sound but leaner fruit, grainy dry tannins. 6-8 mths oak, none new.

★★★☆ **Hill & Dale Malbec** Made by Guy Webber at Stellenzicht; **01** maturing attractively; big, ripe plummy mouthful, good savoury finish with meaty/gamey whiffs. Yr large Fr vats. 13.5% alc. WO Stbosch.

★★★☆ **Landskroon Merlot-Cabernet Franc 02** sophisticated wine, improving in bottle; bramble aromas; soft, juicy palate; lightly Fr oak staved, 71/29 ratio. **03** (★★★★) ✓ obvious but delicious; Xmas pud tones with cinnamon. WO Paarl.

★★★☆ **Villiera Cabernet Sauvignon-Merlot** Elegant, med-bodied **01** has bramble red fruit aromas, wild-hedgerow-fruit flavours; harmonious & tasty. Fr oak, 40% new.

Hill & Dale Cabernet Franc ★★★★ Sparingly wooded (large vats, yr) to amplify spicy/thatchy aromatics. **01** bright blackcurrant aromas; sweet plump fruit, elegant slightly leafy goodbye. **Morgenhof Estate Private Bin 44 Chardonnay** NEW ★★★ Crowd-pleaser by Rianie Strydom; her Mrgnhf version similar to this **03**, sweet (5g/ℓ), fruit-driven; finishes with crème brûlée richness. Portion oaked. EW, WO Stbosch. Following available, not ready for tasting: **Flagstone Strata Series Cape Blend 02**, **Misty Mountain** (white blend in 1ℓbottle, ex-Bon Courage), **Boplaas Private Bin Port** (1.5ℓ).

Babbling Brook range

Pinotage ☺ ★★★ Easy-drinking **02** has a big, sweet bouquet of mulberry jam, slightly meaty palate with fair amount of oak. Made by Horse Mountain. WO Paarl.

Shiraz ★★★★ Latest **02** switches to Fr oak, 20% new; piquant red fruit flavours; elegant, soft fruity finish. From Bon Courage. WO Rbtsn. Not ready for tasting: **Cabernet Sauvignon**, **Merlot**, **Chardonnay** & **Sauvignon Blanc**.

Mont d'Or range

Brut Busy fizz with some interest; touch lime adds freshness, dryness softened by dab sugar. **Demi Sec** Sweeter version with pretty touch of muscat, nice freshness. **Doux** Wafting muscat spice, fresh-faced & light, sweet & very soft. All ★★, ±11.5% alc. NV.

Turtle Creek range

This line-up of easy-drinkers temporarily unavailable.

Thomas Kipling range

Cabernet Sauvignon ★★★ A satisfying, plummy drink, made more attractive by being true to variety & well oaked (all Fr, 30% new, 16 mths). **02** is by Stellenbosch Hills (WO Stbosch). **Merlot** ★★★★ **01** will appeal widely; smooth, soft overripe plum succulence, touch of savoury for food cordiality, dry finish. Used Fr oak. By Bon Courage (WO Rbtsn), as is... **Shiraz** ★★★ 20% new oak (Fr) fairly obvious on **02**, but spicy redcurrant fruit holds its ground; Karoo bush whiffs will please fans of aromatic styles. — *TM/IvH*

Malan Family Vintners

Colourfully and simply attired export range by the Malan brothers of Simonsig.

Sauvignon Blanc ☺ ★★★ Revisited **03** has retained its leafy, grassy vibrancy, palate's tangy freshness. Enjoy solo, or as food partner. 12.4 alc. **Cape Blanc** ☺ ★★★ Step up on pvs; tropical fruits, appealing aromatics, softly rounded tasty palate. Colombard/semillon blend, soupçon riesling, morio muscat. NV. 12.3% alc.

Pinotage ★★★ **02** more complexity than pvs: macerated cherries, plums, with smoky, scrubland nuances. Savoury, chewy palate; ripe tannins with structure to age 3+ yrs. 14. 4% alc. Lightly oaked, as is… **Cabernet Sauvignon-Merlot** ★★★ 53/47 blend, **03** dark fruited, toasty, roasted vegetables, structured for earlier drinking. ±14% alc. **Cape Rouge** ★★ NV, mainly pinotage (85%), mix other reds. Appealing red berry/rhubarb, gently oak-spiced. Easy, juicy, quaffing style. 13.1% alc. **Chardonnay** ★★★ All the ingredients for uncomplicated drinking enjoyment. **03** trademark lemon butter on toast, roundly appealing melon flavours, crisp finish. Lightly oaked. 13.6% alc. **Sauvignon Blanc-Semillon** ★★★ **04** more sauvignon than pvs (66%), adding green fig, gooseberry pungency, while retaining light-textured accessibility. 12.5 alc. WO Stbosch. — CR

Mankazana see Ross Gower Wines

Manley Private Cellar

Tulbagh ▪ Est/1stB 2002 ▪ Tasting & sales daily 9-5 ▪ Fee R15 ▪ Cellar tours 10 & 3 ▪ Closed Dec 25th ▪ Light picnic hampers (or BYO) ▪ Luxury B&B ▪ Gifts ▪ Farm produce ▪ Conferencing ▪ Walks ▪ Owner/winemaker/viticulturist David Jordan, advised by Pierre Wahl (Jan 2003) ▪ 8 ha (cabs s/f, merlot, mourvèdre, pinotage, shiraz) ▪ Target: 4 000 cs 85% red 15% white ▪ PO Box 318 Tulbagh 6820 ▪ info@manleywines.co.za ▪ www.manleywines.co.za ① (023) 230·0582 ☎ (023) 230·0057

There's still a fair bit of wine being made amidst all the other activities at luxurious Hunter's Retreat Guest House in Tulbagh. Retired sailor David Jordan's third vintage produced excellent fruit, though was lighter than expected at under 5 tons/ha. His mainly red vineyards have proved pretty shipshape, having previously earned their stripes under other wineries' labels. Jordan's cellar first-mate is Pierre Wahl from nearby Rijk's.

★★★★ **Shiraz 03** (★★★★) raspberry/pepper notes with mineral element. Sweet mid-palate fruit still overwhelmed by oak (15 mths 60/40 Am/Fr, some new). 14.3% alc. **02** more evident berry fruits, along with earthy notes; dense & well rounded.

★★★★ **Pinotage 03** tasted ex-barrel. Sweet raspberry whiffs, along with coconut notes. Softly opulent mid-palate, featuring refined tannins, persistent flavours. Satisfyingly mouthfilling — helped by 14.8% alc. 16 mths barrel matured 50% Am.

Cabernet Sauvignon NEW ★★★ Carefully made **03** offering cassis/marzipan spice; herbal mid-palate, dense & chunky, with dry tannins. Finish marked by oak (15 mths Fr, 70% new). 14.3% alc. **Merlot** NEW ★★★ **03** introduced by savoury mulberry & smoky aromas. Now dominated by influence of oak (yr Fr, half new), unpolished tannins abounding. Paarl YWS's champ wooded red. 14% alc. **Sauvignon Blanc** NEW ★★ **03** herbal & slightly austere. Dry, with moderate 13.1% alc. WO Coastal. — MF

MAN Vintners

Paarl ▪ Est/1stB 2001 ▪ Tasting & sales by appt ▪ Owner MAN Vintners (Pty) Ltd ▪ Winemaker Tyrrel Myburgh ▪ Viti consultant Pieter Smit (2003) ▪ 120 ha (cab, shiraz, merlot) 40 000 cs own ranges + 15 000 cs for Pangolin ▪ 70% red 30% white ▪ PO Box 389 Stellenbosch 7599 ▪ info@manvintners.co.za ▪ www.manvintners.co.za ① 886·7532 ☎ 887·4340

'We suppose that, like many men, MAN has expanded a bit over the years,' say these partners in wine (brothers Tyrrel and Philip Myburgh of Joostenberg and José Condé of

Stark-Condé). Their business has burgeoned from a modest shipment to Japan in 2001 to 40 000 cases in 9 countries. It's poised to grow some more: during a chat with Charles Back of Fairview, they realised they were in agreement about most things vinous and, by the end of the first beer, a deal was struck. 'Charles brings his enthusiasm, energy and a range of new grape sources to the party.' Their new top-tier Sénga ('to milk' in Xhosa, in-spired by the former dairy farms in the Muldersvlei area where the wines are made) got off to a cracking start with the maiden Shiraz winning gold at the IWC. You can buy the wines at cellar-door prices at Joostenberg and nearby Klein Joostenberg Bistro.

Sénga range

NEW

★★★☆ **Shiraz** Bright, modern, immediately pleasing **02**, with 15% infusion of cab. Touch of perfume on fruity nose; mouthfillingly intense, tasty & well-structured, with big 15% alc adding undeniable weight. For drinking now, next few yrs. IWSC gold.

Merlot & Cabernet Sauvignon 02 ★★★ Attractive, firmly built 60/40 blend, savoury & substantial. Big, slightly heavy 14.7% alc. Appealingly modest wooding — yr Fr, mostly 2nd/3rd fill. Like above, from Muldersvlei grapes. **Limited Release Merlot & Shiraz** discontinued.

Standard range

★★★★ **Cabernet Sauvignon** ✓ Spicy, blackcurrant aromas lead to **03**'s fresh savoury palate, with persistent sweet fruit well supported by gentle tannin & unobscured by 6 mths older oak. Honest, unpretentious & winning. 13.6% alc.

Chardonnay ☺ ★★★ Very decent **03** now blossoming, with plentiful fruit giving dried peach, citrus; moderate 12.7% alc, enlivening acidity. Minimal wood; dash sauvignon.

Pinotage ★★★ Still youthful **03** (with dollop shiraz) offers lush ripe aromas, soft mouthfilling flavours, well-balanced gentle tannins. Briefly oaked; 14.2% alc. **Shiraz** ★★★ Rich ripeness on engaging **03**, & full, baked flavours with earthy touch, but finishes dry & a little hard. Includes dashes cab, merlot. 6 mths Fr oak; 14% alc. **Chenin Blanc** ★★★ **04** from old Paarl vines, a little viognier added. Easy-going, fresh, lightly fruity; unchallenging 12.1% alc. **Sauvignon Blanc** ★★★ **04** pale, light-bodied (mere 12.2% alc), vaguely pungent greengage/grassy flavours, nicely crisp. — TJ

Marcel de Reuck see Crows Nest
Marianne Wine Farm see Mont Destin
Marimba see Kosie Möller Wines

Marklew Family Wines

Stellenbosch ▪ 1stB 2003 ▪ Visits by appt ▪ Tourgroups (max 20) ▪ Walks ▪ Mountain biking ▪ Conservation area ▪ Owners Marklew family (Edward Dudley, Edward William, Lyn & Haidee) ▪ Winemaker Duan Brits, with Wikus Pretorius & Haidee Marklew (all Jan 2003) ▪ Viticulturists Billy Marklew & Duan Brits (Jun 2001/Jan 2003), advised by Cobus van Graan ▪ ±45 ha (cab, merlot, pinotage, chard, sauvignon) ▪ ±300 tons 2 700 cs own label 95% red 5% white ▪ PO Box 17 Elsenburg 7607 ▪ wine@marklew.co.za ▪ www.marklew. co.za ©/🖅 884·4412

When Dudley and Lyn Marklew bought the farm De Goede Sukses ('Good Success') 35 years ago, far-sightedly replanting with new varieties, they could not have known 'the bug' would bite their two children. Yet the elder Marklews had hardly retired when off-spring Bill and Haidee sprang into action, renovating the 180 year old cellar. Two vintages later they made their first wines, released last year. The farm still sells off most of its crop, but a few rows in every block are singled out for the Marklew label. Young winemaker Duane Brits (ex-Muratie) advocates balance in blending. His goal — 'to offset fruity youth with structure' — an appropriate metaphor for the relationship between the generations here. 'Dudley and Lyn have a lot more faith in us than we do,' says Bill M. But then they know 'Good Success' when they see it.

★★★★ **Capensis Reserve** Stringent barrel selection in **03** strongly influenced cab/merlot blend (62/31), with splash pinotage for 'Capeness' (efficacy indeterminate). Plush cassis, plum scents; elegantly fresh; velvety, serene tannin backing; classy oak buff. Good growth potential. Components in separate oak 10 mths, 5 more as blend. Classically dry, easing heavier effects of ±14% alc.

★★★★ **Cabernet Sauvignon 03** brilliant, healthy hue; bright, focused cassis purity, complementary oak spice; svelte, fashioned frame. Demurely elegant — oomph perhaps from time in bottle. 10 mths new/old oak.

★★★★ **Merlot 03** ripe plum temptation; invitingly fresh, no harshness, sensitively oaked (10 mths new/older Fr). Pleasurable, but lacks substance, complexity for long haul.

★★★★ **Chardonnay 04** all popular attractions (bar extra sugar!), without blowsiness, overkill. Dry, roast hazelnut, ripe melon flair; balanced palate weight, richness, lively, fruity acids. Uncomplicated yet more than satisfying. Fermented/5 mths 2nd-fill oak.

Following NEW **04**s sampled ex-barrel, should rate min ★★★★. **Pinotage** Assertive crimson, less outspoken minerally red fruit, enhanced by good Fr oak (20% new). Big, agile, bone-dry as is... **Shiraz** Seriously intended, in restrained, classic mode. Lilies, dark savoury spice delicacy; mellifluous feel, secured by super-fine, firm tannins. Fr & Am oak, 50% new.—*AL*

Marthinus see Bovlei
Martins Red see Major's Hill
Maskam see WestCorp

Mason's Hill Wines

Paarl • Est/1stB 2001 • Visits by appt; tasting/sales also at I Love Wine (see Wine shops section) • Owner Mason's Hill Wines (Pty) Ltd • Winemaker Derek Clift • 10 tons 700 cs 100% red • PO Box 515 Suider-Paarl 7624 • dehoop@mweb.co.za ✆ 863·1710 🖷 863·1601

'To make a wine that is not bounded or classified according to market preferences or ideologies.' That's the rationale behind this micro-winery, specialising in shiraz and owned by table-grape and olive oil producer Derek Clift. Since the previous vintage he's doubled production (something of a trend among SA's *garagistes*) and formed a limited liability company to accommodate all this vinous activity. Written into the business plan are 4ha of new plantings on Paarl Mountain.

★★★★ **Shiraz** Flamboyant, opulent, powerful (14.5% alc) Barossa-style **02** (retasted) will appeal to fans of such wines. Sweet raspberry fruit, juicy textures, whiffs of coconut from Am oak. Mostly older oak, 60/40 Fr/Am. Drinking well now.—*MF*

Matzikama Organic

Olifants River • Est 1999 • 1stB 2001 • Closed to public • Owner/winemaker/viticulturist Klaas Coetzee • 3 ha (cab, shiraz) • 180 cs 100% red • PO Box 440 Vredendal 8160 • info@ matzikamawyn.co.za • www.matzikamawyn.co.za ✆ 082·801·3737

To get the best out of his grapes, Klaas Coetzee farms organically and, says he, pays meticulous attention to timing, particularly, of course, during harvest. Last year the timing was perfect, with quality equal to that of 2001, the year the Elsenburg graduate first made wine. Unlike bigger cellars which can use different blocks to 'build' flavour, Coetzee works with one block per variety, which means each release has the season and site well and truly cooked into its character, as he puts it. Last year Coetzee vinified his first Cab. No doubt it will reveal exactly what cooked in 2004.

Shiraz Warm rich mulberry, subtle oak support, soft ripe tannins in **02**, touch damp earth on finish, delicious drinking. Retasted mid-2004 deserves a notch up; re-rated to ★★★. Yr oak, 80/20 Am/Fr oak. Follow-up **03** ★★★ lighter, red berries, less flavoursome, wisely given less oak — 8 mths, 60/40 Fr/Am. — *IvH*

Mauroma Winery

Walker Bay ▪ Est 2002 ▪ Visits by appt ▪ Fee R10 ▪ Roses (in season) & olives for sale ▪ 2 self-catering guest houses ▪ Winemakers Maurice 'Jacko' & Melanie Jackson ▪ Viti consultant Schalk du Toit ▪ 4 ha (pinotage) ▪ 300-600 cs 100% red ▪ PO Box 23 Stanford 7210 ▪ mauroma@itec. co.za Ⓒ (028) 341·0841 ☎ (028) 341·0286

Untimely rain disrupted the 2004 harvest on surrounding farms but somehow missed the small patch tended by Maurice 'Jacko' Jackson and his daughter Melanie. Not that a bit of bad weather would throw this retired airline pilot. He's been watching his first-release Pinotage fly out of his winery (a hangar, appropriately), and nothing will stop him now. While many are punting shiraz as the most exciting growth market for SA reds, Jackson remains a firm advocate of pinotage — 'the hand-crafted variety', he qualifies, 'with a flavour even those who don't like pinotage love'. No prizes for guessing which Pinotage he's referring to.

★★★★ **Jackson's Pinotage** Attractively light-toned, alluding to grape's pinot parentage; **02** reined-in but soft, supple, well fruited. Delicious **03** (★★★★) again with pinot-like undergrowth on nose, whiffs cherry & vanilla; elegant & juicy, good taut acidity. 11 mths Fr oak, 33% new. 14% alc. — *TM*

Maze Valley see Doolhof

McGregor Winery

Robertson ▪ Est 1948 ▪ 1stB 1978 ▪ Tasting & sales Mon-Thu 8-12.30; 1.30-5 Fri 8-5 Sat 9-2 ▪ Closed Easter Fri/Sun, Apr 27, May 1, Dec 16/25/26 & Jan 1 ▪ Owners 42 members ▪ Manager/winemaker Jacques du Toit, with Chris Smit (Aug/Dec 2002) ▪ Viticulturist Anton Laas (Dec 2000) ▪ 680 ha ▪ 11 000 tons 30% red 65% white 3% rosé 2% other ▪ PO Box 519 McGregor 6708 ▪ mcg@intekom.co.za ▪ www.mcgregorwinery.co.za Ⓒ (023) 625·1741/1109 ☎ (023) 625·1829

Looking for great little quaffers at glee-inducing prices? This winery might have just the thing. Its Pinotage sells from the cellar at R24 a bottle; not surprisingly, it made *Wine's* 2004 list of value-for-money reds — in fact, was one of the top three. More ammunition for the campaign headed by Quintus Basson (ex-WineCorp), marketing manager of the newly established McGregor Wine Company, in which the co-op's 42 members are the main shareholders. The company's job is to promote the McGregor brand nationally. Integral to that is a move from more than a half-century of bulk trading to bottled sales.

Winemaker's Reserve range

★★★★ **Cabernet Sauvignon** Handsomely packaged & seriously structured; from a single vyd, ±14 mths Fr barrelled. **01** food wine featured bright fruit, elegant fine-grained tannins. **02** complex notes of vanilla, cassis & plum pudding; more body, complexity than reds below; soft, supple dry finish. 14% alc.

Chardonnay ★★★ **04** (sample) shy green melon & marzipan whiffs; soft, juicy melon fruit, toffee hint from fermentation/brief ageing on Fr oak. **Sauvignon Blanc** 🆕 ★★☆ **04** grapefruit & quince flavours, rounded, fruity; nutty nuance from fermentation on oak; atypical, but an appealing drinking wine.

McGregor range

Colombard ☺ ★★★ Super picnic wine. **04** effusive guava/floral notes; touch greenpepper, light body, off-dry. **Colombard-Chardonnay** ☺ ★★★ **04** (sample) lively tropical passionfruit & guava aromas; delicious tropical flavours; just-dry, just-right acidity. 50/50 blend.

Pinotage ★★★ **03** strawberry aromas & pinot-like hint undergrowth; lighter easy-drinking mould; sweet-fruited finish. **Ruby Cabernet** ★★☆ Appealing lunchtime quaffer. **02**

smoky aromas, quite firm, medium body, tangy. **Shiraz** NEW ★★★ Shy dusty red fruits on nose, plump black plums in mouth with tobacco, dry savoury finish. 14% alc. **Cabernet Sauvignon-Merlot** ★★★ 02 wild bramble fruit, medium texture with hint dark choc, lick cedar-oak on finish; lightly oaked; 14.5% alc. **Chardonnay** ★★★ Unwooded 04 wafts peach blossom & sweet melon; supple, full & ripe melon flavour; appealing quick-quaff. **Chenin Blanc** ★★ 04 shy apple & pear aromas/flavours; crisp & quite lean. **Sauvignon Blanc** ★★★ Light bodied, for early drinking. 04 shy herby nose, hint of nettle; juicy, sweetly fruited guava palate. **Late Harvest Bouquet** ★ 03 from colombard, muscadel, after extra yr in bottle shows baked apple aromas, very soft sweetness. **Brut** ★★★ Carbonated sparkler from chenin; NV. Big, vigorous bubbles, lemon-zest flavours, smoothly dry rather than brut. **Red Muscadel** ★★★★ Retasted 03, brilliant pinkish ruby; gorgeous spicy nose of potpourri & tea-leaves, Turkish Delight & allspice flavours. 17% alc. **White Muscadel** ★★★ Sweet-scented 03, yr on, has huge petally/spicy nose, hint of mint; light body, peachy fruit, nice apricot-toned acidity. 17% alc. **Cape Ruby** ★★★ Still-available 02, from ruby cab; retaste shows maturing dried fruit/raisin aromas, varnish notes; holding together, won't fall over in next yr/2. 18% alc. — *TM*

MC Square

Est/1stB 1996 ▪ *Closed to public* ▪ *Winemaker/viticulturist Jean-Luc Sweerts* ▪ *300 cs 100% white* ▪ *PO Box 436 Somerset West 7129* ▪ *mcsquare@iafrica.com* ℂ *083·303·5467* 🖷 *852·7740*

He's not a *winemaker*, says Jean-Luc Sweerts, who started his vocation as a *provider of dreams* (his suggested alternative) at Uitkyk near 30 years ago. 'Allow your sensitivity to take over,' he advises, let intuition guide you and be 'ferociously protective of those outstanding barrels and vineyards instead of blending them away'. Using a classic, 'no rush' technique, he focuses on his award-winning Chardonnay, vinifying Franschhoek grapes in a boutique winery on Cape Town's foreshore.

★★★★ **Cuvée Chardonnay** Subtitle – 'Méthode Classique' – sets tone for both vintages tasted to date: **00** fine honeyed patina to elegant marmalade/apricot tones; peaking, must drink. **01** fuller, richer, more youthfully citrus-fruited with attractive hints toast on nose/palate. Yr Fr barriques, ±20% new; bottle-aged extra yr. — *IvH*

Meander see Groot Eiland

Meerendal Estate

Durbanville ▪ *Est 1702* ▪ *1stB 1969* ▪ *Tasting Mon-Fri 10-7 Sat 10-5 Sun 11-4* ▪ *Fee R10 per person, refunded on purchase of 6 btls* ▪ *Closed Easter Fri & Dec 25* ▪ *Attractions/amenities: see intro* ▪ *Owners AW Bester, HN Coertze, JG Adriaanse, AF Swanepoel, R Truter & CG Stride* ▪ *Winemaker Riaan van der Spuy, with Liza Goodwin (Aug 2004/Nov 1998)* ▪ *Viti adviser Paul Wallace (Aug 2004)* ▪ *142 ha (cab, merlot, pinotage, shiraz, chard, chenin, gewürz, sauvignon)* ▪ *±1 000 tons 25 000 cs 80% red 20% white* ▪ *Private Bag X1702 Durbanville 7551* ▪ *info@meerendal.co.za* ▪ *www.meerendal.co.za* ℂ *975·1655* 🖷 *975·1657*

A complete revamp is underway for an estate which perhaps has yet to realise its potential. Purchased by a syndicate of businessmen in 2004, Meerendal has a new winemaker (Riaan van der Spuy, ex-L'Ormarins) and viticultural adviser Paul Wallace. The upgraded cellar and visitor facilities, due for completion in May, include a new tasting centre, deli (for picnics), children's facilities (including nannies), gift shop, conference centre and three new restaurants: the fine dining Wheatfields, buffet-style Starke's Barn & Lawn and the Bistro. Last year's climatic vagaries resulted in uneven ripening. But due to careful hand-picking, the wines are developing 'great fruit flavours reflecting the unique Durbanville terroir' as new GM Bennie Howard, for many years the Nederburg Auction manager, puts it. With this vintage bottled under restyled labels, it appears the resurrection is on schedule.

★★★★ **Cabernet Sauvignon-Merlot** ✓ The renamed 'Cabochon'. **03** in glass shows a lovely bright edge; whiffs cocoa & cigarbox, hint mulberry; modern, lots of ripe fruit, finishes almost dry; plump, silky wine, will have many fans. Yr Fr oak, 2nd/3rd fill. Pvs was elegant & poised **01**, serious wine which needed time to develop.

★★★☆ **Cabernet Sauvignon 03** continues & elaborates on flamboyance of strapping **02**, which boasted 15.5% alc. **03** is a cassis fruit bomb — ripeness taken to the edge; huge mouthful jammy fruit, pulpy fruit-cordial aromas, unsophisticated yet not charmless; yr small Fr oak, 14.2% alc.

★★★☆ **Merlot 02** & pvs releases have shared a sinewy character, ungenerous dark-choc flavour profile. Auspicious vintage **03** (★★★★) ✓ might herald a turnaround: impressively deep & dark; pencilbox whiff; plump, sweet, very ripe plum fruit, wood still prominent but should settle with time. 14.5% alc. Yr Fr oak, 20% new.

★★★☆ **Pinotage** 2 vintages tasted: **01** low-key bouquet but full body, taut mulberry flavours; elegant, earlier drinkable than slightly austere **02**, with powdery tannins, refined sour mulberry flavours. Both yr Fr casks, some new.

★★★☆ **Shiraz** In bygone days the estate's calling card; latest pair of releases not as impressive; **01** muted sage whiffs, sour plum flavours, grainy tannins but wood more controlled than in **02** (★★★), with almost pinot-like aromas, dry stalky finish. 14.2% alc. Yr Fr oak, mostly new.

Chardonnay Waxy baked apple tones on **04**; peachy/tropical fruit tastes, quite a mouthful, balanced by taut & zippy acidity; too young to rate but promising. **Sauvignon Blanc** ★★★★ **04** newly bottled, shows dusty nettle & fig aromas; firm lime/grapefruit flavours, dry flinty tail, structure to develop. **Natural Sweet** ★★★★ **02** from gewürz, soft Turkish Delight aromas, lemony flavour, well-toned sweetness. 14.9% alc. **Gewürztraminer**, **Liberté** & **Blanc de Blanc** discontinued. — *TM*

Meerhof Winery

Swartland ▪ Est/1stB 2000 ▪ Tasting & sales Mon-Fri 9-4.30 Sat 10-2 ▪ Fee R5 ▪ Closed Easter Fri-Sun, Dec 25 & Jan 1 ▪ Meals by appt, or BYO picnic ▪ Tours by appt ▪ Owners Gert & Kobus Kotzé ▪ Winemaker Wrensch Roux (Jan 2003) ▪ ±65 ha (cab, merlot, pinotage, shiraz, chard) ▪ ±320 tons 90% red 10% white ▪ PO Box 1229 Malmesbury 7299 ▪ meerhof@ waccess.co.za ⓒ (022) 487·2524 🖷 (022) 487·2521

Having previously sold all their grapes from their vineyards on the crest of Bothmaskloof Pass between Malmesbury and the Riebeek Valley, Kobus and Gert Kotzé now pursue an independent route. They have their own cellar and a new tasting locale where visitors may sample the wines. Last harvest very dry weather resulted in disease-free vines. Luckily the chardonnay was harvested before the heatwave, says winemaker Wrensch Roux. The reds are ripe and show dark, fruity flavours.

★★★★ **Shiraz** First vintage from young vines was a cracker: **00** fruit-driven, richly flavoured with good length & well-meshed oak (2 yrs new Fr). Current **02** oak-lashed; all pencil shavings & spice; moderate blackberry flavours battle against the wood mid-04. Sample rates ★★★, but could settle, improve. ±14.5% alc.

Cabernet Sauvignon NEW ★★★ Focused, pure-fruited **02** has clean, sweet red fruit aromas, reprised on palate with cassis; firm, slightly dry tannins. **Shiraz-Cabernet Sauvignon** ★★ **02** interesting layered bouquet of fresh-crushed berries, game & forest floor; missing some juice on palate; shortish dry finish. **Pinotage** ★★★ Last tasted was **01** with well-shaped body; full, fine flavours needing time to soften, develop. **Rosé** NEW ★★★ Pale fuchsia-hued **04** (sample), rose-petal & strawberry coulis aromas; refreshing dry finish. Perfect for a hot summer's day. **Chardonnay** ★★★ **04** better balanced than pvs, more zing, less wood; finishes with chamomile-citrus twist. — *JB*

Meerland see Baarsma

Meerlust Estate

Stellenbosch ▪ Est 1693 ▪ 1stB 1975 ▪ Tasting by appt ▪ Fee R60 ▪ Sales Mon-Thu 9–5 Fri 9–4.30 ▪ Tours by appt ▪ Closed public holidays ▪ Owner Hannes Myburgh ▪ Winemaker Chris Williams (Jan 2004) ▪ Viticulturist Roelie Joubert, advised by Paul Wallace (both 2001) ▪ 110 ha (cabs s/f, merlot, pinot, chard) ▪ 600 tons ±50 000 cs 90% red 10% white ▪ PO Box 15 Faure 7131 ▪ info@meerlust.co.za ▪ www.meerlust.co.za © **843·3587** 🖷 843·3274

After 26 years as Meerlust's cellarmaster, Giorgio Dalla Cia last year bid farewell to the Myburghs, 'a Renaissance family supporting me, an artist, and letting me express myself'. An Italian committed to making wine in the French manner, '30 years ago Italy wasn't ready for it'. Dalla Cia found 'an Afrikaner [Nico Myburgh], here in the Cape of all places, who wanted me to help him make a Bordeaux blend'. Rubicon, the wine they created, became an icon. Rejoins Myburgh scion, Hannes: 'My father's supposed 'difficultness' stemmed from his frustration at trying to do things right while so many others could not be bothered… Giorgio helped him do things right.' Happily, there is a sense of continuity with the return 'home' of 'prodigal son' Chris Williams, Dalla Cia's assistant for six vintages until 2000. Viewed as a traditionalist, this confident, enthusiastic young winemaker intends taking Meerlust to the next level, exploiting 'superb fruit from a recent replanting programme by trying dozens of new techniques. We want to make Meerlust wines more distinctive in expressing terrain identity'. After three decades of winemaking, Meerlust, like all greats, will tackle the new age with aplomb.

★★★★★ **Rubicon** One of early Cape Bdx royals — now celebrating quarter century (with this guide!). Regality evident in **00**'s deep, polished robe; imposing yet unintimidating vinous mélange with cedary decoration. Sleek, agreeably fresh, medium-bodied. Present tannic grip suggests no problem 'losing' this for another 6 yrs. **99** dusty, cedar/tobacco notes, fruit still trussed up by lacy tannins. 70% cab, 20% merlot, 10% cab f; 2 yrs Fr oak, 80% new. **98** *Decanter* ★★★★.

★★★★ **Merlot** As with above, brilliant velvety sheen on **00** invites further inspection. Reveals genteel, spice-dusted mocha tones, traditional in lack of puffery, modern in ripe, fresh purity. Fine, compact frame (10% cab stiffening) yields persuasive hints violets; still gripped by dry tannin. Greater succulence may evolve with further 3/6 yr maturation. **99**, voluptuous chewy. 18 mths Fr oak.

★★★★ **Pinot Noir** (No longer with 'Reserve' in name) Positive ruby clarity heralds fresh, fleshy style. Replicated on **00** (★★★★★) in delicate crushed black cherry, newly fallen-leaf fragrance, flavours. Structured tannins more obviously solid than suggested in pvs ed; needs yr/2 to unleash further delights. **99** aromatic, accessible mushroom wildness. 15 mths Fr oak (heavy-toast, tight-grain Allier). 13.5% alc.

★★★★ **Chardonnay** No pussy-footer. Since **95**, in bold, some would say overtly oxidative, oaky mode. **00**, decadent appley/roast hazelnut development, springs to life on palate via core minerality, sumptuous, textured surround. Needs/demands fine food. Legs for 2008. 19 mths Fr oak (100% barrelled). 14% alc. — *AL*

Meerrust see Allée Bleue

Meinert Wines

Stellenbosch (see Helderberg map) ▪ Est 1987 ▪ 1stB 1997 ▪ Tasting & sales at 96 Winery Road Restaurant (see Eat-out section) ▪ Owner/winemaker/viticulturist Martin Meinert ▪ 13.5 ha (cabs s/f, merlot, petit v, pinotage) ▪ 70 tons 5 000 cs 100% red ▪ PO Box 7221 Stellenbosch 7599 ▪ info@meinertwines.com ▪ www.meinert.co.za ©🖷 **865·2363**

Private, particular, philosophical: that's Martin Meinert the winemaker. Artist as well as technician, exceptionally adroit blender, he puts heart, soul, guts, intellect — and anything that's left — into his wines. Everything's carefully considered. The 2004 harvest? 'I prefer not to judge a red wine vintage so early but it was a difficult one to interpret, harrowing at times. Great? No, but just how good we still need to see.' He's added 1ha of cab franc and ½ha petit verdot to his red palette, and a smidgen of semillon is planned for a future white. (Let's not forget considerable merits of the chenins and sauvignons he makes with Ken Forrester.) A market slow-down and competition have driven this reluctant front-man out there: USA and Germany are his main destinations.

★★★★ Synchronicity The standard bearer. Barrel-selected cab, merlot, pinotage, cab f; 44/31/17/8 medley in **01** (★★★★★): enticing aromas echoed on smooth silky palate, masterly fruit/structure integration — seamless ensemble of enduring length. Bold (15% alc), rich & modern, yet still classic. Maiden **00** spotlighted bright fruit, oak vanilla, ripe tannins, imposing 14.4% alc. Now 2 yrs new Fr oak.

★★★★ Devon Crest Named after the beautiful Devon Valley ('amongst the best red grape sites in the world' avers Meinert) home-farm. Retasted **01** bright currant fruit well-napped in integrated structure; subtle, classy frame for rich flavours, replete with 15% alc. Sample **02** lighter toned, more accessible in youth. Cool s-facing vyds gaining gravitas; 63/37 cab/merlot blend. 18 mths new Fr oak. Age 4–6 yrs longer.

★★★★ Merlot An urbane & characterful table companion, loaded with panache. Wood-smoke veil screens red berry fruit of next **02**, tannins marshal good length of flavour. Despite 14.5% alc, slighter than sumptuous **01**, loaded with mulberries & polished tannins, finish bolstered by 15% alc. Need 5 yrs from harvest. 18 mths older Fr oak. — *DS*

Mellasat

Paarl ▪ Est 1996 ▪ 1stB 1999 ▪ Visits by appt, but encouraged ▪ BYO picnic ▪ Owner Stephen Richardson ▪ Winemaker/viticulturist Stephen Richardson, with Poena Malherbe ▪ 9 ha (cab, pinotage, shiraz, chenin) ▪ 90 tons 2 800 cs 85% red 15% white ▪ PO Box 7169 Paarl 7623 ▪ mellasat@mweb.co.za ▪ www.mellasat.com ©/✉ (021) 862·4525

The grapes, particularly pinotage and shiraz, strolled in on African time in 2004, sighs Norfolk-born Stephen Richardson. Ready to receive the dribs and drabs were visitors from the UK, who were 'inadvertently and innocently commandeered to help with the late night punch-downs', leaving Richardson to hold their cameras. The winemaker has started to ferment his reds in smaller batches in open bins to increase extraction. He's installed new tanks, and his next projects are a maturation store for bottled and cased wine, and, after a lengthy delay sourcing suitable vines, a new block of tempranillo.

Cabernet Sauvignon ★★★ Seems to have hardly changed since we tasted last yr; **01** still satisfying, easy drinking, tannins soft, berries flavourful. 20 mths Fr oak, 30% new. **Revelation NEW ★★★** Cab by another name; **02** red cherries plus touches leather & earth, supple tannins; individually styled — won't disappoint fans of this characterful winery. Unfiltered. 15 mths oak, 50/50 Fr/Am. 14.5% alc. **Pinotage ★★★ 02** has a touch of the house's wholesome earthiness, too; adds complexity to ripe plummy fruit. Yr Fr oak, 11% new. 14.4% alc. **Shiraz ★★★ 02** (sample) shows improved tannin management, providing supple platform for cherry/mulberry fruit, with hint eucalyptus. Should rate ★★★★ on release. 18 mths Am small-oak, 2nd fill. **Dekker's Valley Pinotage ★★★** D-V their 2nd label, aiming for an easy drinking style. With extra yr in bottle, **01** succeeds; muted pinotage character but a good fruity mouthful. 6 mths Am/Fr oak. **Dekker's Valley Chenin Blanc ★★ 04** quietly tropical, soft, gentle & lightish bodied. **Tuin Wyn ★★★** Straw wine from air-dried chenin grapes. **00**, which mellowed into velvet mouthful, was the last tasted. — *DH*

Merwespont Winery

Robertson (see map) ▪ Est 1956 ▪ Tasting & sales Mon-Thu 8–12.30; 1.30–5 Fri 8–12.30; 1.30–4.30 ▪ Closed public holidays ▪ Tours during harvest by appt ▪ BYO picnic ▪ Farm produce ▪ Owners 35 members ▪ Winemaker Esmarie Smuts (Jan 2002) ▪ Viti consultant Briaan Stipp (Jan 2000) ▪ 568 ha (cab, pinotage, ruby cab, shiraz, chard, sauvignon) ▪ 8 850 cs own labels 56% red 44% white ▪ PO Box 68 Bonnievale 6730 ▪ merwespont@lando.co.za © (023) 616·2800 ✉ (023) 616·2734

Sakkie Bosman, of the former Nuwehoop Winery, has taken over the management of this cellar to fill the gap left by veteran Dirk Cornelissen's retirement. A hot, humid ripening season resulted in a harvest slightly later than usual, but the winemaking team say they expect excellent quality, particularly in their reds, Chardonnay and Sauvignon. It's a friendly place to visit, and you're welcome to bring your own picnic and make a day of it.

Cabernet Sauvignon ★★★ Unlike pvs, no hint of oak on lightish 01; maturing ruby-red glints reflected in developed aromas of leather & raspberry coulis, pliable tannins. **Cabernet Sauvignon-Merlot** NEW ★★★ Marriage of two SAYWS champs, consummated in 2nd fill barrels, yr; expensive cinnamon/cigarbox spicing to juicy red fruit core; fairly assertive & dry tannins; tame with red meat. 14% alc. **Chardonnay** ★★★ 04 lovely melange of fresh & glacé fruit (melon, kumquat & pineapple); medium body; finishes crisp & very fresh. **Sauvignon Blanc** ★★★ Invariably swiggably light, for earliest enjoyment. **04** (sample) mown lawn & capsicum sniffs; elegant, pleasantly chalky flavours. Pvs **Special Late Harvest** and **Natural Sweet** not retasted.

Agulhas range

White ☺ ★★ Light, refreshing just-dry equal blend chenin, colombard, sauvignon, with pleasant honey & orange blossom aromas. Both NV.

Red ★★ Perky unwooded ruby cab/pinotage mix (50/50) to lightly chill & quaff solo or with food. Spicy nuttiness on nose, soft raspberry preserve flavours. Both WO Breede River, as is Sauvignon.—*JB*

Merwida see Riverstone Vineyards

Middelpos

Swartland ▪ Est 1978 ▪ 1stB 2001 ▪ Tasting & sales see Bellevue ▪ Owner Stephanus du Toit ▪ Vini/viti consultant Dirkie Morkel, with Wilhelm Kritzinger ▪ 57 ha ▪ 100% red ▪ PO Box 59 Riebeek West 7306 ▪ mariedut@mweb.co.za © (022) 461·2375 🖷 (022) 461·2042

Stephanus du Toit and wife Marie, a crafter specialising in quilts, grow mainly reds on their farm in the Riebeek West area. A soupçon of their pinotage finds its way into bottle under the farm name via brother-in-law Dirkie Morkel of Bellevue. To date an 01.

Middelvlei Estate

Stellenbosch ▪ Est 1919 ▪ 1stB 1973 ▪ Tasting & sales Mon-Sat 10-4.30 ▪ Fee R10 ▪ Closed Easter Fri & Dec 25 ▪ Tours by appt Feb & Mar ▪ Small conference facility ▪ Walks ▪ Owners Momberg family ▪ Winemaker Tinnie Momberg (Jan 1992) ▪ Viticulturist Ben Momberg (Jan 1992) ▪ 130 ha (cab, merlot, pinotage, shiraz, tinta, chard, sauvignon) ▪ 1 000 tons 35 000 cs own labels 95% red 5% white ▪ PO Box 66 Stellenbosch 7599 ▪ info@middelvlei.co.za ▪ www.middelvlei.co.za © 883·2565 🖷 883·9546

At this farm on the outskirts of Stellenbosch you'll find the extended Momberg family and their animals, including wallabies, miniature horses and pygmy goats. 'Young blocks of cabernet and merlot have come into production, and surprised us with their quality,' says Ben Momberg, keeper of these vineyards, where they've cut the yield back to a very low 4.5 ton/ha in almost all their top blocks, to up the calibre of the wines. 'The 04s are showing lots of fruit and colour with soft tannins,' says winemaker Tinnie Momberg. Thys Pietersen accompanied him to VinExpo in Bordeaux, a real eye-opener for this cellar foreman who'd never been further than a 100km from Stellenbosch.

★★★★ **Cabernet Sauvignon** Buyers of this wine (& some below) get the considerable benefit of extended estate bottle-maturation – 5 yrs in the case of still-listed **00**; uncorked mid-2004 shows its age attractively in fleeting meaty whiff. Will always be firmer, drier than **01** (★★★★), richer, better balanced, with characteristic austere note to help food-partnering qualities. A satisfying drink, shows a sense of place. 24–26 mths new wood, 25% Am for **01**.

★★★★ **Pinotage 01**, (★★★★) yr on, takes after the pinot parent — understated & elegant, soft strawberry tones, medium body; contrast with big, powerful (& ABSA

THE NEW PEUGEOT 407
PLAYTIME IS OVER

407

Glen Carlou

Having built Glen Carlou Vineyards into a Cape front-ranker over the past 20 years, **Walter Finlayson** and son **David** have now sold their share to long-time partners, the Swiss-based Hess Group. Continuing at the helm, David is overseeing major refurbishments including a new gallery housing part of big-businessman Donald Hess' private art collection.

Overgaauw

Celebrating 100 years of successful farming this year, the Van Velden family are planning 'a number of surprises', including updated livery for their often innovative wines (SA's first varietal Merlot among them). Not new, but perennially charming, is the broekie-laced tasting room where we pictured **Braam** and son **David** against a wintry backdrop of Stellenbosch mountains.

nomacorc®

THE NO.1 SELLING SYNTHETIC CORK IN SOUTH AFRICA

- No cork taint
- Controlled oxygen transfer
- No leakage
- Consistent extraction forces

Co-extrusion, a unique technology ...for a unique preservation.

MCG Industries
Pty (Ltd)

STAY OVER
AND CELEBRATE
THE MEMORY
FOR YEARS TO COME

With our charming winelands hotel, boutique spa and variety
of restaurants, including the unique Cape African experience of Moyo,
the Jonkershuis and Spier Deli, you may find that there simply aren't enough
hours in a day to experience all that Spier has to offer.

So why not stay over? Because, you'll find that Spier offers many other
unexpected pleasures. Like our Wine Centre that boasts an extensive selection
of the finest international and national wines, including our own award
winning Spier Private Collection. All catering for the discerning wine lover,
we'll ensure that every Spier experience is one to remember.

The Village
WINELANDS HOTEL

*To experience these and the many other pleasures
call us on +27 21 809 1100.
email: info@spier.co.za website: www.spier.co.za*

SPIER

Team Platter

The guide inaugurated by John and Erica Platter is now massaged into shape by a team whose size mirrors the growth of the SA wine industry. Raising a glass to 25 years of Platter at this year's five-star blind-tasting in Stellenbosch were, from left, **Irina von Holdt**, **Philip** and **Cathy van Zyl**, Andrew McDowall, Michael Fridjhon, Tony Mossop, Dave

Hughes, **Clive Torr**, **Neil Pendock**, **Tim James**, **Angela Lloyd**, **Steven Hobson** from auditors Fisher Hoffman PKF (CT), **Meryl Weaver**, **Jabulani Ntshangase** and **Dave Swingler**. Meeting tasting deadlines off-camera were **Christine Rudman** and **Richard Kelley**.

Meerlust

Looking as relaxed and jovial as ever is **Giorgio dalla Cia**, Meerlust cellarmaster for more than a quarter century, now a man of (relative) leisure after passing the baton to his sometime assistant, **Chris Williams** (left), free-ranging for some years and now delightedly 'home'. Home, a white-walled Cape-Dutch masterpiece, belongs to **Hannes Myburgh**, sensitively nudging this 300 year old estate to new heights.

Kanonkop

In a notoriously mercurial wine market, Kanonkop's ball-and-cannon emblem represents enduring and exceptional quality. **Beyers Truter**, the estate's winemaker and avuncular public persona since 1980, has handed over the reins to two young guns, **Abrie Beeslaar** and assistant **Jeremy Arries** (left), recent recipient of the Patrick Grubb study bursary. Behind them – a reassuring constant – is the peak that gives the farm its name.

YOUR COMPLETE WINE DESTINATION

Find great quality and incredible value in the vast range of wines available at your nearest Makro liquor store.

Award winners, auction offerings, special bottlings, large formats and great gifts are all on offer alongside super wines for everyday enjoyment, all at great case prices.

Our wine advisors can assist you to locate the perfect wines to meet your requirements. Subscribe to our newsletter and enjoy news of latest releases and upcoming in-store tastings and events.

Get the card. Get the Best Deal in the World.

Classics. Since 1600.

The humble cork has been nurturing and protecting our most precious wines since the 17th century. And, thankfully, nothing has really changed since that time. A pure product of nature, like the wine it cares for, the cork has storage benefits that no amount of engineering can duplicate. It's light. Impermiable. Compresses to half its dimensions with no loss of flexibility. Its surface cells create 'suction cups', giving it a tight fit against glass. Temperature doesn't affect it, it doesn't age and it's biodegradable. And probably most important of all, it has over 400 years of classic vintages to its name!

Certificate No.PTG0940903
SABS ISO 9001:2000

ECI
EUROPEAN CORK INDUSTRIES
A growing force in cork technology and supply

(021)886 7709 www.eci-sa.co.za

EXPORTERS OF WINES FROM THE CAPE

YOUR WINESHOP IN THE VINEYARDS

THE VINEYARD
CONNECTION

Top 10-acclaimed) **00**, showing fruity rusticity & big tannins. 13.5% alc. 11-14 mths oak, mostly Fr, small percentage new. These should keep another 5 yrs.

★★★★ **Shiraz** Appealingly rustic **02** has one's nose follow a trail from gunsmoke through to hints of earth to forest floor, then to dense black plum on palate; fascinating; 21 mths oak, 42% Am; **01** was more harmonious than powerfully built **00**.

★★★★ **Pinotage-Merlot** Understandably popular blend; equal proportions in **00**, re-tasted, shows complexity & good bottle-age character; rich, silky; persistent tannins touch sweetish. 18 mths oak, 22% Am. 14.2% alc.

Chardonnay ★★★ **04** forthcoming fruit salad aromas; uncomplex but attractive, though some would like a touch more zip. 30% oak-fermented.

Hagelsberg range

Literally 'Hail Mountain', allusion to Stbosch's Papegaaiberg; mainly for export. **Merlot-Pinotage** ★★★ Estate's 2nd take on this blend not dumbed down: **02** refined spicy nose, soft, balanced, ripe blackberry taste. 50/50 mix. **Robyn** ★★★ Fruitily unpretentious & warmly engaging blend including tinta, cab, shiraz, pinotage – latter to fore in **03** retaste, with touch earthiness. – *TM*

Migration-Serengeti

Stellenbosch ▪ Closed to public ▪ PO Box 7210 Stellenbosch 7599 ▪ leidersburgwines@ intekom.co.za © **082·856·3560**

'Consumer-friendly but serious' wines styled by Stellenbosch negociant and winemaker Jan du Preez and partners in their bid to offer 'quality, exciting packaging and consistency'. Export destinations include the UK, Holland, Scandinavia and the US, where the range is known as Serengeti.

Pinotage ★★★★ **02** less flamboyant than pvs; ripe plum & banana on nose; palate neatly stacked with berries, juicy round tannins, good oak. Altogether, well pitched/presented. **Shiraz** ★★★★ 'A classy shiraz,' avers JdP. To us, **01** also agreeably old-fashioned, with leathery sniffs & hint of game; rounded, well-tuned palate, accessible. **Cabernet Sauvignon-Merlot** ★★★★ **03** classic nose of greenpepper & red berries; mellow & easy drinking, juicy tannins & mild alc (±13%) slip down comfortably. **Pinotage Rosé** ★★ Gentle red berry notes on **03**; mature & well rounded, fairly lively acidity, gentle honeyed touch. Drink up. **Sauvignon Blanc** ★★★ Food-inclined **03** is light bodied, with green grass, figs & hint of citrus reappearing in tart, racy finish. ±13% alc. – *DH*

Mijn-Burg Wines

Paarl ▪ Est/1stB 1999 ▪ Tasting, sales, tours by appt Mon-Fri 9-4 ▪ Owner W Myburgh ▪ Vini consultant Tyrrel Myburgh (Jan 2003) ▪ Viticulturist FC Truter ▪ ±130 ha (cab, pinotage, chenin) ▪ 99% red 1% white ▪ PO Box 191 Klapmuts 7625 ▪ mijnwyne@new.co.za ▪ www. mijnburg.co.za © **884·4892** 🖷 884·4882

The Myburghs have decided to discontinue bottling wine under their own label and focus instead on supplying bulk-wine for third parties to bottle and market under their own brands.

Migliarina Wines

Stellenbosch ▪ Est/1stB 2002 ▪ Closed to public ▪ Owner/winemaker Carsten Migliarina ▪ 450 cs 100% red ▪ PO Box 673 Stellenbosch 7599 ▪ african_wine@yahoo.com © **072·233·4138**

Keep it simple, don't get too complicated, is the sensible approach of sommelier-turned-winemaker Carsten Migliarina, a thwarted pro surfer whose alternative career in wine is turning out swimmingly. He's increased production of his own-wine, a Shiraz, to 9 barrels, and raised the new-oak component to 60%. The 02 has sold out, and the follow-up 04 was not ready for tasting (03 skipped). But, with 'so few vintages, so much to do', there's plenty on the go, including a white off Elgin vineyards.

Millberg see Franschhoek Vineyards
Millbrook see Arlington

Millers Thumb see Ruitersvlei

Millstream

Range by DGB chiefly for export to the UK, Ireland and the Netherlands. Available locally at News Café branches.

Pinotage ★★★ Balanced easy-drinker; **03** mulberry bouquet with attractive earthy touch; plump, dry savoury flavours. All reds 3 mths Fr oak chips. **Cinsaut-Ruby Cabernet** ★★★ Ripely appealing 50/50 melange in **03**, brambly/smoky tones on nose, seamless carry-through to red-fruit palate. **Rosé** ★★★ Blush-coloured **04** has strawberry/banana whiffs, bouncy fruit acidity, disguising high alc (14.3%). **Chardonnay** ★★★ Will appeal widely. **03** inviting lime-green colour, peaches & cream aromas, perky lemon-peach fruit. **Chenin Blanc** ★★★ Lightish **04**, casual-quaffing dry white, some sprightly melon fruit, not too dry finish. All WO W-Cape.— *TM*

Milton Grove see African Terroir

Mischa Estate

Wellington ▪ Est/1stB 1999 ▪ Tasting, sales & tours (incl vine nurseries in summer) by appt ▪ Fee R200, waived if 6+ btls purchased ▪ Closed public holidays ▪ Snacks & meals by appt ▪ Walks ▪ Mountain biking ▪ Owners JH & JA Barns ▪ Winemaker Andrew Barns (Jan 1999) ▪ Viticulturist Ruiter Smit (Jun 1960) ▪ 40 ha (cab, merlot, shiraz) ▪ 60 tons 3 000 cs own label 100% red ▪ PO Box 163 Wellington 7654 ▪ mischaestate@telkomsa.net ▪ www.mischa.co.za © 864·1016/ 19/20 ☐ 864·2312

'Knowledge transfer from our nursery to our vineyards gives us a large viticultural advantage,' says Andrew Barns. He's the winemaker on this Wellington winery and vine nursery; his brother Gareth looks after the *stokkies*, and is more than happy to share his wealth of knowledge during conducted nursery tours (by appointment). Another advantage is viticulturist Ruiter Smit's intimate knowledge of the soils, climate and vineyards — he's been rooted here for 45 years. With a barrel cellar recently completed, their philosophy remains minimal intervention. They irrigate only when deem essential; don't fertilise; and their entire winemaking process is designed to be gentle on the grapes and wine.

★★★★ **Cabernet Sauvignon** Extraordinarily scented **02** — currants, satsuma plum jam — point to ripeness here. Alc a hefty 15%. Will be attractive to the hairy-chested; huge concentration of sweet ripe fruit, softish ripe tannins, not without robust charm. Elegantly oaked **01** (★★★★) gold at 2003 FCTWS.

★★★★ **Merlot** 🆕 Attractive cassis & lead pencil introduction to **02**, dry minerally palate infused with oak, not overdone, made with regard to variety's softer tannins. A class act. Yr Fr barriques. Alc 13%.

★★★★ **Shiraz** Newest **02** a handsome youth — well built & muscular, with ripe tannins; still a little young but well schooled in oak, yr tight grain Fr. Should improve over min 5 yrs. Riper at 14% alc than stylish, sweet-fruited **01** with rich mouthfeel, attractively soft tannins.

Eventide range

★★★★ **Cabernet Sauvignon 02** ultra-ripe fruit as above, alc more manageable 14.5%. Warm porty fruit, soft irresistible palate, slight sweetness from alc. Step-up **01** (★★★★) dense blackcurrant aromas, fine tannins concealing that sweet hint.

★★★★ **Shiraz** Warmly welcoming **02** offers accessible spicy fruit, ripe & plummy, with hint of tobacco. 14% alc. Drink these Eventides while waiting for the Mischas to come round.— *IvH*

Misty Morning see Lutzville
Misty Point see Barrydale

Monis Wines

Paarl ▪ *Est 1906* ▪ *Closed to public* ▪ *Owner Distell* ▪ *Winemaker Dirkie Christowitz (Aug 1979)* ▪ *22 000 cs 100% fortifieds* ▪ *PO Box 266 Paarl 7620* ▪ *dchristowitz@distell.co.za* ▪ *www.distell.co.za* ℂ *860·1601* 🖷 *872·2790*

Dirkie Christowitz has been winemaker for the Cape's oldest fortified brand for 25 years. The affable dessert-wine-man reports that a wood-matured Muscadel (5 years in French barrels) will be released in upgraded packaging this year, and will become a permanent part of the range. Meanwhile the wine's forerunner, the much-garlanded 92, is still available. The next (96) version of the Port was released too late for inclusion in the guide.

★★★★★ **Muscadel** ✓ Venerable **92** has garnered as many admirers as show gongs (2000 VDG; gold 2001 Muscats of the World, France, Best Muscat trophy 2002 FCTWS, ★★★★★ *Wine*) during its unpretentious tenure in the market place. Re-engaged mid-2004 scintillating amber gaining tawny tints, expansive raisin fruit now fully integrated, sensual silkiness holding. Next release in 375ml screwcap package.

★★★★ **Very Old Tawny Port** Vintage-dated, unusually, hero of many competitions (including Veritas, Peter Schultz, FCTWS) since **89**, recent versions slightly drier (<95g/ℓ sugar), less spirituous (18% alc), shorter time in wood (now 8.5 yrs). Latest **95** (★★★★) red-onion skin hues, marzipan nose adds icing to Christmas-cake tone, venison-pie/pipe tobacco nuances for interest. **93** VDG. No **94**. Paarlberg tinta/cinsaut grapes now joined by Stbosch fruit.—*DS*

Mons Ruber Estate

Little Karoo ▪ *Est ca 1850* ▪ *Tasting & sales Mon-Fri 9-5 Sat 9-1* ▪ *Closed Easter Sun & Dec 25* ▪ *Estate produce for sale* ▪ *Walking trail in proclaimed conservation area* ▪ *Owners Radé & Erhard Meyer* ▪ *Winemaker Radé Meyer* ▪ *Viti consultant Willem Botha* ▪ *38 ha (cab, muscadels r/w, chard, chenin, hanepoot, palomino)* ▪ *±500 tons 10 000 cs own label 50% red 50% white* ▪ *PO Box 1585 Oudtshoorn 6620* ▪ *www.geocities.com/monsr_za* ▪ *monsruber@lantic.net* ℂ/🖷 *(044) 251·6550*

Wine farmers in the Cape are often faced with vine diseases and difficult climatic conditions. But it's not often that a grower reports a plague of locusts in his vines, as was the case with this Little Karoo estate. Apart from that fortunately relatively minor setback, winemaker Radé Meyer says, 2004 was a kind year, with moderate temperatures during the growing season and enough irrigation water available to prevent undue stress in the vines. He's expecting some excellent wines from the vintage.

Cabernet Sauvignon ★★☆ Last tasted was unoaked **00**, lightish, soft, plummy mouthful. **Conari** ★★☆ Uncertified/unvintaged cab, usually light casual quaffing. Orange tint, spiced strawberry aromas; firm & dry, light textured, could be chilled. **Chardonnay** ★☆ **02** presents hints of ginger & honey; full smoky herbal flavours. **Vino** ★☆ 🆕, but **03** (chardonnay) showing bottle-age honey & hints of peach; light, soft, toasted nuts flavours. **Cabernet Sauvignon Jerepigo** ★★★☆ ✓ Unusual dessert. **03**, uncorked again for this ed, cassis, raisin, dried fruit combo; choc-coated cherries & raisins; soft, slightly savoury finish, uncloying. Alternative name Elegantia. **Red Muscadel Jerepigo** ★★★ Velvet-smooth fortified dessert with unmistakable muscat tones; reappraised **02** ambertinted, with sweet waxy/floral bouquet, muscat character growing somewhat less overt. 17.7% alc. **White Muscadel Jerepigo** ★★★☆ ✓ **02** fortified turning a striking bronze shade; fragrant honeysuckle, grape & Turkish Delight aromas. Lightish 15.3% alc nicely balanced, gives creamy effect. **Regalis** ★★★ Latest bottling (NV, 03) of this fortified white muscadel tastes sweeter, more unctuous than version above, less muscatty; caramel & tea-leaf on finish. 16.7% alc. **Hanepoot Jerepigo** ★★★ Retasted **99** maturing well, shows some complexity; honeysuckle & dried peach aromas; concentrated, rich, & weighty. 16.8% alc. Alternative label: Bonitas. **Sultana Jerepigo** ★★ **99**, retasted, notes of smoky raisin & hazelnut, slight sherried tone, unctuous. 18.3% alc. **Port** ★★★ Mellow tawny style, less sweet than many traditional Cape ports; from cab; current is NV blend 98, 99, 00. ±17% alc. Mature-looking russet-ruby, stewed fruit & mocha hints.—*TM*

Montagu Winery

Little Karoo ▪ Est 1941 ▪ 1stB 1975 ▪ Tasting & sales Mon-Fri 8-12.30; 1.30-5 Sat 9-12 ▪ Closed public holidays ▪ Tours by appt during harvest ▪ BYO picnic ▪ Owners 68 members ▪ Winemaker Sonnie Malan , with Collin Wright (Jan 1972/1990) ▪ Viti consultant Willem Botha ▪ 660 ha (cab, merlot, muscadel, shiraz, chard, chenin, colombard) ▪ ±12 000 tons 5 000 cs own label ▪ 10% red 40% white 50% muscadel ▪ PO Box 29 Montagu 6720 ▪ mkwkelder@lando.co.za © (023) 614·1125 ☐ *(023) 614·1793*

Not without reason was this co-op on the fringe of picturesque Montagu village previously known as Sweetwine Farmers. Their fortified muscadels are particularly good, so it's appropriate that there should be 'a strong possibility' of their staging a Muscadel Festival sometime this year, advises Sonnie Malan, manager/winemaker since the year dot. Post-prandial sweets are by no means the sole focus here. 80% of their branded products are unfortified, and include an appealing dry red. Pinotage and shiraz were the star performers in harvest 2004, while the chenin, they regret, was less exciting than usual. The wines weren't ready for tasting this edition, but on the current price list are: Merlot-Ruby Cabernet, Chardonnay (wooded and unoaked), Chenin Blanc, Colombard, Late Harvest, Mont Blanc Semi-Sweet, Vin Doux and Red/White Muscadel.

Mont Destin

Paarl ▪ Est/1stB 1998 ▪ Visits by appt ▪ Owners Ernest & Samantha Bürgin ▪ Winemaker Samantha Bürgin, advised by Bruwer Raats (Jan 2002/Jan 2003) ▪ Viticulturist André van den Berg (Jan 2000), advised by Johan Wiese ▪ 7 ha (cab, cinsaut, grenache, mourvèdre, shiraz, viognier) ▪ 15 tons 1 000 cs 80% red 20% white ▪ PO Box 1237 Stellenbosch 7599 ▪ www. montdestin.co.za © 083·288·4985 ☐ *875·5870*

Having decided to simplify their lives and follow their dream of producing small quantities of hand-crafted reds (and start a family), Samantha and Ernst Bürgin sold a portion of their Simonsberg farm, including the restaurant and guesthouse, to the Dauriac family from St-Emilion, who renamed their section Marianne. Now the Bürgins are pursuing their destiny on just ten hectares, seven of which are being planted with cab, cinsaut, grenache, mourvèdre, shiraz and viognier. Until these new vineyards come into production the line-up will feature a Shiraz, red blend and Chenin (fellow chenin enthusiast Bruwer Raats now consults).

★★★★ **1482** Classy, complex blend; make-up dictated by vintage; **02** dominated by merlot's broad dark-berried richness (81%), splashes cab (14%), shiraz (5%) for backbone, freshness, extra interest. Intelligently oaked: 18 mths, mainly Fr, none new; suavely knit for 3-4 yrs development. 14.5% alc. Not as dense, opulent as **01** (★★★★★) equal cab, merlot, with 20% shiraz. Yr new Fr oak. 13.5% alc.

★★★★ **Bushvine Pinotage 02** (sample) rings with modern, hedonistic tones of pvs. Mint-infused red berries, brushed with sweet oak; voluptuous, loads of sweet, mouth-coating fruit smoothes fine tannins, controls 15% alc. Yr older Fr/Am oak. **01** vibrant minty fragrance; intense velvety palate. 60% equal Fr/Am oak, yr.

★★★☆ **Destiny Shiraz** ᴺᴱᵂ Just 500 bottles **02**, from low-yield, single vyd. Eye-catching looks: hand-labelled/embossed with gilt wax. Matching powerful, very ripe wine with contrasting, almost too silky mouthfeel; pleasant varietal notes currently overwhelmed by new oak coconut/vanillins (15 mths new Fr/Am barrels — one each); but short on substance, frame to allow for benefits of ageing. 15% alc.

★★★★ **CMS** ᴺᴱᵂ Hearty **02** blend, 50% cab with merlot, shiraz. Big, chewy mouthful packed with warming smoky, meaty richness & clever flick red fruit freshness in tail. Buffed & ready for equally hearty winter fare. 14% alc. Yr used Fr oak.

★★★☆ **Chenin Blanc** ✓ Pure, unwooded chenin; substance, flavour increased via time *sur lie*. Preview **04** fine lime-/tangerine-blossom scents; similar flavours well-focused/sustained across lees-enriched padding; rounded, just-dry. 13.5% alc.

Discontinued: **Grenache**, **Sauvignon Blanc**. —AL

▨ *Mont d'Or* see Makro

Mont du Toit Kelder

*Wellington ▪ Est 1996 ▪ 1stB 1998 ▪ Tasting & sales by appt ▪ Owner Stephan du Toit ▪ Winemaker Pieter-Niel Rossouw (Jan 2000), advised by Bernd Philippi (1997) ▪ Viticulturist Alwyn Myburgh (Apr 1999) ▪ 28 ha (alicante bouchet, cabs s/f, merlot, mourvèdre, petit v, shiraz, tempranillo) ▪ ±140 tons ±10 000 cs 100% red ▪ PO Box 704 Wellington 7654 ▪ kelder@montdutoit.co.za ▪ www.montdutoit.co.za ✆ **873·7745** 🖷 864·2737*

Mont du Toit's flagship blend remains top of the heap, winning the trophy in the regional Bordeaux-style red category (wines over £10) at the 2004 *Decanter* World Wine Awards. With the first petit verdot coming on-stream and in the words of winemaker Pieter-Niel Rossouw, 'looking very good', Johannesburg-based lawyer Stephan du Toit is taking on all comers with 'not just another international cab'. A dream come true for him is, sadly, not to be for consultant Bernhard Breuer. The untimely death of this world-renowned champion of modern German wine (to him is attributed the Rheingau riesling renaissance), cut short exciting forays into international red wine production in SA and Portugal. Partner Bernd Philippi will keep the memory alive at Mont du Toit.

★★★★ **Mont du Toit** Burst onto the scene with **98** & gathering fans & accolades ever since. Cab, merlot, shiraz, cab f, proportions dictated by yr, combine dense complexity with supple elegance. Big **00** firmer, more fruity, possibly the standout vintage. **01** smooth velvety allure underpinned by densely packed fruit; new **02** riper, more plummy, more immediately accessible thanks to soft, ultra-ripe tannins. These luxuriously oaked 22+ mths, (25-30% new) imparting loads of spice. Deserve 4-6 yr wait.

★★★★★ **Le Sommet** Selected blocks, barrels & vintages reserved for this bold, individual blend, where winemakers' artistry gets/gives full rein. To date **98**; next is **02**.

Hawequas ★★★ Poured by glass at some of Gauteng's swankiest restaurants. Mix cab s/f, merlot, shiraz with about yr in barrel, ±10% new. **02** blend sweet, ripe, porty, with firm finish. 14.5% alc. All above Wllngtn/Kmuts fruit; WO Coastal. – *IvH*

Monterosso Estate

*Stellenbosch ▪ Est/1stB 2000 ▪ Tasting & sales Mon-Sat 8.30–12.30; 1.30–5 ▪ Closed Easter Fri/Sun/Mon, Apr 27, May 1, Jun 16, Dec 25 & Jan 1 ▪ Tours by appt ▪ Owners Socrate, Orneglio & Francesco De Franchi ▪ Winemaker Orneglio De Franchi (Jan 2000) ▪ Viticulturists Francesco De Franchi ▪ 68 ha (cab, merlot, pinotage, sangiovese, chard, sauvignon, semillon) ▪ 1 800 cs own label 80% red 20% white ▪ PO Box 5 Stellenbosch 7599 ▪ monterosso@mweb.co.za ✆/🖷 **889·5021***

It might have been a temporary front-label but it was adorned several times: the Cab-Merlot of the *fratelli* De Franchi, Francesco and Orneglio (aka 'Meaty'), went from winning a Michelangelo gold to inclusion on the Diners Club Reserve Select list and a best-value award from *Wine*. Now, with a new and eye-pleasing label in classical style, the estate's wines are ready for a marketing campaign. New to the range is a Sauvignon, with a maiden Sangiovese to be launched as the guide went to press, having matured 'favourably', in the brothers' opinion, in French oak.

★★★★ **Cabernet Sauvignon-Merlot 01** restrained red berry flavours & strong tannins; hand-crafted rusticity should please those who bemoan the current fashion for intensely fruity wines. Fermented/14 mths Fr oak (70% new).

Sauvignon Blanc ☺ ★★★ **04** water-white quaffer with peach & floral notes; ideal for summer lunches. – *CvZ*

▨ *Montestell* see Boland Kelder

Montpellier de Tulbagh

Tulbagh ▪ Est ca 1950 ▪ 1stB ca 1968 ▪ Tasting, sales & tours daily 9-12; 2-5 Sat 9-12 ▪ Farm-style guest house ▪ Facilities for children ▪ Tourgroups ▪ BYO ▪ Conferencing ▪ Farm-style guest house ▪ Owner Lucas van Tonder ▪ Winemaker Anton Krynauw (Jan 2003) ▪ Viti consultant Gawie Kriel (Apr 2003) ▪ 50 ha (11 varieties, mainly white) ▪ 300 tons 10 000 cs 30% red 70% white ▪ PO Box 79 Tulbagh 6820 ▪ montpellier@jav.co.za ▪ www.tulbaghwineroute.com ✆ **(023) 230·0723/0656** 🖷 *(023) 230·0723*

Counsellor-at-law Lucas van Tonder and winemaker Anton Krynauw continue their trans-formation of this venerable property, founded by a French Huguenot in 1714. In the vine-yard, they've grubbed up under-whelmers and replaced them with potential high-achievers like cab, shiraz, mourvèdre and petit verdot. Next to take root are chardonnay and viognier, with the eventual goal of an equal red/white mix. Targeting the trade as much as consumers, they point out that all wines are available in both bottle and bulk. And, eyeing tourists, they promise 'an unforgettable experience that forces you to come back again and again', including a rose-ringed hilltop church for weddings, conference fa-cilities, guesthouse and restaurant in progress.

Private Reserve ☺ ★★★ Perfumed **02** with rose-petal wafts, light body, good bal-ance, soft finish; from gewürz, colombard, clairette.

Pinot Noir ★ **02**'s ethereal colour belies immense body (15.5% alc); savoury/forest floor aromas, soft texture. **Colombard** 🆕 ★★★ Muted tropical fruit salad tones, slender body, gently flavourful **04**. **Semillon** ★★ **04** subdued quince & hay aromas, livelier lime-toned palate, clean & dry finish. **Weisser Riesling** ★★ Minerally & dry **02**, now gaining more pronounced terpene tone; lightish & soft palate. **Cap Classique** ★★★ Lightish fruity **02** bubbly mostly from semillon; pear/pineapple aromas, refreshing appley froth. Follow-ing **04**s tasted but too young to rate: **Cabernet Sauvignon** 🆕, **Chenin Blanc**, **Clairette Blanche** 🆕, **Sauvignon Blanc**. – *CR*

Montpellier du Sud

Tulbagh ▪ Est 1965 ▪ 1stB 2000 ▪ Visits by appt ▪ Farm produce ▪ Owner Montpellier du Sud (Pty) Ltd ▪ 35 ha (cab, merlot, pinot, chenin, riesling, sauvignon) ▪ 3-5 000 cs own label 15% red 80% white 5% blanc de noir ▪ PO Box 24 Tulbagh 6820 ▪ jstheron@intekom.co.za ▪ www.montpellier.co.za ✆/🖷 **(023) 230·0631**

New owners have taken over here, and they were assessing the current wines and their potential as the guide went to press. They say they will attempt to extend the red variet-ies planted to equal the whites. The intention is to bottle a Cabernet Sauvignon, Pinot Noir, Blanc de Noir, Pinot Gris, Chenin Blanc, Sauvignon Blanc and Weisser Riesling.

Mont Rochelle Mountain Vineyards

Franschhoek ▪ 1stB 1996 ▪ Tasting & sales Mon-Sat 10-5 Sep-Apr only: Sun 11-2 ▪ Fee R10 ▪ Closed Easter Sun/Mon, Dec 25/26 & Jan 1 ▪ Tours 11, 12.30 & 3 ▪ BYO picnic (R5 cover charge) ▪ Farm produce ▪ Art gallery ▪ Owner Miko Rwayitare ▪ Winemaker Justin Hoy, with Francois Samuels (Sep 1999/1998) ▪ Viticulturist Alwyn Geldenhuys (May 1994) ▪ 19 ha (cab, merlot, chard, sauvignon) ▪ 10 000 cs own label 50% red 50% white ▪ ISO 14001 certified ▪ PO Box 334 Franschhoek 7690 ▪ info@montrochelle.co.za ▪ www.montrochelle.co.za ✆ **876·3000** 🖷 *876·2362*

Even the best-laid plans can go awry. Ask Congolese-born telecommunications entrepre-neur Miko Rwayitare and wife Conso, who were supposed to take up residence at their Franschhoek property last year. But business commitments keep him in Gauteng, and he's become a frequent flier instead, visiting the farm a couple of times a month. The pro-prietor was on hand to lend moral support to Justin Hoy during a very up and down vin-tage, which ended far later than usual. 'The sauvignon fared well,' the winemaker reports. Other news is that they earned an ISO 14001 certification along with several other local wineries as part of a project to promote sound environmental practices in the valley.

★★★☆ **Alchemy** Maiden **02** five-variety blend: cabs s/f, merlot, shiraz, pinotage. Retasted mid-2004, developing savoury meaty, dried biltong notes, smooth & supple. 15 mths oak. 14.5% alc. Should keep 3–5 yrs (& perhaps turn to gold?).

★★★☆ **Cabernet Sauvignon 02** in now familiar style — minty fragrance, hints sage, fennel; ripe mulberry & dark choc intensity. Nudges next rung up. 18 mths Fr oak, 30% new (regimen also for Cab, Syrah below). 14% alc. Will hold 5–7 yrs.

★★★☆ **Merlot 02** plump damson profile; velvety, plush texture. High extract from long skin contact; sweet fruit tannins melding with Fr oak. These reds all WO W-Cape.

★★★☆ **Syrah** NEW **02** from Paarl fruit. Choc-coated prunes, whiff vanilla; savoury meaty flavours, smooth mouthfeel, fine-grained tannins on finish. Huge 15.5% alc.

★★★★ **Oak-Matured Chardonnay 03** unready. **02** at best was full, richly-textured, nutty & complex; retasted mid-2004, tiring: drink soon. 10 mths oak, 30% new. 14% alc.

★★★★ **Natural Chardonnay ✓** Unwooded version with more interest than many. **03** developing smoky, buttery notes, could easily be mistaken for oak. Zesty lemon & melon, some leesy interest from regular battonage over 4 mths. Gutsy 14.5% alc.

★★★☆ **Sauvignon Blanc** Latest **04** bang on form; riper style taste-wise, if not analytically (modest 12.5% alc) — grapefruit & greengage profile, tart as plum skin, lively bouncy wine, tangy finish.

Pinotage discontinued. — *IvH*

Mooiberge see African Terroir

Mooi Bly

Paarl ▪ Est/1stB 2003 ▪ Visits by appt 10-1 ▪ Self-catering cottages (see Stay-over section) ▪ Owner Luc Wouters ▪ Winemakers Luc Wouters, Erik Schouteden & Theunis van Zyl, with consultants ▪ Viticulturists Erik Schouteden & Theunis van Zyl ▪ 16 ha (cab, chard, chenin) ▪ 95 tons ±400 cs own label + 45 000ℓ bulk ▪ 100% white ▪ PO Box 801 Huguenot 7645 ▪ info@mooibly.com ▪ www.mooibly.com ✆ 868·2808/082·371·2299 🖷 868·2808

Four years ago Luc Wouters purchased this small Dal Josaphat farm and installed his son-in-law Erik Schouteden as farm manager. Keen to make their own wine in the French tradition ('nothing overpowered, a pure taste based on the fruit') last year was, as Schouteden puts it, 'a special one'. Not only did Mooi Bly stop delivering grapes to the local co-op, but the farm produced its first Reserve Chardonnay — 225ℓ initially earmarked for blending, but finally deemed too good to dilute. Wouters & co aim for 'an honest product at a fair price'; to this end they concentrate on making a limited quantity of top-quality Chenin and Chardonnay; 2005 should see both wines made in the new own-cellar.

Chenin Blanc ★★ Charmingly named winery offers fitting first vintage **04** bursting with super-ripe guava aromas; light textured, tangy acid. 12.5% alc. — *IvH*

Mooiplaas Estate

Stellenbosch ▪ Est 1963 ▪ 1stB 1995 ▪ Tasting & sales Mon-Fri 9-4 Sat & public holidays 10-2 ▪ Closed Easter Fri-Mon, Dec 25/26, Jan 1 ▪ Fee R10 refundable with purchase ▪ BYO picnic ▪ Conservation area ▪ Owner Mooiplaas Trust ▪ Winemaker Louis Roos (1983) ▪ Viticulturist Tieleman Roos (1980) ▪ ±120 ha ▪ 750 tons 8 000 cs own label 67% red 33% white ▪ PO Box 104 Koelenhof 7605 ▪ info@mooiplaas.co.za ▪ www.mooiplaas.co.za ✆ 903·6273 🖷 903·3474

Shiraz was the red of the 2004 vintage for the Roos family, owner Nicolaas and sons Louis the winemaker and Tielman the viticulturist (celebrating his silver anniversary in these Bottelary Hills vineyards in 2005). Shiraz was also the wine of 2004 for Mooiplaas, the 02 winning the Wine 500 Club Best Shiraz plaudit on the day of its release as well as a Fairbairn silver medal. As he bottled the Sauvignon 04 ('excellent, full flavours again — this was the year to savour the drip irrigation installed 2 years ago on the hilltop vineyards'), Louis R noted: 'Remember that a good sauvignon ages well. Do not ignore the 03 once 04 hits the shelves'.

★★★★ **Cabernet Sauvignon** Always released with a few yrs on them – a welcome bonus these days. About 15% merlot blended in. **99** evidencing lighter vintage (though 13.5% alc), but still very satisfying, unpretentious, well balanced drinking. Drink over next few yrs. More muscular, rich **00** opening up, but still youthful. Abundant ripe, fresh fruit attending juicy big tannins, for savoury lingering finish; cedary notes from 2 yrs oak, mostly Fr, 40% new.

★★★★ **Pinotage ✓ 01** still youthful: fresh, fruity, sleek; pinotage lushness touched with elegance, supported by ripe tannins. Very little wood used. Effortlessly, cheerfully charming rather than over-serious – but certainly not trivial. Drink now or keep 5 or so yrs. **00** stylish & well-fruited; both ±14% alc.

★★★★ **Shiraz** Good honest shiraz, pleasantly fleshy, rounded with soft tannins & dryish savoury finish. **01** (★★★) was surprisingly sullen, unyielding, less graceful than maiden **00** (which continues drinking well). **02** broad, ripe, savoury, with subtle blackcurrant & leather notes; good acid, ripe tannin. 18 mths oak, most Fr, 60% new. Beware 15.1% alc. Should keep happily 5+yrs.

★★★★ **Sauvignon Blanc 03** still showing well mid-2004: fresh, round, supple, nicely mixing green element (peppers, greengage) with tropical fruit. No hurry either with similarly styled **04**; well balanced with succulent acidity & slightly lower 13% alc. – *TJ*

Mooiuitsig Wine Cellars

Robertson ▪ Est 1947 ▪ Tasting & sales Mon-Thu 8-5 Fri 8-3 ▪ Tours by appt ▪ Stay-overs at De Rust Lodge: linda@outdoorarena.co.za ©️ (023) 616·2444 ▪ Owners Jonker & Claasen families ▪ Winemaker Christiaan van Tonder, with Nico van der Westhuizen (Dec 2002/Feb 2003) ▪ Viticulturist Casper Matthee ▪ 3 400 tons ▪ PO Box 15 Bonnievale 6730 ▪ info@ mooiuitsig.co.za ▪ www.mooiuitsig.co.za ©️ (023) 616·2143 🖷 (023) 616·2675

Far more than just a wine producer, this large family-run wholesale business offers a range of local and imported liquors including sherries, brandies and the traditional unmatured firewater, witblits. Newcomers to their own range are two blended wines under the African Wine Adventure label. For travellers, they run a spacious thatched guest lodge, De Rust, ideal for exploring the Bonnievale area's charms. Weddings, conferences and other occasions also catered for.

African Wine Adventure range   `NEW`
No mistaking the Afro-theme here: zebra stripes blazoned on cork as well as label. **Red** ★★★ Fruity dry blend cab/merlot with red-berry tone, ripe tannin. **White** ★★★ Honest to goodness dry white from sauvignon, chardonnay (70/30); light, pleasing. Both NV.

Clemence Creek range
★★★★ **Chardonnay Dessert Wine** Full-sweet jerepiko-style fortified dessert, unusually in SA from chardonnay, ex-Genadekloof ('Vale of Grace'), a single-vyd on Bnvale farm Ardein. Retasted **98** deliciously mature, characterful; alc starting to show so probably time to drink up. ±200g/ℓ sugar. 17.5% alc. 500ml.

Mooiuitzicht range
Overberger ★★★ Chardonnay, sauvignon, chenin trio, charmingly subtitled 'Opwindende Witwyn' ('Exciting White Wine'); in fact: a light, honeyed peach quaff. **Vin Brut** ★★ Light-bodied, bone-dry sparkling with honeyed froth; carbonated, from sauvignon, as is... **Vin Doux** ★★ Tropical flavours & gentle sweetness. **Marsala** ★ Spirity red fortified dessert, made from 'various sweet-wine varieties'. **Nagmaalwyn** (Sacramental Wine) ★★★ Light mahogany colour; pleasant porty character & sweet prune flavours. **Hanepoot** ★★ Sunshine-yellow dessert with low-key muscat sweetness; winemakers say: 'a great winter companion'. **Old Tawny Port** ★ Wood-matured fortified showing distinctly un-tawny purple colour; traditional-style low alc. **Bonwin Ruby Dessert Wine** ★★ Hues nearer mahogany than ruby; rounded & sweet. All NV; fortified to ±17.5% alc.

Oude Rust range

Certified fortified dessert. **Red Muscadel ★★★ 03** pale bronze-pink; gentle, liqueur-like palate; more refreshing, sprightly than pvs. Gold at 2002 Muscadel Competition. **Sweet Hanepoot ★★★** Light golden glints to unctuous, warming **01**. **White Muscadel ★★★ 02** attractive, with honeysuckle scents, lemon freshness to its smooth length. Enjoy in its youth. All 17.5% alc.

Rusthof range

> **Oulap Se Rooi** ☺ **★★★** Jocular labelling distinguishes this all-occasions red; sweet-fruited & juicy; lightly oaked cab, merlot, pinotage. 13.4% alc. Styled to enjoy with a traditional potjie. Also presented in more conventional packaging as Dry Red.

Rosé ★★ Slight berry-like tone on palate but otherwise straightforward semi-sweet. **Blanc de Blanc ★★** Light, gently aromatic off-dry white from chardonnay, sauvignon, chenin; fairly brisk finish. **Premier Grand Cru ★★** Slightly drier version of BdB. **Late Harvest ★★** Balanced semi-sweet with light tropical tone; varieties as for above whites. **Potjie Effe Droog ★★** Similar to BdB above; marketed in 500ml screwtop. All NV. Also available but not tasted: **Red/White Jerepigo** & **Old White Port**. — *DH*

Moonlight Organics see Stellar Winery
Moraea see Overhex

Môreson

*Franschhoek ▪ Est 1986 ▪ 1stB 1994 ▪ Tasting & sales daily 11-5 ▪ Fee R10 ▪ Closed Dec 25 ▪ Tours by appt ▪ Bread & Wine Restaurant & other amenities (see Eat-out section & intro) ▪ Owner Richard Friedman ▪ Winemaker/general manager Anton Beukes, with Jacques Wentzel (1994/2003) ▪ Viticulturist Anton Ferreira (Feb 2002) ▪ 18 ha (pinotage, chard, chenin, sauvignon) ▪ 300 tons 18 000 cs 40% red 55% white 1% rosé 4% MCC ▪ Export brands: Pinecrest & MorningSide ▪ ISO 14000 & Eurogap certified ▪ PO Box 114 Franschhoek 7690 ▪ sales@moreson.co.za ▪ www.moreson.co.za ✆ **876-3055** 🖷 876-2348*

This winery celebrated its 10th anniversary last year, and Anton Beukes, here from the outset, can take much of the credit for the farm's fine reputation. His new assistant is Jacques Wentzel, top student at Elsenburg in 2003, who arrived in time for a dry, cold, challenging harvest. The duo shares a goal of making wines with elegance and balance, which includes aiming for lower levels of alcohol. 'We can't adjust this in the vineyard,' Beukes comments, 'so we'll have to use less efficient yeasts.' Beyond wine, the annual Blessing of the Harvest ceremony, Bread & Wine Restaurant (where, appropriately, you can learn to bake bread), a play area for children and function facilities are some of the allures of this riverside property.

★★★★ **Magia** Bdx-style red named by unidentified Bulgarian at international wine show, who declared the as yet unlabeled **98** 'magia!' (magical). Current **01** from cabs s/f, merlot, grown in Paarl, Stbosch, all subjugated into successful blend (49/24/26); deep plummy nose with herbal/green pepper hints; finely structured. 18 mths Fr oak, some new; holds 15% alc well. **00** (**★★★★**) featured silky fruit, unobtrusive structure. **99** similarly fruit-focused but probably earlier-drinking.

★★★★ **Cabernet Sauvignon** These need yr/2 from release to settle, unwind. **01** (**★★★☆**) still tight, unknit mid-2004, but showing ripely generous cab fruit & oak (18 mths, Fr, 1st/2nd fill). ±14% alc. **00** still inky, oaky, embryonic when tasted last yr; similar to **99**, needing further bottle-maturation.

★★★☆ **Merlot** Enthusiastically oaked, mostly with good results; as in **01**, juicy nose with well-expressed varietal fruit; just needs time for chunky wood to harmonise. 14.5% alc. Initially dark, sullen **00** (**★★★★**) opened out into lovely silky smoothness. 15-20 mths Fr barrels.

★★★☆ **Pinotage 02** (★★★★) fresh, juicy & well-defined version from Stbosch fruit; supple tannins & poised acidity. **01** showed good oak, huge fruit concentration. Invariably high alc: 14.7, 15% not out of place.

★★★★ **Premium Chardonnay 03** raises bar for this label with polished & well wooded fruit, enlivening citrus zip; balanced & focused. 14 mths new & 2nd fill oak. **02** (★★★) was soft & fleshy — and would have been better with livelier acid, more integrated oak. This, following 3 wines, WO Frhoek.

★★★★ **Chenin Blanc 04** fresh & harmonious, undoubtedly chenin. 14% alc. **03** clean, still fresh in spite of faint honeycomb of age in background. From mature bushvines.

★★★★ **Sauvignon Blanc** ✓ Own fruit, night-harvested & made reductively for freshness, zing. **04** delicate floral aromas, well weighted palate exhibits concentration, focus; dry mineral backbone. **03** was tangy, full-bodied & vibrant.

Môreson Cap Classique ★★★ Brut sparkling from chardonnay (90%), chenin. Latest (NV) has the usual busy bready bubbles, but also some lemony austerity missing from pvs riper releases. *Wine* ★★★★.

Pinehurst range

★★★☆ **Cabernet Sauvignon 01** (★★★) fairly big departure from pvs' clever Bdx-like styling. 14% alc prominent; simple, sweet, porty tone. 14 mths oak. **00**, FCTWS 2003 gold, blackcurrant flavours & dusty austere tannins. WO W-Cape.

★★★☆ **Cabernet Sauvignon-Merlot** ✓ **01** (★★★) pleasing unwooded easy drinker, green pepper nose/palate with black fruits & whiff liquorice. **00** also in full-blown modern style, fruity & juicy, with more concentration.

Pinotage ★★★ We last tasted quaffable **02**, honest & forthright. **Rosé** 🆕 **03** from pinotage untasted. **Chardonnay** ★★☆ Unwooded **03**, light, fresh, leesy & vinous. 14.2% alc. **Chenin Blanc** ★★★ **04** youthful pear-drop/mineral tone; dry, leesy flavour; made in a sound commercial style. WO Frhoek. **Sauvignon Blanc** ★★ Undemanding **04** doesn't shout the variety, but shows some vinosity. All above WO Coastal unless noted. — *RK*

Morgenhof Estate

Stellenbosch ▪ Est 1692 ▪ 1stB 1984 ▪ Tasting & sales Nov-Apr: Mon-Fri 9-5.30 Sat/Sun 10-5; May-Oct: Mon-Fri 9-4.30 Sat/Sun 10-3 ▪ Fee R10 ▪ Closed Dec 25 ▪ Light lunches/coffees & other amenities (see Eat-out section & intro) ▪ Tourgroups ▪ Owner Anne Cointreau ▪ Winemaker Rianie Strydom, with Jacques Cilliers (Mar 1994/May 2003) ▪ Viticulturist Pieter Haasbroek (1998) ▪ ±70 ha (cabs s/f, merlot, pinotage, touriga, chard, chenin, sauvignon) ▪ 320 tons 25 000 cs 60% red 40% white ▪ PO Box 365 Stellenbosch 7599 ▪ info@morgenhof. com ▪ www.morgenhof.com ✆ 889·5510 🖷 889·5266

Owner Anne Cointreau (yes, that's *the* Cointreau) has woven a something-for-everyone web at this magnificent venue. There's a sense of history (farm established in 1692) in the French/Old Cape-toned yard, tree-shaded for summer meals; a fire-warmed winter's welcome for diners; spacious tasting venue across the rose garden; chapel for weddings; carolling at Christmastime; an annual art expo; special treats for Valentine's Day; and finally, the star turn — the wine. Which introduces another formidable Morgenhof woman, winemaker Rianie Strydom, mother of three and wife of Rust en Vrede's Louis. She's realistic about prospects post-2004, which she terms a harvest of extremes: 'Wines won't be as good as they were in 2003'. Her plan is to focus on the flagship Première Sélection, which means bringing all the red vineyards up to standard and extending the options as regards blending components (hence the recent planting of a small block of petit verdot). Here Strydom is positioning herself at the vanguard of a trend: more of the top SA properties are aiming for a single *grand vin*, à la the leading estates of Bordeaux.

★★★★★ **Première Sélection** Classically styled, made to age, blend varying with vintage. Latest **01** cab s, merlot, cab f, malbec (60/25/9/6) configuration less austere, more accessible & graceful than pvs. Concentrated, refined dark fruit with ripe sweetness, firm tannins but balanced, lengthy dry finish. 18 mths oak, 60% new. **00** similar but more austere; powerfully tannic. Suggest cellar 6-8 yrs.

★★★★★ **Cabernet Sauvignon Reserve** Fine, deep **01** (★★★★), a barrel selection. Lovely berry fruit with herbal grace-notes in refined setting, magisterial authority tempering austere power with fruitful generosity. 18 mths new Fr oak. Retasted mid-2004, en route to fine maturity 6-8 yrs hence. Pvs was spectacularly flavourful **98**.

★★★☆ **Cabernet Sauvignon** Latest **02** (sample) warm, ultra-ripe dark berried fruits – black cherry & mulberry, almost lumbering under weight of fruit, soft ripe tannins hardly noticeable, redeemed by fine oak component. **00** awarded trophy at FCTWS 2002. No **01**.

★★★★☆ **Merlot Reserve** With flagship styling & massive structure. Maiden **98** was sensual, smoky, substantial. No **99**. **00** (★★★★) had big tannin structure, suggesting hopeful wait of min 5 yrs. **01** re-establishes claim in seductiveness stakes (but very classy & serious), helped by less dominating oak (only 60% new, Fr). Ripe, supple tannin integrating with warm, bright fruit, savoury acid. 5-8 yrs ahead.

★★★★ **Merlot** Serious version, **01** retasted mid-2004 shows benefit of keeping. Delightful – refined, graceful, integrated; beautifully poised & accessible, should maintain peak for 1-2 yrs more. 18 mths Fr oak, 20% new. 14% alc.

★★★★ **Pinotage** Fragrant, generously but elegantly styled, benefits from few yrs' keeping, as retasted **01** shows. Plump, well-balanced, with variety's sweet redcurrant charms, though genuinely dry on finish. Yr oak 90/10 Fr/Am, 40% new. 14% alc.

★★★☆ **Vineyards Red** NEW Deep coloured **02**, all-sorts blend with good depth, attractive mulberry & black cherry given good oak. Properly dry, smooth, approachable tannins. Better than everyday red. Yr oak, 2nd & 3rd fill. 14.6% alc.

★★★★ **Chenin Blanc** ✓ From older vines (mid-30s), always impressive, unobtrusively wooded (7-9 mths, 10% new), usually just about dry. Latest **03** shows signature quince & honey; rich but with distinctive clean acidity of chenin for uncluttered finish, longevity. 14.2% alc.

★★★★ **Brut Reserve** Latest **01** assertive dry bubbly with good yeasty attack. Tasted *sur pointe* (undisgorged, before final dosage). Base wine barrelled yr, on lees 2½. Good depth after time on lees, biscuity, burgeoning complexity, chardonnay dominant, shows in fine length. Blend (60/40) chard/pinot noir.

★★★☆ **Noble Late Harvest** Reappears with **02**. Attractive orange marmalade bouquet, & barley sugar twist, not over-sweet at 105g/ℓ with good balancing acidity, slight caramel notes, dry finish. Rather good. Barrel fermented/aged 6 mths.

★★★☆ **Late Bottled Vintage 99** from tinta, touriga, matured 4 yrs in used barriques; drier style (96g/ℓ sugar), alc a delicate 17.5% though. Appealing meat richness, cloaked subtly in oak, some dry tannin on finish. Nice integration of spirit.

★★★★ **Cape Vintage** Last was **00** tinta/touriga in drier Portuguese style.

Sauvignon Blanc ★★★ Middle of the road version, won't knock your socks off, nor disappoint. **04** echoes of capsicum & fig, pleasantly fruity, noticeable sweetness on finish (4.8g/ℓ). **Chardonnay** ★★★ Label resuscitated with lightly wooded **03**, with understated oak & peach flavours, silky/creamy attractions but heavy hand with sugar shows on finish. **Natural Sweet** NEW ★★★ Barrel-fermented, bottle-matured 2 yrs. Less sweet than many at 90g/ℓ sugar, soft acidity, subtle oak on nose/palate. Lightish 12.6% alc. NE. **Sauvignon Blanc-Chenin Blanc**, **Malbec-Merlot**, **Cabernet Franc-Cabernet Sauvignon** discontinued.

Fantail range   NEW

Rosé ☺ ★★★ **04** pinotage immediately recognisable from sweet candyfloss nose; palate comes as lovely surprise – bone-dry & zingy, lightish at 12.7% alc.

Pinotage ★★☆ **02** sweet spiced plum aroma, but palate properly dry & tangy, good dry finish. Bit austere. **03** (★★★) waiting in wings, more succulence & juice; better welcome altogether. **Merlot** ★★★ Fared well in difficult **02** vintage, some attractive cassis & berry sleekness, smooth & supple. 18 mths oak, 30% new. Lowish 12.7% alc. **Vineyards Red 03** ★★★ All-sorts red, but cab-dominated, pleasing & fruity, soft approachable tannins, made with accessibility foremost. Tastes much sweeter than 2.5g/ℓ sugar suggests, should ensure commercial success. NE; WO W-Cape. **Vineyards White 04** ★★★ Blend chenin, sauvignon (80/20), former mainly oaked. Tropical & lime invitation to dry juicy palate, tangy acidity, good fruity lingering finish. — *IvH*

Morgenster Estate

Stellenbosch (see Helderberg map) ▪ Est 1993 ▪ 1stB 1998 ▪ Tasting & sales Mon-Fri 10-5 ▪ Fee R10 ▪ Closed public holidays ▪ Tours by appt ▪ Estate-grown olive oil & olives products ▪ Owner Giulio Bertrand ▪ Winemaker Marius Lategan, with Cornea Cilliers (Aug 1999, Jan 2004), advised by Pierre Lurton ▪ Vineyard manager Basie Fismer, with Sandré Colyn, advised by Francois Viljoen ▪ 40 ha (cabs s/f, merlot, petit v) ▪ 160 tons 100% red ▪ PO Box 1616 Somerset West 7129 ▪ wine@morgenster.co.za ▪ www.morgenster.co.za ✆ 852·1738 ☎ 852·1141

It's all systems go at this internationally acclaimed wine and olive estate. But in the typically understated style of its Italian owner, Giulio Bertrand. With all 40ha of vines and a spanking new winery finally in full production, 2004 represented a pinnacle of achievement: the release of the first wine made in commercial quantities in the property's cellar from 100% own grapes. The 2001 Morgenster 'estate blend' (second vintage) and its stablemate Lourens River Valley (a second label in the Bordeaux tradition — Ch Cheval Blanc's Pierre Lurton consults) is to be aggressively marketed internationally (USA and Scandinavia particularly) by new sales/marketing manager Hardie Basson. Providing added drive are recent appointees, MD Gerrie Wagenaar (ex-Boschendal) and assistant winemaker Cornea Cilliers.

★★★★★ **Morgenster** Probably destined for Cape showcase greatness — showing, says modest Marius L, the hand of bordelais consultant Pierre Lurton. Merlot-dominated **01** (51%; with cabs s & f) delicate with already tertiary nose, but tight restrained palate suggests keeping for 5+ yrs. More ripely opulent & big (though 14.5% alc not obvious) than pvs, though still refined. Excellent, impressive **00** (retasted) blend of the cabs only, improving in bottle. Limpid but laden with flavours, supple texture for elegance, bearing the mark of the Old World. Still needs time. 16 mths Fr oak, 80% new; 14 % alc.

★★★★★ **Lourens River Valley** This Bdx blend seems set to keep pace with the flagship. **01** (★★★★), 55% merlot, with cab, dash of cab f, had firm tannin grip from 16 mths new Fr oak, & mineral, fennel palate. Upcoming **02** has close to equal quantities same 3 varieties. Taut tannins & tea-leaf finish should ease back in short term to let underlying berry fruit come to the fore. Structure & balance (14.5% alc unobtrusive) to improve with cellaring. — *RK/CvZ*

Morning Mist see Cape Wine Cellars
MorningSide see Môreson

Mostertsdrift Noble Wines

Stellenbosch ▪ Est/1stB 2001 ▪ Visits by appt ▪ Fee R5 ▪ Meals by appt ▪ Owners Anna-Mareè Mostert-Uys & André Mostert ▪ Winemaker Anna-Mareè Mostert-Uys (Jan 2001) ▪ Viticulturist Nico Mostert (Jan 2001) ▪ 7.5 ha (cab, chard, hanepoot) ▪ 29 tons 600-800 cs 50% red 50% white ▪ PO Box 2061 Dennesig 7601 ▪ mostertsdrift@telkomsa.net ✆ 889·5344 ☎ 887·1780

Excitement in 2004 for owner André Mostert and his sister, winemaker Anna-Mareè Mostert-Uys: 'We harvested the first cab from our own block and we're delighted with the results.' This in spite of a difficult and challenging harvest, though the varieties picked while it was still cool delivered wonderful flavours, they report. With the goal of making wine more accessible to the person in the street, the winemaker hosts regular tastings. She also wants to show the world that local wines can stand proud against all comers.

Cabernet Sauvignon ★★★ 02 retasted, now well rounded, still lots of vivacious fruit to match the obvious tannin. 14 mths oak, 2nd-3rd fill. Preview **03**, featuring Bnvale fruit, seems step up: big, fuller, more flavoursome/interesting. **AnéRouge ★★★** Lightly oaked cinsaut/cab with ripely rounded strawberry flavours; latest (NV) is 80/20 blend. **Chenin Blanc Wooded** None since Fr-oaked **02**, with honey-cream topping to ripe tropical fruit. **Chenin Blanc ★** The unwooded version; honeyed **03** a little tired now. **Blanc de Blanc ★★** 100% sauvignon from Frhoek; lightish **04** tropical tones with hints gooseberry, green grass; lively apple zest finish. — *DH*

Mountain Oaks Winery

Worcester ▪ Est/1stB 2003 ▪ Tasting, sales & tours by appt ▪ Organic farm produce ▪ Owners Stevens family ▪ Winemaker Christine Stevens (Jun 2003), advised by Ross Gower ▪ Viti consultant Paul Wallace ▪ 20 ha (cabs s/f, mourvèdre, pinotage, shiraz, chard, chenin, viognier) ▪ 40-50 tons 2 000 cs 30% red 70% white ▪ PO Box 68 Rawsonville 6845 ▪ eikenbosch@iafrica.com © (023) 344·3107 ≏ (023) 344·3688

'Let the vines do the work' is Christine Stevens' maxim. A newcomer to winemaking — she and husband Mark bought the old Cape Dutch property known as Eikenbosch and built a new cellar there — she's being advised and mentored by ex-Klein Constantia wineman Ross Gower. They bottled their first wines in 2003/4, and more recently took delivery of two 6 000ℓ wood fermenters from a cooper in France. In harmony with the organic theme is the produce now on sale at a farmstall attached to the tasting room.

★★★☆ Pinotage 03 robust, aromatic, gamey notes, supplemented by rhubarb whiffs; palate shows well handled, dense tannins contributing to a firm fine finish. 11 mths 80/20 Fr/Am oak. Unfiltered. 14% alc.

Chenin Blanc ★★★ Elegant, persistent **03**'s unshowy pear aromas lead on to lime-tinged grip. Pleasingly moderate 13% alc. **Chenin Blanc Barrel Reserve ★★★** Revisited (but still unreleased mid-2004), from old vines, now rather closed (winemaker suggests it will open up). Unshowy, austere lime palate with evanescent apricot; 13.5% alc; good length. 4 mths oak well integrated. **Le Jardin 03 ★★** Crisp chenin-dominated quaffer (30% chard), food-friendly & undemanding. Name a tribute to the farm gardens. **Chardonnay 03 ★★★** Dominated now by oak (11 mths Fr, 70% new), though with fine citrus finish promising some fruit development over time. No cold stabilisation — hence harmless crystals present. 14% alc. All 🆕 except where noted as retasted; all from organically farmed vyds. — *MF*

Mountain River Wines

Paarl ▪ Est 1993 ▪ 1stB 1998 ▪ Closed to public ▪ Owner De Villiers Brits ▪ Winemaker De Villiers Brits with consultants ▪ 38 700 cs 60% red 40% white ▪ 146 Main Road Paarl 7646 ▪ dev@mountainriverwines.co.za mattie@mountainriverwines.co.za ▪ www.mountainriverwines.co.za © 872·3256/7 ≏ 872·3255

Grapes and wine for his ranges are bought in, but owner De Villiers Brits now has 2ha of his own shiraz planted on land acquired some years ago. He also has a newly built storage facility for his bottled wine. The 2004 harvest, Brits predicts, will yield 'very, very nice' wines from the varieties pressed later rather than usual.

Cabernet Sauvignon-Merlot ★★★★ 01 retasted, improving with age; mellow cherries/strawberries joined by sweet spice & slight savoury touch, light tannins. 13.5% alc. Stbosch grapes; 16 mths older Fr small-oak. **Merlot 🆕 ★★** Classic flavour profile of plums & mocha, **02** round & fruity entry yet fairly strong tannic comeback; give time. 14% alc. **Pinotage-Shiraz ★★★** Ripe, flavoursome **02**, yr on, pvsly noted big dry tannins now show as firm but friendly, nice minerally touch too. Yr Fr/Am oak; 14.5% alc. **Chardonnay ★ 02** now with pronounced honeyed tone to the soft lemony fruit. Rbtsn grapes.

Maankloof range

Shiraz ☺ NEW ★★★ Bright purple sheen introduces bouncy, fragrant **02**, Karoo scrub, woodsmoke & plums in bouquet; plentiful rounded flavours. Could be cellared 2/3 yrs.

Pinotage NEW ★★☆ **03** ripe plummy aromas mingle with spicy cherries in palate, with fairly firm ripe tannins; better with a food accompaniment. **Chenin Blanc** ★★★ **04** light & pretty with ripe tropical tones, bright & fresh, balanced acidity. Enjoy soon. **Sauvignon Blanc 04** untasted. Both ranges WO W-Cape unless noted. — *DH*

Mountain Shadows see Vinfruco
Mountainside see Fairseat Cellars, Ruitersvlei
Mount Claire see Cordoba
Mount Marble see Simonsvlei
Mount Maskam see WestCorp

Mount Rozier Estate

Stellenbosch (see Helderberg map) ▪ *Est/1stB 1997* ▪ *Tasting, sales & tours by appt* ▪ *Closed public holidays* ▪ *Conservancy area* ▪ *Owner Atlantic Wine Agencies, Inc* ▪ *Winemaker Jacques Fourie (Sep 2001), advised by Christopher Burr & Larry Cherubino* ▪ *45 ha (cab, merlot, shiraz, chard, sauvignon, semillon)* ▪ *±1 500 cs own label 40% red 60% white* ▪ *PO Box 784 Somerset West 7129* ▪ *wine@mountrozier.co.za* ▪ *www.mountrozier. co.za* ✆ **858·1130** ✉ 858·1131

Extending the cosmopolitan tone of the Helderberg's Schaapenberg area, US-incorporated Atlantic Wine Agencies has taken over the 105-hectare Mount Rozier property next to Vergelegen, and intends to upgrade and expand it into a world-class wine estate with hotel, leisure facilities and high-end housing development. The aim is to establish Mount R as 'a leading SA-orientated New World premium brand' in Europe and US, and to this end group CEO Harry Chauhan has marshalled the international expertise of top Aussie winemaker Larry Cherubino and viticulturist and Master of Wine Christopher Burr to supplement the talents of resident cellarmaster Jacques Fourie. For the prestige Mount Rozier range, emphasis is on identifying and cosseting the best-performing blocks within the existing vineyards. 'This will allow us to trade up in terms of price,' says AWA's SA chief Adam Mauerberger, 'which is a key objective not just for us but for the industry as a whole.' The earlier-drinking Rozier Bay and Rozier Reef ranges contribute to a marine conservation project. Empowerment is another focus, and Monique Lyddell, wife of estate manager Dave, is spearheading a programme to engage the local community.

★★★★ **Cabernet Sauvignon** New release **02** (★★★★) a casualty of difficult vintage, understated dark-berried fruit overshadowed by oak, awkward tannins, unbalanced at 15.2% alc. 27 mths oak, Fr 16% new. Redeemed by **03**, bang on form — ripe mulberry fruit, rings true with cab cedar, mulberry & supportive oak, tannins still young but balanced. 15 mths, Fr 35% new.

★★★★ **Shiraz** NEW Stylish & very elegant. Fragrant choc & cinnamon in **02**, still under the influence of oak, excellent fruit will fight back. Poised despite big build, dark berries abound, hints of smoke & leather. 14.7% alc. Completed fermentation in barrel: Am/Fr all new. Preview of **03**, still bigger, sumptuous, a feast, but loss of elegance. 15.6% alc; also 15 mths Fr /Am, all new, one barrel chestnut!

★★★☆ **Merlot 02** (★★★) another blockbuster, at 15% alc, idiosyncratic blueberry, redolent of furniture polish (27 mths oak), still with firmish tannin; ultra-ripe & spicy from huge oak component. **03** much more recognisably merlot with ripe meaty fruit, balanced oak. 15 mths, Fr 20% new.

★★★☆ **Sauvignon Blanc 04** big notch up on previous. Attractive ripe gooseberry, tropical whiffs, boldly flavoured, slight sweetness from high alc (14.7%), soft acidity.

Shiraz Merlot, Pinotage, Annie Rozier discontinued.

Rozier Bay

All samples, ratings provisional. **Cabernet Sauvignon** ★★★ Inky black, whiff cedar to **03**; mulberry ripeness, but also cab's firmer tannic structure, some youthful astringency, but nice oak there, too. 14% alc. **Merlot** ★★★ **03** sweet, concentrated fruit recalls choccoated prunes, ripe tannins allow for easy accessibility. Alc at 15.5% solid roadblock to easy quaffing. **Pinotage** ★★★ Rich, luscious, lumbering under weight of extrovert fruit in **03**; sweet jammy, ripe tannins, ready to drink. Like a fruit cordial. 14.7% alc. Proportion barrelled. **Chardonnay** ★★★ **04** big & bold, a real upstart! Loads of ripe yellow fruits — peach, apricot, huge whack oak, sweet finish thanks to 14.9% alc. Love or hate style. **Sauvignon Blanc** ★★ **04** unusually scented for sauvignon: baked apple fruit, touches spice, delicious but lacks sauvignon's punch. 12.2% alc.

Rozier Reef

All samples. **Pinotage** ★★☆ **04** ripe pruney fruit, very dry, youthful tannic grip on finish. 14.3% alc. **Merlot** ★★★ Ripe, loads blackcurrant fruit in **04**, fat & juicy tannins to match, subtle oak. 13.5% alc. **Ruby Cabernet** ★★☆ **04** still a bit rough around the edges; robust, crammed with plummy cab-like fruit, just what a ruby is supposed to be.14.3% alc. **Chardonnay** ★★☆ **04** shy with good underlying ripeness, dried peach flavours, smooth acidity. 14% alc. Small proportion staves. **Chenin Blanc** ★★ Dried fruit, nuts on **04**, slender build, tangy. 12.1%alc. **Sauvignon Blanc** ★★★ **04** looks a winner. Packed with green fig & tropical aromas/flavours, lovely sweet-sour tang, mouthwatering finish. — *IvH*

Mount Vernon Farm

Paarl ▪ Est/1stB 2003 ▪ Visits by appt ▪ Closed Easter Fri/Sun, Dec 25/26 & Jan 1 ▪ BYO picnic ▪ Walks ▪ Mountain biking ▪ Owners David & Debbie Hooper ▪ Winemaker Debbie Hooper, with Marius Hector (Jan/Jul 2003) ▪ Viticulturist Phillip du Toit ▪ 28 ha (cab, malbec, merlot, petit v, pinotage, shiraz, chard) ▪ 150 tons 7 000ℓ ▪ mountvernon30@hotmail.com ▪ PO Box 348 Klapmuts 7625 ℂ/🖷 875·5073

Simonsberg-Paarl growers David and Debbie Hooper are reputable suppliers of quality fruit, seeing clients win international awards with their chardonnay, shiraz and pinotage particularly. So, having declined a 1998 dinner-party offer from a vintner friend of winemaking lessons, Debbie H accepted the challenge in 2002. She so enjoyed it, that a shed on their farm was converted into a cellar for the following harvest. Next thing she knew, she had several barrels stashed away. Her inspiration for 'good quality, value-for-money wines'? David Finlayson (nearby Glen Carlou), Jeff Grier (Villiera) and John Nel (Camberley). Her philosophy? Small is beautiful — and an advantage of dealing with small quantities is that 'I'm able to learn new techniques without jeopardising a vast amount of wine'.

Three Peaks Chenin Blanc ☺ ★★★ Whiffs dried pear, spiced melon & quince in maiden **04**, full flavoured & luscious, just the wine to show visitors how delicious SA chenin can be. From low-yielding bush vines. People-friendly 12.5% alc. — *IvH*

Mouton-Excelsior see Mouton House of Wines
Mouton du Cap see Mouton House of Wines

Mouton House of Wines

Cape Town ▪ Est 1988 ▪ 1stB 1985 ▪ Closed to public ▪ Owner Pater Familias Trust ▪ 20 000 cs 70% red 30% white ▪ PO Box 51596 Waterfront 8002 ▪ moutonhouseofwines@wol.co.za ℂ 439·6946 🖷 439·5250

There's been a spring-cleaning here, as negociant Gerda Mouton pares down her range to suit a re-focused marketing strategy. Premier wines under the newer Mouton du Cap label, unready for tasting for this edition, are destined for export, while Itakané, budget-priced wines made on order, is the only label to survive from the past.

Mulderbosch Vineyards

Stellenbosch ▪ Est 1989 ▪ 1stB 1991 ▪ Sales: Mon-Fri 8-5; tasting by appt only ▪ Closed on public holidays ▪ Owner Hydro Holdings ▪ Cellarmaster Mike Dobrovic (1991) ▪ Winemaker Clinton le Sueur (Jun 2001) ▪ Viticulturists Dawid van Papendorp & Desmond Hendriks (vyd manager), advised by Albert Strever ▪ 27 ha (cabs s/f, malbec, petit v, chard, chenin, sauvignon) ▪ 500 tons 30 000 cs 30% red 70% white ▪ PO Box 548 Stellenbosch 7599 ▪ info@mulderbosch.co.za ▪ www.mulderbosch.co.za © 865·2488 ☎ 865·2351

There's a sense of questioning and humour about this cellar — a very bearable lightness of being. (Their answers to our annual list of questions had us rolling with laughter, we wish we could print them all but alas....) Small steps towards organic cultivation appear to be bearing fruit. The petit verdot blocks they experimented with last harvest showed little to no disease. (The spray used was a combination of fulvic acid and orange oil, sardonically named 'Oros' by vineyardist Dane Williams.) The only difficulty during the crush was uneven ripening. 'Sorting tables were hauled out, and most of us suffered from post-harvest hypnotic grape disorder,' says winemaker Mike Dobrovic. An avid reader of philosophy, psychology and poetry, Dobrovic's current favourite is Mowlana Jalaluddin Rumi. Nobody leaves the farm without a sample of the 13th-century Sufi mystic's writings. Dobrovic's parting shot: 'Finally it may be that the sole purpose of my existence is to serve as a warning to others....'

★★★★ Beta Centauri Occasional 'stellar' offering (Alpha, twinkled in **98**) **02** plush modern partner to more laid-back 'Hound'. Gorgeous cedary scents, leafy/minty freshness; 44% cab f important to elegant fruit richness (+ 44% cab, petit v); vibrant tannin needs good few yrs ageing. Effortlessly absorbs 18 mths new Fr oak. 13.5% alc.

★★★★ Faithful Hound 02 (★★★★) Bdx quintet with claret-like lightness (in texture; 13.5% alc), emphasised by very fresh spine. Forward cedary, tobacco scents; slight herbal edge. Tasty, understated; for shorter-term drinking than pvs where quality, excitement increased. **01** enticing ripe red/blackberry. 90 pts *WS*. 13.5% alcs. 50% cab, 35% merlot + petit v, malbec, cab f; 18 mths Fr oak Fr oak, 50% new.

★★★☆ Shiraz 🆕 Dobrovic's considered approach evident in this **02**, with 10% petit v. Hearty smoked meat, savouriness expanded by red fruits, spicy undertones; silkiness diminished by charry oak intrusions, may merge, warrant higher rating after yr/2. 13.8% alc. Fr oak, half new, 18 mths. Young Stbosch/Stanford vyds.

★★★★ Chardonnay Finely poised blend barrel/tank-fermented dishes up usual approachable, satisfying **03**. Forward but not showy creamy lime attractions. Ripe, mouthfilling persistence firmed by touches toasty oak, refreshing minerally acid. Will benefit from yr/2. **02** dense, tapered. 60% fermented/8 mths oak, half new. *WS* favourite: **02**, **01** both 92.

★★★★ Chardonnay Barrel Fermented Adorned with laurels since maiden **97**. Latest **03**, FCTWS trophy, stylish New World refinement; nuanced pickled lime zest, buttered toast; very contained, sleek with fantail finish. 6-8 yrs potential. **02** (★★★★) more obviously oaky, ripe. Developed melon, buttery bouquet; bold, sturdy build. 13.7% alc. CWT gold. Native yeast fermented, 11 mths new Fr oak. All with ±5g/ℓ sugar.

★★★★ Steen-op-Hout ✓ One of first new-wave chenins using oak; 'op-hout' indicating perennial background note. **03** with usual food-friendly affability. Delicate yet persuasive floral-honeyed whispers; grows in mouth to succulent conclusion. From distinguished old hilltop bushvines, brushed (5%) with 2nd fill Am/Fr oak.

★★★★★ Sauvignon Blanc Consistent Cape benchmark over 14 vintages. Recognised for its giddy, pure-fruited vibrancy. **04** greengage/quince/gooseberry deluge. Brilliant, assertive with resounding flavour conclusion, with ±5g/ℓ sugar assistance, as does whole range. 12% alc. Seduces *WS* (and locals): both **03**, **02** 92 pts. —*AL*

Muldersvlei see Westbridge

Muratie Estate

Stellenbosch ▪ Est 1685 ▪ 1stB ca 1920 ▪ Tasting & sales Mon-Fri 9-5 Sat & Sun 10-4 ▪ Fee R20 (incl glass) ▪ Closed Easter Fri, Dec 25 & Jan 1 ▪ Picnic hampers by appt ▪ Tours by appt ▪ Guest house ▪ Art gallery ▪ Owner Melck Family ▪ Winemaker Guillaume Nell (Apr 2003) ▪ Viti consultant Paul Wallace (1998) ▪ 38 ha (cabs, merlot, pinot, shiraz, chard, hanepoot, port varieties) ▪ 210 tons 6 000 cs own label 85% red 15% white ▪ PO Box 133 Koelenhof 7605 ▪ muratie@kingsley.co.za ▪ www.muratie.co.za © 865·2330 ℻ 865·2790

It's finally goodbye to the practice of medicine for Rijk Melck: 'I've decided to spend all my time and energy on the farm. We have a great team and I'm sure we are going to kick butt.' An element of team-building last season must have been the hearty meal 'prepared by our "mother superior", Marieta Kuipers' for the farm's picking staff after every day's harvesting, as is customary in the French winelands. It was, Melck believes, the most extended crush since his arrival at Muratie in 1987 but it yielded 'stunning' merlot and shiraz. Investment in the cellar saw a new pump and crusher installed, and good new French oak in the barrel hall. For winemaker Guillaume Nell, 2004 will have been memorable as his first consultant-less vintage. Two assistants were brought in to help, one from London and the other from Darling, and they 'teamed up wonderfully'.

★★★★ **Cabernet Sauvignon 00** generously built, not yet approachable, promises future pleasures, but touched by austerity. **01** retasted, has developed ripe mulberry notes, deep-pile velvet richness, tannins loosening their grip. Lingering finish has dry tannic element over hint of sweetness. Fine wine, seriously built; 5-8 yrs ahead. 14% alc, yr Fr oak, 25% new. All the major Muratie reds made in mix traditional open fermenters & modern stainless steel.

★★★☆ **Merlot** Current **01** retasted, has developed a meaty dimension to rich dark-berried fruit & charry oak; tannins softening, nearing approachability. 13.9% alc; Fr oak, 25% new. MIWA 2003 gold.

★★★★ **Pinot Noir** SA's first pinot vines planted here just over 75 yrs ago. **01** retasted for this edition, retreating into its shell, quite earthy & austere, tannins still firm — will they relax? Yr Fr oak, 25% new, 14.7% alc.

★★★★ **Shiraz** Seductively fragrant **03** (sample) has black cherry, prune & dark choc aromas, similar flavours. More berries, & more graceful & approachable than previous — both **02** & **01**, deep & dark, full of ripe fruit, savoury acid balancing the firm dry tannin (latter VDG). Properly dry, wrapped in lots of spicy, charry oak (Fr/Am). 13.5% alc. Cellar 5 yrs. Hedonistic maiden **00** (**★★★★★**) was a star of its year.

★★★★ **Ansela** Stylish blend named after slave freed in 1695 who married farm's first owner. **02** right on the money: terrific whiff cab cedar & dark choc, follows through for finely wrought complexity, more relaxed & graceful than the estate's single varieties. Blend cab s, merlot, cab f, 50/30/20, 16 mths Fr oak, 25% new. Modest 12.3% alc. For shorter-term ageing. **01** was from cab s & f only; succulent & ripe.

★★★★ **Isabella** (Sample) **04** terrific yeasty brioche, dried peach invitation; creamy breadth already evident, long resonating finish. Let's hope this fine chardonnay makes it into bottle as is. Whole bunch pressed, barrel fermented, still in oak mid-2004, Fr 18% new. **02**, **03** untasted, sold out. 13% alc.

★★★★ **Cape Vintage** Continues with more classical approach in **01** (**★★★★**), vinified in open fermenters; traditional port varieties, tintas b/r/f, souzão, 3 yrs oak. Deep mulberry hue, plummy depths misleading as this is surprisingly easy drinking. More LBV-style approachability. Sweet & warm for cold winter's evenings.

Melck's Red ★★★ All-sorts black grapes (four varieties, cabs ruby & sauvignon dominant) in latest **02**; ripe, pruney fruit, still some harsh tannins; honest & no frills. **Port ★★★** Youthful berry quality to current release, light & fruity. Not overly sweet, warm alcoholic heart. Made Ruby style for more casual wintertime tippling. Sugar 107g/ℓ & alc 19.1%. From Portuguese varieties; NV. **Amber Forever ★★★** Fortified muscat d'A, popular for over 75 yrs. Like a lollipop, but a delicious one. Fragrant with mint & honey, deliciously fresh, sweetness enlivened by sprightly acidity in **03**. – *IvH*

Mystery Wine Corporation

Cape Town ■ *1stB 2002* ■ *Owner Saul Gorin* ■ *4 000 cs 40% red 50% white 10% rosé* ■ *PO Box 281 Sea Point 8060* ■ *info@mysterywines.co.za* ■ *www.mysterywines.co.za* ℂ *083·628·5160* 🖷 *403·4867*

The only mystery that needs solving here is how Saul Gorin manages to pour this much value into these bottles, with their famously full-bodied labels. He's sticking to his guns when it comes sourcing the best possible wines for his growing base of customers. Bronze medals at the FCTWS for two consecutive Dry White vintages are a good indication of consistent quality. With real cork a cost, alternative closures will be used in future bottlings, probably synthetics while Gorin considers his verdict on screwcaps.

Dry Red ★★★ Ultra-suave **02**, mouthfilling & juicy; retasted: spicy aromas, balanced red berry flavours & appealing grip; blend ruby cab, cinsaut, shiraz, pinotage, lightly oaked. **Tickled Pink** ★★ **02** rosé from merlot; now herbaceous rather than red fruit aromas, seeming a bit tired. **Dry White** ★★★ Mainly chenin, jazzed up with 10% sauvignon; **03** attractive lemon cream aroma, tastily fresh & zingy-dry, hint passionfruit on finish. **Melon** NEW ★★★ Naming outstanding features of nude on front-label or flavour inside bottle? Both are apt, though flavour's the more reigned in, & touch sweet for some palates. Clean & easy drinking, though — will win plenty of fans. Enjoy young. — *JB*

Nabygelegen Private Cellar

Wellington ■ *Est 1712* ■ *1stB 2002* ■ *Tasting & sales Mon-Fri 10–5 Sat 10–1* ■ *Tasting fee R10 incl glass* ■ *Closed Easter Fri/Sun, Apr 27, May 1, Dec 25 & Jan 1* ■ *Tours anytime by appt* ■ *BYO picnic* ■ *Walks* ■ *Owners Avalon Vineyards (Pty) Ltd* ■ *Winemaker Charles Stassen (Jan 2003)* ■ *Viti consultant Johan Wiese (May 2001)* ■ *18 ha (cab, merlot, petit v, tempranillo, chenin, sauvignon)* ■ *2 800 cs 40% red 60% white* ■ *PO Box 302 Wellington 7854* ■ *avalonwines@icon. co.za* ■ *www.nabygelegen.co.za* ℂ *873·7534/ 082·829·1189* 🖷 *873·7534*

Stone Age implements and hand axes are regularly unearthed in these deep red soils by the vineyard team (some are on view in the tasting room). Nabygelegen has a long history of winemaking, too, and mindful of maintaining the link with the past, present owner James McKenzie has restored the original cellar's thick buttress walls and deep cool tanks, and installed the latest equipment. With extensive and on-going replanting of the vineyards, the wines already starting to gain acclaim — and sold-out status.

★★★★ **1712** NEW ✓ Characterful **03** classic Bdx blend merlot, cab, petit v (64/29/7), showing spicy red fruit notes on a serious structure, supported by yr oak. 14% alc fairly modest for area. Youthful; should develop 3+ yrs still.

Chenin Blanc ★★★ Last sampled was sensuously emphatic, lightly wooded **03**. **Sauvignon Blanc** ★★★★ Step-up **04** lively floral, grassy nose, with gooseberry & pineapple fruitiness; big acid; light (12.8% alc), dry & lingering finish. **Chenin Blanc-Sauvignon Blanc** ★★★ Melon & peaches from 81% chenin, sauvignon's grassiness; honey & cream hint from dash semillon on **04**. Flying with Aeroflot in style. 13% alc; dry, but touch sugar for richness. — *NP*

Naledi see Savanha
Namaqua see WestCorp
Namaqua Organic see Stellar Winery

Napier Winery

Wellington ■ *Est 1993* ■ *1stB 1994* ■ *Visits by appt* ■ *Owners: see intro* ■ *Winemaker/viticulturist Leon Bester (Apr 2000)* ■ *34 ha (five Bdx reds, shiraz, chard, chenin)* ■ *±5 500 cs 36% red 64% white* ■ *PO Box 638 Wellington 7654* ■ *napwines@iafrica.com napierwines@ mweb.co.za* ■ *www.napierwinery.co.uk* ℂ *873·7829* 🖷 *864·2728*

After bidding a farewell to co-founders Chris and Val Kühn, who recently retired, a new team slotted into place: chairman Chris Bertie, wine aficionado and head of the Halcyon group (Bay Hotel in Cape Town among its landmarks); Maria Constantinides, taking charge of marketing; and Laurent Desfarges, technical and infrastructure. Leon Bester still makes the wines and manages the estate. Changes include a cellar redesign by Paarl architect Johan Wessels to accommodate 13ha of vines coming on-stream this year.

★★★★ Red Medallion Individual Bdx-inspired blend cabs s/f, merlot, 18–24 mths in Fr barrels, ±30% new, 2 yrs bottle-matured at cellar. Next-up **01** (sample) unveils a plushness not seen in recent yrs. Dark-choc & mocha tones; velvety ripe palate with dry savoury tannins. 60/20/20 assemblage, 14.5% alc. Promising.

St Catherine Barrel-fermented/aged chardonnay, **02** not ready for tasting. **Greenstone Chenin Blanc ★★★** Latest **03** juicier, less austerely dry & firm than pvs; spicy apple & lemongrass sniffs, slight waxiness to palate adds to appeal; ex-35 yr old vines; aged *sur lie* 3 mths. — *TM/JB*

Nature's Group see Oranjerivier
Natuvin see Stellar Winery

Nederburg Wines

Paarl ▪ Est 1792 ▪ 1stB ca1940 ▪ Tasting & sales Mon-Fri 8.30-5; Sat 10–2 (Apr-Oct); Sat 10-4 & Sun 11-4 (Nov-Mar) ▪ Informal tasting fee dependent on wine; tasting & tour: R20 ▪ Closed Easter Fri, Dec 25 & Jan 1 ▪ Tours in Afrikaans, English, French & German by appt ▪ Picnic lunches by appt Mon-Sun Nov-Mar ▪ Corporate & private lunches/dinners by appt ▪ Tourgroups ▪ Gifts ▪ Conferences ▪ Conservation area ▪ Owner Distell ▪ Cellarmaster Razvan Macici (Jan 2001) ▪ Winemakers Andrea Freeborough & Elunda Basson (whites, reds, Jan 2000/2001), with Wellington Metshane & Pieter Badenhorst (reds, whites, Mar 2001/Jan 2003) ▪ Viticulturist Hannes van Rensburg ▪ 15 000 tons ▪ 1.1m cs ▪ Private Bag X3006 Paarl 7620 ▪ nedwines@distell.co.za ▪ www.nederburg.co.za © 862·3104 🖷 862·4887

Nederburg as the flagship of Cape wine? A possible Penfold's of SA? If it comes to pass, this most audacious of transformations may have begun in 2004. The right crew's in place: Cpt Razvan Macici (the thoroughly engaged — and engaging — Romanian cellarmaster); mates Andrea Freeborough (white wines) and Elunda Basson (reds). And the great old winery Nederburg, finally declared shipshape after an R80m overhaul. There's space for micro-vinification (small blocks, longer skin contact, whole-bunch pressing) but also macro quantities (thanks to large-scale automation). A phenomenal 8 000 barrels are deployed, offering a choice of French, American, Hungarian and Romanian oak. Ranges and labelling have been streamlined. It's full steam ahead: 130% off-shore growth by early 2004; 700 000ℓ of Sauvignon projected sold out by end-2004, allocations pending; Chardonnay set to follow; Edelrood, Baronne, Cab alone totalled 3.7m litres. On the horizon: sauvignon and shiraz are 'focus varieties'. Finally, the helmsman poses a question: 'Aren't we in danger of becoming so terroir-obsessed that we are foregoing one of wine's greatest joys: its complexity of character?'

Private Bin wines for Nederburg Auction

The Nederburg Auction, now in its 31st yr, is SA's biggest. It's open to any producer whose wine passes the selection process (Nederburg also subject to strenuous screening). The gavel is wielded by Patrick Grubb MW, inaugural & still incumbent auctioneer. 2004 sales of R6.7m were down on 2003's record R7.5m, mainly due to the stronger rand and difficult trading conditions. Local buyers, led by retail chains Pick 'n Pay, Makro and Checkers, again accounted for more than 80% of purchases. The average price per btl was R100 (compared with R1.50 in 1975!). The highest prices in 2004 were paid for: Monis Collectors Port 'Stamp Collection' 1948 (R2 000/btl); Lanzerac Pinotage 1964 (R1 033); Hamilton Russell Chardonnay 2001 (R266); De Wetshof Edeloes (R300; 500ml btl); JC le Roux Chardonnay MCC (R530; 3ℓ btl); Nuy White Muscadel Full Sweet 1997 (R68). The Nederburg wines below are made in small quantities, usually from special vyd blocks, offered in lots of ±500 cs. Originally labelled under a meaningless Bin number, prefaced by a letter (R=dry red, D dry white, S dessert, C Cap Classique), they now also carry the variety/blend.

★★★★ **Cabernet Sauvignon Private Bin R163** 'New World' style – cellar's premium selection of ripe fruit infuses sappy finesse into **02**: dense colour, deep cassis flavour with minty freshness, liquorice tail. Yard off big, rich **01**; focused blackberry fruits embroidered with smoothly sweet tannin. ±14% alcs.

★★★★ **Cabernet Sauvignon-Merlot Private Bin R109** Signature ripe, juicy cab frame softened, broadened by meaty merlot in **02** (60/40 blend). Quieter than emphatic **01**: concentrated cassis, super length of fruit interwoven with lacy tannins; 2 yrs 'best wood'; entirely modern makeover from **00**.

★★★★ **Cabernet Sauvignon-Shiraz Private Bin R103** Sports-model version of the Baronne family sedan; now 50/50 blend from **02**, & shiraz takes centre stage: choc sheen to richly spiced red/black berries, bolder than mint-toned **01** which 60/40 cab/shiraz, sweet edge from 20% Am oak. Now 2 yrs Fr oak. ±14% alcs.

★★★★ **Shiraz-Cabernet Sauvignon Private Bin R115 02** billows with fried spices, coriander/pimento fullness dusted with white pepper, hung-game girth to palate. Sweet tannins. No **01**. 60/40 Darling/Dbnville combo, lavished with 2 yrs Fr oak.

★★★★ **Merlot Private Bin R181** Pedigree upgrade secured by **02** in line with elegance from **01**. Latest offers ripe red fruits mingled with choc/bacon characters, enduring tapered mouthful, gentle tannins & late mint lift. **01** elevated quality plane; layers of violets, smoked meat unobtrusive in sculptured frame. 500 cs.

★★★★ **Pinotage Private Bin R172** Selection vyd fruit not unscathed in patchy harvest yr, next **02** (★★★★) trenchant prune/plum character, chewy mouthful. Serious **01** lashed with 2 yrs new oak; essence of ripe, spicy red berries in vinous fabric.

★★★★ **Shiraz Private Bin R121** 'Shiraz doesn't mind the vintage', avers Macici & it shows in **02**. Fennel, liquorice hues to zippy, spiced fruit, thoroughly delicious mouthful, approachable even in youth. Masterly **01** well-tailored fruit & roasted spice; dash viognier (9%) adds perfume, softens peppery tone. ±14% alcs.

★★★★ **Sangiovese-Barbera-Nebbiolo Private Bin** A mouthful in name & glass as noted (not retasted); maiden **01** 'Italian Blend' became kaleidoscope of sumptuous black cherry & berry flavours. 70/20/10 blend; mix Hungarian, Fr, Am oak. No **02**.

★★★★ **Petit Verdot Private Bin R104** Fruit ex-Plaisir de Merle, now tailor-made for Auction. **02** redolent of purple pastilles, bursting with juicy cherry/red berry fruits, shepherded into line by fine, yielding structure. **01** in similar style with grassy, linear finish. VDG. Ladles of novelty, limited 6 000ℓ.

★★★☆ **Malbec Private Bin R101** Bags of individuality dished out by ripe Bottlry fruit. **02** still closed mid-2004, but colour intensity, tannic core should yield tapered fruit in time. **01** (★★★★), juiced-up choc-mint succulence, 14.5% alc. VDG.

★★★☆ **Cabernet Franc Private Bin 01** one-off bottling for Auction. New interest: ripe plum sheen to dark-choc/currant flesh, oak succulence. Not retasted for this ed.

★★★★ **Chardonnay Private Bin D270** Striking **03** (★★★★) shifts focus to minerally, stony intensity; fabulous fruit gains patina from top-end Burgundian barrels. Revisited mid-2004: developed richness, finish tethered by crisp acidity. 13 mths Fr oak. Stbosch, Dbnville sources. **Private Bin D166** discontinued after **02**.

★★★★ **Sauvignon Blanc** Two distinct sources & styles: similar class. **Private Bin D215** spotlights pithy tropical characters of Dbnvlle; **04** cornucopia of peaches & pines, mid-palate boost tails off. **03** more delicate. **Private Bin D234** Form given on **04** to racy intensity of Darling vyd's capsicum character with herbaceous explosion in mouth. Length of finish suggests a match for **03**, Macici's 'best yet': penetrating gunpowder flintiness, rivetting focus of flavour. VDG.

★★★☆ **Sauvignon Blanc-Chardonnay Private Bin D253** NEW **04** closed on nose mid-2004, rich creamy breadth to tingling core suggests flavour will unfold in 1-2 yrs. 70/30 blend; chard barrel-fermented 3 mths, full malo.

★★★★ **Sauvignon Blanc-Semillon Private Bin D252** Green-pea **02**; **03** 60/40 blend tingled with sauvignon flint; no **04** as quality semillon in short supply.

★★★☆ **Semillon-Viognier Private Bin D224** NEW As 'the suits' dithered in allocating a bin number (usually the clone for single varieties; blends more arbitrary), Macici decided his birthdate (22 April) would do. 'Having fun' embodied in **03**: peach-pip aromas jest with full waxy spice in exotic 60/40 assemblage (both 2nd fill Fr oak).

★★★★ **Semillon Private Bin D266 03** intensely reductive fruit to match brisk frame. Not retasted for this ed. No **04** due to a paucity of quality semillon.

★★★★ **Viognier Private Bin 03** Poised muscat scents, ripe apricot-pip fruits & gentle oak (30% ferment in new Fr). Not retasted. No **02**.

★★★★ **Gewurztraminer Private Bin D259** 🆕 Macici's viticultural 'Save the rhino' – to prevent grubbing-up of low-yielding old vines (made Günter Brözel Winemaker of the Year in 1985!). **04** alluring scents at entry to very ripe, deeply concentrated – powerful – palate. Refreshingly dry 2.5g/ℓ sugar, potential ★★★★ when ready.

★★★★ **Edelkeur** Queen of SA botrytis desserts holds court again with unctuously rich new-millennium releases. Sample **04** bulging with flavour in infancy, massively concentrated, celestial potential. **03** & **02** not tasted for this ed. **01** glistening tangerine twist to apricot/peach nose, great palate complexity. 100% chenin.

★★★★ **Semillon Noble Late Harvest** Always good value at Auction. No **03**. **02** brooding sheep's wool tones, quince in elegant length. Sugars on 200g/ℓ. Not retasted.

★★★★ **Weisser Riesling Noble Late Harvest Private Bin S316** 'A bastard to make, but it makes us proud', says RM. Delicate, perfumed, aromatic pistachio nuttiness to next **03**, rich botrytis balanced by refreshing – near spearmint – viscosity. **02** not tasted for this ed. Very ripe **01** has citrus tang to cut the honey richness.

★★★★ **Eminence** 100% muscadel provenance flaunted in grapey character; easier than sweet siblings above. Sample **03** big in all ways: scents, structure… & 200g/ℓ sugar. More retiring **02** interplay muscat allure, layered botrytis texture ends in juicy tangy tail, lighter 120g/ℓ sugar.

Other Private Bin wines

★★★★ **Cabernet Sauvignon** Restoration of former Nederburg finesse from **00**. Marks time in **02**: juicy structure hinged with mint, blackcurrant fruits still reticent. Super **01** (★★★★). 2 yrs Fr, eastern European oak.

★★★★ **Shiraz** Emerging as cellar signature; **02** (★★★★) with purple radiance, smoky, fried spice fruit, soft, yielding tannins. 2 yrs oak (2nd as blend of Philadelphia, Dbnvlle components. **01** marked return to stable – and quality. Expanded 40 000 ℓ quantity.

★★★★ **Chardonnay** Flamboyant modern style pleasing judges as far afield as Prague. **03** aromatic relief to concentrated citric fruit; more delicate than fulsome **02** with bold, nutty, white pear flesh. Fermented/13 mths new oak; full malo, big ±14% alcs.

★★★★ **Sauvignon Blanc** 'Sensational', says Macici of **04**: we agree. Judicious blend Darling & Dbnville fruit affords piercing flavour intensity bridled into riveting focus. ±1% infusion of semillon made in NLH style adds flesh; sweeter (4g/ℓ sugar) than focused fig fruit polished by green tints in dry **03**.

Classic range

★★★★ **Edelrood** Quintessential Nederburg red back in its rightful place, deflects difficult **02** harvest with ease (helped, perhaps, by 'new technologies' like oak staving, micro-oxygenation). Herbaceous tints introduce sweetly ripened red/black berries, meaty characters enliven firm finish. Pace set by warm choc/tar **01**. 60/40 cab/merlot blend, the Cellarmaster's housewine.

★★★★ **Baronne** Riper fruit & succulent oak have delivered this stalwart back to reliable respectability since **01**. **02** tops 1.5m ℓ without missing a beat: chunky, richly spiced shiraz fruit leads palate, juicy cab provides undercarriage (40/60 blend).

★★★★ **Cabernet Sauvignon** Fresh, sappy **02**: linear blackberry fruit formed by clean wood, grippy finish satisfies. Well-juiced currant flesh on **01**. (**99** last to bear 'Paarl' name.) Now 1.2m ℓ.

★★★★ **Shiraz** 'Still a baby' (in volume), Macici's bet for Nederburg's future, relaunched with bold spicy **01** after 4 yrs. **02** fruit now from Darling, Dbnville, Philadelphia. Smoky interest to juicy, ripe-berried fruit, chewy tail. 14.5% alc.

★★★☆ **Sauvignon Blanc** Entry-level bottling of cellar's 'focus' white variety achieves above its station, though volumes grown to 0.7m ℓ in **04**: tropical sweet gooseberry flesh layers reductive nettled core, firm finish. Steely, green pepper **03**.

★★★☆ **Rhine Riesling** ✓ **04**, with 10% gewürz, enticingly aromatic, floral perfume boosted by fleshy quince, crisp racy tail. Touch drier (9.5g/ℓ sugar) than ripe raisin-enriched **03** that raised the bar. 'Almost Private Bin (70 000ℓ) quantities.'

★★★★ **Noble Late Harvest** Sumptuous 'sticky' in league of the Auction stars above; ditto demand. **03** upholstered peaches & cream opulence toned by cool tropical lines, fantastic fresh finish. **02** honeyed botrytis lifted by acid fillip. **01** IWSC gold. Chenin, Cape Riesling, muscat. Sugars 200g/ℓ. 375 ml.

Rosé ☺ ★★★ 'Pink makes me happy' says Macici of this charming mouthful of cranberry fruit flecked with savoury interest, from cinsaut. **04** crisp finish carries 20g/ℓ sugar. Dry version exported to Germany.

Pinotage ★★★ Unambiguous **02** offers typical ripe cherry, warm spicy berries. Acetone edge but not jammy or bitter. **Chardonnay** ★★★☆ Unabated overseas demand for this generous style likely to be fuelled by **03**'s clever melange citrus fruit warmed by partial oaking, breadth of malo. **Prelude** ★★★ 65/35 blend sauvignon-chardonnay, latter briefly in oak, gears up in **04**: white pepper backbone fleshed out by creamy fullness. **Paarl Riesling** ★★★ Exponential demand limited by grape supply (crouchen blanc). **04** true to form, thatchy, crisp finish. Enjoy fresh. **Premier Grand Cru** ★★ Usual bracing steely finish lifted by fruity tones from ripe chenin in latest NV (04). <2g/ℓ sugar. **Stein** ★★ Ever-popular semi-sweet with fresh chenin touch on **04**. **Special Late Harvest** ★★★ Lavish raisin botrytis lifts **04** – clean, fresh, full. Uncloying 50g/ℓ sugar. **Chenin Blanc** discontinued.

Lifestyle range
Duet ★★★ 75/25 pinot/cab blend a wow in Germany – **03** sold out, not tasted. **04** smiling cherry fruit unobscured by wood or tannin. **Lyric** ★★ **04** Inoffensive off-dry quaffer due for fruit upgrade late 2004: chenin to replace crouchen in sauvignon/chardonnay fusion.

Sparkling range
Premiere Cuvée Brut ★★★ NV. Base wine now finished at sister-cellar JC le Roux, carbonated, crisp & dry, always refreshing. Discontinued: **Blanquette**; **Premiere Cuvée Doux**; **Kap Sekt**. – *DS*

Neethlingshof Estate

Stellenbosch ▪ Tasting & sales daily 9-7 (closes at 5pm Mar 1-Nov 30) ▪ Fee R25 (R30 incl cellar tour) ▪ Also tasting/sales of Stellenzicht wines ▪ Closed Easter Fri & Dec 25 ▪ Tours by appointment ▪ Lord Neethling Restaurant, Palm Terrace ▪ Play area for children ▪ Tourgroups ▪ Conferences ▪ Owner Lusan Premium Wines ▪ Winemaker DeWet Viljoen ▪ Viticulturists Hannes van Zyl & Peet Blom ▪ 210 ha ▪ 50 000 cs 70% red 30% white ▪ PO Box 104 Stellenbosch 7599 ▪ info@neethlingshof.co.za ▪ www.neethlingshof.co.za © 883·8988 ✆ 883·8941

Winemaker De Wet Viljoen had a baptism of fire (almost literally, given the scorching heat of February 2004), doused by rain two months later. He was grateful for the latter, however, as it obviated the need for post-harvest irrigation. His general feeling is the vintage will produce a few very good wines, with the NLH the best of them. Talking of the best of wines: the Lord Neethling Pinotage 00 won a gold at the 2004 IWSC in London. News of the award coincided with 'growing sales in an increasingly tough international market'.

Lord Neethling range
★★★★★ **Laurentius** Splendid & serious blend, launched with **97**, largely cab, with 10% merlot, dollop malbec; **98** was cab/shiraz, DG at 2003 Michelangelo; **99** (★★★☆) cabs s/f, merlot, shiraz (70/14/8/8), somewhat less dazzling mid-2004; stalky edge to fragrant black fruits; dry, tight; needs time. Yr oak, 10% Am. 14% alc.

★★★★ **Cabernet Sauvignon** Current **00** (★★★) harks back to the more severe tones of **98**, which needed some yrs to open. The new version is unsophisticated, very dry with pronounced acidity. 14% alc. **99** was a classic Cape cab: ripe mulberry fruit backed by fine new oak, with ripe tannic structure. ±16 mths Fr oak.

★★★★ **Cabernet Franc** Latest is **02** (★★★), with pronounced green pepper character, very dry finish. 14% alc. Fr oak, some new, 14 mths. No **01**. **00** was a hedonist's delight – gorgeous bouquet, pristine fruit undimmed by expensive oak. **99** won gold at 2002 IWSC. Off vines planted in 1987.

★★★★★ **Pinotage** Usually has more style, personality than version below, so **01** (★★★) doubtless a fleeting diversion into quieter, sparser territory; very dry, unyielding; nowhere near as expressive as IWSC-lauded blockbuster **00**, almost a caricature of pinotage, so concentrated, rich; **99** also arresting.

★★★★★ **Chardonnay** Show-stopping **02** not retasted. Pvsly we noted wafting vanilla oak, ripe stone fruit, touches mimosa, cinnamon – truly fragrant. Generously built & fleshy, luxurious. Barrel-fermented/aged 7 mths new Fr oak. 14.3% alc.

Standard range

★★★☆ **Cabernet Sauvignon 01** green pepper nose & simple, sweet oak; minty palate fleshed out with easy red fruit. 2 yrs Fr oak, 1st-3rd fill. **00** had all the correct flavours – cedar, cassis, pencil shavings – to satisfy cab lovers.

★★★★ **Shiraz** Usually obliging & amiable, though current **01** youthfully brooding, introverted; needs time to harmonise & develop. 19 mths barriques, some new. 14.5% alc. **00** had huge ripeness (14.9% alc) well concealed beneath elegant oak.

★★★★ **Cape Blend** Mostly for export, though some available from estate. Current **01** not retasted for this ed; mainly unwooded red, blend of cabs s/ f, pinotage (40/28/22) with dash cab. Mid-2003 youthful tannins were still in charge.

★★★★ **Gewürztraminer** Lovely example, could even subvert those who only drink dry. Refined & elegant, ±10g/ℓ sugar softens rather than sweetens when well balanced by acidity, as in **04** (sample) classic rose-petal bouquet, soft grapey flavour. Includes splash riesling. **03** had perfect poise, bigger build (14.2% alc) than pvs.

★★★☆ **Sauvignon Blanc** From their False Bay-facing vyds; **04** (sample) youthful, generously fruity, appealing citrus/tropical flavours. **03** was an attention-grabber (★★★★★); a real achievement from this demanding variety.

★★★★★ **Weisser Riesling Noble Late Harvest** Much decorated since **90**, national champion NLH of yr. Recent in more modern, generally drier mode (118g/ℓ), in keeping with current taste. **04** not ready for tasting; **03** had delightful tangerine peel, orange marmalade & honey tones.

Merlot ★★★ The new (**01**) version not tasted; **00** was blended with 15% cab, showed as somewhat gruff & forbidding, needing time. **Pinotage** ★★★ Now more seriously oaked – 17 mths Fr/Am for **01**, with old-style organic/acetone whiffs, pinot-like flavour spectrum, dry finish. 14%. **Cabernet Sauvignon-Merlot** ★★★★ We latest tasted **00**, classically constructed, intelligently oaked. **Chardonnay** ★★★ **03** has strapping 14.8% alc, equally obvious toasty oak from 50% wooded portion (4 mths, Fr). Overt butteriness cushioned by racy acidity on the finish. — RK

Neil Ellis Wines

Stellenbosch • 1stB 1984 • Tasting & sales Mon-Fri 9.30-4.30 Sat & public holidays 10-2 • Fee subject to quotation • Closed Easter Fri/Sun, Dec 25/26 & Jan 1 • Owner Neil Ellis Wines (Pty) Ltd • Winemaker Neil Ellis • 35 000 cs • 50% red 50% white • PO Box 917 Stellenbosch 7599 • info@neilellis.com • www.neilellis.com © 887·0649 ▤ 887·0647

Two decades ago, Neil Ellis took a pioneering step away from the tradition of growing grapes and then surrendering their identity to the big producers. As SA's first negociant, he bought in grapes he'd identified as special (presciently, as it turned out), and vinified them in a leased cellar. Now the acknowledged leader draws on three main areas: Elgin (on the chardonnay-only Hall Farm, an empowerment project), Groenekloof in the Darling foothills, and Jonkershoek, on the Oude Nektar estate owned by his long-time partner Hans-Peter Schröder. 'I'm taking a bigger look at Elgin,' reveals Ellis. 'One of my growers there has put in some reds and we've made some wines that I'm very excited about.' As we spoke, he was on his way to the area to investigate some more pockets of land. His thinking now is that terroir-specificity will extend to producing several unique wines from a single block. On a personal note, Ellis's son Warren graduated in viticulture and oenology at the end of 2003 and embarked on a Master's. 'He probably won't go into winemaking but end up as an academic,' says his father, wryly. For what it's worth, another local big-shooter, André van Rensburg of Vergelegen, is one who believes the youngster has potential to reach the pinnacle of SA winemaking. Listening, Jnr?

Vineyard Selection range
Single-vyd 'reserves', WO Jonkershoek Valley, for long maturation.

★★★★★ **Cabernet Sauvignon** Understated class from these cooler Oude Nektar vyds. Benefited from long-ripening **01** with trademark expressive deep dark-berry, cedar-oak aromas, taut minerally mouthfeel; promises unfolding over time. No **02** – not up to standard. New oak (Fr, 18 mths), 13.5% alc. Pedigree recognised in **01** 90 pts *WS;* **00** Wine ★★★★☆; *Decanter* ★★★★; IWC gold; VDG.

★★★★ **Shiraz** Last tasted **01** (★★★★★), 90 pts *WS,* epitomises Ellis principle of 'power with elegance'. Ambrosial allspice scents, spicy fruits, ripe fine-grained tannins. Wonderfully 'cool' finish. Will reward patience – enjoy from 2008. No **02**. 16 mths new Fr casks, 13.5% alc.

Premium range
★★★★☆ **Stellenbosch Cabernet Sauvignon** ✓ Classic cab – moderate alcohols, understated oaking, with modern refinements – ripe fruit, tannins, always with vintage character. Herbal touch to lighter, leaner & paler **02** (★★★★). Agreeable, if less complex than usual; enjoy while waiting for brilliant **01**'s juicy cassis fruit, fine-tuned tannin, mineral intensity to mature. ±18 mths Fr oak, 50% new.

★★★★ **Stellenbosch Pinotage** ✓ **03** sampled ex-cask, as were two following reds, illustrates excellent vintage. Bright, healthy colour; full flavour spectrum with modern refinement, medium body. Confidently structured for lengthy life. **02** svelte interplay of clove-spiked plums & well-meshed tannins. Polished ±15 mths Fr oak.

★★★★ **Stellenbosch Shiraz** These dense, substantial but never rustic, chunky or overblown. **03** hugely concentrated, yet refined; layers mulberry/dark spicy flavours; long, digestibly dry. Will be magnificent in maturity, 11-13. **02** accessible earlier than intense, complex **01**. ±15 mths Fr oak.

★★★★ **Stellenbosch Cabernet Sauvignon-Merlot** Stylish, distinctive blend. **03** stunner-in-making (min ★★★★★). Resonating layers perfectly ripe black berries, cassis; fine, dusty grip, minerally length. Great presence, complexity. Deserves 2/3 yrs before broaching; long-lived: ±8 yrs. **02** broader choc-sheen, fleshy meat notes. Super finish. Usually approachable young; better after five yrs. Fr oak ±15 mths.

★★★★ **Stellenbosch Chardonnay** This & Elgin **03** below, twins in elegance, though far from identical. Quality yr displayed cooler profile than usual in Stbosch. Fresh tropical lime intensity in rippling, supple mouthfeel, some hazelnut/toasty oak enrichment on tapered finish. Complementary Fr oaking (fermented/±10 mths). Potential to 2008. Home vyds. **02** powerful; excellent length. 13.5% alc.

★★★★ **Elgin Chardonnay 03** (★★★★☆) not a feature out of place; minerally tension, compact form resonant of high, cool vyds. Initial daintiness, then embryonic savoury oatmeal depths; focused, tangy length. Should be long-lived (to 2010-13). Oaking (as per above) tightens rather than expands. **02** delicate spiced cream, minerally tapered palate. 13.5% alc.

★★★★★ **Groenekloof Sauvignon Blanc** ✓ Has helped put SA on world map. Consistent fruit quality upholds perfect match with Atlantic-influenced Darling site. **04** usual show-stopping form in bigger, more luscious mode. Rich, juicily concentrated gooseberry, fig flavours unfurl with incredible length; paced by regular scythe savoury acidity. Racy **03** more taut grass, piercing nettles. 13.5% alc. – *AL*

Nelson Estate
🍴 🍷 ◎ ⊚⊚ ♿

Paarl ▪ Est/1stB 1993 ▪ Tasting & sales Mon-Fri 9-5 Sat 9-2 Sun by appt ▪ Fee R10, waived on purchase of 6 btls ▪ Closed Easter Fri/Sun & Dec 25 ▪ Tours Mon-Sat 10; Sun by appt ▪ Meals/refreshments by appt ▪ Facilities for children ▪ Tourgroups ▪ Gifts ▪ Walks ▪ Conference/function/lapa venue ▪ Conservation area ▪ Owner Alan Nelson ▪ Winemaker Jean van Rooyen, with Natasha Kotzé (Dec 2003/Mar 2004) ▪ Viticulturist Walter Schloms (Dec 2001) ▪ 60 ha (cab, merlot, pinotage, shiraz, chard, sauvignon) ▪ 340 tons 20 000 cs own label 65% red 30% white 5% own label ▪ PO Box 2009 Windmeul 7630 ▪ info@nelsonscreek.co.za ▪ www. nelsonscreek.co.za Ⓒ 869·8453 🖷 869·8424

It's been a watershed year for the Nelson family. They celebrated 10 years on the estate, and patriarch Alan hung up his advocate's gown after 25 years in Cape Town practice to focus full-time on the rapidly expanding winery. Stellenbosch University-trained daughter Lisha polished her skills with a further season at Mulderbosch and visits to Australia and France before joining Jean van Rooyen (ex-Waboomsrivier) and assistant Natasha Kotzé, fresh from Cape Technikon, in the home-cellar. The visitor facilities, already impressively varied, were extended with the opening of a third conference and function venue. A tourist attraction in own right is Victor Titus, their 'cellar-door manager'. Ranked by Alan N as 'the most highly qualified man of colour in the SA wine industry', Titus offers 'one of the most informative and interesting cellar and vineyard tours in the country'.

Nelson Estate range

- ★★★★ **Cabernet Sauvignon-Merlot** The **02** Cab & Merlot tasted from barrel last yr were blended to produce this stylish ensemble (81/19), all Fr oak, 18 mths, 80% new. (All N-E reds feature saignée-style drawing-off some juice pre-fermentation, for heightened flavour concentration; here 30% was bled). Classic cassis/cigarbox aroma; firm, slightly grainy tannins; solid ripe fruit core; wood a deftly applied condiment. Just needs couple of yrs to soften, unfold. 14.8% alc.

- ★★★★ **Pinotage 02** denser, (even) bigger than N-C version below (15% alc); has settled down with extra yr in bottle, initial big dry tannins now less feisty; suffused with a rich mocha/smoked meat character — appealingly showy. 18 mths Fr oak.

- ★★★★ **Chardonnay** Forceful, creamy style, lots of concentrated flavour & structure, imparted by native yeast fermentation, extended lie-in on lees (11 mths); 75% new Fr, 25% unwooded for freshness, balance; **02** revisited shows rich lemon cream biscuit character — flagrant New-World styling with some balance. **03** (★★★★) somewhat quieter mid-2004, more Old World; also attractive, possibly needs time.

Shiraz ★★★★ Extra yr has tamed the exuberance; **02** now shows as full but not overpowering; well layered with peppery red fruit, warm toast & coffee tones. 14.8% alc.

Nelson's Creek range

- ★★★★ **Merlot** Medium-bodied, soft dry red; quietly appealing; **00** (★★★) low-key aromas, jammy red-fruit palate. 18 mths 2nd fill Fr oak. **99** quiet, generously padded.

- ★★★★ **Pinotage** Unwooded **02** drinks well now; grape's signature banana/mulberry tones embellished with wholesome earthy tinge; silky texture. 14% alc. **Pinotage Limited Edition** This barrelled version tasted as early sample for pvs ed, not revisited. **02** was lashed with oak (±60% new, of which 10% Am) mid-2003; ripe, strapping, but brimming with potential (★★★★★?) Set for release after stocks of above N-C 02 have sold out.

Cabernet Sauvignon ★★★ Current release is russet-edged **00**, with smoked meat & sweet potpourri nose; dry, savoury, slightly earthy flavours, approaching peak. Yr 1st/2nd fill barrels. **Shiraz** ★★★ From single vyd; matured in 2nd-4th fill oak, 10% Am. **00** dense & chunky with gamey whiff; slightly reductive character, so give plenty of air before serving. **Albenet** ★★★ **03** (sample) rustic but appealing pasta wine with spice-tinged mulberry fruit, firm acid; mainly merlot plus cabs s & ruby, pinotage, shiraz. ±14% alc. **Cabernet Sauvignon Rosé** ★★★ 'Unwooded, easy-drinking *dry* rosé', emphasises winemaker; **04** (sample) soft strawberries & cream nose; unstinting red fruit flavours. **Chardonnay** ★★★ **03** thickly padded with grapefruit & butterscotch taste, retains some sprightliness via

70% unwooded portion (rest barrel-fermented). **Sauvignon Blanc** ★★★ **04** has a ripely generous sweet-fruit tone throughout (plus 4g/ℓ sugar to broaden the palate); dry, pleasantly firm almost minerally finish. **Chenin Blanc Limited Release** & **Semillon** now discontinued as standalones & channelled into… **Triple Creek** ★★★ Chenin-led, semillon-fragranced, chardonnay-fattened **04** (sample); full-flavoured, bone-dry compatible blend, has some minerality. **Marguerite** ★★★ Scented semi-dry chenin, muscat d'A (80/20) blend; **03** hint of muscat; balanced sweetness; persistent kiwi fruit flavour; good with spicy food. — *TM*

New Beginnings Wines

Paarl ▪ Tasting & sales Mon-Fri 9-5 ▪ Fee R10 for groups ▪ Vineyard tours by appt ▪ Owner Klein Begin Farming Association ▪ 13 000 cs 60% white 40% red ▪ PO Box 2009 Windmeul 7630 ▪ nbwines@iafrica.com ⓒ/☎ 863·8612

This small winery, an offshoot of Nelson Estate and one of the original Cape empowerment ventures, has devised a novel way to fund their vineyard expansion. Called 'Adopt a Vine', it enables members of the public to 'sponsor' one vine and, in return, receive a beautifully boxed bottle of New Beginnings wine and — delightful touch — a photograph of your new offspring to keep in your wallet. The wines below were made by New Beginnings's Solly Hendricks and Nelson Estate's winemaker Jean van Rooyen.

Cabernet Sauvignon ★★★ Latest release shows a new seriousness — lots more extract than pvs, **03** big, solid feel (brawny alc too: 15%), deep blackberry flavour, assertive but good oaking. **Pinotage** ★★★ Same revitalised tone: **03** plump yet forceful, youthfully muscular (15% alc); banana whiffs, smoky complexity. Good auguries for future. **Chardonnay** ★★★ 25% barrel-fermented, 03 striking green tinge, pervasive attractive creaminess with baked apple whiff, nicely poised; alc well contained too (13.3%). — *TM*

New Cape Wines

Worcester ▪ Est/1stB 2000 ▪ Closed to public ▪ Owner/winemaker Christiaan Groenewald ▪ 80 ha ▪ 40% red 60% white ▪ PO Box 898 Worcester 6849 ▪ christiaan@ncw.co.za ▪ www. newcapewines.co.za ⓒ (023) 340·4112 ☎ (023) 340·4132

Christiaan Groenewald harvested 12 tons in 2004 for his two own-labels, Eagle's Cliff and Dwyka Hills, with satisfactory *and* less pleasing results: 'The sauvignon was better than 2003, the pinotage not so good.' The maturation facility has been upgraded and additional barrels bought in.

Dwyka Hills Shiraz 🆕 ★★★ **03** well behaved, with shy plum tones on nose, fairly open texture, sweetish finish tinged with fennel. Light oaking. 14% alc.

Eagle's Cliff Reserve range

Cabernet Sauvignon ★★★ Last ed's charry oak has become better meshed with time in bottle; **02** now proffers smoky cassis aromas & cinnamon spicing, plump juicy black plum fruit. **Shiraz** ★★★ **02**, revisited, estery whiffs, bit of peppery fruit & blatant charred oak; not a lot of finesse. 14.5% alc. **Sauvignon Blanc** ★★★ **03**, with extra yr's bottle-age, offers quiet lemon aromas, echoing in palate. Contrast with below's ebullience.

Eagle's Cliff range

Merlot-Cabernet Sauvignon ★★★ **03** reticent nose, hints of smoky stewed prunes; sweet-sour character, not much fruity presence. **Shiraz-Pinotage** ★★★ Plummy **02** 70/ 30 blend, yr on, pleasantly sweet fruited, plump & silky. 14.5% alc. **Chardonnay** ★★★ Lightly oaked & ready for drinking; **04** shy peardrop aromas, very light wood presence; firmer, less effusive than pvs. **Chenin Blanc** ★★★ Aromas of guava & dried flowers on **04**, & good crisp acidity. Light 12.5% alc, as is… **Sauvignon Blanc** ★★★★ **04** full flavoured, zestily fruity with pungent coriander tone. Enjoy soonest. All WO Wrcstr. — *TM*

Newton Johnson

Walker Bay ▪ Est 1996 ▪ 1stB 1997 ▪ Tasting & sales Mon-Fri 9–4 Sat 10–12.30 (Sep 22-Apr 29 only, otherwise by appt) ▪ Closed public holidays ▪ Owners Dave & Felicity Johnson ▪ Winemaker Gordon Newton Johnson (Jan 2001) ▪ Viticulturist Johan Montgomery (Jun 2002) ▪ 8 ha (pinot, shiraz, chard, sauvignon) ▪ 120 tons 6 000 cs 40% red 43% white 17% rosé ▪ PO Box 225 Hermanus 7200 ▪ wine@newtonjohnson.com ▪ www.newtonjohnson. com © (028) 312·3862 🖷 (028) 312·3867

'What? Is the harvesthon over? Can I go surfing now?' was Gordon Johnson's reaction to the longest and most difficult vintage in this family-owned cellar. Quality wasn't in question, but 'the forces-that-be made absolutely sure you worked hard for it. I also can't remember signing up for Extreme Cellar Space Management 101. With this bumper harvest I was ready to prime my bath for extra fermentation space.' Development of their vineyards in Hemel-en-Aarde Valley continues, and plans are being drawn up for a gravity-based cellar which will permit separate vinification of the various sites. Gordon J comments: 'We want to get to know our soils, and learn how best to translate their essence through the winemaking process. Moving forward means refining these principles.' With sales of the FirstCape joint-venture brand scaling new heights, their Sandown Bay range is in abeyance. The Cape Bay easy-drinkers, on the other hand, remain a popular feature. They are listed separately.

★★★★ Cabernet Sauvignon Again features dollop shiraz from Dbnville; cab ex-Bot River. **02** (★★★★) interesting liquorice twist to dark smoky fruit — not very cab-like; firm tannins, chunky & chewy mid-2004, need time. ±14% alc. ±Yr Fr barriques, 40% new. **01** was splendid example of richly flavoured cab with minerally, cool finesse.

★★★★ Pinot Noir 03 continues the more delicate & refined mode introduced by **02**; latest shows an alluring suppleness & juiciness, silk tannins, plus surprising youthful complexity: meaty/cherry tone spiked with damp earth/forest floor, whiffs cigarbox & dried fruit. Slightly more in-sourced fruit than pvs (70%), otherwise specs similar to pvs: 9–10 mths Burgundian oak, 35–40% new. Significantly bigger wine than pvs at 14.4% alc, but retains **02**'s pleasing finesse, light-textured flavour purity.

★★★★ Shiraz-Mourvèdre 🆕 New World meets the Old in this elegant, darkly delicious Rhône-style blend; aromatic excitement from black pepper & dried herbs; warm sweet-dry flavours of smoky plums, **03** hint of old leather on finish; modern but not jammy/sweet — in fact, tightly wound still, could do with time to develop. 12–13 mths Burgundy barrels, small % new. 14% alc. W Bay, Dbnvlle, Pdberg vyds.

★★★☆ Félicité ✓ Pinot, picked specifically for this sophisticated, food-friendly, dry rosé; soupçon shiraz also features in luminous coral-pink **04**, though it's pinot's strawberry & cherry on nose/palate; juicy, firm zesty finish. As pvs, winner in all respects, including appealing packaging. Stbosch/Elgin/Dbnvlle fruit. ±13% alc.

★★★★ Chardonnay Reflects Gordon NJ's considered approach: no malo for tighter, minerally core; lees-stirring for creamier mouthfeel. Carefully judged oak (40% new Burgundian) highlights fruit identity of lofty Kaaimansgat ('Crocodile's Lair') vyds at Villiersdorp. **03** well-structured; beautiful butterscotch, toffee apple, passionfruit notes; overt sweetness (±6g/ℓ) cut by pervasive limy tang. **02** was also refined, polished; **01** a Nederburg Auction selection.

★★★★ Sauvignon Blanc ✓ From own s-facing vyd & another H&A Vlly block nearby, broadened as always by splash oaked Bot R semillon; plenty of appetising flavour & varietal verve in **04**, one of the more expressive this vintage; tasty mouthful green nettle, grapefruit & coriander, elegantly presented. ±13% alc. — *TM*

New World see The Winery

Nicholas L Jonker Estate see Jonkheer

Nico van der Merwe Wines

Stellenbosch • Est/1st 1999 • Closed to public • Owners Nico & Petra van der Merwe •
Winemaker Nico van der Merwe • 45 tons 3 500 cs 85% red 15% white • PO Box 12200
Stellenbosch 7613 • wilhelmshof@xsinet.co.za Ⓒ/🖷 903·9507

The Nico Plan is taking shape: the Saxenburg winemaker, here producing as an independent, was poised to launch his new Nicolas van der Merwe blends as this guide went to print. A red and a white, they should be his bulk business in the future. Also in that future lies the Botrivier land owned by the winemaker and his wife Petra, which is due for planting in 2005. All will be cultivated without trellising, and pruned *en gobelet* to form compact bushes. The size of the property, limited water resources and windiness of the area have something to do with this decision, but 'as a *paysan* I would like to use this method to grow some nice wines with their own character'. Exports are looking up; NvdM identifies Asia and the US as having potential, as does the home-market provided that conditions for tourism are improved and locals are better educated as wine drinkers.

★★★★★ **Mas Nicolas** 'The label says "Cape" but this will *never* be a blend with pinotage.' Nico vdM is emphatic. He believes shiraz/cab is *the* 'Cape Blend' & this singular offering posts his colours pretty high. Statement stuff, understated delivery; distinctly leans more towards Old World than New. **01** densely opaque, delicate perfumes, beautifully tailored spice folded into blackberry fruits. Fine-grained tannins – soft but for the long haul. Retasted mid-2004, ready for the impatient. Savoury **00** (★★★★★) has similarly early-approachable but peak on distant horizon. 14% alc. Latest 52/48 K/River shiraz, Simonsberg cab; 14 mths Fr oak, 50% new.

★★★☆ **Robert Alexander Merlot** Ripe mulberry signature for **03** (sample), fleshy fruit, soft tannins, emphasis on early approachability. Yr oak, 2nd/3rd fill Fr/Am. **02** in overt, chunky style; open, easy finish. Stbosch grapes.

★★★★ **White NEW** (Sample) 50/50 blend sauvignon & semillon in **04**. Ripe gooseberry notes mingle with peach & subtle oak, tastes riper than 13.5% alc. Deceptively soft & easy – charm disguises serious purpose. Oak fermented, long on lees. Semillon oaked, sauvignon not, blend briefly wooded before bottling.

Robert Alexander Shiraz 01 last of the Trawal Cellar cooperation from Olifants vyds, made by NvdM's brother Alkie. Retasted mid-2004, leather aromas, soft, accessible but fading, re-rated to ★★★. **Robert Alexander Chardonnay** ★★★ **02** was last, replaced by white blend above. – *IvH*

Nico Vermeulen Wines

Paarl • Est/1stB 2003 • Closed to public • Owner/viticulturist Nico Vermeulen • Winemaker Nico Vermeulen, with Judy & Izelle Vermeulen • 1 000 cs • 3 Pieter Hugo Str Courtrai Suider-Paarl • 13657631@sun.ac.za Ⓒ/🖷 863·2048

Havana Hills winemaker Nico Vermeulen makes these own-wines in conjunction with H-H owner Kobus du Plessis and Bloemendal's Jackie Coetzee. The aim, Vermeulen says, is to make affordable wines, 'new and young in spirit, which will have people dancing with excitement'. Sounds like our kind of fun!

The Right Two Reds ★★★☆ Maiden **03** proffers aromatic violets mingled with riper earthier notes, firm yet supple palate in satisfying finish. Will open in 2–4 yrs. 63/37 merlot/cab blend; cool, pure Dbnvlle fruit seasoned 15 mths in Fr oak, 30% new. **The Right Two Whites** ★★★★ Compatible 2:1 sauvignon/semillon alliance, **04** sporting touch of oak on semillon part; scrub wildness tempered with creamy vanilla, good grippy finish. Unoaked **03** (55/45) weighty, roundly dry. ±13.5% alc. – *DS*

Niel Joubert Estate

Paarl • Est 1898 • 1stB 1996 • Visits by appt • Reception venue with fully equipped kitchen • Tourgroups • Walks • Owner Joubert family • Winemaker Ernst Leicht (May 2000) • Viticulturist Daan Joubert • 350 ha (cab, merlot, pinotage, shiraz, chard, chenin, sauvignon) • 1 900 tons

40 000 cs own label 40% red 60% white • PO Box 17 Klapmuts 7625 • wine@nieljoubert.co. za • www.nieljoubert.co.za ©/🖷 875·5936

At this peaceful property, kept so by Byter the boerbull, winemaker Erni Leicht has started using riper grapes, resulting in bigger wines. The four year old cab planted in his first year here is showing 'beautiful berries'. They've added a Viognier to the range, and redesigned the labels. Further afield, the wines are 'going down singing' in Ireland. They also received a gold medal for the Shiraz 02 at the IWSC in London, a star turn repeated locally by gold at Michelangelo for both the Shiraz 02 and 03 (a bit like winning the Currie Cup *and* the World Cup, they say). A new air-conditioned wine store now completes the tasting and sales facility.

★★★★ **Christine-Marie** Impressive blend of cab & merlot, roughly equal proportions; to date only the **01**.

★★★★ **Shiraz** Am oak imparts obvious sweet vanilla tone, magnified by beefy alc — 15% in latest **02**, beloved of IWC judges. Rich, ripe dark berries & sweet spice, already well rounded & succulent, unlike **01**, revisited mid-2003, enters sweet, turns spicy mid-palate (greenpepper, cinnamon), finished very dry even after extra yr; needed more time. 16-18 mths oak, 90% Am.

Cabernet Sauvignon ★★★ Last tasted was **01**, with eucalyptus-scented fruit, easy-ish tannins. **Merlot** ★★★★ **02** colour/viscosity of bull's blood! Attractive ripe plum nose, dollops choc & coffee; roundly but solidly structured, so could be cellared 3-4 yrs. 14.5% alc; 100% oaked, 20% 1st fill barrels. **Pinotage** ★★★ **02** mirrors pvs vintages' generous dimensions (14.5% alc), slightly higher oaked portion (20%) reflected in firm wood backing to plum/banana fruit, succeeds in retaining a rugged elegance. **Chardonnay** ★★★★ Partially casked **04** a step up; more structure, sweeter fruit with lively citrus tang. 2-3 yrs in store. **Chenin Blanc** ★★★ Settled into style which cleverly hides 8g/ℓ sugar, enormous alc (±15%) among some of the zingiest fruit around — passionfruit & guava in **03**, rounded but crisp finishing. **Sauvignon Blanc** ★★★ **04** racy-sweet passionfruit & guava tones, big flavour, modest alc (13% alc). Portion fruit ex-Rbtsn. **Viognier** NEW **04** unrated work in progress shows potential; beefy alc (15%), de rigueur here, matching structure, richly fruited with peaches & apricots. Maturing in combo barrels/staves. — DH

■ *Niels Verburg see Luddite*

Nietvoorbij

Stellenbosch • Est 1963 • 1stB 1992 • Tasting & sales Mon-Fri 9-4; phone ahead on Sat • Fee R1/wine • Closed public holidays • Conferencing • Owner Agricultural Research Council • Winemakers Kous Theart & Adéle Louw (Apr 1975/1997) • Viticulturist Guillaume Kotze (Apr 2002) • 32 ha (cab, malbec, merlot, petit v, pinotage, shiraz, chard, sauvignon) • 150 tons 6 000 cs own label 54% red 45% white 1% port • Private Bag X5026 Stellenbosch 7599 • shirley@infruit.agric.za adele@infruit.agric.za © 809·3091 🖷 809·3202

Owned by the Agricultural Research Council, Nietvoorbij is the outright winner of the 'Most wines made in one cellar' title. How's that? Well, since every wine's an experiment, free rein is allowed, with the best results for sale — at very reasonable prices — on the premises. Production processes and packaging range from traditional to hi-tech, going as far as screwtops for the whites and dry red wines.

★★★★ **Cabernet Sauvignon** ✓ Satisfying cab; relaxed tannins impart early drinkability plus 2/3 yrs cellaring potential. Yr oaked. Two vintages in stock: **02** plump & sweet-fruited, attractive nutty-berry aromas; shows some development. **01** deeper colour, more complexity, intensity, despite lower alc (13 vs 13.4%).

Pinotage ★★★ ✓ Hints banana & clove in **02**; fruitier, more structured than pvs, obvious pinotage mulberries. Yr older oak. 14.6% alc. **Dry Red** ★★★ Convivial pizza/pasta companion from trio cabs (sauv, franc, ruby) & pinotage; lightly oaked; **03** (sample) loaded with sappy berry fruit & light touch toast. **Sauvignon Blanc** ★★★ **04** (sample) forthcoming greenpepper/coriander aromas & hint guava; bright flavourful palate; medium body. **Chardonnay-Sauvignon Blanc** NEW ★★ Shy candyfloss & talcum powder aromas on **04**, crisp, refreshing quaffable 60/40 blend. **Dry White** ★★ **03** blend chenin/chard with gewürz from Dbnville; lees & bottle-age character now evident; sweetish finish. — *TM*

Nieuwedrift Vineyards

Swartland ▪ Est 1996 ▪ 1stB 2003 ▪ Visits by appt Mon-Sat ▪ Light/buffet meals for groups of 5-74 by appt ▪ Self-catering/B&B guesthouse ▪ Facilities for children ▪ Tourgroups ▪ Conferencing ▪ Walks ▪ Owners Johan & Teubes Mostert ▪ Winemaker Johan Mostert, advised by Marais de Villiers & Theo Brink ▪ Viti consultant Jurie du Plessis ▪ 29 ha (shiraz, chard, chenin, colombard) ▪ ±7 tons 35% red 65% white ▪ PO Box 492 Piketberg 7320 ▪ nieuwedrift@telkomsa.net ✆ (022) 913·1966/082·824·8104 🖷 913·1966

The Swartland, noted for vinegrowing and hospitality, features a new producer epitomising both. Owner/winemaker Johan Mostert was so inspired by successful *garagiste* producers that just tending his award-winning vineyards (Swartland vineyard block winner in 2003/04) was not good enough. With help from Marais de Villiers (Main Street) and Theo Brink (Porterville), JM made his first chenin and shiraz (still in barrel) in his new small cellar (the rest of his crop goes into the Porterville and Kumala ranges). A restaurant and tasting room, incorporating part of the original stables and decorated with his wife's paintings, exudes rustic charm, giving visitors a tangible sense of the wholesome farming lifestyle.

> **Chenin Blanc** ☺ ★★★ Attractive fruit-filled chenin, layered with guava & lemon, full, nicely rounded, long crisp aftertaste. **04** sample tasted. 13.8% alc. — *DH*

Nitida Cellars

Durbanville ▪ Est 1992 ▪ 1stB 1995 ▪ Tasting & sales Mon-Fri 9-5 Sat 9.30-1 ▪ Closed Easter Fri/Sun, Dec 25/26, Jan 1 ▪ Tours by appt ▪ BYO picnic by request ▪ Owners Veller family ▪ Winemaker/viticulturist Bernhard Veller with Jacus Marais (1995/1999), advised by Eugene van Zyl & Johan Wiese ▪ 15 ha (cab s/f, merlot, pinotage, shiraz, sauvignon, semillon) ▪ 140 tons 7 500 cs own label 45% red 55% white ▪ PO Box 1423 Durbanville 7551 ▪ nitida@mweb.co.za ▪ www.nitida.co.za ✆ 976·1467 🖷 976·5631

'A dry winter followed by a dry summer made the harvest very stressful for vines and staff' is owner/winemaker Bernhard Veller's summation of the 2004 season, so prolonged that he was still harvesting cab in early May. A firm believer in hand-making small quantities of wine the traditional way, Veller considers the specificity of small areas to be paramount. Commenting on possible further subdivisions of the Tygerberg district (a new ward within the area, Philadelphia, has just been demarcated), he points out that Tygerberg came into being 'because Durbanville did not see any value in being enlarged. The creation of new divisions is great as long as each has a terroir that is definable in the bottle.'

★★★★ **Cabernet Sauvignon** This cooler-climate cab more austere in difficult vintage **02** (★★★★), notes cedar & black berries, hefty 14.5% alc. Should keep well ±5 yrs. Usual wooding regime: 18 mths Fr oak, 40% new. Not in league of well-proportioned, supple **01** which should outlast it.

★★★★ **Pinotage** Aromas of **02** (★★★) promise a lively quaffer. Minty, acetone, banana notes on palate, huge 15% alc a little down on that of smooth **01**. These 10-12 mths Fr oak, none new.

★★★☆ **Shiraz** Brambles, mint aromas/flavours on **02**. Fruit-driven, with restrained oaking — yr older barrels. Another big wine: 15% alc.

★★★★ **Calligraphy** Less kind vintage conditions made for lesser, bosky-toned **02** (★★★), from merlot, cabs f/s (35/25/30). Yr oak, 25% new. 14% alc. Wilder than elegant merlot-led **01** (45%) blend with delicious pruney, fleshy substance.

★★★★★ **Sauvignon Blanc Club Select** NEW ✓ **04** another fine Dbnvlle example of the variety. Ignore unusual pink grapefruit hue, and enjoy floral aromas with grassy back-up; subtle fruitiness & racy acidity. Very young — try to resist for few yrs.

★★★★ **Sauvignon Blanc 04** more approachable than above version: gooseberry, grass notes with zingy acidity. Modest & very drinkable 12.5% alc. Drinks well now but will keep 3 yrs. Retasted **03** (★★★★★) developing beautifully: gooseberry essence, New Zealand-style 'sweatiness', great length, concentrated. 13.2% alc.

★★★★ **Semillon ✓ 03** (★★★★★) best yet of these new-wave charmers. Still very young; lanolin & honey notes starting to show. Excellent balance acid & fruit, supported by skilful wooding (oak fermented, half new). Richness will develop further over, say, five years, whereas **02** was for earlier drinking.

★★★★ **Chardonnay 03** restrained citrus aromas, austere peach fruit, resinous notes; oak still dominates (3 mths, 20% new). 14.1% alc. — *NP*

Noble Cape see Origin Wine
No Name see Pick 'n Pay

Nordale Winery

Robertson ▪ Est 1950 ▪ Tasting & sales Mon-Thu 8-5 Fri 8-4 ▪ Closed public holidays ▪ Tours by appt ▪ BYO picnic ▪ Owners 31 members ▪ Winemaker Simon Basson (Dec 2001) ▪ Viti consultant Newald Marais ▪ 500 ha (shiraz, chard) ▪ 8 000 tons ▪ 1 500 cs own label + 5.8m litres bulk 15% red 85% white 1% other ▪ Ranges for customers: Rocco Bay (Sweden), Tabiso (Denmark) ▪ PO Box 105 Bonnievale 6730 ▪ info@nordale.co.za ▪ www.nordale.co.za © (023) 616·2050 ☎ (023) 616·2192

Having made the move from part-time consultant to full-time GM of this Bonnievale operation, ex-Nederburg kingpin Newald Marais is involved in both vineyard and cellar. A goal now is to achieve sustainability: 'To embrace long-term business practices so that there's security for our members'. To further their ambitions, the team is collaborating with other wineries in a major export drive to the Scandinavian countries.

★★★★ **Red Muscadel** Last tasted was jewel-bright **01**; follow-up is **04**; preview looks promising: quieter on nose than White but flavourful; sweet, viscous palate has a rich toffee-apple tone.

★★★★ **White Muscadel** Mouthwatering, lusciously smooth fortified; pvs was **02** VDG, from old vines on Gelukshoop farm. **04** (sample) powerful aromas of pineapple, whiff jasmine; palate slightly less striking: unctuous, quite spirity (±17% alc); provisionally ★★★★, but may just need time to settle. 375ml.

Vin Rouge ☺ ★★★ Unpretentious everyday red with fleshy, rounded body. Current **01** shiraz (40%) + 2 cabs — sauvignon & ruby; peppery hints, zesty sour-plum flavours.

Captain's Drift Shiraz ★★★ Still-stocked **01** ex-single vyd, yr oaked, all Fr barrels. Now has meaty/bouillon hints; drying tannins — suggest drink soon. 14% alc. **Double Cabernet** ★★★ Sauvignon & ruby are the alluded-to cabs, ±50/50; fragrant **01** continues to appeal; dry; fairly prominent eucalyptus tone; firm savoury finish. **Captain's Drift Chardonnay** ★★★ Buxom barrique-fermented **04** (sample) pale yellow-gold; eager butterscotch & marmalade-toast aromas; finishes sweet. Drink young. **Chenin Blanc** ★★ Dry version; light-bodied **03** very demure; lanolin hint, crisp lemon palate; slightly honeyed finish. **Steen** ★★ Off-dry, also lightish; **03** brushed with bottle-age but still juicy, supple. **Sauvignon Blanc** ★★★ **04** blast of gooseberry/guava on nose; palate quieter, discernibly dry & touch coarse. — *TM*

Norton Wines

Stellenbosch ▪ Est/1stB 2002 ▪ Closed to public ▪ Owner Anthony Norton ▪ Vini consultant Nicolette de Kock ▪ 50 cs 100% red ▪ PO Box 6045 Uniedal Stellenbosch © 082·807·4447

No new releases from young Gauteng lawyer Anthony Norton. The maiden Merlot 01 was made to his spec by Gusto Wines' Nicolette de Kock.

Nutwood Grove see De Morgenzon

Nuwehoop see Groot Eiland
Nuwe Wynplaas see Coppoolse Finlayson

Nuy Wine Cellar

Nuy (see Worcester map) ▪ *Est 1963* ▪ *1stB 1967* ▪ *Tasting & sales Mon-Fri 8.30-4.30 Sat 8. 30-12.30* ▪ *Fee R15 for groups of 10+* ▪ *Closed Easter Fri/Sun, Dec 25 & Jan 1* ▪ *Braai facilities* ▪ *Conferences* ▪ *Owners 23 members* ▪ *Manager/winemaker Christo Pienaar, with Juan Slabbert (Sep/Oct 2003)* ▪ *Viti consultant Newald Marais (Oct 2002)* ▪ *9 500 tons* ▪ *20% red 68% white 12% muscadel* ▪ *PO Box 5225 Worcester 6849* ▪ *wines@nuywinery.co.za* ▪ *www. nuywinery.co.za* ✆ *(023) 347·0272* 🖷 *(023) 347·4994*

It's been a hard act to follow, but Christo Pienaar, formerly of Slanghoek, has taken over the reins from Wilhelm Linde and, with his assistant, Elsenburg-trained Juan Slabbert, is beginning to stamp his own personality on the range. New are a dry Chenin, a promising NLH and a Shiraz that's been matured 18 months in new French barrels. The (Cape) Riesling is being dropped from the range. Newald Marais, formerly of Nederburg, keeps a practised eye on the winemaking since being appointed consultant in 2002.

★★★★ **Red Muscadel** ✓ Beautifully poised & intense fortified dessert, great character & charm; ages brilliantly. As with white version, moderate 16.5% alc just right for power without spirituous burn. **02** shot through with fresh, nervy acidity to balance massive 232g/ℓ sugar. **03** (★★★★★) more depth, complexity, potential; curious & delightful toffee whiffs; pristine ripe fruit — not a raisin in sight. Even sweeter at ±250g/ℓ, yet 4.2g/ℓ acid (though low-sounding) imparts required verve.

★★★★ **White Muscadel** ✓ Luxurious fortified dessert; rich & flavoursome. **03** worthy heir to long line of medal winners. Raisins spiked with mint, hint eucalyptus; touch more complexity than pvs; exceptional cellaring potential. Finishes with lovely a citrus tingle. ±245g/ℓ sugar, 4.2g/ℓ acid.

Rouge de Nuy ☺ ★★ Still-available **02** remains fruity, juicy, braai friendly; cab/merlot, lightly oaked. **Sauvignon Blanc** ☺ ★★★ Summery & quaffable **04**; tropical tones, lightish, dry & refreshing. **Chant de Nuit** ☺ ★★★ Satisfyingly racy NV white blend; Ferdinand de Lesseps table variety's pineapple's fragrance more obvious this yr; dry, lightish (alc 12%). **Colombard Semi-Sweet** ☺ ★★★ Relaxed poolside quaffer; **04** brims with ripe guava & honeysuckle, delicate sweetness. **Sauvignon Blanc Sparkling Vin Sec** ☺ ★★★ **04** gentle off-dry tropical bubbles; plenty of foaming fun. NV.

Cabernet Sauvignon ★★★ Yr in bottle has been kind to **02**, now suffused with flavourful mellowness. Retains its easy food-friendly dry finish. Lightly Fr-oaked. **Chardonnay** ★★★ Tasty **04**, light peach tones quickened by acidity; oak hardly perceptible. **Chenin Blanc** NEW ★★★ Lightly fruity dry **04**, appealing mixed fruit tones. **Colombard Dry** ★★★ **04** as pleasant as ever. Lightish, with bright guava scent; well balanced for early, easy downing. **Fernão Pires** ★★ Undemanding, light (11.6% alc), off-dry **04**, with delicate tropical tone. **Noble Late Harvest** NEW **04** preview shows very obvious botrytis character woven with ripe apricot-toned fruit; gentle flavours, poised, slight citrus touch in tail. Should rate ★★★★ on release. 10.8% alc. From chenin & hanepoot, harvested end Apr. *— DH*

▮ *Oakdene* see Bovlei

Oaklands Wine Exporters

NEW

Est 2002 ▪ *1stB 2003* ▪ *Closed to public* ▪ *Owner Danie Zeeman* ▪ *Brands for customers: Boschenmeer & Ukusa (Germany)* ▪ *PO Box 12898 Die Board 7613* ▪ *info@oaklandswines. com* ▪ *www.deza.co.za* ✆ *886·9626* 🖷 *887·0441*

Danie Zeeman, the man behind this new negociant company, has extensive experience of wine-making and -trading, having worked at cellars like Longridge locally and as production director of a wine wholesaler in the Netherlands. He sources wines locally for clients in Europe for marketing under their own brands, and in some cases creates special blends to suit clients' requirements. Deza is his own label, and it flies to America and Holland.

Deza Collection

Reserve Shiraz ★★★★ Modern-style **03**; ripe black fruit, hint coffee; well stuffed with summer pudding flavours, lots of toasty wood (combo Fr/Am 80/20). 14% alc. **Shiraz-Pinotage** ★★★ 55/45 mix, fruit ex-Wllngtn, not oaked; **03** melange red/black berry fruits & tobacco whiff; savoury/meaty tone, assertive but ripe tannins. **Sauvignon Blanc** ★★★★ **04** subtle but typical greenpepper & grapefruit-pith aromas, fresh & lively; full flavoured, grapefruit carrying through into persistent finish. All WO W-Cape. — JB

Oak Lane see BoweJoubert
Oak Ridge see Shoprite Checkers

Oak Valley Wines

Elgin ▪ Est 1898 ▪ 1stB 2003 ▪ Tasting & sales Mon-Fri 9-5, otherwise by appt ▪ Closed Easter Fri-Mon, Dec 25/26 & Jan 1 ▪ Attractions/amenities: see intro ▪ Owner AG Rawbone-Viljoen Trust ▪ Winemaker/viticulturist Pieter Visser ▪ 35 ha (cabs s/f, merlot, pinot, chard, sauvignon) ▪ 2 100 cs 100% white ▪ PO Box 30 Elgin 7180 ▪ wines@oak-valley.co.za ▪ www.oakvalleywines.com ℂ 859·4110 ℻ 859·3405

Finally, the original source of quality fruit from Elgin's famous cool-climate vineyards is claiming its own identity. Anthony Rawbone-Viljoen's historic Oak Valley farm has supplied grapes to several big names (including Bouchard Finlayson, WhaleHaven, Rupert & Rothschild, Flagstone). Debuting is a Sauvignon, and a Merlot blend, Chardonnay and Pinot will follow in 2006-8. Made by Pieter Visser, intimately familiar with vines he's overseen since 1993, at Paul Cluver's Elgin cellar, these bottlings represent the coming-of-age of Elgin's landmark venture into commercial wine-grape cultivation by industry experts since 1985. Vineholdings will be upped to an eventual 60ha by 2006, and a winery is planned. (Great-grandfather Sir Antonie's cellar was used until decommissioned in the 1940s.) Tasting room visitors note: this 1 780ha spread is a major supplier of apples, pears, greenhouse cut-flowers and naturally reared beef-cattle, and boasts 30ha of protected-in-perpetuity English oaks and 500ha of mountain *fynbos* reserve.

★★★★☆ **Sauvignon Blanc 03** stunning debut, fine advert for cool-climate sauvignon. Classically styled with elegant, nettley aromas, whiffs of green fig. Dense, herbaceous mid-palate fruit, yet in a restrained ensemble (13.2 alc moderate these days) with a sustained finish. Still youthful, ample maturation potential. — MF

Oak Village see Vinfruco

Obikwa

Value-priced Distell brand, exported to North & South America, Europe and the Far East.

Cabernet Sauvignon ★★★ Fruit-grenade **03** bursts with cassis; palate lifted by sugar (4. 5g/ℓ), though furry tannins probably better in another yr. **Merlot** ★★★ **03** cherry fruitcake nose; lively, smooth, slides down easily. **Pinotage** ★★★ **03** your basic plummy pinotage, with banana whiff & youthfully abrasive tannins; ends fairly quickly. **Shiraz** ★★★ Dark fruits & smoke in the greeting; **03** lighter texture/weight than pvs, grippy tannins need few mths to settle. Above mainly Fr oak, staves/barrels. **Chardonnay** ★★★☆ Carefully wooded **04** (sample), soft & mellow peach/bosc pear flavours; unoaked portion keeps ripeness in check. **Chenin Blanc** ★★★★ Lively, refreshing style; **04** again with Granny Smith apple zing; lovely mouth-juicing crispness; food enhancing. Low 11.7% alc. **Sauvignon Blanc** ★★★ **04** a fruit salad with lots of crunch & freshness. Again light bodied (11. 8% alc) for comfortable summer imbibing. All WO W-Cape. — CR

Oddbins see Shoprite Checkers

Odyssey

Low-alcohol (7-9%) Natural Sweets by Robertson Winery appealing to youth market. In 1ℓ resealable packs splashed with 'astral imagery'. See Vinimark entry for details.

Rosé Delicate rose-pink, sweet & juicy. Ruby cab, merlot, pinotage. **White** Crowd-pleaser, fresh, sweet tropical flavour. Muscadel, colombard, chenin. Both ★★, NV. – *DH*

Oewerzicht

Greyton ▪ *Est/1stB 2002* ▪ *Visits by appt* ▪ *See intro for attractions/amenities* ▪ *Vini consultant Wynand Lategan (2002)* ▪ *Owner/viticulturist Kootjie Viljoen (2002)* ▪ *3 ha (cab)* ▪ *1 000 cs 100% red* ▪ *PO Box 18 Greyton 7233* ▪ *oewerzicht@telkomsa.net* ©/🖃 *(028) 254·9831*

This brand new riverside cellar – one of a small handful in the Greyton area – has plenty to offer in addition to its wine. Conference facilities accommodate up to 40 people, with seven comfortable cottages, luxury guest tents and a large kitchen for catered functions. There's also a mountain bike trail for the more energetic, as well as hiking paths. Visitors are welcome to bring their own picnics. The cellar will concentrate on a Cab from vines planted six years ago. Vinification is by Wynand Lategan of Lourensford Winery, here in an advisory capacity.

Cabernet Sauvignon ★★★ Gently basket-pressed **02**'s herbal notes & rustic aromas belie the fine tannins & quite sweet finish. Subtle oak. 14% alc. WO Overberg. – *MF*

Old Bridge Wines

Closed to public ▪ *Owner Paulinas Dal Farm Holdings (Pty) Ltd* ▪ *20 000 cs 60% red 40% white* ▪ *PO Box 50002 Waterfront 8002* ▪ *rickety@iafrica.com* © *082·777·1519*

Export-focused producer and negociant sourcing wines for a variety of brands, including private labels for specialised corporate clients. The wines, untasted, include limited edition African Gold Collection: Cabernet-Merlot, Shiraz, Merlot mainly for US, Europe and Far East; Big Six Collection: boxed sets of Cabernet, Merlot, Shiraz, Pinotage, Sauvignon, Chenin for local game lodges/retreats and for export; Old Bridge: Cabernet, Merlot, Shiraz, Pinotage, Sauvignon, Chenin.

Old Brown see Sedgwick's
Old Chapel see Robertson Winery

Old Vines Cellars

Est/1stB 1995 ▪ *Closed to public* ▪ *Owners Irina von Holdt & Françoise Botha* ▪ *Winemaker Irina von Holdt* ▪ *11 000 cs own label + 2 000 for client Park House* ▪ *22% red 78% white* ▪ *50 Liesbeek Road Rosebank 7700* ▪ *fran@oldvines.co.za* ▪ *www.oldvines.co.za* © *685·6428* 🖃 *685·6446*

What's this, a cat among the proverbial pigeons? Or are 'pigeons' far too tame a tag for the team and the only women's empowerment winery in the Cape? Expansion over the past year led owners Irina von Holdt (taster for the guide and originator of the SA chenin revival) and daughter Fran Botha to appoint Richard Hilton (of Vinus Via) their international sales and marketing manager. 'It's nice to have some testosterone around here,' laughs Botha, recently selected one of 28 of 'the most awesome women in SA' by *Cosmopolitan* magazine, largely because of her women's empowerment efforts. Margaret Gobeni, who joined as a cleaner, completed her secretarial training and is now responsible for office administration. They celebrated with their new Vintage Brut sparkling, made, unsurprisingly, from chenin. 'Our objective of raising the profile of SA chenin is gathering momentum locally and overseas,' says IvH. In line with this, they're stepping up their exports of premium chenin to Europe and Japan.

★★★★ **Blue White** ✓ 'Blue' bottle broke the mould, 'White' unwooded chenin from old Stbosch vines has raised the bar for SA chenin since inaugural **95**. Current **03** wet wool nose & apple compôte palate lifted by mere touch of sweetness. 14%

alc. **04** sample should live up to pvs. These gain waxy complexity with bottle-age, best at 4-7yrs.

★★★★ **Old Vines Chenin Blanc** A different angle on the unwooded genre: small fraction botrytised grapes adds honeycomb complexity in older wines. Elegant **03** packed with honeysuckle & elderflower; refined dry finish. 13.5% alc. **02** sold out before we could taste.

★★★★ **Old Vines Barrel Reserve Chenin Blanc** The wooded version. Ripe **03** cosseted in spice, lavender & bees wax. Smidgen sugar (3.9g/ℓ) plumps out mid-palate. Structure to develop, as did pvs **99**, maiden **98**. 6 mths Fr casks, none new.

★★★★ **Old Vines Vintage Brut** From chenin (of course, but unusual for MCC); 2 cool hillside Stbosch bushvine vyds. **01** crafted with help from 'Sparkling king', Villiera's Jeff Grier. **01** ebullient bubbles, easy, friendly, no brut-ish severity. Toffee apple aromas & flavours, weighty, fruit-sweet palate from 24 mths on lees. Small portion bottled, remainder on lees to be degorged on demand. 9.8g/ℓ sugar; 12.9% alc.

Spring Valley range

Chenin Blanc-Sauvignon Blanc ☺ ★★★ Happy-go-lucky **04** blend, with tasty white peach notes, Granny Smith apple crispness to finish. 14% alc.

Shiraz-Merlot ★★★ Cellar's only red; lightly wooded. **03**'s solid 14.5% alc smothered by raspberry fruit & same easy-going feel as pvs. — *CvZ*

Onderkloof

Stellenbosch (see Helderberg map) ▪ Est 1998 ▪ 1stB 1999 ▪ Tasting Mon-Fri by appt ▪ Sales & tours by appt ▪ Private functions (lunch/dinner) by appt ▪ Schaapenberg Nature Conservancy ▪ Owners Daniël Truter & Beat Musfeld ▪ Winemaker/viticulturist Daniël Truter, with Truter Willemse (May 2003) ▪ 25 ha (cab, pinotage, shiraz, chenin, crouchen, muscat d'A, sauvignon) ▪ 100 tons 4 000 cs own label 30% red 70% white ▪ PO Box 90 Sir Lowry's Pass 7133 ▪ wine@onderkloofwines.co.za ▪ www.onderkloofwines.co.za ℡ 858·1538 📠 858·1536

'It's very exciting to work with this variety,' says Daniël Truter, reflecting on his second shiraz harvest in 2004 and describing the wine in the barrel as 'looking good'. Looking ahead, the Onderkloof co-owner and winemaker, now assisted by another Truter — Truter Willemse — thinks the Schaapenberg area is showing its mettle, not just for white wines but 'most definitely for reds'. On Sir Lowry's Pass, originally known as the Onderkloof, the Truter vineyards are unirrigated, which presented something of a challenge in 2004, but 'concentrated wines' were the result. Mirroring Truter and wine-partner Beat Musfeld's eco-bent, the farm is a founding unit in the new Schaapenberg Conservancy.

★★★☆ **Cabernet Sauvignon Reserve** Latest **01** concentrated aromas of raspberry & cherry, mouthcoating flavours, slightly furry tannins — all auguring well; just needs bit more time. Dryland vyd on Schaapenberg, 18 mths Fr barriques, 15% new.

★★★★ **Chardonnay** ✓ **02** retasted, shows Marie biscuit nuttiness/toastiness; still juicy; lively; wonderful racy concentration; could go few more yrs. Bunches harvested/selected by hand, barrel-fermented/matured 8 mths, 20% new wood. **01** had this wine's signature creaminess, tossed with salad of apples & pears.

★★★☆ **Sauvignon Blanc** ✓ **01** was cellar's first; elegant & steely dry. **02** freshly cut grass on nose, zesty palate, touch asparagus; extra year in bottle has upped the pleasure, added complexity & character without sacrificing freshness. From single vyd, est 1989.

Pinotage Reserve ★★★★ **02**, retasted, has acquired a delicious banana custard creaminess on nose; savoury & charry flavours from oak, very dry finish; could do with another yr to soften, integrate. 12 mths Fr oak, 10% new; unirrigated bushvines; 14% alc. **Chenin Blanc** ★★★ **02** retaste, ripe melon aromas, slightly herbal, still crisp finish; could go another yr/2. **Floreal** ★★★ ✓ Suitably floral semi-dry blend chenin, muscat de A, crouchen (50/40/10). **03** super-intense almost overpowering grapey bouquet — chenin a mere delivery platform for pure hanepoot fragrance, scented gewürz-like finish. Gorgeous aperitif at a giveaway price. — *CR*

Onyx see Darling Cellars

Oom Tas

One of SA's top-selling budget-priced brands (2m cases a year, all in returnable glass), produced 24x7 by Distell. Amber hue looks 'sweet', but latest (NV) ★★ is decidedly dry, as always; nutty/tea leaf aromas; dry but easy, no sharp edges. — *CR*

Opstal Estate

Slanghoek (see Worcester map) ▪ Est 1950 ▪ 1stB 1978 ▪ Tasting & sales Mon-Fri 8.30-5 Sat 10-1 ▪ Closed Christian holidays ▪ Tours by appt ▪ Amenities: see intro ▪ Owner Stanley Louw ▪ Winemakers Stanley Louw, with Jaco Theron (Jan 1999) ▪ Viticulturist Kobus Theron (1978) ▪ 103 ha (13 varieties, r/w) ▪ 1 500 tons 10 000 cs own label 35% red 65% white ▪ PO Box 27 Rawsonville 6845 ▪ opstal@lando.co.za ▪ www.opstal.co.za © (023) 344·3001 ✆ (023) 344·3002

Stanley Louw is an enthusiastic apostle (and chair) of Breedekloof Wine & Tourism, the newly declared wine-tourism destination. Opstal's doing its bit to promote the area — the winelands between Paarl and Worcester — with a new small conference centre as well as a tasting facility and wine restaurant offering a view of the Slanghoek Valley. 'Ghost tours' of the cellar are another attraction; on the more serious side, students of viticulture will appreciate Louw's moisture-metering and dedicated weather station for disease-detection. Ultra-modern cellar practice and night harvesting have also made a difference to quality in recent years, says Louw, particularly in the case of aromatic varieties.

Chenin Blanc ☺ ★★★ **02** ageing in bottle without honeyed decadence; tinned pineapple hint to palate, which is lifted by lemony acidity.

Cabernet Sauvignon ★★★ Characterful **01** ageing gracefully, showing good rounded red berry flavours. ±Yr Fr oak. **Merlot Blush** Last tasted was **03** (sample), full-bodied & discernibly dry. **Chardonnay** ★★★ Lightish **03** offers guavas, peaches & tropical fruit, oak staving shows in fairly obvious vanilla coating; finishes fresh. **Hanepoot** ★★★ **03** has retained enough of its acidity to be a fresh, warming, appealingly smooth & fragrant drink.

Carl Everson range
Cabernet Sauvignon-Shiraz NEW ★★★ **02** curious melange of black & green pepper, plums & pronounced oak, full but light textured. A more traditional — not unappealing — style. **Classic Red** ★★★ Slight formula change (to shiraz, merlot, pinotage, ruby cab) upped the enjoyment in **01**; retasted, combo red berry fruit, fresh herbs & savoury even rounder, more inviting. **Sauvignon Blanc** ★★★ **03** touched by good bottle-age, guava & tropical tones, soft, but enough acid to refresh. **Sauvignon Blanc-Semillon** discontinued. This range NE. — *DH*

Oracle

Distell export brand launched July 2002, initially into the UK retail market; the name an allusion to the 'ancient wisdom of Africa'.

Cabernet Sauvignon ★★★★ **01** offers lightly savoury carpaccio-like whiffs over red berries, attractively light but not lean fruit; firm unaggressive tannin. Fr oak casks/staves 9 mths. **Pinotage** ★★★★ Dbnvlle/Hldbrg fruit in **03**; brooding Bovril & tar bouquet leavened by airy texture/body (12.7% alc), lots of dry tannins. Combo barrels, Fr staves, unwooded. **Shiraz** ★★★★ Am oak adds vanilla seduction to sweet, succulent brambleberry fruit; versatile **03** (sample) enjoyable solo or with food. Portion Fr oak staves. **Chardonnay** ★★★★ **03** ingratiatingly smooth & soft; English toffee & butterscotch richness (from fermentation/ageing 6 mths on oak) offset by lifted citrus freshness on finish. **Sauvignon Blanc** Zingy **04**'s passionfruit & cape gooseberry jump out of glass; tangy, sinewy structure/flavour show remarkably fine concentration for low 12% alc. Sample could rate ★★★★ on release. All WO Coastal. — *CR*

Oranjerivier Wine Cellars ♙♟&

Lower Orange (see Northern Cape map) ▪ Est 1965 ▪ 1stB 1968 ▪ Tasting Mon-Fri 8–4.30 Sat 9–11.30 ▪ Fee R5 for 5 wines ▪ Sales Mon-Fri 8–5 Sat 8.30–12 ▪ Closed public holidays except Easter Sat ▪ Tours Mon-Fri 9, 11 & 3 Jan-March ▪ Owners ±930 shareholders ▪ Winemakers Johan Esterhuizen (Upington cellar), Jan Steenkamp (Grootdrink), Chris Venter (Groblershoop), Deon Truter (Keimoes) & Bolla Louw (Kakamas), with Alicea Hamman/Jopie Faul, George Kruger/Jannie Britz, Henno Ludick, Tinus Kotze/Riaan Liebenberg & Johan Dippenaar (in same cellar order) ▪ Viti consultant Dirk Malan (since Jan 1989) ▪ 3 308 ha (pinotage, ruby cab, chenin, colombard) ▪ ±184 000 tons 995 019 cs own label 28% red 63% white 9% rosé ▪ Export labels: Living World, Wozani ▪ Ranges for customers: Vine Collection, Cape Fest & Liquor Boys (Liquor City); Country Cellars & Carnival (Spar); Nature's Group ▪ HACCP, ISO, BRC & Eurogap certification in progress ▪ PO Box 544 Upington 8800 ▪ marketing@owk.co.za ▪ www.owk.co.za © (054) 337·8800 🖷 (054) 332·4408

Last year one of the largest wineries in the southern hemisphere (close to 800 active members spread along 300km of Orange riverbank) chalked up the biggest harvest ever recorded here: 184 361 tons – roughly equivalent to 37 000 elephants! And if that wasn't enough reason to celebrate, 'OWK' (as they call themselves) turns 40 this year. Despite their monolithic size, they've out-manoeuvred many of their co-op competitors, increasing local market share alone to 6%. Besides hiring a full-time viticulturist in 2003 to provide their growers with complete site analyses (quite a job given the huge number and variety), OWK has also spent more than R20m over the past 2 years on an extensive upgrade of cellar equipment and bottling facilities, among these a sophisticated laboratory, completed last year. The next goalpost? Producing 30m litres of good wine.

★★★★ **White Muscadel** Pvsly tasted **96** had evolved into something delicious & characterful; Madeira-like tone, ultra-smooth & balanced; **02** (★★★) quite intense on nose, silky palate, sleek; hint of raisin but no real complexity.

All below NV unless noted. **Cabernet Sauvignon** NEW ★★ Sweet perfumes greet the nose, mid-weight body, somewhat short with touch eucalyptus. **Ruby Cabernet** ★★★ Always attractive. **03** crushed berry, leaf/thatch aromas, quite juicy, simple but satisfying. **Shiraz** ★★★ Brambley **03** has hint of white pepper, warm savoury/earthy palate, soft tannins. **Riverstale Classic Red** ★★★ Smoky/savoury **02** blend cab, shiraz, pinotage, ruby cab (components all from single vyds, 6 mths oak-staved); retasted: blackberry jam, hint of smoky vanilla oak; light, slightly grainy dry flavours. **Blanc de Noir** ★★ Pale salmon pink; mere whiff of strawberry, nice red-berry mouthfeel. 13.7g/ℓ sugar on the high side for the acid. **Chenin Blanc** ★ Latest is NV; clean & off-dry. **Colombard** ★★ Semi-dry styling; **04** shy, dusty, peardrop nose; attractive ripe off-dry zesty/lemony flavours. 12.4% alc. **Grand Cru** ★ Water-white & not as bracingly dry as expected. **Nouveau Blanc** ★★ Popular talcum-powder-scented semi-sweet from chenin, very light though not too sweet. **Red Muscadel** ★★★ Invariably appealing, with well-judged sweetness & alc (±17.5%). Latest bottling is scented, spicy; lots of strawberry & apricot flavour. **Jerepigo Red** ★★★ From ruby cab; pretty garnet colour; powerful raisined bouquet with hints woodsmoke, tar; concentrated & well balanced fruit-cordial flavours. **Red Port** ★★★ Traditional-style fortified from ruby cab; like pvs, the new version shows lowish alc (18.2%), nice fruit though not much grip; fairly straightforward with gamey/plummy tones. Pinotage, **Rouge**, **Rosé**, **Blanc de Blanc**, **Chardonnay**, **Light**, Stein (semisweet), **Late Harvest**, **Special Late Harvest & Classique Petillement** (carbonated fizz), **Sweet Hanepoot** & **White Jerepiko** not available for tasting. — *TM*

Origin Wine

Stellenbosch ▪ *Est/1stB 2002* ▪ *Closed to public* ▪ *Owners Bernard Fontannaz & Rhyan Wardman* ▪ *Winemaker Rhyan Wardman, with Julia Andrag, David Smit & Grant Michales (Jan/Jun/Sep/Jan 2003)* ▪ *Viti consultant Thys Greeff (Jan 2003)* ▪ *4m cs* ▪ *55% red 40% white 5% rosé* ▪ *Export brands: Palm Grove, Sunbird, Cape Original, Noble Cape & ranges below* ▪ *PO Box 7177 Stellenbosch 7599* ▪ *reception@originwine.co.za* © *882·9004* 🖷 *882·9006*

Recognising the importance of quality control and corporate social responsibility, Bernard Fontannaz (who partners Kiwi immigré Rhyan Wardman in this venture) recently added Origin Service to the parent company and its subsidiary Origin Bottling. MD of Origin Service is Jaco van der Merwe, whose target is to put in place a quality control system for the Origin operation and its key suppliers (Origin works with eight main cellars). VdM, as chairman of WIETA (the Wine Industry Ethical Trade Association, which aims to improve the working conditions of employees) is ideally positioned for his other portfolio: to achieve WIETA compliance. First step towards this goal was establishing a supplier forum. As Fontannaz says: 'To be meaningful and effective, this needs to be achieved throughout the supply chain and not only at the end of it.' Social development is happening in conjunction with Western Wines — a project at Ikaya Primary School in Stellenbosch has funded a pre-school facility. Another Origin initiative is its Growers' Challenge, which acknowledges winegrowers within its orbit, stimulates competition among them and encourages feedback with quarterly get-togethers and wine-tastings.

Cape Original ★★★ From shiraz, ruby cab; smoky, earthy, leathery aromas; chewy tannin to balance the sweet fruit. 3ℓ bag in box. 15% oaked. NV/03.

African Horizon range

Shiraz ★★★ 04 honest, well-made with good varietal character; soft & supple, pleasing juiciness. 15% Am oaked; **Chardonnay** ★★★★ 04 (sample) good ripe citrus fruit, toned with butterscotch.

Cape One

[NEW]

Shiraz ★★★ 04 (sample) peppery & herby intro, very dry tannins & finish make for a food wine. 14.1% alc. 25% Am wooded. **Selected Red** ★★★ Friendly 04, equal pinotage/merlot mix; red berries on a spicy bed of oak. **Chardonnay** ★★ Fruity part-wooded 04 (sample) has a nice citrus tweak to tail. **Selected White** ★★ Tropical fruits with boiled sweet hint; crisp, undemanding 04.

Evolution range

Merlot ★★★ Latest version not tasted; 03 was coffee-tinged, lively, plummy. **Pinotage** ★★★ Partly wooded 04 mingle of red fruits, gentle tannins for easy drinking. **Shiraz** [NEW] ★★★ Peppery touch to 04, palate padded by touch sugar ±4g/ℓ. Similar to Cape One version above. 20% Am oaked. **Rosé** [NEW] ★★★ From pinotage; 04 plummy red berry character, crisp & refreshing, satisfyingly dry. **Merlot-Ruby Cabernet** [NEW] ★★★ Rhubarb tartness to plum & choc flavours; firmish tannins; 04 appealing now & enough stuffing/ structure to develop over few yrs; 15% Fr oaked. **Chardonnay** ★★★ Portion wood-aged; 04 (sample) peaches & cream aromas, vanilla whiff, crisp liveliness. **Colombard** ★★★ 04 tropical fruit aromas, crisp, boiled-sweet aftertaste. **Sauvignon Blanc** ★★★ 04 (sample) light bodied, English gooseberry intro; sweet fruit, nicely rounded, lively acidity. **Semillon-Chardonnay** ★★★ [NEW] 04 light tropically toned nose, citrus tang, to drink early. 20% Fr oaked.

Cape Grove range

Latest versions of **Shiraz** & **Chardonnay** (both ★★) not tasted. **Rosé** ★★★ [NEW] Mainly pinotage. 04 pretty strawberry aromas with peppery touch (from soupçon shiraz), house's rounded quaffability. **Sauvignon Blanc** ★★★ Pleasant casual dry quaffer. 04 (sample) English gooseberries mixed with tropical fruit, zinging freshness to finish.

Cape Tradition range
Shiraz Made more interesting by dollop seldom-seen roobernet; berries & shiraz spice, more spicing from oak (20% Am), **04** supple, flavourful, cheerfully drinkable. **Chardonnay** 20% Fr oaked, which shows in understated butterscotch tone; sweet-fruited, full but balanced. Shows potential. Both **04**, tasted as samples, provisionally ★★★★.

South Point range
Both **04**. **Dry Red** ★★★ Red berries & plums, smoky touch, smoothed by 4.5g/ℓ sugar; pleasant BBQ/al fresco wine. Mainly pinotage & shiraz, with dash ruby cab. **Chenin Blanc** ★★★ Gentle, fresh-tasting guava flavours, styled for undemanding quaffability. All ranges WO W-Cape. – *DH*

Ormonde Estate

Darling (see Swartland map) ▪ 1stB 1999 ▪ Tasting & sales Mon-Fri 9-4 Sat & public holidays 9-1 ▪ Closed Easter Fri, Dec 25/26 & Jan 1 ▪ Vineyard tours by appt ▪ Picnic baskets by appt or BYO ▪ Function hall ▪ Facilities for children ▪ Farm produce ▪ Walks ▪ Owners Basson family ▪ Winemakers Theo Basson & Wouter Pienaar ▪ Viticulturist Theo Basson ▪ ±300 ha (cabs s/f, merlot, mourvèdre, petit v, shiraz, chard, chenin, sauvignon, semillon) ▪ 1 700 tons 11 000 cs own label 40% red 60% white ▪ PO Box 201 Darling 7345 ▪ ormondevineyards@iafrica.com ▪ www.ormonde.info.co.za ℂ (022) 492·3540 ℻ (022) 492·3470

The sheer scale of this sea-breeze-cooled property at Darling on the West Coast blows visitors away: the farm gates are literally in town, and the roughly 300-ha vineyard fans out from there, rolling up into the hills behind the village. Siting has been done with care: sauvignon, for example, looks out over the cold Atlantic; where ground is unsuitable for vines, olives grow. Since the last edition the portfolio has grown and the wines have been split into Ormonde ('reserve') and Alexanderfontein ('lifestyle') ranges. Young viticulturist and co-winemaker Theo Basson is a traditionalist with access to the latest technology. Looking at what's ahead for the area, he sees only stars.

Ormonde range
Cabernet Sauvignon-Merlot ★★★ **02** 60/30 blend, with cab f & petit v the balance. Attractive nose, then opulent smooth mouthfeel, broad palate well balanced, with black berries, plums. 20+ mths Fr oak. Will improve 2/3 yrs. **Sauvignon Blanc** ★★★ **03** Easy, crisp drinkability, pleasant unobtrusive green berry fruit & grass; respectable 12.9% alc. **Chardonnay** ★★★ Double butterscotch nose on **03** & good citrus flavours; needs at least more varietal character to achieve declared icon intent. 13.5% alc.

Alexanderfontein range
Given in last edition under separate 'Alexanderfontein' entry.
- ★★★☆ **Cabernet Sauvignon** ✓ **02** Classic cool climate cab with restraint & elegance (13.5% alc), firm tannins. 9 mths Fr oak, 30% new. As with **01**, should improve yr/2, but tempting in its good-natured youth.
- ★★★★☆ **Sauvignon Blanc** Extraordinary leap from light, angular **03** (★★) to **04**'s attractive lemon/lime, with racy acidity & concentration of flavours leading to long finish. Lunch-friendly 12.9% alc.

Merlot ★★★ **03** has herbal nose with dark choc, plums; lingering flavours. Needs 2/3 yrs to settle down & meld. **Chenin** ★★☆ **03** retasted mid-2004 showing bottle age rather than former greengage freshness. Drink soon. 12.8% alc. **Chardonnay** ★★★ **03** lightly elegant & fresh, with shy, subtle pear notes. Judicious wooding: fermented/6 mths older oak; some native yeasts. 13.5% alc. – *NP*

Oubenheim Estate

Olifants River ▪ Est/1stB 2002 ▪ Closed to public ▪ Owners DW Viljoen & Philip Viljoen ▪ Winemaker Philip Viljoen ▪ Merlot, pinotage, shiraz, chenin, sauvignon ▪ 500 cs 100% red ▪ PO Box 52 Vredendal 8160 ▪ oubenheim@telkomsa.net ℂ 083·509·9885 ℻ (027) 213·5624

Elsenburg-qualified Philip Viljoen's father and grandfather made wine on family-owned Morgenzon farm in the 1960s before closing the cellar to help kick-start nearby Spruitdrift winery. Philip has re-commissioned the cellar, and re-registered Morgenzon and two other properties as Oubenheim, the first 'estate' in the Olifants River area. He's looking to release his first Shiraz later this year, having had encouraging ratings for his Merlot and Pinotage at the Michelangelo, Swiss International and FCTWS competitions.

Oude Jongh see Le Manoir de Brendel

Oude Kaap

Range by DGB for export mainly to Germany, Scandinavia and the Low Countries.
Cabernet Sauvignon ★★★ **03** fairly evolved aromas of roast meat & dried red fruit; soft, potpourri-scented palate. All reds 3 mths Fr oak chips. **Pinotage** ★★★ **03** shows meaty/savoury edge to the sweet-berry bouquet; comfortable tannins; dry, with concluding tobacco hint. **Cabernet Sauvignon-Merlot** ★★★ Tasty, harmonious equal partnership in **03**; bramble/game notes with food-cordial savoury finish. **Rosé** ★★ From pinotage, **04** with variety's signature mulberry aromas; sweetish, very gentle finish – some might prefer more zip. **Chardonnay** ★★★ Styled for the pop palate; **03** lively pale lime hue, slight melon/butterscotch note; creamy, balanced. **Chenin Blanc** ★★ Light-bodied, softly dry **04** offers hint of guava, tangy lemongrass tail. **Elegant Wit** ★★ NV blend of 6 grapes; shy pear/marzipan aromas, melon flavour; drier taste than (17.8g/ℓ) would suggest. Light 11.7% alc. All WO W-Cape. — *TM*

Oudekloof Private Cellar

Tulbagh ▪ Est 1752 ▪ 1stB 2000 ▪ Closed to public ▪ Owners Francois Rozon, Lyndsay Webster-Rozon, Paul & Lucille O'Riordan ▪ Winemaker Emile Gentis (Aug 2004) ▪ Arnold Hugo (Jan 2000) ▪ 22 ha (cab, shiraz, chard, chenin) ▪ 1 000 cs ▪ 25% red 75% white ▪ PO Box 191, Oudekloof Farm, Tulbagh 6820 ▪ Oudekloof@mweb.co.za ✆ (023) 230·1925 📠 856·4595

There's a sense of history on the Rozon-O'Riordan farm on the western slopes of the Tulbagh Valley. It was established in 1752 but a national monument on the property marks the date of the first reconnaissance of the area in 1658. An old cannon is a relic of times when the news was signalled to the hinterland that boats had entered Table Bay. Skipping a few centuries, there is also history in a block of chenin bushvines planted almost 50 years ago. Outgoing winemaker Gert Theron experimented with the Beaujolais style 'with great success', says co-owner Francois Rozon. Thinking is that it suits the reds growing in Oudekloof's microclimate. Next to come into production is chardonnay.
Cabernet Sauvignon 04 unrated work-in-progress shows well-formed fruit with smoky currant jam nose & hint green olive. 14% alc. **Shiraz** ★★★ Modern, ripely fruity **03**, spice emporium smells amid thickly padded plummy fruit; full, powerful stewed fruit palate with obvious oak, dark choc finish; yr Fr oak; 14% alc. **Forgeron** ★★★ **02** rustic fusion of pinotage (70%) & cinsaut, off unirrigated low-yielding vyds. Volatile, soft, sweet & jammy. Only ±500 btls made. **Chenin Blanc** ★★ Off ±50 yr old bushvines. **04** (sample) sweet-melon & honeysuckle whiffs; soft, quite juicy; lightish pleasant apple tastes. — *TM*

Oude Rust see Mooiuitsig

Oude Wellington Estate

Wellington ▪ Visits by appt ▪ Tasting fee R15 ▪ Closed Dec 25 ▪ A la carte restaurant ▪ Guest house & self-catering cottages ▪ Tourgroups ▪ Facilities for children ▪ Conferencing ▪ Owners/viticulturists Rolf & Vanessa Schumacher ▪ Winemaker Vanessa Schumacher (Jul 1995) ▪ 13 ha (cab, ruby cab, shiraz, chard, chenin) ▪ 80 tons ±2 500 cs own label 60% red 20% white 20% rosé ▪ PO Box 622 Wellington 7654 ▪ info@kapwein.com ▪ www.kapwein.com http://estate. kapwein.com ✆ 873·2262 📠 873·4639

Last harvest Vanessa Schumacher (now with ten years under her winemaking belt) heard Cape farmers were struggling to ripen their red grapes. 'Fortunately we didn't have any difficulties. The only problem is, I don't know exactly what we did right or how to repeat it, there are so many variables', she shrugs. Last year marked the maiden vintage from their shiraz vineyard. They're seeing more local folk in their tasting room, which means a lot to her and husband Ralph because 'pleasing local winelovers remains our most important endeavour'. A guesthouse, self-catering cottages and brandy cellar (Ralph's domain) complete the picture at this characterful Wellington *weingut*.

Currant Abbey ☺ ★★★ Anagram of ruby cabernet, from which it is made. Unwooded **01** thatch & earth tones; fruity tannins now smoothed by bottle-age. **Gewürztraminer** ☺ ★★★ Absolutely classic bouquet of roses, **03** sweetly scented yet dry-tasting despite 6g/ℓ sugar, thanks to brisk acidity. Lowish 12% alc.

Cabernet Sauvignon ★★★★ Emphatic Wellington red, Fr oak aged, 14 mths for latest **01**; dark berry fruit on attractive spicy sweet-oak background, fruity roundish tannins; could do with yr/2 to soften, develop. **Ruby Cabernet** ★★★ **98** has mellowed with bottle-age but still has juice & body (14% alc); woody/earthy tones, nice dry tannins. Fr oak. **Blanc de Noir** ★★ From ruby cab. **03** glows a coppery pink, light fruit, pleasing freshness; rounded rather than sweet (7.5g/ℓ sugar). **Chardonnay Barrique** ★★ Am oak aged (8 mths, 2nd fill), new to the guide but already **02** pleasantly honeyed; whiffs dried peach/vanilla; balanced wooding. **Chardonnay Unwooded** ★★ **04** (sample) understated peach & citrus tones; rounded, clean & fresh. Best in its youth. — *DH*

Oude Weltevreden see Weltevrede
Our Founders see Bellingham
Out of Africa see African Terroir
Out of the Blue see African Terroir

Overgaauw Estate 🍷 ♿

Stellenbosch ▪ Est 1905 ▪ 1stB 1971 ▪ Tasting & sales Mon-Fri 9-12.30 2-5 Sat & public holidays 10-12.30 (closed Mar 21, Easter Fri-Sun, Dec 25/26 & Jan 1) ▪ Fee R10 ▪ Tours by appt ▪ Owner Braam van Velden ▪ Winemaker Chris Joubert (1990), with David van Velden Jnr (Nov 2002) ▪ Viti consultant Johan Pienaar ▪ 75 ha (11 varieties) ▪ ±360 tons 17 000 cs 60% red 40% white ▪ PO Box 3 Vlottenburg 7604 ▪ info@overgaauw.co.za ▪ www.overgaauw.co.za ✆ 881·3815 📠 (021) 881·3436

One hundred years ago Abraham Julius van Velden bought a portion of the family farm from his grandfather, naming it Overgaauw. To celebrate four generations of successful farming, the Van Veldens are planning a number of surprises for 2005, including brand new packaging. What they won't spring on us is the 02 Tria Corda or Cab – a vintage they say simply doesn't meet their exacting standards. Last year's harvest is producing good flavour, with fruitier and softer reds (particularly the merlot and shiraz) expected to be ready earlier than 03 or 01; the exception is (again) the cab, which they find somewhat disappointing. Of the 04 whites, chardonnay is the one to watch.

★★★★★ **Tria Corda** Benchmark, early 'Cape claret' blend, offered in better yrs only (so no **02**). Sample **03** signals fantastic promise lurking in barrel: beautiful, sculpted huckleberry/blackcurrant fruits well ordered in juicy, sweet-ripe tannin scaffold. Lipsmacking now, should prove to be sensational 2007 onwards. **01** in classic style: all currants & plums, with trademark leafiness for interest. VDG. **00** *Decanter* ★★★★. Cab, merlot, cab f blend (65/25/10), 18 mths new Fr oak, 14% alc.

★★★★★ **Cabernet Sauvignon** Always in strapping mode, with 18+ mths in oak, all new for lavish **03** (sample): concentrated juicy blackcurrant fruit wreathed throughout huge, ripe tannin latticework. Most promising. No **02**. **01** similarly impressive build, cassis jostling with wood, a typical cab profile in classic dry finish. 14% alc.

★★★★☆ **Merlot** The first Cape bottling of this variety, now a seriously styled wine that needs few yrs' maturation. Sample **02** shows deceptively open loganberry fruits, but tight-grained tannins keep door closed for now. **01** mocha-toned, with supple yet juicy flavours; a true-to-style local example. Unobtrusively 18 mths used Fr oak.

★★★★ **Shiraz-Cabernet Sauvignon** Pulpy sweet bilberry flesh another arrow for cellar's 'Old World' quiver. Just-bottled **02** (mid-2004): plump, juicy, berried richness with 20% cab spine. Delicious now-2007. Untasted **01** VDG. 18 mths older oak.

★★★★ **Chardonnay** While others vacillate, the family stays true to a style that has done the business for yrs. **03** big & buttery, redolent of vanilla and toffee, a rich mouthful freshened by acid seam. **02** marzipan, asparagus & hints of burnt match. 7 mths Fr oak (equal measures new & 2nd fill). Ready on release.

★★★★☆ **Sauvignon Blanc 04** changes course: now in racy, pacey cut-grass mode, offering sprightly green characters calling for food accompaniment. **03** a tropical riot of gooseberry-&-guava scents, grapefruit flavours. Lower (12%) alc than pvs.

★★★★☆ **Sylvaner** A speciality for over three decades, the sole Cape example of this grape. **03** has developed a waxy spice depth to floral perfume; supple, earthy style, finishes full & dry (2.7g/ℓ sugar). Proven track record for bottle maturation.

★★★★★ **Cape Vintage** ✓ Pioneers of using Portuguese varieties locally, (but no whisper now of p-word on the label); adherents to classic style — lower sugars, higher alcs. **97** ('**Reserve**' in pvs eds; ★★★★★), still tannic & youthful in true vintage style, maturing into real excellence. Great balance, with intensity & grip. Early (at 7 yrs!) complexity promises long development. Blend touriga with tintas b/f/r, souzão & cornifesto. 2½ yrs 1 300ℓ casks.

Discontinued: **Pinotage-Cabernet Franc.** – DS –

Overhex Private Cellar

Worcester • Est/1stB 2002 • Tasting & sales Mon-Fri 8-5 • Closed public holidays • Tours by appt • BYO picnic • Farm produce • Owners George Smit, Gerhard van der Wath & Kobus Rossouw • Winemaker Kobus Rossouw, with Willie Malan (Jun/Jan 2003) • Viticulturist Henri du Plessis (Oct 2003) • 10 000 tons • Export brands: Balance, Five Senses, Yammé & Cape Rock • Ranges for customers: Warthog (America, Europe), Country Cellars (SA) • HACCP, BRC & ISO 9000 certification in progress • PO Box 139 Worcester 6849 • overhex@intekom.co.za • www.overhex.com ⓒ (023) 347-5012 🖷 (023) 347·1057

Overhex have bottled their first two organically produced wines, a Pinotage and Pinotage Rosé. Watch this space for more organic releases in future. The enthusiastic management team here are determined to make a bigger impact on the market and have appointed new personnel to handle marketing and logistics, as well as a new viticulturist. Two new ranges, Balance and Five Senses, have been launched, and a Cab should soon be added to their flagship Overhex line. They're excited about their latest red wines, which they say are accessible and early drinking. The tasting area has undergone a complete facelift and can now accommodate groups of up to 50 at a time. They have no own vines at present, and buy in selected grapes, but planting will begin this year.

Overhex range

Cape Rock Lizabelle 🆕 ★★★★ **02** striking red blend of ruby cab, roobernet, pinotage & shiraz with intriguing nose of sweet black berries & pine needles; big & chunky, lots of juicy tannins, dry savoury finish. Following **04**s tasted as samples, ratings provisional. **Chardonnay** ★★★ **04** light tropical tone, touch of ripe peach, gentle vanilla; clean, well made. **Sauvignon Blanc** ★★★ **04** strikingly aromatic with green grass & ripe guava; full & sweet-fruited. **White Muscadel** ★★☆ Powerfully sweet & muscatty. **Red Muscadel** ★★★ Better balanced than white version; muscat billows out of the glass with earthy touch, sweetness balanced by high acidity, alc (6g/ℓ, 17.9%).

Balance range

NEW

All **04**s, many tasted as samples, ratings provisional. **Merlot-Cabernet Sauvignon** ★★★ Coffee & choc on nose, some leafy & floral notes, amenable tannins, smooth persistence. Could be cellared 2-3 yrs; same for... **Shiraz-Merlot** ★★★★ Unusually aromatic: proffers smoky blackberries & pepper; ripe berries & plum flavours; firm, full tannins; long floral finish with hint of rosemary. **Pinotage Rosé** ★★★ Pretty ripe-plum nose, lots of berry flavours, touches Ribena & banana, smooth, good zip of acidity refreshes. **Chenin Blanc-Colombard** ★★★ Off-dry, with guava & pineapple in bouquet; dry, lively & refreshing. **Colombard-Chardonnay** ★★ Shy tropical nose, more forthcoming on palate, fresh dry acidic finish. Note: the Moraea and Intrusa ranges featured in pvs ed now for export market/buyers own brands only. — *DH*

Overmeer Cellars

No-frills quaffing range launched in 1996. All NVs in 5ℓ boxes, WO W-Cape. By Distell.
Selected Red ★★ Light-hued braai slosher; plummy, earthy & rustic, with some tannins. **Premier Grand Cru** ★★ Crunchy melon-toned quick-quaff; fruit maintains low profile, as always. **Selected Stein** ★★ Gulper for the sweeter tooth; soft lemony flavours. **Late Harvest** ★★★ Fractionally sweeter, fuller version of Stein; subdued glacé fruit aromas/flavours, yielding texture. All alcs ±11%. — *CR*

Overvaal see Hartswater
Paarl Heights see False Bay Winery

Paarl Wine Company

Paarl • Closed to public • 9 Zuidmeer Str Huguenot Paarl • winesales@ffbc.co.za ℂ 862·0616 🖷 862·6400
Wine wholesalers and owners of, among others, the Fairbridge, Spencers Creek and Casa Portuguesa ranges.

Paddagang Wines   🍷🍽️ ⚭ 🔖

Tulbagh • Est 1987 • Tasting & sales daily 9-4 • Fee R5 • Paddagang Restaurant daily 8.30–4.30 • Closed Easter Fri, May 1, Dec 25 & Jan 1 • Guest house • Gifts • Owners Paddagang Vignerons • Winemakers Carl Allen & Elsabé Roux (Aug/Dec 2002) • Viticulturist Callie Coetzee (Dec 2002) • 5 300 cs 52% red 21% white 27% other • PO Box 303 Tulbagh 6820 • paddagang@mweb.co.za • www.tulbagh.net • ℂ (023) 230·0394 🖷 (023) 230·0433
The five shareholders of Paddangang Wines succeed in injecting a little humour into the sometimes too-serious wine market though their amusing name wines and frog-theme labels. These make wonderful souvenirs to take home after a good traditional Cape meal at the Paddagang Restaurant, where several Cape artists have their works on display. A recent addition to the historic restaurant complex is the Danie Theron Guest House, which can accommodate up to eight guests.

Paddarotti ★★★ Appropriately wide-girthed (±14% alc); a blend of shiraz/cab (60/40) in latest version; peppery currant aromas, jammy red fruit flavours, dry savoury finish. **Paddajolyt** ★★★ Easy unwooded *vin ordinaire* from pinotage & ruby cab (50/50); shy earthy/leafy bouquet; lightish body, tangy dried-fruit finish. **Paddadundee** ★★ Chardonnay, latest subtitled 'Limited Release'; striking green-gold colour; fragrant passionfruit hints; creamy dry finish. **Paddasang** ★★ Lightish sauvignon, its apple/pear tones tinged with bottle-age; needs drinking. **Paddapoot** ★★★ Hanepoot, back in the froggy fold by popular demand — & fans will be pleased: deliciously aromatic & fresh; lovely passion- & grapefruit aromas/flavours, very soft & sweet (sample tasted). **Brulpadda** ★★★ Good old Cape port, from ruby cab & pinotage; with fairly developed aromas of stewed plum; soft, sweet, quite silky, pleasant. Low 16.5% alc. — *TM*

Palm Grove see Origin Wine
Pangolin see MAN Vintners
Panorama see Lost Horizons

Pulpit Rock

Swartland ▪ 1stB 2003 ▪ Tasting & sales Mon-Fri 8-5 Sat 9-1 ▪ Closed Easter Fri-Mon, Dec 25 & Jan 1 ▪ Restaurant daily Tue-Sun; or BYO picnic ▪ Tours by appt ▪ Tourgroups ▪ Walks ▪ Conservation area ▪ Winemaker Piet Kleinhans (Dec 2003) ▪ Viti consultant Johan Viljoen (Jun 2004) ▪ 400 ha (cab, merlot, petit v, pinotage, roobernet, shiraz, chard, chenin, sauvignon) ▪ 570 tons 8 500 cs own label +300 000ℓ bulk 80% red 20% white ▪ Owner Brinkshof Wines (Pty) Ltd ▪ PO Box 1 Riebeek West 7306 ▪ info@pulpitrock.co.za © /🖷 **(022) 461·2025**

Piet Kleinhans, former member of the Stellenbosch Vineyards winemaking team, now has his own charge: all-new Pulpit Rock Winery on one of the Brink brothers' Riebeek West farms. His maiden vintage (2004) produced small quantities of barrel-matured wines for export to the US and EU under the Pulpit Rock label. More commercial quantities/styles are marketed locally as Cape Haven. The remainder of a 4 000-ton crop is sold in bulk. Kleinhans was thrilled to garner three golds at the 2004 SAYWS. A tasting room was opened in October, and a restaurant was opening as we went to press.

Both ranges were tasted as samples; reds in this line-up all **03**. **Cabernet Sauvignon** fairly underplayed blackcurrant & plum aromas; deftly extracted; silky, dry savoury tannins. Potential ★★★★. **Merlot** Smoked meat aromas, firm but silky tannins, very ripe sweetish fruit; handles its towering 15.5% alc better than the next wine. Possible ★★★★. **Pinotage** An 'ultra' wine – extremes of everything, from colour (pitch black) to aroma (porty, exotic whiff salami) to flavour (sweet & boneless) to alc (15.6%). Highly idiosyncratic. How to rate? ★★★? **Shiraz** Peppery red plums on nose, slightly dusty; very attractive dark choc flavour with sour-plum tang, dry finish. 'Only' 14.7% alc. Yr Fr oak, as are all above. Could rate ★★★★. **Chardonnay 04** impressively deep burnished gold, impressive alc too (15.5%); deep wells of peach flavour tinged with ginger. Too young to rate. Fr-oak-fermented/8 mths, partial malo.

Cape Haven range

Chardonnay Gutsy, full-bore version. Great chunks of peach fruit, potently active 15% alc which imparts overtly sweet finish. Possible ★★★. **Chenin Blanc** Considerably quieter & better mannered than Attila the range-mate; also quite a mouthful though; exotic spicy nose with touches grapefruit, asparagus; zesty acidity. Likely ★★★★. **Cabernet**, **Merlot**, **Pinotage** & **Shiraz** not ready for tasting. All in this range **04**. – *TM*

Papillon see Van Loveren

Papkuilsfontein see Tukulu

Paradyskloof

Stellenbosch ▪ Est/1stB 1981 ▪ Tasting Mon-Fri 9-4 only by appt ▪ Sales Mon-Fri 8.30-4 ▪ Tours & meals/refreshments by appt ▪ Owner Landgoed Vriesenhof (Pty) Ltd ▪ Winemaker Jan Coetzee, with Richard Phillips (2001) ▪ Viticulturist Hannes Coetzee, with Schalk du Toit (2002) ▪ 37 ha (cabs s/f, merlot, pinot, pinotage, chard) ▪ ±500 tons 85% red 15% white ▪ PO Box 155 Stellenbosch 7599 ▪ info@paradys.co.za ▪ www.paradys.co.za © 880·0284 🖷 880·1503

Jan Coetzee has dropped the 'Domaines' moniker for his stable, Vriesenhof, Talana Hill and Paradyskloof. Whatever his reason, the straightforward 'Paradyskloof' is more representative of the burly former Springbok loose-forward's shirt, shorts, no shoes persona (which, it must be said, belies his vinous sophistication). A long-standing passion for pinot is now matched by Coetzee's belief that (a) pinotage finds its finest expression in a blend, (b) has a non-negotiable role in a definitive 'Cape Blend'. Hence the new assemblage, Enthopio (Greek for 'indigenous'); and the culling of the single-varietal Pinotage from the Vriesenhof range. Completed in 2004 was another Coetzee creation: 'a Rolls Royce sorting facility with destemmer and press', based on hi-tech equipment seen in Europe. One step closer to a fully gravity-fed cellar by 2007.

Vriesenhof range

★★★★ **Enthopio** Greek for 'truly indigenous' — alludes to presence of pinotage in this attractive, carefully assembled red. The 'local' grape's qualities more evident in **01** than maiden **00**. Tiny quantities of shiraz, cab f & merlot in both vintages provide evanescent support. Oaked ± yr, new/used barrels. 13.1% alc. **01** fruitily sinuous — more Olympic athlete than indulged Greek god. **00** also focused & honed. **02** barrel sample shows generous proportions & heady, complex bouquet. Potentially exciting.

★★★★ **Pinot Noir** No closet pinotphile, JBC gives dense farmyard & cherry aromas free rein in **03**. Structure a contradiction in terms — ethereal yet firm, it pleads cellaring. 13% alc. No **02**; **01** nodded in direction of Burgundy. From Dijon clones in varying soils. Generously oaked.

★★★★ **Kallista** Flagship Bdx-style blend led by merlot (± 40%), with cabs s/f, structured for long-term rather than quick gratification. Moreish **01** (★★★★★) savoury & plummy with signature earthy finish & fine sour cherry twist. Pitch black **02** barrel sample packs baskets of fruit, liquorice & cigar box. Long finish with judicious alc (13.5%) & gossamer tannins. Potentially even more starry.

Cabernet Sauvignon; **Pinotage**; **Chardonnay** discontinued.

Talana Hill range

★★★★☆ **Royale** Long-established blend cabs s/f & merlot. **01** (★★★★) initial oak-vanilla attack loses against rising tide of opulent black fruit & attention-grabbing alc (14%). Maturing gracefully. 8 mths Fr oak, new/2nd fill. Sample **02** lavish with berry ice-cream flavours & vanilla fudge aromas. Aggressive tannins will soften.

★★★★☆ **Chardonnay 03** continues where weighty, oaky **02** left off: as big as its ex-rugby Springbok maker. Dash of citrus zest cuts buttered scone nose. Relatively lofty alc (13.5%) ensures lingering finish. Single-vyd wines worth cellaring a few yrs.

Paradyskloof range

Pinotage 02 ★★☆ Easy drinking **01**, lanolin/raspberry aromas with slight acetone whiff; robust earthy/organic flavours. 13% alc. **Cabernet Sauvignon-Merlot** ★★☆ **02** for imbibing not intellectualising; floral, with herbaceous finish. **Chardonnay** ★★☆ **03** delicate lemon blossom nose & palate given punch by 'hot' alc (13.5%). **Sauvignon Blanc-Chardonnay** discontinued. — *CvZ*

Patrys

Range launched in 2003 by Woodlands Import Export of Somerset West, mainly for export to Europe. See Assegai for contact details.

Cabernet Sauvignon ★★★ **02**, on retaste, shows tarry smoked meat aromas, scrubby palate, firm dry finish; could be aged further. ±9 mths Fr oak. 14% alc. **Merlot** ★★☆ **03** sweetly fresh berry fruit, light-textured, lacks intensity, finishes quickly. 6 mths equal Fr/Am oak. 14% alc. **Pinotage** ★★★★ ✓ **03** smoky dried banana nose; creamy/toasty palate with underlying sweet spice; nicely weighted & dry for variety; no hurry to drink up. 3-9 mths Fr/Am oak. 14.5% alc. **Shiraz** ★★★ **02** startlingly dark; concentrated, creamy blackfruit nose; strong tannins need further cellaring. 14% alc. 8 mths Fr oak. **Cinsaut-Ruby Cabernet** ★★★ **03** fruity but leaner & less amendable than pvs; very dry. **Chenin Blanc** ★★★ **04** Granny Smith apple nose, crisp, zesty palate. Good summer refresher. **Sauvignon Blanc** ★★ **04** delicate pear-drop aromas, leafy green-toned palate, not as much character as pvs. All WO Paarl. — *CR*

▨ *Paul Bonnay* see Robertson Winery

Paul Cluver Estate

Elgin ▪ Est 1859 ▪ 1stB 1997 ▪ Tasting & sales Mon-Fri 8-5 Sat & public holidays 9-5 ▪ Fee R10 for groups of 8-12 ▪ Closed Easter Fri/Sun, Dec 25 & Jan 1 ▪ BYO picnic ▪ Guest house ▪ Summer sunset concerts in amphitheatre ▪ Conservation area ▪ Owners Cluver family ▪

Winemaker Andries Burger (Nov 1996) ◼ Viticulturist Wayne Voigt, advised by Kevin Watt (Mar 2003) ◼ 100 ha (cab, merlot, pinot, chard, gewürz, riesling, sauvignon) ◼ 300 tons 20 000 cs 50% red 50% white ◼ PO Box 48 Grabouw 7160 ◼ info@cluver.co.za ◼ www. cluver.com © 844·0605 ⌨ 844·0150

Paul Cluver, neuro-surgeon and major player in the deciduous fruit industry, helped engineer Elgin's entrée to wine scene in the 1980s while there was still an official taboo on vine planting in the area, despite its cooler climate. The family winery has since quietly sneaked in among the big names. In 'one of our better harvests', Andries Burger rates riesling a 'highlight'. The lowlight was handling the crush with a broken arm after falling off a press. Uneven ripening was merely 'a problem' sorted out by… well, sorting tables, part of a new grape intake system and other winery extensions, including a barrel cellar.

★★★★ **Cabernet Sauvignon 01** still as cool & elegant as we now expect, with berry scents/flavours, cedar overlay, dry finish. 13.5% alc is 1% lower than in **02** (★★★★), yet latter speaks of difficult vintage through slightly diminished substance, poise & length, & more obvious, dryer tannins — probably earlier-maturing. But still an attractive, savoury mouthful. Usual ±18 mths Fr oak, 60% new.

★★★★ **Pinot Noir** Has helped build reputation of cool Elgin over the year, but retasted **02** (★★★), while well structured, strives too hard to overcome vintage. Very ripe, heavily extracted fruit, but now a touch severe, over-big 14.5% alc, finishing fairly short & a little bitter. Happily **03** promises well: long, dark & handsome; rich fruit firmly supported, subtly oaked (Fr, third new, ±11 mths). 14.5% alc.

★★★☆ **The Elgin Blend** 🆕 Cheekily but proudly named **03** blend home cab & (now dominant) bought-in Elgin merlot. Choc, berries to sniff. Fine fresh acidity, firm, unobtrusive savoury tannins. Not challenging the flagships above but pleasantly, though seriously, supporting them. Typically sensitive oaking: 15 mths, 10% new. 13.5% alc. Will benefit from few yrs keeping, and last longer. NE.

★★★☆ **Gewürztraminer** Delicately aromatic, forcefully elegant **04** more serious & less blowsy than most. Pleasing crisp acidity controls lingering Turkish Delight flavours & touch sugar — effectively dry, like similarly attractive, food-friendly **03**.

★★★★ **Chardonnay** Elegant, fine tones from Elgin's mild climate characterise these. Toasty, spicy youthfulness on **03**, green lime flavours, in harmonious, silky ensemble. Big fresh acid should guard over few yrs' development. Fermented in Fr oak (75% new), partly with native yeasts, then 9 mths in barrel. 13.5% alc **02** (★★★) more bitty, with sweet edge to over-acidic limey core.

★★★★ **Weisser Riesling** A most sophisticated wine, with **04** offering the tingle of excitement that (for some) only this great variety can give; it's partly inherent fineness, partly the subtle balance fruit, moderate 12% alc, acid & a little sweetness (8. 7g/ℓ sugar). Intense, peachy loveliness will develop complexity over 5+ yrs. Lightly intense **02** (★★★☆) already quite developed.

★★★★☆ **Weisser Riesling Noble Late Harvest** Elegantly packaged version from consistently excellent vyd. **03** (★★★★★) still with thrilling tensions of sumptuous fruit, sweetness & nervy acid, honeyed botrytis & peach/muscat/pepper notes. Long, interesting life ahead. IWSC gold. No **02**. **01** also excitingly balanced, opulent yet restrained; shows a complex fruit array with brush mellower botrytis. 14.5% alc.

Sauvignon Blanc ★★★★ **04** more floral, finer balance than pvs — lighter 12.5% alc helps. Earthy & green notes, fresh acidity, lingering passionfruit finish. Discontinued: **Weisser Riesling Special Late Harvest**. — *TJ*

▨ *Paul Wallace Wines* see Terroir Wines

Pax Verbatim Vineyards

Stellenbosch ◼ Est 2004 ◼ Closed to public ◼ Owner/winemaker Richard Hilton ◼ 100 cs 100% red ◼ 21 Topaz Street, Heldervue, Somerset West 7130 ◼ info@paxverbatim.co.za ◼ www.paxverbatim.co.za ©/⌨ 855·5244

'Having been in the business for 13 years, I've long wanted to make and bottle a single wine for which I am wholly responsible,' says wine marketer Richard Hilton. In 2003, he had the wherewithal to make four barrels 'at a quality level I'd be happy with' – and took the plunge. Dream fulfilled, he named his wine brand Pax Verbatim – 'True Peace'. A full yet seductively soft, spicy Syrah is his goal, and he draws inspiration from celebrated Rhône Valley exponents like René Rostaing and Alain Graillot. The grapes are from unirrigated bushvines on the Groenekloof hills along the West Coast, vinified in a private cellar in Stellenbosch. His maiden vintage is dedicated to grape farmers, 'who are seldom mentioned yet provide the intrinsic backbone for the potential quality of any great wine'.

★★★☆ **Blazing Hill Syrah** Ground pepper aromas, restrained dense tannins, elegant, unflamboyant, fine linearity. **03** in good balance with 14% alc, supportive acid. Groenekloof fruit. Needs few yrs to start showing its best. 60% new Fr oak 16-18 mths. – MF

Peaks View see Bovlei
Pearl Springs see Cape Vineyards
Pearly Bay see KWV International

Perdeberg Winefarmers' Co-operative

Paarl ▪ Est 1941 ▪ Tasting & sales Mon-Fri 8-12.30; 1.30-5 ▪ Closed public holidays ▪ Tours by appt during tasting hours ▪ Owners 49 members ▪ Winemakers Kobus de Kock & Ewald Kellerman (1989/1997) ▪ Viticulturist Stephan Joubert (2001) ▪ 3 000 ha ▪ 20 000 tons 5 000 cs own label 60% red 40% white ▪ PO Box 214 Paarl 7620 ▪ info@perdeberg.co.za ▪ www.perdeberg.co.za ✆ 869·8244/8112 🖷 869·8245

What's new here is the best design award at the 4th Construction New Media Awards for their interactive website. Well worth a visit, as it's well padded with food and wine matching ideas and a selection of recipes. The physical Perdeberg is also worth popping into, of course, especially for a first taste of the additions to the Reserve range. The labels on these and the standard wines depict the quagga which once roamed the Paardeberg Hills. Other news is that winemaker Niël Groenewald has moved to Bellingham.

Reserve range

★★★★ **Pinotage** We last tasted **01**, a reserved Reserve, with evident but soft tannins.

Cabernet Sauvignon 🆕 ★★★★ ✓ **02** offers rich concentration of cassis & sweet oak; modern yet elegant; ripe tannins provide a comfortable backing. 14 mths Fr barrels. **Chardonnay** 🆕 ★★★★ ✓ Shows some refinement, breed. **03** vanilla & butter tones well meshed with ripe fruit flavours, peach uppermost; focused dry finish. 13.7% alc.

Perdeberg range

Cinsaut ☺ ★★★ **03** bright & light textured, as always, succulent cherry tone; hides its 14.1% alc very well.

Shiraz ★★★ **03** good spread of black/red fruits, slight savoury pepperiness & chunky tannins make this a good braai-mate. 14.8% alc. **Cabernet Sauvignon-Merlot** ★★★ **03** modern fruity styling, satisfying, though fairly puckering tannins could do with more cellaring. **Pinotage** ★★★ ✓ Unoaked version a benchmark for this style. **03** perky, clean cherry flavours, lots of ripe tannins; could keep a few yrs. **Chenin Blanc Dry** ★★★ **04** straightforwardly pleasant; well flavoured with pears, apples & guavas; balanced refreshment. **Sauvignon Blanc 04** not ready for tasting. **Chenin Blanc Semi** ★★★ 'Semi', as in semi-sweet though **03** not all that sweet on analysis or taste (10g/ℓ sugar); otherwise similar to dry version. **Cinsaut Liqueur Wine** ★★★ Unusual, attractive & long-lived fortified dessert with cherry/strawberry whiffs, moderate sweetness; **01** good solo or with fruit preserves and nuts. 17.7% alc. – JN

Perold see KWV International

Philip Jordaan Wines

*Rawsonville ▪ Est/1stB 1998 ▪ Closed to public ▪ Owner/winemaker Philip Jordaan ▪ Viti consultant Schalk du Toit ▪ 1 ha ▪ 500 cs 100% red ▪ PO Box 55 Rawsonville 6845 ▪ philipjordaan@intekom.co.za ✆ **(023) 349·1601** 🖷 (023) 349·1581*

Philip Jordaan, by day cellarmaster at Du Toitskloof, makes a small quantity of Cab Franc for his own label. He's upbeat about the quality of 2004, and about the fact that his wine featured at the Nederburg Auction last year. From 02, features revamped packaging.

★★★★ **Cabernet Franc** Establishing a name for silky refinement. **02** offers pleasant coffee character, notes of prune & mint. Well integrated tannins. But **01** (★★★★) particularly impressive: same coffee character but more elegance, spice & perfume; excellent balance. These yr oak; 14% alc; WO W-Cape. — *NP*

Picardi Rebel Liquors

*Est 1994 ▪ PO Box 18130 Wynberg 7800 ▪ lenor.cw@picardirebel.co.za ✆ **700·5500** 🖷 700·5515*

Well-established national drinks chain (80+ stores) sourcing value-wines and special parcels for sale under their house brand Hippo Creek (see entry). Also a range of 5ℓ bag-in-boxes, made to spec by Robertson Winery: Classic Red, Vin de Noir, Stein, Blanc de Blanc and Late Harvest.

Pick 'n Pay

*Enquiries Elsa Gray ▪ Bahrain Drive Extension, Airport Industria 7490 ▪ egray@pnp.co.za ▪ www.picknpay.co.za ✆ **936·8400** 🖷 934·2639*

This national chain of supermarkets and hyperstores offers its No Name house-brand in 5ℓ bag-in-boxes, as well as convenient fridge-door-fitting 500 ml budget packs, all made by Robertson Winery. **Dry Red** ★★ Easy quaffing fruity red, with amenable tannins which switch easily from standalone to table. **Rosé** ★★ Blush-coloured semi-sweet with light fruit. **Dry White** ★★ Smooth, easy, gently dry. **Stein** ★★ Light textured, with delicate sweetness. **Late Harvest** ★★ Soft but perky semi-sweet, with tropical fruit flavours. **Dry White Light** ★★ Light (9.6% alc) & juicy, smooth acidity, tasty. — *DH*

Pier 42 see Goedverwacht
Pierre Jourdan see Càbriere
Pinecrest see Môreson
Pinehurst see Môreson

Plaisir de Merle

*Simondium (see Franschhoek map) ▪ Est 1993 ▪ 1stB 1994 ▪ Tasting & sales Mon-Fri 8.30-5 Sat 10-4 (Nov-Mar) 10-2 (Apr-Oct) ▪ Fee R20 (informal), R30 (tasting & tour) ▪ Closed public holidays ▪ Tours by appt during tasting hours ▪ Small private functions by appt ▪ Overnight stays (B&B) by appt ▪ Tourgroups ▪ Conferencing ▪ Owner Distell ▪ Winemaker Niel Bester (Jan 1993) ▪ Viticulturist Hannes van Rensburg ▪ ±400 ha (cab, merlot, shiraz, chard, sauvignon) ▪ 900-1 000 tons 55 000 cs own label 80% red 20% white ▪ PO Box 121 Simondium 7670 ▪ nbester@distell.co.za info@plaisirdemerle.co.za ▪ www.plaisirdemerle.co.za ✆ **874·1071** 🖷 874·1689 (sales) 🖷 874·1488 (cellar)*

In our 1995 edition, we noted the introduction of 'a revolutionary Cape red' from this imposing winery, advised then and now by Ch Margaux director Paul Pontallier, 'almost instantly approachable, but with striking complexity'. The wine was the Cab 93, made by the same founding winemaker, Niel Bester, who continues to garner bouquets for his wines from wine critics locally and abroad. In 2004, the 01 version of the Cab so impressed the judges of the Sélections Mondiales in Canada, they awarded it the SA Prix du Jury. (Our own preference now is probably for the Merlot and, on recent showing, the blend.) Bester, though understandably pleased, assures he's not out to impress. 'I try to make elegant, food-friendly wines for drinking rather than showing. In the case of the reds, I want them to last 10 years or longer.'

★★★☆ **Cabernet Sauvignon** Currently **02** fairly typical of the vintage: elegant, soft, through not especially complex or intense; for early enjoyment. More firmly structured **01**, a good performance given major quantities: now up to 28 000 cs. ±Yr Fr oak, 35% new. Should grow, keep few yrs.

★★★☆ **Merlot 00** splashed with shiraz. **01** took on 6% cab, 9% petit v. Current **02** returns to monovarietal; light, elegant, gently wooded. Attractive & restrained with well focused palate; more elegance than power in spite of gutsy 14.5% alc. 11–17 mths Fr oak, 1st-3rd fill. **03** will be sold through Bergkelder Vinoteque.

★★★☆ **Shiraz** Modern **01** (★★★★), designed for obvious pleasure: lush, sweet-fruited, burly but gentle tannins. **02** soft & generously oaked, needs time for wood to integrate, acidity to settle. 60% aged in new & 2nd fill Am/Fr oak, 12–16 mths.

★★★★ **Grand Plaisir** Latest releases spark a raised general rating for this red, launched ahead of Diners Club 'Cape Red' category with **97**, cab, merlot, shiraz, petit v (50/20/20/10); same blend in **01**, but bigger, riper. Soupçon malbec joins in **02** for final 50/24/10/10/6 make-up; again a big wine (14.6%) but classically taut, promising red fruit cornucopia on palate just needs few yrs to harmonise. 16 mths Fr oak.

★★★☆ **Chardonnay** Always a fine, excellently wooded example. Citrus-toned **02** less concentrated, in line with vintage, but well structured, poised. **03** exhibits good citrus fruit, clever oak. Light & delicate.

★★★★ **Sauvignon Blanc** Blend of two younger, earlier-harvested vyds & older, riper-picked block; no longer oaked & only briefly lees-aged (2½ mths) in **04** (sample); returns to aromatic style with lemongrass, light honeyed/savoury notes, fynbos whiff too; lots of soft-textured freshness. 13.4% alc. Has more to give than simple though greenly refreshing **03** (★★★). — *RK/CR*

▪ *Podium* see Baarsma
Pongrácz see JC le Roux
Porcupine Ridge see Boekenhoutskloof

Porterville Cellars

*Swartland ▪ Est 1941 ▪ Tasting & sales Mon-Fri 9-5 ▪ Closed Easter Fri-Mon, Dec 25/26, Jan 1 ▪ Tours by appt ▪ Picnic baskets/light meals by appt or BYO ▪ Tourgroups ▪ Owners 94 members ▪ Winemakers André Oberholzer (Dec 1996) & Theo Brink (July 2003) ▪ Viticulturist Jurie du Plessis (Jun 2003) ▪ 1 490 ha (cab, pinotage, shiraz, chard, chenin, colombard) ▪ ±16 000 tons 12 000 cs own label 16% red 84% white ▪ Range for customer: Kumala (UK) ▪ PO Box 52 Porterville 6810 ▪ info@portwines.co.za ▪ www.portervillecellars.co.za © **(022) 931-2170** 🖷 (022) 931-2171*

Heat waves, drought, this land of extremes was beset by both last harvest. But carefully tended vineyards (some of the fruit from which goes into the high-flying Kumala brand) withstood the onslaught. The resultant wines, processed in the upgraded cellar, are 'particularly flavourful,' say the crew. Unlike the weather, the wines have been performing well, and the Pinotage, Shiraz and their red blend, Visage, have proved particularly popular internationally. The stylish new tasting area comfortably accommodates up to 60 visitors. Picnic lunches can be booked ahead to further enhance the experience.

Unfiltered Reserve range

Cabernet Sauvignon ★★★☆ **02** correct in all respects – balanced oak, juicily lush cassis fruit; approachable, with some maturation prospects. Reds all barrel matured. **Pinotage** ★★★ **02** not too extracted; red plum tone with pleasant sweet-sour tussle, vanilla-spice finish. 14.3% alc. **Shiraz** ★★★☆ **02** still with youthful purple edge; arresting spicy fynbos/red berries bouquet (best aromatics of all these); ends with toasty mocha lick. 15.2% alc well integrated. **Visage** ★★★☆ 'Enigma' in pvs edition; ripe, jammy combo shiraz, pinotage, merlot, cab (50/20/15/10); with benefit of another yr's maturation, shows some complexity; roast meat/vanilla nose, sweet clove on good grainy palate. 14.5% alc. **Chardonnay** ★★★ Vinified in wood, **03** voluptuous nose of tropical fruit; plumply forceful palate; enough stuffing, alc (14.7%), to stand up to full-flavoured food. **Chenin Blanc Unfiltered** ★★★ Wood-fermented **03** now fairly richly swathed in lanolin & lime marmalade, suggestion of butterscotch/caramel; full-bodied & balanced.

Disa range

> **Rosé** ☺ ★★★ Chug-a-lug style **04**, deep cochineal pink (from pinotage), fresh strawberry nose, succulent off-dry mouthful. NB: 14% alc. **Chardonnay** ☺ ★★★ **04** (sample) unwooded, lightish yet mouthfilling, generous; white peach scents, zingy lemon flavours. **Xation** NEW ☺ ★★★ Off-dry white swigger with delicate green pear aroma; fruit salad flavours; tweak of fruity sweetness in **04** (sample). WO Coastal.

Pinotage ★★ Medium-bodied **03** shows muted plum tones, still some dusty tannins. **Cape Red** ★★ Soft, pinotage-dominated **02** blend with merlot, cab (69/18/13); plummy, harmonious, finishes sweetish. ±14% alc. **Chenin Blanc** ★★★ **04** (sample) subtle melon/green pear aromas, livelier palate of green apples, racy fruity acidity. **Sauvignon Blanc** ★★ **04** perfect foil for succulent braaied snoek; austere capsicum/crushed nettle character, bracing flinty acidity. **Chanaché** NEW ★★ 'More serious white blend' chenin, chard & grenache blanc; **04** sample shows shy lemon whiffs & hints of almond; lime flavours, dry crisp finish. **Snakebite** NEW **02** (unrated sample) unusual fortified, leaning more towards sherry than port; quite spirity, sweet. WO Coastal. **Red Jerepiko** ★★★★ Lovely ruby glints to latest version of full-sweet dessert (NV), from pinotage, cab, cinsaut, fortified to 17%. Potpourri fragrance; silky, light-tripping palate with spiced herbs; firmer & drier tasting than… **Golden Jerepiko** ★★★ From hanepoot; latest NV (02) burnished yellow-gold; ambrosial Turkish Delight whiffs; smooth & honeyed with creamy finish. **Blanc de Blanc, Grand Cru** & **Late Vintage** discontinued.— *TM*

▨ *Portmore Wine Company* see The Foundry

Post House Cellar

Stellenbosch (see Helderberg map) ▪ *Est/1stB 1997* ▪ *Tasting & sales Mon-Fri 8.30-5 Sat by appt 8.30-1* ▪ *Closed Easter Fri/Sun/Mon, Dec 25/26 & Jan 1* ▪ *Owner/winemaker Nicholas Gebers* ▪ *Viti consultant Paul Wallace (1999)* ▪ *37 ha (cab, merlot, petit v, pinotage, shiraz, chenin)* ▪ *±200 tons 2 000 cs own label* ▪ *PO Box 5635 Helderberg 7135* ▪ *ngebers@iafrica.com* ▪ *www.posthousewines.co.za* ⊘/🖷 *842·2409*

At his postage-stamp-sized cellar, Nicholas Gebers follows a minimal-interventionist approach. He ferments with native yeasts, uses as little sulphur as possible and refrains from filtering his wines before bottling. Last year was as bright a vintage as the antique postbox which stands sentinel outside (a relic from the days this farmhouse served as a post office for the tiny missionary town of Raithby). Gebers vinified the first petit verdot and declared the crush as a whole 'very promising'.

★★★★ **Cabernet Sauvignon** Middleweight, dark-fruited **02** for drinking soon; sweet-oak finish. Lighter-textured than 14.3% alc suggests. Foursquare, rather rustic **01** has intense flavours, tough tannins needing ±3 yrs to soften. Balanced oak (35% new, 20 mths) on both.

★★★★ **Merlot** Workmanlike **01** (★★★) retasted mid-2004 shows seductive gamey nose; more austere on palate (though backed by fleshy black fruit) than attractive, luscious **00**. 18 mths oak, 35% new.

★★★★ **Chenin Blanc** Modern, intense **03** joins **02** (★★★★★) on high road taken with FCTWS 2003 trophy win. Opulent lemon flavours, creamy/leesy texture (from barrel-fermentation) & obvious biscuity oak (10 mths, 14% new); steely dry finish. Should grow in cellar for ±5 yrs. 13.5% alc.

Shiraz NEW **03** barrel sample lush with red fruit, white pepper, lily fragrance. Oak still rampant (16% new); should subside with bottle-age. 14.5% alc. Potential★★★★ . — *CvZ*

░ *Post Stones* see False Bay Winery

Premium Cape Wines

Stellenbosch ▪ Est 2003 ▪ Closed to public ▪ Owner Premium Trust ▪ PO Box 12149 Die Boord 7613 ▪ ansgar@gravitywine.com ©/🖷 **886·8515**

This new negociant company supplies wines to supermarkets and direct sales companies in Germany, sourcing the wines from several Cape cellars. The business is run locally by Ansgar Flaatten, who has had experience at Audacia, Cape Classics and merchant houses in Europe.

Imvelo range
Cabernet Sauvignon ★★★ Undemanding but characterful **03**, rich, ripe plum pudding bouquet; not too full bodied, well pitched for earlier/easier drinking. **Sauvignon Blanc** ★★★ Zesty, crisp & dry **04**, food-cordial with leafy/nettly aromas & flavours.

De Sonnenberg range
Dry Rosé ★★★ Deeply coloured **03**, ripe macerated red berries on nose, some appealing mature notes on palate, needing to be enjoyed fairly soon. **Natural Sweet Blanc** ★★★ **03** lovely sweet confectionary nose, light body, drier palate than expected, very soft. **Natural Sweet Rosé** ★★ Fruit gum aromas in ebullient **03**; semi- rather than full-sweet, slightly lacking in acidity grip. **De Sonnenberg Natural Sweet Red** ★★★ **02** warmly ripe basket of red fruit, more structured than others, even has touch tannin. Certainly doesn't need disguising, but a great base for Glühwein.

Uhambo range
Dry Red ★★★ Cinsaut/ruby cab blend with mulberry tone, **02** still youthful, uncomplicatedly juicy, though after the sweet-ripe fruit, the finish is unexpectedly dry. **Dry White** ★★★ Chenin-colombard mix, **03** youthful & fresh, pear-drop bouquet & zinging if somewhat curt appley finish. **Semi-Sweet White** ★★★ Same varieties as for Dry, more characterful on nose, appetising fruit salad tone, soft & easy to drink. **Natural Sweet White** ★★★ Repeat of above varieties, here with Golden Delicious apple on nose; more grip & flavour; a good quaffing style for the sweet of tooth. **Semi-Sweet Red** ★★ Same grapes as dry version, different fruit profile; **02**'s jammy & plummy, fairly slender, much less sweet than name implies. – *CR*

Prospect 1870

Robertson ▪ Est 1990 ▪ 1stB 1998 ▪ Closed to public (tasting & sales at The Wine Boutique, Main Rd, Ashton) ▪ Owners Louis, Chris & Nic de Wet ▪ Winemakers Johan van Wyk & Philip Louw ▪ Viti consultant Francois Viljoen ▪ 45 ha (cab, merlot, pinotage, shiraz, chard, sauvignon, viognier) ▪ 700 cs own label 80% red 20% white ▪ PO Box 141 Ashton 6715 ▪ nic@lando.co.za ▪ www.prospectwines.com © **082·878·2884** 🖷 *(023) 615·1913*

The name of this De Wet family farm refers to the year of founding, which makes this their 135th anniversary. Nic, Louis and Chris dW, the present (5th generation) owners, concentrate on the American market and have added two more US states to their sales area during the past year, bringing the total up to 10. Vineyard Varieties, their stateside distribution arm, handles their own wines as well as those of selected clients.

Cabernet Sauvignon ★★★ **98** lively colour still; mature aromas with tobacco leaf & sandalwood; fruit starting to dry out a bit, we'd enjoy soon. **Chardonnay** NEW ★★★ Ripe melon & apricot aromas on **03**, creamily assertive wood, finishes more than a shade oaky. 6 mths new Fr barrels. Early picked for moderate 12% alc.

Leatherwood range   NEW
Cabernet Sauvignon ★★★ **02** spicy red fruit aroma, attractive woody whiffs; gentle ripe-fruit flavours, quite rich but firmed by mouthcoating tannin. 14% alc. **Shiraz-Viognier** NEW ★★★ **02** aromas of red cherries & violets, spicy red fruit flavours, all heavily accented by wood (6–12 mths Fr, 2nd fill). 5% viognier. All WO W-Cape. – *JB*

Provin see Douglas Winery

Pulpit Rock

Swartland ▪ 1stB 2003 ▪ Tasting & sales Mon-Fri 8-5 Sat 9-1 ▪ Closed Easter Fri-Mon, Dec 25 & Jan 1 ▪ Restaurant daily Tue-Sun; or BYO picnic ▪ Tours by appt ▪ Tourgroups ▪ Walks ▪ Conservation area ▪ Winemaker Piet Kleinhans (Dec 2003) ▪ Viti consultant Johan Viljoen (Jun 2004) ▪ 400 ha (cab, merlot, petit v, pinotage, roobernet, shiraz, chard, chenin, sauvignon) ▪ 570 tons 8 500 cs own label +300 000ℓ bulk 80% red 20% white ▪ Owner Brinkshof Wines (Pty) Ltd ▪ PO Box 1 Riebeek West 7306 ▪ info@pulpitrock.co.za ©/🖃 (022) 461-2025

Piet Kleinhans, former member of the Stellenbosch Vineyards winemaking team, now has his own charge: all-new Pulpit Rock Winery on one of the Brink brothers' Riebeek West farms. His maiden vintage (2004) produced small quantities of barrel-matured wines for export to the US and EU under the Pulpit Rock label. More commercial quantities/styles are marketed locally as Cape Haven. The remainder of a 4 000-ton crop is sold in bulk. Kleinhans was thrilled to garner three golds at the 2004 SAYWS. A tasting room was opened in October, and a restaurant was opening as we went to press.

Both ranges were tasted as samples; reds in this line-up all **03**. **Cabernet Sauvignon** fairly underplayed blackcurrant & plum aromas; deftly extracted; silky, dry savoury tannins. Potential ★★★★. **Merlot** Smoked meat aromas, firm but silky tannins, very ripe sweetish fruit; handles its towering 15.5% alc better than the next wine. Possible ★★★★. **Pinotage** An 'ultra' wine — extremes of everything, from colour (pitch black) to aroma (porty, exotic whiff salami) to flavour (sweet & boneless) to alc (15.6%). Highly idiosyncratic. How to rate? ★★★? **Shiraz** Peppery red plums on nose, slightly dusty; very attractive dark choc flavour with sour-plum tang, dry finish. 'Only' 14.7% alc. Yr Fr oak, as are all above. Could rate ★★★★. **Chardonnay 04** impressively deep burnished gold, impressive alc too (15.5%); deep wells of peach flavour tinged with ginger. Too young to rate. Fr-oak-fermented/8 mths, partial malo.

Cape Haven range

Chardonnay Gutsy, full-bore version. Great chunks of peach fruit, potently active 15% alc which imparts overtly sweet finish. Possible ★★★. **Chenin Blanc** Considerably quieter & better mannered than Attila the marge-mate; also quite a mouthful though; exotic spicy nose with touches grapefruit, asparagus; zesty acidity. Likely ★★★★. **Cabernet**, **Merlot**, **Pinotage** & **Shiraz** not ready for tasting. All in this range **04**. — *TM*

Quagga Ridge see Horse Mountain

Quando

Robertson ▪ Est/1stB 2001 ▪ Visits by appt ▪ Owner Irene Bruwer Family Trust ▪ Winemaker/ viticulturist Fanus Bruwer ▪ 80 ha (sauvignon, mourvèdre) ▪ 15 tons 1 100 cs own label 100% white ▪ Eurogap certified ▪ PO Box 82 Bonnievale 6730 ▪ quandowines@mweb.co. za ©/🖃 (023) 616-2752

'We're bursting at the seams,' says Fanus Bruwer, who makes his Sauvignon in a hand-built cellar on a gravelly kink in the Breede River. Everything here is done by hand, from bringing in the grapes in small lugs to traditional basket-pressing. In spite of the cramped conditions, Fanus B turned out 1 100 cases in 2004 ('no mean feat'), having vanquished patches of the sour rot that blighted many lower-Breede vineyards last harvest. It still turned out 'the best of all vintages', says he, partly due to the extra oomph provided by maturing vineyards.

★★★★ **Sauvignon Blanc** ✓ Consistently satisfying wine, capable of maturing beneficially few yrs. **04** adds hints asparagus to light tropical fruit & savoury green core; juicy acidity, dry finish, moderate 12.5% alc — all working together for refreshing drinkability. — *TJ*

Quantum see Lost Horizons
Queen of Sheba see Eshkol

Quoin Rock

Stellenbosch ▪ Est 2000 ▪ 1stB 2001 ▪ Tasting, sales & tours by appt ▪ Owner Talacar Holdings ▪ Winemaker Carl van der Merwe (Jan 2002) ▪ Viticulturist Jaco van der Westhuizen (2000) ▪ 60 ha (cab, merlot, pinot, shiraz, chard, sauvignon) ▪ 180 tons 5 000 cs own label 70% red 30% white ▪ PO Box 1193 Stellenbosch 7599 ▪ wine@quoinrock.co.za ✆ 888·4740 🖷 888·4744

Winemaker Carl van der Merwe has two preoccupations — making wine in SA and sampling wine in France. So if he isn't in some château in Bordeaux, he's back here, working his own alchemy. Last harvest uneven budding and ripening required a great deal of viticultural work, as well as a second sorting table to ensure that only healthy berries made it into the bottle. Working with grapes from very different sites, Stellenbosch and Elim near Cape Agulhas, Van der Merwe says he is still in the process of getting to know his vineyards. No doubt the relationship, like a good marriage, will continue to bear fruit.

★★★★★ **Merlot** Imposing, blue-blooded red. As with entire range, emphasis on texture, structure rather than straightforward variety. **01** sets tone with striking dark choc smoky nuances; sumptuous, densely layered, very ripe; heavier effects of 15% alc eased by fine, dusty tannins, dry finish. **02** (★★★★) similar; compact, dense, less luxurious meaty, savoury spread; should flesh out over 4-5 yrs. Yr Fr oak, 50% new. 13.5% alc. Sample **03** real elegance with power; multi-layered, rich flavours; taut, fine tannin. 60/40 mix home/Agulhas vyds. 14% alc. Fr oak, 50% new.

★★★★ **Cape Blend** Three vintages, three blends & no release date yet! **01, 02** pinotage plays third fiddle to shiraz/merlot (28/40/32; 10/39/51). Former remains vigorous; boisterous sweet fruit dominated by burly tannined frame. **02** more focused; light-texture, tidily built with sultry red plum/choc softness, toasty oak. **03** (sample) adds influential dollop cab to mix; seemingly more cohesive. Fr/Am oak, 50% new.

★★★★ **Oculus** Flagship dry white, its goal 'a statement of site' (single home-farm vyd), not varieties (undisclosed). Maturation benefits clear in delicious **01**, unusual (for Cape) French-style savoury decadence. **02** full, grippy. **03** (sample) youthful, primary, though follows traditional style. Oak hints (fermented/yr Fr, 20% new) in tune with concentration, broad frame. Like pvs, uncompromising, made for fine dishes & time.

★★★★ **Chardonnay** Vinosity rather than varietal prominence, well-meshed oak thumbprint. **02** some developed, tropical-tones, firmer & ready sooner than **01**'s deep, oxidative complexity, lively core. Preview **03** promises finest yet. Incredible viscosity, savoury length; built to mature. 14% alc. Fermented/ yr Fr oak, 60% new. Home/Agulhas vyds.

★★★★ **Sauvignon Blanc** ✓ Rather elegantly restrained, structured; food style par excellence, with ageing potential. **03** cool, steely chalk/gooseberry whiffs; great presence, uncluttered intensity without heaviness, harshness; brisker edges padded by 6 mths on lees. Bone-dry. 65/35 blend Agulhas/home vyds.

Following impressive 🆕 wines still in barrel. **Shiraz 03** dark-hued, rumbling spice, smoked meat nuances; rich, weighty; fine tannin. **Vine Dried Natural Sweet 04** from sauvignon. Orange-blossom, honey scents; unctuous but uncloying 140g/ℓ sugar; 13.5% alc. — *AL*

R62 see Joubert-Tradauw

Raats Family Wines

Stellenbosch ▪ Est/1stB 2000 ▪ Visits by appt ▪ Owners Bruwer & Jasper Raats Jnr ▪ Winemaker Bruwer Raats ▪ Viticulturist Jasper Raats Snr (2003) ▪ 20 ha (cab f, chenin) ▪ 3 500

cs 15% red 85% white ▪ *PO Box 2068 Dennesig 7601* ▪ *braats@mweb.co.za* ▪ *www.raats.co. za* ⓒ *881·3078* 🖷 *885·1290*

Last year was a great one for Raats Family Wines. They installed themselves on a small property in the Polkadraai area and built a tasting room. Chenin, one of two varieties focused on by Bruwer Raats and his brother Jasper, ripened at lower alcohol levels than usual, leaving them with high expectations for 'an exceptionally good year'. US *Wine Spectator* gave the 02 bottling a 91-point rating, one of the highest yet for this variety (the States their biggest growth market; volumes almost double every year). UK *Decanter* named the 03 one of the best value-for-money wines under £15. Raats J and B believe local producers should work together 'to build a Brand SA in wine-buying countries around the world'. They're certainly doing their bit.

★★★★ **Cabernet Franc 02** (★★★★) has Bdx-like austerity, showing leather notes, some stalkiness & a lot of wood (16 mths Fr oak, third new). 13% alc. Nudges higher rating, but shy fruit flavours a victim of vintage. Significantly, maiden **01** took 18 mths mainly new wood in its attractive, fragrant stride.

★★★★ **Chenin Blanc 03** guava & honey notes from 90% fermented/6 mths Fr oak, 10% new. Unwooded component gives citrus lift, granadilla tang to freshness. Big 14. 5% alc & off-dry 6g/ℓ sugar add to richness. These stats a little higher for flamboyantly delicious **02**. Both Stbosch/Paarl fruit; WO Coastal.

★★★★ **Original Chenin Blanc** The unwooded version. Honeysuckle, citrus notes on **04**, fine acid aids elegance, balances 13.5% alc (these lighter, drier than above). **03** (★★★★★) delivers on last yr's sample promise, with richness & opulence. – *NP*

▮ *Radford Dale see The Winery*

Rainbow's End Estate

Stellenbosch ▪ *Est 1978* ▪ *1stB 2002* ▪ *Visits by appt* ▪ *Fee R15 refundable on purchase of 4+ btls* ▪ *Owners/winemakers/viticulturists Jacques, Anton & Francois Malan* ▪ *16 ha (cabs s/f, malbec, merlot, petit v, shiraz)* ▪ *400-800 cs 100% red* ▪ *PO Box 2253 Dennesig 7601* ▪ *hbmeng@iafrica.com* ⓒ *083·411·0170/082·413·7285/885·1719* 🖷 *885·1722*

Frère Jacques et fils were delighted to 'personally introduce our wines and small winemaking business' to the public in spring 2004. The amateur duo of civil engineer Jacques and accountant son Anton are equally enamoured to have newly qualified oenologist, son/sibling Francois, stepping up to the plate in 2005. A varietal Cab, Cab Franc, Merlot and Estate blend (eventually to include newly planted petit verdot and malbec) will join the current 2002/2003 Shirazes. Completed plantings bring to 28ha the total mix of classic reds; the remainder to be a private fynbos reserve.

★★★☆ **Shiraz** Maiden **02** still showing well, attractive fruit flavours supported by firm &savoury acid/tannin structure. Ripe **03**'s greater depth of fruit, intensity, character reflects maturing vines. Alc at 14% up on pvs, but wine still on tastily elegant side of extrovert modernity. Spicy evidence of Fr/Am oak ageing will meld in. A label to watch, we can now repeat with even more confidence. – *TJ*

Raka

Walker Bay ▪ *Est/1stB 2002* ▪ *Tasting & sales Mon-Fri 9-5 Sat during peak season otherwise by appt* ▪ *Fee R10 for 4 wines* ▪ *Closed Easter Fri & Dec 25* ▪ *Tours by appt* ▪ *BYO picnic* ▪ *Walks* ▪ *Nature conservancy* ▪ *Owner Piet Dreyer* ▪ *Winemaker Teresa Fourie, advised by Bertus Fourie* ▪ *Viti consultant Dawie le Roux* ▪ *44 ha (five Bdx reds, pinotage, sangiovese, shiraz, sauvignon, semillon)* ▪ *11 000 cs 75% red 17% white 8% rosé* ▪ *PO Box 124 Caledon 7230* ▪ *rakawine@ telkomsa.net* ▪ *www.rakawine.co.za* ⓒ/🖷 *(028) 341·0676*

A quiet spell during harvest was the eye in the storm for the team at this winery in the soon-to-be-standalone appellation Kleinrivier, who were hit with an unprecedented 240 tons to process in the last 10 days. Hard-pressed winemaker Teresa Fourie assures, however: 'All the grapes show promise, especially the sauvignon and shiraz'. When not growing wines, Piet Dreyer spends his time skippering a fleet of squid boats – the winery is named after his favourite fishing vessel. His and wife Elna's farm, Remhoogte, is a part of the Akkedisberg Bio-conservancy, offering mountain hikes through indigenous fynbos. Nearby Stanford, known for its arts and crafts, also boasts numerous guest farms, several restaurants, a cheese factory, micro-brewery, fresh water fishing and more.

Raka range

★★★★ **Biography (Shiraz)** Acclaimed (VDG, SAA, SAYWS gold) **02** from own, Swtlnd fruit. Impressively full, dark, ripe plummy nose heralds dense but not overweight palate, with savoury spice. Juicy, lip-smacking. 14 mths Fr/Am oak. 15% alc.

★★★★ **Quinary** 'Erica Five Maidens' in pvs ed — trademark issues required renaming. Supple, rich, berry fruits & choc/mocha warmth to well-sprung build of **02**. A Bdx quintet with Cape flavour. House grapes, plus W Bay, Stbosch & other. Fr oak. 14% alc.

★★★★ **Sauvignon Blanc** ✓ Strikingly 'different' option from cool Stanford: quintessential sauvignon but both tropical & herbaceous — & more. **04** offers herby aromas, super body encompasses summer melon & gunflint, intriguing smooth-stone finish. **03** aromatic stewed guavas, green pepper & grass; forceful lime finish. ±13% alc.

★★★★ **Semillon-Sauvignon Blanc** NEW **04** Unoaked 60:40 blend more muted grass/savoury tones, but bigger feel — woollen brush to figgy fruit — than above. Gentle 12% alc. Could develop with interest.

> **Rosé** ☺ ★★★ One of the nicest around, & dry to boot. **04** sangiovese adds body to cheery cherry fruits (mostly pressed juice of Bdx blend). **03** fuller (sangiovese lightly oaked!) but similar fresh dry finish. 13.5% alc.

Spliced ★★★ ('Red' in pvs ed) **03** clever blend cab, merlot, ruby cab & shiraz, rafts of accessible fruit licked into semblance of sophistication by 6 mths oak. **02** baked, earthy, rustic. 14% alcs. **Cabernet Sauvignon-Merlot** ★★★ W Bay merlot joins own cab in easy juicy marriage. **02** last, support act to Quinary above. Yr oak. **Shiraz** ★★★ **02** fruit-bomb packed with sweet blackcurrant contrasted with leather & Oxo tints, from own/Rville grapes. 15% alc. **Pinotage** NEW ★★★ Emphatic, trenchant, unequivocal — unmistakably pinotage in anybody's language. **03** brimming with purple pastille, plum fruit amplified by vanilla oak. Yr Fr & Am casks. 14% alc. **Shannonea Sauvignon Blanc** ★★★ Semillon infusion (7%), 2 mths new Fr oak, brings spiky tickle to tropical character of **03**. Release undecided. — DS

Ravenswood

Budget wines made by Robertson Winery for Vinimark.

500ml & 2/5ℓ packs; all comfortably light (±11% alc unless mentioned), NV. **Dry Red** ★★ Easy-quaffing *vin ordinaire*; fruity, with amenable tannins. **Rosé** ★★ Pale, sweet & lightly fruited. **Grand Cru** ★★ Fruity-dry white with zesty finish. **Light** ★★ Dry white with clean perky fruit. Low 9.5% alc. **Johannisberger** ★★ Quiet but pleasant fruity off-dry white. 10% alc. **Selected Stein** ★★ Honeyed semi-sweet, gentle in every way. **Late Harvest** ★★ Soft but lively semi-sweet, with tropical flavour. — DH

Red Wolf see Wolvendrift

Remhoogte Estate

Stellenbosch ▪ Est 1994 ▪ 1stB 1995 ▪ Tasting & sales 9-4 by appt ▪ Tours anytime by appt ▪ Olives & olive oil for sale ▪ Conservation area ▪ Exhibition of SA hunting trophies ▪ Owners Boustred family/Murray Boustred & Michel Rolland ▪ Cellarmaster Murray Boustred, advised by Michel Rolland & Auguste Natter ▪ Viticulturist Hendrik de Beer (1999), advised by Johan Pienaar (1994) ▪ 30 ha (cab, merlot, pinotage, shiraz, chenin) ▪ ±180 tons 6 500 cs own label 100% red ▪ PO Box 2032 Dennesig 7601 ▪ remhoogte@adept.co.za ☏
889·5005 🖷 889·6907

It's been a busy 10 years since the first 5 barrels of Remhoogte were made. The vineyards on the Simonsberg have been extensively replanted (4ha of shiraz last year) and the cellar redone (fashionable oak fermentation vessels now dominate the production area). Three years ago Murray Boustred persuaded Michel Rolland, arguably the world's most influential winemaker, to join forces with him. The co-owners toasted their partnership with the release last year of a new red blend, aptly named Bonne Nouvelle ('Good News'). With commitments all over the world (Rolland advises more than 100 wineries), winemaker Auguste Natter flies in from Sancerre for the harvest – and 2004 was excellent…. As they might say in France: *Vous n'avez vu rien encore.*

★★★★ **Bonne Nouvelle** ⬛ Joint venture with roving bordelais star Michel Rolland already well noted internationally with maiden **02**: Concours Mondial gold; 90 pts *WS*. Merlot-dominated blend (25% pinotage, 17% cab). Polished, sumptuous & super-ripe (note massive 15% alc); tannins add weight, texture to slightly evanescent fruit, but savoury, plummy notes & good length. 16 mths in 80% new Fr oak.

★★★★ **Estate Wine** ⬛ Elegant **02** has spicy plum & cassis on the nose; marzipan, cassia & nutmeg on mid-palate; fine texture, good lengthy finish. 14% pinotage well hidden by equal parts cab, merlot. 15 mths Fr oak, 40% new. 14% alc. Still evolving, should do so for 5+ yrs. These all WO Simonsberg-Stbosch.

★★★☆ **Cabernet Sauvignon** Classically styled example. Revisited **01** (★★★★), with 12% merlot infusion, offers fine cassis almond aromas, supple elegant tannins, sweet mid-palate fruit. Persistent & refined. 13.5% alc. 18 mths oak, third new. Suggest keep 5 yrs.

★★★★ **Merlot 01** (★★★★) on retaste advancing savoury mulberry notes; slightly herbal tannins, concentrated dry finish, with element of austerity enhanced by 15% cab. 14% alc. 18 mths Fr oak, third new. **00** gold at IWC 2003.

★★★☆ **Aigle Noir** Blend merlot-cab, with dollop pinotage. On chunky **03** (★★★) marzipan, raspberry whiffs prelude to tannic mid-palate; austere estery finish. Yr oak, 20% new. Maiden **02** more accessible, less oaky, sweeter finish. – *MF*

R & de R-Fredericksburg see Rupert & Rothschild
R & R see Rupert & Rothschild

Reyneke Wines 🍷🍴🏠

Stellenbosch ▪ Est 1863 ▪ 1stB 1998 ▪ Tasting & sales by appt ▪ Uitzicht B&B ▪ Owners Reyneke family ▪ Winemaker Georg Meissner, with Johan Reyneke (2004 harvest) ▪ Viticulturist Johan Reyneke (1992) ▪ 20 ha (cab, merlot, pinotage, shiraz, sauvignon) ▪ 1 500 cs own label 70% red 30% white ▪ PO Box 61 Vlottenburg 7604 ▪ wine@reynekewines.co.za ▪ www.reynekewines.co.za © (021) 881·3517 ✉ 881·3451

'It takes nature up to 500 years to build up one inch of good topsoil, but conventional agriculture reduces it to a mere growing medium. It's paradoxical to make a big deal about the uniqueness of your terroir if you then effectively destroy it.' While many claim to work closely with nature, Johan Reyneke lives by the maxim 'no artificial yeasts, no enzymes, no funny additives, no hardcore chemicals'. It's potentially risky but, given the saturation of the 'conventional' market and the long-term sustainability of organic methods, Reyneke has no doubt it will pay off. Besides, he says, there is already the pleasure of strolling about the vineyard without the whiff of poison in the air. Last year winemaker and surf-buddy James Farquharson moved to Boschendal, so Reyneke imported Georg Meissner from Germany for the 2004 harvest.

★★★★ **Reyneke Reserve** Sample **03** (likely ★★★★) mugged by oak (60% new Fr): mocha, vanilla dominate ripe fruit & spice. Mostly shiraz, with splash merlot. Natural, minimalist approach: vyd in conversion to organic; native yeasts, no additives, unfined (as for Pinotage below). 14 % alc. No **02**. **01** was classically taut & minerally blend shiraz, merlot, cab (82/14/4).

★★★★ **Pinotage** From a small biodynamically farmed vyd; electric, characterful **03** (★★★★★) has ripe loganberry fruit, excellent length, sour cherry & bitter choc notes. 13.5% alc. Fr oak 18 mths, 30% new. Last was stylish **01**

★★★★ **Cornerstone** Shiraz/cab/merlot blend (45:44:11) in **03**. Appealing nose; palate slightly tannic but with fruit to hold it together; tea-leaf finish. 13% alc. 18 mths Fr oak. No **02**. **01** (★★★) growing dusty now; full-bodied, dry, fennel & earth flavours. 14 mths oak, 25% new. Blend here 25/48/27.

Sauvignon Blanc Sample **04** likely ★★★. Reductive nose, light grapefruit, leesy, wild character from wild yeast ferment, 13% alc. — NP

Rheboksloof Private Cellar

Paarl ▪ 1stB 1989 ▪ Tasting & sales daily 9-5 ▪ Fee R8 (informal) or R15 (incl tour) ▪ Tours by appt ▪ Restaurant (see Eat-out section) ▪ Play area for children ▪ Tourgroups ▪ Gifts ▪ Conferences ▪ Conservation area ▪ Owner Rheboksloof Farming & Trading ▪ Winemaker Daniël Langenhoven (May 1998) ▪ Viticulturist Carel van Niekerk (Jun 2003) ▪ ±84 ha (cab, merlot, chard) ▪ 420 tons 28 000 cs 60% red 40% white ▪ PO Box 7141 Noorder-Paarl 7623 ▪ info@rheboksloof. co.za ▪ www.rheboksloof.co.za © 869·8386 🖷 869·8504

We've come to expect forthright answers from this crew: 'It was a difficult harvest … despite that, the quality of the red wine grapes was very high but the white wine grapes were somewhat disappointing,' they say, sights firmly focused on new markets such as south-east Asia. Encompassing two valleys and bordered by Paarl Nature Reserve, much of the property is still covered in wild fynbos. On a horseback trail through vineyards and forest you may well meet the shy buck which feature on the front-labels. Options suit everyone, from beginners to experienced riders, with short and long trails, hunting, endurance riding and sedate horse-drawn wagon rides. Much like the wines, which suit most palates and pockets. An exclusive extra virgin olive oil, from trees planted between the vineyards, is available in limited quantities directly from the farm.

★★★★ **Cabernet Sauvignon** The flagship, grown in two vyds ±17 yrs old; only Fr oak, 20% new, 14 mths. **00** retasted, warrants further cellaring. Luxurious upholstery of ripe red/black berry fruit, touches cherry & tobacco; deliciously round, full & mellow, still securely laced with tannin to continue improving 4-5 yrs or more. Alc 14.8%.

★★★★ **Cabernet Sauvignon-Merlot** ✓ Warm-hearted blend & gorgeous mouthful, always with a terrific ripe-berried intro. **02** no different despite troubled vintage; spicy-rich flavours subtly permeated with vanilla, firmly round tannins; long life ahead. 18 mths Fr oak, 10% new. ±13.5% alc. **01** sold out before we could taste. **00** had a plush feel, ripe tannins adding needed textural contrast.

★★★★ **Chardonnay Grande Reserve** More obvious wood than version below, thanks to barrel-fermentation/ageing in 100% new oak, ±11 mths. **03** still suffused with vanilla/butterscotch & spice mid-2004, hinting at good fruit lurking, hinting at good development over 3-5 yrs. Huge 15% alc will need time to meld. **02** was also very ripe but not overdone (13.9% alc), some oak tannin helped rein in the richness.

★★★★ **Chardonnay Sur Lie** Unashamedly New World styling — with some elegance. **03** slightly toned-down version of G-R above (it's all relative — 15% alc!), similar sweet-fruited richness but slightly less oak, more lemon-lime tang. Readier, but should also age well. 8 mths oak, only 30% new barrels, no malo. Showy **02** (★★★★) billowed ripe peach & vanilla oak. **01** was clove-scented with creamy palate.

Tamay Sparkling ☺ ★★★ Reliable not-quite-brut style fizz from chardonnay & riesling, splash hanepoot for fragrance. Lovely creamy mouse, tropical fruit flavours, suggestion of spicy sweetness in the finish. NV.

Merlot ★★★★ **00** retasted, ageing with benefit. Ripeness the immediate impression (15% alc), similar appealing tobacco hint as cab. 16 mths Fr oak, 2nd/3rd fill. **Pinotage** ★★★ **02** plum, banana & vanilla flavour combo, generous despite farily slender build (12.

5% alc), pleasantly unsophisticated. 14 mths oak, 2nd/3rd fill. **Shiraz** ★★★☆ **03** (sample) promising deep colour, thick pile of fruit & spice, firm tannic finish; looking good. **Weisser Riesling** ★★★ Recent releases less engaging than pvs; **04** (sample) shyly pleasant; lightish lime & lemon flavours, touches earth & spice, bone-dry finish. Should rate ★★★★. **Gamay Noir** discontinued.

Rhebok range

> **Dry White** ☺ ★★☆ Charming, easy-drinking **04**, chardonnay/riesling blend (80/20), crisp, fresh & fruity, to be enjoyed young.

Cabernet Sauvignon-Merlot NEW ★★★ Worthy companion to the premium version above; **03** inviting fresh-berry bouquet; choc-toned palate, savoury note in long finish. 9 mths Fr oak, 10% new. **Dry Red** ★★★ Tangy, savoury-dry blend pinotage, gamay, cab (55/30/15); **02**, yr on, tannins have softened, drinking easily. **Chardonnay** ★★☆ **04** (sample) light white-peach fragrance; clean apple-zest flavour. 12.5% alc. **Sauvignon Blanc** NEW ★★☆ **04** (sample) light figgy tones, fresh, crisp & dry. **Chardonnay-Sauvignon Blanc** ★★☆ Varieties make a complementary combo in early-harvested **04** (sample), chard adds juice, sauvignon verve. 80/20 blend. **Bouquet Blanc** ★★☆ **04** (sample) lightly fragrant, crisply fruity everyday quaffer from chenin. **Chenin Blanc** discontinued. — *DH*

Rickety Bridge Winery

Franschhoek ▪ Tasting & sales Mon-Fri 9-5 Sat & public holidays 9-1 ▪ Closed Easter Fri, Dec 25/26 & Jan 1) ▪ Fee R5 refundable on purchase ▪ Tours by appt ▪ BYO picnic ▪ Gifts ▪ Owner Duncan Spence ▪ Winemaker Wilhelm van Rooyen (Jan 2001), with Dawid Gqirana (Jun 1998) ▪ Viticulturist Wilhelm van Rooyen ▪ 16 ha (cab, merlot, shiraz, chard, chenin, semillon) ▪ 120 tons 5 000 cs own label 65% red 35% white ▪ PO Box 455 Franschhoek 7690 ▪ sales@ricketybridgewinery.com ▪ www.ricketybridgewinery.com ✆ 876-2129/3669 🖷 876-3486

'No news is good news', shrugs Wilhelm van Rooyen, chugging along quietly under a quaintly named brand which long ago ceased to describe the farm or the winery, and certainly not what's in the bottles. The winemaker works in a contemporary, gravity-fed cellar, and the wines are equally modern and stylish. Much of the action appears to happen off-site: owner Duncan Spence, a Channel Islands-based entrepreneur, has many irons in many fires. His most recent local ventures include a wine-and-lifestyle tie-up with Kosie Möller of Kosie Möller Wines, part of which involves redeveloping one of the original Paarl farms, Kleine Parys.

★★★★★ **Shiraz** Cellar's polished signature. Hallmarks are concentrated, mouthfilling, black fruit, well-controlled by spicy oak. **02** forthcoming, excellent bouquet blackberry & cherry, touch black peppercorn, deep flavoured & classy with oak adding fine-grained tannins. 20 mths Fr barrels, now reduced to 20% new. 14% alc. **01** brightly aromatic & sensuous; **00** *Decanter* 2004 World Wine Award.

★★★★ **Paulinas Reserve** Limited-release barrel selections honouring farm's founder, Paulina de Villiers. Latest **02** (sample) signals change in blend to 66/34 cab s/merlot with more classic claret-like grip & feel, dark-berried tone with firm dry tannins. Fr oak, 25% new. **01** (★★★★★) was unblended merlot, from Stbosch fruit; wonderful suppleness coupled with firm backbone. This, above, WO Coastal.

★★★☆ **Merlot** Ripe damson fruit on **02**, touches lead pencil, roast beef; palate full-bodied & rich, crammed with ripe fruit, firm dry finish a touch harsh, reflects difficult vintage. 17 mths Fr oak, 20% new. Big at 14.5% alc. WO Coastal. No **01**.

★★★★ **Cabernet Sauvignon** Latest **01** (★★★★) shows polished dark-berried fruits with the signature cedar & cigar box of fine cab. Full bodied, slight sweetness from perfectly ripe berries, sleek & groomed by oak; classic dry finish. Includes splash malbec. 19 mths Fr oak, 40% new. **00** featured compact, tannic Ribena fruit on release, which softened a tad when tasted last yr.

★★★★ **Chardonnay** Bright fruit acidity a signature for these deep-flavoured New World versions, **03** true to form: ripe citrus, tropical lime, juicy but rich, well oaked. All the components to age 2/3 yrs with style. New-oak fraction: 17% vs 83% used, all Fr, 10 mths. Showy ripe peach, vanilla oak in **02**, supple grapefruit notes on finish.

★★★★ **Semillon** Serious, made to last, small-barrel style continues with **03**. Smooth creamy palate threaded through with tropical lime & sweet apricot, seems sweet thanks to fruit concentration; lengthy finish. **02** elegant & creamy. These aged in oak, 18-30% new; aged 9-14 mths. Medium-bodied, poised & complex; should age with distinction.

Sauvignon Blanc 04 unready for tasting.

Duncan's Creek range

> **Classic Red** ☺ ★★★ **03** now cab, shiraz & merlot. Perhaps more meaty & muscular than pvs, enlivened by firm acidity, with added attraction of some oak — 9 mths used Fr. Better than everyday, should develop, too. 13% alc. WO Coastal.

Classic White discontinued. — *IvH*

Ridder's Creek

Wellington ▪ Tasting by appt ▪ Owners George de Ridder & partner ▪ QC consultant Jeff Wedgwood ▪ PO Box 72 Wellington 7654 ▪ ridders@iafrica.com ▪ www.ridderscreek.co. za ©/☎ 873·7746

Negociant George de Ridder and a partner launched the Ridder's Creek range, sourced and made to their specs, in 2002. Wines and blending components are sourced from various regions and assembled under the experienced eye of Jeff Wedgwood. The team also does bottling for clients as well as local and international bulk-wine trading. Also limited-release corporate gift packs yearly. Details on their website.

> **Cape Red** ☺ ★★★ **03** shows youthful purple gloss; bright summer fruits in a round & juicy package. Some structure, too, for short term development. 13.5% alc.

Cabernet Sauvignon ★★ Blackberries & touch oak on muted **01**; firm grip on finish. **Shiraz** ★★★ Understated nose hinting at blackberries & pepper; more expressive palate; still firmish but drinkable **01**. **Chardonnay** ★★★ Like so many **04** unwooded whites, retiring on nose; palate peppier, tropical, brisk. Sample tasted. **Sauvignon Blanc** ★★ Light in most departments; **04** some peach & apricot accents. **Cape White** ★★★ 100% chenin with appealing deciduous fruit & floral tones; sample **04** tasted. — *DH*

▓ *Rider's Valley* see Ruitersvlei

Ridgeback Wines

Paarl ▪ Est 1997 ▪ 1stB 2001 ▪ Tasting & sales Tue-Sat 10-4 Sun (Sep-Mar) 10-3 ▪ Fee R15 ▪ Closed Easter Sun, Apr 27, Dec 16/25 & Jan 1 ▪ Deli-style light meals Sat/Sun ▪ Tours by appt ▪ Owners Kilimanjaro Investments ▪ Vini consultant Cathy Marshall (Jan 2000) ▪ Viti consultant Paul Wallace (Apr 1997) ▪ 34 ha (cabs/f, merlot, shiraz, sauvignon, viognier) ▪ 200 tons ▪ 8 100 cs own label 68% red 32% white ▪ Eurogap certified ▪ PO Box 2076 Windmeul 7630 ▪ ridgeback@mweb.co.za lesleyco@mweb.co.za ▪ www. ridgebackwines.co.za ©/☎ 869·8068 or © 082·554·0176 ☎ 794·1070

'It was a year for reds,' say the team from this Agter-Paarl farm, resulting in 'robust big wines, lots of elegance, more in line with 2001'. Winemaker Cathy Marshall needed all her expertise and experience to get the best out of a difficult vintage with uneven ripeness and particularly low yields from sauvignon. The usual niggles associated with operating a new winery smoothed out, the next challenge was establishing a tasting room in landscaped gardens. Now they're working towards their Master's Choice Syrah, the 04 crushed with a dash of viognier for a Côtes-du-Rhône style (mourvèdre and grenache to spice up future releases). Rhodesian ridgebacks are close to owner Jerry Parker's heart. Rudolf, 'older but still a bit of a rebel', is featured on the charming front labels.

★★★★★ **Shiraz 02** (★★★★) rich & meaty; bold frame, vigorous tannins still holding sway. Will benefit from further 2-3 yrs, though probably not as multi-dimensional as **01** with *garrigue*-like aromas, fennel, bay leaves. 80% new barrels, Fr/Am. 14% alc.

★★★★ **Cabernet Franc-Merlot** 🆕 **03** distinctive 54/46 blend. Modern, lifted spicy, leafy elegance; creamy, well-weighted fruit, clamped by serious, ripe tannins. Most attractive; worth cellaring to 2008/10. Fr oaked 14 mths. 14% alc.

★★★★ **Merlot** Velvet-touched palms, green olives distinguish **03**. Supple, mouthcoating; fruit enriched by well-absorbed 100% new Fr oak; savoury length. Harmonious now, good potential to 2007/09. 14.5% alc. **02** med-bodied, savoury.

★★★★ **Viognier** 🆕 Planted as partner for Shiraz above; Cathy M made **03** 'to see what fruit looked like'. Verdict: very promising. Broad-based, sumptuous; noticeable oak matched by expansive, apricot scents, flavours, richly dry finish. Bold, balanced 15.5% alc. Partial spontaneous ferment/15 mths new Fr oak.

★★★★ **Sauvignon Blanc 04** tasted just after bottling, still unsettled. Cool, sleek profile; good weight, concentration; fig/passionfruit flavours extended by solid acid spine, 5g/ℓ sugar. Food style; will benefit from ageing.

Vansha Chenin Blanc-Sauvignon Blanc ★★★ **04** balanced, persistent, forthcoming ripe tropical tones; fruitily dry. Uncomplicated yet satisfying, everyday drinking. 13.5% alc.—*AL*

Riebeek Cellars

Swartland ▪ Est/1stB 1941 ▪ Tasting & sales Mon-Fri 8-5 Sat 8.30-2 ▪ Closed Easter Fri/Sun, Dec 25 & Jan 1 ▪ Tours strictly by appt ▪ BYO picnic ▪ Farm produce ▪ Owners 63 shareholders ▪ Winemakers Zakkie Bester & Eric Saayman (Dec 1999/Jan 1997), with Kenneth Whiley ▪ Viticulturist Hanno van Schalkwyk (Sep 2000) ▪ 1 400 ha (cab, merlot, pinotage, shiraz, chard, chenin, colombard, sauvignon) ▪ 14 000 tons 45 000 cs own labels + 40 000 cs for customers, incl Rocheburg & Broken Rock (both UK) ▪ 35% red 60% white 5% rosé ▪ ISO certification in progress ▪ PO Box 13 Riebeek Kasteel 7307 ▪ riebeek@mweb.co.za ▪ www.riebeekcellars. com Ⓒ (022) 448·1213 🖷 (022) 448·1281

From this Swartland cellar the message is 'an exceptional red wine year', particularly for shiraz . Ripeness at low sugar levels resulted in wines with slightly lower alcohols, report Zakkie Bester and Eric Saayman. Malbec and petit verdot were produced on a commercial scale for the first time, and the chenin looks 'exceptionally good'. They planted the first 15ha of sauvignon, and this year they'll harvest a maiden viognier. Riebeek is one of the partners in Cape Coastal Wines, a new marketing company set up to increase exports, initially to the US (their Few Good Men range already flies there). An empowerment project will see 150 farm and cellar workers in joint-ownership of a newly developed wine farm.

A Few Good Men range

★★★★ **Cabernet Sauvignon 00** mellowed & improved while retaining its basic firmness; **01** inherently smoother, more supple, mouthfilling, lubricated by 15% alc. Appealing sweet blackcurrant/choc character. Yr Fr oak.

★★★★ **Merlot ✓ 00** was soft, open-textured, with some food-friendly grip. Current **01** shows maturity on nose/palate; starting to peak; hint cigarbox; soft & elegant despite beefy 14.3% alc. 9 mths oak, none new.

★★★★ **Shiraz 00** aged with some distinction; toasty mocha whiffs from Am-oaked portion (30%, ±9 mths). Similarly wooded **01** shows some attractive bottle-age complexity on nose, *confiture* character on palate; dry savoury finish. 14.7% alc.

Chardonnay ★★★ 100% barrel-fermented/aged 6 mths, Fr/Am oak (50/50); **03** a fruit salad explosion, supple & juicy, spicy supportive oak, integrated. Their finest to date. All above ex-selected vyds, their growers being the eponymous Few Good Men.

Riebeek range

★★★★ **Shiraz Reserve** Rich, brawny, aromatic wine; pvs **00** had forward smoky aromas; fairly strong but supple tannins. **02** equally punchy, strapping; toast/mocha on finish. Still closed, but good prospects. 18-24 mths Fr/Am oak, some new. 14.5-15% alc. WO Swtlnd.

★★★★ **Red Jerepiko** ✓ Delectable full-sweet winter-warmer from tinta. 17% alc. NV. Latest version has huge, pungent sealing wax aromas/flavours with hints blackcurrant & dried flower; a rich, luxurious confection. 17% alc.

★★★★ **Cape Ruby** ✓ Excellent & bemedalled blend tinta, souzão (80/20), portion small-oaked 24 mths; rich & delicious; latest bottling has prune & tobacco hints; correct Ruby style: fruity, soft, drinkable. Vibrant, not raisiny. 19.8% alc. NV.

Cinsaut-Pinotage NEW ☺ ★★★ **03** light-coloured/toned easy-drinker with slightly sweet spicy fruit; unwooded. Quaff with caution: 14.2% alc. **Pinotage Rosé** NEW ☺ ★★★ Charming al fresco drink with pinotage's crushed mulberry nose; nearly dry, balanced flavours with touch tannin to tame the sugar. 12.5%. **Stein** ☺ ★★ Soft, sweetish, undemanding quaffer with hint of apricot. Light-bodied NV from chenin, muscadel.

Cabernet Sauvignon ★★★★ Exuberant **03** chock-full of backcurrant/Ribena fruit, jumps out of the glass but behaves on palate, finishes nice & dry. Deserves 2/3 yrs. 14.3% alc. Yr Fr oak, ditto for... **Merlot** ★★★ Well-made **02** has warm-climate cooked plum tone; bright, sappy fruit; herby touch to finish. 14.2% alc. Last two WO Swtlnd. **Pinotage** ★★★ **03** charred wood nose from oak chipping; light savouriness; muscular yet elegant for its 14% alc. **Shiraz** ★★★★ ✓ Rich, meaty, concentrated **03** impresses without trying; smoked black fruit, whiff of tar; good varietal expression; Fr oak; even better in another 2-3 yrs. 14.5% alc. **Redneck** NEW ★★★ Vibrant Mediterranean-style red with food-friendly dry savouriness, spicy red fruit; **03** partly oaked equal mix shiraz, malbec. WO Swtlnd, as is... **Chardonnay Reserve** ★★★ 100% Fr oak-fermented, lees-aged; **03** has subdued fruit-salad flavours, sweetish impression though technically dry. **Chardonnay** ★★★ Partly & subtly oaked **03** shows fair complexity; pear & butterscotch tones; apple/hazelnut finish. **Sauvignon Blanc** ★★ **04** pale, shy, dry, lightish-bodied/flavoured. **Chenin Blanc Reserve** NEW ★★★ Pedigreed **03**, grand champ on local Young Wine Show; barrel-fermented, new Fr oak; rich, leesy character, dry & restrained; needs time. Low-keyed oak. WO Swtlnd. **Chenin Blanc** ★★★ **04** expresses variety clearly & fully; guava whiffs, soft appley finish. ±12% alc. Enjoy young. **Brut** ★★ Easy, refreshingly brisk & dry carbonated sparkle with clean lemon tones. NV. All in range WO Coastal unless mentioned.

Montino range

Montino Petillant Light ☺ ★★ Lively, spritzy white with gentle grapey nose; chill well for instant summer refreshment. Light 9% alc. NV.

Off-Dry Rosé NEW ★★★ More substantial than Pinotage Rosé above; shows more red-wine character; soft toffee apple aroma. NV.

Cape Table range

NV range of lowish-alc 1ℓ packs; current boxings (not retasted, descriptions from pvs ed): **Cellar Red** Light, fruity, dry *vin ordinaire*. **Cellar Rosé** Light & not too sweet. **Natural Sweet Rosé** Crisp & uncloying. **Chardonnay** Firmish, with good varietal character. **Cellar White** Simple dry quaff. **Cellar Gold** Honeyed semi-sweet. **Natural Sweet White** Citrusy sweetness. **Cellar Lite** Unusually flavoursome for style. — *TM*

Rietrivier Winery

Little Karoo ▪ Est 1965 ▪ 1stB 1990 ▪ Tasting & sales Mon-Thu 8-5 Fri 8-3 ▪ Closed public holidays ▪ Tours by appt ▪ Light meals daily 8-5; or BYO picnic ▪ Amenities/attractions: see intro ▪ Owners 46 members ▪ Manager/winemaker Chris-Willem de Bod, with Petrus

Bothma (Oct 1999/Jan 1994) ▪ *Viti consultant Willem Botha (Jan 2001)* ▪ *300 ha (merlot, shiraz, chard)* ▪ *5 700 tons 10 000 cs own label + 4m litres bulk 50% red 49% white 1% rosé* ▪ *PO Box 144 Montagu 6720* ▪ *rietrivier@lando.co.za* ▪ *www.rietrivier.co.za* Ⓒ/ 🖩 *(023) 614·1705*

Like many wineries on the scenic Route 62 between Montagu and Barrydale, 40 year old (this year) Rietrivier has woken to the great potential of tourism. A brand new tasting venue and shop are being added alongside the cellar. It will be the perfect place for a birthday party or wedding reception, they say, and light meals will be served there daily in summer. It's set to become a popular family tourist stop, with special facilities for children, a gift shop and farm stall, hiking trails, mountain biking and an off-road trail.

★★★★ **Montagu Red Muscadel** ✓ Still a standout in area recognised for sweet fortified desserts. Made jerepiko-style (no fermentation), fortified to 17.5%. **02** a pleasure to revisit: billowing muscat perfumes, fine fruity structure. Marvellous; long life ahead. Manageable 500ml bottle a plus.

Rosé 🆕 ☺ ★★★ Lightish, not too sweet pink with engaging plum pudding & custard aroma, succulent red fruit flavour, clean finish. **04** from pinotage. **Petite Blanc** ☺ ★★★ Crisp, light-bodied dry white; latest subtitled 'Kuierwyn' ('Sociable Quaffer'), which it is. 500ml screwcap. **Sparkling Vin Doux** ☺ ★★★ Fresh, low-alc (11.5%) sweet fizz from sauvignon. Latest (NV) with winegum aroma, juicy freshness. Has interest/character.

Merlot 🆕 ★★ **03** youthful & fresh, prominent plummy nose; needs time to mellow. **Pinotage** ★★★ Last tasted was **03**, with charry touch to volatile ripe-banana character. **Shiraz** ★ Some herby/smoky notes on **03**, huge 15.2% alc, very dry finish. **Petite Rouge** ★★ Rustic red from pinotage, ruby cab (80/20), unwooded. Latest (NV) shy, firm; not as gluggable as pvs. 500ml screwcap. **Route 62 Red** ★★ High-octane pinotage, merlot (90/10) mix, unwooded; overripe mulberry fruit on **03**. **Chenin Blanc** ★★ **03** not tasted. **Sauvignon Blanc** 🆕 ★★ Peardrops & grapefruit in subdued, lightish **04** quick-quaff. **Colombar-Chardonnay** ★★ **04** tropically toned fruity blend, smooth & ripe. **Late Harvest** ★★ NV (04). Rounded light tropical sweetness which slides down easily. **Montagu White Muscadel** ★★★ Persistent, slightly raisined, silky **02**. Splash some into venison potjie, winemakers recommend, or over crushed ice for summer refreshment. 17.5% alc. **Montagu Hanepoot** ★★ **02** gold on local Bottled Wine Show; pleasant cream-textured full-sweet fortified with honeysuckle fragrance. Alc as above. **Montagu Ruby Port** 🆕 **02** from pinotage, with highly idiosyncratic mulled wine character. — *CR*

Rietvallei Estate

Robertson ▪ *Est 1717* ▪ *1stB 1975* ▪ *Tasting & sales Mon-Fri 8.30-5 Sat 9.30-1* ▪ *Closed Easter Sat-Mon, Dec 25/26 & Jan 1* ▪ *BYO picnic* ▪ *Facilities for children* ▪ *Tourgroups* ▪ *Owner Johnny Burger* ▪ *Winemakers Johnny & Kobus Burger (1973/2001)* ▪ *Viti consultant Briaan Stipp (2000)* ▪ *137 ha (cab, chard, sauvignon, riesling)* ▪ *2 040 tons ±20 000 cs own label 40% red 45% white 15% fortified* ▪ *Export brand: Wild Rush* ▪ *PO Box 386 Robertson 6705* ▪ *info@ rietvallei.co.za* ▪ *www.rietvallei.co.za* Ⓒ *(023) 626·3596/4422* 🖩 *(023) 626·4514*

A new range emerged from this family cellar last year, named John B after the senior winemaker and owner, Johnny Burger. Resplendent in modern packaging, it offers an easy-drinking red blend and a white of the same sociable sort. Well worth a visit if you're on the farm (picnic baskets are popular) is a block of red muscadel, four years short of its centenary, source of the winner that recently took a Veritas and Michelangelo honours. Relatively new to the international market — the Burgers have been exporting only since 2003 — Rietvallei doubled volumes in a year and has established itself in 10 countries.

★★★★ **Cabernet** Light berry fruit on **02**, with tang of bitter choc; good balance & ripe tannins, not overtly sweet with 4.3g/ℓ sugar. 13.5% alc. 7 mths Fr oak.

★★★★ **Shiraz** Retasted **02** has come into its own: bursting most appealingly with red berries, spice; lovely lingering aftertaste. 13.5% alc. Yr mix Fr/Am oak.

★★★★ **Chardonnay** ✓ **03** needed yr to reveal quality that pleased Chardonnay-du-Monde judges. Notes of apples & pears, offering elegance, lingering finish. 40% wood-fermented, rest tank. 13.6% alc.

★★★★ **Red Muscadel** ✓ Ever-reliable quality here. Whiffs of rooibos tea & raisins; richly sweet (265g/ℓ sugar), full-flavoured; moderate 16% alc. Be adventurous: it's brilliant with apple pie or bacon & eggs!

★★★★☆ **Muscadel 1908** From the Cape's oldest red muscadel vyd (tiny-yielding bushvines planted in 1908). Retasted **02** gets better & better. Slightly drier than above version — along with firm acid, means fine balance with intense raisin character. MIWA gold; VDG.

Chardonnay Special Select ★★★★ Last tasted of this barrel selection was maiden **02**: nutty & peachy, with lingering sweetness-touched finish. **Sauvignon Blanc 04** ★★★ Light tropical fruit, pear-drops & grapefruit; lunchtime-friendly 12.7% alc. **Gewürztraminer** 𝗡𝗘𝗪 ★★★ **03** in just-dry style has typical rose-petal aromas; lightish (12.5% alc) & delicate litchi-toned palate.

John B range   𝗡𝗘𝗪

Bouquet Rouge ★★ Cheap & cheerful 65/35 blend tinta b & cab; sweet zesty fruit, spicy & approachable, with light oak influence (ex-staves); 13.5% alc. NV as is... **Bouquet Blanc** ★★★ Easy-drinking screwcapped blend colombar, chenin, sauvignon; lively, refreshing — with 12% alc also very moreish. Discontinued: **Generations Cabernet**, **Chardonnay**, **Sauvignon Blanc** & **White**. — *NP*

Rijk's Private Cellar

Tulbagh ▪ Est 1996 ▪ 1stB 2000 ▪ Tasting & sales Mon-Sat 10-4 ▪ Fee R5/wine ▪ Closed Easter Fri-Mon, Dec 25 & Jan 1 ▪ Tours during tasting hours ▪ Country Hotel ℂ (023) 230·1006 ▪ BYO picnic ▪ Tourgroups ▪ Conferencing ▪ Walks ▪ Owner Neville Dorrington ▪ Winemaker Pierre Wahl (Jan 2002) ▪ Viti consultant Johan Wiese (Mar 1996) ▪ 28 ha (cab, merlot, pinotage, shiraz, chard, chenin, sauvignon, semillon) ▪ ±180 tons 11 000 cs own label 70% red 30% white ▪ PO Box 400 Tulbagh 6820 ▪ wine@rijks.co.za ▪ www.rijks. co.za ℂ (023) 230·1622 🖷 (023) 230·1650

In a wine-world dominated by talk of terroir, Neville Dorrington's scepticism about its importance ('I have an award-winning block of semillon right next to an award-winning block of pinotage') is refreshingly different. But then this former luxury leather goods manufacturer can afford to be breezy. Since the maiden-vintage Sauvignon won double-gold at Veritas, Rijk's has enjoyed rich acclaim (it was the 2nd most successful entrant overall at last year's Fairbairn show, for example). Last year the last of Rijk's vineyards went into full production, and Dorrington now is intent on developing an adjacent 12ha. 'I'm going to fix all the mistakes I made,' he deadpans. Winemaker Pierre Wahl concurs: 'The goal is to keep improving year upon year.'

★★★★ **Bravado** Suitably bold name for house's first 'reserve' red; blend 60% cab, 30% merlot, 10% shiraz; **01** retasted for this ed, either in dull phase or derailed with some porty notes on top of baked flavours. Nearer ★★★on present form; drink up or wait to see what happens. 20 mths Fr oak, 70% new.

★★★★☆ **Cabernet Sauvignon** Small block, intensively managed for ripe fruit: debut **00** MIWA gold. **01** (★★★★), retasted, developing brilliantly: perfume & mineral notes, good mouthfeel, excellent balance despite massive 14.8% alc. Generously oaked: 20 mths 70% new Fr barrels.

★★★★☆ **Pinotage 02** Mocha notes, plus rubber & chocolate; grainy tannins. Plenty of evidence of 18 mths largely new Fr/Am oak (65/35); 14.8% alc. Pinotage Top Ten 2003, VDG. Heavier than sleek, intense **01** (★★★★).

★★★★☆ **Shiraz** Revisited fruit-driven **01** (★★★★) still shows rippling spiced fruit under guard of fine tannins, better able to carry 14.75% alc than show-gilded **00**. 18 mths Fr/Am oak, half new.

★★★☆ **Chardonnay** Forcefully styled, with great track-record for pleasing show judges. **03** has rich, opulent buttery nose, round full flavours, hefty 14.4% alc. Fermented/yr Fr oak, 70% new. Flavour-packed **02** billowed fresh new oak.

★★★★ **Sauvignon Blanc 04** (★★★★) big flavours, fields of cut grass & fresh hay thanks to 30% grapes Mbury, leesy/lemony extra dimension to own grapes; night-harvested, reductive style **03**, tropical fullness tempered by flinty edge, bracing tail. Gentle 13% alc.

★★★★ **Chenin Blanc 03** (★★★★) even splashier expression of new-wave styling. Ripe fruit, big alc (14.6%), wood influence (60% fermented/yr oak, 20% new), all deliver rich toasty flavours, full mouthfeel; fresh guava edge from tank component. Off-dry 6.2g/ℓ sugar. **02** also ultra-ripe, with showy oak, sweet finish.

★★★★ **Semillon 03** continues with winning recipe of full mouthfeel, waxy lanolin & creamy honey, with good balance, length – & sweet element. But turns down the volume on alc (14.6%) & sugar (6.2g/ℓ) on rich, FCTWS trophy-winning **02** (14.9%, 8g/ℓ respectively). Fermented/yr Fr oak, 20% new.

Merlot ★★★★ Less rumbustious red. Revisited **01** has elegant bouquet, punchy red fruit plus mint; accessible now. 18 mths 60% new Fr oak; 14.2% alc. – *NP*

Rising River see Kosie Möller Wines
River Grandeur see Viljoensdrift
River's Edge see Weltevrede

Riverstone Vineyards

Rawsonville (see Worcester map) ▪ Est 1963 ▪ 1st 1975 ▪ Tasting & sales Mon-Fri 8-12.30; 1.30-5 Sat 9-1 ▪ Fee R10 refunded on purchase ▪ Closed Easter Fri-Mon, Dec 25 & Jan 1 ▪ Merwida Country Lodge ℂ (023) 349·1435 ▪ Owners Schalk & Pierre van der Merwe ▪ Winemakers Magnus Kriel (Dec 2000), with Sarel van Staden (Aug 1982) ▪ Viticulturist Magnus Kriel ▪ 630 ha (cab, merlot, shiraz, chard, chenin, sauvignon, semillon, viognier) ▪ 10 000 tons 20 000 cs own label 40% red 60% white ▪ PO Box 4 Rawsonville 6845 ▪ wines@merwida.com ▪ www.merwida.com ℂ (023) 349·1144 🖷 (023) 349·1953

This high-volume, family-owned cellar, formerly Merwida, continues to expand with the addition recently of an 1 100m² fermentation cellar. A new public relations officer, Anchen Barnard, has joined the team. Most of their production reaches the market under labels other than their own, as they specialise in making wines to the specs of clients who order in bulk for their own bottling and marketing. The in-house ranges, Riverstone and Heron, are attractively packaged, affordable and offer enough variety to keep consumers returning for more. 'Riverstone' alludes to the 4m deep bed of river stone underlying the vineyard soils.

Riverstone range

Shiraz ★★★ **02** muscled but benign. Showing good bottle-development/complexity; red berry fruit, scrubby touch, tasty; enjoy (with food – 15% alc!) in the next yr. **Shiraz-Cabernet Sauvignon** ★★★☆ **02** 80/20 blend, Fr-oaked; retasted, still something in hand; red/black berries on toasty background, huge rounded palate (15% alc), sweet ripe tannin. **Ruby Cabernet** ★★★☆ Unwooded **02** another friendly monster in this range: 15% alc, still packed with fruit; plum & cherry, touch rhubarb, rounded tannin; could safely be cellared another yr/2. **Cabernet Sauvignon** ★★ **03** vague strawberry nose; full oaky palate with obvious tannins; give time. Positively Liliputian at 14.2% alc. WO Goudini, as is... **Sauvignon Blanc** ★★★ **04**, gentle ripe gooseberry nose, pleasant soft flavour ably tweaked by acid. Drink young. 11% alc. **Family Reserve Viognier** ★★★ Simply 'Viognier' in pvs ed. Switches to unoaked in **03**, SAYWS class winner, with gentle lemon-lime aromas, well rounded palate gliding easily to a citrus finish. Already touch mature, so not for extended ageing. 14% alc. **Chardonnay-Viognier** ★★★ Gracefully mellowing **02** offers soft, gentle citrus & vanilla tones; pleasant but needs drinking. Briefly oaked. 14.5% alc. **Muscadel** 🆕 ★★★★ ✓ **03** effusive aromas of honeysuckle & muscat, light toned & satin smooth, lovely citrus tang followed by spiritous lift. 16.5% alc. WO Wrcstr. **Cuvée Brut**

★★★ The last NV carbonated sparkling tasted was a lightish, gently dry sauvignon. Both ranges WO Brde Rvr Vlly unless noted.

Heron range

> **Shiraz-Petit Verdot** ☺ ★★★ 03 rare varietal pairing (70/30 ratio) achieves friendly quaffability via exuberant plum fruit & balancing smoky/toasty note. So fruity, you don't notice the 14.5% alc. **Chenin Blanc-Viognier** ☺ ★★★ Unusual & appealing 60/40 blend; 03 tropical fruit salad with citrus, still enough acid to give a nice grip, satisfy; enjoy soon. — *DH*

Robertson Winery

Robertson ▪ Est 1941 ▪ 1stB 1987 ▪ Tasting & sales Mon-Thu 8-5 Fri 8-5.30 Sat 9-3 ▪ Closed Easter Fri, Dec 25 & Jan 1 ▪ Tours by appt ▪ BYO picnic ▪ Gifts ▪ Tourgroups by appt ▪ Small wine museum ▪ Owners 43 members ▪ Winemakers Lolly Louwrens, Francois Weich, Jacques Roux & Neil Hawkins (May 1995/Sep 1997/Jan 2000/Nov 2001) ▪ Viticulturist Anton Laas (Nov 2000) ▪ 1 700 ha (cab, merlot, pinotage, ruby cab, shiraz, chard, chenin, sauvignon) ▪ 27 000 tons ▪ 40% red 60% white ▪ No 1 Constitution Rd Robertson 6705 ▪ johann@vinimark.co.za ▪ www.robertsonwinery.co.za ℂ (023) 626·3059 🖷 (023) 626·2926

Unlikely as it may seem, the biggest news from this 1m cases a year winery centres on a minuscule 16 barrels. Naturally they aren't just any old casks. They hold — or held, until their contents were transferred to bottles — Robertson's new flagship, a Shiraz they've named No. 1 Constitution Road, after their catchy sounding street address. Extending their successful varietal range are three new blends under the Old Chapel label, spotlighting the original place of worship first used as a winery in 1941. All the wines now fly the 'Proudly South African' flag, signalling the winery's support for the nationwide programme promoting creation and economic growth. On which subject, cellarmaster and GM Bowen Botha is justifiably proud that the Department of Trade & Industry named them one of SA's top 300 companies for their contribution to expansion and employment.

Vineyard Selection range

★★★★★ **No. 1 Constitution Road** NEW Cellar's new standard bearer, sibling to shiraz below, inviting inevitable comparisons. With maiden 02, this version has the edge; fine spread of vivid aromas (ripe black cherry to Karoo bush); spicy, full-fruited palate; generous pliable tannins; loads of potential. Same abundant oak, alc, as below.

★★★★ **Wolfkloof Shiraz** ✓ Maiden 02 excellent ripe shiraz; full & very rotund; comforting, all-enveloping; velvety tannins to match. follow-up 03 also striking yet finer, more elegant; similar huge but balanced alc (15%), generous but harmonious oak.

★★★★ **Prospect Hill Cabernet Sauvignon** Warm-country cab with generous build, 02 ripe, meaty aromas, quite individual. 03 (★★★★) ✓ unfolds slowly in glass to reveal more refined, structured wine; real summer pudding flavour melange, generous supply of ripe tannins, vanilla oak. 14% alc.

★★★★ **Kings River Chardonnay** NEW ✓ Gentle white peach waft introduces quite an outspoken wood-matured white; waves of lime & lees followed by butterscotch & fudge; all nicely focused & packaged. Excellent now, good prognosis for development over 2-4 yrs. 14% alc.

★★★★ **Retreat Sauvignon Blanc** Grapes from eponymous farm, owned by Jac de Wet. 04 grabs the attention with array of pleasantly contrasting ripe-tropical, 'green' & citrus tones; fine weight with dry lip-smacking finish. 13.6% alc.

★★★★ **Almond Grove Weisser Riesling Noble Late Harvest** From Almond Grove farm & the original NLH in this line-up; now seems outshone by the jewel below, but genteel, understated 03 has its own attractions including beautifully poised & balanced sugar/acid; deserves time to show its potential. 10.5% alc.

★★★★★ **Wide River Reserve Noble Late Harvest** New to the guide, but VDG in 2002, **01** tour de force takes this Vyd Selection range to the next level. From botrytised riesling, a deep golden nectar of remarkable richness, concentration; aromas of orange marmalade & cinnamon merge with hint of ginger, caramel on palate. Ample bracing acidity to ride out the wine's weight, viscosity, & carry into grand maturity 5+ yrs hence. 9.5% alc.

Robertson range

★★★☆ **Cabernet Sauvignon** ✓ Briefly oaked style not for laying down. **03** sweet mulberry/green pepper tones with toast/vanilla; smooth & soft, approachable.

> **Ruby Cabernet** ☺ ★★★ Terrific, youthful **03**, robust, lashed with plum & strawberry flavour, juicy & mouthwatering. Perfect quaffer, moderate alc this yr (13.4%). **Beaukett** ☺ ★★★ **04** lightish, aromatic semi-sweet wafting Turkish Delight/honeysuckle perfume; very pretty, not over-sweet; shows attractive delicacy.

Merlot Latest **03** not tasted. **Shiraz** ★★★★ ✓ powerfully aromatic & muscular **03**; black pepper, smoke & leather aromas; wide sweet-spicy palate, amenable tannins. 14% alc. **Pinotage** ★★★★ ✓ Supercharged berries/cherries over ripe, rounded tannins in **03**, showcasing variety's lovely sweet-fruit tone. Enjoy over the next 2-3 yrs. **Cabernet Sauvignon-Shiraz** Latest **03** untasted. **Chardonnay** ★★ **03** has developed broad citrus/vanilla character, rather than tiring bottle age (20% oaked), but should be enjoyed soon. **Chenin Blanc** ★★ **04** step up; satisfies with full, ripe tropical fruit in pleasingly compact body (12% alc). **Colombard** ★★★ Last tasted was **03**, dry, lightish, with soft acidity. **Sauvignon Blanc** ★★★ **04** night-harvested to retain zingy green-fruit character; rounded yet crisp appley finish. Moderate 13% alc. **Gewürztraminer Special Late Harvest** ★★★ Delicious scented dessert, **04** rich & smooth; honeysuckle & rose-petal aroma plus whiff botrytis; enjoy in its youth. 11.5% alc. **White Muscadel** ★★★ **03**, yr on, has apple & litchi fragrances, luscious sweetness given life by crisp acidity, tangy finish. 16.5% alc. **Cape Ruby Port** ★★★ Last tasted was **02**, youthful, lively dryish, light spirit (16.5%).

Old Chapel range

> **Red** ☺ ★★ Round juicy tannins form scaffold for thatch & bramble aromas, ripe red berry flavours. Pleasant everyday glassful.

Rosé ★★ Bright pink colour; sweet, light & lively, clean fresh finish. **White** ★★★ Tropical-toned nose/palate, crisp, fruitily dry finish. Low 11.5% alc. Both NV.

Natural Light range

Low alc wines (7.5-9.5%), all NV; mainly Natural Sweets. **Red** ★★ Sweet ripe plums & berries with fresh acidity. **Rosé** ★★ Baby-pink hue; soft, fruity & gently sweet. **White** ★★ Delicate, light & easy. **Dry Light** ★ Aptly named: decidedly dry & fresh.

Sparkling wines

NV carbonated bubblies from chenin, colombard, with lightish alcs (10-11%). All ★★. **Brut** Tart green-apple fruit, busy bubbles, firm dry acidity. **Sec** Pretty bouquet of honeysuckle, ripe melon; slight sweetness nicely balanced by fresh acidity. **Doux** Honeyed aroma, (not bottle age) very sweet, busy bubbles.

Two-litre boxed range

Certified bag-in-boxes with varietal labels & vintage dates. Includes two NVs.

> **Ruby Cabernet** ☺ ★★★ Some attractive warm plum fruit with touches cooler capsicum; **03** epitome of an easy-swigger. 14% alc.

Merlot 03 untasted. **Chardonnay** ★★ Broader build than other whites; **04** light citrus flavours. Also in 3ℓ. **Chenin Blanc** ★ **04** Light & easy, off-dry. **Sauvignon Blanc** ★ Pleasant, dry **04**. **Extra Light** ★★ NV attractive freshness, almost dry, very light; has charm. Low 9.5% alc. Also available in 3ℓ box: **Cabernet Sauvignon 03**.

Vinipak range

Good-value anytime wines in 500ml/1ℓ packs, with welcome low alc (±7-11.5%) for easier quaffing. All NV. **Smooth Dry Red** ★★ Full flavoured, round, gratifying; could be chilled in summer. **Dry White** ★★ Smooth, easy, undemanding. **Light White** ★★ Light (9.6% alc) & juicy, smooth acidity, tasty. **Stein** ★★ Light, with pleasing sweetness. **Late Harvest** ★★ As usual, drier than expected from this style, good fresh acidity. **Johannisberger Sweet Red** ★★ Light-bodied, soft acid, sweet plum juice flavours, no tannins. **Natural Sweet Rosé** ★★ Light, appealing, full of ripe fruit & balanced sweetness. **Natural Sweet White** not tasted. – *DH*

Robertson Wide River Export Company

Joint venture between Robertson Winery and Vinimark, handling all Robertson Winery exports. See Vinimark for contact details.

Kaapdal range   [NEW]

Cabernet Sauvignon ★★★ **03** characterful, with variety's firmish tannins, cedary dry finish. **Merlot** ★★★ **03** low-tannin style, smooth, good ripe fruit. **Pinotage** ★★ **03** full-blooded style, approachable with tannins in reserve for keeping few yr/2. **Ruby Cabernet** ★★ **03** soft & easy, berry-fruit tones, tannins firm the finish. **Shiraz** ★★★ Generous **03**, warm cherry/plum fruit, touch of toast, nicely padded palate, softish tannins. Alc for above ±12.5-13.5%. **Shiraz Rosé** ★★ Lightly floral **04**, perfectly pleasant, easy, gently dry. **Chardonnay 03** not tasted. **Chenin Blanc** ★★ **04** rounded tropical tones, fresh & clean. Light 11.5% alc. **Sauvignon Blanc 04** not ready for tasting.

Kleindal range

Mainly for Germany & the UK. **Cabernet Sauvignon** ★★★ **03** some nice cab character, mulberry with cooler cedar touches, firmish tannins, properly dry. **Merlot** ★★★ **03** dark-berried smoothie, lip-smacking fruit, no tannins to speak of, dry. **Pinotage** ★★ **03** hot-country redcurrant style, touch medicinal, pleasantly rounded, tannic finish. **Ruby Cabernet** ★★ **03** nicely fruity, some berries, soft & easy, some tannin on finish. **Shiraz** ★★★ **03** warm cherry/plum fruit, touch of toast, nicely padded palate, softish tannins. Alc for above ±12.5-13.5%. **Shiraz Rosé** [NEW] **04** not tasted. **Chardonnay** ★★ Ripe citrus fruits on **03**, nice plumpness yet still quite firm. **Chenin Blanc** ★★ Still youthfully shy, **04** some citrus notes, firm acid, dryish. **Sauvignon Blanc** ★★ **04** non-assertive style, gentle tropical whiff, almost dry.

Silver Sands range

Chiefly for the UK. **Cabernet Sauvignon** ★★★ **03** nice whiff cab cedar/tobacco, quite ripe & fleshy, soft tannins & honestly dry. **Pinotage** ★★ **03** extrovert variety, scented, well rounded fruit though tannins need bit of time to soften. **Ruby Cabernet** ★★ **03** lovely berry quality, juicy, no worrying tannins. **Shiraz** ★★ **03** whiff ripe red-berried fruits, touches roast/toast, firm acid, almost ready. **Merlot** ★★ Some seductive chocolate & cassis aromas on **03**, soft, easy style. **Chardonnay** ★★★ **03** good whiff oak, citrus fruit, dryish. **Chenin Blanc** ★★ **04** modestly fruity, juicy with firm acidity, finish softened by dab sugar. **Sauvignon Blanc** ★★ **04** though lacks varietal punch, easy-drinking tropical tones. Alcs as for Kleindal.

Sinnya range

These destined mainly for Germany & Canada. **Cabernet Sauvignon** ★★★ **03** good varietal flavours: mulberry, cedar, friendly structure, firm dry finish. **Merlot** ★★ **03** nice choc/cherry, ultra-soft tannin, easy quaffing style. **Pinotage** ★★ **03** unusual medicinal flavour, nice rounded fruit, toughish. **Ruby Cabernet** ★★ **03** juicy berry fruits, pleasant freshness, easy. **Shiraz** ★★ **03** some sweet red cherry fruit, roast beef, fresh acidity, ready.

Chardonnay ★★ 03 some citrus fruit, dryish. **Chenin Blanc** ★★ 04 citrus & nuts, already some interesting development, slight sweetness on finish. **Sauvignon Blanc** ★★ 04 less shrill than most, touch tropical, dryish. Alcs as for Kleindal.

The Veldt range

Mostly for Scottish market. **Cabernet Sauvignon** ★★★ 03 modest cedary whiff, fair varietal character, some welcome fleshiness, dryish finish. **Merlot** ★★ 03 pretty whiff choc box, soft tannins; attractive quaffer. **Pinotage** ★★ 03 quite weighty, unusual medicinal flavour, some fairly gawky tannins. **Ruby Cabernet** ★★ Lovely crushed-berry character sets 03 apart; juicy, tangy, easy. **Shiraz** ★★ Tangy 03, some sweet red cherry fruit & plums; ready. **Chardonnay** ★★ 03 soft, easy, dryish. **Chenin Blanc** ★★ 04 curiously scented, bouncy fruit, soft landing via touch sugar. **Sauvignon Blanc** ★★ 04 lacks varietal character, smooth acidity, not bone dry. Alcs as for Kleindal.

Vruchtbaar range

The Netherlands is the chief market for these. **Cabernet Sauvignon** ★★★ 03 shows good typicity, some nice berries under vanilla spice. **Merlot** ★★★ 03 delicate cassis aromas/flavours, softish tannins. **Pinotage** ★★ Warm redcurrants on 03, fruity, easy, edgy tannins. **Ruby Cabernet** ★★ 02 softly fruity, some cab gruffness. **Shiraz** ★★★ 03 attractive roast/toast edge to ripe fruit, softish tannins. **Chardonnay** ★★ 03 ripe citrus zing, smoothly rounded. **Chenin Blanc** ★★★ Attractive fruitiness on 04, firm fleshed, fresh acidity softened by dab sugar. **Sauvignon Blanc** ★★ Shy; some tropical fruit, hint of fresher salad greens in 04, almost dry. Alcs as for Kleindal. — *DH*

Robert's Rock see KWV International
Robusto see Rudera
Rocco Bay see Nordale
Rocheburg see Arlington, Riebeek Cellars
Rockfields see Du Preez Estate
Rock Rabbit see International Wine Services
Rock Ridge see Vinfruco
Rodini see Goudini
Roland's Reserve see Seidelberg

Romansrivier Cellar

Wolseley (see Worcester map) ▪ *Est 1949* ▪ *1stB 1976* ▪ *Tasting & sales Mon-Fri 8-5 Sat 10-1* ▪ *Closed Easter Fri-Sun, Dec 25/26, Jan 1* ▪ *Tours by appt* ▪ *Tourgroups* ▪ *BYO picnic* ▪ *Conference facilities* ▪ *Owners 30 members* ▪ *Winemaker/viticulturist Francois Agenbag (2002)* ▪ *500 ha (cab, chard, chenin, colombard)* ▪ *8 000 tons 5 000 cs own label 40% red 60% white* ▪ *PO Box 108 Wolseley 6830* ▪ *romans@cybertrade.co.za* ✆ *(023) 231·1070/80* 🖷 *(023) 231·1102*

This enterprising cellar near Wolseley now receives grapes from as far afield as Malmesbury and Vredendal. Cellarmaster Francois Agenbag believes that good wine makes itself if the grapes are of a high enough quality. He adds that the 2004 vintage produced very fruity white wines and intense, full-bodied reds. He believes co-op wineries have to become more market-driven to survive in today's competitive world.

Mountain Ridge range

Chardonnay Unwooded NEW ☺ ★★★ Epitome of peaches-&-cream character on nose, sprightly texture with crisp citrus finish in 04 (sample). Note: 14% alc. **Sauvignon Blanc** ☺ ★★★ 04 (sample) water-white, rather subdued nose but lively & bright fruity palate, clean finishing; enjoy this summer.

Cabernet Sauvignon & **Shiraz**, both NEW & 04, tasted as early barrel samples, too unformed to rate; both aged in 100% new Fr/Am oak; alcs ±14.5%. **Pinotage** NEW ★★★★ Charming 03 offers ripe mulberry & plum aromas, sweet-tasting fruit, soft, slightly smoky tannins. 14.5% alc. **Malbec-Pinotage** ★★★☆ Unusual combo, unwooded; 03 has developed since last tasted; thickly layered with plums & strawberries, slight smokiness adds interest. **Chardonnay Wooded** ★★★ 04 (sample) tropical fruit & spicy oak, joined by peaches in palate, crisp lime-tinged finish. **Colombard-Chardonnay** NEW ★★★ Attractive combo peaches, guava & tropical fruit, light & vivacious, for early enjoyment. **'Bordeaux Blend'** & **Colombard** discontinued. All WO Brde Rvr Vlly. — *DH*

Romond Vineyards

Stellenbosch ▪ Est 1993 ▪ 1stB 2003 ▪ Visits by appt ▪ Owners André & Rhona Liebenberg ▪ Winemakers André Liebenberg, advised by Inus Muller & Marais de Villiers (Jan 2003) ▪ Viticulturist De Wet Theron (Oct 2002) ▪ 33 tons 2 500 cs ▪ 100% red ▪ PO Box 5634 Helderberg 7135 ▪ romondwine@iafrica.com ✆ 855·4566 🖷 855·0428

A dream becomes reality. André Liebenberg successfully swops the TV ad director's chair for the cellarmaster's hot seat. With the Helderberg in his viewfinder since the 1980s, he eventually spots a steep eucalyptus-infested slope, next to Cordoba, in 1993: a portion of a property first farmed in 1772 by one M Romond. Five years of land reclamation follows ('I knew the battle was won when indigenous pioneer grasses appeared'). Now 9ha of cab, merlot, cab franc and pinotage are 'mollycoddled' there. Stonewall's 'charming, honest and sociable' old cellar provides the perfect combination of modern and old-fashioned. Despite reverse pumping pitfalls and tank tumbles, learner Liebenberg is loving 'every nerve-straining, back-breaking minute'.

★★★☆ **Rebus** Stylish blend cab f & s; franc the senior partner, just, at 56%. 03 (sample) quality grapes show in deep concentrated flavours, lively acidity. Wafting vanilla, still very youthful, tart finish. Matured on staves 15 mths, 13.2% alc. — *IvH*

Roodeberg see KWV International

Roodezandt Wines & Vineyards

Robertson ▪ Est 1953 ▪ Tasting & sales Mon-Fri 8-5.30 Sat 9-12.30 ▪ Closed Easter Fri-Mon, May 1, Dec 25/36 & Jan 1 ▪ Tours by appt ▪ Owners 54 members ▪ Winemakers Christie Steytler & Elmo du Plessis, with Piet Bruwer (May 1980/Oct 1999/Feb 1985) ▪ Viticulturist Anton Laas (Dec 2000) ▪ 1 400 ha (cab, merlot, pinotage, ruby cab, shiraz, chard, chenin, colombard, sauvignon) ▪ 23 000 tons ▪ PO Box 164 Robertson 6705 ▪ roodez@intekom.co.za ▪ www.roodezandt.co.za ✆ (023) 626·1160 🖷 (023) 626·5074

The wine industry is enough to turn your hair grey before its time, murmurs manager Abé Rossouw. 'We're trying to achieve export targets because the local market seems as dead as a dodo.' What's more, it isn't easy to compete internationally because so many countries subsidise their export producers. But there's good news, too, at Roodezandt. The vintage produced wines of a very reasonable quality, particularly in their single-vineyard wines. 'We're not doing anything fancy here', says Christie Steytler, who's experienced boom as well as gloom in his quarter-century with this co-op. 'Good wines are made in the vineyard and it's up to each winemaker to apply his or her own recipe to guide them to their maximum potential.'

★★★★ **Red Muscadel** Appealing winter warmer, best in fragrant youth; 03 (★★★) inviting bouquet of strawberries & tea-leaves; bright acidic lift for juicy effect; strawberry jam flavour with hint of cream. 18.5% alc much higher than pvs 01.

Keizer's Creek ☺ ★★★ Unwooded NV blend led by ruby cab; damp thatch & stewed plums; soft, full, juicy; quick but quaffable. 13.5% alc. **Keizer's Creek 'The White'** NEW ☺ ★★★ Just-off-dry, light-bodied, supple & juicy poolside tipple. NV. **Special Late Harvest** ☺ ★★★ From chenin, muscadel; scented 04 billows full-sweet honeysuckle aromas/flavours; delicate 12% alc heightens the charm.

Balthazar Classic Cabernet Sauvignon ★★★ Limited release honouring winery's ex-chairman, Baltus Kloppers. Unfined/unfiltered. ±13% alc. **00** now shows savoury mince-pie aromas, hint rum & raisin; gaining stewed character — peaking, must drink. **Cabernet Sauvignon** ★★★ **01** herbal aromas with eucalyptus hint; cocoa flavours, quite soft, lean & leafy. Yr older Fr casks. 14.5% alc. **Syrah** ★★★ (Pvsly 'Shiraz') Cross between aromatic & wood-powered style; **03** pepper & spice over soft plummy fruit, pervasive on oakiness on palate (which not unappealing); 13% alc. **Chardonnay** Pvs 'Balthazar Classic' to be replaced by another version, unavailable at press time. **Sauvignon Blanc** ★★ Usually from cooler river-fronting sites; ±13% alc. **04** slightly confected talcum powder nose, soft, dry white-fruit palate, lacks zest to finish. **White Muscadel** ★★★ **02**, retasted this ed, improving; brilliant yellow-gold colour; huge Turkish Delight bouquet; zippy peach flavours & cleansing acidity. 17.5% alc. **Port** ★★★ From ruby cab, fortified with brandy spirit to 18.5%; **00**, retasted, soft dried prune nose, hints raisin & meat; silky sweet palate not showing much grip. **Colombar** discontinued. — *TM*

Rooiberg Winery

Robertson ▪ Est 1964 ▪ 1stB 1974 ▪ Tasting & sales Mon-Fri 8-5.30 Sat 9-3 ▪ Closed Easter Fri/Sun, Dec 25 & Jan 1 ▪ Tours by appt ▪ Farmstall and tea garden with gift shop; also BYO picnic ▪ Facilities for children ▪ Tourgroups ▪ 4×4 trail ▪ Audio-visual on video/CD ▪ Owners 30 members ▪ Cellarmaster André van Dyk, winemaker Eduard Malherbe, vini consultant Newald Marais (all Oct 2002) ▪ Viti consultant Briaan Stipp (Jan 2000) ▪ 600 ha (cab, merlot, pinotage, ruby cab, shiraz, chard, chenin, colombard, sauvignon) ▪ 11 000 tons 75 000 cs own labels 20% red 70% white 10% rosé ▪ Export brands: African Collection, Amandalia, De Sonnenberg, Goeie Tye, Signum, Umculi & Zebra Collection ▪ PO Box 358 Robertson 6705 ▪ info@rooiberg.co.za ▪ www.rooiberg.co.za ☏ (023) 626·1663 ▨ (023) 626·3295

Cellarmaster André van Dyk's report card for harvest 2004 varies from 'good' (the chardonnay) to 'average' (the chenin and sauvignon) to 'good to average' for the reds. A black mark, however, for the rot that affected the chenin to a degree, a not uncommon vintage problem in the Robertson valley. With an eye to what the market wants, the production team has added a Pinotage Rosé and a Chenin-Sauvignon to the product range. The winery's still preferred supplier to Stellenbosch Vineyards of chardonnay for its Shamwari range, which is in turn sold on to the global wholesaler Constellation Wines. Plenty of fun to be had here, for dads (4x4 trailing), moms (wine-accessory shopping) and children (playpark and pets), with picnics for the whole family for afters.

Reserve range

★★★★ **Cabernet Sauvignon 01** in ripe, international style; shows plump cassis fruit, dense structure, finely-grained tannins & elegant, dry, subtly-oaked finish. Charming, if slightly baked, aromas on still youthful **02** (★★★★), leading to sweet cassis fruit & soft ripe tannins on well-balanced palate, but reflecting vintage in lesser concentration, gravitas. These 13.7% alc; 18 mths Fr oak.

★★★★ **Pinotage** Last tasted was **01**, satisfying wine ready to mature with distinction.

★★★☆ **Chardonnay** 🆕 Appealing spice & oatmeal on nose of **03**, also showing wood influence (fermented/9 mths Fr) on crisply clean forthright palate, along with pleasant lime notes. Drier than 3.4g/ℓ sugar suggests; 14.3% alc.

Standard range

★★★★ **Henri Roselt** This flagship already sailed its last, to be replaced by Reserve range.

★★★☆ **Cabernet Sauvignon-Merlot (Roodewyn) 03** (★★★), like last-tasted **01**, a sweetly-fruited blend, pleasant from first baked jam aromas to friendly, mild-tannined farewell. Not one for keeping. Yr older Fr oak; 14% alc.

★★★☆ **Pinotage** ✓ **03** big, ripe & outgoing, offering boiled sweet flavours, & just enough structure to give stability & character to the fruity charm. 14% alc; yr Fr oak.

★★★☆ **Shiraz** ✓ **03** repeats last-tasted **01**'s fine warmly savoury/spicy effort. Cherry & hillside scrub notes; well balanced, with some succulent ripe tannins adding a serious touch to the friendly effect. 14% alc. Yr Fr oak.

★★★★ **Red Jerepiko** ✓ Excellent unwooded fortified dessert. **96**, from single pinotage vyd in Eilandia area, still on offer & still interestingly delicious, with a range of flavours from floor polish to apricots & orange marmalade, while racy acidity controls the sweetness. 17.5% alc.

★★★★ **Red Muscadel** ✓ Unutterably cheerful **03** is rosy-coloured, with copper gleams. Scented, flowery, raisiny aromas pour out a welcome; intense flavours no less good-hearted. Rather lovely as well as unctuously comforting. 16.5% alc.

★★★☆ **White Muscadel** ✓ Revisiting **00** only a pleasure: lovely luscious gold, with grapey nose, rich & velvety marmalade flavours, a good acidic counter-thrust, warm flavourful finish. Less sweet, higher alc (17.5%) than Red version.

Merlot ☺ ★★★ Quiet aromas on **02**, but big lush palate, very ripely soft & little backbone. Lightly wooded. Good of its cheerful, friendly type. Yr Fr oak. **Selected Red** ☺ ★★★ Generous, forthright & honest – great start to a warm friendship (though this one finishes a little short). NV lightly oaked blend. 13.5% alc. **Pinotage Rosé** ☺ ★★☆ Crisply refreshing lunchtime (or midnight snack, for that matter) pale red quaffer; lots of cherry & strawberry flavour, good dry finish.

Cabernet Sauvignon ★★☆ **03** warm, sweet-fruited, easy & very pleasant to drink, without being trivial. Modest 13% alc. Yr Fr oak. **Natural Sweet Red** ★★★ **02** mouthfilling dark choc, juicy plums; cleverly balanced with some refreshing acid/tannin grip to complement sweetness (33g/ℓ sugar). **Natural Sweet Rosé** ★★★ **03** pleasant, light-hearted stuff, redolent of fruit & flowers; doesn't cloy. Blend red muscadel, colombard. 11% alc. **Chardonnay** ★★☆ Previewed **04** restrained, dry & crisp, even steely, with sufficiently satisfying fruit, brush of oak adding interest. 14.3% alc. **Chenin Blanc** ★★☆ Creamy texture but fresh balance in **04**, light & virtually dry; evanescent green flavours & earthy notes. 12.5% alc. **Sauvignon Blanc** ★★☆ **04** light insubstantiality with vague, green-tinged & quickly disappearing flavour. **Cape White** ★★★ **04** pretty, face-powdery, flowery character on this crisply balanced, off-dry quaffer. Easy-going 11% alc. **Rhine Riesling** ★★☆ Floral, spicy notes on **04** (just) remind the sipper of the variety's great nobility; just-off-dry, with a quickening acidity marking the finish. **Natural Sweet Blanc** ★ Grapey nose the best part of this soft-centred, insubstantial, insipidly sweet **04** blend. Low 10% alc. **Brut Sparkling** ★★ Jovially frothy carbonated NV (as all these bubblies) from sauvignon crouchen, light & dry enough – not much substance, but let's not be pedantic or precious here. **Flamingo Sparkling Flamingo Sparkling** ★★ Flying high with all the above, plus a dash of pinotage for colour. **Vin Doux Sparkling** ★★ Festive (or anytime) sweetly foaming, with bright grapey aromas/flavours. **Hanepoot** ★★★ **00** still available, still floral, grapey & sweet – rather coarser, duller than Rooiberg's fine muscadels. 16.5% alc. **Ruby Port** ★★★ **02** pleasant fruitcake bouquet, mild flavours; structured more by acid than tannin, with a little richness. – *TJ*

Roothman Wines

Bonnievale ▪ Est 2003 ▪ Visits see Jonkheer ▪ Owner/winemaker Erhard Roothman ▪ PO Box 13 Bonnievale 6730 ℂ 082·376·7974 🖷 (023) 616·2744

These are the own-wines of Erhard Roothman, stalwart of the Jonkheer winery for the past thirty years. His guiding philosophy is to offer exceptional value for money.

Klassieke Rooiwijn ☺ ★★★ Selection of merlot & cab from the **00** vintage; forthcoming sweet plum aromas, whiffs tobacco pouch & mint; fruit drying a bit, enjoy soon.

Klassieke Witwijn ★★★ 03 shy lemon- & green-grass bouquet, dry rhubarb flavours; honey bottle-age starting to creep in; drink soon. From chenin. Both WO W-Cape. — *TM*

Rose Garden see Domaine Brahms

Ross Gower Wines

Walker Bay ▪ Est 2003 ▪ 1stB 2004 ▪ Tasting & sales Mon-Fri 9-5 ▪ Closed public holidays ▪ Tours by appt ▪ Picnic baskets/light lunches by appt; or BYO ▪ Amenities/attractions: see intro ▪ Owners Ross & Sally Gower/JM Family Trust ▪ Winemaker/viticulturist Ross Gower (Jun 2003) ▪ 5 ha (sauvignon) ▪ 1 500 cs 30% red 60% white 10% MCC ▪ PO Box 161 Elgin 7180 ▪ rossgower@worldonline.co.za ⓒ/🖷 844·0197

Ross Gower spent 2000 pinpointing the 'ideal spot to buy a retirement farm'. He and wife Sally found it on an apple spread in the south-east corner of Elgin. Retiring? Hardly. Establishing Klein Constantia's winery ('home' for 19 years) honed his hands-on skills: throwing concrete for his new cellar (assisted by his sons), installing equipment himself, including the cooling; surviving an exploding press (Sinatra classic 'Fly Me to the Moon', he chuckles, is his new signature tune); sourcing sauvignon for his maiden 2004 vintage; and planting 5ha of his own (to come: muscadel, shiraz, merlot, sangiovese and chardonnay/pinot noir). Plus olives (oil and eating), lavender, citrus, dairy cows, a bistro and function venue. And winemaking for Elgin Vintners. Whew! Biodynamic practices are partly inspired by the proximity of the Kogelberg Biosphere World Heritage Site (guests at the Gowers' self-catering cottages can hike, mountain-bike). For he who knew at 13 that he wanted to be a winemaker, farming 'our heavenly little patch of earth holds great joys'.

★★★★ Mankazana Sauvignon Blanc 🆕 Tank sample **04** from Bottelary fruit seduces with overt fleshy tropicality — veritable fruit salad — lifted by tapering nettle finish, brisk 13.7% alc. For sunny summer libation within yr of harvest. — *DS*

Rotsvast see Baarsma
Route 101 see Du Preez Estate, Thirty-Two Degrees South
Route 303 see Ultra Liquors

Royle Family Vineyards

Paarl ▪ Est 2000 ▪ 1stB 2001 ▪ Closed to public ▪ Owner Noel Woods ▪ Vini consultant Cathy Marshall (Oct 2000) ▪ Viti consultant Paul Wallace (May 2000) ▪ 45 ha (cab, merlot, pinotage, ruby cabernet, shiraz, viognier) ▪ 750 cs own label 100% ▪ PO Box 298 Klapmuts 7625 ▪ noelwoods@roylewines.com ▪ www.roylewines.com ⓒ/🖷 875·5363

Gauteng businessman Noel Woods' policy is to release wines only once they meet his 'good drinking' standards. By press time last edition only limited amounts of the Shiraz had done so. This year there's more: the next Shiraz vintage and a new Cab. Woods bought this farm near Glen Carlou and Backsberg to keep himself occupied after he'd retired, but already has his shoulder to the wheel (with advisers Cathy Marshall and Paul Wallace, and manager Johan Southey), and is looking to boost exports to the East.

Cabernet Sauvignon 🆕 ★★★★ 02 minty cherry nose, broad spectrum of stone fruit flavours with bitter choc finish. Dry, but blockbuster 15% alc gives impression of sweetness. 14 mths Fr oak. **Syrah ★★★** Name change from 'Shiraz' for **02**, but same style: toasty mocha nose, lightly spiced fruit. 13.9% alc. 11 mths Am/Fr oak. Revisited **01** shows good integration, some smoked beef aromas, with fine soft tannins & a tasty mid-palate with good length. 13.5% alc. — *NP*

Rawson's see Cape Vineyards
Route 101 see 32 South

Rozendal

Stellenbosch ▪ 1stB 1983 ▪ Tasting, sales & tours by appt ▪ Luxury auberge with restaurant & amenities ▪ Conference facilities ▪ Walks ▪ Owners Kurt & Lyne Ammann ▪ Winemaker Kurt Ammann ▪ 6 ha (cabs s/f , merlot) ▪ 2-3 000 cs 100% red ▪ PO Box 160 Stellenbosch 7599 ▪ rozendal@mweb.co.za © 809·2621 ☎ 809·2640

Marigold and Pearl have joined the dedicated winegrowing team at Rozendal. These two cows are an essential part of being fully biodynamic, producing the homemade manure which is used to make 'compost tea' to spray the vines. The resulting 2004 crop was very healthy, plagued by neither pestilence nor disease. The wine fermented naturally and, like the 2003, is entirely biodynamic. The only disappointment for the Ammanns was the disbanding of the SA Biodynamic Association leaving them and the two other bio-producers, Reyneke and Groenvlei (near Spier), to look overseas for accreditation once their current certificate expires. The 02 vintage of the Ammanns' top-class red blend is bottled but not ready for release, though eagerly awaited by customers locally and in the USA, UK, Germany and Scandinavia.

Ruby Sunset see Lutzville

Rudera Wines

Stellenbosch ▪ Est 1999 ▪ 1stB 2001 ▪ Closed to public ▪ Owners Teddy & Riana Hall ▪ Winemaker/viticulturist Teddy Hall ▪ 18 ha (cab, shiraz, chenin) ▪ 3 400 cs 45% red 50% white 5% NLH ▪ PO Box 2868 Somerset West 7129 ▪ info@rudera.co.za ▪ www.rudera. co.za ©☎ 852·1380

Home for these outstanding wines is neither farm nor winery, but Teddy and Riana Hall's hearts and hands. Teddy H, three-times Chenin Challenge winner and Diners Club 2002 Winemaker of the Year, side-steps 'fame'. Winemaking was a lifestyle choice for this ex-stockbroker, family man, food-and-wine lover (stogie clenched between teeth), pianist, private pilot.... His maiden vintage (2004) as an independent renting cellar space was as 'glorious' as his first solo flight, despite frustrating botrytis conditions nixing any hopes of an NLH (*Wine Spectator* scored the 03 92 points). Producing only 1 000 cases from own grapes, 2 500 from bought-in fruit, he's revelling in the 'luxury' of manicuring vineyards, handcrafting each wine (though still vinifying for Katbakkies, Amarava and the Wine Society). Growth opportunities? 'Chenin blanc – watch this space.'

- ★★★★★ **Cabernet Sauvignon** Made in minuscule quantities (102 cs + a few 3ℓ bottles). **01** a beauty; no problem with ripeness: cassis & black plums, sugared-violet nuances, richly oak-spiced. Stylish palate, beautifully balanced, well-served by firm yet ripe tannins. A keeper, with 8+good yrs ahead (though likely to be finished well before that). New Fr barriques, 23 mths. 14.5% alc. 91 pts *WS*. Maiden **00** excited international palates (including US-based Robert Parker), local critics too: *Wine* ★★★★. MIWA gold. Off leased vyds in Stbosch, as are wines below.
- ★★★★★ **CWG Auction Reserve Cabernet Sauvignon** ⬛ Like the winemaker, big, impressive, lots of depth. **02** violets, lead pencils, wet heath nuances interplay with cassis core; cedar spice from expensive oaking, 23 mths new Fr oak. Supple, fine-grained tannins permit immediate access, but don't be deceived, still young – will reward 8+ yrs cellaring. Unfiltered. 14.5% alc. Only 60 cs.
- ★★★★ **Syrah** Dark-fruited **02**, layers woodsmoke, white pepper, more than nod to Rhône but palate pure New World: cherry-pip flesh, softly amenable, long creamy finish. Delicious now or keep ±3 more yrs. Partly fermented in Fr barrels, 11 mths aged, 20% new. 13.5% alc. Veritas-gonged **01** had spicy fruit in manicured tannin frame.
- ★★★★ **Chenin Blanc** From old bushvines, yielding small crops – ±5 t/ha in **03** shimmering peach & quince fragrance/flavours; voluptuous body, mouthfilling intensity. 8 mths Fr barrel fermentation/maturation adding to complexity, structure. 7.2g/l acid stiffens backbone, will help it to age beautifully. 14% alc. **02** rich marmalade-orange

depth has super-fine integration of fruit/oak on sumptuous palate, finishes dry despite 6.4g/ℓ sugar. Buffed, a beauty. 91 pts *Wine International*. Native yeasts.

★★★★ **Robusto Chenin Blanc** 'Robust' but controlled — the palate weight of these almost balanced by the show-topping hardware in the cupboard (Chenin Challenge, *SA Wine*, Diners Club, Michelangelo etc). **02** (★★★★☆) yr on, just gets better. Voluptuous, honeyed tropical fruit, some marmalade tones & full-bodied palate richness from perfect ripeness, signature plumping 15.7g/ℓ sugar. Scrumptious, and still many yrs ahead. 14% alc. **01** had a chalky nuance.

★★★★ **Chenin Blanc Noble Late Harvest** Hand-selected botrytised berries; 100% native yeast-fermented in new Fr barriques. Latest **03** (★★★★☆) pervading tangerine, orange peel perfume; the silkiest, tangy marmalade texture imaginable. Beautifully balanced: racy acidity (8g/ℓ) invigorates sweetness, giving length & ageing ability. So good, shouldn't be shared with food. 13% alc. 137g/ℓ sugar. 92 pts *WS*. Sit-up-and-take-notice electricity in **02**; with penetrating balanced spicy finish.

★★★★★ **CWG Auction Reserve Chenin Blanc Noble Late Harvest** NEW Natural-yeast ferment in new Fr barriques for **03**. So much to admire: concentration, complexity, balance. Sumptuous tropical fruits, mango, peach, assail the nose, promising riches to come; mouthfilling honeyed sweetness is tempered by bracing acidity, leaving intense nutty, citrus-tang impression long after wine is finished. Good 5+ yr cellaring potential. 132g/ℓ sugar. 12.5% alc.— *CR*

Rudi Schultz Wines

Stellenbosch ▪ Est 2002 ▪ 1stB 2003 ▪ Closed to public ▪ Owner/winemaker Rudi Schultz ▪ Viticulturist Dirkie Morkel ▪ 400 cs 100% red ▪ rudi@thelema.co.za ✆ 082·928·1841

New York, here he comes! Rudi Schultz's own-label Shiraz, made on borrowed (from Thelema) time and space off selected vineyards, was snapped up in 2004 by his American agent. 'The USA loves our (SA's) shiraz and sauvignon.' What hasn't headed offshore has taken to the skies, after being selected by SA Airways for its First and Business Class winelists. Lucky for locals, Schultz was able to double production this past vintage. Wine lovers will also like his views on pricing. 'Ridiculous prices are asked for ordinary wines. We have to keep the quality and price related.'

★★★★ **Syrah** Standout wine, in refined style, from Bottlry fruit. Revisited **02** shows raspberry fruit breaking through oak-induced dense mocha; mid-palate sweetening out, soft tannins, & good spice on finish. Ripe (14.5% alc), but not flabby. **03** less oaky, more peppery, more succulent grape presence; lower 13.8% alc means greater elegance. Needs time to harmonise. 14 mths oak, most Fr, half new. — *MF*

Ruiters see Fairseat Cellars

Ruitersvlei Wines

Paarl ▪ Est 1692 ▪ 1stB 1995 ▪ Tasting & sales Mon-Fri 9-5 Sat 9-3 Sun 11-3 ▪ Fee R10 (incl glass) ▪ Closed Easter Fri, Dec 25 & Jan 1 ▪ Italian-style lunches Tue-Sun 10-5; evenings by appt ▪ Tours by appt ▪ Farm produce ▪ Facilities for children ▪ Tourgroups ▪ Gifts ▪ Reception/ conference venue ▪ Conservation area ▪ Owner John Faure ▪ Winemaker Reino Kruger, with Yvette Moolman (Jan 2004/Dec 2003) ▪ Viticulturist Kobus Mostert (Nov 2001) ▪ 289 ha (cab, merlot, pinotage, shiraz, chard, chenin, sauvignon) ▪ 1 400 tons 50 000 cs own labels 70% red 29% white 1% rosé ▪ Export brand: Rider's Valley ▪ Ranges for customers: Vaughan Johnson, Steven Rom, Millers Thumb Restaurant & Casa do Mar ▪ PO Box 532 Suider-Paarl 7624 ▪ Sales@ruitersvlei.co.za ▪ www.ruitersvlei.co.za ✆ 863·1517 🖷 863·1443

It's another year of change on John Faure's farm, with winemaker Reino Kruger arriving from Daschbosch and assistant Yvette Moolman, fresh from Elsenburg, completing the team. Yield from their first harvest here was the average 1 400 tons — cinsaut was the only newly planted variety to have come on-stream — but that should rise thanks to recent plantings of cab, merlot and sauvignon. The farm restaurant, La Masseria, continues to draw visitors who enjoy fine Italian fare served under the walnut and almond trees overlooking the vineyards. Added attractions are a free-range area for children and a characterful function hall for weddings and parties.

★★★☆ **Cabernet Sauvignon Reserve** Concentrated, delicious & easy to drink. **02**, revisited, dead ringer for an Aussie: mouthfilling Ribena fruit, ripe, soft, low acid, plump; wood (Fr barriques) obvious but well synched.

★★★☆ **Merlot Reserve 01** retasted, offers ripe stewed plums & warm blackcurrants, smells sweet; palate full of soft choc-coated fruit, yet ends cleanly dry. Malo in Fr/Am oak. 14.7% alc.

★★★☆ **Merlot 02** meaty hints to black fruit, vanilla/cedar overlay; tannins opened after bit of ageing. **04** (unrated early sample) shows quite a lot of complexity, wood still apart on palate but well-fruited, balanced.

★★★☆ **MCC** Classically styled brut sparkling from pinot, chardonnay; latest (58/42 ratio) tasted prior to *dosage* (final RS ±5g/ℓ); brioche & baked apple whiffs; lively yeast-toned froth; firm, vibrant limy flavour. NV (02).

> **Mountainside Red** ☺ ★★★ Powered by merlot (44%) & 4 other grapes, without the usual smoothing grain sugar — & all better for it: **04** lively, juicy red-fruit nose, touch mocha; fruit-cordial flourish on palate, finishes nutty, nice & dry.

Pinotage ★★★ 'Fruit-driven for early consumption' say winemakers; **04** striking crimson hues, effusive mulberry nose with estery hint, quaffable, nicely handled fruit. **Shiraz** ★★★ **04** (unrated sample) farmyardy/meaty nose, still with fermentation characters mid-2004; Am oak staves. 14% alc. **Cabernet Sauvignon-Merlot** ★★★ **04** touch more cab than pvs (55%); sample is quietly aromatic, whiffs cigarbox & cassis; youthful blackberry palate; **03** also downbeat on nose; softly plump & sweetish, lacks structure. Both samples. **Cinsaut-Cabernet Sauvignon** ★★★ **04** again a 75/25 alliance, sample offers cherry fruit & tea-leaves; fruity, light/medium body; nice food wine. **Shiraz-Merlot** ★★★ We last tasted **02** 63/37 blend; a big, sweet-spicy mouthful. **Rosé** ★★★ Last was the chenin, pinotage mix from **03**; open & immediately appealing. **Chardonnay Wooded** ★★★ **04** fermented on Fr/Am staves, showing understatedly as vanilla spice; **04** fleeting lemongrass whiffs, clean lemony fruit, soft apple finish. **Chenin Blanc** ★★★ **04** preview sweet melon & beeswax hints; soft quince-toned palate. **Sauvignon Blanc** ★★★ **04** shy marzipan/green nettle character, medium body, lacks acid on finish, tails off quickly. **Sauvignon Blanc Special Selection 04** NEW ★★★ (sample) holds together better, guava fruit, zesty acidity, focused mineral/flint dimension. 5 mths *sur lie*. **Chardonnay-Chenin Blanc** ★★ Casual quaffer; **04** very shy, whiff of fruit salad. 51/49 blend, lightly oaked. **Mountainside White** ★★ Changes to four-way equal blend in **04**, zesty, pear-dropped-toned quaffer, med-bodied. **Port 04** previewed from barrel (unrated), potentially very good; rich, warming aromas (clove, molasses, fennel, choc); will be aged min 2-3 yrs, 2nd fill barriques. 18.5% alc perhaps shade low — would benefit from slightly more spirit grip. — *TM*

Rupert & Rothschild Vignerons

Simonium (see Paarl map) ▪ Est 1997 ▪ 1stB 1998 ▪ Visits only by appt Mon-Fri 9-4.30 ▪ Fee R10 for groups of 10+ ▪ Closed Easter Fri-Sun, Dec 25 & Jan 1 ▪ Owners Rupert family & Baron Benjamin de Rothschild ▪ Winemaker Schalk-Willem Joubert (Jun 1997), with Clive Radloff & Yvonne Schröder (Jun 1997/Sep 2001) ▪ Viticulturist Renier Theron (Oct 2003) ▪ 145 ha (cabs s/f, merlot, shiraz, chard) ▪ 750 tons 33 000 cs 90% red 10% white ▪ ISO 14001 certified; HACCP accreditation in progress ▪ PO Box 412 Franschhoek Valley 7690 ▪ info@rupert-rothschildvignerons.com ▪ www.rupert-rothschildvignerons. com ✆ 874·1648 🖷 874·1802

Forged by two powerful dynasties, the Rupert family (here fronted by scion Johann) and the Rothschilds (represented by Baron Benjamin de R), R&R is a cross-pollination of French and local winemaking (bordelais guru Michel Rolland jets in four times a year to advise). As far as winemaker Schalk-Willem Joubert is concerned, 2004 will be an outstanding vintage, comparable to 1997. Cool nights allowed for slow ripening, matched by an equally slow-paced harvest — three weeks later than usual, with pickers combing the rows again and again to harvest at peak. With a choice of 85 vineyards on a wide variety of sites, new viticulturist Renier Theron has his work cut out, but he has both international and domestic experience to bring to work.

★★★★☆ **Baron Edmond** Pedigreed flagship; more opulent, ageworthy than blend below, though **02** (★★★☆) lacks gravitas of **01**. Same 66/34 cab s/merlot blend; solid ruby, oak nicely paced with light, fleshy feel, uncomplicated plummy, toffee sweetness; touch short, green. 15% alc. **01**, temporarily tightened up, less expressive than yr ago (open well in advance if drinking now). Sound structure, fruit richness for evolution over next 3-7 yrs. Stbosch, Darling, Paarl, Dbnvlle vyds. 80% native yeast-fermented. 19 mths new Fr oak. **99** *Decanter* ★★★★; IWSC gold.

★★★☆ **Classique** Elegant, accessible Bdx-style blend (though includes soupçon pinotage). **02** (★★★) victim of problem cab vintage (53%, merlot/pinotage 41/6). Some garnet development; straightforward fruity sweetness gently oak-brushed (18 mths Fr, some new); best within yr/18 mths. 14.5% alc.

★★★★★ **Baroness Nadine** Grand, complex chardonnay in classic style. **03** just bottled, unsettled but promisingly elegant; skilfully oak-enhanced fresh peach/roast nut character; creamy, rich but not over-heavy; polished length. Likely 4-5 yr maturation. 80% fermented/yr Fr oak, third new. 13.5% alc. Simonsberg, Gr Drknstn, W Bay vyds. **02** first to show slightly fruitier, livelier approach; savoury roast nut, pickled lime complexity, creamy texture.—*AL*

Rustenberg Wines 🍷 ⊙⊙ ♿

Stellenbosch ▪ Est 1682 ▪ 1stB 1892 ▪ Tasting & sales Mon-Fri 9-4.30 Sat 10-1.30 Sat 10-3.30 (Dec/Jan) ▪ Closed Easter Fri, Dec 25, Jan 1 ▪ Farm-style cheeses ▪ Owner Simon Barlow ▪ Winemaker Adi Badenhorst, with Gareth le Grange (Dec 1999/Jan 2003) ▪ Viticulturist Nico Walters (Nov 1999) ▪ 150 ha (cabs s/f, merlot, shiraz, chard, sauvignon) ▪ 900 tons 55 000 cs 70% red 30% white ▪ PO Box 33 Stellenbosch 7599 ▪ wine@rustenberg.co.za ▪ www.rustenberg.co.za ✆ 809·1200 🖷 809·1219

There's a youthful spring in the step of this grande dame for a while, probably largely unnoticed, because there's been little trumpeting their successes. In the latter half of 2004 alone, they garnered an IWSC best chardonnay trophy for the 01 Five Soldiers, and a top rating for the John X Merriman of the same vintage in a *Wine* Bordeaux-style blends evaluation. In the words of owner Simon Barlow: 'While ensuring that Rustenberg wines remain true to our terroir, we're very aware that today's world wine trends are consumer-led.' Tousle-haired, T-shirted Adi Badenhorst produces the goods ('great' cab and 'spectacular' chardonnay in 2004) and the excitement (the first wine from 'fantastic' Rhône white grape roussanne). Modernist moves come also in the form of screwcaps for Brampton reds from 2004, having been introduced on the 2003 whites.

Single Vineyard range

★★★★★ **Peter Barlow** A flagship, all cab, as handsome as its Simonsberg origin. Meticulous focus from grape (multiple prunings; bunches individually tagged at start of each growing season; stringent bunch/berry selection during harvest) to cellar (20 mths Fr barrels, 70% new, egg-white fined, unfiltered). **02**'s bold, strong (15% alc) canvas for ripe blackberry fruit held back from ungainly opulence by fine tannins. FCTWS gold. **01** deep, layered black cherry, red berry & cassis. Rivetting intensity, grand structure. 92 pts *WS*. **99** (★★★★★) among Cape's best, *Decanter* ★★★★★. No **00**: mountain fires singed vyd. Deserves cellaring up to 10 yrs.

★★★★ **Five Soldiers** Five stone pines give this characterful chardonnay its name. **03** not ready mid-2004. **02** has grown into a true beauty: nuanced complexity threads from alluring aromas through to its echoing length. A fine dry white, rather than just another chardonnay. **01** mineral-rich, gravelly palate. 91 pts *WS*. Natural fermentation in Fr oak (90% new), 14 mths, full malo. 14.5% alc.

Regional range

★★★★★ **Stellenbosch John X Merriman** Fine Bdx red, from 28 parcels of fruit, 22 mths Fr oak, 40% new. **02** (★★★★) 52:46 cab/merlot, shot cab f as for others, 15% alc; oozes plump mulberries in overt, ripe structure; **01** (53:42 merlot/cab, 14.5% alc) more meaty, smoked characters, lighter in mouth, 91 pts *WS*. Release of **97** in magnum (80/15 cab/merlot) spurs fascinating retrospective: tobacco, pencil-lead, savoury features in dusty, mineral core, svelte elegance – & moderate 12.5% alc – reward for slow-ripening vintage. Proof of (proper) cellaring's reward.

★★★★ **Stellenbosch Chardonnay** Firm, ripe, assertive, fruitier than above version. Sample **03** shows wood; rich apricot/almond depth in minerally chassis likely to settle into complex ensemble in 1-2 yrs. **02** as confident; muesli flavours, ordered stony grip. 90 pts *WS*. Native yeast ferment/yr Fr oak, 40% new. 14.5% alc.

★★★★★ **Straw Wine** Bought-in chenin (WO Coastal); on beds of straw 6 wks until wizened into raisiny sweetness; long, slow barrel-fermentation. Old-gold **02** revisited; reclusive jasmine/tangerine-scents but explosive depth of flavour in tight acid-balance. ±400g/ℓ sugar, gentle 6.5% alc. 375ml. Release still to be decided.

★★★★ **Brut** NEW MCC returns to range after several yrs. 2/1 chard/pinot. Languid bead, discreet fresh brioche nose, generous mousse heralds firm black-grape texture. Not too tart, most refreshing. For conviviality, celebration. 11.5% alc. NV.

Brampton range

★★★★ **Shiraz-Viognier** ('Shiraz' in pvs ed) Viognier makes peach-pip impact in **03**, albeit mere 3% of blend. Savoury, milled pepper infusion afforded juicy tang with choc sheen in late, perfumed rush. 15 mths oak, 30% Am. 14% alc.

★★★★ **Old Vines Red** Familiar wild heather stamp of 1970s, 80s Rustenbergs with next **03** (sample) blend cab, merlot, splash shiraz: spicy, dark-choc fullness to mocha/coffee tones, more accessible than sinuous, comparatively rustic **02**, which included carignan, mourvèdre, malbec. 17 mths Fr oak, 15% new.

★★★★ **Chardonnay Unwooded** fruit purity supported by lees of pvs yr's Stbosch Chardonnay. **04** (★★★) lime/pine, consistent tail. 14% alc. Less complex than pvs.

★★★★ **Viognier** Crammed with scented fruits, boosted by oak: proves jaded adage that wine offers constant variety. **03** as noisy as pvs: jasmine perfume jostles with orange blossom, tangerine twists; turbo ripeness parried by wood. 14.5% alc.

★★★★ **QF** Weighty NLH-style. Intermittent appearance, when nature affords good botrytis. Lasted tasted **QF2** (**00**), FCTWS trophy, from sauvignon; original **QF1** (**97**) from chardonnay. **QF3** (pvs ed) not released, rerouted to Natural Sweet below.

★★★★ **Natural Sweet** NEW Sumptuous alternative when botrytis insufficient for QF. NV (**01**) copper-toned colour a warm up to juicy apricot, fleshy peach, honeycomb. Moreish. Ex-sauvignon, natural fermentation in oak, 190g/ℓ sugar, 13.5% alc.

Sauvignon Blanc ★★★ Tank sample **04** generously overt tropical basket: salad of passionfruit, litchi, & gooseberry, amplified with asparagus, ordered by classic flint grip. Pvs 'Silver Capsule' one-off **02** (★★★★) from single Hldrberg vyd. **Port** ★★★ NV Well fortified, drier style from melange Portuguese varieties. Evokes images of smoking jackets, both cigar leaf and paisley. Ends touch hard in youth. Discontinued: **Cabernet Sauvignon-Merlot**. – *DS*

Rust en Vrede Estate

Stellenbosch ▪ Est 1694 ▪ 1stB 1981 ▪ Tasting & sales Mon-Fri 9-5 Sat: 9-4 Oct-Apr; 9-3 May-Sep; public holidays 9-4 ▪ Closed Easter Fri/Sat, Dec 16/25, Jan 1 ▪ Tours during tasting hours ▪ Gifts ▪ Walks ▪ Nature conservancy ▪ Owner Engelbrecht Trust ▪ Winemakers Louis Strydom, with Ettienne Malan (1998/2002) ▪ Viticulturist Wessel Combrink (Jun 1998) ▪ 50 ha (cab, merlot, shiraz) ▪ ±300 tons 15 000 cs own label 100% red ▪ PO Box 473

Stellenbosch 7599 ▪ info@rustenvrede.com ▪ www.rustenvrede.com © *881·3881* ✉ *881·3000*

Away from the loud media headlines of family imbroglios, the real business continues serenely. The vision, winemaker Louis Strydom declares, remains to unite the estate's extraordinary vinous assets into a single, superlative red blend. The process leading up to that point now looks to be more protracted than originally envisaged, however. 'R&V's terroir has a very strong personality', Strydom says. 'We're probably about four years away from our one Estate Wine.' If, in parsing that statement, admirers of this internationally acclaimed property conclude that the maturing (but youthful) vines are still too feisty to meld into an harmonious *grand vin*, we're almost certain the reaction would be: Who cares? We love the wines the way they are. The critics (including ourselves) do too. For the fourth consecutive year, R&V made the Top 100 Wines of the World list compiled by US *Wine Spectator*, the 00 vintage of the Estate Wine meriting 92 points (out of 100), among the highest for an SA wine. Which should encourage Jean Engelbrecht to continue 'pursuing wines that are internationally relevant to the modern palate'.

★★★★★ **Estate Wine** Patience required for full splendours of latest **01**; richness, grandeur still sheathed in fine, dense tannin. Bit more powerful, demonstrative than pvs, but seamless cab/shiraz/merlot alliance (53/35/12), overall balance, distinction of this acclaimed *grand vin* remains. **00** *Wine* ★★★★★; 92 pts WS; FCTWS 2003 trophy. Hallmark understatement, solid structure; fresh, pure. Regularly 20 mths new Fr/Am oak. ±14% alc. These need ± 8-10 yrs. **99** (★★★★★) lighter. Also in magnum.

★★★★★ **Shiraz** Great finesse, subtlety in **01**. Understated yet insistent fresh spice, smoked meat purity; silky but substantial, authoritatively structured; still tight, should blossom over 3-6 yrs. Effortlessly absorbs 15 mths new Fr/Am oak. 14% alc. **00** first to benefit from new-clone input. Light-textured, cool, refined. Fr/Am oak, 20% new. 90 pts WS, VDG.

★★★★ **Cabernet Sauvignon** Benefits of good vintage, increased clean vine material evident in **01**. Compact, austere yet with ripeness in body (14% alc); supple fruit, in usual understated mode. 14% alc. 15 mths new Fr oak. **00** (★★★☆) lighter, less complex, though firmly structured. 13.3% alc. 90 pts WS; Concours Mondial gold.

★★★★ **Merlot** Increased sophistication, textured elegance in recent vintages. Preview **03** poised ripe/fresh contrast; sophisticated dark choc/plum concentration in velvet mouthfeel. Extra class, polish from yr in new Fr oak. Possible ★★★★★. **02** polished, ripe; some flesh, contrasting bright red plum tension. 14% alc.—AL

▪ *Rusthof* see Mooiuitsig

Rusticus

Robertson ▪ Est 2001 ▪ 1stB 2002 ▪ Tasting & sales Tue-Fri 9-4 Sat 10-2 ▪ Closed Easter Fri & Dec 25 ▪ Tours on request ▪ BYO picnic ▪ Self-catering cottages & guest houses ▪ Tourgroups ▪ Gifts ▪ Conferencing ▪ Walks/hikes ▪ Conservation area ▪ 4x4 trail ▪ Mountain biking ▪ Owner/ winemaker/viticulturist Pat Busch, with Stephan Busch ▪ 20 ha (merlot, pinot, pinotage, chenin) ▪ 200 tons 1 300 cs own label ▪ PO Box 579 Robertson 6705 ▪ patbusch@intekom.co.za ▪ www.patbusch.co.za ©/✉ **(023) 626·2033**

Journey back to nature and back in time, to rural Klaas Voogds, home of Rusticus wines. Made in a working museum featuring an antique wooden press, brightly painted refurbished pumps and open cement kuipe, the grapes harvested from Pat Busch's 20ha of hillside vineyards. Rusticus — 'Of the Land' — aptly describes this down to earth and jovial farmer/winemaker, assisted by son Stephen and spouse Karin ('Behind every successful man is a tired wife'). Their 2 000ha property, on which they've rusticated since 1979, offers the visitor not just wine but accommodation, conference facilities, and 4x4 and mountain bike trails. On the wild side, guests can also take a walk or game drive in the Pat Busch Private Nature & Game Reserves.

Cabernet Sauvignon ★★★☆ Modern blockbuster, though made with antiques. Port-like concentration on **02**, intense blackcurrant aromas, flavours masking the vast 16% alc.

Swashbuckling but well polished. Yr older wood. All these WO Klaas Voogds. **Pinot Noir** ★★★ **03**'s spicy cherry aromas lead to marzipan mid-palate, with intense berry character. Unobtrusive older oak only (like all these reds). 14+% alc. **Pinotage** ★★★ **03**'s varietally typical strawberry/banana whiffs lead to palate with dense tannins, food-friendly grip. 15.5% alc. **Merlot** ★★★ Super-ripe **03**, massively fruited, intense plum character, opulent palate dominated by 15.5% alc. **Ruby Cabernet** ★★ Robust **02** with gamey whiffs, chunky palate, 14.3% alc. **Shiraz** ★ **02** porty notes, jammy, unrefined. — MF

Sable View

This Distell export range, launched in 1990, now discontinued.

Sadie Family

Malmesbury (see Swartland map) ▪ Est 1999 ▪ 1stB 2000 ▪ Tasting & sales by appt ▪ Owners Sadie family ▪ Winemakers/viticulturists Eben & Niko Sadie ▪ 7 ha (grenache, mourvèdre, shiraz) ▪ 650 cs 90% red 10% white ▪ PO Box 1019 Malmesbury 7299 ▪ sadiefamily@mail.com © 869·8349 ⌨ 869·8101

Peripatetic Eben Sadie is back in this year's guide's five-star rankings with his 2002 Columella (the maiden 2000 conquered in 2003). Having hit the headlines as Spice Route's talented young maverick, Sadie left after five vintages, setting up shop in a humble, whitewashed Perdeberg bodega. His love affair with the warm Swartland led him to sunbaked Priorat in Spain, where he has another humble, stone bodega to vinify his Dits del Terra grenache/carignan blend from 4ha of 'young' vines (60-80 years!). Without 'letting things slip' here, Sadie is now 'often' in Spain. And a new disciple of biodynamic winegrowing. 'Anything less is just McDonalds. With biodynamic, it's possible to take winemaking to the next level. Watch me, I'm going to blow the roof right off.'

★★★★★ **Columella** These sophisticated, modern expressions of the Swtlnd grown & made with great (& expensive) attention to detail since maiden **00**. **01** (★★★★☆), with 14% mourvèdre, had lovely, full-bodied, confidently balanced structure, persistent flavours — & refined despite the 14.8% alc. **02** similarly constituted & built, but more obvious New World style, with sweet ripeness, roasted warmth. Superbly smooth tannins a savoury, sensuous delight. Native-yeast fermentation in open wood; 2 yrs Fr oak, ± 70% new. Unfined, unfiltered. These should mature many yrs.

★★★★☆ **Palladius** Swartland blend of 40% chenin, equal parts viognier, chardonnay, grenache blanc in youthful **02** — where aromatic viognier now in peachy ascendant. Mouthwatering fresh flavours, with depth & power (heady 15% alc) carried on satin-textured intensity. Long finish. 18 mths Fr oak, 30% new. With 3.8g/ℓ sugar, beneficially drier than also-splendid maiden **01**. Excellent balance means probable ageability, but near-irresistible now (don't over-chill!). Unfined/filtered. — TJ

▪ *Safeway* see Daschbosch
Safiki see Goudini

Sanctum Wines

Stellenbosch Est/1stB 2002 ▪ Closed to public ▪ Owners Mike & Alice Dobrovic ▪ Winemaker Mike Dobrovic ▪ 3.2 tons 240 cs 100% red ▪ PO Box 11 Koelenhof 7605 ▪ dobrovic@mweb.co.za © 865·2483/082·882·2488

For this own-wine, Mulderbosch founding winemaker Mike Dobrovic returns to his first love, red wine. It's a family project, he says, their most ambitious thus far. The name means 'one's private place', and the front-label has an appropriately intimate, almost spiritual air. It shows a wooden tabernacle door and a quartet of angels — one of the treasures (circa 1750) which unexpectedly came with a Johannesburg house they bought in the 1970s. 'To make wine of great character and quality,' is the goal. 'Above all to have fun doing it and maintain a respect for life.'

★★★★ **Shiraz** NEW Initial silkiness on **02** suggests delicate style. Full textural/flavour spectrum currently restrained by grainy tannins, though hints of spice, smoked meat with toasty oak suggest future complexity. May rate higher with another yr. From young Stanford, Stbosch vyds. 18 mths new Fr oak. 14% alc. — *AL*

Sandown Bay see Newton Johnson
Sandy River see Zandvliet

Saronsberg

Tulbagh ▪ Est 2002 ▪ 1stB 2004 ▪ Tasting & sales Mon-Fri 8-5 Sat 9-1 ▪ Closed Easter Fri-Mon, Dec 25/26 & Jan 1 ▪ Tours by appt ▪ Owner Saronsberg Cellar (Pty) Ltd ▪ Winemaker/viticulturist Dewaldt Heyns (Oct 2003) ▪ 25 ha (cab, malbec, merlot, mourvèdre, petit v, shiraz, viognier, chard, sauvignon) ▪ 65% red 35% white ▪ PO Box 361 Tulbagh 6820 ▪ info@saronsberg.com ▪ www.saronsberg.com ✆ (023) 230·0707 📠 (023) 230·0709

A month after publicity-shy Pretoria businessman Nick van Huyssteen bought fruit farms Waveren and Saronsberg (historically part of Twee Jonge Gezellen) in 2002, fire devastated the orchards and vines. From the ashes has risen a state-of-the-art winery. Starting with a clean slate, ex-Avondale winemaker/viticulturist Dewaldt Heyns is relishing his 'independence and hard work'. By year-end, he'll have planted 40ha of individually primed and managed blocks, each just 1ha in size. This panoply of sites will provide the components for a Rhône- and a Bordeaux-style blend, and a varietal Shiraz due out in next year. The current releases are from selected Tulbagh, Malmesbury and Darling vineyards.

★★★★ **Sauvignon Blanc 04** maiden from Stbosch & Mbury fruit. Predominantly herbaceous style, nuances of passion- & tropical fruits also in the mix. Racy acidity with 'wet pebble' minerality. Deserves intellectual consideration, not mindless quaffing.
Red trio (from 2004 vintage, for 2006 release) too young to rate, but showing promise with pure fruit, clever oaking, precise balance. '**Bordeaux Blend**' dominated by cab/merlot, with petit v, drop malbec. **Epicentre** (Area has earthquake history!) Lush shiraz (63%) as backbone, with mourvèdre (30%) & viognier. **Shiraz** spicy & black as Hades, with a rim of cerise the only light. — *CvZ*

Savanha

1stB 1997 ▪ Tasting, sales & tours at Spier ▪ Owner Winecorp ▪ Winemakers/viticulturists: see Winecorp ▪ 300 ha ▪ 25 000 cs 65% red 35% white ▪ PO Box 99 Lynedoch 7600 ▪ winecorp@iafrica.com ▪ www.winecorp.co.za ✆ 881·3690 📠 881·3699

This Winecorp-owned label features fruit grown by contracted farmers in the Darling, West Coast & Paarl areas, vinified at the Spier cellar outside Stellenbosch. Bordeaux winemaker Alain Moueix is the advisor for the Naledi and Sejana labels. The Sulanga wines ('langa' means 'sun' in Sotho) are for export. See also Winecorp.

★★★★ **Naledi Cabernet Sauvignon** Aim here, with Merlot below, super-league quality within a classical context. Last tasted was **01**, built for longer haul.
★★★★ **Sejana Merlot** Last was complex & individual **01**.

Premium range

★★★★ **Merlot** Sophisticated **02** has rich complex depths. Sleek muscular frame with supple ripe tannins, already approachable, but will reward 4-5 yrs cellaring; lots more to give. 11 mths small Fr, third new. 14.5% alc. **01** was also deep, opulent, complex with potential for 5+ yrs. Combo Coastal, Dbnville fruit.
Cabernet Sauvignon ★★★★ Stylish **02** step up; better balanced, more accessible than pvs. Well-spiced dried meat, roasted fennel, on ripe black plum base. Lithe structure, poised tannins, yet with 3-4 yr development potential. Oak as above. 14.2% alc. **Shiraz** ★★★★ Raises the bar in **02**: layered complexity, creamy spice, dark-fruited richness, woodsmoke, touch scrub, within sleekly muscular structure. Ripe, smooth tannins, yet 3-4 yr good future ahead. Oak as above. 14.8% alc. **Sauvignon Blanc** ★★★★ Zinging

freshness characterises **04** (sample), nettles, kiwi fruit, green figs etc. Bone dry, but heaps of interest, long finish. Perfect for hot summer's day, or with food. 13% alc. **03** VDG.

Sulanga range

For export, all WO W-Cape. **Cabernet Sauvignon** ★★★ **03** back to usual style after standout pvs. Light-textured & -toned: wild berries/sour cherries with gentle herbaceous hints, smoky spice. Easy, accessible, not for ageing. 8 mths older oak. 13.3% alc. **Merlot** ★★★ Cherry-choc, slightly herbaceous tones in **02**; medium-weight, chewy dry tannins add stiffening. Will keep few yrs, but designed for earlier drinking. Portion Fr barrel matured. 13.9% alc. **Shiraz** ★★★ **03** shows varietal tipicity: whiffs white pepper, fynbos to brambleberry ripeness. Despite only portion oaked, finishes firm & food-compatibly dr. Will improve with few yrs ageing. 14.7% alc. **Chardonnay** ★★★ Fragrant floral, peach intro to **03**, lightly oaked, which doesn't interfere with freshness, approachability. — CR

Savisa see African Terroir

Saxenburg

Stellenbosch ▪ Est 1693 ▪ 1stB 1990 ▪ Tasting & sales Mon-Fri 9-5 Sat 9-4 Sun 10-4 (closed Sun-Tue in winter) Public holidays 10-4 (closed Easter Fri, Dec 25 & Jan 1) ▪ Fee R3-6 ▪ Guinea Fowl Restaurant & 'Lapa' (see Eat-out section) ▪ Farm produce ▪ Conferencing ▪ Miniature game park ▪ Owners Adrian & Birgit Bührer ▪ Winemaker Nico van der Merwe (Nov 1990), with Marius Prins (Dec 2003) ▪ Viticulturist Len Coetzee (Jun 2001) ▪ 85 ha (cab, merlot, pinotage, shiraz, chard, chenin, sauvignon) ▪ 440 tons 50 000 cs 80% red 20% white ▪ Export brand: Bosman's Hill ▪ PO Box 171 Kuils River 7580 ▪ info@saxenburg.com ▪ www.saxenburg. com ✆ 903·6113 🖷 903·3129

A whoop of joy from Nico van der Merwe, celebrating his 15th year as winemaker here: *'Boetie kom huis toe!'* (Little brother's coming home.) He's double-harvested every year since 1995, at the French and Stellenbosch farms owned by Adrian and Birgit Bührer, but now he's giving up that demanding lifestyle and looking forward to get closer to the Saxenburg product, assisted by newcomer Marius Prins (Koos Thiart having departed for WestCorp). The flagship Saxenburg Shiraz Select is now made entirely from home-farm grapes. 'We are now self-supplied and, in fact, have 30% more grapes than needed, so we can be very selective', says NvdM. In future, the only buying-in will be when and if required for blends. Coincidentally, a new red blend is poised for launch. Also on the cards are a cellar upgrade, vineyard replanting and boosted expenditure on marketing. And more of the winners the market has come to expect — the winemaker is lyrical about the 2004 vintage's full-bodied reds, and the 'nice ripe flavours' of the sauvignon.

★★★★★ **Saxenburg Shiraz Select** Pricey showpiece deserving 7-10 yrs' bottle-ageing; **01** cohesive blend of refined fruit & fragrant oak (one third Am), firmly but elegantly bound with perfectly ripe tannins. Class of **00** apparent in focused intensity; resonating mix dark fruits, new oak; fluid texture tensioned by sweet tannins. No **99**. New oak, two-thirds Am (some sourced from Spain), remainder Fr. 14.5% alc. Only ±200 cs. At R420 ex-cellar, approaching Adrian B's target R500/btl price tag.

Private Collection range

★★★★ **Cabernet Sauvignon** Elegant & generous style; **01** first from 100% Sxnbrg fruit (pvsly 50% bought in); cornucopia of cassis, red berries marshalled by deliciously soft tannins, upholstered finish. Mid-2004, immensely stylish, ready. **00** (★★★★★) more compact, refined; sleek feel of new-clone fruit. **99** lighter, pliable texture. Yr Fr oak, 60% new. 14% alc. Worth cellaring 5-7 yrs.

★★★★ **Merlot 01** quieter than pvs, though still generously coloured/fruited; juicy mouthful mulberry/choc fruits unimpeded by yielding tannins. Mid-2004, ready to drink. Extracted **00** showed opulent vinosity firmed by fresh mineral core. Included splash cab. Yr Fr casks, 40% new.

★★★★ **Pinotage** 'Did everything to avoid bitterness' avows NvdM. Charming **01** tingles with fresh raspberry tones; supportive tannins. Mid-2004 almost ready. Contrasts with **00**, all savoury meats & truffles. Yr oak, 60/40 Am/Fr, 25% new. 14% alc.

★★★★★ **Shiraz** Long one of the farm's best advertisements, consistently excellent since maiden **91** VDG; recent vintages show more richness, power. **01** complex composition 'cool' slightly minty red fruit lifted by palate spice, beautifully judged ripe tannins. On mid-2004 showing, needs another ±yr. **00** bigger, yet remained supple. 100% new clones, 90% Sxnbrg grapes, rest sourced elsewhere in Kuils River. 50/50 Fr/Am oak, third new. 14% alc.

★★★★ **Chardonnay** No compromising in well oaked, boldly flavoured **03**. Fat, rich ripe peach tone with butterscotch, soft acidity enhanced by 100% malo. Fine concentration seen in lengthy finish. 14 mths Fr oak, 50% new. 14% alc. **02** focused & intense lemon/lime tones, sumptuous oak, all creamily poised.

★★★★ **Sauvignon Blanc** Reflects gentler, ripe vintage in **04**, less assertive, but more friendly, welcoming. Delicate gooseberry, some fresh-mown grass, touch lime; curvaceous with charming tropical tones. 13.8% alc. **03** full, bluegum whiff to fruit, touch off scintillating, tangy **02**.

Le Phantom Brut Cap Classique ★★★ NV (96) sold out, follow-up vintage not available mid-2004. **Natural Sweet Le Rêve de Saxenbourg** ★★★ NV non-botrytised dessert, retiring 50/50 sauvignon/chenin partnership, soft, light textured. 375ml.

Guinea Fowl range

★★★★ **Guinea Fowl** 'The workhorse for the future', says NvdM, 'made to enjoy young or to mature'. Bright mulberry fruit in **03** (sample) ripe & dark-berried, hint mulberry leaf mirrored in fresh acidity. Nicely rounded, pleasing friendly style with minimal tannins, lightly oaked. Blend third each shiraz, cab, merlot.

Cabernet Sauvignon ★★★ **00** accessible fruit, dusty tannins, tangy. Last vintages, to be discontinued: **Merlot 00** ★★★★ Fine-textured, spicy, savoury, ready. **Pinotage** ★★★ **00** rich, black cherry flavours with Fr new-oak trim. Ready, will go 2-3 yrs.

Selection Famille

★★★★ **Gwendolyn** ✓ First in blended range named after Bührers' children. 60/40 shiraz/cab in **01**; warm spice, choc notes in med-bodied mouthful, softly gathered by tannins. Retasted mid-2004, poised & elegant, ready. **00** reflection of hot yr; robust blackberry compote, sturdier palate. Yr Fr/Am oak, none new. 13.5% alc.

★★★★ **Manuel** ✓ Comfortable cab/merlot (65/35) blend, partly from Dbnville; notch-up **00** (★★★★) shows dusty layers of minty cassis, good dry tannins. Ready mid-2004. Yr seasoned Fr oak. 13.5% alc.

Completing this range are **Apollonia 00** white blend featuring chardonnay, viognier, roussanne, **Fiona 00** cabs s/f, merlot, syrah, grenache & **Adrianus 99** syrah/grenache, all from Bührers' Ch Capion in France (& so untasted).

Concept range

Grand Vin Rouge ☺ ★★★ Warming fruity quaffer, spicy savoury bite of southern France. 50/50 Capion/Sxnbrg union, includes 8 red varieties with dab white. **Grand Vin Blanc** ☺ ★★★ Zingy lemon-tinged fruit, minerally twist to finish. Latest 60/40 Saxenburg chenin, Ch Capion chardonnay. Both NV. — IvH

Scali

Paarl ▪ Est/1st 1999 ▪ Visits by appt ▪ Olive oil ▪ Guest accommodation ▪ Owners/winemakers Willie & Tania de Waal ▪ Viticulturist Willie de Waal ▪ 70 ha (cab, merlot, pinotage, shiraz, chardonnay, chenin, sauvignon, viognier) 910 cs 100% red ▪ PO Box 7143 Noorder-Paarl 7623 ▪ info@scali.co.za ▪ www.scali.co.za ⓒ 869·8340 ▤ 869·8383

'We have to wow the wine world with ever improving quality throughout our industry. Consumers have to feel they're getting much better wine than they're paying for', say Willie and Tania de Waal, infectiously enthusiastic vignerons in Agter Paarl and, for our money, shoo-ins (should such positions ever come into being) for SA wine ambassadors at large. Their own vintning operation is tiny: just 900 cases, all red, vinified on-site from grapes cherry-picked from their 66 producing hectares. Mad about syrah and the Rhône, they're combining both in their latest project, by dense-planting new shiraz vineyards (to a claustrophobic 7 250 vines/ha), and training the plants individually – 'à la Côte Rôtie'.

★★★☆ **Pinotage 02** Unalloyedly pleasant side of the grape: fruity, well structured & balanced. 12 mths oak, half new, 90% Fr, 10% Am for coconuts & spice, 50% new. 14.5% alc gives more weight than on refined, fine-tannined **01**.

★★★☆ **Syrah 02** bursting with red fruit & spice; obviously deft use of wood (2 yrs Fr, 50% new), but too 'hot' at 15% alc. Clumsier than fine-textured **01** with roast nuts/dark spice infusion for elegant palate. – *NP*

Scarborough see Cape Point Vineyards

Schalkenbosch Wines

Tulbagh ▪ Est 1792 ▪ 1stB 2002 ▪ Tasting & sales daily 9.30-4.30 ▪ Closed Dec 25/26 & Jan 1 ▪ Tours, meals & accommodation (B&B or self-catering) by appt ▪ Tourgroups ▪ Walks ▪ Conservation area ▪ Mountain biking ▪ Owner Platinum Mile Investments ▪ Winemaker Josef Krammer (Nov 2002) ▪ Viti consultants Johan Wiese & Andrew Teubes ▪ 35 ha (cab s/f, merlot, mourvèdre, petit v, shiraz, chard, sauvignon, viognier) ▪ 100 tons 7 500 cs 80% red 20% white ▪ PO Box 95 Tulbagh 6820 ▪ info@schalkenbosch.co.za ▪ www.schalkenbosch.co.za © (023) 230·0422 ✆ (023) 230·0422

Sold Out. Always a satisfying feeling, all the more so when it happened their first year. Like so many others, farm manager Peter Jackson says the 2004 harvest was difficult due to uneven ripening, but the wines are now showing 'strong promise, with good fruit and body'. Having run out of stock once, Jackson plans to expand, procuring equipment for up to 350 tons. The range has been expanded and stratified: Ibis, the entry level, successfully launched into the export market last year; Edenhof, 'early-release, easily-accessible reds'; and Schalkenbosch, their signature 'old-world classic' reds.

Edenhof range

★★★☆ **Cabernet Sauvignon** 🆕 Elegant, balanced **02** ex-Stbosch fruit; leafy cassis aromas, soft lightish mid-palate & sweet finish; fine tannins. Yr older oak. 13.5% alc. Sample **03** less promising, with intense oak dominant; slightly volatile.

Merlot 🆕 **02** not tasted. **Shiraz** 🆕 ★★☆ Attractive nose on **02** – like light rosé colour, more likely on pinot! Smooth palate, pleasant strawberry fruit. **Cabernet Sauvignon-Merlot** 🆕 ★★ Vegetal nose on **02**; thin & light, with some medicinal flavours. **Glen Rosa** ★★ (As with Sauvignon below, **03**; only tasted last ed as sample; **04**s not tasted.) Appealingly rustic red, savoury quintet of Tbgh grapes. **Rosé** migrates to Ibis range below. **Sauvignon Blanc** ★★★ Light & lively, packed with tropical fruit. **Blanc de Blanc** ★★★ Herbaceous whiffs & crisp honeysuckle notes on **03**; easy drinkability enhanced by low 12% alc. Both ranges WO W-Cape.

Ibis range 🆕

Dry Red ★★★ Cinsaut (55%) dominates unwooded **03** blend, with ruby cab & cabs s & f adding to structure. Mouthfilling & richly textured, lingering finish. 14.2% alc. **Rosé** ★★★☆ ✓ **03** delicious, readily accessible blend chenin, sauvignon, shiraz. Dry but not tart, ample texture & length. Moderate 12.7% alc helps make for lovely lunchtime drinking. **Dry White** ★★★ **03** 60/40 chenin/chardonnay blend, with former most evident in attractively fresh fruit salad aromas. Generous mid-palate, crisp dry finish; 13% alc. – *MF/NP*

Scholtzenhof see Ken Forrester
Secluded Valley see Tulbagh Winery

Sedgwick's Old Brown Sherry

The original SA 'old brown' (launched 1886), and still a good warming drop. By Distell. Actually a blend muscat jerepiko & dry sherry; latest (NV) bottling ★★★ rich coffee & molasses aromas; prune hints, well-defined clean finish. 16.8% alc. WO W-Cape. — *CR*

Seidelberg Estate

Paarl ▪ Est 1692 ▪ 1stB 1989 ▪ Tasting & sales Mon-Fri 9-6 Sat/Sun & public holidays 10-6 ▪ Fee R10 ▪ Closed Dec 25 ▪ Tours daily (by appt for groups of 5+) ▪ De Leuwen Jagt Restaurant (see Eat-out section) ▪ Play area for children ▪ Farm produce ▪ Conferences/functions ▪ Tourgroups ▪ Gifts ▪ Walks ▪ Hiking trail ▪ Conservation area ▪ Owner Roland Seidel ▪ Winemaker Cerina de Jongh (Jun 2002) ▪ Viticulturist Conré Groenewald (Nov 1999) ▪ 110 ha (cabs s/f, merlot, pinotage, shiraz, chard, chenin, sauvignon, viognier) ▪ ±500 tons ▪ 40 000 cs 70% red 20% white 10% rosé ▪ PO Box 505 Suider-Paarl 7624 ▪ info@ seidelberg.co.za ▪ www.seidelberg.co.za © 863·5200 ☐ 863·3797

'Long term, wine's not a fashion business,' marketing manager Guy Kedian points out. So the philosophy on Roland Seidel's estate is to resist the temptation to cater to mass market tastes and please instead those consumers who want more than 'recipe wines full of up-front fruit with very little else'. That's the current SA formula, opines Kedian, and if it continues 'it won't be long before we're asking "Do you want fries with that?"' Vintage 2004 was generally good, with the viognier doing the team proud and yielding 'a gutsy wine'. In the cellar, there was much more use of open fermentation on the reds. The estate's now even more congenial — apart from boasting a popular restaurant, it has a glass-blowing studio and gallery, an art exhibition and an air-conditioned tasting room.

Roland's Reserve range

★★★★ **Cabernet Sauvignon** Muscular but shapely wine, intimidating; all hallmarks present in latest **02**: blackcurrant whiffs, firm dry tannins, cassis flavours; big alc (15%) not out of place.

★★★★ **Merlot** ✓ Flashy, broad-shouldered style of **99**, **00**, toned down in pvs **01**, with grainy tannins needing time, and now in **02** (★★★★) introverted, in line with vintage; thatchy whiffs & dried-fruit tone on leaner but still supple palate. These Yr-14 mths Fr oak, none new; ±14.5% alc.

★★★★ **Syrah** Showy, extracted **02** has peppery Karoo bush aromas; huge choc/mocha palate with hint of dark plums. 15% alc consistent with 'overripe' style which has its adherents. **01** was more elegant/drinkable than Seidelberg version of same vintage. 13.5% alc. Yr-14 mths oak, ±30% Am.

★★★★ **Pinotage** Last tasted was **01**, pleasantly youthful, 3-4 yrs development potential.

Seidelberg range

★★★★ **Un Deux Trois** ✓ Still the pick of this bunch; blend of equal portions cabs s/f, merlot, 8-12 mths Fr staves, expertly applied. **01** shows laudable elegance, harmony; expensive cigarbox tone (& some 'lowly' farmyard sniffs too). Fairly genteel alc (13.6%). **00** developed attractively; last ed showed classy ripe fruit, dry finish.

> **Rosé** ☺ ★★★ Semi-dry blush from red muscadel. **04** refreshing & supple with some red-wine structure/heft; try with Parma ham & melon. **Chenin Blanc** ☺ ★★★ Off oldest producing vyd on estate; **04** lightish, well flavoured with quirky herbal tone, clean melon acidity. For early enjoyment.

Cabernet Sauvignon ★★★☆ **02** immediately convinces with rich colour, refined claret-like aroma; palate has full cassis/tobacco flavour; savoury dry finish. High 14.4% alc does not detract. **Merlot** ★★★ **02** holding up. Aromas evoke cream on a strawberry-jam scone; fairly elegant, slightly grainy finish. Full-bodied (14% alc). **Pinotage** ★★★☆ **03** SAYWS champion of 2003; strapping, concentrated, unsubtle (15% alc); fruit-sweet palate ends with dry tobacco twist. Fr/Am staves. **Shiraz** ★★★☆ Last tasted was **02**, a wine on steroids. **Cabernet Sauvignon-Merlot** ★★★★ Unwooded **02** shy on nose; similar to Cab but fractionally fleshier, livelier, fruitier. **Chardonnay** ★★★ Fermented/aged 4 mths on staves. 14.2% alc. **03** bold butterscotch & toast nose; baked apple palate; quite a blowsy number. **Sauvignon Blanc** ★★★ Juicy, easy-drinking **04** offers talcum whiffs, minerally dry finish, undaunting 12.8% alc. **Viognier 04** (sample) big improvement on pvs; refined peachy/terpene bouquet; full green melon/passionfruit flavour; potentially ★★★★. 14% alc. Partly bunch-pressed; 30% 2nd fill Fr oak.

De Leuwen Jagt range

Chardonnay Unwooded ☺ ★★★ Juicy, medium-bodied **04** shy on nose yet ebullient on palate; apples & pears zested with clean acidity. **Nuance** ☺ ★★★ **04** fragrant off-dry tipple from muscadel & chenin. **04** sweet talcum powder nose, hints lime & rhu-barb on finish. **Stein** ☺ ★★ Light (12.3% alc), charming semi-sweet; white muscadel gives the delicate rose-petal fragrance, crouchen the creamy fruit salad flavours.

Cabernet Sauvignon ★★★ **02** somewhat muted (a vintage dip?), some cassis character & sweet-sour palate. Unwooded, as are all reds in range. **Merlot** ★★★ **03** with this wine's signature leafy character on nose; red berries & currants on lively palate; moderate 13% alc. Appealing food wine. **Pinotage** ★★★ Real bottled sunshine in **03**; opaque plum col-our; banana ice-cream aroma; big, fat, ripe & sweet (6.8g/ℓ sugar). 13.8% alc. Swtlnd fruit, as is... **Shiraz** ★★★ **01** no great shakes, just honest earthy/fynbos flavour with pep-pery touch to savoury finish. 14.2% alc. **Cabernet Franc-Merlot** ★★★ Exuberant 50/50 partnership, very drinkable. **03** ripe, plummy, full bodied & soft. **Leuwenrood** ★★★ Cab/merlot blend; **02** an amiable rustic; forest floor hint; full prune & choc flavours. 14.5% alc. **Rosé** NEW ★★★ Quaffable semi-dry **03** from own cab, Bnvale white muscadel; delightful Turkish Delight colour/aroma; dried fruit palate. **Leuwenblanc** ★★ From chenin. **04** plain soft dry white with shy candyfloss whiffs. **Red Muscadel** ★★★★ √ Sophisticated NV for-tified dessert with developed tawny colour; sweet 'floor polish' aroma; quite dry for style (102g/ℓ). Unusual. All above NE; WO Paarl, W-Cape, Coastal.– *TM*

Sejana see Savanha
Semaya see Jonkheer

Sentinel Vineyards

Stellenbosch ▪ 1stB 1995 ▪ Tasting & sales Mon-Fri 9-4.30 Sat 9-2.30 Sun 10-2 Public holi-days 9-4.30 ▪ Fee R5 ▪ Closed Easter Fri, Dec 25 & Jan 1 ▪ Light meals Mon-Fri 10-4 Sat/Sun 9.30-4, or BYO picnic ▪ Facilities for children ▪ Conferencing ▪ Display of military artefacts ▪ Owners Rob Coppoolse, Walter Finlayson & Viv Grater ▪ Winemakers Adele Dunbar & Danielle du Toit (Aug 1998/Apr 2002) ▪ Viti consultant Johan Pienaar (2001) ▪ 23 ha ▪ 20 000 cs 75% red 25% white ▪ ISO 9001:2000, HACCP & BRC certified ▪ PO Box 4028 Old Oak 7537 ▪ wine@sentinel.co.za ▪ www.cfwines.co.za © **982·6175** ☎ 982·6296

Not many people can say 'We'll meet you at the castle'. These wine-partners can, and they'd be referring to the crenellated building perched on a hill outside Stellenbosch, home of the newly repackaged Sentinel range. A tasting facility was opened here recently, and among the attractions are 20 antique muzzle-loading cannons ('to keep any bad wine spirits away'). It's the largest and most diverse private collection in Africa. Each gun has a nickname and a fascinating history (there's a retired noonday gun and even one from a pirate ship). Cannon expert Gerry de Vries is called upon for regular and dramatic firings (the neighbours may just need earplugs for Sentinel's 10th anniversary next year). The surrounding vineyards are being replanted, and existing chardonnay is being joined by sauvignon, merlot and shiraz. The purpose is to make site-specific wines, all under the watchful eye of cellarmaster Walter Finlayson and his son-in-law, Swiss winemaker Jean-Claude Martin, who was joining the team as we went to press.

★★★★ **Shiraz** New release **03** in established style of spicy, savoury fruit, wisp of cigar smoke; broad expansive flavours – black plum, roast beef & dark choc richness, oak completely submerged. 10 mths Am oak barriques. Firm, yet approachable on release with potential to grow. **02** (★★★★★) unusually intense, piquant & velvet-textured; fermented/aged Fr oak, yr.

★★★★ **Pinotage** ✓ No longer labelled 'Reserve' but ongoing march towards higher quality another step forward with **03**. Perfumed redcurrant & raspberry, soft berry fruits, oak working behind the scenes. Soft acidity, high alc (a numbing 15.3%) help towards seductive style. FCTWS 2004 Best Pinotage & Discovery of the Show.

★★★★ **Chardonnay** Toasty **03** (sample); riper fruit (±14% alc) & 10 mths Fr oak barriques delivered a bonny bouncing chardonnay, full of lusty life. Juicy peach, lime marmalade & toasty oak make for delightful drinking, will keep 2-3 yrs, too.

Cabernet Sauvignon ★★★☆ **02** smooth ripe mulberry, touch of mint a constant here. Supportive oak adds firmish tannins, dry finish. 14.8% alc. **Merlot** ★★★☆ Latest **03**, slathered in dark choc, succulently ripe, slightly spicy. Yr+ Fr oak. 14.2% alc. **Sauvignon Blanc** ★★★ Sample **04** pushes all right buttons – hints grass, lime, passionfruit; fullish body, juicy sweet/sour fruit interplay though properly dry. WO Stbosch. **Cape Snort** ★★★☆ Cellar's 'Cape Port' renamed to show displeasure with envisaged banning of word 'Port'. **99** less sweet, à la Portuguese styles, but alc a modest 17.4%. Dark, fruitcake richness, slight tannic grip on finish. WO Coastal unless noted. – *IvH*

Serengeti see Migration
Seven Falls see Barrydale
Shamwari see Stellenbosch Vineyards
Shepherd's Creek see Clos Malverne
Sherwood-Berriman see High Constantia
Shibula see Klompzicht

Ship Sherry

Not 'sherry', but a jerepiko-style fortified from two muscats & chenin. By Distell. Latest (NV) ★★★ raisiny, viscous; finishes with a clean, firm, savoury grip. WO W-Cape. – *CR*

Schoonberg

Upper Langkloof ▪ Est 1999 ▪ 1stB 2002 ▪ Visits by appt ▪ Walks ▪ Mountain biking ▪ 4x4 trail ▪ Owner Morné Jonker ▪ 17 ha (cab) ▪ 200 cs 100% red ▪ PO Box 689 Oudtshoorn 6620 ▪ morné@schoonberg.co.za ▪ www.schoonberg.co.za ℭ (044) 888·1707 🖷 (044) 203·3715

Soaring 750m above sea level in the Outeniqua Mountains north of George on the Wilderness coast, Morné Jonker's 'extreme' vineyards enjoy an annual average temperature of just 17°C, making them possibly the coolest in the country. Grapes are hauled 450km to Fairview in Paarl, where the wine is made, but as far as Jonker is concerned, the major work is already done: 'It's time the industry gave more recognition to the viticulturist than the winemaker,' he asserts, adding: 'Our vineyards are our pride and joy. The farm has the most interesting terroir in our country – come and have a look.' Jonker shows no interest in the export market, so you'll find his Schoonberg Cabernet only at selected Garden Route restaurants and golf resorts.

Schoone Gevel see La Motte

Shoprite Checkers

National wine-buyer Stephanus Eksteen ▪ 30 000 cs 60% red 35% white 5% rosé ▪ PO Box 215 Brackenfell 7561 ▪ seksteen@shoprite.co.za ▪ www.shoprite.co.za ℭ 980·4000 🖷 980·4012

A panel of winemakers, wine experts and consumers meets regularly to select these well-priced in-house ranges for the nationwide retail chains Shoprite and Checkers. A packaging upgrade for the Oddbins range sees the old 'brown paper' labels replaced with much more attractive livery, on par with the Oak Ridge 'reserves'.

Oak Ridge range

> **Merlot** ☺ ★★★ **02** vastly different to strict, unyielding pvs; this is jovial & plummy; roly-poly profile matched by sweet ripe tannins. Should hold 2-3 yrs.

Cabernet Sauvignon ★★☆ **03** lightish bodied but shows variety's strong structure/ tannins, mellowed somewhat by vanilla oak. 12.7% alc. **Shiraz** ★★★ Honest to goodness *vin rouge*; **02** now with touch of maturity & fairly evident oak spicing; still effortlessly drinkable. All WO Stbosch.

Oddbins range

Limited editions sourced directly from estates & private cellars; bin numbers change as batches are replaced by new lots.

> **Merlot Bin 173** ☺ ★★★ All purpose, well flavoured dry red; **03** plummy tones, comfortable tannins. WO Coastal. **Merlot Rosé Bin 84** ☺ ★★★ Poolside quaffer par excellence. Purple-tinged **04**, delightfully fragrant & sappy, lively just-off-dry palate. WO Stbosch. **Sauvignon Blanc Bin 169** ☺ ★★★ Light & perky **04**; gooseberry & hint of capsicum; on the outer limit of dry (4.8g/ℓ), which fills out the aftertaste. WO Stbosch.

Cabernet Sauvignon Bin 175 ★★ Red-fruited **03** a braaied steak partner rather than solo drink, given its booming dry tannins. WO W-Cape. **Shiraz Bin 182** ★★☆ **03** ready to drink, no rough edges; abundant juicy fruit & hint smoky oak. Could keep 2/3 yrs. ±14% alc. WO Stbosch. **Cabernet Sauvignon-Merlot Bin 186** ★★★ **03** 50/50 partnership with surprising (at price) claret-like tones, mineral grip to minty black fruit palate. Could improve in bottle. WO Coastal. **Pinotage-Shiraz Bin 178 03** ★★☆ compatible blend, no variety dominant. Bags of ripe red fruit, big (14.5% alc) but easy. WO W-Cape.— *DH*

Signal Hill

Cape Town ▪ Est/1stB 1997 ▪ Not open to the public ▪ Owners Ridon Family Vineyards ▪ Winemaker Jean-Vincent Ridon (1997), with Khulekani Laurence Buthelezi & JC Steyn (1998/2004) ▪ Viticulturist Marietjie Marais (1997) ▪ 5 ha (cab, merlot, shiraz, pinot, muscat d'A) ▪ 45 tons ±3 000 cs ▪ 70% red 27% white 3% rosé ▪ PO Box 12481 Mill Street Cape Town 8010 ▪ info@winery.co.za ▪ www.winery.co.za ✆ 461·9590 ▤ 465·0342

French-born Jean-Vincent Ridon has an eye for marketing (and more than a dash of chutzpah): having studied the suitability of Cape Town city's slopes for viticulture, he called on landowners with more than 100m² 'spare' to allow him to rent and plant vines (this at a time when agents and developers hover like eagles over every potential centimetre). So far, he has only a soupçon of city-bowl shiraz (½ha, planted 2003) but, undeterred, continues to source grapes from selected Boland vineyards. Last year's dry conditions resulted in a dearth of botrytised fruit, so the NLH is missing from his 2004 line-up. Ridon has hired JC Steyn as 2nd assistant winemaker and, in keeping with the 'we make wines, not engineered products' philosophy, introduced gravity flow into his winery.

- ★★★★ **Antica MM** Cab, made with minimal intervention to express the essence of mature Simonsberg bushvine fruit; we last tasted **00**.
- ★★★★ **Petit Verdot 01** seductive, soft bouquet of dark plums, violets & fragrant oak. Palate still tight; firm tannins keeping fruit in check. Has structure to improve ±4-7 yrs. ±40 mths (!) in mainly 2nd fill Fr casks. 14% alc. **00** exotic, with dark choc & prune notes, dry, elegant tannins.
- ★★★★ **Malwenn** From pinotage, off Paarl, Simonsberg vyds. Youthful **04** exhibits pinotlike earthy, cherry bouquet, bright cinsaut-like strawberry flavour. Too young to judge conclusively: rasping tannins & alcoholic heat (14.1%) should integrate with time. **03** sold out untasted by us. Yr Fr oak, 20% new.

★★★★ **Pinot Noir 04** barrel sample suggests all classic pinot components in place, auguring well. As with **02**, **03** sold out before we could confirm last yr's note of vibrant cherry, gripping fruit acidity & savoury, chalky tannins.

★★★☆ **Grand Rouge de Constance** Winter warming red mostly from Constantia pontac, tinta & soupçon cab f. **02** abundant prunes, red/yellow plums & farmyard aromas. 18 mths older 500ℓ vats. 14% alc.

★★★★ **Climat de Corsaire Chardonnay** Name 'Clos Corsaire' mooted last yr was disallowed. **03** (★★★★) orange/lime, creamy flavours undimmed by exuberant alc (14. 5%), caramel oak. No **02** made. **01** waxy, honeyed tones; firm, complex & limy finish. Frhoek, Stbosch grapes, bunch-pressed, fermented in Fr oak, 30% new.

★★★★ **Tête Blanche** Partly-oaked chenin, from selected low-yield Simonsberg, Polka-draai vyds. **03** melon & lemon fruit augmented with floral notes, cleansing lemon acidity. As with rich, maiden **01**, should gain honeyed complexity with age. No **02** made.

★★★★ **Vin de l'Empereur** Natural Sweet from muscat d'A vyd on Simonsberg. Arresting **03** (★★★★★) flush with hazelnuts & almonds, tropical/citrus fruits – not a grapey aroma to be found. 10% botrytis adds apricot flavours & citrus acidity. Uncloying (98g/ℓ sugar vs last **00**'s 115); lingering goodbye. **00** grapey, litchi aromas with barley-sugar on tongue. 13.5% alc.

★★★★ **Vin de Glacière** Extraordinary 'assisted icewine' – muscat d'A grapes coldroom-chilled to super-concentrate flavours. None since **00**'s glacé-fruit notes; balanced, tangy palate. J-V R promises revival.

★★★★ **Crème de Tête Muscat d'Alexandrie NLH** Barrel-fermented & yr *sur lie*. Hedonistic **03** liberally touched by apricots (from botrytis), raisin, toffee & burnt sugar flavours. Silky, thanks to near-perfect sugar/acid balance (225:7g/ℓ). Drink young. ±10% alc. No **01**; **02** untasted but *Wine* ★★★★★.

★★★★ **Straw Wine** Unknown field blend (possibly chardonnay, chenin, riesling), air-dried on straw mats as traditional *vin de paille* style demands. Only **01** so far; mid-2004 peach & honey with nutty, sherry-like notes. Caramel palate unctuous from 250g/ℓ sugar. Arduous, two yr fermentation, yielding just 10% alc.

★★★★★ **Mathilde Aszú 6 Puttonyos** Characterful orange-tawny Tokaji lookalike, again a Cape first. Botrytised Swtlnd furmint, Simonsberg sauvignon. MIWA DG; 91 pts *WS*. **02** bouquet unfolds in glass to amazing array of aromas – orange peel, caramelised sugar, candied almonds, apricots, lavender. Racy, thanks to sugar/acid balance (185/14g/ℓ). Long dried-fruit finish.

Grenache NEW ☺ ★★★ Unwooded, early drinking dry red for the thrifty. Bramble fruit, tea-leaf aromas, pliable tannins on **03**.

Malbec NEW **04** unrated barrel sample cock-a-hoop mouthful; resplendent sweet-and-sour cherry fruit, mint finish. **Argile Rouge** NEW Merlot from Simonsberg treated to 'Pomerol winemaking' (says J-V R) 'including micro-oxygenation & lees lie-in'. **02** work-in-progress indulges in chocolate, plummy fruit; tannins already luxurious; currently shows at least ★★★★ potential. **Rosé de Saignée** NEW ★★★ J-V R asserts this is SA's first blanc de noir from petit v (ex-Stbosch). Herbs & raspberries, **03** delightfully dry. Firmer than many in this category thanks to fermentation in 3rd fill Fr oak. Ideal *charcuterie* accomplice. 14% alc. **Cabeça Tinta** discontinued.

La Siesta range

★★★★ **Grenache Blanc** NEW Claims to be SA's first varietal bottling. Maiden **03** lives up to potential highlighted in pvs edition (listed as simply 'Blanc'). Mid-2004 boasts a dusty lemon blossom nose, almond & peach palate with bracing acidity (7.5g/ℓ), juicy-fruit finish. Welcome addition to retail shelf bulging with the usual suspects.

★★★★ **Grenache** (Pvsly 'Rouge') **02** shows true southern French style of pvs: happy artisanal red berry fruit, fennel high-notes, friendly tannins & refreshing acidity to enliven rustic stews. Fermented, aged in 20% new Fr wood.

Gamay Noir discontinued. — *CvZ*

Signature Series see Jean Daneel
Signatures of Doolhof see Doolhof Estate
Signum see Rooiberg
Silver Sands see Robertson Wide River
Simonay see Simonsvlei International

Simonsig Family Vineyards

Stellenbosch ▪ Est 1953 ▪ 1stB 1968 ▪ Tasting & sales Mon-Fri 8.30–5 Sat 8.30–4 ▪ Fee R7/R10 (incl glass) ▪ Closed Easter Fri, Dec 25 & Jan 1 ▪ Tours Mon-Fri 10 & 3 Sat 10 (min 5; booking essential for groups) ▪ BYO picnic ▪ Play area for children ▪ Tourgroups by appt ▪ Walking trail ▪ Owners Malan brothers ▪ Winemaker Johan Malan (1981), with Van Zyl du Toit & Debbie Burden (Dec 97/Nov 99) ▪ Viticulturist Francois Malan (1980), advised by Johan Pienaar & Di Davidson ▪ 205 ha (cab, merlot, pinotage, shiraz, chard, chenin, sauvignon) ▪ 2 000 tons 46% red 38% white 17% MCC ▪ HACCP certification in progress ▪ PO Box 6 Koelenhof 7605 ▪ wine@simonsig.co.za ▪ www.simonsig.co.za ℂ 888·4900 ✆ 888·4909

While others talk the talk about how shiraz could become SA's most exciting red, Simonsig walks it. Every vintage since 97 has garnered gold on a major wine show, and last year the 01 saw off 160 competitors to take the inaugural Shiraz Challenge (the follow-up 02 secured two international golds). But while 2nd-generation winemaker Johan Malan has a deep affection for the cultivar (flying to Australia to attend the 2004 International Shiraz Alliance), his talents are clearly not confined to that grape. Besides winning the usual clutch of awards, Malan last year made his first viognier (from bought-in grapes — he wants to play before he plants), opened a novel 'Labyrinth Vineyard' walking trail, and appointed Ross Hobbs as GM of marketing/sales. Like many of his Cape colleagues, Malan revelled in the unusually cool season, yielding excellent fruit intensity. In short, 2004 looks set to become a collector's year.

★★★★ **Frans Malan** Stylish tribute to visionary patriarch; pinotage attracts spotlight, supported by cab (24%), dash merlot. **02** pulpy mulberry/plum character, sweetly spiced from generous oaking (18 mths equal Fr/Am, 77% new); boldly flavoured, with juicy accessibility, but really designed for longer development, 7+ yrs. 15.1% alc. **01** bigger fruit than pvs, backed by enough oak for longer haul. VDG among strings of awards.

★★★★ **Tiara** Excellent Bdx blend, friendly on release, deserves ageing for black/red berry fruits to penetrate dense tannins. **02** cab's predominance (71%) dictates style; complex interleaving roasted fennel, creamy fruit, cigarbox. Merlot, cab f & Johan M's favoured petit v add interest. Of all reds in lineup, this for longest haul, 10+ yrs, will show beautifully from ±5. Mainly Fr oak, dab Am, ±90% new. Bold 15.3% alc, but wine's depth, structure handles it. **01** offered fruit concentration, ripeness.

★★★★☆ **Merindol Syrah** Frequently garlanded single vyd in lighter sandy loam soils, specially groomed. **02** ultra ripe, opulent plum/mocha depths, tantalising whiffs Parma ham & coriander. Plush, velvet fruit punctuated by sinewy tannins from 16 mths new Fr/Am (68/32) barriques; tempting to drink all now, will reward 6+ yrs. 14.8% alc. FCTWS gold. **01** retasted, just keeps getting better: intensified mocha/choc, complex layers underbrush, smoked meat, within seamlessly integrated, sleekly elegant structure. Pure class. FCTWS trophy winner, VDG, MIWA double-gold.

★★★★☆ **Shiraz CWG Auction Reserve** To date only beautifully crafted **02**, built for 7+ yrs. From low-yielding vyds (3.7 t/ha).

★★★★☆ **Petit Verdot CWG Auction Reserve** 𝗡𝗘𝗪 One of very few standalones on the market. **02** distinctive, sophisticated, necessarily minuscule quantities (146 cs). So much to admire: complex layers mulberries/loganberries, meat extract, forest floor, even gunflint; classically styled, elegant, fine-grained tannins reflecting expensive oaking (16 mths Allier barriques). Already accessible, but will get even better over next ±6 yrs. 14.2% alc. Small portion cabs s/f & merlot.

★★★★ **Shiraz** Trademark campfire tendrils in **02**, spicy dark fruit, creamy texture. Integrated ripe tannins deliver accessibility, but will continue to please for another 4+ yrs. Mainly seasoned barrels, 17 mths. 15.1% alc. **01** showed attractive succulence with a firm structure.

★★★★★ **Redhill Pinotage** Burgeoning list of awards for this standout, fruit from 40+ yr old bushvine vyd 'Rooibult', embellished with hefty dollop new oak. **02** intensely perfumed, flavoured; sour cherry, wild berries, with smoky underbrush toning; easily accommodates 16 mths small new Fr/Am oak, benefiting from savoury overlay, lithe musculature. 5+ yr ageing potential. Fine modern, individual pinotage. 14.8% alc. FCTWS gold. **01** also showed extraordinary complexity, depth, build to last 6+ yrs.

★★★☆ **Pinotage** ✓ Steady performer stays resolutely unwooded. **03** rhubarb & brambleberry typicity, arresting fruit-dominant body, long tasty finish. Smoothly appealing. 14.9% alc. **02** well-structured, juicy fruit-driven style.

★★★☆ **Chardonnay 03** lemony interplay with biscuity oak; balanced silky structure, eminently drinkable. 10 mths oaking, third new, easily assimilated. 13.9% alc. **02**'s big oak presence (40% new) accommodated by lemon cheesecake nose, tropical flavours.

★★★★ **Gewürztraminer** ✓ Frequently awarded SLH (though not labelled as such). **04** upholds reputation. Fragrant rose-petal greeting, seductive silk-textured sweetness, very good length. Mild 11.3% alc. **03** gewürz at its best; again the beguiling rose-petals, balanced sweetness, irresistible. No **02**.

★★★★ **CWG KV Cuvée Chêne** Last was **00**, chard-dominated MCC, subtly oak-influenced from used-barrique fermentation.

★★★★ **Cuvée Royale** Prestige sparkling made only in exceptional yrs. Original **91** marked 20 yrs of Simonsig bottle-fermented bubbly, re-released after 10 yrs on lees. **92** buttered-croissant nose, bone-dry, firm acidity regenerates lengthy finish. Retasted **96** proof of how well good bubbly ages: lemon/orange peel & honey cream fragrance, richly curvaceous body, good length. Drinking beautifully, probably at peak. 50/50 chard/pinot.

★★★★ **Kaapse Vonkel** ✓ More than 30 yrs on, demand undiminished for SA's first bottle-fermented bubbly. Latest **03** lemon/brioche fragrance, flavours; exuberantly zesty texture & finish. Given weight, extra taste dimension from 15% wood fermentation. Chard/pinot noir, dash pinot meunier (unique amongst local bubblies). 12.2% alc. **02**, **01**, **00** sold out before we could taste. Also in magnum, 3ℓ, 9ℓ.

★★★★ **Encore** NEW ✓ Off-dry sec-style MCC. 3 yrs bottle-age evident in pronounced bready richness on **00**, tangy sweet-sour citrus flavour demands attention, impresses. Brisk acidity (7.8g/ℓ) gives drier finish than 22g/ℓ sugar suggests. 12.3% alc. Worthy encore to rest of bubbly range.

★★★★ **Vin de Liza** Outstanding, elegantly presented NLH, honouring family matriarch. Usually a blend, as in **03** (★★★★☆), semillon/sauvignon showing more layered complexity than pvs; botrytis richness evident as vivid honeycomb, glacé fruit aromas assail the nose; generous oaking (10 mths, 45% new) adds savoury dimension to tangy apricot/quince flavours. Irresistibly delicious. 13.1% alc. 82.6g/ℓ sugar. **02** pure sauvignon, also delectable. **01**'s floral apricots nudged to complexity by oak.

Chenin Blanc ☺ ★★★ Eminently drinkable house style. **04** tangy pear drop & crunchy apple freshness, lively, flavourful.

Cabernet Sauvignon ★★★☆ **01** deep creamy layers cassis, mocha-choc speak of perfect fruit ripeness, soupçon merlot addition, good cellar care. Stylish, accessible, yet backbone for 4+ yrs ageing. Mainly seasoned Fr/Am oak, 15 mths. 13.9% alc. Also in magnums. **Cabernet Sauvignon-Shiraz** ★★★★ Export only. **03** perfect partnership (53/47) where shiraz brings smoky savouriness, cab juicy berry fruit, sinewy structure. Lightly oaked, designed for early enjoyment. 12.8% alc. **Sauvignon Blanc** ★★★ **04** green apple, gooseberry fragrance, flavours; satisfyingly rounded texture, brisk finish, make it oh-so-easy to drink. 13.3% alc. **Vin Fumé** ★★★ Among first wooded sauvignons in SA. **03** light oaking loses none of variety's fig/passionfruit character, just adds flavour, interest, as does 15% semillon. Balanced, food-friendly; amenable 12.5% alc. **Mustique** ★★★ Buket/riesling-driven off-dry blend laced with muscats (ottonel, morio). **03** yr later, lost none of its charm, aromatics or drinkability. Friendly 11.9% alc, 8.1g/ℓsugar. **Franciskaner** ★★☆ **02** sample retasted mid-2004 as finished product. More rounded, palate's voluptuous grapey sweetness still main attraction. Will make many friends. Buket/chenin. 11.6% alc. **Port** discontinued. — *CR* —

Simonsvlei International

Paarl ▪ Est/1stB 1947 ▪ Tasting & sales: Mon-Fri 8-6 (8-5 in winter) Sat 8.30-4.30 Sun 11-3 ▪ Fee R5 for 5 tastings ▪ Closed Easter Fri & Dec 25 ▪ Tours by appt ▪ Restaurant 101 ▪ Facilities for children ▪ Tourgroups ▪ Gifts ▪ Farm produce ▪ Function/conference facilities for small groups ▪ Owners 65 shareholders ▪ Winemakers Francois van Zyl & Rolani Lotz (2000/2002) ▪ Viticulturist Jannie Underhay (Dec 2002) ▪ 1 200 ha (cab, shiraz, chard, chenin) ▪ 10 000 tons 220 000 cs own labels + 300 000 cs for customers, incl Long Neck (US) & others ▪ 30% red 70% white ▪ PO Box 584 Suider-Paarl 7624 ▪ info@simonsvlei.co.za ▪ www.simonsvlei.co.za ☏ 863·3040 🖷 863·1240

All sorts of business buzzwords come to mind here — empowerment, enabling, value-added. But progressive's the term for the first company in SA to qualify for 3 international certificates to do with hygiene, good housekeeping and quality: Simonsvlei met ISO 9001, HACCP and British Retail Consortium standards in 2004. Another female winemaker joined the team — Mari van der Rijst as assistant to Rolani Lotz — and at the end of 2003 five members of staff graduated from the Cape Wine Academy's cellar education programme. Customer-friendliness became even warmer with the introduction of a card which allows 10% discount at the cellar, and summer sales hours were extended. But to the wine: the Mount Marble name gives way to Simonsvlei Lifestyle, describing a range of value-for-money easy-drinkers. Equally easy on the pocket and palate are Simonay boxed wines, now with a Johannisberger added.

★★★☆ **Cabernet Sauvignon-Merlot** ✓ Claret-style red, 50/50 blend tweaked for approachability with scope for cellaring. **02** well-fruited with plums & mulberries, enough tannin for 2-3 yrs. **03** (★★★) closed, hints dusty red fruit, oak apart & prominent mid-2004, needs more cellaring for harmony. Oak as for Cab.

Simonsrood ☺ ★★☆ Simple but flavoursome Mediterranean red; NV; four-way blend, not oaked. Robust (14% alc) & very drinkable. Forthcoming cherry, dried fruit & pot-pourri whiffs, medium bodied, dry, savoury. **Rosé** ☺ ★★★ 'What a tantaliser!' enthuses marketer Heila Brand. Semi-sweet-style **04** lurid ruby colour; strawberries & cream aromas; fruity strawberry-jelly tone, slight rasp of tannin balances the sugar. **Premier Chenin Blanc** ☺ ★★★ Stylish quaffer. **04** fairly powerful nose, sweet apple & quince fragrances, fruit salad flavours with tinge of lanolin.

Zenzela ★★★ Individual **01** blend shiraz (50%), equal cabs s/f, 6-9 mths Fr oak. Retaste reveals a lovely clean-thatch fragrance, cab f coming to the fore; good full palate, oak (as for Cab 03) nicely integrated now. 14% alc. **Cabernet Sauvignon 01** (★★★★) complex blackcurrant, cigarbox, forest floor array; plump, spicy-dry palate, serious but nicely handled wood (100% new oak, Fr/Am). Limited quantities still available ex-cellar. **03** (★★★) less effusive nose, some redcurrant, leaner flavours. 14% alc. 6-9 mths European oak, as are reds below. **Pinotage** ★★★ Muted mulberry & banana aromas introduce **03**, supple & juicy, sprightly palate tone, mid-weight easy drinker. **Shiraz** ★★★ Cracked pepper spicing to **02**, fuller flavoured/bodied than companions, mocha flavours, pleasant drinking now. **Chardonnay** ★★★ Sweet melon preface to **03**, low-key vanilla hint (2-4 mths European oak); lemon cream biscuit flavour, tangy grapefruit finish, medium body. **Sauvignon Blanc** ★★★ Water-white **04**, shy green aromas (fig, nettle, -pepper), lime palate; for early drinking; try with Red Roman cooked over coals, suggest winemakers. **Premier Bukettraube** ★★☆ Characterful & full-flavoured Late Harvest-style; light coloured but full flavoured **04**, soft, uncloying. **Simonsblanc** Off-dry white partner to Simonsrood not ready for tasting. **Humbro Red Jerepiko** ★★★ NV winter warmer from muscadel, fortified to ±17% alc. Lovely ruby glow; shy tea-leaf & strawberry aromas, sweet fruit-cordial character, though not as much structure or interest as pvs. **Humbro Hanepoot** ★★★ Latest (NV) bottling of this jerepiko-style fortified shows restrained honeysuckle & muscat aromas, notes of dried fruit & orange rind; very full bodied, perhaps too spiritous for some (±17% alc). All WO W-Cape.

Lifestyle range

All NV, unwooded. **Charming Red** ★★★ Well-fruited semi-sweet from four red grapes, would be more charming with less than the 26g/ℓ sugar. **Blanc de Blanc** ★★ Dusty nettle & guava intro; light bodied, austere, bone-dry. **Stein** ★★ Another take on chenin; hint of peach blossom, dryish for style, peachy finish.

Simonay range

1ℓ & 5ℓ boxed wines untasted; well priced. **Classic Red**, **Blanc de Blanc**, **Stein**, **Late Harvest**. — TM

Simunye

This joint-venture between California winemaker Zelma Long, her viticulturist husband Phil Freese and Backsberg's Michael Back has been discontinued and the brand sold.

Sinnya see Robertson Wide River

Six Generations see Rietvallei

Siyabonga

Wellington ▪ Est 1998 ▪ 1stB 1999 ▪ Closed to public ▪ Owners H Investments #121 (Pty) Ltd ▪ Winemaker Graham Knox ▪ Viticulturist Andrew Pratt (2003) ▪ 15 ha (cabs s/f, merlot, pinotage, semillon, viognier) ▪ 3 000 cs own label ▪ PO Box 1209 Wellington 7654 ▪ doolhof@ mweb.co.za ℂ 864·3155 🖷 864·1744

This is man-about-the-vineyards Graham Knox's on-Broadway production. Bordeaux bigname Alain Moueix stars, Knox is director/understudy, the new find is Corlea Fourie (née Van Wyk; top 2003 Stellenbosch winemaking graduate, newly married to Diemersfontein winemaker Bertus Fourie). This 'brilliant scholar' has 'masterminded the refreshing of the farm's wonderful old vineyards'. Mostly bushvines (25-35 years old) have been cut away, young wood trained for future bearing, old trunks/extensive root systems retained. The farm produces its first crops only after 5 years; full production at 7-8 years. While trying to shorten this interval, the cast will keep yields small to ensure concentration. Meanwhile, between busy periods, protea blossoms are harvested (vineyard blocks are hewn out of a fynbos wilderness).

★★★★ **Cabernet Sauvignon-Merlot 02** complete & refined. Firm, but not too dense/ tense for present drinking, or keeping 4-6 yrs. Pure fresh scents ripe soft black berries; supple, juicy with tapered, sweet-fruited length. Young home vyd. **01** intense; minerally grip. Partly fermented/yr Fr oak. 14% alc.

★★★★ **Pinotage 02** retasted, now with greater finesse, pleasure offered by tasty, ripe gamey notes sitting well with soft-tannined succulence, satiny smooth finish. Happily harmonised now/further 2 yrs. 14% alc. **01** elegant, med-bodied. Low-yielding vyd on own farm. Yr Fr barriques.

★★★★ **Severney** Serious dry white, designed to age. Usually with chenin, semillon from 30+ yr old vines: 60/40 blend in barrel-fermented **03**. Well-structured, firm, dry, vinous concentration appropriate to its reputation as popular partner to diverse menus. 14% alc. **02** adds in chardonnay; dry but with presence, richness. — AL

Slaley Estate

Stellenbosch ∎ Est 1995 ∎ 1stB 1997 ∎ Tasting & sales Mon-Fri 8.30–4.30 Sat 10–4.30 ∎ Fee R20, refunded on purchase ∎ Closed Easter Fri/Sun, Dec 25/26 & Jan 1 ∎ Tours by appt ∎ Farm produce ∎ Owners Hunting family ∎ Winemaker Shaun Turnbull (Mar 2002) ∎ Viticulturist Jaco Mouton (Jun 1999) ∎ 70 ha (cab, merlot, pinotage, shiraz, chard, sauvignon) ∎ 350 tons 12-15 000 cs own label 89% red 10% white 1% rosé ∎ Eurogap certified ∎ PO Box 119 Koelenhof 7605 ∎ info@slaley.co.za ∎ www.slaley.co.za © 865·2123 ℻ 865·2798

It's the name of a village outside Newcastle, where Charles Hunting built Slaley Hall and expanded the shipping business his father had established in 1874. Was Slaley Estate co-owner Lindsay Hunting feeling that ancestral pull when he built his own boat in 2004, with the help of his children? Also floated in 2004 was a new range: Lindsay's Whimsy is what winemaker Shaun Turnbull calls a 'social label', offering the wittily-named Shatot Planque and Shatot Plinque, a rosé. At the other end of the scale, the maiden Slaley 2002 Pinotage was an ABSA Top Ten selection. Pinotage is the variety that Hunting's cut down on — plantings have been reduced 50%. 'The market's not there,' explains Turnbull, 'and it's quite an expensive crop.' Against trend, riesling is going into the ground instead.

★★★★☆ **Merlot Reserve** Distinctive aeronautical label-theme for experimental Reserve range, represented on current list by elegant, silk-textured **99**; revisited mid-2004 shows sweet berry notes have translated to more savoury, beefy flavours, oak completely absorbed. Fine wine, ready. 20 mths new Fr oak. Unfiltered. Harmonious 13.2% alc. Will easily keep, say 3 yrs. Magnums only; 450 made.

Hunting Family range

★★★★ **Cabernet Sauvignon-Merlot** Latest **02** (★★★★) 65/35 blend reflects lesser vintage, still well made — cab cedar & merlot choc muted, lighter textured & flavoured, despite 14.2% alc. 14 mths oak, all Fr, 40% new. **00** (cab ±70%) had pure, sweet fruit, poised & delicious, still many yrs ahead. No **01**.

★★★★ **Merlot** Latest **02** roast/toast welcome, much riper at 14.8% alc. Big wine, soft ripe tannins, still manages some elegance. Yr Fr oak, 40% new. **00** relaxed & open mid-2004; ripe dark-berried & fruitcake flavours. Fine-textured tannic presence, well-managed supportive oak ~18 mths new Fr. 13.4% alc. No **01**.

★★★★ **Pinotage** Spicy, berry-redolent **02** from 45-yr-old vines; less classic than others in range, emphasising sweet, ripely rich fruit, intense tannic & alcoholic power, 14.6% alc. Balanced, though, & on course for another 5 yrs when retasted mid-2004. 14 mths oak, 90% new, 60/40 Fr/Am. ABSA Top Ten 2003.

★★★★ **Shiraz** Latest **02** intensely coloured & flavoured. Rich, muscular, scented with smoked beef, prune; firm fleshed, tannins unobtrusive, almost ready. 14 mths oak, Fr/Am 66/34%, 58% new. 14.2% alc.

★★★★☆ **Chardonnay** Vanilla backdrop to juicy yellow peach flesh which seems to absorb 7.8g/ℓ acid with ease in **03**. 95% fermented/aged 10 mths new Fr oak, balance unwooded. **02** (★★★) looking a little tired.

Broken Stone range

★★★★ **Shiraz 02** (★★★★) another victim of difficult vintage; firm & robust, tangy acid, dry finish. 14 mths main Am oak, 35% new. Serious but hearty **01**, full-flavoured, velvet-textured, satisfying savoury solidity based on fruit & big ripe tannin.

★★★★☆ **Cabernet Sauvignon-Shiraz** ✓ **02** has 6% merlot, shows attractive berries on palate, smoothly rounded, soft tannins, fresh acid. 14 mths Fr oak, 40% new. Almost ready. **00** exuberantly flavourful, with savoury acid, soft tannin.

★★★★☆ **Pinotage** Big, bold **01** has masses of bright savoury fruit, well-balanced, supportive tannins & sensitive oaking (14 mths older barrels). 14.4% alc. **02** (★★★) now bottled, lighter textured & firm with freshening acidity, reflecting vintage.

Sauvignon Blanc ★★★ Sample **04**, definitely notch above pvs; gooseberry & grass, pleasant fullness despite modest alc (12.5%). Thrilling fruit/acid balancing act. Bone-dry.

Shatot range

> **Lindsay's Whimsy** ☺ ★★★ **02** lighter textured, gently fruity, graceful 'Cape blend'. Merlot, pinotage, shiraz (46/42/12), lightly oaked & very accessible.

Plinque ★★★ Distinctive blueish Pink from pinotage in **04** (sample), full-bodied at 13.7% alc yet fresh & lively. Bone-dry, great for summer tippling. **Planque** ★★ Blend shiraz, cab (68/32) **02** easy, plump & fruity, lightly oaked; some will find bitterness on finish. —*IvH*

Slanghoek Winery

Slanghoek (see Worcester map) ▪ Est 1951 ▪ Tasting & sales Mon-Fri 8-12.30; 1.30-5.30 Sat 10-1 ▪ Closed public holidays except Easter Sat ▪ Picnic baskets by appt or BYO ▪ Tours 11 & 3 by appt ▪ Tourgroups ▪ BYO picnic ▪ Audio-visual presentation ▪ Gifts ▪ Conferencing ▪ Walks ▪ Conservation area ▪ Owners 25 members ▪ Cellarmaster Pieter Carstens (Aug 2002) ▪ Winemakers Nicolaas Rust, with Jacques de Goede , Nico Grundling & Johan Jordaan (Oct 2003/Dec 2001/Dec 2002/Nov 2003) ▪ Viticulturist Francois Nel (Dec 2000) ▪ 1 600 ha (17 varieties, r/w) ▪ 40 000 cs own label + 14m litres bulk 20% red 60% white 10% rosé 10% fortified ▪ Export brand: Zonneweelde ▪ PO Box 75 Rawsonville 6845 ▪ slanghoek@lando.co.za ▪ www.slanghoek.co.za ✆ (023) 344·3026/7/8 ▦ (023) 344·3157

It may have been a difficult year for some, but for Slanghoek 2004 was not only its biggest harvest to date, yielding 30 000-plus tons, but one of its best: 'Quality was outstanding; sauvignon and pinotage were exceptional,' raves Nicolaas Rust. Ex Seidelberg, he was appointed senior winemaker late in 2003 and heads up a team recently joined by Johan Jordaan, fresh from Elsenburg but with some French seasoning. The Slanghoek honours list has been extended by Veritas and SAA plaudits for the Sauvignon, Vinay White and Pinotage. 'Bigger *and* better' is the winery's answer to ever-tougher marketing challenges, hence close co-operation between the viti and vini teams, new plantings, upgraded equipment and expansion of the cellar.

★★★★ **Noble Late Harvest** One of SA's acclaimed botrytised desserts, though recent releases less impressive at our mid-yr tastings; **03** case in point: laudable spread of flavours (incl vibrant pineapple), fine balance — but all in subdued form. Pvs **01** lauded by Diners Club Club, yet to our palate less concentrated, more honeyed than pvs. Mainly chenin, dollop hanepoot; all roughly 7g/ℓ acid, 160g/ℓ sugar, 12% alc. Unwooded. 375ml.

★★★★ **Red Muscadel** Delicious silk-textured **03** was kept lively & fresh by well-tweaked acidity & spirit; **04** (★★★) seems overtly sweet & alcoholic, doesn't show all that much muscat character. 16.8% alc.

> **Vinay Red** ☺ ★★★ Four-way blend, fruity & wickedly drinkable (so watch the 14% alc). Red berry & plum flavours/aromas, light touch of oak. **Vinay Rosé** ☺ ★★★ From pinotage, made dry; satisfying red-wine character; fresh & firm, delightful crisp finish. 'Drink within the year of purchase,' says back-label, accurately. Vinays above, below, in 1 000ml bottles, NV. **Chenin Blanc** ☺ ★★★ **04** peach-toned quaffer, refreshing, midweight & comfortably dry. **Vinay White** ☺ ★★ Supple, lightish off-dry quaffer; blend sauvignon, chenin, colombard; fresh pineapple & guava flavours; surprise DG at 2003 Veritas. **Special Late Harvest** ☺ ★★★ From hanepoot; good sugar-acid tension for effortless lightish sipping. **04** has guava & pineapple aromas & flavours.

Latest releases of **Camerca** (★★★★ Bdx blend), **Cabernet Sauvignon** (★★★) & **Merlot** (★★★) not tasted. **Pinotage** ★★★ **02** textbook plum & banana tones, suggestion of wood, touch bottle-age complexity, savoury finish; could be cellared few more yrs. Fr barriques aged. **Shiraz** ★★★ **01** retaste, ripe plum flavours now somewhat dominated by spicy oak (yr barriques, 30% Am). **Chardonnay** ★★★★ Fr oak-fermented; last tasted was **03** (sample), soft, ripe & peachy. **Sauvignon Blanc** ★★★ **04** grass & asparagus notes; sterner than pvs, more food orientated. **Semillon** ★★★ Fresh, lively **03** supportively oaked; new-clone nettles on nose, nicely rounded. **Riesling-Semillon** ★★★ Lightish 70/30 blend crouchen, semillon. **04** brisk & bone-dry; good food style. **Natural Sweet** ★★★ Dessert wine from hanepoot, chenin; vyds selected for high sugars & regular botrytis; noble rot character fairly evident in **03**, good sugar/acid balance; tropical fruit tones, surprisingly dry at 91g/ℓ sugar; now in 500ml. **Vin Doux** ★★★ NV carbonated sparkler with billowing tropical fruit tones; refreshingly frothy, delicate, not too sweet. **Red Jerepiko** ★★★ Penetratingly sweet fortified dessert from pinotage; **04** soft & grapey, 17% alc sure to warm the cockles. **Sweet Hanepoot** ★★★★ Last ed we noted label's swansong, but here's an **04**, in fine fettle to boot: light, delicate, well-made & clean. Good over crushed ice in summer, say Team S. 16.5% alc. **Cape Ruby** ★★★ Now mainly touriga, tiny splashes malbec, barbera in **03**; impressively deep hues; full, rich red berry & plum flavour, earthy undertone. Still traditional low alc (16.5%); only older oak. — *DH*

Smook Wines

Paarl ▪ Est/1stB 2000 ▪ Visits by appt; tasting/sales also at I Love Wine (see Wine shops section) ▪ Owner Anthony Smook ▪ Winemaker Anthony Smook, with Francois Louw (2000) ▪ Viti consultant Johan Wiese (2001) ▪ 30 ha (cab, merlot, pinotage, shiraz, chard, chenin) ▪ 36 tons 2 500 cs 80% red 20% white ▪ PO Box 7038 Noorder-Paarl 7623 ▪ asmook@mweb.co.za ▪ www.smookwines.co.za ✆ 872·1804 🖷 872·2867

Anthony Smook has a sensible view on the vagaries of the export-plaguing rand: 'Don't depend on a favourable exchange rate. Build a proper long-term local market.' France is an unusual export destination for SA producers so he's lucky to have recently established a French link; taking a five-year view, he identifies China as a potential market. The winemaker upgraded his pressing equipment in 2004, which produced wines with 'good fruit and structure'. Structuring meals that harmonise? Smook offers food and wine matching advice, as well as tastings, of course, but call ahead for an appointment.

Pinotage ★★★ Gear shift from mega-ripe pvs to medium-intensity **02**, more Burgundian in tone; soft, supple palate with forest floor notes. All Fr barrels, 15 mths. **Shiraz** ★★★ **02** cask aged (50% new, 90% Fr); again hefty alc (14.8%) but not clumsy or over-extracted; aromatic coriander hint; sweet red fruit palate. **Shiraz Reserve** NEW **03** (sample) concentrated version of above, wattage upped with 100% new oak; smoky black fruit nose with meaty edge; more structure, complexity, ripeness. Provisional ★★★★ . **Merlot-Cabernet Sauvignon** ★★★★ This Bdx blend is merlot-led in **02** (50%, with 40% cab, soupçon cab f); soft & sweet-fruited, hints game & red meat, sweetish fragrant finish with cigarbox whiff from 50% new Fr oak. 14.5% alc. **Chardonnay** NEW ★★★★ European feel to **03**, elegant & well balanced; supple lemon/brioche flavours with clean, lingering dry finish. All above off single-vyds in Voor-Prdberg area. — *TM*

Soek die Geluk see Goedverwacht

Somerbosch Wines

Stellenbosch (see Helderberg map) ▪ Est 1950 ▪ 1stB 1995 ▪ Tasting & sales Mon-Fri 9-5 Sat 9-3 (9-1 Apr-Aug) ▪ Fee R10 refundable with any purchase ▪ Closed Easter Fri/Sun, Dec 25/26 & Jan 1 ▪ Tours by appt ▪ Owner Roux family ▪ Winemakers/viticulturists Marius & Japie Roux (1987/1995) ▪ 80 ha (cab, merlot, pinotage, shiraz, cinsaut, chard, chenin, sauvignon) ▪ 60% red 40% white ▪ PO Box 12181 Die Boord 7613 ▪ enquiries@somerbosch.co.za ▪ www.somerbosch.co.za ✆ 855·3615 🖷 855·4457

The convivial Roux brothers of Die Fonteine farm this year mark the 10th anniversary of their wine brand Somerbosch (an allusion to their cellar's situation at the mid-point between Somerset West and Stellenbosch). Much older — dating from their father Wally's era, in fact — are 1967-vintage cinsaut bushvines, still going strong. Marius and Japie R continue their steady programme of increasing their own-label production (and exporting it to Europe and Thailand) while selling off grapes to selected clients.

★★★★ **Cabernet Sauvignon** Balanced & elegant dry red, sparingly oaked (yr Fr/Am oak, none new). Retasted **02** (★★★★) dried fruit/cassis in spicy vanilla frame; savoury dry finish. Satisfying, if not as youthfully beguiling as last yr; **01** featured piquant redcurrants & herbs, well-tempered tannins. 13.5% alc.

★★★★ **Cabernet Sauvignon-Merlot Limited Release** Occasional label; we last tasted **00**, settling & gaining complexity; had life for further 3-4 yrs min.

Chenin Blanc ☺ ★★★ Quaffable & refreshing **04**, with quince & candyfloss aromas, rich if fairly uncomplex melony fruit. NB: 14% alc.

Merlot ★★★ **02**'s gripping tannins are coming round, plump dark choc flavours becoming accessible; slightly sweet finish. 14.5% alc. Fr/Am oak, 2nd-4th fill, yr. **Shiraz** ★★★ **02** acquiring a secondary dried-fruit character, slight savouriness which makes it food-friendly. Not over-oaked (as above). **Pinotage** ★★★★ **02** refreshingly unforced expression of the variety; elegant, emphasising the pinot parentage. Only 50% wooded (Fr, yr). Contrast with... **Pinotage Limited Release** NEW ★★★★ Very different oak polishing: 50% new, combo Fr/Am, imparts vanilla-spice to **01**'s fruit compôte character; slight gaminess apparent; still, not uncontrolled, over-alcoholic (13.5%). **Chardonnay** ★★★ **04** unwooded this yr; leesy lemons on nose; crisp Granny Smith apple on taste, zippy acidity. 14.5% alc. **Chenin Blanc Barrel Fermented** ★★★★ **03** more complex, serious than above version, Fr-oaked component (80%, yr) shows attractively in rich toffee-toned flesh. 14% alc. 25 yr old bushvines. **Sauvignon Blanc** ★★★ Pale **04** shows marzipan & lees aromas; flinty, austerely dry flavours. Foil for rich linefish. 13.5% alc. **Late Bottled Vintage Port** NEW ★★★ From cab, 4 yrs in oak; ripe prunes & smoked ham aromas, hint of raisin; firm & dry. **99** already drinkable, as style should be; not for purists but a good effort. 19.5% alc.

Seugnet range

Blanc ☺ ★★★ Latest version of this bright outdoorsy tipple hits the spot. **04** shy & pale, but well fruited with green apples/pears; refreshing. 50/50 chenin/semillon.

Rouge ★★★ **03** new blend (merlot, shiraz, pinotage), same easy drinkability; delicate spicy/leafy aromas, juicy fruit cordial-like palate. Portion oak-staved. — *TM*

Somerfield see Cape Grace, International Wine Services
Somerlust see Viljoensdrift
Something Else see Kosie Möller Wines
Sommelier's Choice see Wine Concepts
Songloed see Coppoolse Finlayson
Sonnigdal see Goue Vallei
Sonop Organic see African Terroir

Southern Right ▮▮

Hemel-en-Aarde Valley ▪ Est 1994 ▪ 1stB 1995 ▪ Tasting & sales at Wine Village- Hermanus (see Specialist wine shops section) ▪ Owner Anthony Hamilton Russell ▪ Winemaker/viticulturist Hannes Storm, with Bernard le Roux (2004/2003) ▪ ±13 ha (pinotage, sauvignon) ▪ 225 tons 17 000 cs 40% red 60% white ▪ PO Box 158 Hermanus 7200 ▪ hrv@hermanus. co.za © (028) 312·3595 ▤ (028) 312·1797

The 'delicious mystery' in last year's guide? Pushing the envelope on pinotage, Anthony Hamilton Russell planted a research block of a few rows each of cab, shiraz, cab franc, malbec and petit verdot to evaluate their performance and ability to add complexity and character to Southern Right's favoured red. Further vinous R&D included trial vinifications at different yields in a single pinotage vineyard. (Range-sibling sauvignon was subjected to separate vinifications at different ripeness levels.) S-R's commitment to re-defining pinotage is reflected in the exciting new wine below. Bastenburg is a family name given to a high-density vineyard planted in clay-rich soil in 1996. The 18 barrels of the first vintage is an attempt at a 'classy, classically styled' pinotage.

★★★★★ **Bastenburg** NEW Limited release of this estate-grown pinotage coincides with the first decade of Southern Right, though Anthony HR's vision for Bastenburg is to have its own identity. **01** bordelais in structure with distinct varietal edge. Will evolve into a Cape blend over time, partnering Bdx varieties. Trials continue.

★★★★☆ **Pinotage 03** youthfully unevolved, but very good representation of the variety; wood & slightly grainy tannins just need time to settle. 75% W Bay fruit, with Swtlnd (18), Stbosch. 9 mths Fr oak, 50% new. 14% alc. **02** showed further refinement with both Rhône & Burgundy nuances, yet still distinctly pinotage. **01** led with pristine varietal aromas; more restrained palate & barely noticeable wood.

★★★★ **Sauvignon Blanc 04** (sample) figgy, green fruit nose/palate, intense & weighty. Shows the familiar zinging cool-climate tone; promising. WO W-Cape, fruit from W Bay, Vdorp, Stbosch; **03** ripe, exotic; excellent structure. **02** had vivacious & exotic aromas/tastes, superb concentration. — *RK*

Southern Sky Wines

*Paarl ▪ Est 2002 ▪ Tasting & sales at I Love Wine, Main Rd Paarl, Mon-Sat 9-4 ▪ Coffee & light meals 9-4 ▪ Closed Dec 25/26 & Jan 1 ▪ Crafts, homeware & gifts ▪ Owner Andrew Milne ▪ Vini consultant Johann Jacobs (Mar 2004) ▪ 10 000 cs ▪ 80% red 20% white ▪ 92 Main Street Paarl 7646 ▪ sales@southernskywines.com ▪ www.southernskywines.com ✆ **871·1437/ 082·876·8878** 🖷 871·1437*

'Winemaking is much like making love. It has to be memorable,' ventures Andrew Milne, who took the plunge into wine from an advertising, events and marketing platform. The range of services he offers is almost as wide as the southern sky, and encompasses sourcing, packaging and branding of wine. He's also focused on building his own young brands. Not ready for tasting, but available during the currency of the guide are the Tara Hill Cab and Sauvignon Blanc, and Imagine Shiraz and Chenin (reds 03, whites 04).

South Point see Origin Wine

South, South West

Also known as SSW, a geographical allusion to Cape wine country, these affordable easy-drinkers from African Wines & Spirits are sold in 1 000 ml bottles.

Ruby Cabernet-Pinotage ☺ ★★★ Retasted **01** still gluggably smooth & light-toned; ruby cab's thatch aromas well melded with dried fruit whiffs; slightly sweet finish.

Chardonnay-Chenin Blanc ★★★ **03** lightish 51/49 blend now shows attractive creaminess on palate from extra yr in bottle; fresh apple/peach whiffs. Both WO Rbtsn. — *TM*

Spar SA

*Est 1963 ▪ PO Box 1589 Pinetown 3600 ▪ ray.edwards@spar.co.za livingworld@mweb. co.za ✆ **(031) 719·1900/1844** or (012) 998·4737 🖷 (031) 719·1991 or (012) 998·4736*

When it comes to districts, wards, wineries, growers and varieties... one word fits all: 'various'. Add 14 winemakers and 3 000 000ℓ of wine, and you get an idea of the size of the Spar supermarket chain's wine-sourcing operation. Ongoing market research highlights what customers want to buy. 'Fruity, balanced, early accessible wines,' says consultant Tinus van Niekerk. 'Consumers shy away from wines which are too prominently wooded. And of course everyone wants value for money.' The group's house brands, Country Cellars and Carnival, are listed separately.

Special Selection see Laibach
Spencers Creek see Paarl Wine

Spice Route Wine Company 🍷

Swartland ▪ Est/1stB 1998 ▪ Tasting & sales at Fairview (see that entry) ▪ Owner Charles Back ▪ Winemaker Charl du Plessis (Dec 2001) ▪ Viti adviser Andrew Teubes ▪ 123 ha (shiraz, mourvèdre) ▪ 450 tons ±18 000 cs 70% red 30% white ▪ PO Box 645 Malmesbury 7299 ▪ spiceroute@iafrica.com Ⓒ (022) 485·7139 🖷 (022) 485·7169

Sealing the Swartland in a bottle, is how Charl du Plessis sums up his job at this cutting-edge Malmesbury cellar, owner by Fairview's Charles Back. Their wines certainly reflect the region: wide, warm, spicy, slightly out of the mainstream. Having made an international mark with regular warm-blooded reds (shiraz, merlot, pinotage), the home farm (though planted predominantly with shiraz and mourvèdre) is seeing the first fruits of more adventurous varieties. Two barrels of 2004 Petite Sirah look 'outstanding'. A Sangiovese and Barbera are due out soon. Grenache, carignan, tannat, souzão, tempranillo, primitivo (zinfandel) and... and... wait in the wings. Among white wine farm Amos Kuil's site-selective plantings is a crouchen/semillon cross: nouvelle.

★★★★★ **Malabar** NEW At last, name/blend of this truly Swtlnd red finalised; **02** shiraz/merlot/grenache (58/26/16) union holds torch for future — cellar's best 02. Unshowily exudes confidence; fine, aromatic freshness intricately mixing spice, red fruits, projecting vinosity not varieties; gorgeously sensuous, silky; ending with densely textured elegance. Seamless oaking: fermented large wood, Fr casks 22 mths. Unfiltered. 15.4% alc.

Flagship range

★★★★★ **Syrah** New-wave shiraz on classic lines, but with Swtlnd warmth, generosity. Latter expressed to extreme in über-ripe **02** (★★★★); unusually aggressive tannin currently throttles underlying meaty, savoury richness — sufficient to leave 15.3% alc not over-intrusive. Less complex, shorter-term prospects than elegant, seamless **01** (14.3% alc); well-structured; textured fruit; focused, long & savoury. As per last ed, delicious, plenty in store. 91 pts *WS*, *Decanter* 2004 World Wine Award. 16 mths Fr oak; unfiltered.

★★★★★ **Merlot** Full-blooded red; richly-hued, textured as the deep red soils of its origin. **02** characteristic tannin sheath over rich red vinosity; tighter, more introverted than pvs, quieter meaty/plum tones vs usual expansive red fruit/earthy minerality. Best of 02 Flagships; could develop with classic aplomb, over 3-4 yrs. 15% alc. Unfiltered. **01** richer, bigger than pvs with savoury vinosity; needs further yr/2 for fruit/tannin resolution; then potential 4+ yrs. 18 mths Fr oak, 50% new.

★★★★★ **Pinotage** Unusually wild, gamey **02** (★★★★). Broad shoulders, refined demeanour but lesser fruit richness; plays up variety's more assertive tannins. Should harmonise over 2-4 yrs. 14.8% alc. No **01**. Fine-textured **00**; 14.7% alc; 18 mths Fr oak, 40% new.

Standard range

★★★★ **Pinotage** Extravagant fresh black cherry, raspberry tone puts **03** firmly in modern camp. Very big (15% alc) but friendly; great fruit concentration, smooth tannin, buff from sweet Am oak, 40% new. Enjoy — in sips — while harmony tightrope act lasts.

★★★★★ **Chenin Blanc** Barrel fermentation enhances honeyed richness of these Swtlnd grapes. Honey-gold **03** already has some waxy oxidative development. Opulent structure replete with dried apricots, peaches, tangy tangerine peel. Barrel sample **04** similarly concentrated, plus brush botrytis, touch livelier acid. From ±26 yr old Mbury bushvines. Fr oak-fermented/aged, 26% new. 14.5% alc.

Discontinued: **Sauvignon Blanc, Shiraz, Andrew's Hope Pinotage.** — *AL*

Spier

Stellenbosch ▪ Est 1767 ▪ 1stB 1996 ▪ Tasting & sales daily 9-5 ▪ Fee R8 (informal) or R12 (formal) ▪ Tours by appt ▪ Meals, refreshments & picnics, see Eat-out section ▪ Luxury hotel & wide variety of attractions/amenities ▪ Owner Winecorp ▪ Winemakers/viticulturists: see Winecorp ▪ 110 ha (cab, merlot, pinotage, shiraz, chard, sauvignon) ▪ 200 000 cs 60% red 40% white ▪ PO Box 1078 Stellenbosch 7660 ▪ francoisvdw@spier.co.za winecorp@ iafrica.com ▪ www.spier.co.za ▪ www.winecorp.co.za ℂ 809·1100 🖷 809·1143

The latest attraction of this manicured, riverside pleasure dome is Moyo, an 'outdoor African eating experience' with Arabian Nights-style tents (and a tree-house platform) providing exotic settings for a bountiful buffet (chilly Cape winter nights warmed by large braziers/woolly blankets). An hotel, conference centre, open-air amphitheatre, five other restaurants, a deli (offering picnic hampers), golf course, equestrian centre, wildlife close encounters… and fine wine (from an SA-showcasing shop). Spier's home-cellar master Frans Smit (also Winecorp stablemate Longridge overseer) has red-wine maker Kobie Viljoen conjuring with cab (Concours Mondial gold medal), and new shiraz (top wine at the 2004 SAYWS). Eleonor Hoogendijk's specialist treatment of especially chenin, semillon and viognier are regular showstoppers. Find these gems under Spier's Private Collection single-vineyard 'selections within selections', as Smit calls them.

Private Collection

★★★★ **Cabernet Sauvignon** Multi-faceted wine for keeping. **02** richly cassis-perfumed, with cedar overlay, hints meat extract, wet heath; lots of class & depth. Firm but ripe tannins provide platform for long ageing, need time to reveal potential. 14.7% alc; 10 mths Fr oak. A little more oak (14 mths, 80% new) on similarly ripe, forceful **01**; also needed yr/2 for accessibility; good for 7+. Concours Mondial gold.

★★★☆ **Merlot** Back to tight-knit house style with **02**, after more amenable **01**. Smoky, dark choc, minted red berry aromas/flavours; will reward patience as it develops. 14% alc. **01** (★★★★) spices, mocha-choc adding to black plum core; fruit richness. These seriously oaked for longer (5+ yrs) haul: ±14 mths Fr, 80% new.

★★★★ **Pinotage** Sleek, supple, modern example. **02** still an infant mid-2004. Opulent black-fruit, cigarbox, roasted spice fragrance, flavours; firm fine-grained tannin support for 8+ yrs in cellar. 14.7% alc. **01**'s lithe suppleness hid firm structure. These ±14 mths Fr/Am oak, ±80/20, 60% new.14.6% alc. IWSC gold for both.

★★★★ **Chenin Blanc 03** (★★★★☆) raises bar on already acclaimed wine. Wonderfully perfumed, layers baked apple, barley sugar, candied lemon-peel, even tropical fruit, yet an unwavering freshness, zing in the tail that speaks of youthful vigour, ageability (5+ yrs) & superb food compatibility. Fermented/6 mths Fr oak. 13.2% alc. No **02**. **01** Mondial gold; *Wine* ★★★★★; 2003 Chenin Challenge runner-up.

★★★★☆ **Sauvignon Blanc** Powerful, full-flavoured. Previewed **04** promises complex interweaving of grapefruit, nettles & gooseberries, lip-smacking zesty freshness, long flavours. 13% alc. Follows impressive **03** with exciting mineral, green edginess.

★★★★ **Viognier 03** offers wafting peach kernel, jasmine, spice & friendly, peachy approachability: well balanced, with plumping up by 6.3g/ℓ sugar. Larger part fermented in wood, for weight & structure. 14% alc. Concours Mondial gold.

★★★★ **Noble Late Harvest** Last tasted was delicious **00** from riesling & chenin; honey, marmalade & dried peach notes, sweetness (106g/ℓ) offset by refreshing acidity (8g/ℓ). Nutty overlay from 18 mths Fr oak adds complexity, appeal. 13% alc.

Semillon discontinued.

Spier range

★★★★☆ **Sauvignon Blanc 04** (sample) focuses on freshness & flavour: green figs, gooseberry-rich fruit salad. Tangy, zesty, crisp finish, just what's needed for ideal food partnership. 13.1% alc. WO Coastal (whole range this or WO W-Cape).

Chenin Blanc ☺ ★★★ **04** (sample) exuberantly fresh & juicy; pear-drop, guava fragrance/flavours, mouth-tingling crispness & long fruit-laden finish make a tasty quaffer.

Cabernet Sauvignon ★★★ **03** deep-veined cedar-cassis intro, but still tight-knit – leave yr for tannins to meld, soften. 10 mths Fr oak. 14.1% alc. **Merlot** ★★★ **03** bitter-choc, dark berries, heaps of spice, creamily presented in accessible, medium-weight package. Tasty early drinking. Oak as above. 14.6% alc. **Pinotage** ★★★ Classic varietal styling on **03**: rhubarb, brambleberries; smoothly ripe & accessible. Deft oaking, 10 mths Fr/Am, provides support, gentle spicing. Enjoy now, 2/3 yrs. 14.6% alc. **Shiraz** ★★★ Lighter-toned **03**, earlier drinking than pvs, but same impressive aromas: smoked meat extract, black pepper, hint of scrubland. 9 mths small Fr, 20% new. 15.1% alc. **Chardonnay** ★★★ **03** Tasty lemon/lime & peach aromas, flavours, softly rounded (off-dry 6.9g/ℓ sugar), friendly. Only smidgen oak for those who prefer chard unadorned. 13.8% alc. **Bouquet Blanc** ★★★ **03** pretty as a picture: jasmine, litchi & preserved pineapple tones in an easy-drinking, light-textured offering. Semi-sweet. 12.3% alc. – CR

Spitz see Bellingham

Springfield Estate

Robertson ▪ Est/1stB 1995 ▪ Tasting & sales Mon-Fri 8-5 Sat 9-4 ▪ Closed Easter Fri/Sun, Dec 25 & Jan 1 ▪ BYO picnic ▪ Owners Bruwer family ▪ Winemaker/viticulturist Abrie Bruwer, with Johan van Zyl (Jun 2000) ▪ 150 ha (cabs s/f, merlot, chard, sauvignon) ▪ PO Box 770 Robertson 6705 ▪ info@springfieldestate.com ▪ www.springfieldestate.com © **(023) 626·3661** 🖷 *626·3664*

Adventurer, philosopher, challenger of convention; yet a traditionalist, a man of the soil. Abrie Bruwer, celebrating a decade producing his star-studded Springfield wines, never ceases to surprise. He's a keen fisherman (2004 harvest deemed first-rate because of a good yellowtail run), private pilot, frustrated yachtsman (but last year managed to fit in a month's sailing along the Croatian coast with his family). Refreshingly, he downplays his hard work and commitment. 'Johan [van Zyl] makes the wine; I make the mistakes.' Anything new? 'We are traditional, so everything tends to stay the same.' So he's still pushing the limits with his native-yeast fermentations (and winning, often spectacularly). Still ripping up and re-aligning north-south vines to run east-west for even ripening. And, now, upping vine density to a sardine-can-like 7 000/ha (5 000 is the norm), for extra flavour concentration. His view of recent estate legislation changes? 'An embarrassment. It's about the pocket, not purity of origin.'

★★★★★ **The Work of Time** Fleshy, fruit-crammed yet elegant blend cab f & merlot (40/40), with cab s & soupçon petit v. Realisation of a 10 yr old dream to make a Bdx-style red on the estate. We'd say worth the wait. Maiden **01** revisited for current ed shows all pvs delights in smoother, more seamless package. Marvellous concentration of ripe berry fruits (black-, logan-), hint of choc, fresh prune & savoury – big but beautifully proportioned. 18 mths Fr oak, some new. 14.5% alc. **02** not ready for tasting.

★★★★★ **Méthode Ancienne Cabernet Sauvignon** Steep, rocky, thorn-strangled site cleared 23 yrs ago for this cab vyd (abandoned ox wagon also removed); 'ancient' winemaking methods (100% native-yeast fermentation of whole berries in new Fr oak; ageing 2 yrs each on lees & in bottle; unfined/-filtered) give life to marvellous **99**, aromas of fresh berries & classy oak; intense chocolatey palate. Again the admirable purity of fruit seen in **98**, the same bright texture & ultra-soft tannins. Delicious now, with muted power hinting at a great future. 13.5–14% alc.

★★★★★ **Whole Berry Cabernet Sauvignon** ✓ Cellar's quest for gentlest possible flavour/tannin extraction – via fermentation of uncrushed berries with native yeasts – reflected here too; **02** maintains stellar quality of pvs vintage; delightful fresh-crushed blackcurrant tone, cosseting tannins. **01**, finest since maiden **99**, offered cassis-like lushness melded with mocha-toned oak. These gorgeous on release, with potential to improve up to ±8 yrs. ±Yr Fr oak, some new. 14% alc.

★★★★★ **Méthode Ancienne Chardonnay** Bruwer-style extreme winemaking taken to the limit in this version, 'inspired by ancient Burgundy': native-yeast-fermented in barrels, all Fr, 80% new; yr on lees sans sulphur, bottled un-everything (-filtered, -fined, -stabilised). **99**, only the 2nd successful attempt in 5, now followed by **02**, a tour de force: aromatic toasted oatmeal & lime introduction; open, lusciously creamy texture; clean, dry, emphatic finish. 14% alc. Unquestioned ageability: 'Made to last (we hope) a lifetime,' winemakers say. **03** is next.

★★★★ **Wild Yeast Chardonnay** Unwooded, characterful version, off well aged (22 yrs) block; vinification as above; 13 mths *sur lie*, 100% through malo, which shows in creamily rich texture of **02**; retasted mid-2004, a lovely note of bottle-age peeps though the peaches, citrus & white flowers; still that refreshing citrus tang. 14% alc. Luckily **03**'s waiting in the wings.

★★★★ **Special Cuvée Sauvignon Blanc** Muscular style, distinct from 'extra-flinty' version below; from mature (20 yrs), extra-cool riverine vyd. **04** piercing combo flint & fragrant tropical fruit, exotic persimmon whiff; light-bodied but ripe, sweet-fruited, kept in trim by bracingly fresh finish. Best in its youth.

★★★★ **Life from Stone Sauvignon Blanc** ✓ Striking & individual elixir eked from estate's rockiest soils. Our general rating upped on basis of **03**, finest of recent vintages, & matching **04**, showing extraordinary complexity in youth (spectrum covers cordite to fresh tropical fruit); great depth too, elegantly delivered without alcoholic punch (12.3%). Abrie B believes this will continue to improve over 6 yrs. — *DH*

Spring Grove see Zorgvliet
Spring Valley see Old Vines Cellars
Spruitdrift see Westcorp
S/SW see South, South West

Stark-Condé Wines 🍷

*Stellenbosch ▪ Est/1stB 1998 ▪ Tasting & sales by appt ▪ Owner Jonkershoek Cellars (Pty) Ltd ▪ Winemaker José Condé ▪ Viticulturist Pieter Smit ▪ 40 ha (cab, shiraz) ▪ 60 tons 3 000 cs 100% red ▪ PO Box 389 Stellenbosch 7599 ▪ info@stark-conde.co.za ▪ www.stark-conde.co.za ℰ **887·3665** 🖷 887·4340*

Graphic designer-turned-winemaker José Condé completed an 18-month cellar renovation just as last harvest got into swing. 'It took a great deal of sweat, but I think it was worth it. Nothing fancy, just practical and clean.' Next project was a tasting room, set to open to the public as the guide went to bed. This is a small but meticulous operation. Everything is just so, including the styleful packaging (designed by JC, of course). What *is* lacking here, by definition, is quantity, though fans will be heartened by a mini-cornucopia coming their way: dual vintages of Stark Cab (01 and 02) released only 6 months apart (we'll let the winemaker explain why). Fresh excitement comes via two new wines: a Merlot from Jonkershoek grapes and a Shiraz, partly off an older block in Paarl farmed under JC's supervision. (For a different taste of the latter vineyard, see the Sénga Shiraz under MAN Vintners, a JC joint venture). His take on 2004? 'All the wines look great.'

★★★★★ **Condé Cabernet Sauvignon** Restraint & harmony, fine ripe fruit & supple tannin the hallmarks here. **02** brings merlot & shiraz (5% each) into play. Brooding cassis aromas, leafy whiffs lead to intense, ripe but reined-in palate, with seamless tannins, persistent flavours. 14.1% alc. 22 mths Fr oak, third new. Unfined, unfiltered. Sweeter, less reductive than gamier **01** (retasted; ★★★★), where more organic notes dominate pure cab version; 13.8% alc. Both in same mould as densely fruited, sumptuous **00** FCTWS trophy 2002. Will benefit from ±5 yrs cellaring.

Stark range

★★★★ **Cabernet Sauvignon** Leafy rather than black-fruited **02**, with austere fine mid-palate tannins, elegant but unconcentrated, herbal finish. 14.1% alc. Less sumptuous than **01** where spice, violets & blackcurrant notes abound. 92 pts *WS*. In Fr oak 22 mths, third new.

★★★★ **Shiraz** 🆕 Raspberry, allspice notes on **02**. Succulent sweet & ripe berry fruit flavours on sumptuous mid-palate; no real grip but an elegant polished finish. Attractive & accessible, with big 14.5% alc quite well submerged. Home vyds supplemented by Paarl fruit. 22 mths Fr oak, 10% new.

★★★★☆ **Merlot** 🆕 **02** another elegant offering. Minty, mulberry prelude to richly textured mouthful, with slight herbal notes, and a good finish marked by cassia, marzipan. 14.1% alc. Oaking as cab above; unfined, unfiltered. — *MF*

Starke see Westbridge

St Clements see Frost Vineyards

St Dalfour see Lost Horizons

Steenberg Vineyards

Constantia ▪ Est 1990 ▪ 1stB 1996 ▪ Tasting & sales Mon-Fri 9-4.30 Sat & public holidays 9.30-1.30 ▪ Closed Easter Sun/Mon, Dec 25/26, Jan 1 ▪ Fee R5 (4 wines), R10 (full range) ▪ Tours by appt Mon-Fri 10 & 3 Sat 10 ▪ Catharina's Restaurant; five-star Steenberg Hotel; championship golf course etc (see Stay-over/Eat-out sections) ▪ Owner Shamwari Holdings ▪ Winemaker John Loubser, with Ruth Penfold (Nov 2001/2003) ▪ Viticulturists Herman Hanekom & Johann de Swart (1990/1999) ▪ 63 ha (cab, merlot, shiraz, sauvignon, semillon) ▪ 450 tons 35 000 cs 40% red 60% white ▪ PO Box 224 Steenberg 7947 ▪ info@steenbrg.co.za ▪ www.steenberg-vineyards.co.za ✆ 713·2211 📠 713·2201

The first day of spring 2004 saw this high-flying Constantia cellar mark 10 years of its Sauvignon with a vertical tasting and matching dinner. The anniversary coincided with SA's much-celebrated 'decade of democracy'. We're not sure which Namibian-born cellarmaster John Loubser was more enamoured of. Maybe both milestones were overshadowed by his delight at winning the 2003 Diners Club Winemaker of the Year (category semillon) — not with a Steenberg (that came second) but with neighbouring Constantia Uitsig's Reserve, which he makes on a consultancy basis. But sauvignon is Steenberg's star; 2004's cool, late vintage promises something celestial. 'There's a great demand for sauvignon,' avers Loubser, especially in Europe and the US. What's required to capitalise? 'Sustained quality and perfect service.' He's sure the 'great new member' of the team, energetic, keen young winemaker Ruth Penfold will help up the ante.

★★★★★ **Merlot** Soft red-berried minty elegance at new levels concentration, subtlety in previewed **03**. Cool, creamy with lovely back-palate richness, telling mineral thread. **02** bolder, more sturdily framed, smoky highlights to rich fruit concoction. Ageing will benefit; most for early or med-term drinking. 14 mths new Fr oak.

★★★★ **Catharina** Flagship, from **02** (★★★★☆) in new, distinctive guise: 5-way 'unique blend' says winemaker (for eponymous lady's quintet of consorts) — cab, shiraz, merlot, cab f (36/26/25/11) & nebbiolo. Engaging, refined; farm's red-berry/mint thumbprint plus savoury, minerally adornments. Light-textured, deeply flavoursome, with tannin nip to sweet-fruited length. 20 mths new Fr barriques. 14% alc. **01** firm sleek, savoury trio cab, merlot, shiraz.

★★★★ **Nebbiolo** Improvements each vintage in colour, character. **03** with telling lustrous ruby clarity, high-toned violet fragrance, reverberating minerally tannins. Most satisfying, balanced to date. **02** convincing red-wine hue; savoury; with immense dry tannin. Comes into its own with creamy Italian cuisine. Yr older Fr oak. 15% alc.

★★★★ **Shiraz** Constantia fallen off map a bit with its 1970s trademark red; this & others should start redressing situation. **03** yet to settle, integrate; inklings of future charms in delicately handled fruit, tannins; complementary oak still ruling spicy red berries, toasty-gamey undertones. 14% alc. Yr new oak, 60/40 Fr/Am. **02** white spice, red fruits; big & supple, enlivening fresh spine. Portion fermented in oak.

★★★★★ **Sauvignon Blanc Reserve** Cape signature sauvignon from first **94**; richer, more demanding style with more staying power than regular bottling. **04** real power-house (toy with it at your peril!). Potent dried grass intensity; sweet-fruited, viscous, penetrating mouthful delivered with flair, poise to fantail, dry conclusion. Bigger than **03** statement wine; penetrating yet agile. VDG, *Wine* ★★★★★, 14% alc. Single vyd.

★★★★ **Sauvignon Blanc** 'Can't make enough', says John L of this classy, unflashy favourite. **04** lithe, succulent, bouncily dry with heady cool climate fruit purity – citrus, gooseberry, dried grass; extra flavour, friendly mouthfeel also from 14% semillon. 13% alc.

★★★★★ **Semillon** Distinctive new-breed Cape semillon. Stylish **04** (★★★★★) arrives with exuberant lemon, mandarin, honey flags flying; mth in new Fr oak merely adds weight, dimension to joyous ensemble. Breathtaking now; has concentration for sophisticated maturity. Single vyd. **03** powerful, fine; 3-4 yr development. ±14.5% alc always elegantly carried. *Wine* ★★★★★; Diners Club runner-up.

★★★★ **Steenberg 1682 Brut** Demand for this MCC sees quantities now more than double to 26 000 bottles. Current **03** chardonnay/pinot (68/32) blend, given as NV, yields authentic brioche/biscuity focus; small barrel-fermented portion enriches fine, creamy bead; ends properly 'brut', but no harshness. 12.5% alc. – *AL*

Stellar Winery

*Olifants River ▪ Est 1998 ▪ 1stB 2001 ▪ Tasting & sales Mon-Sat 8-8 ▪ Closed Easter Fri/Sun & Dec 25 ▪ Tours by appt ▪ Farm produce ▪ Tourgroups ▪ Owner Stellar Organics (Pty) Ltd ▪ Winemaker Dudley Wilson (Jan 2002), with Martin Theys & Bertie Jones (2000) ▪ Viticulturist Dudley Wilson ▪ 100 ha (merlot, pinotage, shiraz, colombard, sauvignon, muscat d'A) ▪ 1 000 tons 45 000 cs own labels + 400 000ℓ bulk + 10 000 cs for clients, incl Natuvin (Holland), Namaqua Organic (international), Tappery Nook (UK) ▪ 80% red 17% white 2% rosé 1% other ▪ HACCP & Eurogap certified ▪ PO Box 4 Klawer 8145 ▪ info@ stellarorganics.com ▪ www.stellarorganics.com ⓒ **(027) 216·1310** 🖷 (027) 216·1537*

This innovative winery on the Cape winelands' outer fringe intends 'leading the way in the major growth market of organic wines over the next five years,' informs winemaker Dudley Wilson. Cellar growth and experimentation continue apace. They've developed a time-saving method to turn the cap on tank-fermenting reds using filtered, compressed air ('pneumetage' Wilson calls it). A giant mechancial sieve for reclaming pips (by variety!) for up-coming organic grapeseed oil production. They are also now Fairtrade accredited, committing them to internationally accepted, sustainable market practices. Sauvignon on a hill brushed by afternoon breezes was the big surprise of an overall cooler 2004. Shiraz and ruby cab also performed. The new additions below to their cosmically inspired range will soon be joined by a few others; new clients include a German international and a US distributor.

The Sensory Collection

Shiraz Re-tasted **02** (★★) disappoints now – hasn't held up. Shoe-polish whiffs, light flavours. Best serve chilled. Wood element from powder. 14% alc. **Pinotage** Again, yr not kind to revisited **02** (★★): clumsy oaking evident on palate, finishes rather bitter. **Cabernet** NEW **03** barrel sample (likely ★★★★) shows aromas/flavours rhubarb & cassis; better-balanced wood (Fr/Am mix), fruit & acid.

Stellar range

Sauvignon Blanc NEW ☺ ★★★ Pineapple, tropical fruit aromas on **04**; good balance of fruit with crisp acidity; easy-going ±12% alc well suited for lunchtime pleasure.

Cabernet Sauvignon 🆕 ★★ **03** crème fraiche & black berry notes make for a most unusual cab. 13.3% alc. **Shiraz** ★★★ **02** in Rhône style: leathery, gamey, savoury; well balanced. Wood element from powder, as for all these reds. 14% alc. **01** (★★★★) more concentration, wood character, fruit. Retasted, as are all the **02** wines here. **Pinotage** ★★ **02** has morphed into old style, redolent of acetone, bananas, rubber; rather hard tannins. **Merlot** ★★★ Honest varietal expression & unobtrusive 14.4% alc make **02** easy drinking now, & for short term. **Muscat d'Alexandrie** ★★★★ Well-preserved floral nose on **02**, with characteristic rose-petal aromas/flavours; light (12.4% alc), virtually dry palate a good match for Thai, Vietnamese dishes. **Colombar 02** now flat, with only memories of honeyed fruit to balance 14.5% alc. **Colombard-Sauvignon Blanc** ★★ (Pvsly 'Wooded White') 62/28 blend, the wood influence courtesy of a little Am wood-powder. **02**'s fruit now fading fast now — drink up. 13.8% alc. **Heaven on Earth Vin de Paille** 🆕 **03** tank sample a convincing statement from muscat d'A dried on straw & rooibos tea. Unctuous mouthfeel (300g/ℓ sugar), with heavy middle palate of cooked apricot, cream & rooibos.11.5% alc. Perhaps even ★★★★★ on release.

Live-A-Little range

> **Moonlight Shiraz** ☺ ★★★ Fiendishly drinkable **03**; unadorned shiraz with distinctly savoury mix roast meat, spice & dark red fruits in friendly frame.

Wildly Wicked White ★★★ (Pvsly 'Colombar') **03** clean, light colombard; pleasant, but not much varietal character; quaffable 12.5% alc. (Also under **Firefly White** label.) Retasted **Colombar** ★ **03** is tired, flat. **Really Ravishing Red** (Pvsly 'Dry Red') **02** ★★★ Fruity nose; generally unpretentious unwooded blend of ruby cab, pinotage & shiraz, probably nicest slightly chilled. Moderate 12.3% alc. (Also labelled **Firefly Red**.) — *NP*

Stellekaya Wines

Stellenbosch ▪ Est/1stB 1999 ▪ Mon-Thu by appt Fri & Sat 10-4 ▪ Fee R10 (incl glass) ▪ Sales daily 9-4 ▪ Closed public holidays ▪ Meals by appt ▪ Facilities for small tourgroups ▪ Owner Dave & Jane Lello ▪ Winemaker Peet le Roux, with Nontsikilela Biyela (1998/2004) ▪ ±60 tons 100% red ▪ PO Box 12426 Die Boord 7613 ▪ stellekaya@iafrica.com ▪ www.stellekaya.com ✆ 883·3873 ☎ 883·2536

Jane and Dave Lello are heavily involved in developing the old KWV brandy site in Stellenbosch, now called Bosman's Crossing after the historic railway junction once in Dorp Street. By the spring of 2004 Phase I of a 'community village' had been built, with a town square due for completion at the end of this year. The Stellekaya cellar, an integral part of the complex, is open for tours, tastings and (pre-booked) meals. Peet le Roux continues to oversee this reds-only operation, with Stellenbosch graduate Ntsiki Biyela joining as assistant winemaker last harvest. Stellekaya ('Home of the Stars') has been given new packaging, featuring the star charts of 17th century astronomer Johannes Hevelius. The first labels depict the constellations of Taurus, Scorpio and the Southern Cross.

★★★★ **Cape Cross** 🆕 **02** flagship Cape blend of merlot, pinotage, cab (50/30/20). Perfumed notes & attractive red fruits; well balanced palate, supported by tannic structure to ensure few yrs development. 13.5% alc. 22 mths Fr oak, 30% new.

★★★★ **Cabernet Sauvignon** Fine-tannined & classically styled **02** (★★★★★) a remarkable achievement in a weak vintage. Dark choc, cassis fruit harmonising with ripe tannins, 14.2% alc. 22 mths Fr oak, 60% new. **01** (★★★) was elegant if somewhat austere & herbal.

★★★★ **Merlot 02** light (13.3% alc lower than usual) & lively; with red plum & green olive notes. 22 mths Fr oak, 25% new. Not for keeping: enjoy now. Revisited **01** now a little medicinal, though good fruit, soft finish. 14.3% alc.

Boschetto Rosso Red ★★★★ Pvs was 'Merlot' by name & constitution; step-up **03** blends merlot with cab/shiraz (40/40/20). Fruit-driven, approachable pizzeria wine with element of complexity, good tannin support. 13.5% alc. — *NP*

Stellenbosch Hills

*Stellenbosch • Est 1945 • 1stB 1972 • Tasting & sales Mon-Fri 9-4.45 Sat 9-12.15 (sales close 15 mins later) • Fee R10 • Closed Easter Fri, Dec 25 & Jan 1 • Owners 20 members • Winemakers Kowie du Toit & PG Slabbert (Aug 1973/Jan 1997) • Viticulturist PG Slabbert (Jan 1997), advised by Johan Pienaar • ±1 000 ha (cab, merlot, pinotage, shiraz, chard, chenin, sauvignon) • 8 000 tons 20 000 cs own label 65% red 35% white • PO Box 40 Vlottenburg 7604 • vlottenb@netactive.co.za • www.vlottenburg.co.za © **881·3828/9** ᗏ 881·3357*

New brooms swept thoroughly: the name change (it was 'Vlottenburg Winery') for this 60 year old co-op coincided with another portfolio — that of manager — for winemaker PG Slabbert; stylish new labels; a revamp of the wine-making area; and extensions to the tasting room. After something of a Muscat de Hambourg drought, visitors should now be able to taste and buy this unusual and popular wine: new vines were planted three years ago and harvested for the first time in 2004. Gnarled old vines, by contrast, are those in a pinotage block planted in 1972 and still in production.

- ★★★★★ **1707 Reserve** ＮＥＷ Intended as flagship, which it achieves with aplomb. Stylish **01** densely packed dark choc core with hints mint, black cherry & lead pencil; convinces as classic Cape Bdx blend (50/50 cab/merlot). Sleek & compact, with not so much as a glimmer of tannin out of place. Alc 13.5%. Keep 5+ yrs.
- ★★★★ **Cabernet Sauvignon** ✓ Ripe mulberry intro to **02**, then shows savoury meaty fruit & touches of cool cedar, firmish tannins. 16 mths Fr oak, 30% new. Could do with 3/4 yrs in cellar. Alc 13.5%. **01** another good expression of the variety.
- ★★★★ **Merlot** ✓ Latest **02** maintains excellent track record with this variety — an achievement in difficult vintage. Classically styled with ripe cassis & coffee aromas/flavours, clean spice of good oak (Fr, 20% new). Standout **01** clinched two top 2003 FCTWS awards: Best Merlot & Discovery of Show.
- ★★★☆ **Pinotage 02** (★★★) classically constructed & bone dry; ripe pruney fruit given good dose of oak – yr older Fr. Layered spice, touch green on finish. 13.5% alc.
- ★★★☆ **Shiraz** Well-structured, medium-bodied style with soft ripe tannins in **02** (★★★) Choc/meaty depth & well oaked, almost ready. 16 mths oak, 50%new (Fr/Am), balance used Fr. **01** pervasive sweet-spicy vanilla, hints smoked meat.
- ★★★☆ **Chardonnay** ✓ Latest **04** (sample) gorgeous whiff toast to lime marmalade fruit; rich, buttery — full breakfast special. Ample proportions, threaded with vibrant acidity. Hope it makes its way intact to bottle (provisional rating).
- ★★★★ **Muscat de Hambourg** Normally fine example of this unusual variety, fortified jerepiko-style. **04** unready for tasting; in 375ml bottles.

Blanc de Blanc ☺ ★★★ Unpretentious NV from chenin, sauvignon (60/40); lightish, off-dry. Latest with juicy green-apple flavour, touch sugar on finish. This, Rouge below, 1 000ml flagon screwcap.

Rouge ★★ NV unwooded blend pinotage, cinsaut 50/50, unusually scented — baked bread & tart red berries, dry & savoury with tannic flick in tail. **Sauvignon Blanc** ★★★ **04** (sample) shows greenpepper, cut grass & gooseberry intensity; mouthwatering acidity, long finish. **Chenin Blanc** ★★ **04** (sample) restrained like pvs **03** & similarly showing demure green melon aromas. Off-dry, easy drinking. 13% alc. **Cabernet Sauvignon Limited Release**, **Pinotage Limited Release** discontinued. — *IvH*

Stellenbosch Vineyards

Stellenbosch • Est 1997 • Tasting at Helderberg Winery: Mon-Fri 9-5.30 Sat 9-5; Welmoed Winery: Mon-Sat 9-5 Sun 10-4 Public holidays 9-5 • Closed Easter Fri, Dec 25 & Jan 1 • Meals/refreshments – at Welmoed: Duck Pond Restaurant, daily, © 881·3310; Helderberg Restaurant, Mon-Sat, © 842·2012 • Play areas for children • Tourgroups • Owners 190 shareholders • Winemakers Chris Kelly, Carmen Stevens, Morné van Rooyen, Pieter Kleinhans &

*Danie van Tonder, with Albert Basson & Anthony Meduna ▪ Viticulturists Francois de Villiers &
Johan Hewett ▪ 2 000 ha (cabs s/f, merlot, pinotage, shiraz, chard, chenin, sauvignon, semillon, viognier) ▪ 10 000 tons 850 000 cs 70% red 30% white ▪ ISO 9001:2000 & BRC certified ▪
PO Box 465 Stellenbosch 7599 ▪ info@stellvine.co.za ▪ www.stellvine.co.za ℂ **881·3870** 🖷
881·3102*

Maintaining high quality in large commercial volumes is no mean feat, particularly if the
directive is to make the wine as price competitive as possible. Last year cellarmaster
Chris Kelly noted that to meet this challenge, consolidation was an option, if the right
partner could be found. The words were hardly spoken when the story broke: in June
2004 Stellenbosch Vineyards and Vinfruco announced their intended merger — not yet
approved at press time but likely, given the considerable cost-cutting benefits. Kelly (for
whom the superb 2004 vintage will always be memorable — he formalised the chemistry
in the cellar with winemaker Carmen Stevens in a marriage proposal) adds that SA suffers a shortage of marketing skills rather than a surplus of wine, particularly red wine,
which he identifies as the real growth opportunity.

Genesis range

★★★★ **Cabernet Sauvignon** Showstopper label but in restrained, sophisticated rather
than overt mode. **01** richer, riper; everything beautifully in place, blackberry/mul-
berry intensity interleaved with cigarbox spicing, fine-grained tannins. 18 mths Fr
oak, 30% new. 14.5% alc. No hurry to drink these. **02** unready for tasting.

★★★★★ **Merlot** Always ultra-ripe. Last tasted was **01**, with more sinewy structure to voluptuous plum-pudding/choc/spice tones. Tightly knit, youthful tannins match fruit
concentration. 18 mths Fr oak, 40% new. 13.7% alc.

★★★★★ **Shiraz 02** deep-fruited & sumptuously oaked, shows exceptional complexity in
meaty/woodsmoky/creamy spice layers around dark-berried fruit. Easily absorbs
oak (18 mths Fr/Am, half new), 14.5% alc. Complex **01** JCMA trophy.

★★★★ **Chardonnay 03**'s big build not at expense of elegance. White peach & vanilla pod
intro, creamy smooth texture, soft acidity enhances generous build, richness. 40%
native yeast fermented; ± yr oak, 40% new. 14% alc. **02** sold out early; untasted.

Kumkani range

★★★★ **Shiraz** ✓ Impressively complex at this early age, latest **02** follows in path of elegantly structured **01**. Manages difficult act of balancing good flesh/fruit with unobtrusive structure. Intermingling scents/tastes — smoked meat, veld fire, black
plums — provide continual discovery, pleasure. 15 mths Fr/Am oak (70/30).

★★★★★ **Pinotage 02** (followed 99); multi-layered complexity confirms class discerned in
sample; red berry/banana ripeness shot through with scrub/cedar; muscular, built
to last 6+ yrs. Only half oaked, yr Fr/Am.

★★★★ **Merlot-Cabernet Franc** ✓ Designed to impress – & does. Last tasted was 70/30
blend **01** with heady perfume; seamlessly oaked (18 mths Fr). 13.4% alc. No **02**.

★★★★ **Shiraz-Cabernet Sauvignon 02** poised, integrated blend 75/25 in traditional
savoury style, satisfyingly dry. Rich, dense pruney fruit given 15 mths in mainly Fr
barriques. **01** (★★★★) polished & taut; 14% alc.

★★★★ **Sauvignon Blanc** ✓ **04** (sample) showy like **03**, but justifiably so, as there's substance in this great food wine (moderate 13% alc). Fresh nettle/green fig aromas,
intense, mouthfilling lime/passionfruit flavours, smooth acidity, long finish.

★★★★ **Viognier** Maiden **03** sampled last ed, now firm-fleshed, less curvaceous but still
well endowed, the jasmine/peach fragrances a signature. Perhaps a shade too
much oak (new Fr) for fruit. Acid/tannin provides backbone, definition. 13.5% alc.

★★★★ **VVS** Big, modern **03**, tasted pre-bottling last yr, has developed well. Innovative
blend viognier, verdelho, sauvignon, seducing with ripe peach, lime & grapefruit
aromas. Rich, creamy mouthfeel; classy, concentrated fruit threaded by green (not
unripe) flavours, enlivened by firm acidity. 14% alc.

Infiniti range
★★★☆ **Brut MCC 00**'s honeyed bottle age on nose contrasts with bone dry & lean palate, with crisp, biscuity feel & texture. Mostly chardonnay, with 5% pinot. Elegant & stylish. Alc 12.4%. **99**, same blend & similar style, now peaking.

Versus range

> **Red** ☺ ★★★ **03** allsorts quaffer, very essence of red berries, lively & juicy. Dash oak adds firmness, flavour to fruit-driven charm. 13% alc. **Rosé** ☺ **NEW** ★★★ Gorgeous shell-pink beckons seductively; **04** shy-ish but pleasing crushed berry flavours plumped to off-dryness with 12.5g/ℓ sugar; a real quaffer from pinotage, shiraz, merlot. **White** ☺ ★★★ Bright fruit, perky & lively, **04** blend chenin/sauvignon shows neat balancing act of touch sweetness & zesty acidity for easy drinkability.

@Six range
Shiraz-Cabernet Sauvignon Rosé discontinued.

Welmoed range
★★★☆ **Cabernet Sauvignon** Retasted 02 (★★★) now revealing lean, savoury style. Restrained herbaceous/red berry fragrance, flavours; cedar dusting, firm backbone enhanced by yr Fr barriques. Moderate 12.8%. A bit short on fullness, ripeness.
★★★☆ **Pinotage** ✓ Early-drinking **03** recognisable from the first whiff of Star pink-sweets, raspberry & cherry, to lip-smacking palate, crammed with red & black berries.
★★★☆ **Merlot 02** retasted mid-2004, with black cherry & spicy plums having taken on some gravitas; the tannins still need yr/2 to soften. Yr Fr oak; 14% alc.
★★★☆ **Shiraz 03** ripe, heady, spiced fruitcake, prune & smoke, well-judged oak (yr Fr barriques) imparts muscular beefy style. Drink now, next ±4 yrs. 14% alc.
★★★☆ **Chardonnay 03** more restrained (but delicious) after **02**'s extrovert debut, but also shows signature butterscotch/marmalade richness, with more oak for firmness, weight & seriousness. 50% in Fr oak, 6 mths. 13.9% alc.

> **Blanc de Blanc** ☺ ★★★ Sample **04** combines zesty lemon scents/flavours with creamy length, lovely weight & style. Better than everyday, & very drinkable 12.7% alc.

Sauvignon Blanc ★★★ Less arresting **04** has distant echoes of fig & capsicum; pleasantly fruity, dry. **Chenin Blanc** ★★★ **04** offers baked apple flavours, is lightish in feel & intensity, though 13.5% alc.

Helderberg range
★★★☆ **Shiraz** ✓ Stylish **03** back on form; liquid dark choc, with smoked beef, prune notes; gently oaked (seasoned Fr), a better than everyday drink. 13.3% alc.
★★★☆ **Pinotage 03** signals return to range. Showy sweet redcurrant & vanilla flavours, lush body, bite of tannin on finish. All Stbosch grapes (like above). 3 mths staves.

> **Chenin Blanc** ☺ ★★★ Welcome reappearance with **04**. Bouncy version, well padded with juicy melon & lime fruit, just asking to be taken to the beach or the pool. Easy tippling at 11.5% alc. **Sauvignon Blanc** ☺ ★★★ **04** light, tasty & vibrant. Tangy citrus flavours, mouthwatering & fresh, almost dainty. Bone dry & zingy, perfect for tomato & mozzarella salad in the garden. **Shiraz-Carignan** ☺ ★★★ **03** lighter style red with juicy red cherry fruit & soft tannins, touch of sugar neatly bypasses brashness & austerity of young reds. Easy drinking 12.6% alc.

Cabernet Sauvignon ★★★☆ **03** delicious, ripe dark mulberry flavours & juice, then cab's firmer tannins kick in — a wake-up call that this is rather more serious. Oak staves 3 mths. Drinkable 12.4% alc. **Merlot-Cabernet Sauvignon** ★★★ **03** herbaceous cab now a signature, fresh capsicum & cassis mingle easily without any jarring notes; soft tannins signal early accessibility. 13.3% alc. Drink over next few yrs. **Cabernet Sauvignon-Pinotage** NEW ★★★ Unlikely **03** partners combine well — sweet fleshy pinotage with cab giving a touch of cedar & a flick of tannin in tail. 3 mths staves. Easy-going 12.5% alc. **Chenin Blanc-Sauvignon Blanc** ★★★ **03** last ed promised fruit salad aromas/flavours & food-friendly verve. 12.9% alc. **04** unready for tasting. **Chardonnay** ★★★ **04** (sample) lively & bouncy, ripe peach juiciness with contrasting, mouthwatering tang of greengage skin; 3 mths oaking well hidden. **Semillon-Chardonnay** ★★★ Fruit-focused **04** (sample) plenty of peachy ripeness, juice, around firm minerally core; zesty acidity for balance.

Shamwari range

Shiraz ☺ ★★★ **03** reprises **02**'s Karoo scrub, red berry attractions, but more meat & muscularity, some gruff tannins to match. Very food-friendly, & alc a modest 13.2%.

Merlot-Cabernet Sauvignon 03 pre-bottling sample promises to be a hit (provisional ★★★★); dusty capsicum & cedar of cab (30%) with the flesh & sensuous appeal of merlot; poised, balanced, & dangerously easy to drink! **Chardonnay** ★★★ **04** (sample) ripe musk melon aromas/flavours, softly smoky, good fleshy weight nicely balanced by smooth acidity. Unoaked. — *IvH*

Stellendrift

Stellenbosch ▪ Est/1stB 1996 ▪ 1stB 1996 ▪ Tasting & sales daily 9-5 at Vredenheim (see entry for amenities/attractions) ▪ Fee R2 ▪ Closed Dec 25 ▪ Owner/winemaker/viticulturist Fanie Cilliers (SHZ Cilliers/Kuün Wines) ▪ 12 ha (cab, merlot, pinotage) ▪ ±5 000 cs 90% red 10% white ▪ PO Box 6340 Uniedal 7612 ▪ fcilliers@wam.co.za © 887-6561/082-372-5180 ⊟ 887-6561

Vintage 2003 was the year of the broken arm; 2004 was the year of the lightning strike. Make that plural — Fanie Cilliers and his foreman were felled ('just for a while, luckily') by the first bolt which hit a harvesting trailer; the second struck at Vredenheim, where FC vinifies, while pumping was in progress, knocking out the phones (but fortunately not the workers). On the upside, it was a year of independence: the winemaker and his own staff manned the cellar, and he marketed most of his grapes himself. And some acclaim: the Merlot was named a Best Value by Wine of the Month, following on a similar award for the Cab-Merlot from *Wine* magazine at the end of 2003.

Cabernet Sauvignon ★★★ **02** retasted, still youthfully berry-toned with attractive old-oak backing; characterful. 8 mths Fr/Am oak; lightish 12.5% alc. **Merlot** NEW ★★★ **02** combines fresh ripe plums & eucalyptus in an individual styling, sweet-sour tingle cushions the firm tannins. Yr Fr/Am oak. **Cabernet Sauvignon-Merlot 'Memoir'** ★★★ **01**'s ripe berry fruit showing well; should be enjoyed soon while at peak. — *DH*

StellenHills

Stellenbosch ▪ Est/1stB 2001 ▪ Visits by appt ▪ Owner/winemaker Johann Slazus, with David Lockley (2000) ▪ ±700 cs 36% red 64% white ▪ PO Box 415 Stellenbosch 7599 ▪ orders@stellenhills.co.za ▪ www.stellenhills.co.za © 083-252-2020 ⊟ 887-7745

In this relatively new wine venture, David Lockley (of Yonder Hill, here in an advisory capacity) and owner Johann Slazus, an ophthalmic surgeon, make two contrasting styles of chardonnay, using new and second/third-fill barrels for fermentation and maturation. Their aim is to produce wines that truly reflect their origin.

Charade ★★★★ Uncertified (due to administrative glitch) dry red from shiraz (60%) & cab, fermented in open wood vats, aged yr in new Fr oak. Approachable, soft & plump; some meaty/plummy notes, powdery but harmonious tannins; modest 13% alc. **Barriques Nouveau** ★★★★ Chardonnay, barrel-fermented/aged in new Fr oak; from single vyd. **03** faintly exotic introduction, glimpses passionfruit & toasty oak; fat tropical fruit flavours, mouthfilling (14% alc), engaging. **Chardonnay** ★★★★ Only 2nd/3rd fill oak for this version, 11 mths; **03** shy herby nose, hint grapefruit rind; crisper than above, slightly better focused lime-citrus flavours; rich-ish crème brûlée finish. Alc as above. — *TM*

░ *Stellenvale* see Ultra Liquors

Stellenzicht Vineyards

Stellenbosch ▪ Tasting & sales Mon-Fri 9-5 Sat/Sun & public holidays 10-4 ▪ Fee R15 (R25 incl glass) ▪ Owner Lusan Holdings ▪ Winemaker Guy Webber, with Ilse van Dijk ▪ Vineyards Gary Probert ▪ 70% red 30% white ▪ PO Box 104 Stellenbosch 7599 ▪ info@stellenzicht.co.za ▪ www.stellenzicht.co.za Ⓒ 880·103/4 ▤ 880·1107

It was the SAA Shield taste-off in 1995 that put this Lusan-owned winery on the map, when its Syrah 94 placed ahead of names to conjure with. Ten years later, it's worth noting that it's one of *Wine* magazine's Top Ten wineries, based on performance over a decade. But there's no laurels-lolling for Guy Webber & co: in a drive for the most scientific approach they've tapped the expertise of Eben Archer, associate professor of Viticulture & Oenology at Stellenbosch University and latterly full-time viticulturist for the Lusan wineries, mapped soils, installed drip irrigation and established weather stations. News from the cellar is the release of a Cape red, Rhapsody. 'It's my baby,' confesses the winemaker. 'It's a wine I really like.' Also new is elegant packaging for the Golden Triangle range, with a distinctive golden triangle in one corner, as though the label has been folded back. 'Triangle', of course, refers to the farm's situation in the prime, slope-rich area between Stellenbosch and the Helderberg.

★★★★☆ **Syrah** Set a new Cape shiraz benchmark with dramatic **94**; quality level sustained with latest **02**, but the real excitement will come only around turn of decade, when currently restrained, ripe, smoky fruit emerges from strong tannin sheath. Worth waiting for. IWC 2004 gold for **01**, with headily spicy bouquet & electrifying, sustained finish, lavish 15.8% alc. ±19 mths Fr, Am, Hungarian oak. From mature vyd named 'Plum Pudding Hill'.

★★★★ **Stellenzicht** Cab-dominated Bdx blend (±50%), tempered by merlot (30%), equal parts cab f, malbec. Nothing since **00**, which displayed a polished structure.

★★★★ **Cabernet Sauvignon 00** a one-off. Showed huge colour, flavour concentration; 30 mths new Fr oak. Will reward another ±5 yrs cellaring. 14% alc.

★★★★★ **Semillon Reserve** Usually serious dry white, though latest **03** (★★★★) somewhat less striking mid-2004; shows elegance but lacks definition of pvs; overt butteriness dominates palate, finishes abruptly; whereas **02**, retained usual complexity in spite of lesser yr. Recent alcs 14.5+%. 85% wooded, new/2nd fill Fr, Am, Hngrian oak 9 mths.

Rhapsody 𝗡𝗘𝗪 ★★★ Blend pinotage/shiraz (53/47), 16 mths mainly new oak, Fr/Am/Hngrian; **02** light coloured/fleshed, slightly earthy; very dry.

Golden Triangle range

★★★★ **Cabernet Sauvignon** Tailored mouthful, for those averse to full-frontal fruit. Last tasted was **99**, with fragrant cedar, more slender build than pvs.

★★★★ **Merlot** None sampled since **00**, with trademark clean-fruited succulence bolstered by ripe meaty frame.

★★★★ **Pinotage 01** was among top 10 in *Wine*'s 2003 Pinotage champs; lovely creamy aromas; juicy cherry fruit-pulp ordered by sweet tannins. **02** (★★★) shows old-style acetone character, firm acidity & charry oak, obvious 15.5%.

★★★★ **Shiraz** Enviable show record, usually characterful, rewarding. VDG for **01**, pepper-and-spice aromas with plump accessible fruit, firm ripe tannins for keeping. **02** (★★★) just about handles forceful 15.5% alc. Expressive fruit, but needs time for charry wood to settle. ±15 mths mix new/seasoned oak, mostly Fr.

★★★★ **Sauvignon Blanc 04** like pvs in the tropical-fruit spectrum – on nose & palate, with tingling sherbety acidity. **03** (★★★) had a generous collage of tropical flavours, ended with hint of sweetness.

Chardonnay ★★★ Barrel-fermented/matured **03**, creamy, spicy & savoury; fair amount of sweet-sour acidity exposed in tail. — *RK/CR*

Sterhuis

*Stellenbosch ▪ Est 1980 ▪ 1stB 2002 ▪ Visits by appt ▪ Closed Christian holidays ▪ Facilities for children ▪ Conservation area ▪ Owners Kruger family ▪ Winemaker Johan Kruger ▪ Viticulturist Thys von Solms, advised by Kevin Watt ▪ 48 ha ▪ 300 tons 800-2 000 cs own label 50/50 red/white ▪ PO Box 131 Koelenhof 7605 ▪ sterhuis@intekom.co.za ©/🖻 **906·1195***

The weather during ripening of the 2004 vintage resulted in wines that are developing more slowly than usual, comments André Kruger from the family farm on the Bottelary Hills, 'and they should last much longer than the previous vintage'. Two hectares of sauvignon blanc and one of merlot went into the ground last year, a cool 350-400m above sea level; irrigation is being installed to further vine health. Son Johan, previously at Jordan, is now winemaking at Diemersdal, whose cellar he will use for the family brand.

★★★★ **Merlot** Fruit shy at present on **03** (★★★), some berry notes on palate, but now dominated by oak (16 mths Fr, 40% new), concealing 15% alc under dry tannins. Lacks more succulent savoury notes of maiden **02**, now developing spicy, olivaceous character; elegant, with persistent flavours. 14% alc.

Sauvignon Blanc ★★★ Rather soft, dilute maiden **03** (retasted), less balance & restraint than stepped-up **04** (tank sample; still on lees, but potential ★★★★), with lingering green fig, greenpepper notes. Classical style, dry-finishing, belies 14% alc. — *MF*

Stettyn Winery

*Worcester ▪ Est 1964 ▪ 1stB ca 1984 ▪ Tasting Mon-Thu 8-4.30 Fri 8-3.30 ▪ Closed public holidays ▪ Tours by appt ▪ BYO picnic ▪ Walks ▪ 4x4 route ▪ Owners 11 shareholders ▪ Winemaker Albie Treurnicht (Nov 2000) ▪ Viti consultant Schalk du Toit ▪ 300 ha (cab, cinsaut, merlot, pinotage, shiraz, chard, chenin, colombard, sauvignon, semillon) ▪ ±4 600 tons 3 000 cs own label + 3.6m litres bulk ▪ 55% red 45% white ▪ Export brands: Baobab, Tyne & Dalby ▪ PO Box 1520 Worcester 6849 ▪ stettyncellar@telkomsa.net ▪ www. stettyncellar.co.za ©/🖻 **(023) 340·4220***

'It definitely wasn't a classic year,' says Albie Treurnicht, manager/winemaker at this 11-member co-op, adding that the grapes had a fair amount of botrytis. No, the wine isn't made in the vineyard, he declares, it's managed in the vineyard. 'The cellar's just a facility where grapes are turned into wine as naturally as possible.' The Stettyn cellar has been upgraded and, in the vineyard, planting of a port block completed. An interesting empowerment/skills transfer programme here: likely learners in the community are identified and trained during the harvest, with an eye to filling middle management positions.

Millstone Pinotage ★★★ **01** satisfying ripe plum & red cherry flavours; charry touch to long fruity tannins. 14% alc. 14 mths 3rd fill barrels. **Signature Reserve Shiraz-Cabernet Sauvignon** ★★★★ Elegant shiraz (60%), cab blend; **01** well rounded, big smooth tannins feature benignly in long mineral finish. **Sauvignon Blanc** ★★★ **04** charged with 5% oaked semillon for extra flavour; English gooseberries & nettles in lively, zesty, light-bodied package (only 11.5% alc). **Semillon-Chardonnay** 🆕 ★★★ Fermented with Oregon oak; **03** bears its wood lightly, allowing citrus/tropical fruit ensemble plenty of leeway; attractively light 12% alc. **Vin de Paille** ★★★ **01** characterful dessert from air-dried hanepoot. Brilliant coppery gold; botrytis whiff enlivening marmalade & apricot richness; intriguing sweet-sour kumquat tone in finish. WO Wrcstr & W-Cape. — *DH*

Stonewall Wines

Stellenbosch (see Helderberg map) ▪ Est 1828 ▪ 1stB 1997 ▪ Visits by appt Mon-Fri 9-5 Sat 9-1 ▪ Closed Easter Fri/Sun, Dec 25/26 & Jan 1 ▪ Conferencing ▪ Owner/viticulturist De Waal Koch ▪ Vini consultant Ronell Wiid (May 2000) ▪ 75 ha (cabs s/f, merlot, pinotage, shiraz, chard, sauvignon) ▪ 2 500 cs own label 90% red 10% white ▪ PO Box 5145 Helderberg 7135 ▪ stonewall@mweb.co.za ℂ 855·3675 🖷 855·2206

The historic significance of the stone wall separating farmyard from vineyard — it dates back to the 19th century — gives De Waal Koch's brand its name. He keeps only 10% of his grapes for his wines, whose front-labels depict the historic homestead; the rest he sells off to Distell. 'Top quality' is his evaluation of the 2004 vintage.

★★★★ **Cabernet Sauvignon** Hallmark is great concentration from low-yielding (4-6 t/ha) old bushvines. **00** was beautifully fleshy, showed slight sweetness of ripe fruit. **01** a super wine, deserved 4-5 yrs cellaring to realise its potential. **02** shrugs off difficult vintage with ripe fruitcake aromas; confident structure (more so than blend below, dark plum & cassis flavour; should develop well. 18 mths Fr oak. 14% alc.

★★★★ **Rubér** Forceful cab/merlot blend, structured for keeping. **00** was soft, enticing; **01** similar but more inscrutable, needed lots of time. **02** (★★★★) fruit-forward New-World styling, Ribena-like aromas with gamey/savoury notes; approachable, vanilla-oak sweetness in tail; 18 mths oak, blended just before bottling. 14% alc.

Pinotage ★★★★ No new release since fleshy, slightly sweet **02**. **Chardonnay** ★★★★ **03** notch above pvs; bright lemon-gold colour; aromas of crème brûlée & 'burnt match'; supple, good carry-through; well crafted, balanced. 5 mths oak. 14% alc. — *TM*

Stoney Croft

Stellenbosch ▪ Est 2000 ▪ 1stB 2001 ▪ Visits by appt ▪ Owner Sacramento Trading (Pty) Ltd ▪ Winemaker Danie Steytler, with Charl Coetzee (Jan 2001/Mar 2003) ▪ Viticulturist George Steytler (Mar 2000) ▪ 3 ha (shiraz) ▪ 25 tons 2 000 cs 100% red ▪ PO Box 239 Koelenhof 7605 ▪ cstone@absamail.co.za ▪ www.frontierlifestyle.co.za/stoneycroft.htm ℂ/🖷 865·2360

'Savouring a Stoney Croft wine should be an experience to remember,' says Carmen Stone who, with father John, is determined to produce an exceptional wine aimed at a discerning market. Their maiden Shiraz has received favourable, 'even flattering' reviews. Quality of the 2004 harvest, though difficult due to delayed ripening, is 'on a par', and winemaker Danie Steytler of Kaapzicht is pretty optimistic. Recently released was the special bottling, Jenny's Legacy, named for the family's late wife and mother.

★★★★ **Shiraz** Revisited **02** very appealing now. Fynbos nose, herbal flavours brushed with peppermint, good mulberry fruit, tea-leaf character, supported by ripe tannin. 15 mths new Fr/Am oak (90/10). 14% alc. Even finer, more impressive **01** (★★★★★), already approachable. Meaty nose, spices & smoke, concentrated flavours. Big 14.5% alc. Yr Fr oak, 35% new. — *NP*

Stony Brook

Franschhoek ▪ Est 1995 ▪ 1stB 1996 ▪ Tasting & sales Mon-Sat 10-1 or by appt ▪ Closed Easter Fri/Sun/Mon, Dec 25/26, Jan 1 ▪ Fee R10 (refund on purchase of 12 btls) ▪ Owners Nigel & Joy McNaught ▪ Winemaker Nigel McNaught ▪ Viti consultant Paul Wallace ▪ 14 ha ▪ 80 tons 5 500 cs 60% red 40% white ▪ ISO 14001 certified ▪ PO Box 22 Franschhoek 7690 ▪ mcnaught@iafrica.com ℂ/🖷 876·2182

The 'stony brook' became a raging torrent during the winter of 2003, destroying the road and gouging a 3m ditch through the cab vineyard. The road's now tarred (but overlaid with gravel for a rustic look) and the vines obviously suffered no damage: Nigel McNaught considered 2004 a good harvest 'but it took so bloody long to finish you thought there was no mid-year holiday this time'. Another endeavour that took its time was achieving ISO 14001 certification for Stony Brook and nine other wineries in the Franschhoek valley, as one unit. For the future, there's the new Ghost Gum label, for wines produced from selected parcels of the best fruit and with longer maturation times. Even further ahead, there's a plan to produce sauvignon (from a newly bought property in Elgin) and shiraz for the US market, at competitive prices.

★★★★ **Cabernet Sauvignon Reserve** Excitement following first release (**98**) continues unabated. **02** still crammed with berries mid-2004, top-note of spice & toast; has lost its youthful gawkiness but 5-6 yrs from peak. 14% alc. ± Yr Fr oak, some new.

★★★★★ **Ghost Gum** NEW A different an equally worthy take on this winery's cab; here with 10% merlot, cab f & petit v for added complexity; selection of best barrels, aged 27 mths in new oak; **02** very striking & individual; packed with berries & cassis, very obvious oak still; mouth-expanding flavour, slight greenpepper tang; full house of ripe tannins needing/deserving plenty of time.

★★★☆ **Cabernet Sauvignon 01** a miniature version of the reserve – all correct flavours, maturing rather stylishly, as retasting mid-2004 reveals; nice & rounded tannins, good drinking now while the others develop.

★★★★ **Pinotage 01**, retasted, maturing with distinction; tannins smoothing out, fruit still sweet, good length/potential. 13.5% alc. **00** was smoother on release, amiability enhanced by choc/vanilla tone. 10 mths Am/Fr oak.

★★★☆ **Merlot** First vintage **00** refined & gentle; follow-up **01** sleek, cassis-scented; **02** copybook plums, violets, choc & coffee; hint of clean oak; all aromas repeat on palate; smoother & juicier tannins than the others, developing more pronounced roundness & mellowness; enough tannin/alc to develop over 3-4 yrs. 14.5% alc.

★★★★ **Shiraz Reserve 01**, 'best wine I've had the privilege to make,' per Nigel M, trounced by **02** (★★★★★), still showing exceptional vinosity, concentration, balance; similar to pvs; herbal touch (from 2% semillon seasoning?), bold structure, firmly rounded musculature. 14.5% alc. Deserves cellaring other 5/6 years. Mbury, Frhoek fruit, yr 3rd-fill Fr oak.

★★★☆ **Reserve** First release was **99**, selected barrels of mainly cab, merlot, dashes petit v, malbec. Current **01** (★★★★), from own vyds, incl dash cab f. Revisited, developing nicely; savoury intro followed by array of berries & red deciduous fruit; en route to pleasurable maturity. 14.5% alc. ±yr Fr wood, 70% new.

Shiraz ★★★★ Bold & powerful **02**, retasted, loaded with ripe fruit; developing well but needs more time for tannins to soften. Alc 15%; partly native yeast fermented; combo new Am oak, older Fr. **Camissa** NEW ★★★★ Ripe black berry entry to promising blend merlot & cab in equal proportions, with 10% shiraz; latter makes presence felt in peppery touch to **03**, still firmly encased in sweet tannin & oak, needs few yrs to soften; shows ★★★★ potential. Fr/Am oak, ±yr. **Chardonnay** ★★★ **01** was the last tasted; it featured sweet ripe stone fruit & mellow bottle-age. **Semillon** ★★★☆ **03** aromatic mix lemon/lime, lees, vanilla & smoke. Lovely rounded flavours, acidic touch smoothed by succulent ripe fruit; some development already showing – suggest drink soon to catch at peak; barrelfermented, 3 mths new Fr oak. 12.9% alc. **Sauvignon Blanc** ★★★ **04** tropical fruit on nose, recurring on palate, appealing herby touch on back-palate. Light 12.5% alc. **Annie's Wine** Characterful uncertified NLH-style dessert; last was **01**, richly textured with dryish finish; mere suggestion of botrytis. Now **03**; sauvignon with dash semillon, to be aged 2+ yrs. Unrated preview appears spicier than pvs, again lightly botrytised. Mainly Frhoek WO, some Coastal. —*DH*

Stormy Cape see Thelema
Stoumann's Wines see Excelsious
Stata Series see Flagstone
Suikerbosch see Zidela

Sumaridge Wines

Hemel-en-Aarde Valley (see Walker Bay map) ▪ *1stB 2001* ▪ *Tasting daily 10-3; sales Mon-Fri 10-3 Sat/Sun 8-4.30* ▪ *Fee R10* ▪ *Closed Easter Fri/Sun & Dec 25* ▪ *Light lunches daily 12-2.30* ▪ *Self-catering guest house (up to 6 people)* ▪ *Conferencing* ▪ *Walks* ▪ *Owner Brenda Harcourt-*

Cook ■ ±25 ha (merlot, pinot, pinotage, shiraz, chard, sauvignon) ■ 120 tons 6 000 cs own label
50% white 40% red 10% rosé ■ PO Box 1413 Hermanus 7200 ■ sumaridge@itec.co.za ■
www.sumaridge.co.za © (028) 312·1097 🖷 (028) 312·2824

Swings and roundabouts in the Hemel-en-Aarde Valley: Kevin Grant, formerly of Hamilton Russell Vineyards, has moved to over-the-rise Sumaridge (in an advisory capacity), while Hannes Storm, ex-Sumaridge winemaker and a Grant protégé, has moved to… you-know-where. But not before Storm presided over the 2004 Sumaridge harvest, one of the most difficult to date, with uncharacteristic weather and the presence of his younger brother, Ernst (now off to California), to keep him on his toes. But Hannes S took it all in his stride, living by his motto that 'everything always works out for the best, so no need to stress'. Grant also advises other wineries in the valley and plans to launch his own label.

★★★★ **Syrah 03** Big fruity aromas & flavours. Unbalanced mid-2004, but few yrs should re-establish harmony — should keep longer. 14% alc. Partly native yeast fermented. 16 mths Fr oak, half new. Retasted **02** has lactic & matchstick notes on nose, with black berry fruit, herbal hints. A little more alc, less wood than subsequent.

★★★☆ **Pinot Noir 03**'s excellent colour, fine berry flavours will please, but some mocha notes would disturb the purist. 11 mths Fr oak, half new. Mature 3+ yrs yet. Maintaining improvements of **02**.

Merlot ★★★☆ 03 idiosyncratic milky aromas, plus pleasant red plums, choc. Fine taut flavours demand 3+ yrs. 14% alc. Oak matured, 40% new. Revisited leafy, herbal **02** (★★★) with mocha notes, elegant, supple profile; yr Fr oak adds spice, which emphasises cool-climate flavours. Big 15% alc. **Pinotage ★★** Boiled milk nose & rather unbalanced **03**, edgy palate. 11 mths older Fr oak; 13.6% alc. **Dry Rosé ★★★★ 04** from merlot, spent 16 mths in Fr barrels, 40% new — unusually serious treatment. And worth it: attractive colour, good balance, fresh fruity flavours tinged with liquorice. Dry — another bonus. 13.8% alc. **Chardonnay ★★★☆** Lightly wooded appley-style on sample **04**, with lashings of elegant cool climate appeal. Still in oak (20% new) mid-2004 — rating provisional, as it is for..
. **Sauvignon Blanc ★★☆** Reductively styled **04** ex-tank has sweaty nose, with some citrus notes. 13.5% alc. Retasted **03 ★★** a little sour, short. — *NP*

Sunbird see Origin Wine
Sunny Day see Lutzville

Swartland Wine Cellar

Swartland ■ Est 1945 ■ Tasting & sales Mon-Fri 8-5 Sat 9-12 ■ Closed Mar 21, Easter Fri/ Sun, Dec 25/26 & Jan 1 ■ Tours during tasting hours by appt ■ BYO picnic ■ Play area for children ■ Tourgroups ■ Gifts ■ Farm produce for sale ■ Conferencing ■ Owners 56 members ■ Cellarmaster Andries Blake ■ Winemakers Andries Eygelaar, Pieter van Aarde & Hugo Truter ■ Viticulturist Johannes Mellet (Jun 2000) ■ 3 000 ha (cab, merlot, pinotage, shiraz, chenin, sauvignon) ■ 21 000 tons ■ 50% white 47% red 3% rosé ■ Exported as Leeuwenberg & labels below ■ BRC certified (ISO 9001 in progress) ■ PO Box 95 Malmesbury 7299 ■ andries@swwines.co.za ■ www.swwines.co.za © (022) 482·1134/ 5/6 🖷 (022) 482·1750

This winery just outside Malmesbury has always set the benchmark for progressive cooperative wine farming and it's still leading the way. Not only was it among the first with a boutique-quantity premium brand, Indalo, but in 2004 it commissioned a cellar specially for Indalo production. 'The wines are very promising,' says cellarmaster Andries Blake, adding that previous releases performed well at Veritas 2003. Not that the winery's everyday offerings have been neglected: recent general refurbishment came into its own in 2004 and 'made a perceptible different in quality'. For the first time, Swartland harvested more reds than whites (55 vs 45%). Barely on the shelves, the new Eagle Crest range (poised between Indalo and Swartland labels) has already won its spurs: the Chenin was judged an outstanding wine at Le Rendezvous de Chenin 2004, held in the Loire, home of the variety.

Indalo range

- ★★★★ **Cabernet Sauvignon-Merlot 02** (sample) was the last tasted; less austere than Cab below, more amiable, but also shade less power, presence.
- ★★★★ **Cabernet Sauvignon 03** (sample) impressively dark & deep; ripe mulberries & green/black pepper whiffs; full bodied/flavoured with deft oak underlay heightening minerality. Deserves time to settle & smooth; exciting future. Suave **02** was fuller than **01**, offered mulberry flavours with cab's firm but ripe tannins.

> **Sauvignon Blanc** ☺ ★★★ Attention-focusing cat's pee, greenpepper & cut grass intro to **04** (sample), lively, zinging green flavours on a lightish texture.

Shiraz 03 announces seriousness with deep purple glow, mulberry/cherry/toast array, robust but sweet juicy tannins, good mineral tinge. Sample shows ★★★★ potential. **Pinotage** ★★★★ Follows vanilla-oak-sloshed style, densely packed Morello cherry palate; **03** (sample) zingier, more drinkable than pvs. **Chenin Blanc** ★★★ Last we tasted **03** dry, assertive, grassy & floral.

Eagle Crest   `NEW`

> **Chenin Blanc** ☺ ★★★ **04** good old-fashioned guava flavour, understated but bright; for early enjoyment.

Cabernet Sauvignon-Merlot ★★★ **02** black berries, hint choc & vanilla on nose; juicy ripe tannins; lots of fruit through to finish; grain sugar (3.3g/ℓ) ups the swiggability. **Shiraz-Cabernet Sauvignon** ★★★ **02** full-blown black/red berry palate with hint vanilla & sweet spice; also some fairly strict cab tannins. 13.7% alc. **Chenin Blanc-Chardonnay** ★★★ **04** presents lightish tropical fruit flavour, pleasant, for everyday imbibing.

Swartland range

- ★★★☆ **Shiraz** ✓ Enticing intro of Karoo scrub & biltong – a real SA special; **03** (sample) has more berry character than pvs, more toasty oak too.
- ★★★★ **Red Jerepiko** ✓ Graceful, elegant NV from pinotage. Latest is velvet-like & warming, oozes into endless soporific finish tinged with fruit pastille. 15.6% alc.
- ★★★★ **Vintage Port** Last tasted was **99**, showing distinctive cellar styling: not quite Portuguese but not old-Cape either. Tinta, cab, shiraz; 2 yrs small oak.

> **Dry Red** ☺ ★★★ Latest version (NV) brings red berries & Bovril to taste, satisfying fruity-tangy persistence. Not over-alcoholic at 13.5%, making it the ideal quaffer. **Chenin Blanc** ☺ ★★★ Bouncy drink-now styling for **04**, offering ripe guava & hint pineapple, fresh zippy acidity.

Cabernet Sauvignon ★★★ Cab roars out of the **03** glass, as do chunky oak, big dry tannins need taming with rustic food. ±14% alc. **Pinotage 04** (sample) reprises exuberance of pvs; sweet plums/cherries, touch mint on solid oak background; juicy tannins. Should rate ★★★★ on release. **Cabernet Sauvignon Merlot** ★★★ Label revived with attractive **02**; yr on, more rounded, lightly fruity with spicy whiffs; should hold further yr/2; unoaked; 14.2% alc. **Merlot** ★★ Nose of **03** beguiles with choc-licked super-sweet plums/cherries, firm tannins come as surprise; better in another yr/2. **Tinta Barocca** ★★★ Unoaked **04** (sample) contrasting cherry & savoury tones, hints earth & raisin; chunkily ripe, as always, with firm tannins. **Rosé** ★★ NV. Generous red berry aromas; ripe plum on fresh & fruity palate, bright acidic lift; not to be kept hanging about. 12.8% alc. **Blanc de Noir** ★★★ **04** gentle red berry nose, nicely rounded, ends with delightful fruity tang. **Chardonnay** ★★ **04** unoaked; bright, fresh & fruity, pleasing peach & lemon tones. **Sauvignon Blanc** ★★ **04** very light on nose; hint green grass; crisp & dry. ±13% alc. **Blanc de Blanc** ★★ NV. Latest touch honeyed but still has enough grip for satisfying casual quaffing. **Grand Cru** ★★ NV. New version more foursquare; crisp, but not much to hold the attention. **Light** ★★ Good lunchtime tipple with low alc (9.6%) from fernão pires. Latest NV

(04) crisp acidity, floral/citrus touch; more flavour/body than most. **Bukettraube** ★★ Gentle, light-bodied sweetie, **04** soft floral fragrance, fresh finish. Drink young. 10.6% alc. **Hanepoot** ★★★ Almost a Cape institution; latest NV has richer aromas than pvs, bigger, more chunky, bracing alc (18.2%) ideal for winter de-icing. **White Jerepiko** ★★★ NV. Latest has signature rooibos aroma, very sweet & syrupy. From chenin. 15.8% alc. **Port** ★★☆ Recent releases (NV) have been from tinta, though alcs remain non-classically low at ±17%. Latest is smooth, pruney, earth-tinged. **Cinsaut** & **Baron van Imhoff** discontinued.

Sparkling range

Budget-priced carbonated NVs. **Cuvée Brut** ★★★ Pleasantly fullish & fruity (12.8% alc). Busy bubble adds zest; not quite extra-dry as label suggests. **Demi Sec** ★★ Subtitled 'Special Reserve' but fragrantly unstuffy; fresh & bright; uncloyingingly sweet. **Rosette** ★★★ Latest version of this light-bodied pink fizz not tasted.

D'Vine range

Untasted this edition; 500ml, 1.5ℓ glass, 2 & 5ℓ casks, all NV. **Dry Red**, **Rosé** 🆕, **Dry White**, **Johannisberger/Semi Sweet** & **Light** 🆕.

Boxed range

2 & 5ℓ casks untasted this edition; **Grand Cru**, **Blanc de Blanc**, **Stein** & **Late Harvest**, all NV. — *DH*

▓ *Sweetwell* see Terroir Wines

SylvanVale

Stellenbosch (see Stellenbosch map) ▪ Est 1997 ▪ 1stB 1998 ▪ Tasting & sales daily 11-7 ▪ Fee R7.50 refundable with any purchase ▪ Open public holidays ▪ Tours by appt ▪ Flavours Restaurant , Vineyard Terrace & Cedarwood Lounge (see Eat-out section) ▪ Picnics by appt ▪ Luxury 40 room hotel (see Stay-over section) ▪ Conferences ▪ Tourgroups ▪ Play area for children ▪ Walks ▪ Owners LGI Hotels & Vineyards ▪ Vini consultant Mark Carmichael-Green (2002) ▪ Viti consultant Lorna Hughes-Roos (1997) ▪ 10 ha ▪ 4 600 cs 90% red 10% white 10% rosé ▪ PO Box 68 Stellenbosch 7599 ▪ info@sylvanvale.com ▪ www.sylvanvale.co.za ℃ 865·2012 🖷 865·2610

The new owner of these vineyards and the Devon Valley Hotel at their heart is the Louis Group, fronted by Craig Seaman. Since takeover late in 2003 the organisation has been upgrading the hotel, aiming for four-star status. The bar, refurbished and fitted with deep leather armchairs, is used for tastings when the new-look Vineyard Terrace is uncomfortable weather-wise. The hotel slogan, 'Handmade hospitality', is being applied to the vineyards, whose 'handmade wines' are intended to express the character of the valley. As well as bringing in 80 new barrels, Seaman & co have bought selected cab grapes (previously earmarked for Thelema's Gyles Webb) from SylvanVale viti-consultant Lorna Hughes, wife of the celebrated Dave (a taster for this guide). Pinotage and shiraz from the new owners' farm Eshwaleni will add variety to the hotel's well-aged vines.

★★★★ **Pinotage Reserve 03** shows variety's modern face: sweet, oak-laced raspberry/ cherry purity, soupçon fresh earth interesting extra; luscious sweet fruit; fine tannin grip. Still v young, fresh, unlike **02** evolving with ripe gamey notes, spicy, chewy, touch rustic (especially nip finishing bitterness) but indisputably individual. Generally native-yeast ferment; 16 mths Fr oak, half new. Single vyd ±30 yrs old.

★★★☆ **Chenin Blanc** (pvs Laurie's Harvest) ✓ All change in **04** (★★★★); pvs unwooded, now third each unoaked, barrel/stave-fermented — adds structure, richness to (botrytis-brushed) honeyed/floral generosity; balance, concentration & fresh persistence augur well for development. 13.9% alc. **03** shows nutty bottle-age; still some creamy viscosity, but better sooner than later. From 25+ yr old vines

★★★★★ **Vine Dried Chenin Blanc** Unctuous dessert from desiccated berries, ±30 yr old vines. **02** (★★★★) essence-of-chenin; dried peaches, apricots, mangoes, in honey-laced viscosity. Good winey feel despite low 9% alc; finishes little tamely compared with **00**, where unctuous sweetness cut with rapier acidity. 14 mths new Fr oak.

★★★★ **Vine Dried Pinotage** Broodingly dark dessert **00**, buchu, spice-rack bouquet; warmly smooth, balanced 16% alc. Ultra-ripe grapes, fermented with native yeasts. 18 mths older Fr oak. 375ml. Next **04** currently slumbering in all-new oak.

Dry Cabernet Sauvignon Rosé ☺ ★★★ Food-friendly, serious yet unintimidating. **04** wins from striking ruby translucence to prolonged wild red berry farewell; small 20% barrel-ferment portion broadens, intensifies brilliant cab fruit. 14% alc. — *AL*

Tabiso see Nordale
Table Bay see Ultra Liquors

Table Mountain

This Distell range was launched into the Japanese market in 1997 and is still a strong seller there as well as in the UK and Denmark.

Cabernet Sauvignon ★★★ **03** similar to pvs but more savouriness to the spicy plum-pudding tone; gripping, not unpleasantly austere tannins. **Merlot** ★★★ Better fleshed than Cab. **03** soft, smooth mulberry palate cut by clean tannin. **Chardonnay** ★★★★ **04** (sample) deftly part-oaked, giving ripe-peach fruit room to blossom; wood not yet knit mid-04, but sound structure augurs well. **Chenin Blanc** ★★★★ Lively & refreshing **04**; green-apple bounce & mouthwatering crispness; good foil for seafood & summer salads. Low 11.7% alc a bonus here and in… **Sauvignon Blanc** ★★★ **04** what the variety should be: crunchy, fresh, aromatic & fruity. All WO W-Cape. — *CR*

Talana Hill see Domaines Paradyskloof

Tanagra Private Cellar

McGregor ▪ Est 2000 ▪ Tasting & sales daily 10-4.30 ▪ Closed Easter Sat/Sun, Dec 25 & Jan 1 ▪ BYO picnic ▪ Facilities for children ▪ Walks ▪ Conservation area ▪ Owners/winemakers/viticulturists Christoph Reinhold & Felicia von der Schulenburg ▪ 12ha (cabs s/f, merlot, pinotage, shiraz) ▪ 10 tons/480 cs own label ▪ ▪ PO Box 92 McGregor 6708 ▪ ffvdscar@ lando.co.za ℂ (023) 625·1780 ▤ (023) 625·1847

Christoph Reinhold and wife Felicia (von der Schulenburg, a cartographer for National Geographic Society; he an architect) were inspired to make wine by Abrie Bruwer. The Springfield owner, they say, is blessed with 'infectious joie de vivre'. We'd say they have plenty of their own: their farm's very name is Vrolykheid ('Joy'), and the place is alive with a Durrellesque cast of animals and other people: four young children, a terrier who imagines she's a pig, a pair of ball pythons, a macaw named Caesar…. 'Chaos,' they note (euphemistically?), 'rings throughout the farm.' More orderly is their winegrowing operation. Their vineyards lie amongst the Langeberg and Riviersonerend ranges, hence the Latin brand name, 'Mountain'. Starting with a 'patchwork of neglected varieties', they replanted with noble reds, pinotage and chardonnay. After a spell of delivering grapes to the co-op by day and by night 'quietly practising next to the tractors in our small garage', they made a barrel of Cab in 2000. A 'grand success', they quickly polished it off. Still literal *garagistes*, albeit since slightly upgraded ones, they plan to expand their facilities within the next year.

All tasted as samples, ratings provisional. **Cabernet Sauvignon-Merlot-Cabernet Franc** ★★★ Proportions are 54/36/10, ±yr oaked, unfiltered/unfined (as is red below). **03** black & red berries on nose, oak & leather whiffs, boldly structured with burly but rounded tannins. Unusual; deserves time to show its best. 14% alc, as is… **Shiraz-Cabernet Sauvignon** ★★★ **03** notes of cedar & smoke over ripe plums & berries, black pepper touch; forceful ripe palate, approachable tannins; promises to develop interestingly. **Rosé 04** pinotage, chardonnay blend, to young & unformed to rate. **Chardonnay** ★★

Native yeast fermented in new oak — shows fairly stridently in **04**'s vanilla-toast tone; lurking are ripe fairly smooth peach & tropical fruit flavours, needing time to emerge. —*DH*

Tappery Nook see Stellar Winery
Tara Hill see Southern Sky

Tarentaal

Range launched in 2003 by Woodlands Import Export of Somerset West, mainly for export to Europe. See Assegai for contact details.

Pinotage ☺ ★★★ Unwooded charmer from Wrcstr fruit; **04** vibrant red berry aromas, appealing on palate too, with interesting wild scrub scent. Modern & stylish. **Chenin Blanc** ☺ NEW ★★★ **04** passionfruit/pineapple tones in a flavourful, crisp-finishing package which slips down easily; could handle food well. **Sauvignon Blanc** ☺ ★★★ **04** light-bodied (12% alc) & well stocked with sauvignon character; value for your euro.

Shiraz ★★★★ √ Harmonious **03** proffers khaki bush & smoked meat on nose, loads of spice, quite elegant, firm but not harsh. Fruit ex-Swtlnd, portion barrelled. **Shiraz-Cabernet Sauvignon** NEW ★★★ Dark fruit aroma/flavour subtly pervaded with smoke; juicy fruit; **03** deftly blended for easy/early drinkability. 66/34 mix, unwooded. **Chardonnay** ★★★ **04** lively lemon-butter aromas; warm, ripe, appealing & definitely for early drinking. Most tasted as samples; all WO W-Cape.—*CR*

Tassenberg

Gluggable dry red affectionately referred to as 'Tassies', launched 1936 & still associated with good times. Latest (NV) ★★★ effortless, very soft cinsaut/cab blend (60/40), light-textured with redcurrants & fruit pastilles on taste. By Distell. WO W-Cape.—*CR*

Taverna Rouge

Juicy budget-priced red from Distell. NV blend cinsaut, cab, ruby cab; technically off-dry (8g/ℓ sugar) but somehow not unctuous. Latest ★★★ offers sweet-ripe berries, easy plummy flavours. Light 12% alc. WO W-Cape.—*CR*

Tempel Wines see Kleine Draken
Terra del Capo see L'Ormarins

Terroir Wines of SA

*Stellenbosch ▪ Est 2002 ▪ 1stB 2003 ▪ Closed to public ▪ Owners/viticulturists Inus Muller & Bennie Diedericks ▪ Winemaker Inus Muller (2002) ▪ 5.5 tons 340 cs 100% red ▪ PO Box 5435 Helderberg 7135 ▪ inus@terroirwines.net inusmuller@absamail.co.za bennad@telkomsa.net ℂ **082·825·9001/082·452·7263** 🖷 842·2373*

This is a one-stop winegrowing advisory service owned and run by Inus Muller and Bennie Diedericks (Marais de Villiers of Main Street Winery no longer officially involved), providing assistance to a new generation of artisan winemakers. Clients include Amarava, Leeurivier Wines & Olives, Paul Wallace Wines, Romond and Sweetwell, some listed separately. Muller and Diedericks now also make small quantities of wine for their own account under the brand name Karmosyn.

Tesco see Vinfruco

Text

DGB range launched late 2003 in packaging calculated to appeal to 'fashion-conscious trendsetters in the 25 to 35 age group'. 15 000 cases.

Chenin Blanc ☺ ★★★ Fragrant deciduous fruit whiffs, apricot flavours, firm but juicy, dry. Modest 12.5% alc.

Ruby Cabernet-Merlot ★★★ Smoky, leafy notes & hint of mulberries; dry entry to palate but the finish is fruity & comfortable. Lightly oaked. Both NV, WO W-Cape. — *TM*

Thabana Li Meli see Bartinney Cellars

Thabani Wines

Stellenbosch ▪ *Closed to public* ▪ *PO Box 1381 Stellenbosch 7599* ▪ *thabani@iafrica.com* ▪ *www.thabani.co.za* ✆ **883·9640** 📠 883·2562

Jabulani Ntshangase remains *thabani* ('joyful') about his and partner Trevor Steyn's venture, the first wholly Black-owned wine company in SA. Always fast-foward, JN decelerates long enough to taste wine for this guide and to shepherd groups of black oenology students though the system. (For a look at his newest protégées, see the Photo gallery.) As for the future, he's playing his cards close to his chest. All he'll reveal is that having had no fixed address since its birth, 'Thabani is at last preparing to move to a new home. The launch will take place around harvest, and we'll unveil the latest vintages then'. Slated for release are the Shiraz, Merlot and Cab-Merlot, all 03s, and the Sauvignon 04.

Thandi Wines

Elgin ▪ *Est 1996* ▪ *1stB 1997* ▪ *Tasting & sales Mon-Sat 9-5* ▪ *Fee R10 for groups of 10+* ▪ *Closed Easter Fri/Mon, Dec 25/26 & Jan 1* ▪ *Traditional meals 9-5* ▪ *Tours by appt* ▪ *Gifts, crafts & farm produce* ▪ *Owners Lebanon Fruit Farm Trust* ▪ *Winemaker Patrick Kraukamp (Jan 1997)* ▪ *Viti consultant PD Koegelenberg* ▪ *26 ha (cab, pinot, chard)* ▪ *140 000ℓ 80%red 20% white* ▪ *PO Box 12730 Die Boord Stellenbosch 7613* ▪ *rydal@thandi.com* ▪ *www.thandi.com* ✆ 886·6458 📠 886·6589

Thandi means 'Love', and that's what gets poured into the making of these wines. So says Rydal Jeftha, general manager of what is both a wine brand and a community transformation project, based on fruit farming as a generator of income. The venture began with the Lebanon village community in the Elgin Valley (local winegrower Paul Cluver, Capespan/Vinfruco and others providing mentorship), and recently expanded to Misgund farm in the Langkloof. Here some 130 farm workers have obtained full ownership of a 240ha property. Misgund is one of the first farms in the world recognised by the Fair Trade Labelling Organisation, meaning the working and living conditions of the workers have passed a strict 'ethical audit'. The Thandi wine brand, meanwhile, goes from strength to strength, their Chardonnay taking a gold medal at the IWC in 2003.

★★★★ **Chardonnay** Pleasantly fresh, with nutty & citrus notes on **02**. Elegant acidity copes well with touch of enriching sugar, aids lingering finish. Well integrated Fr oak — fermented/8 mths, 30% new; 14 % alc. IWC gold. No hurry to drink up.
Cabernet Sauvignon ★★★ Forward, friendly **01** offers tobacco & blackcurrant aromas/flavours. Previewed **02** has more of the same solidly well-built, satisfying attractions. Both 13.5% alc; 2 yrs Fr oak. **Pinot Noir** ★★★ Lighter than pvs, **02** has classic notes of strawberry, undergrowth; firmly structured, perhaps a bit lean, ungenerous. — *TJ*

The Berrio see Flagstone
The Blends see Bellingham

The Foundry

Stellenbosch ▪ *Est 2000* ▪ *1stB 2001* ▪ *Visits by appt* ▪ *Owners Chris Williams & James Reid* ▪ *Winemaker/viticulturist Chris Williams, with selected growers* ▪ *20 tons 1 000 cs 90% red 10% white* ▪ *PO Box 12423 Die Boord Stellenbosch 7613* ▪ *thefoundry@mweb.co.za* ▪ *www.thefoundry.co.za* ✆ **082·577·0491** 📠 843·3274

'The Foundry has taken up residence at Meerlust,' announces Chris Williams, former assistant and now successor to Meerlust cellarmaster Giorgio Dalla Cia. 'That's four vintages in four cellars.' Not that it's a problem, mind. Williams makes magic wherever he is at the time. He and James Reid, his wine-partner in this brazenly brilliant young label, are on a mission to 'discover great vineyards that feel right, then care for the vines, harvest ripe fruit and help it become wine'. Their maiden Syrah rated five stars in last year's guide — a Williams 2004 highlight; others include being best man at his brother's *and* best friend's weddings, and, naturally enough, his Meerlust homecoming. While others clutch their vinous jewels to their bosom, these unstuffy enthusiasts cast their pearls far and wide: with total production of just 1 000 cases, they export to all of eight countries.

★★★★★ **Syrah 02** (★★★★★) holds great promise, though youthful tight, less immediately expressive; will reward 5-8 yrs patience. Textural delicacy, fruit richness (Williams' thumbprint), clearest reflection of maiden vintage; present curtain insistent, fine tannin holds possibly greater complexity within spicy, meaty, red fruit depths. Blend Stbosch, Paarl vyds. 16 mths Burgundian oak, 10% new. 14.2% alc. Classically-styled **01** benchmark SA shiraz; delicious in youth, for good 10 yrs. Both native yeast fermented, unobtrusively oaked. Malo in barrel. 14.4% alc.

★★★★ **Double Barrel 01** highly praised (over above wine), by UK guru Jancis Robinson. Has shed puppyfat, emerged sleek, sophisticated. Gentle, light-textured feel, emphasised by fresh earth, mineral elegance. Delicious savoury vinosity. Tinta, cab blend (69/31). 15 mths oak. Fr/Am, 64% new. Aged Stbosch, Paarl vyds.14.5% alc.

Viognier NEW Refined newcomer. Native yeast, no sulphur; made in unused Fr oak. **04** sample haunting lime, apricot/mineral aromas. Gorgeous heavy-silk texture; balanced though noticeable 5g/ℓ sugar — may become absorbed. Should rate ★★★★. 14.8% alc. —AL

The Heads Collection see Knysna Cellars

Thelema

Stellenbosch ▪ Est 1983 ▪ 1stB 1988 ▪ Tasting & sales Mon-Fri 9-5 Sat 9-1 ▪ Closed public holidays ▪ BYO picnic ▪ Tourgroups by appt ▪ Owners McLean & Webb Family Trusts ▪ Winemakers Gyles Webb & Rudi Schultz (1983, Dec 2000) ▪ Viti consultants Aidan Morton & Phil Freese ▪ 50 ha (cab, merlot, shiraz, chard, sauvignon, riesling) ▪ 25 000 cs 40% red 60% white ▪ Export brand: Stormy Cape ▪ PO Box 2234 Stellenbosch 7601 ▪ wines@thelema.co.za ▪ www.thelema.co.za ⓒ 885·1924 🖷 885·1800

Cellarmaster Gyles Webb has a frenetic work schedule. His time is divided equally between his family's Thelema and big-businessman GT Ferreira's next-door Tokara, and attempting to pin Webb down is like trying to catch the proverbial greased porker (he's a long-time member of the unruly Wine Swines tasting fraternity). Even more so now that he zips about in a Mini Cooper S ('my stress relief'). Self-deprecating as he is, his reputation for fine Cape wines is inescapable. Thelema invariably rates at or near the top of authoritative lists of leading SA wine producers. (This, it can safely be said, has nothing to do with the aspirin that irrepressible matriarch 'Ed' McLean insists they add to their headache-free wines.) What is key to their lofty stature is meticulous vineyard management. Some of the original vines on the home-farm are now being replaced and Elgin plantings of chardonnay and sauvignon are soon to come on-stream. Recreational time? Not much, though having an eye for the birds, he (& wife Barbara) were off to the Galapagos as the guide went to press to spot the feathered variety.

★★★★☆ **Cabernet Sauvignon** Viticultural/winemaking teams' fanatic attention to detail responsible for commendable **02** in troubled cab vintage — hand-sorting unripe berries one quality-booster. Vintage character reflected in fresh-scented cassis, mulberry notes, fine-boned frame. Sensitively judged tannin, Fr oaking (50% new, 20 mths), showcases attractive, sweet fruit. For ±6/7 yrs ageing. Elegant **01** for the long haul. 91 pts *WS*. **00** (★★★★★) sensational. *Decanter* ★★★★.

★★★★ **Merlot 02** good drinking (to ±2007) while bigger vintages mature. Readily recognisable fennel, heady damson identity, some sweet-fruit richness set off by finely-tuned structure. 20 mths Fr oak, 20% new. 14.3% alc. **01** (with 14% cab) in usual stylish, impressively firm form. 90 pts *WS*.

★★★★☆ **Merlot Reserve** Webb reduced price (rare step in Cape) by 25% in difficult **02**. But we see no reduction in quality of this traditional best-barrel selection. Rich bitter choc, minerals easily absorb 75% new-oak enhancement. Graceful feel, comfortably firm build, touch better balanced alc (13.9%) than regular bottling promises satisfying 4-6 yr development. **01** svelte & elegant. *Wine* ★★★★☆.

★★★★ **Shiraz 02** perfectly formed in slighter, earlier-maturing style. Gently rounded, supple mouthfeel highlights truffle, spice, red fruit array, lifted by sensitive Fr/Am oak (80/20) maturation. Moderate 13.5% alc adds to comfortable drinking. **01** heady peppercorn/dusty scrub scents, beefy 14.6% alc. 91 pts *WS*.

★★★★ **Pinotage** Big **02** (★★★) flourishes explicit ripe redcurrant/summer pudding generosity. Bold, sweet-fruited mouthful, with twist of 14.4% alc grip in tail. 18 mths oak. **01** more restrained 13.4% alc. Coastal WO (Fruit ex-Klapmuts).

★★★★ **Chardonnay** Proof of Cape's potential for chardonnay. Distinctive **03** (★★★★☆) captures consummate refinement, balance, in usual unshowy Thelema style. Seamless marriage enriching oak, supple swathes creamy hazelnut concentration; mineral core firms, freshens for super-fine length. Will reward 8+ yrs' cellaring. **02** (★★★★☆) refined; shade less opulent. 14% alc. Fermented/9 mths Fr oak, 33% new.

★★★★ **Ed's Reserve** As many fans of this chardonnay from 166 clone as for tasting room supremo, Edna McLean, for whom it is named (that's her childhood face on the label). Fruitier profile, less apparent oak influence than above, though same regime. **03** subtle pickled lemon freshness; creamily supple, rich length. 13.5% alc.

★★★★ **Blanc Fumé** Resurrected after 12 yrs. **03** barrel-fermented/matured in weighty food style. Broad spread tropical ripeness, toasty embellishments driven by incisive fresh core; rounded, dry persistence. Will benefit from yr/2 ageing. 14% alc.

★★★★ **Sauvignon Blanc** ✓ Among best value, most consistent (**02** blip apart) in quality, speed of sales. **04** powerful, tightly focused. Ultra-cool greengage, winter-melon intensity; steely dry, invigoratingly moreish. 13.9% alc. **03** 90 pts *WS*.

★★★★ **Rhine Riesling 03** ups the ante (& price – Webb wants to raise image of this classic grape). Racily brilliant; vivid limey/peppery purity, concentration set off by bone-dry finish. Webb suggests 10 yrs potential (**93** still beautiful). 13% alc.

★★★★ **Muscadel** Honey-coloured dessert. Current NV multi-vintage blend (96-00), old oak matured. Interesting *rancio* notes to mellowing muscat nutty flavours. Warmingly luscious, but not over-heavy. 16.9% alc.

Muscat de Frontignan ☺ ★★★ **04** perfectly poised poolside refreshment. Dainty passionfruit, tangerine peel attractions; relaxed 10.9% alc. Fruitily off-dry. — *AL*

The Mask see Baarsma

The Observatory

Cape Town ▪ 1stB 2000 ▪ Tasting by appt ▪ Owners Tom, Catherine, Elizabeth & André Lubbe ▪ Winemaker/viticulturist Tom Lubbe, with Catherine Lubbe (Jan 2000/Jun 2002) ▪ 15 ha (pinotage, shiraz, chenin) ▪ 12 tons 500 cs 75% red 25% white ▪ syrah@netactive. co.za ▪ PO Box 1098 Malmesbury 7299 ▪ syrah@netactive.co.za ©/🖷 *(022) 487·3023*

A sybarite, Tom Lubbe (luckily for us): he considers the imparting of pleasure to be one of his winemaking goals. It pains him that organic and biodynamic wines are 'thought laughable by most big SA producers'. He's not laughing: having recently collaborated in the production of 2 000 bottles of 'pure mountain carignan' from granitic soils in the south of France, where he works each year, he's determined to cater for the organic/biodynamic market locally. For starters, he uses no pesticides or herbicides on their newly acquired farm in the Paardeberg. Facing the west coast, it has shiraz growing at 400m above sea level. In a couple of years, Lubbe hopes, he'll be able to move his cellar here from its present Cape Town site. Expect 'shockingly gorgeous' wine (he's borrowed the quote) from 2004, but 'unfortunately there is very little of it'. And he does have a promising pinotage: 'We thought we'd give it a go before pulling the vines and were pleasantly surprised.'

★★★★★ **Syrah** Rigorously selected fruit from low-yielding, granitic Paardeberg (Swtlnd) vyd. **01** fine, subtly gorgeous & harmonious; 14.8% alc, 60% new Fr oak. Unique, remarkable **02** only older wood, so intense grape purity & powerful delicacy untrammelled, giving perfumed spice, raspberries, lilies, with mineral depths. Fine acidity, supple tannins; 14% alc. These should develop 5 yrs min, keep much longer, giving increasing satisfaction.

★★★★ **Carignan-Syrah** So far, only the innovative maiden **02** sweet-fruited & touch jammy, with balanced & firmly constructed palate. Light-hearted seriousness or very serious fun? — TJ

The Ruins see Bon Cap

The Saints

Enduring range of easy drinkers by DGB. About 250 000 cases per annum, 60% white, rest equal portions red and rosé.

St Raphael ☺ ★★★ Smooth & comfortable cinsaut, ruby cab (50/50) blend; latest bottling 'ideal around a braai' says back-label; effusive black fruit aromas, smoky/mocha notes, light textured, soft & dry. **St Morand** ☺ ★★★ Fresh, appealing white from chenin & 2 muscats; grapey whiffs, sweetness lifted by peachy acidity. **St Anna** ☺ ★★★ Ethereal Natural Sweet white; low alc (±8%). Full-on fruit salad flavours, passionfruit uppermost, lovely blend of perfumed varieties including gewürz.

Reds all lightly Fr oak chipped. **St Celine** ★★★ Latest same blend as St R, slightly more muted, bit jammy & sweet. **St Claire** ★★★ Soft Natural Sweet rosé with low alc (8%); latest uncharacteristically foursquare, sweet; lacks vinosity. **St Vincent** ★★★ The new bottling mainly sauvignon (60%), with chenin & colombard. Aromas of pear & marzipan, soft & refreshing, light bodied. All NVs, WO W-Cape. — TM

The Sensory Collection see Stellar Winery

Theuniskraal Estate

Tulbagh ▪ Est 1705 ▪ 1stB 1947 ▪ Tasting & sales Mon-Fri 9-12; 1-4 Sat 10-1 ▪ Fee R5 refundable on purchase ▪ Closed Easter Fri/Sun, Dec 25, Jan 1 ▪ BYO picnic ▪ Tourgroups ▪ Owners Rennie & Kobus Jordaan ▪ Winemaker Andries Jordaan (1991) ▪ Viticulturists Jordaan brothers ▪ 140 ha (13 varieties, r/w) ▪ ±1 600 tons ±35 000 cs own label 10% red 90% white ▪ PO Box 34 Tulbagh 6820 ▪ tkraal@lando.co.za ▪ www.theuniskraal.co.za © **(023) 230·0687/88/ 89/90** ▤ *(023) 230·1504*

Nearly 60 years on, the Jordaans' (Cape) Riesling remains a fad-resistant evergreen, an icon of 'Old Cape' in an area which is arguably the fastest-changing in the winelands. In other nods to continuity, the cellar still produces more white than red wine, and is still a registered estate: 'Perhaps the term adds character,' says winemaker Andries J, 'especially in the case of farms where family is involved.' And family is very much involved here: from Kobus and Rennie, the sons of founding father Andries, to their wives and their sons, Andries Jnr and Wagner.

★★★★ **Semillon-Chardonnay** ✓ Varieties seamlessly married in **04** (sample) — neither semillon freshness nor chardonnay fatness dominating; vibrant, satisfying tanginess the lingering impression. Unwooded 56/44 blend, exactly as for **03**.

Prestige ★★★ The Jordaans' only red, blend of ruby cab & cab (67/33) in **03**; 'early-drinking, fruity style' say they, though to us saturated & dense, spicy more than fruity; serious tannins need time — 2/3 yrs. **Riesling** ★★★ Enduring brand, launched 1947; from crouchen, aka Cape riesling; **04** more accessible than pvs; dry rather than steely; shows light leafy freshness & variety's signature hay aroma. **Natural Sweet** ★★★ **03** fragrant melange buket/gewürz (40/60); full-blown sweet bouquet of candied fruit & ripe, fleshy grapes; palate admirably restrained & uncloying. — *CR*

The Veldt see Robertson Wide River

The Winery

Stellenbosch ▪ Est/1stB 1998 ▪ Closed to public ▪ Owners Alex Dale, Edouard Labeye, Ben Radford, Heather Whitman & Christophe Durand ▪ Winemakers Ben Radford, Edouard Labeye, Christa von la Chevallerie (1998/1999/2004) & Clive Torr (pinot noir only, 2004), with Tubby May (Feb 2003) ▪ ±120 ha (cab, merlot, shiraz, chard, chenin, sauvignon, semillon) ▪ ±850 tons 30 000 cs own label 50/50 red/white ▪ Ranges for customers: Churchaven, Three Gables (UK) ▪ Postnet Suite 124 Private Bag X15 Somerset West 7129 ▪ thefunwinery@thefunwinery.co. za ▪ www.thefunwinery.com ✆ 855·5528 ▯ 855·5529

Blood, guts, joy and passion go into every wine from this extraordinary collaboration (MD and spokesman Alex Dale; Christa von la Chevallerie, ex-Steenberg winemaker, who co-ordinates vineyard operations and liaises with Barossa-based Ben Radford and Rhône oenologist Edouard 'The Bee's Knees' Labeye; Clive Torr, Cape Wine Master and co-owner of Topaz Wine; assistant winemaker Tubby May; his wife Fran, export administra-tor). A 'puzzlingly' erratic 2004 vintage had all hands on deck. But, bolstered by copious bottles of Burgundy from Dale's personal collection, they ended up, for the first time since inception, with 'not a single wine or tank that is not worthy of what it was produced for'. Which is? 'Drinking wines with individuality, balance, elegance and subtlety'. Six years into a 'fascinating journey', the vinous alliance's creative juices still flow: new in 2004 are the flagship Radford Dale Gravity, a Pinot and the Rhône-inspired Black Rock range.

Radford Dale range

★★★★★ **Gravity** NEW **03** seamlessly combines merlot, shiraz, cab; impresses with pure, sa-voury vinosity in soft frame; sleek, fine-boned, full presence revealed only after last sip. Name derives from vinification: even 'press' juice from pressure of grapes themselves, not machinery. Should delight — now to at least 2008 — anyone able to find some of mere 290 cs. Partly barrel-fermented, 14 mths wood. 14.5% alc.

★★★★ **Merlot** Pleasurable drinkability, concentration/structure for 4-5 yrs improvement. **02** tasty, savoury mouthful; delivers velvety smooth satisfaction, in slighter, earlier-peaking mode. 14.5% alc. 14 mths 85% Fr oak, some new. Previewed **03** more em-phatic, striking; rich, intense aromas/flavours on confident structure. 14.% alc. 16 mths mostly Fr oak. Hldrberg/Devon Vlly grapes.

★★★★ **Shiraz** Seeks balance of firm structure with spicy, peppery abundance. **03** spot on: delicious rich mouthful dark spice/berries with fresh, lively core for great savoury length; dense, supple tannins encourage current drinking; further 4-5 yr potential. **02** (★★★★) slightly sullen, overripe edge; smooth mouthful; lack of usual freshness favours early drinking. 14.5% alc. Unfiltered. ± 90% Fr oak, bal Am, 40% new.

★★★★ **Chardonnay** Complex in subtle, understated manner. **03** layered, cool elegance; soft oatmeal, lemon cream pinpoint minerally fresh core; supportive, enriching wood. **02** sold out; not tasted. 13.5% alc. No malo. Fermented/±yr oak, 20% new.

Pinot Noir NEW Crafted by team Burgundy-seasoned specialists, including Dale & Radford; **04** mix Dijon/BK5 clones from Darling, Stbosch. Dark, clear ruby; very ripe black cherry character. Too young to realistically rate. Maturing in Burgundy casks, none new.

Black Rock range

Two promising NEW **04**s previewed, from Pdberg slopes in Swrtlnd. Shiraz, grenache & carignan (75/15/10) in piquant spicy '**Red**'; full-bodied but bursting with minerally fresh-ness, juicy tannin. 66% oaked, mainly Fr, some new. The '**White**' chenin-led with char-donnay, viognier; textured, very fine, suavely insistent; partly barrel-fermented.

Vinum range

★★★☆ **Cabernet Sauvignon** Invariably hits the team's goal of refined structure with accessible fruit. Elegant **03** prime example: reverberating cassis, soft berry scents, flavours; sleek; mouthwatering juiciness; harmonious, sappy tannin frame. 13.5% alc. 30% wooded, mainly from Hldrberg/Devon Vlly.

★★★★ **Chenin Blanc** ✓ From prime, mature Hldrberg vyds. **03** Rendez-vous du Chenin selection; pure lemon-blossom scents; tapered mineral length, great finesse; most characterful & appealing. **04** (sample) riper, greater orange zest/honey intensity; substantial mouthful clean, pure flavours with minerally intensity, delicate oak expansion. 5% barrel-fermented, new Fr oak. ±14% alc.

New World range

Shiraz ★★★ Invitingly dark **04** exudes sweet dark berry/spice juiciness; firm yet smoothly drinkable; rich & lingering. Oak-seasoned. **Cabernet Sauvignon-Merlot** 🆕 ★★★ **03** medium-bodied 60/40 blend. Light-textured, smoothed for readiness by wild strawberry/plum fruity sweetness. **Shiraz-Pinotage** ★★★ **04** peppy, easygoing 60/40 partnership. Substantial, expressive flavour richness, warmingly long. Unoaked. **Semillon-Chardonnay** ★★★ Satiny **04** unoaked 60/40 mix; flavoursome waxy lemony intensity, good zippy length. **Sauvignon Blanc** ★★★ Forthcoming warmer-region tropical ripe aromas; contrasting grassy zesty flavour on medium-bodied, dry **04** crowd-pleaser. — AL

▓ *Thierry's Wine Services* see Cape Grace

Third World Wines

Est 2001 ▪ MD Jonathan van Blerk ▪ Vini consultant Kosie Möller ▪ The Stables, Westcot, Wantage, OX12 9QA UK ▪ wineorders@3rdworld.co.uk wineorders@gatsbyhotels.com ▪ www.3rdworld.co.uk www.gatsbyhotels.com ℂ 0944·779·191·3044 🖷 0944·123·575·1755

A UK-based company, producing its flagship Jay Gatsby brand and value-for-money Third World range from grapes bought in from selected growers in Stellenbosch, Franschhoek and Paarl. Winemaker Kosie Möller, who earned his spurs at KWV, vinifies in Paarl. Distribution is exclusively to the hospitality trade, notably the 32-member Gatsby International group of hotels, lodges, penthouses and tented camps.

▓ *Thirty-Three Degrees South* see Wamakersvallei

Thirty-Two South Ltd 🆕

Stellenbosch ▪ Est 1998 ▪ Closed to public ▪ 100 000 cs 55% red 45% white ▪ PO Box 12149 Die Boord 7613 ▪ UK office: Millennium Harbour, 202 Pierpoint Building, Westferry Rd, London E14 8NQ ℂ 0944·207·987·1241 🖷 0944·207·536·9721 ▪ 32south@btconnect.com ℂ/🖷 887·9112

This wine export company was established about six years ago specifically to find or create wines to suit the needs of individual European buyers. 'Our approach is to put the cart before the horse,' says director Louis Meyer. 'Rather than reserving huge quantities of wine and trying to find a buyer, we find the buyers first, then find, or order, wines to suit their requirements.' The approach seems to work well, and now they're expanding with a line-up under the Isabelo label, launched at the showcase London Generic Tasting.

Cape American Oak Pinotage ☺ ★★★ Unmissable in curvaceous Mercurochrome-hued bottle. Lovely bright-fruited contents to match — cherries, strawberries, raspberries — sweetly lashed with vanilla from Am oak (10 mths, 50% 1st fill). Delightfully OTT. Made by Bergsig, responsible for all in this range except Merlot. **Elephant Trail Pinotage-Shiraz** ☺ ★★★ **03** decidedly user-friendly anytime sort of wine; combo blackberries & sweet spice, soft, nice. 75/25 blend. **Leopard Canyon Merlot** ☺ ★★★ **03** an all too rare sighting in SA: soft, plump, undemanding merlot. Bouncy boiled-sweet flavours, fruity & ripe. 14% alc. **Limited Release Gewürztraminer** ☺ ★★★ Soft, semi-dry **04** (sample) with quince & sweet-spice aromas; lightish effortless quaffing. WO W-Cape. **Sweet Surrender Pudding Wine** ☺ ★★★ Scented NLH dessert, well made in ethereal, easy-sipping style for instant gratification. **03** quince aroma unfolds, authentic botrytis dustiness too.

Route 101 range

Red ☺ ★★★ Well-juiced melange of shiraz, merlot & petit v; ripe plum flavours & touch pepper for steakhouse friendliness.

White ★★ Dry three-way blend with sweet guava & floral whiffs; soft fruity palate. Both by Rockfields Wines, vintage **04**.

Isabelo range

Shiraz ★★★ **02** soft & generous, with loads of succulent black-plum fruit, contrasted with whiffs smoke & white pepper. **Chenin Blanc** ★★ **04** juxtaposes retiring talcum powder bouquet & assertive acidity. Probably too fresh for solo, but good with seafood. **Sauvignon Blanc** ★★★ Hints grapefruit & nettle; sweet-sour palate with sherbety acid; **03** best enjoyed soon. WO Brde Rvr Vlly unless noted. — *JN/TM*

Thomas Kipling see Makro
Thornhill see Veenwouden

Thorntree Wines

Est/1stB 2001 ▪ Closed to public ▪ Owner/winemaker André Badenhorst ▪ 70 000 cs 50/50 red/white ▪ Export brands: Cape Mist, Witteboomen ▪ Suite 310 Private Bag X16 Constantia 7848 ▪ andrebad@iafrica.com ©/☏ 794·7679

Born on Groot Constantia, wine veteran André Badenhorst lived and worked in Constantia Valley all his life, never really leaving the 'nest'. All that's changed since embarking on his relatively new wine business, focused on marketing value-for-money wines, something he says SA has in abundance. Nowadays he ventures far from his comfort zone and works with producers across the winelands. 'I never really appreciated the incredible diversity of the regions and their terrains before,' he says. A constant presence in the US the past few years has culminated in an exciting deal with one of the biggest distributors there.

Cabernet Sauvignon ★★★☆ Inviting whiff vanilla to **03** mulberry fruit, tannins nicely tamed. Good quality grapes, carefully put together, even shows some elegance. Staves for 4 mths, alc 14%. **Merlot** ★★★ Robust & rustic red. Dark plummy fruit, firm tannins on **03**, very dry. 14% alc. **Pinotage** ★★ Fleshy plummy fruits with firmish tannins in **03**, muscular & meaty, good concentration; some would find bitterness on finish. Unoaked. **Shiraz** NEW ★★★ Ripe pruney fruit & some leather of older-style shiraz in **03**. Very dry. Good meaty red for winter tippling. Alc 14.3%. **Chardonnay** ★★★ Unoaked **04** (sample) shyish on nose; impressively fruity palate though, fullish body from extra time on lees. **Chenin Blanc** ★★★ **04** (sample) shows quality fruit — bouncy & ripe with greengage/melon flavours & twist lemon on longish finish. **Sauvignon Blanc** ★★★ Fresh & fruity **04** (sample), grapes ex-Paarl, light citrus flavours, bone-dry. Alc 13%. All WO W-Cape. — *IvH*

Three Anchor Bay see Cape First

Three Gables see The Winery
Three Peaks see Mount Vernon
Three Rivers see Bon Courage
Thys Drift see Goedverwacht

Tierhoek

Citrusdal ▪ Est 2001 ▪ 1stB 2003 ▪ Closed to public ▪ Owner Tony Sandell ▪ Vini/viti advisers Johan Delport & Johan Viljoen ▪ 2.5 ha (chenin) ▪ 150 cs 100% white ▪ 12 Ferndale Drive, Ottery, Cape Town 7800 ▪ tsrw@iafrica.com ✆ 704·1122/082·536·7131 📠 704·1110

Nestling in a circle of mountains on the edge of the Cederberg lies Tierhoek, a farm owned by the Marais family from 1886 until 2001, when bought by Tony and Shelley Sandell. Considered an Historically Significant Sandveld Site, the farm and its buildings are being lovingly restored. So too is a small block of chenin, a venerable 35 years old. At 780m above sea level, it's watered by double the rain and records temperatures 9 degrees C cooler than neighbouring sites. Organic feeding and meticulous pruning have boosted yields from a miserly 2.5 t/ha to around 8. Vintage 03, an FCTWS bronze medalist, was made by Chris Williams (Meerlust, The Foundry); 04 by Citrusdal's Johan Delport.

★★★★ **Chenin Blanc** Testing the water (& showing the potential here) with fine semi-sweet **03**. Sumptuous pear, apricot aromas; lime-tinged melon on the rich palate. 21g/ℓ sugar in fact well balanced, almost concealed by fresh acidity. 14% alc quite evident, though. Ageworthy. WO W-Cape.— *MF*

Timbili see Ernst & Co
Tin Mine see Zevenwacht
Todo see Helderkruin

Tokara Winery

Stellenbosch ▪ Est/1stB 2000 ▪ Tasting & sales 9-5 Sat 9-1 ▪ Closed public holidays ▪ Tours by appt ▪ Tokara Restaurant for lunch & dinner Tue-Sat ▪ Farm-grown olive oil ▪ Art exhibits (enquiries: Julia Meintjes ✆ 083·675·1825) ▪ Owner GT Ferreira ▪ Winemaker Miles Mossop (Jan 2000), with Dumisani Mathonsi (Jan 2004) ▪ Viticulturist Aidan Morton (Nov 2000) ▪ 62 ha (cabs s/f, merlot, mourvèdre, petit verdot, shiraz, chard, sauvignon) ▪ 300 tons 40 000 cs own label ▪ 60% red 40% white ▪ PO Box 662 Stellenbosch 7599 ▪ wine@tokara.com ▪ www.tokara.com ✆ 808·5900 📠 808·5911

Winemaking involves both art and science, and neither artists nor young vineyards (<6 yrs) are to be rushed. New plantings of chardonnay and sauvignon in Elgin and the Hemel-en-Aarde Valley will need nurturing (and ultimately provide greater choice). Precision viticulture techniques, including remote sensing, continue to be practised on the three Helshoogte properties. Dumisane Mathonsi now assists Miles Mossop in winemaking. These developments, noteworthy as they are, pale by comparison to the $64 000 question: when will the first branded releases from this showcase cellar, owned by big-businessman GT Ferreira, see the light? Turns out there's an auspicious 03 red roosting in the barrel hall. Will it take flight? The final decision rests with cellarmaster Gyles Webb, and at press time he was off on a birding trip to South America. So: to be 'T' or not to be? Meanwhile the watchwords are 'zip-lipped' and 'Zondernaam' (the medal winning second label, listed separately). At a venue with spectacular views, regular visual arts exhibitions, fine food, wine and olive oil — there's plenty to feast the creative body and soul on.

Tokolosh see International Wine Services
Tom Lubbe Wines see The Observatory
Tomorrow Wine Company see Kosie Möller Wines

Topaz Wine ♀

Stellenbosch • Est/1stB 2000 • Visits by appt • Owners/winemakers Clive Torr & Tanja Beutler • Viticulturists Willie de Waal & James Downes • 0.4 ha 355 cs 100% red • 26 Topaz Str, Heldervue, Somerset West 7130 • topazwines@mweb.co.za © 855·4275 ☎ 855·5086

Verandah-gistes Clive Torr and Tanya Beutler, proud new parents of baby Juliet, last year fermented their shiraz in a 5 000ℓ container, easily breaking the record for the largest vessel ever used in Topaz Street. That's little more than a thimbleful in the greater scheme, but their grape intake of up to 4 tons/day put quite a strain on their Somerset West home's small working area. Last harvest was 'great for shiraz', and their bought-in Elgin pinot ripened very gently in cool weather ('Much like Burgundy', says Torr, co-owner of a domaine there). So expect 'great finesse and elegance' in the wines. Torr, who completed his 21st consecutive Argus Cycle Tour, has left the Cape Wine Academy to concentrate on wine-making, -tourism and -education.

★★★★ **Pinot Noir 03** (★★★★) from Stbsch, Elgin grapes, has Burgundian notes of forest mushrooms, taut berry flavours; convincing & satisfying; 13.5% alc better balanced & more elegant than massive **01** (14.5%). Low-yields (5 t/ha); ±14 mths oak, 50% new. 13.5% alc.

★★★★ **Syrah 03** (★★★★★) concentrated, powerful yet controlled cracker off Stbosch, Pdberg vyds. 'Made from buchu & dagga,' chortles Torr, 'it's addictive.' Definite heathery aromatics (jury's out on the cannabis); attractively untamed; 13.5% alc. Penetrating aromatic aftertaste. Cellar 5 yrs (though hard to resist now). 14 mths new Fr oak. 93 pts in *Wine International*; leap up from elegant **02**. — *NP*

Tower see Fairview
Towerkop see Ladismith
Tradouw see Barrydale
Travino see Klawer
Trawal see Klawer
Tribal see African Terroir

Tukulu ♀

Groenekloof • Est 1998 • Tasting & sales at Bergkelder • Owners Distell, Leopont 98 Properties, Maluti Groenekloof Community Trust • Winemaker Adian Fry (2003) • Viticulturist Hannes van Rensburg (1998) • 245 ha (cab, pinotage, sangiovese, shiraz, chard, chenin, sauvignon, viognier) • 4 500 cs own label • 60% red 40% white • PO Box 184 Stellenbosch 7599 • info@ tukulu.co.za • www.tukulu.co.za © 809·8305 ☎ 883·9651

Due for completion this year is a planting programme on Papkuilsfontein farm near Darling which supplies the grapes for Tukulu (and upper-tier Distell ranges such as Nederburg). Of the 330ha earmarked for vines, 85% will be red, the source perhaps of more award-winners such as the 01 Tukulu Pinotage, *Wine*'s Pinotage of the Year in 2003. The farm is a black empowerment project in which a community trust has a 15% stake, the rest belonging to a consortium involving black taverners and major shareholder Distell. Ultimately grape-farming profits will engender the capital for a Distell buy-out by the black partners. At the end of 2004, Papkuilsfontein worker accommodation was upgraded so that it's in line with housing on the other farms where Distell has an interest.

★★★★★ **Pinotage** Retasted **02** developing well, with rich berried nose, opulent fruit & subtle gentle tannins on palate. 14.5% alc. Acclaimed **01** had sweet raspberry fruit; from 7-30 yrs old bushvines. Yr small Fr/Am/East Eur oak, mostly new.

★★★★ **Chenin Blanc 04** pleasant pineapple & melon fruit salad with some citrus notes. Good dry finish. 13.7% alc. In popular style of delicious **03**, with vibrant juicy fruit from low-yielding old vines. Both these wines from Darling dryland fruit. — *NP*

Tulani see Diemersfontein

Tulbagh Mountain Vineyards

Tulbagh ▪ Est 2000 ▪ 1stB 2003 ▪ Tasting, sales & tours by appt ▪ Owners Jason Scott & George Austin ▪ Winemaker/viticulturist Chris Mullineux (Dec 2002) ▪ 16 ha (cab, mourvèdre, shiraz) ▪ 19 tons 95% red 5% straw wine ▪ PO Box 19 Tulbagh 6820 ▪ winegrower@tmv.co.za ▪ www.tmv.co.za ✆ (023) 231·1118 🖷 (023) 231·1002

TMV is the 'huge gamble' of Jason Scott and George Austin, two British wine mates who gave up the good life in the City (London) to settle on 180ha of virgin land near Tulbagh and create 'one of the best red wines in the world'. They have developed the vineyards using organic methods, and the winery to enable minimal intervention throughout the vinification. The decision to go organic, explains Chris Mullineux, is as much due to the suitability of the climate and quality of the site as their heartfelt convictions. 'Wine grown from fertilised soils mostly reflects the terroir of the chemical companies,' he believes. 'That said, organics only appeal to a small part of the population. Our wines will stand or fall on whether people enjoy drinking them or not.' We had hoped to taste their first release for this edition, but the final blend had not yet been assembled. Watch this space.

Tulbagh Winery

Tulbagh ▪ Est 1906 ▪ Tasting & sales Mon-Fri 8-5 Sat 9-1 ▪ Closed public holidays except Easter Sat, May 1 & Sep 24 ▪ Gift shop ▪ Owners 32 members ▪ Cellarmaster Carl Allen (Aug 2002) ▪ Winemaker Elsabé le Roux (Dec 2002) ▪ Viticulturist Jan-Carel 'Callie' Coetzee (2002) ▪ 550 ha ▪ 5 200 tons 70 000 cs own label 70% red 20% white 7% rosé 3% other ▪ Range for customer: Paddagang ▪ PO Box 85 Tulbagh 6820 ▪ tkw@tulbaghwine.co.za ▪ www.tulbaghwine.co.za ✆ (023) 230·1001 🖷 (023) 230·1358

'Our whole production team are still rookies in the Tulbagh area,' says winemaker Elsabé le Roux, 'it's only our second vintage here and we're learning a great deal. There are many different sites in the area and if we learn to manage each properly we can expect some great wines in future.' A longer than usual ripening period has taught them that grapes in the better soils maintain a good sugar-acid balance throughout, while less well-sited vineyards lose acidity before ideal sugar levels are reached. Their semillon, cinsaut and ruby cab suffered from this, she says, while colombar and merlot came up tops. Vineyard manager Callie Coetzee married recently and his wife was expecting their first offspring at the time of going to press. It's obviously a fertile valley.

Cabernet Sauvignon ★★★ 03 has some muscle & exuberance; spicy sweet jam intro; full-bodied. Reds in range lightly wood chipped, alcs around 14.5%. **Merlot** ★★★ Smoky redcurrant jam lead-in to 03; med-bodied, with zinging acidity. **Pinotage** ★★★ Ripe mulberry & cream nose; 03 simple but sappy wine, balanced. **Shiraz** ★★★ 02 fruitier, juicier than Rsv below; more varietal character. **Chardonnay** ★★ 04 herby & 'green' tones to nose, otherwise just a dry white. **Chenin Blanc** ★★★ 04 shy candyfloss & pear-drop aromas; juicy guava flavours, lightish toned, good limy finish. **Sauvignon Blanc** ★★ Early-picked 04, crisp, flinty & lightish (±12% alc). No fresh bubbles to taste this ed; we last listed: **Brut** ★★★ Boisterously bubbly, very brut; **Vin Doux** ★★★ Lightish, with berry flavours. Both carbonated, NV. **Port** ★★★ NV from pinotage & ruby cab; latest bottling overtly fruity, jammy; more 'sweet fortified than 'port'. 17.6% alc.

Klein Tulbagh range

Special vineyard selections, aged ±yr in oak, further yr in bottle, prior to release in elegant packaging. **Cabernet Sauvignon Reserve** Classically austere 02 (★★★), redcurrant & green olive aromas; medium body; grainy but fairly soft tannins. 03 (★★★) similar but more appealing, supple. **Merlot Reserve** ★★★ Massively ripe, unsubtle style; has its fans. 02 russet-rimmed; spicy, mint & dried fruit bouquet, lightly structured/toned, almost lean; 03 deeper coloured, more extracted; stewed plums & dried fruit; grainy tannins. **Pinotage Reserve** ★★★ 03 mulberry aromas & vanilla suggestion; riper, more satisfying than above wines. **Shiraz Reserve** ★★★ 02 shy strawberry nose, woodsmoke sniffs; soft & quaffable, not definitively shiraz but a good drink. ±14% alc. **Vintage Port** ★★★ From pinotage; 01 developing pleasingly; forthcoming ripe-plum/mocha bouquet;

shows some alc/spirit but no roughness yet; **02** (sample) earthy/gamey tones, slightly more extract, bit closed still. ±20% alc.

Secluded Valley Magnums

No updates on this 1.5ℓ NV range, pvsly noted as exclusive to Pick 'n Pay hyperstores.

Tulbagh Magnums

We last noted availability of the following 1.5ℓ NVs without tasting them: **Cabernet Sauvignon, Merlot, Pinotage, Vin Rouge, Rosé, Chardonnay, Blanc de Blanc**.

Village Collection

NVs in 1 & 2ℓ packs, 750 ml and 500 ml screwtops.
Classic Red ★★★ Equal blend pinotage, ruby cab with attractive spicy nose & hints of dark choc; plump, soft & fruity. *Wine* value award. **Natural Sweet Red** ★★ Russet hue, tomato jam aromas, sweet-sour plum flavours, light-toned/flavoured, low 9.5% alc. **Natural Sweet Rosé** ★★ Coppery salmon hue; very demure pinotage-chenin blend with low 8.8% alc. No new bottlings of **Chenin Blanc** (★★) or **Blanc de Blanc** (★★). **Crispy White** 〈NEW〉 ★★ Floral, appropriately crisp blend colombard (90%), sauvignon; lemony, quaffable. **Extra Light** ★★ Blend of five white grapes including fernão pires; arresting new translucent front label, readable from opposite side of the clear bottle. Contents nice too; scented bouquet, appropriately light (9.5% alc), herby, semi-dry finish. No new versions of **Stein** (★★), **Late Harvest** (★★) or **Natural Sweet White** (★★). — *TM*

Turtle Creek see Makro
Tutuka see Buthelezi Wines

Twee Jonge Gezellen Estate

Tulbagh (see Tulbagh map) ▪ Est 1710 ▪ 1stB 1937 ▪ Tasting & sales Mon-Fri 9-4 Sat & public holidays 10-2 ▪ Casual tasting: no charge; formal tasting: fee on request ▪ Tours Mon-Fri 11 & 3; Sat & public holidays 11 ▪ Closed Easter Fri-Mon, Dec 25-26 & Jan 1 ▪ Farm-style produce ▪ Owner/winemaker Nicky Krone ▪ 120 ha (petit v, pinot, muscat de F, chard, chenin, riesling, sauvignon, semillon, viognier) ▪ 1 000 tons 7% red 85% white 8% rosé ▪ PO Box 16 Tulbagh 6820 ▪ tjg@mweb.co.za ▪ www.tjwines.co.za ⓒ **(023) 230·0680** 🖷 (023) 230·0686

Nicky and Mary Krone were just getting their breath back after finalising a mammoth half-million bottles of MCC, including a limited-volume prestige cuvée in imported French bottles, when they gave us their bullish take on the new estate dispensation (allowing previously non-estate producers to produce 'estate wine'): 'We need unity and a combined drive in striving for excellence. The new legislation is more accommodating and lays the foundation to build a quality code. It's a stepping stone for the future.' The first red in the Krone range, a Syrah made from night-harvested grapes and matured in French oak, was launched last year. Third son Matthew, who's apprenticed in all aspects of the family business, is now a full member of the team.

Krone range

★★★★ **Borealis Brut** ✓ Fine, subtle, critically acclaimed vintaged MCC, 50/50 chardonnay-pinot; traditional vinification including bunch-pressing, free-run juice only. **97** pinot very evident; lightish feel & texture from chardonnay, lively, rather more length than breadth. **98** more weight, breadth. Lightish alcs (±11.5%), dry (±11g/ℓ sugar). Unusually, **98** released ahead of **97**, latter less approachable in youth. Both retasted mid-2004, demonstrates wisdom of cellaring bubblies; now with distinct champagne-like bouquet & nuance. In smart new livery.

★★★★ **Syrah** (Pvsly 'Shiraz') **02** now safely bottled, attractive dusty berry & dried prune quality, fine-grained tannins, carries 14.5% alc with ease. Truly dry, only sweetness from ripe fruit flavour, attractive biscuity finish with touch earth. New attempt at red, tried & abandoned mid-80s. 20 mths Fr oak, 2nd fill.

Balm of the Night ★★★ Fortified muscat de F ('Beaumes-de-Venise style' says Nicky K); **99** shows barley sugar sweetness balanced by clean acid, unorthodox heather/peat aftertaste; warming, soothing. Modest 15.5% alc. 500 ml, as is... **Engeltjipipi** ★★★ Delicate botrytised **01** from semillon, chenin, riesling, ageing serenely. Honeyed, mouthwatering citrus flavours, firm acidity, lovely balanced sweetness.

TJ range

Schanderl ☺ ★★★ After Nicky K's ex-teacher at Geisenheim College. **03**'s youthful honeysuckle/spice has developed into Rose's Lime Juice & spice aromas. Off-dry, zesty, the most assertive of the dry whites. Perfect lunchtime tipple at 12% alc. 100% muscat de F. **Rose Brut** ☺ ★★★ Fun bubbly; chardonnay with dash pinot for colour, extended lees stay-over for authentic effect; latest tasted mid-2004 has some delicious bottle-age. NV, carbonated.

Thirty Nine ★★★ Riesling dominated blend (39=clone number). **03** dry with delicate floral, lemon peel notes. Modest 12.5% alc. These whites all delicate, slenderly built, but show excellent length. **Light** ★★★ Low alc (8%), low kilojoule, wafting muscat bouquet, firm dry palate comes as delightful surprise. **03** mid-2004 retains appeal. Long approved by Heart Foundation. **Night Nectar Natural Sweet** ★★★ **03** fresh, graceful sweetie with delicate acidity, would never guess sugar is 80g/ℓ. Chenin, touch gewürz; light ±9% alc. Perfect for bobotie/curries. — *IvH*

Twin's Peak see Lateganskop
Two Cubs see Knorhoek

Two Oceans

Launched September 1996, these good-value wines from Distell are mostly for export, though some distributed locally and available for tasting at Bergkelder.

Pinotage ★★★ Lightish-bodied **03**'s dark-toned mulberry fruit dominated mid-04 by combo oak barrels/staves; should settle with brief bottle-ageing. **Shiraz** NEW ★★★ Juicy & savoury **03** has hints smoked meat & game, so should be good with, say, roast duck or venison. Fr staves/chips. **Cabernet Sauvignon-Merlot** ★★★★ ✓ Cut above these easy-drinkers; 60/40 mix in **04**; classy clove & lead pencil whiffs, minerally touch; palate fruitier but fairly stern; should settle, soften soon. **Merlot-Shiraz** NEW ★★★ Good middle-of-road style; 65/35 ratio, partly barrelled; **04** expressive fresh-picked berry character with vanilla; agreeable dry finish. **Cape Red** ★★★ Aka Fresh & Fruity Red. **03** minimally oaked cab, pinotage, ruby cab (40/30/30) with quite a bit to say; heathery fragrance, vegetal touch; smooth & flavoursome. **Rosé** ★★★ Coral-pink **03** still-fresh hotchpotch pinot, cab, pinotage, carignan; now with red-berried richness, which best enjoyed soon. **Chardonnay** ★★★ Retasted **03** lightish, well integrated lemon palate with biscuit overlay; not much length but has flavour. 40% in Fr oak barrels, 6 mths. **Sauvignon Blanc** ★★★ Well-pitched & appealing, grain sugar for rounded mouthfeel; **04** guava & lemon-drop redolence; fresh rather than crisp. **Semillon-Chardonnay** ★★ **03** uncomplex quick-quaff now shows more texture than flavour. Partly wood-fermented. **Chenin-Chardonnay** NEW ★★★ Medium-bodied **03** gentle peach & lemon zest aromas; soft; subtly oaked. **Cape White** ★★★ Aka Fresh & Fruity White. Friendly, lightish chenin, colombard fusion; grassy summer fruits, guava touch; pleasant limey zing to finish. All WO W-Cape. — *CR*

Tygerberg see Altydgedacht
Tyne & Dalby see Stettyn
Uhambo see Premium Cape Wines
Uiterwyk Estate see DeWaal Wines

Uitkyk Estate

Stellenbosch ▪ Tasting & sales Mon-Fri 9-5 Sat/Sun 10-4 ▪ Fee R15 (R25 incl glass) ▪ Picnics in summer ▪ Owner Lusan Holdings ▪ Manager Rudi Buys ▪ Winemaker Estelle Swart

(2000) ▪ ±870 tons ▪ 20 000 cs ▪ PO Box 104 Stellenbosch 7599 ▪ info@uitkyk.co.za ▪ www.uitkyk.co.za © **884·4416** 🖷 884·4717

This gracious estate, tucked away behind neighbour Kanonkop, is worth a visit just for the handsome manor house and its elegant neoclassical fresco. But there's also a *boules piste*, tasting room with a tinkling mountain spring running its length, picnics in summer (we could go on and on). And of course there's wine, made by Estelle Swart from well-tended vineyards with evocative names like *Jakkalskloof* ('Jackal's Ravine') and *Bobbejaanberg* ('Baboon Mountain'), sweeping up the Simonsberg.

★★★★ **Sauvignon Blanc** A fruity, genteel version, smooth & easy-drinking. **04** well structured; enjoy before the next vintage comes along. Fresh & attractive **03** included dash semillon.

Cabernet Sauvignon ★★★ Last tasted was **99**, lighter than pvs, delicate & leafy. **Cabernet-Sauvignon Shiraz** ★★★ **01** equal blend with some black fruits & light savouriness. Fresh, juicy acidity, though touch dry on finish. Hearty 15% alc. 14–18 mths oak, mainly Fr, some new. **Chardonnay** ★★★ **03** vinous rather than fruity, with firm acid finish. 9 mths oak, mainly Fr, 42% new. ±13% alc. — *RK*

Uitvlucht Co-op Winery

Little Karoo ▪ *Est 1941* ▪ *Tasting & sales Mon-Fri 8-5.30 Sat 9-1.30* ▪ *Fee R5 for groups of 20+* ▪ *Open public holidays* ▪ *Owners 48 members* ▪ *Winemaker/viticulturist Kootjie Laubscher (Jun 1993), with Willem Botha* ▪ *325 ha* ▪ *5 000 tons 12 000 cs 36% red 22% white 28% muscadel 14% sparkling* ▪ *PO Box 332 Montagu 6720* ▪ *uitvluchtwine@lando. co.za* © **(023) 614·1340** 🖷 *(023) 614·2113*

Range not tasted this ed. Pvs have included: Cabernet Sauvignon, Merlot, Ruby Cabernet, Sauvignon Blanc, Blanc de Blanc, Colombar, Chenin Blanc, Late Harvest, Vin Doux, Vin Sec; Red/ White Muscadel (also in 250ml); Muscat de Frontignan and Port.

Ukusa see Oaklands Wine Exports

Ultra Liquors

Independent discount liquor chain offering a wide range of in-house-branded wines, selected from top wineries by its national wine-buying team to offer good value as well as character and interest. See Specialist wine shops section for contact details and opening hours. Enquiries: Chris Minikin.

Stellenvale range

Secret Cellar Barrel No. 25 Cabernet Sauvignon ★★★ Meaty, earthy complexity in **00**; touch of mint-choc; yr new oak well integrated; ready, drink soon. **Secret Cellar Barrel No. 15 Cabernet Sauvignon-Merlot** ★★★ **99** stewed red plum & leather notes, evidence of some bottle-age complexity in dried fruit/potpourri flavours; needs drinking. **Secret Cellar Barrel No. 35 Cabernet Sauvignon-Merlot** ★★ **02** richer, more youthfully ruddy colour above; stewed plumy nose, very ripe & sweet entry turning chunkily dry & tannic on finish. Needs time or food. **Cabernet Sauvignon** ★★★ **02** assertive plum jam/stewed fruit aromas, plump black fruit palate with tight minty edge. Partly barrelled, 30% new oak, yr. **Merlot** ★★★ Most open, generous of the reds. **01** (sample) attractive Xmas cake aromas; well padded & supple, nice flick of tannin. **Pinotage** ★★ Toffee/fruitcake aromas, rich, inviting nose; **01** palate unexpectedly dry & taut. Yr older oak; moderate 13% alc. **Shiraz** ★★★ Savoury, with hints game, forest floor, earthy finish; **01** tight, food friendly. Oak as for cab, 25% new. **Chardonnay** ★★★ Muted green-fruit nose of apple & pear; unwooded **04** (sample) sprightly acidity for summer upliftment. **Sauvignon Blanc** ★★★ **04** (sample) perfumed with guava & green fig; fresh lemon on palate, zesty & pleasantly light. WOs Stbosch, Paarl, Coastal, W-Cape.

Table Bay range

Dry Red ★★★ Four-way unwooded blend fronted by cinsaut; shy red-berry tones, gently dry finish. **Dry White** ★★ Chenin, with shy green melon nose, hint honeysuckle, slightly downbeat finish. Both NV, fruit ex-Paarl, as is following range.

Route 303 range

Dry Red ★★★ Chunky, savoury all-sorts blend; dusty/leafy notes, hints mulberry & mocha. 14.2% alc. **Dry White** ★★ Mix of chenin, crouchen, colombard; pear-drop & talcum powder aromas, bone-dry, verging on austere yet quite zesty.

Beaufort range

5ℓ bag-in-boxes, untasted. **Grand Cru**, **Johannisberger**, **Late Harvest** & **Dry Red**. — *TM*

Umculi see Rooiberg
Umfiki see Goudini

Umkhulu Wines

*Stellenbosch ▪ Est/1stB 2000 ▪ Closed to public ▪ Owner Fiona Phillips ▪ 20 000 cs 80% red 20% white ▪ PO Box 132 Simondium 7670 ▪ info@umkhulu.co.za fiona@cybercellar.co.za ▪ www.umkhulu.com ©/🖷 **874·2106***

It's been a bumper year for owner Fiona Phillips and husband Adam. They had their first child, Jessica, and, in a double blessing, quantities of their Umkhulu brand jumped to 20 000 cases because their suppliers, Bellevue, were able to deliver twice the previous volume. Sales are through the website, Cybercellar.co.za (which also hosts this guide's internet pages, Platteronline.com). The wines are finding an enthusiastic market in the US, and Fiona P is very excited about a Cape Blend, soon to be released.

★★★★ **Tian** (Pvsly Titan, renamed to avoid conflict in US, but says Phillips, 'also the name of my new puppy'). Mulberry & cinnamon bouquet in **02**. Deep-coloured, youthful & still taut Bdx-style blend from full-house of cabs s/f, merlot, malbec, petit v. Extracted, modern; tannins polished for earlier approachability with potential. Stylishly oaked (12 mths Fr, 50% new), not overripe at 13.4% alc.

★★★★☆ **Pinotage** In bright, modern guise, early accessible. **02** soft, plush, plummy fruit almost ready. Slight sweetness to fruit hauled back by firmish oak tannins which add needed texture, dryness. Yr Am oak, 30% new. Drink now & over next 2-3 yrs.

Malbec ★★★☆ Spicy blackberry, sprig mint on **02**, properly dry, tannins already approachable. For drinking now, over next 3-4 yrs. Fr oak, 10 mths. 14% alc. **Shiraz** ★★★☆ Unshowy, workmanlike version in **02**, hints smoked beef, good oak; disciplined black cherries, still some youthful tannic grip. 12 mths Fr oak. 14% alc. **Akira** ★★★☆ (Pvsly 'Atticus') Latest **01** in 60/40 cab/pinotage formula, latter shows in slight sweetness to padding around sturdy tannic backbone. Ripe & deceptively easy, no pushover. 9 mths Fr/Am oak. Drink now & over next ±4 yrs. Alc 13%. **Sauvignon Blanc** ★★★☆ **04** unusually scented: tropical fruits, hints of capsicum, fresh green tomato! Softish acidity, bone-dry & easy drinking, modest typicity. **Chardonnay** Not available for tasting. **Sauvignon-Chardonnay** discontinued. — *IvH*

Unity see African Terroir
Unplugged 62 see Joubert-Tradauw
Upington see Oranjerivier

Upland Estate

*Wellington ▪ Est/1stB 1998 ▪ Visits by appt ▪ 2 self-catering cottages ▪ Distillery ▪ Farm-grown/made olives & tapenade ▪ Owners Edmund & Elsie Oettlé ▪ Winemaker/viticulturist Edmund Oettlé ▪ 12 ha (cab, chenin, crouchen) ▪ 30 tons 500 cs 100% red ▪ PO Box 152 Wellington 7654 ▪ oettle@intekom.co.za ▪ http://organicwine.co.za © **082·731·4774** 🖷 873·5724*

'Look after the soil, and the wine looks after itself,' is the philosophy of Edmund Oettlé, in-vitro fertilisation scientist with two PhDs, and one of the first local wine farmers to turn to organic cultivation. Since 1994 Oettlé has witnessed dramatic improvements in soil and crop quality, and significant reductions in erosion. With nutrients and trace elements maximised in the soil, Upland vines are better able to withstand disease. Despite this, 2004 was difficult, and uneven ripening led to late picking and low sugars. But Oettlé remains a firm believer in organic wine's superior ability to absorb and express its natural terroir, and provide a quality product (like the new 5-year-old brandy, released this year). 'These are wines I want to drink every day, knowing they are good for me and the environment, and that I can keep making them ad infinitum.'

★★★★ **Cabernet Sauvignon** Authentic 'bio wine' from low-cropped, organic vyds; barrel-matured ± yr. Quality trio tasted mid-2004: **01, 00, 98.** Ripe brambleberry fruit, sweet & inviting; fleshy, honest ripe fruit on palate, **00** odd-man-out (★★★), savoury, touch austere. **98** rich, ready. **01** very similar, arguably the best. **99** fleshy, generously intense (gold at MIWA).

Merlot ★★★ Latest **00** under 'Maske' label; grapes from neighbour's vyd, Oettlé vines suffered downy mildew; retasted mid-2004, black cherries, now with touches tar, fragrant cigar in bouquet, easy palate. NE. *– IvH*

Urbane Wines

Walker Bay • Tasting/sales & contact details: see Bartho Eksteen Family Wines

When winemaker Bartho Eksteen and IT consultant-turned-vintner Gerhard Britz bottled Urbane's maiden vintage in 2002, one of their key assets was an inside track on one of the world's most lucrative markets. Having consulted in the US for a number of years, Britz simultaneously developed many good contacts in the wine industry. Those have borne fruit: Urbane grew 400% in its first two years, and exports have now expanded into the UK. Last year, Wine of the Month Club voted their Shiraz Best Value. To sample it and the rest of the range (as well as other fine wines, either created or selected by Eksteen), visit Wine & Company, his and wife Suné's delightful Hermanus wine shop.

Chardonnay ☺ ★★★ Touch honeyed but holding up; appealing 'sweet lemon' fragrance; nice ripe sweet-melon mouthful; at peak, drink soon.

Shiraz ★★★ Warm stewed plum whiffs, slightly earthy with hint choc on finish; plump. 14% alc. Unwooded. **Sauvignon Blanc** ★★★ Fresh lemongrass nose; dry & flinty nettle flavours; medium body, slight coarseness easily countered by fishy accompaniment. All **03**, WO W-Cape. *– TM*

Usana

Stellenbosch • Est/1stB 2003 • Tasting by appt • Owner Joubert Family Trust • Vini consultant Mike Dobrovic, with Clinton le Sueur (both Mar 2003) • Viticulturists Joubert brothers • PO Box 7087 Stellenbosch 7599 • usana@xsinet.co.za • www.usana.co.za ☎ **082·896·3437/083·625·2301** 🖷 865·2441

For eight generations, the Joubert family have owned and nurtured vineyards on their three Stellenbosch farms. They grow 80% of the grapes that go into Mulderbosch's highly rated sauvignon, so there's every reason to expect good things from this label, pronounced Oo-sar-na, a Xhosa word meaning 'small child' or 'new beginning'. A donation of the proceeds of sales goes to the Beautiful Gate organisation in Cape Town for the upliftment of children infected and affected by Aids.

Sauvignon Blanc ★★★ Easy drinking **03** with herbal, greenpepper notes, soft palate, some grip on finish, softening to sweetness. 13% alc. Tank sample **04** looks set to be a notch up: tauter, greener & more textured, some sappy notes, food-friendly finish. *– MF*

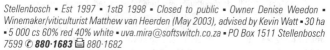

Uva Mira Vineyards

*Stellenbosch ▪ Est 1997 ▪ 1stB 1998 ▪ Closed to public ▪ Owner Denise Weedon ▪ Winemaker/viticulturist Matthew van Heerden (May 2003), advised by Kevin Watt ▪ 30 ha ▪ 5 000 cs 60% red 40% white ▪ uva.mira@softswitch.co.za ▪ PO Box 1511 Stellenbosch 7599 ✆ **880·1683** 🖨 880·1682*

Matthew van Heerden says he's happy with the 2004 harvest, the first made in the new 100-ton cellar on the farm high on the Helderberg (the 2003s, first to emerge after short break in commercial production while the vineyards were replanted, were made at Tokara). 'The relative smallness of the winery enables us to focus very strongly on quality,' MvH says. 'For example, past harvest we were able to ferment batches of just 1 ton.' The top range (Vineyard Selection) will eventually consist of a Chardonnay and a red blend of merlot, shiraz and cabernets franc and sauvignon. Both will be selections from top-performing blocks. There will also be a second range, Cellar Selection, similar or better in quality to the wine below ('not a "cheaper" or "supermarket" brand', MvH emphasises). This line will include the current Sauvignon and a Bordeaux-style red. Designer Anthony Lane has been engaged to re-brand the wines, and owner Denise Weedon has her eye on export markets such as Japan and China.

Sauvignon Blanc ★★★ Mellow hints to ripe, tropical tones on **03.** Full-bodied, sturdy with some luscious filling. — *AL*

Vals Baai see False Bay Winery

Van Loveren Private Cellar

*Robertson ▪ Est 1937 ▪ 1stB 1981 ▪ Tasting & sales Mon-Fri 8.30-5 Sat 9.30-1 ▪ Closed Easter Fri/Sun, Dec 25 & Jan 1 ▪ Tours on request ▪ Sweetcorn fritters available Sat 9.30-1 or BYO picnic ▪ Tourgroups ▪ Conference/function venue ▪ Walks ▪ Owners Nico, Wynand, Phillip, Hennie, Bussell & Niel Retief ▪ Winemaker Bussell Retief ▪ Viticulturists Niel & Bussell Retief ▪ 220 ha (cab, red muscadel, sauvignon) ▪ 3 900 tons 300 000 cs 33% red 33% white 34% rosé ▪ PO Box 19 Klaasvoogds 6707 ▪ info@vanloveren.co.za ▪ www. vanloveren.co.za ✆ **(023) 615·1505** 🖨 (023) 615·1336*

With all four Retief cousins now married and two 'klein cousins' on the way, what better way to celebrate than with the addition of a Natural Sweet to the Four Cousins range? Family ties are no mere marketing ploy. The remarkable and sustained success of Van Loveren is attributable to their close-knit bond, says winemaker Bussell Retief, as it enables them to keep overheads to an absolute minimum. This in turn helps the winery compete in the most price-sensitive markets, despite the world-wide glut of wine. The 2004 harvest was smaller than usual, but Bussell R is delighted with his sauvignon, and says his reds are progressing well too. You can sample the wines in their lovely garden tasting area or, in inclement weather, in a new indoor tasting room, warmed by a fire.

★★★★ **Limited Release Cabernet Sauvignon** Latest **03** (★★★) shy & understated, even for house's already unshowy style. Nothing out of place, though; good chewy dark fruit, softish tannins, dry finish. Yr Fr oak. 14.7% alc.

★★★★ **Limited Release Shiraz** Serious example from single-vyd. **02** retasted mid-2004, whiff woodsmoke, tangy/savoury fruit has developed white pepper & scrub notes, drier & less fleshy than friendly **01**. Ripe tannins already approachable, very dry finish. Yr oak, 70/30 Fr/Am. 13.5% alc.

★★★★ **Pinotage** ✓ **03** in stylish new livery, more in keeping with pumped-up persona. Subtle dark-berried fruit, discreet oak; suave, well groomed with savoury dry finish. Lightly oaked. Big 14.7% alc.

★★★★ **Limited Release Chardonnay** ✓ Pvsly 'Reserve'. Latest **03** (★★★★) with gorgeous toasty oak support for ripe citrus, grilled almond fruit. Deep flavoured & decently dry, firm acid has been easily absorbed into flesh of wine, long dry toasty finish. Fermented/aged 100% new Fr oak. **02** also generously & well built.

★★★★ **Red Muscadel** ✓ Bright luminous pink in youthful **04**, wafting muscat spice introduction. Still edgy/youthfully unsettled when tasted; freshening acidity adds welcome lift. Made in more delicate style. 17.5% alc.

Wolverine Creek label has made way for smart new Van Loveren livery. **Cabernet Sauvignon-Shiraz** ★★★ **03** in 70/30 blend, cab aged with staves, shiraz barrelled. Whiff smoked beef; tangy, savoury flavours; neat, not overdone or flashy, properly dry. Riper at 14% alc. **Blanc de Noir Red Muscadel** ★★★ **04** Palest shell-pink, pretty semi-sweet version tastes drier as modest sugar balanced by fresh acid. Subtle muscat tone, lightish at 11.5% alc. Drink within the yr. **Blanc de Blanc** ★★ **04** light, dry quaffer (12% alc) from colombard/sauvignon. Also in 500 ml screwcap as **Vino Blanc**. **Colombard** ★★ Floral touches to **04**, pretty, off-dry, drink within the yr. **Fernão Pires** ★★ **04** soft, just off-dry, easy drinking, light textured. **Cape Riesling** ★★ **04** good expression of variety (now almost endangered species). Tangy citrus flavours, zingy acid, bone dry. **Semillon** ★★ Now made riper, **04** has lost the bright fruit quality of pvs, firm fleshed, sullen when tasted. Good concentration, though, seen in long finish. 14% alc. **Chardonnay** ★★★ Pvsly 'Spes Bona Chardonnay'. Pleasing **04**, tropical lime whiffs, plumply fruity, lingering finish. Unwooded. Ripe at 14% alc. **Special Late Harvest Gewürztraminer** ★★★ **04** still shy after bottling, but delicate rose-petal bouquet starting to bloom. Fresh, with delicate sweetness; elegant, lovely acid balance. Easy to drink, especially at just 12% alc.

Merlot ☺ ★★★ **03** for those who like their reds honest, unfussy & distinctly dry, here's a savoury dark-berried charmer, ready to drink, lip-smacking. 60% barrel-aged, 4 mths. 14% alc. **River Red** ☺ ★★★ Savoury, affordable everyday red. **03** follows formula of pvs — shiraz, merlot, ruby cab (50/30/20), unoaked 13.5% alc. Also in 500ml screwcap. **Blanc de Noir Shiraz** ☺ ★★★ Fun aroma of red jelly beans in **04**, bone-dry, soft red cherry flavours, delicate in well established style. Terrific! Light 12.5% alc. **Sauvignon Blanc** ☺ ★★★ Delicate capsicum in lightish, juicy-dry **04**. Flies with United Airlines Business Class, but not so fancy it can't go with fish & chips. **Colombar-Chardonnay** ☺ ★★★ Back to original 60/40 sauvignon/chardonnay in **04**, more bounce & style, bone dry, soft citrusy flavours. Lovely summer quencher. **Pinot Gris** ☺ ★★★ **04** continues in style of pvs with intriguing talcum-powder-scented fruit, soft & fleshy. Honest, attractive version, one of very few from Cape.

Four Cousins range

Dry Red ★★★ Smooth, tangy red with soft tannins for easy quaffing. Clone of River Red. **Sweet Rosé** ★★ Gentle sweetie with low alc at 7.5% (but not for slimmers at 70g/ℓ sugar!). Fresh & appealing. **Dry White** ★★ Fresh as morning dew, pleasing lightweight quaffer from colombard, sauvignon (70/25) with dollop muscat for perfume. All in party-size 1ℓ bottles, all NV.

Four Cousins Natural Sweet range   **NEW**

Red Gives term 'sweet/sour' whole new dimension! Sugar of 70g/ℓ, freshening acidity & brush of tannin in red wine/grape juice blend. 9.5% alc. **Rosé** Appealing freshness in charming pink, really sweet at 78g/ℓ, low alc at 7.5%. **White** Diabetics beware! 50/50 blend white muscadel/chenin hides 60g/ℓ sugar with ease; smooth, fruity. All ★★, NV.

Papillon sparkling range

Colour-coded butterfly labels on these budget-priced, lowish alc (11–11.5%) NV carbonated bubblies. **Brut** Fresh lemony tang, dryness cushioned by 12g/ℓ sugar. From colombar & sauvignon. **Demi-Sec** Fragrant, semi-sweet, but balanced by fresh acidity, blend (Rhine) riesling, muscat de F. **Vin Doux** Deep coral-pink, not oversweet. Unblended muscat de F. All ★★. – *IvH*

Van Schoor Wines

Robertson ▪ Est/1stB 2001 ▪ Tasting & sales Mon-Fri 8-5 Sat & public holidays 9-1 ▪ Tours on request ▪ BYO picnic ▪ Owners Melt & Mike van Schoor ▪ Winemaker Mike van Schoor,

*advised by Tommy Loftus & Eben Rademeyer ▪ Viticulturist Francois van Schoor ▪ 83 ha
(cab, merlot, pinotage, shiraz, chard) ▪ 5 000 cs own label 80% red 20% white ▪ PO Box 65
Robertson 6705 ▪ mike@vanschoorwines.co.za ▪ www.vanschoorwines.co.za © **(023)
626·1633** ▤ (023) 626·6455*

No new releases from blacksmith-turned-winegrower Melt van Schoor. We last tasted a
Cabernet Sauvignon, Shiraz and Pinotage, all 02s, and an NV red blend, Blacksmith.

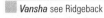 *Vansha* see Ridgeback

Van Zylshof Estate

*Robertson ▪ Est 1993 ▪ 1stB 1994 ▪ Tasting & sales Mon-Fri 9-5 Sat 9-1 ▪ Closed Easter Fri, Dec
25 ▪ Tours by appt ▪ Owner Van Zylshof Trust ▪ Winemaker/viticulturist Andri van Zyl ▪ 32 ha
(cab, merlot, chard, chenin, sauvignon) ▪ 10 000 cs 10% red 90% white ▪ PO Box 64
Bonnievale 6730 ▪ vanzylshof@lando.co.za © **(023) 616·2401** ▤ (023) 616·3503*

This small family farm in Bonnievale is becoming more visitor-friendly, with the revamping
of the cellar exterior and the erection of shaded parking for visitors. In the cellar, a new
destalking machine will speed up the handling of the grapes at harvest time. Though they
follow the Robertson region's trend toward fine red varieties, the Van Zyls recently
planted a new block of sauvignon in soil specially selected to suit this fashionable variety.

> **Chardonnay** ☺ ★★★ Friendly, with touch complexity via 10% new Fr oak. Pudding-like
> **03** oozes peaches & creamy butterscotch; light textured despite generous 14.3% alc.
> Should be enjoyed soonest. **Chardonnay Riverain** ☺ ★★★ **04** (sample) 10th anniver-
> sary of this label; intially sauvignon, latterly unwooded chard; sweet fruited, loaded
> with tropical flavour. NB alc: 14%. **Chenin Blanc** ☺ ★★★ Epitome of a good quaffer:
> clean & lightish; tropical fruit salad & lemon flavours; well made. 12.4% alc. **Sauvi-
> gnon Blanc** ☺ ★★★ Bright, lovely wine; light-toned; delicious tropical flavour & clean
> fruity acidity.12.2% alc.

Cabernet Sauvignon-Merlot ★★★★ Andri vZ extracts the same sappy fruitiness from
this red as his flavourful whites; barrel ageing (new & used oak) adds the necessary seriousness; **03** (sample) full, rounded black berry palate with floral note, well-tuned oak,
ripe tannins. 14.6% alc. – *DH*

Van Zylskloof

*Swartland ▪ Est/1stB 2002 ▪ Visits by appt 10-5 ▪ Owner Johan van Zyl ▪ Vini consultant
Gerda Willers ▪ Viticulturist Johan Viljoen ▪ 50 ha (cab, cinsaut, grenache (r/w), pinotage,
tempranillo, chard, viognier) ▪ 250 tons 320 cs own label ▪ PO Box 251 Citrusdal 7340 ▪
bergdal@kingsley.co.za © **(022) 921·3328** ▤ (022) 921·3326*

The Van Zyls were the first to plant vines in the Piekenierskloof back in 1923, but it would
be almost 80 years before Johan 'Oubaas' van Zyl – inspired by Charles Back, among the
first modernists to recognise and develop the Piekenierskloof's winemaking potential –
finally took the plunge and made his own wines. The vineyards, on mountain terrain
above the Olifants River (high enough to occasionally be covered with snow), are night-
harvested and the fruit trucked to Franschhoek for vinification by consultant Gerda Willers. It was warm and dry in 2004, and Van Zyl, whose grapes have garnered awards under another label, expects his pinotage and grenache (the latter harvested for the first
time) to be complex and intense. Sample them in the new tasting room on the property.

Chardonnay ★★★ **03** ripe, tropical, buttery aromas; advanced though not unpleasant
chewy oxidative character; less appealing hot, unyielding finish. 14% alc. 8 mths Fr oak,
50% new. **Pinotage** ★★★ **03** high-toned, slightly spirity raspberry aromas 'sweetened'
with oak (yr, 50% new, 20% Am); raspberry/vanilla cuts gutsier elements of 15.5% alc.
Will need careful monitoring. **Pinotage Natural Sweet** ★★★ **03** neither quite dessert
nor table wine. Generously-oaked blockbuster, varietally indeterminate; raisiny

sweetness controlled by assertive tannins. 22.4g/ℓ sugar. 15.5% alc. 75% new oak, 8 mths. **Grenache 04**, sampled ex-vat (unrated), broad-shouldered; earthy/red pepper persistence; fresh focus to solid 14% alc. — *AL*

Vaughan Johnson's Wine & Cigar Shop

Cape Town (V&A Waterfront Pierhead Cape Town) ▪ Est/1stB 1985 ▪ Sales Mon-Fri 9-6 Sat 9-5 Sun 10-5 ▪ Open public holidays ▪ Selection of gourmet cheeses, open sandwiches, olives & coffees available ▪ Gifts ▪ Owner Vaughan Johnson ▪ PO Box 50012 Waterfront 8002 ▪ vjohnson@mweb.co.za ▪ www.vaughanjohnson.com ✆ 419·2121 🖷 419·0040

His emporium on Cape Town's V&A Waterfront has been a landmark and magnet for an estimated 2m home-town and visiting palates. This year the urbane Vaughan Johnson celebrates another milestone — two decades of purveying fine wines and canny advice on most things vinous. He launched his often ground-breaking approach to retailing in Illovo, Johannesburg, where he opened SA's first wine 'boutique' — rather, was temporarily prevented from doing so by the local Liquor Board: 'They rejected my application because I had not drawn 6 lines, each 4cm long, to denote the shelves in the shop on the plan of the shopping centre,' he recalls. It was not the last run-in with officialdom. In 1995, after years' fruitless lobbying for permission to trade on a Sunday, Johnson simply opened the doors and served his customers as usual. And was promptly clapped in irons by raiding police. Today it's business seven days a week, on the Waterfront and at Dublin's fashionable Temple Bar, and the clientele stretches as far as the Caribbean island resort of Petit St. Vincent. Meanwhile Johnson's unpretentious, amusingly labeled housebrand continues to hit the right spot, on price as well as on palate.

Sunday Best Red ★★★ 'Authentic & Agreeable' reads label; ripe jammy black-fruit aromas & hint tobacco, blackcurrant jam flavour; perhaps not quite as agreeable as pvs (a function of higher percentage cinsaut (75) this yr, lower % cab?). **Good Everyday Cape Red** ★★★ A hit in Ireland, V-J reports; subtle but ripe red fruit, sandalwood hint; fairly firm tannin & evident oak. Mainly ruby cab & merlot, dashes tinta & carignan. **Good Everyday Cape White** ★★★ Still sells for less than R16/btl. Subtle guava aromas/flavours, hint of sweet lemon blossom; pleasant if quick. **Sunday Best White** ★★★ From chardonnay, chenin (51/49); bit more gravitas than pvs; stone fruits & creamy lemon flavours, good persistence, balance, concentration. To enjoy young, as are all the VJ wines. **Seriously Good Plonk (Red/White)** discontinued.

Waterfront Collection

Great White ☺ ★★★ 'For Supersport-channel watchers' recommends VJ. Latest certainly a crowd pleaser, unexpectedly rich, with lime cordial tone, satisfying.

Nautical labels distinguish this value-priced, quaffable duo. **Captain's Claret** ★★★★ ✓ Honest, appealing everyday red. ±60/40 shiraz/merlot; allspice aromas, rich & well balanced, supple tannin, med-bodied & quite fine. This should have been the 'Sunday Best'! All above NV, mainly Paarl/Frhoek vyds. — *JB*

Veelplesier see Baarsma
Veelverjaaght see BoweJoubert

Veenwouden Private Cellar

Paarl ▪ Est 1989 ▪ 1stB 1993 ▪ Tasting sales Mon-Fri 9-4.30 ▪ Fee R200/btl if no purchase made ▪ Closed public holidays ▪ Sales & tours by appt ▪ Owners D & SJ van der Walt ▪ Winemaker Marcel van der Walt, with Faried Williams (Jan 1994/1995) ▪ Viticulturists Marcel van der Walt & Sias Louw (Jan 1994/1995) ▪ 14 ha (cabs s/f, malbec, merlot) ▪ ±80 tons 5 500 cs own labels 99% red 1% white ▪ PO Box 7086 Noorder-Paarl 7623 ▪ veenwouden@intekom.co.za ▪ www.veenwouden.co.za ✆ 872·6806 🖷 872·1384

Devoted parents and able-bodied vineyard/cellar managers Charles and Sheila van der Walt have retired, after a decade helping celebrity son Deon's cellar achieve cult status. Ex-Cape Vineyards marketer Henriëtte Jacobs now manages; winemaker Faried Williams and viticulturist Sias Louw assist Deon vdW's brother Marcel. This stylish little winery is consolidating. Upgrades include a new barrel cellar (also designed to accommodate impromptu recitals by the owner, a world-renowned Zürich-based tenor). Their Thornhill Shiraz is now made with 100% own-grapes from their Wellington vineyard, wood-matured for an extra six months. Though down from 80 to 70 tons due to cropping dictated by uneven ripening, Marcel vdW rates 2004's flavour, colour, concentration 'great'.

★★★★☆ **Merlot** Serious & classy, introduced with fanfare & still prized a decade on. Mainly new Fr oak, ±2 yrs, always bolstered by dash cab, for longer bottle maturation. **02** ethereal scents of violets & hung pheasant already stirring, beautifully structured palate of fine, densely pleated tannin demands time. **01** (★★★★) less focused, complex than exhilarating **00**, which full yet elegant, powerful yet restrained. Single low-yielding vyd on home farm, over 10 yrs old. Latest less new oak – 70%. 14% alc.

★★★★☆ **Classic** Featuring cabs s/f, merlot &, latterly, soupçon malbec. **02** back on track, in ripe genre. Opulent forest-floor fruits fleshed out further with mocha hints, trademark lace tannins the key to restraint. **01** (★★★☆), capricious on initial view mid-2003, has settled with yr in bottle. 14% alc. Revised oaking as above.

★★★★ **Vivat Bacchus** Fine grained, more understated than above cellarmates – & emphatically moreish. **02** proffers generous butcher-shop aromas, damson & red berry fruits in downy tannin. Delicious on release, will reward 2-4 yrs. **01** subtle, gently complex. Now 70% merlot, with malbec, cabs s/f. 50% new Fr oak. 14% alc.

★★★☆ **Thornhill Shiraz** Bold, fruity, dramatic shiraz, gaining complexity as 1.5ha house-owned Wllngtn vines mature. **03** not ready for tasting. **02** revisited mid-2004: focused peppery flavours now layered with gamey meat tones, tightly knit, very firm tannins still on guard. 10% cab stiffening. Yr Fr oak, 25% new. 14% alc.

★★★★☆ **Chardonnay Special Reserve** With mere 200 bottles, from 4 vyd rows, both a 'reserve' (commanding R250 ARP), and 'special'. **03** back to finessed form with white truffle richness kept in order by mineral structure, lacy tannins. Super length to svelte finish: elegance regained. Turbo-powered crème brûlée fullness plumped up **02** (★★★★). New Fr oak fermented/aged *sur lie* 14 mths. 13% alc. —*DS*

Vendôme

Paarl ▪ Est 1692 ▪ 1stB 1999 ▪ Tasting & sales Mon-Fri 9.30–1 (1–4.30 by appt) Sat 9.30–12.30 ▪ Fee R5 refunded on purchase ▪ Closed public holidays ▪ Tours on request ▪ Conferencing/functions for up to 60 ▪ Owner/viticulturist Jannie le Roux ▪ Winemaker/viticulturist Jannie le Roux Jnr ▪ 40 ha (cabs s/f, merlot, shiraz, chard, chenin, colombard) ▪ 20 tons 1 400 cs own label 70% red 30% white ▪ PO Box 36 Huguenot 7645 ▪ lerouxjg@icon.co.za ▪ www.vendome.co.za ✆ ***863·3905*** 🖷 *863·0094*

Just because they like it rustic at this old Cape *werf* with its ancient oaks, pebbled paths and gabled cellar, doesn't mean the Le Roux family aren't plugged into what's happening globally. Owner Jannie le Roux Snr is chair of Boland Kelder and a mover behind the new Paarl/Wellington-focused Cape Coastal Wines export concern. JleR's son, tenth-generation Jannie, made wine in Australia, Bordeaux and California before returning to this farm sprawled on the banks of the Berg River.

★★★★ **Cabernet Sauvignon** Features natural yeast fermentation & small portion cab f for complexity; standout **00** improved in bottle, offered minerals & oak seasoning melded attractively with fruit. Retasted **01** (★★★) shows elegant tomato cocktail-like tones; appears to be peaking; moderate ±12.5% alc; yr Fr small-oak, 3rd-4th fill. No **02**, went into wine below. Attractive old-style label.

★★★☆ **Le Roux Merlot-Cabernet Sauvignon** Equal blend in **01**, tasted last ed showed as fruity, easily drinkable; **02** slightly more merlot (55%) manifests as mocha/choc edge to aromatic ripe plum tone; plump & eager; well supported by oak (regimen as above).

Chardonnay Unwooded ★★★★ **03** lovely nose of tropical fruit salad; flavours of granadilla & grapefruit marmalade; big mouthful (14.3% alc) with supple waxiness adding texture. Paarl Young Wine Show chard champ. **Chardonnay-Chenin Blanc** & **Chardonnay Classique** discontinued. — *TM*

Vera Cruz Estate see Delheim

Vergelegen

Stellenbosch (see Helderberg map) ▪ Est 1700 ▪ 1stB 1992 ▪ Tasting daily 9.30-4.30 (sales close at 5) ▪ Fee R2-R10/wine ▪ Closed Dec 25, May 1 & Easter Fri ▪ Lady Phillips Restaurant: à la carte lunches daily; Rose Terrace: al fresco restaurant Nov-Apr; picnics Nov-Apr ▪ Guided winery tours daily 10.15, 11.30 & 3 ▪ 'Interpretive Centre' depicting farm's history; also self-guided tour to the homestead ▪ Gifts ▪ Tourgroups ▪ Owner Anglo American Farms ▪ Winemaker André van Rensburg (Jan 1998) ▪ Viticulturists Spekkies van Breda & Niel Rossouw ▪ 112 ha (cabs s/f, merlot, shiraz, chard, sauvignon, semillon) ▪ 47 000 cs 60% red 40% white ▪ ISO 9002 & 9000/2000 certified ▪ PO Box 17 Somerset West 7129 ▪ vergelegen@amfarms.co.za ▪ www.vergelegen.co.za ⓒ 847·1334 ▤ 847·1608

Once upon a time a winemaker took his staff to see *Shrek*, to 'show them who they're dealing with'. The wacky, wild-eyed, grumbling winemaker with a heart of gold: that's André van Rensburg. He treats five 2004 FCTWS trophies as a given. Americans asking to taste Vergelegen's entire range were bluntly told: No, only the Reserves; he didn't want to create the erroneous impression that California could compete with him. But, like Shrek, the man has layers. 'I'm getting old (43!) — I have to make my mark.' Passion, dedication are redemptive. Having won a battle for vineyard control, he promises 25-year-old virus-free vines on Vergelegen upon retirement. Worried that he might have (subconsciously) neglected his whites, he's making amends with this season's stellar 03s. A softened Shrek since marrying his Princess Fiona (cellar assistant Maritza Steenkamp)?

★★★★★ **Vergelegen** For nearly a decade, Cape Bdx blend showing its class in immaculate fruit, alluring texture, suave tannins. Mainly cab s with merlot & seasoning of cab f. **02** supple, more rounded than pvs, thanks partly to lower (54%) fraction cab (half of crop wiped out — 'But when you're focused on terroir, you have to reflect it regardless of vintage', shrugs AvR). 14% alc. **01** retasted mid-2004, shows starbright fruit, great polish & character, structure to improve 6-10 yrs. 14.5% alc. Best red blend at FCTWS 2003, best red wine overall. From relatively warmer Rondekop vyd, imparting fruity succulence. Native-yeast fermentation; ±2 yrs new Fr oak.

★★★★★ **Vergelegen CWG Auction Reserve** Barrel selections of above; 21 mths new oak. Last tasted was **01**.

★★★★★ **Vergelegen V** Crafted to grab attention of US cult-wine fans (& influential US critic Robert Parker?); dramatically different to 'terroir-driven' style. Retasted **01** not for the oak-averse: luxurious black plum/cassis lashed with wood (21 mths new); behind the pyrotechnics, densely layered fruit is waiting to unfold over the next 5-10 yrs. Single-vyd cab, blended with merlot, tiny seasoning cab f (90/9/1);

★★★★★ **Cabernet Sauvignon** Classically styled benchmark, usually blended with smidgen merlot. **98** re-emerged as FCTWS 2004 best museum-class red; tasted mid-2004, showed confident, Bdx-like bottle-age. No **02**. **01** (★★★★★) now has fine-boned velvet texture; focused, sweet fruit masking hefty 15% alc; likely to mature 10 yrs+. Handsome muscular **00** retreating into its shell: needs time. Healthy tannins & fruit concentration augur well. 2 yrs Fr oak, ±50% new.

★★★★ **Merlot** Vergelegen's first premium red, launched to wide acclaim with **94**. Current **01** (★★★★★) retasted mid-2004, bold (15 alc %) & beautiful: mulberry-plum flavours folded with choc, clove & cinnamon. Ingratiating tannins; long mint/coffee goodbye. 20 mths Fr oak, 60% new. ±10% cab most yrs. **00** paired liquorice & minerals with structured palate. No **02**.

- ★★★★☆ **Shiraz** Classically Rhône-styled version. **02** (★★★☆) from poorer vintage, has a distinct 'green-stick' edge. Restrained & delicate red fruit, forest floor hints, limpid tannins. Not unattractive, but not up to heights of **01**, which took 2003 FCTWS trophy. Latter, retasted mid-2003, wafted violets, liquorice, choc; supple palate good for another 5-8 yrs. Fr oak, 40% new, for spice.

- ★★★★ **Mill Race Red** ✓ Admirably consistent blend cab, merlot (40-50% each) & drop cab f. **02** (★★★☆) biggest bottling ever (17 000 cs) — as cab & merlot declassified into this wallet-pleaser. Selling faster, too, than ever before, especially in new market Finland. Herbaceous, less overt fruitiness than pvs; smoky, minty end. **01** ripe; **00** gold at 2003 IWC. No scrimping on oak (± 60% new, 16 mths). 14% alc.

- ★★★★★ **Vergelegen White** A polished leader of the white pack; **03** & **02** best blend at FCTWS in 2004 & 2003 respectively; **02** *Wine* ★★★★★. **03** lovely duet between semillon's waxy white peach & sauvignon's melon/citrus tones. Perfectly balanced, tightrope-taut. 14% alc. **02** mouthfilling rich fruit & minerally tension with classy, subtle, spicy oak (new barrel ferment; then 10 mths). AvR keeps upping fraction of his beloved semillon: 22% in **01**, 67% in **02**, 78% in **03**.

- ★★★★☆ **Chardonnay Reserve** Vyd on lower Schaapenberg hillside, delivering full-bodied fruit core & mineral finish. Bunch-pressed, fermented/matured in new Burgundian oak. **03**'s elegant fruit so impressed AvR he bottled 150 magnums, a first for this farm. Ethereal white peach & orange blossom tones cosseted in creamy oak. **02** & **01** also thoroughbreds.

- ★★★★ **Chardonnay** Oak plays second fiddle to fresh stone fruit flavours in a potion that could convert critics of the variety's sometimes blowsy characters to chard lovers. **03** wholly barrel-fermented, so poised oak is barely detectable and then only as creamy texture; 40% malo adds to lighter palate-feel. **02** finely balanced. ±14.5%.

- ★★★★☆ **Sauvignon Blanc Reserve** Site-specific sauvignon from AvR's favoured, windswept Schaapenberg vyd. Skin contact mandatory to lower grapes' piercing acidity. **04** a standout vintage, scintillating & rapier-sharp, lemongrass & wet slate character. **03** showed trenchant, extra fine minerality. Unwooded. Moderate 13% alc.

- ★★★★★ **Schaapenberg Reserve** Says AvR: 'I want this to be the best Sauvignon in the world.' Prestige bottling (50 cs) of Sauvignon Blanc Reserve given weight, spice by oak (10 mths, no malo); grapes plucked from single rows. Rare (in SA) & haunting blackcurrant-leaf bouquet on **03**, also fynbos & honey, wonderfully cool 'river stone' palate. For mid-2005 release; should still give pleasure up to or beyond 2010. **02** bottled as CWG Schaapenberg Auction Reserve. ±14% alc.

- ★★★★ **Sauvignon Blanc** ✓ While others chase Holy Grail of greenpepper, this deliberately embraces broader spectrum: passion- & grapefruit to nettles to minerals. As with **03**, **04** has 10% semillon uplift. Unlike pvs, **04** not all home fruit: 25% from vyd near Koekenaap on West Coast, 1 metre (!) above sea level. No oak, no malo.

- ★★★★★ **CWG Auction Reserve Semillon 03** first since **99** (untasted by us), which took museum class trophy at FCTWS 2004. Minuscule bottling (75 cs — 50 for auction). Gorgeous honey/nougat & lime-zest flavours; persistent waxy 'wet-pebble' finish. Great structure, concentration for ageing. Bunch-pressed, barrel-fermented/10 mths Fr, 60% new, which shows in brush of caramel/spice.

- ★★★★ **Vin de Florence** ✓ Chard out, sauvignon & riesling in, with stalwarts chenin, semillon & muscat de F in fragrant, spicy off-dry **04**. 7.8g/ℓ sugar. AvR's sterling contribution to complementing Thai cuisine. 13.5% alc.

- ★★★★☆ **Noble Late Harvest Semillon** Last were elegant, wooded **98**, **00**. — *CvZ*

Vergenoegd Estate

Stellenbosch ▪ Est 1773 ▪ 1stB 1972 ▪ Tasting & sales Mon-Fri 8-5 Sat 9.30-12.30 ▪ Closed public holidays ▪ Tours by appt ▪ Owners John Faure Family Trust & Strauss family ▪ Winemaker John Faure (1984) ▪ Vineyard manager Chris van Niekerk (May 2003), advised by Drikus van der Westhuizen ▪ 90 ha (cabs s/f, merlot, shiraz) ▪ 500 tons 10 000 cs own label 95% red 5%

port ▪ PO Box 1 Faure 7131 ▪ enquiries@vergenoegd.co.za ▪ www.vergenoegd.co.za ©
843·3248 🖷 843·3118

A highlight in 2004 for John Faure, apart from the celebration of his 20th year as
winemaker, was a gold won at Europe's biggest wine show, the Concours Mondial in
Brussels, for his Cab. Another significant event was the opening of the original homestead, dating back to 1773 and recently restored, as a venue for tastings and sales. If
you're off to buy and you're wondering how Vergenoegd is affected by the proposed
Dreamworld film studio on the property, fear not – it's sited on land unsuited for production. On the cultivated portion, there are fresh blocks of malbec, petit verdot and cab, the
first two being new to the farm. Motorists on the N2, which bisects the property, might
have noticed a large vineyard vanish before their eyes. 'It was old virus-infected shiraz,
replaced for now with a cover crop which will help break down populations of unwanted
insects in the soil before we replant with vines again.'

★★★★★ **Vergenoegd** ('Reserve' till 01) Forceful cab-based blend, resisting market pressure for showy, simple fruitiness – as with all these reds; all also need & deserve
maturing 5+ yrs yet. **01**, with 24% merlot, 8% cab f; 14.5% alc, showing well mid-
2004: lovely sweet fruit coping with imposing structure; rich, powerful, savoury &
satisfying. Reflecting lesser vintage, **02** (★★★★) lighter in colour, flavour, depth. Appealing, though, with perhaps more compensating elegance, & readier earlier
(probably shorter-lived). These 20+ mths in mostly new Fr oak – 11% Am in **02**.

★★★★ **Cabernet Sauvignon** Macho stuff, needing time to soften, develop. Deeply glowing **01**, with 8% merlot, sumptuously spreads red berries, plums over serious dry
tannins. 14.3% alc. Keep, while drinking **02** (★★★☆): lighter, less intensity, also tannic but not the same rich fruit. ±20 mths oak, ± 60% new.

★★★★ **Merlot** Follows house style: grand, serious, satisfyingly conservative. Also follows
recent vintage pattern. Still youthful **01** retains well-balanced, savoury, herb-
tinged seriousness, with deep sweet fruit & chewy, powerful structure. Will keep
many yrs. Less concentrated **02** (★★★★) adds coffee notes to choc-mint fragrance;
peaking sooner. These 20+ mths oak, ± 55% new, some Am in **02**.

★★★★ **Shiraz** Handsome, muscular **01** offers ripe fruit, notes of herb, leather, smoke. Un-
exaggerated, well-balanced, satisfying. 13.%% alc. 20 mths in barrel – over half
new, mostly Fr, some Am. **02** a touch more graceful now, despite bigger alc (14.
5%); roast coffee notes, red berries showing appealingly.

★★★★ **Old Cape Colony Vintage Port** Classically profiled – around 90g/ℓ sugar, 20%
alc; fermented in open *kuipe*, old-wood-matured 18 mths. **00**, from tinta, well balanced, with spice, plum pudding aromas/flavours & firm structure. Rich, orange-
zesty **01** (★★★★★) a step forward, maybe thanks to 34% touriga: deeper-coloured,
more refined, complex; good grip. Try to resist youthful deliciousness – rather mature min 5 more yrs.

★★★☆ **Terrace Bay** Always serious, even a little stern for a 'second label', but with
good fruit asserting itself, as in spicy, red-fruited **01**. **02** a touch gentler, more
delicate, with dry tannic finish. On Vergenoegd model: massive alcs (14.5%);
substantial ageing in barrel (20+ mths); mostly Fr, some Am; older wood – 15%
new in **02**. – *TJ*

Versus see Stellenbosch Vineyards

Vilafonte

*Paarl ▪ Tours by appt ▪ PO Box 2 Elsenburg 7607 ▪ mike@warwickwine.co.za ▪ www.
vilafonte.com* © **884·4410** 🖷 884·4025

California's first lady of wine, Zelma Long, her viticulturist husband Phil Freese and US-
based fine-wine merchant Bartholomew Broadbent have joined forces with Mike
Ratcliffe of Warwick, here in a personal capacity, to produce 'a high-end brand targeted
at the top of the American market'. They've bought a property between Fairview and Glen
Carlou in the Paarl area, and plan to build a cellar there in time for the 2007 crush (the 03

and 04 vintages made at Tokara). The existing 14ha of vineyard will be developed to a maximum of about 35ha of classic varieties. Zelma L says the goal is 'to produce a wine that reflects the magnificent site. Expression of terroir is the key to the project'. The first wines – red blends with cab, merlot, cab franc and malbec – will be released in June.

Viljoensdrift Wines

Robertson ▪ Est/1stB 1998 ▪ Tasting & sales Mon-Fri 9-4 (cellar); Sat 10-2 & 1st Sun of month 11-2 (riverside) ▪ Closed Mar 21, Easter Fri, Jun 16, Dec 25 & Jan 1 ▪ Breede River cruises Sat & 1st Sun of month 12 noon, weather permitting; booking essential; weekdays for groups of 15+ by appt ▪ Create your own picnic from the deli (Sat & Sun) ▪ Tours by appt ▪ Owners Fred & Manie Viljoen ▪ Winemaker Fred Viljoen ▪ Viticulturist Manie Viljoen ▪ 120 ha (cab, pinotage, shiraz, chard, chenin, sauvignon) ▪ 1 200 tons ±80 000 cs 50% red 48% white 2% rosé ▪ Export brands: Die Breedekloof, Elandsberg, Keurfontein & Somerlust (Netherlands & Belgium) ▪ PO Box 653 Robertson 6705 ▪ viljoensdrift@lando.co.za ▪ www.viljoensdrift.co.za ℂ (023) 615·1901 ▤ (023) 615·3417

At their Robertson farm on the Breede riverbank, brothers Manie and Fred Viljoen work in harmony: the former in the vineyards, where more stringent practices resulted in a much lower yield last year; the latter in the cellar, now equipped with additional tanks. On which subject, Fred observes: 'When someone asks you when you're going to bottle your wine, send him to the tank and tell him to ask it himself. Wine decides when it is ready to be bottled.' At present some 60% of their production is marketed under their own label, but one day it will be 100%, the brothers envisage. For the leisure inclined, a cruise on Uncle Ben, a motorised raft which operates from their riverside tasting area, is must. It's ever better if you create your own picnic from the deli (Saturdays and first Sunday of every month) to enjoy on deck.

River Grandeur range

★★★★ **Cabernet Sauvignon** ✓ Gregarious **03** in same mould as **02**: rich cassis, herbaceous flavours, hint of bouillon; laid-back tannins. Technically dry, finishes fruit- & oak-sweet. Already drinking well. Open fermenters for all reds in range, yr Fr oak. 13.5% alc.

★★★★ **Pinotage 03** (★★★★) packed with dark fruit/boiled sweet tastes. Firm tannins, slight bitter nuance cuts creamy vanilla/mulberry palate. Drink young. **02** also generously fruity but smoother. Mainly Am oak, yr. 14.5% alc.

★★★★ **Shiraz** ✓ Flavoursome **03** concentrated by 'bleeding' off juice pre-fermentation. Vivid farmyard/floral notes; boisterous 15% alc reined in by sweet-oak & red fruit flavours. Approachable now but has structure to improve ± 3 yrs. **02** fully ripe & fragrant, with vanilla oak & choc-cherries. Yr 50/50 Fr/Am oak, ±30% new.

★★★★ **Chenin Blanc** ✓ Bunch selection ensures fruit quality, as in **04**, which has aromas of dried apple & musk sweets; lovely dry floral palate – like tasting spring! Alc a moderate 13%. **03** weightier (14% alc), food-friendly.

Chardonnay ★★★ **04** (sample) hints lime/lemon & spicy oak; rich palate courtesy judicious oak, 2 mths lees ageing & touch sugar (5g/ℓ) – all given zip by fresh acidity. 30% new Fr oak fermented/matured. 14.5% alc. **Sauvignon Blanc** ★★★ Feather-light **04** with restrained alc (12.5%) & subdued grassy apple flavours. Refreshing finish.

Viljoensdrift range

Merlot-Shiraz ☺ ★★★ Substantial winter-warming 60/40 blend. **04** with now-customary meaty flavours, soft tannins. **Colombar-Chenin Blanc** ☺ ★★★ Picnic quaffer with tangy lime/pineapple profile in **04**. **Rosé** NEW ☺ ★★★ **04** made from bled-off juice of shiraz, pinotage. Outgoing lollipop flavours; firm, dry, clean finish.

Cabernet Sauvignon, Pinotage, Shiraz, Chardonnay for export, not tasted. **Semillon** ★★★ Style change in **03**, now rich & creamy following spell on lees. No **04**. – *CvZ*

Village Collection see Tulbagh Winery

Villiera Wines

Stellenbosch ▪ Est/1stB 1983 ▪ Tasting & sales Mon-Fri 8.30-5 Sat 8.30-1 ▪ R7.50 p/p for groups ▪ Closed Easter Fri/Sun, Dec 25, Jan 1 ▪ Self-guided tours anytime during tasting hours; guided tours by appt ▪ Annual St Vincent's Day dinner (closest Sat to Jan 22) ▪ BYO picnic in summer ▪ Owners Grier family ▪ Winemakers Jeff Grier, with Anton Smal (Oct 1992) ▪ Viticulturist Simon Grier ▪ 260 ha (13 varieties, r/w) ▪ 1 800 tons 100 000 cs own label 32% white 42% red 4% rosé 22% sparkling ▪ PO Box 66 Koelenhof 7605 ▪ wine@villiera.com ▪ www. villiera.com ℂ 865-2002/3 ▣ 865-2314

As cellarmaster Jeff Grier celebrated his 21st vintage on this consummately professional property last year his first-born, appropriately, also fledged: 'He has his freedom now… and a car.' Typically, the affable Grier clan has never taken its continuing acclaim for granted. Cousin Simon's eco-friendly vineyard practices now include probe-monitored drip irrigation (which increases a vine's optimal production capabilities and conserves water), and leaf/soil analysis to detect malnutrition. Grier J is cutting down on (legal, of course) additives and preservatives, and experimenting with natural yeasts. He is also making greater use of micro/macro oxygenation for easier tannins, and extended on-lees ageing. Sister Cathy, Cape Wine Master and queen of customer care, constantly gathers intelligence from the market and wine competitions. Says Grier J: 'I believe in reacting to a clear message.' An example: pre-empting a pending EU ban on the use of the term 'port' by non-Portuguese vintners, Villiera is relaunching its LBV as 'Fired Earth'. As if not sufficiently challenged by all this, Grier J tried skydiving. His first jump: a tandem with his daughter. Verdict? 'Scary!'

★★★★ **Monro** Successor to Cru Monro as flagship red, **00** stepped up with international-style sleekness. 57/43 merlot/cab, firm depth of ripe fruit, structure. **01** 50/50 blend also successfully straddles conservatism/modernism. Rich, sweetly ripe; savoury & fruity, well balanced with gently firm tannins. Still quite oaky mid-2004, evidencing 20 mths in 70% new Fr barrels, needs yr/2 to integrate; will keep well 5+ more. 13.5% alc.

★★★★ **Cabernet Sauvignon** ✓ Invariably well-mannered, honest. **02**'s good varietal nose, spiced with tobacco notes, leads to decently flavoursome palate, with appropriately unassertive tannins. Splash of merlot. Yr Fr/Am oak. 13.4% alc. Will keep few yrs.

★★★★ **Merlot** ✓ Quietly attractive **02** with lighter feel than **01**, though same big 14.4% alc gives warmly glowing finish. Fresh, plummy, choc aromas/flavours, well-structured palate, unobtrusive yr oak, 25% new Fr.

★★★★ **Shiraz 02** developing well, still fragrant with spice & lilies; flavoursome, lively, elegantly structured & balanced. Unobtrusive support from yr in barrel, not excessive 14% alc. **01** had similar choc/violet fragrance.

★★★★ **Cellar Door Cape Blend** ✓ New name for Merlot-Pinotage (prefix used for Villiera's reserve wines in best years). **02** lightish in colour (as are many of this yr), compatible 65/35 merlot/pinotage blend, with some sweetly jammy rusticity tamed & disciplined. Bright fruit, ripe, firm tannins. Few yrs should increase harmony. Yr oak: merlot in new Fr, pinotage in Am. 14.6% alc.

★★★★ **Chenin Blanc** ✓ Always a fine bargain. **04** continues tradition of fruit-salad exuberance, with touch of straw, earthiness. Powerful (13.9% alc), silky, vibrant. Some wood influence (30% barrel-fermented) adds to effect, does not dominate. Dry, but a little sugar for added easy richness.

★★★★ **Cellar Door Chenin Blanc** Made only in best yrs, fermented/matured in new Fr oak 7 mths. No **02**, but **03** worth waiting for. Bright pale gold, with lovely aromas/flavours (including spicy evidence of wooding); leesy, rich & creamy, well-balanced acid, long dry finish. 14.3% alc. Will develop, keep good few yrs.

★★★★ **Traditional Bush Vine Sauvignon Blanc 03** had notes of passionfruit, melon, thatch; attractive & balanced, with weight threaded by fine acidity. 13.4% alc, like previewed sample **04**, promising good core of fruit, but perhaps softer, less focused than usual.

★★★★ **Sauvignon Blanc** Soft-textured **04** (★★★) with a splash semillon, a little less zippily elegant than pvs, but offering pleasant fig & tropical fruit aromas/flavours. Some grainy sweetness on modest finish. 13.7% alc. **03** was ripe, rich but also elegant, balanced.

★★★★ **Rhine Riesling** Always graceful, fresh, dry example of this great variety, deserving few yrs keeping. **03** tank sample was green-appley but very promising last yr; no **04** — insufficient grapes for own label as well as supplying Woolworths.

★★★★ **Inspiration** Luxuriously silky NLH from hand-selected botrytised chenin. **03** hints of raisin whiffs, with typical honeyed, marmaladey yellow-gold rich silkiness. Returns to lighter refined style of **01**, with 115g/ℓ sugar, 12.6% alc both lower than **02** — which also most elegantly balanced, both light & intense. Same clean, airy, almost dry finish. These fermented/aged ± 9 mths Fr oak. Will keep/develop well, though delicious in youth.

★★★☆ **Tradition Brut** ✓ NV indeed a good, consistent Cape tradition for some 20 yrs bottling. Latest from chardonnay, pinot, pinotage (50/35/15) is, as always, light, dry & gently lively, with subtle fruit & hint of minerality. Also in 1.5ℓ and 375ml.

★★★★ **Tradition Rosé Brut** Charming colour from ripe, soft pinotage added to blend of pinot, pinotage, chardonnay juice (45/40/15) in latest (★★★★) NV classically made bubbly, which proclaims the black grapes, with simple fruity aromas. A shade less refined, lingering than pvs. Dry, soft finish; 9g/ℓ sugar.

★★★★ **Monro Première Cuvée Brut** Lovely old-gold glints set off the biscuity aromas in the fine, well-matured **99**. Rich, silkily textured, with dry, gently lingering finish — low 9g/ℓ sugar. Extra depth from barrel-fermented/matured chardonnay (55%) in partnership with unwooded pinot.

★★★★★ **Brut Natural Chardonnay** ✓ Nobly refined MCC made in most yrs since **98**, supplementing 'nature' only with the yeast used in second, bubble-forming fermentation — no sulphur or other additives. Standout **01** (★★★★★) with delightful baked apple, cinnamon aromas, & subtly complex, creamy, bone-dry richness (unusually, no sugar added either), fine acidity & long finish. Latest **02** similar profile, but a touch lighter, leaner. These, if kept to beneficially mature more than yr/2, need even more careful storage than sulphur-protected wines.

★★★★ **Fired Earth** Imaginative, EU-pleasing new name for pvs LBV Port with **00**. Classically styled with high 20% alc, moderate sugar, from unorthodox (but successful) combo shiraz, pinotage, gamay — now plus some tinta, souzão. 3 yrs in older oak. Like slightly drier **99** (85g/ℓ), warmly, uncomplicatedly inviting; ready.

Down to Earth [Red] ☺ ★★★ Don't-worry-be-happy coming together of 6 commingling varieties, succulently ripe & tasty. Lightly oaked, 13.8% alc. **Down to Earth [White]** ☺ ★★★ Pleasant partnership of half chenin with sauvignon, semillon; as zippy & flavoursome in **04** as ever. Should please most, but suitability for vegetarians expressly ensured, say Griers. **Gewürztraminer** ☺ ★★★ Usual rose-petal exuberance from **04**, but, surprisingly, rather elegant in a soft, succulent way. Well calculatedly just off-dry. 14.1% alc. **Sonnet** ☺ ★★★ Charming, flower-fragrant, fresh **04** from muscat ottonel/chenin pleasantly off-dry.

Pinotage ★★★ **02** as friendly as ever, chunkily rustic & soft — but plenty of tannin & bold bright fruit. Yr Am oak; 14% alc. Discontinued: **Cellar Door Pinotage**; **Blanc Fumé**; **Vintage Brut**. — *TJ*

Villiersdorp Cellar

Worcester ▪ Est 1922 ▪ 1stB 1980 ▪ Tasting Mon-Sat 8-5 Sun 9-3 ▪ Sales Mon-Sat 8-5 ▪ Fee R10 for groups of 7+ ▪ Closed Easter Fri & Dec 25 ▪ Fully licensed restaurant, farm stall & gift shop ▪ Owners 55 growers ▪ Winemakers Danie Conradie & WS Visagie (both 2001) ▪ Viticul-

turist Danie Conradie ▪ 500 ha ▪ 5 600 tons 4 000 cs own label 20% red 60% white 6% rosé 14% fortified ▪ PO Box 14 Villiersdorp 6848 ▪ info@vilko.co.za ▪ www.vilko.co.za ⓒ (028) 840·1151 ☎ (028) 840·0957

Many visitors to this cellar on the fringe of Villiersdorp go there to enjoy the relaxed atmosphere of the licensed restaurant, where light meals are the order of the day and good home-baked delicacies are on sale seven days a week. Part of the rural charm is that tourgroups are not welcomed, so you can be assured of an unhurried and quiet visit any day of the week. The wines? Affordable and easy-drinking as ever.

> **Cabernet Sauvignon** ☺ ★★★ **03** notes of plums & cherries, full, generous, subtly oaked; good spicy length. Could happily be cellared few yrs. **Chenin Blanc** ☺ ★★★ **04** (sample) lovely fresh, clean tropical aromas, smoothly dry, quaffable. **Sauvignon Blanc** ☺ ★★★ **04** (sample) basket of sweet tropical fruit on nose/palate, lively light texture & poised acidity. Enjoy in yr of vintage.

Chardonnay ★★☆ Citrus & tropical fruit in **04**, fresh, whistle-clean dry finish; unwooded. **Bouquet Blanc 03** from chenin/hanepoot, untasted. Following NVs (04) tasted as samples: **Hanepoot Jerepiko** ★★★☆ Full-sweet fortified dessert with fresh honeysuckle aroma, lifted palate, finishes with a very attractive spirity tang. 17% alc. **Port** ★★★ Traditional Cape-style fortified with fruity/jammy character. — *DH*

█ *Vine Collection* see Oranjerivier

Vinfruco

Est/1stB 1992 ▪ Closed to public ▪ Owners 13 shareholders ▪ Winemakers Nicky Versfeld, Werner Engelbrecht, Celéste Truter (Jul 2001, Mar 1997, Jun 2000) ▪ 47.5% red 52% white 0.5% rosé ▪ ISO 9001 & HACCP certified ▪ Export brands: Mountain Shadows, Tesco & ranges below ▪ UK offices: Moorbridge Court, 29–41 Moorbridge Road, Maidenhead, Berkshire SL6 8LT ⓒ 0628·763·769 ☎ 0628·763·770 ▪ Stellenbosch offices: PO Box 12730 Die Boord 7613 ▪ info@vinfruco.co.za ▪ www.vinfruco.co.za ▪ www.arniston-bay. co.za ⓒ 886·6458 ☎ 886·6589

There's no gearing back for this wine export dynamo, headquartered in the historic Oude Molen manor house in Stellenbosch. Alliances are part of their philosophy of 'leadership through partnerships', so the intended merger with Stellenbosch Vineyards, in final stages of negotiation as the guide went to press, should come as no surprise. The amalgamated company would generate an annual turnover of some R400m, providing the muscle to compete more effectively in domestic and international markets. Meanwhile it's business as usual, with a string of accolades awarded across the brands: As they put it: 'We want Vinfruco to be known as a producer of high-quality wines that over-deliver on price across the market.'

Credo range

★★★☆ **Cabernet Sauvignon** Initially oaky **99** has settled, harmonised; still firm but pleasantly so, acidity comes back on finish. Drinking well, will keep for few yrs more. 2 yrs Fr oak.

★★★☆ **Shiraz** Delicious, manages power with subtlety. **02** black cherry, hints leather, smoked beef; terrific choc-coated prunes, smooth ripe tannins, good finish with brush of dry tannin. 18 mths Fr/Am oak, all new. 14.5% alc. No **01**. Mouthfilling **00** improved in the bottle.

★★★☆ **Groenekloof Sauvignon Blanc** Sample **04** pushes all the right buttons. Trim figure, loads of style; cool climate fig/crushed nettle, properly dry with gorgeous sweet-sour tang, further freshened by spritzy touch. Should be a winner. 13.7% alc. **03** gold at Concours Mondial.

Arniston Bay range

★★★☆ **Méthode Cap Classique** Classically dry (but only just: 15g/ℓ sugar) sparkling ex-Tlbgh; apple aromas with hints lemon/herb; full, creamy mouthful. Chardonnay & pinots blanc/noir. Mid-2004 still fresh & vibrant; 36 mths on lees. NV.

> **Ruby Cabernet-Merlot** ☺ ★★★ Gulpable style, unoaked, **03** lively, soft & juicy. Well-styled for standalone drinking. 13.5% alc. **Pinotage-Merlot** NEW ☺ ★★★ **03** bright juicy fruit with sweet-sour twist, high-toned fruit pastille flavours, a real show-off. Quaffable 13.5% alc. **Chardonnay-Semillon** NEW ☺ ★★★ **04** more weight & concentration than in Chenin-Chardonnay below, lemon & lime aromas/flavours, tastes drier, too, smooth silky texture, unoaked.

Merlot Reserve NEW ★★★ **03** (sample) ripe mulberry, touch leafiness adds freshness to smooth fleshy build, minimal tannins. Easy drinking. **Shiraz** ★★★ **03** style changes to juicy & light flavoured, though still 14% alc. Good picnic red, cherry/raspberry fruits, delicious. Small portion oaked. **Shiraz-Merlot** ★★★ Latest **03** richer, more concentrated than single-variety Shiraz. Dark cherries, wisp smoke, Karoo scrub with dry, lightly tannic finish. 14% alc. Unoaked. **Rosé** ★★★ Quaffing-style pink from pinotage, soft easy redcurrant flavours. Manageable 12.5% alc. **Chenin Blanc-Chardonnay** ★★★ Among biggest SA brands in Britain. Latest **04** more slenderly built, fresh & bouncy, pear-drops with touches spiced apple, sweetness on finish. 13.5% alc.

Oak Village range

Cabernet Sauvignon ★★★ **02** good whiff cedar, nicely judged dark plummy fruit, shows the firmer tannins of the variety; almost ready. 30% cask-aged. 14% alc. **Pinotage** ★★★ Frequent flyer with SAA, unsurprising given fruit-driven styling (not wooded); **01** light-toned with soft finish. Retasted mid-2004, still lively. **Vintage Reserve** ★★★ Latest **03** (sample) still a bit rough, but pleasing blackberry fruit, chunky build, fresh acidity. Unoaked blend cab s, merlot, cinsaut, shiraz. 14.3% alc. **Chardonnay-Chenin Blanc** ★★★ Juicy yellow peach & spiced apples mingle in fresh **04**, soft easy palate. 13.7% alc. **Sauvignon Blanc** ★★ Pleasant dry white, little sauvignon punch in **03**, echoes of fig, some tangy lemon notes.

Rock Ridge range

Cabernet Sauvignon ★★★ **02** pleasurably firm; flavours deepening & darkening, red berry palate with fresh acidity on finish. **Merlot** ★★★ Take-home-and-drink-tonight styling; **03** suave, groomed version, mid-weight cassis flavours. Lightly wooded, manageable 13.5% alc. **Pinotage** ★★★ Latest **03** choc-box sweet vanilla tone; palate contrasts with dry, savoury flavours, grippy tannins. Ripe at 14.5% alc. **Chardonnay** ★★★ Partially cask-fermented mini-blockbuster, 14.5% alc with crème brûlée nuance; **03** honestly dry, firm, balanced; will have wide appeal. WO Rbtsn. **Sauvignon Blanc** ★★★ **03** shy, not much varietal punch, lemon-lime on palate. Lightish, full of zip. WO Coastal/W-Cape. — *IvH*

Vinimark

Stellenbosch ▪ *Closed to public* ▪ *Directors Tim Rands, Cindy Jordaan & Guys Naudé* ▪ *PO Box 441 Stellenbosch 7599* ▪ *info@vinimark.co.za (exports: jennyr@vinimark.co.za)* ▪ *www.vinimark.co.za* ✆ *883·8043/4* 🖷 *886·4708*

Wine merchants styling various ranges with local partners, including Jonkerskloof, Kleindal, Long Beach Café, Ravenswood, Silver Sands and Zomerlust, listed seperately.

Vins D'Orrance

Est 2001 ▪ *1stB 2002* ▪ *Tastings by appt 8.30-4.30* ▪ *Owner Christophe Durand* ▪ *Winemaker Christophe Durand, advised by Edouard Labeye* ▪ *530 cs 100% red* ▪ *10 Squirrels Way Newlands 7735* ▪ *christophe@vinum.co.za* ✆ *855·2244* 🖷 *855·0095*

Immigré Christophe Durand's Vins D'Orrance label is attached to a Shiraz and a Chardonnay (the first of the latter was bottled as the guide went to press); the Cuveé Ameena label is used for a Syrah. All are exported to the States, Sweden, Belgium and the winemaker's country of birth but 'being a French winemaker,' he says, 'it has been very rewarding for me to be recognised in SA'. His philosophy is to maintain traditions 'and to respect the wine'. Tannin management, he says, is key. In a separate venture, Chris D and partners in The Winery produce in rented space from grapes from leased vineyards.

★★★★ **Syrah 'Cuvee Ameena' 02** from single Simonsberg vyd, realised with French flair. Vibrant, bone-dry; complementary dark spice, berries with gamey slick in textured elegance, savoury length. Fr oak 14 mths. Well balanced to disguise 14.5% alc. **01** (★★★) had austere but elegant; persistent finish. — AL

Vinum see The Winery

Vinus Via

Stellenbosch ▪ Est/1stB 2004 ▪ 10 000 cs (projected) 50/50 red/white ▪ 21 Topaz Street, Heldervue, Somerset West 7130 ▪ info@vinusvia.co.za ▪ www.vinusvia.co.za
©/🖷 **855·5244**

At a career crossroads last year, wine marketer Richard Hilton blew the dust off a long-nurtured business plan and decided it was time to fly solo. His fledgling company boasts a range of four wines, all priced in the R20-R30 category, all promising good value in packaging which reflects UK-born Hilton's continuing love affair with the Cape. Flexibility is the key to the flight plan, allowing Hilton to accommodate future fashion dictates. With the local operation settling into a comfortable cruise, Vinus Via is cleared for take-off into the export arena.

Shaka Zulu Shiraz ★★★★ ✓ **03** crushed pepper spice & almond notes, dense succulence, persistent red berry fruit finish. Some Fr oak support from staves. Above all else, accessible — especially with friendly 12.6% alc. **Rockhopper Pinotage** ★ Varnishy character to rustic **03**; chunky tannins. Wooding as above. WO W-Cape, as are all these. **Wild Lily Chardonnay** ★★★ **04** grapefruit/tropical whiffs, fresh (unoaked) palate, lingering pineapple flavours. 14% alc. **Jackass Chenin Blanc** ★★ Zesty, food-friendly **04**, with some guava-apricot tinged charm, easygoing 11.9% alc. — MF

Vin-X-Port

*Paarl ▪ Est 2001 ▪ Closed to public ▪ 191 Main Rd, Paarl 7646 ▪ marketing@x-port.co.za ▪ www.x-port.co.za © **872·0850** 🖷 872·0849*

Negociant house specialising in procuring, producing and shipping quality wines, and in creating and marketing new brands. Its current portfolio of own-ranges (none tasted) includes African Treasure, Cape Circle and BunduStar, exported to the UK, Belgium, Russia, The Netherlands and Germany.

Virgin Earth see Havana Hills

Virginia

'The wine for men who enjoy being men' is one of SA's long-standing big-volume white brands. Sold in 4.5ℓ flagon; NV ★★ nominally semi-sweet yet finishes dry; tropical fruit salad nose; gluggagle. By Distell. WO W-Cape. — CR

Vlottenburg Winery see Stellenbosch Hills
Volmaak see Baarsma

Von Ortloff

Franschhoek ▪ 1stB 1994 ▪ Tasting, sales & tours by appt ▪ Owners/winemakers/viticulturists Georg & Eve Schlichtmann ▪ 15 ha (cab, merlot, shiraz, chard, sauvignon) ▪ 6 000 cs own label

60% red 40% white ▪ PO Box 341 Franschhoek 7690 vortloff@mweb.co.za © ***876·3432*** 🖷 *876·4313*

After a long, challenging and tiring 2004 harvest, Eve and Georg Schlichtmann treated themselves to a few pints of Guinness – in Ireland. Commissioned in time for the crush were two new open fermenters, notable for their 'astonishing height to width ratio' – a design feature intended to ease the punching-down of the cap during vinification. Yet no sooner had fermentation begun ('as always on a weekend, when the two of us are alone in the cellar') than a stainless steel mixer slipped from one of their hands and vanished into the new-fangled tank's opaque depths. Undeterred, red-haired Eve S plunged in and, after some thrashing about, succeeded in retrieving the submerged implement. Something about the way she stirred up the must appeared to set off a benevolent reaction, for when the fermented wine was drawn off, the results were '10 barriques of real, real good merlot – definitely a hot contender for our new top range, Quintessence'.

★★★★☆ **Cabernet Sauvignon-Merlot** These have style & presence, showing attention to detail: only free-run juice, individual oaking for components. Latest **01** (★★★★) blend 76% cab, 24% merlot; ripe cassis fruit, less taut, continues trend to easier accessibility. Cab 24-26 mths barriques, 60% new; merlot 24 mths, 50% new, all Fr. Standout **00** has a complex weave of mulberry & spice; silky smooth texture, fine-grained ripe tannins approachable on release. Both 14.5% alc.

★★★★ **No. 7** ✓ From merlot. Brilliantly fruity **03**, forthcoming cassis, mint choc/mocha introduction to meaty dry palate, manageable tannins. 9 mths Fr oak, 10% new, 13.5% alc. **02** more savoury, subtle oak support, house's signature drinkability.

★★★★ **Chardonnay** Elegant barrel-fermented example since **93**. Latest **03** in more consumer-friendly style (★★★★), misses some of the classic restraint of earlier vintages. Riper at 14.5% alc, fruit centre-stage, oak in the wings. **02** had a tangy palate & extraordinary length. 12-14 mths, all Fr, 70% new.

No. 5 ★★★★ 'Sauvignon Blanc' **04** says back-label, similarly bright-fruited to excellent **03**. Whiffs fig, gooseberry & passion fruit; exciting sweet/sour play on palate. Delicious.

No. 3 ★★★★ Unwooded chardonnay, showing remarkable intensity in **03**; retasted, ripe with yellow peach juiciness & flesh to match. Round, looser weave than wooded version, more accessible in youth. 14% alc. – *IvH*

▓ *Voorspoed* see Baarsma

Vooruitsig

Paarl ▪ Est 1998 ▪ 1stB 2002 ▪ Closed to public ▪ Owner Mozelle Holdings (Pty) Ltd ▪ Vini consultant Jean-Vincent Ridon (2002) ▪ 3ha (merlot) ▪ 500 cs 100% red ▪ PO Box 6080 Uniedal 7612 ▪ www.prime-invest.co.za/vooruitsig.htm ▪ vooruitsig@prime-invest.co.za © ***082·566·4700/082·564·3231*** 🖷 *855·3028*

If 'location, location, location' is everything when it comes to property, these directors of a real estate company specialising in wine farms knew when to choose the neighbourhood to get their venture off to a good start. It's right next door to fine red-wine house Veenwouden. Only 3ha of merlot are in production, but new blocks of cabs sauvignon and franc, shiraz and malbec will follow. Cape Town-based winemaker and partner Jean-Vincent Ridon (of Signal Hill) makes the wine.

Merlot 02 (sample) rich in all respects; deep, youthful purple hues; intense damson bouquet with pencil-shaving whiffs from new Fr oak (25%, 18 mths). Full mid-palate, ripe mouthfilling tannins. 14.2% alc. Minimum ★★★★ on release. An auspicious debut. – *JB*

Vrede en Lust Farms

Paarl ▪ Est 1996 ▪ 1stB 2002 ▪ Tasting & sales daily 10-4 ▪ Fee R10 ▪ Closed Dec 25 & Jan 1 ▪ Tours 10-4 by appt ▪ Cotage Fromage Deli & Restaurant ▪ Guest accommodation in two guest cottages & manor house ▪ Play area for children ▪ Tourgroups by appt (max 26 people) ▪ Gifts ▪ Farm produce ▪ Conferences & functions ▪ Owners Dana & Etienne Buys ▪ Winemaker

Stepháne de Saint Salvy, with Bongani Shandu (Dec 2001/2002) ▪ *Viticulturist Etienne Buys (Jun 1998)* ▪ *42 ha (cab, malbec, merlot, petit v, shiraz, chard)* ▪ *20 000 cs own label* ▪ *ISO 14001 certified* ▪ *PO Box 171 Groot Drakenstein 7680* ▪ *info@vnl.co.za* ▪ *www.vnl.co.za* ℂ *(021) 874·1611* 🖷 *(021) 874·1859*

This thoroughly modern operation, built on a heritage of more than 300 years, has a marketing strategy that's as advanced as the 500-ton cellar. It's the brainchild of IT specialist Dana Buys, who drew up the basic business plan while studying an advanced management programme at Harvard Business School. They follow what they term 'anti-distribution', marketing directly to consumers via computer-based software (designed by Buys' company). The aim is to steer as many people to their winery and website as possible. SA is their prime market, and their end-target is 35 000 cases a year. Back at the cellar, Bordeaux-born Stepháne de Saint Salvy, assisted by Bongani Shandu, 'believes in blends rather than single varieties to achieve more complex wines'.

Vrede en Lust range

★★★☆ **Marguerite** Altogether more punch & focus in 03; chardonnay, classically styled & toned; ripe citrus spectrum, wood supportive & well tucked away. Whole-bunch pressed, Fr cask fermented & matured 10 mths.

> **Barbère** ☺ ★★★ Rosé 03 like lighter-style red, fullish & vinous; juicy all-sorts — 5 varieties — bone-dry but ultra-soft acidity gives impression of sweetness; good food partner.

Jacques de Savoye range

Following wines all **02**s:

★★★★ **Classic** Well named Bdx blend — the suave, smooth sibling to two more unruly numbers below. Merlot-led with cab, petit v, malbec (52/24/15/9). Supple & elegant with sleek cassis, choc & hint of cedar, ripe & round but under the civilising influence of good oak. Yr Fr oak, 25% new.

Cara ★★★ More robust, riper, tannins still untamed & mouthcoating. Blend merlot, shiraz, cab (62/22/16), spicy & black-fruited. Oaking same as Classic. **Simond** ★★★ Unoaked cab, merlot, shiraz, malbec (40/30/25/5) union. Ripe & rustic, abounding with dark-skinned fruits, shiraz veldfire aromas emerging. 14.5% alc. WO Coastal. — *lvH*

▮ **Vredendal Winery** see Westcorp

Vredenheim Wines

Stellenbosch ▪ *Tasting & sales Mon-Fri 9-5 Sat 9.30-2 (Dec 9-5)* ▪ *Fee R2/tasting* ▪ *Closed Easter Fri, Dec 25 & Jan 1* ▪ *Barrique Restaurant* ℂ *881·3001* ▪ *Hudson's Coffee Shop* ℂ *881·3590* ▪ *Other amenities: see intro* ▪ *Owners Bezuidenhout family* ▪ *Winemaker Elzabé Bezuidenhout, advised by Fanie Cilliers* ▪ *80 ha* ▪ *10 000 cs 60% red 40% white* ▪ *PO Box 369 Stellenbosch 7599* ▪ *trendsetter@vredenheim.co.za* ▪ *www.vredenheim.co.za* ℂ *881·3637* 🖷 *881·3296*

Co-owner Elzabé Bezuidenhout is back in the winemaking role at this family-friendly farm, within cycling distance of Stellenbosch town. She's able to draw on the winemaking and viticultural expertise of Fanie Cilliers, who makes his Stellendrift and Cilliers Cellars ranges here. Both products of both wineries are available for tasting and sale on the property, which features two eat-outs (picnic baskets on request), a gift shop, characterful old cellar (hireable for weddings, birthdays or conferences), a rose garden, and — special treat for children — a menagerie featuring various antelope, ostriches and more.

★★★☆ **Reserve 214** Pick of this crop. 03 cab, shiraz & merlot (46/37/17), tidily packaged & tasty; array of cherry, plum & sweet oak-spice whiffs, suggestion of mint; medium body, ripe & supple. Yr Fr oak, further 18 mths in bottle.

Shiraz ★★★ 01 vibrant colours; allspice aromas with smoked ham hints; fullish, integrated but assertively fresh finishing. 3 yrs (!) Fr oak. **Pinotage** ★★★ WO Coastal (Paarl fruit); **03** ringer for variety: aromas of mulberries & strawberry-yoghurt (creaminess from yr new Fr oak); ripe red fruits, healthy tannins. All above 13.5% alc. **Rosé** ★★★ Ostensibly chenin & cab, but definite muscat whiffs, fairly intense grapey palate; well balanced. NV/ uncertified; low 11.5% alc. **Chenin Blanc** ★★★ **04** light & unsophisticated; soft stone-fruit aromas, Golden Delicious apple flavours. **Angel's** ★★ Returns to guide with **04**, still in Natural Sweet style, from chenin; summer meadow scents; sweet, lightish grapey flavours. **Vredenvonkel** ★★★ Demi-sec style sparkling from chardonnay; lots of exuberant bubbles; apple crumble nuance to its mild sweetness. 12% alc. NV. — *JB*

Vreughvol see Baarsma
Vriesenhof see Paradyskloof
Vruchtbaar see Robertson Wide River

Waboomsrivier Co-op

*Worcester ▪ Est 1949 ▪ 1stB 1950 ▪ Tasting & sales Mon-Fri 8-12.30; 1.30-5 Sat 8-10 ▪ Closed public holidays ▪ Cellar tours by appt ▪ BYO picnic ▪ Owners 40 members ▪ Winemaker Chris van der Merwe (Oct 1987), with Wim Viljoen (Sep 1991) ▪ ±15 500 tons 40% red 42% white 8% rosé 10% other ▪ PO Box 24 Breede River 6858 ▪ wabooms@ mweb.co.za ✆ **(023) 355·1730** 🖷 (023) 355·1731*

The major event of the year in this cellar was the installation of a Flash Dente system for extracting the maximum flavour, colour and tannins from the fruit in the minimum time. The grapes are briefly heated to soften them, then subjected to a vacuum to burst the cells within the berry skins, releasing flavour components instantly. Winemaker Chris van der Merwe reports that 2004 was the driest summer in this area in more than 30 years. Maybe the new technology will help to compensate for uneven ripening in the vineyards.

> **Cabernet Sauvignon** ☺ ★★★ **03** friendly, approachable, with mineral touch; bright red berry flavours; enough structure for some bottle development. **Roodewagen** ☺ ★★★ Rounded, accessible **03**, terrific red berry aromas/flavours; pinotage & cinsaut for succulence, cab for structure, merlot for fun. **Merlot-Ruby Cabernet** ☺ ★★★ **03** ripe plums touched with thatch & prune; sweet amenable tannins; drinks well now, should hold yr/2. Note high alc: 14%. **Cabernet Sauvignon Rosé** ☺ ★★★ Fluorescent pink **03** holding up well; tasty, rounded yet pleasingly crisp on finish. Enjoy within the yr.

Pinotage ★★★ Nothing genteel about these; **02** full, decidedly spiritous (14.4% alc); strong tannins need proverbial fatty chop. Quite unlike... **Ruby Cabernet** ★★★ Unoaked **01** soft & rotund, light thatchy & savoury touches, ready to drink. **Blanc de Blanc** ★★★ We last tasted lightish, dry **03**, from sauvignon/colombard. **Chenin Blanc Late Harvest** ★★★★ ✓ **03** has improved with botte-age; shows lovely honeyed tropical fruit flavours; still fairly brisk. **Rubellite Sparkling** ★★★ Last-tasted version of this blush-coloured NV carbonated bubbly was explosively fizzy, lightish & very sweet. **Hanepoot** ★★★★ Last we tasted this NV fortified dessert, we noted unusual choc-mint whiffs & floral touch, enlivened by acidity. **Port** ★★★★ ✓ **03** ruby-style fortified from ruby cab, gaining charm in bottle; brims with sweet warming damson/cherry fruit. ±18% alc. — *DH*

Wamakersvallei Winery

*Wellington ▪ Est 1941 ▪ Tasting & sales Mon-Fri 8-5 Sat 8.30-12.30 ▪ Closed public holidays except May 1 ▪ Tours by appt ▪ BYO picnic ▪ Owners 40 members ▪ Winemakers Bennie Wannenburg & André Swanepoel ▪ Viti consultant Johan Viljoen ▪ Viti consultant Dricus van der Westhuizen ▪ 1 400 ha ▪ 55% red 45% white ▪ PO Box 509 Wellington 7654 ▪ sales@ wamakers.co.za ▪ www.wamakersvallei.co.za ✆ **873·1582** 🖷 873·3194*

Like many wineries in the area, Wamakersvallei has planted limited quantities of scarcer varieties such as mourvèdre, petit verdot, zinfandel and viognier, to provide an extended palette with which to create its ranges. An ongoing emphasis, says new winery manager

Johan Truter, is to select the best grapes from the wide area farmed (it stretches from Riebeeck-West through Paarl to Wellington). 'We aim to select only the best for the particular style, so we are able to produce wines of a consistent quality.' Bolstering the team are two new recruits: winemaker André Swanepoel and experienced vine-man Johan Viljoen. The tasting area at the winery was recently upgraded, and the portfolio enlarged: there's a Shiraz in the mid-priced Bain's Way range, and a blended quaffer under the label 33 Degrees South, a reference to the winery's location on the map.

La Cave range

★★★☆ **Cabernet Sauvignon** Striking, modern cab, lauded by various show judges; maiden **01** had a minerally tone & satisfying firmness. **02**, on retaste, shows shy black fruit aromas; supple & juicy, fennel tinge to dark plum fruit. 15.5% alc.

★★★★ **Pinotage** High-kicking/flying (ABSA Top Ten, CWT, WOM) version, from a single vyd, 8 yrs old, taken to extremes of ripeness — 15.5% alc in still-available **02**, now showing an aromatic forest floor character. Plump black fruit, hugely ripe & in fact turning slightly jammy, noticeably sweet, so possibly time to start drinking up.

★★★★ **Shiraz 02** steps into different league (**01** ★★☆) with plush black fruit nose spiced with pepper & dried flowers; full, chunky but supple palate laden with black berries; still youthful though slight meatiness starting to show on finish. Brash modern style with blockbuster alc (15.5%) to match; unfiltered. 1st fill Fr/Am oak, as are above.

Merlot ★★★ **02** another bold but modulated statement; mid-2004 retaste highlights a bit of russet on rim, currant jam aroma with hint of savouriness creeping in; watchfulness needed if cellaring further. 14.5% alc.

Bain's Way range

★★★☆ **Pinotage** Invariably the standout in range; **03** gently extracted, leaning towards the pinot side of the grape's persona; attractive earth/forest floor notes, soft sappy finish. Elegant & not too alcoholic at 13.5%.

Cinsaut ☺ ★★☆ This team has cinsaut taped. Aside from a bargain price, **02** now also brings you some complexity in form of dried-fruit whiffs, tea-leaf nuance on finish. Can you resist? **Chenin Blanc** ☺ ★★☆ **04** pale green tint presages appealing greenfruit tone (coriander, sundry leaves); touch guava, well made, quaffable. 12% alc. **Sauvignon Blanc** ☺ ★★☆ **04** hits the spot with floral wafts, nettle & pear flavour; rhubarb tartness on finish; lightweight 11.5% alc. **Sparkling Vin Sec** ☺ ★★☆ Zesty, refreshing any occasion bubbly; NV from sauvignon.

Following reds matured in small oak, 2nd/3rd fill. **Cabernet Sauvignon** ★★★ **03** a more elegant expression than pvs, better controlled alc (14% alc); cassis & hints of tobacco, some grainy, by no means unpleasant, tannins. **Merlot** ★★★ **03** extends the 'breakfast special' analogy of pvs into dinnertime with meat/bouillon/game tone to soft, sweet fruit. 14.5% alc. **Shiraz** NEW ★★★ Sensitively extracted **03**; good varietal character (smoke & leather), zingy dried fruit smack to leaven the serious alc (14%). **Chardonnay** ★★★ **04** unwooded, with juicy acidity, lilting peach blossom & peardrop aromas, sweetish finish from 14% alc.

Thirty-Three Degrees South range

Dry Red NEW ★★★ Soft & sweetish, as you'd expect from cinsaut (with 20% pinotage, neither wooded), complementary plum jam/tomato purée aromas; supple, dark-choc tinged flavours. **Dry White** ★★ Changes to 100% chenin for latest bottling; creamily dry; shy apple & pear flavours. Both NV.

Dessert range

Fishermans Jerepigo ★★★☆ Fortifying salty sea dogs since 1941; hanepoot, offering bright jasmine & honeysuckle aromas, soft peach/passionfruit tastes; quite exotic, very sweet & creamy. 16% alc. **Jagters Port** ★★ Suitably rustic & earthy 'Hunter's Port', from cab. Latest (NV) bottling not sampled. — *TM*

Wandsbeck see Agterkliphoogte
Warthog see Overhex

Warwick Estate

Stellenbosch ▪ Est 1964 ▪ 1stB 1984 ▪ Tasting & sales Mon-Fri 10-5 Sat 10-4 (all year) Sun 10-4 (Oct to Apr only) ▪ Closed Easter Sun, Dec 25 & Jan 1 ▪ Tours by appt ▪ Mediterranean picnic baskets by appt, or BYO ▪ Gifts ▪ Walks/hikes ▪ Owners Ratcliffe family ▪ Winemaker Louis Nel (Jun 2001) ▪ Viticulturist Ronald Spies (Aug 2001), advised by Phil Freese ▪ 60 ha (cabs s/f, merlot, pinotage, shiraz, chard, sauvignon) ▪ 250 tons 13 000 cs 85% red 15% white ▪ PO Box 2 Elsenburg 7607 ▪ info@warwickwine.co.za ▪ www.warwickwine.co.za © 884·4410 ☎ 884·4025

A year of celebration (40th anniversary of Ratcliffe ownership; 20th vintage of Warwick's first commercial Cab) became one of sorrow when Stan Ratcliffe's sudden passing. But his talented family prevails. Son Michael (MD/marketer) has introduced an innovative scheme, keeping 50 cases of each wine for five years before re-release – one way of handling over-subscription thanks to international awards and worldwide restaurant/presidential banquet listings! In a private capacity, he's also collaborating with Californians Phil Freese and Zelma Long (viti-vini husband-and-wife team) on a top-notch Vilafonte red blend from a Paarl vineyard. Wife Norma R, pioneering Cape woman vintner,) remains *en pointe*, while acknowledging winemaker Louis Nel and viticulturist Roland Spies as worthy successors to the Stan/Norma show. Daughter Jenny (Cape Wine Master, gourmet chef & marketer) spreads the wine word.

- ★★★★☆ **Trilogy (Estate Reserve)** Bdx-style blend's pedigree confirmed at 2004 vertical tasting of 1990 onward. **02** from 'a year of firsts', says Norma Ratcliffe – first full vintage for winemaker Louis N, first full harvest for vinegrower Ronald S, first use of sorting tables to raise bar on fruit quality. Higher than usual merlot/cab f content (30/28) and lower alc (14%) offer more diverse flavours than pvs. Cellaring should soften oak (2 yrs Fr, some new). **01** elegant in spite of 14.5% alc, bountiful cab fruit & lingering finish. 90 pts *WS*, Concours Mondial gold, only SA wine served on Queen Mary 2.
- ★★★★ **Three Cape Ladies** The 'other flagship', balanced & poised pinotage blend with cab, merlot. **02** generous strawberry & forest floor aromas, juicy fruit flavours still wrapped in oak (2 yrs Fr, some new). More open, accommodating **01** has grown mellow & balanced with extra yr in bottle. 91 pts *WS*. 14-14.5% alc.
- ★★★★ **Cabernet Franc** Perfumed **02** emerges from oak cocoon (24 mths older Fr) with dry, leafy tannins & sweeter raspberry fruit than pvs. 14.5% alc. Standout **01** (★★★★★) proffered fynbos notes complemented by curry spices & coriander; seamless palate, hallmark finesse.
- ★★★★ **Old Bush Vines Pinotage** From low-yielding vines. **03** & **02** picked less ripe than **01**, giving more submissive alc (14% vs ±15). 18 mths seasoned Fr oak. **03** plush, with signature strawberry fruit & slight acetone lift. Drinks well now but has structure for cellaring. **02** complex berry, 'nail varnish' & farmyard aromas. Also for earlyish enjoyment.
- ★★★★ **Chardonnay** At 14.5% alc, **03** not for the faint-hearted. sensitively oaked to highlight variety's honeyed cream & lemon flavours. **02** (★★★★) revealed more oak, angularity than usual. (fermented/9 mths Fr oak, some new)

'Professor Black' Sauvignon Blanc ★★★★ Herbaceous, tropical **04** aged 3 mths *sur lie* to extract flavour/texture. Acidity toned & finish lengthened by touch sugar (3.5g/ℓ). Confirms class & stature of **03**, VDG & 91 pts *WS*. **Merlot** & **Cabernet Sauvignon** discontinued. – *CvZ*

Waterford Estate

Stellenbosch ▪ Est/1stB 1998 ▪ Visits Mon-Fri 9-5 Sat 10-1 ▪ Fee R20, negated on purchase ▪ Closed Easter Fri, Dec 25 & Jan 1 ▪ Owners Jeremy & Leigh Ord, Kevin Arnold ▪ Winemaker

Kevin Arnold, with Francois Haasbroek (Jul 2004) ▪ *Viticulturist Lombard Loubser* ▪ *45 ha (barbera, cabs s/f, malbec, merlot, mourvèdre, petit v, shiraz, chard, sauvignon)* ▪ *250 tons 35 000 cs 80% red 20% white* ▪ *PO Box 635 Stellenbosch 7599* ▪ *info@waterfordestate.co.za* ▪ *www.waterfordestate.co.za* ✆ *880·0496* 🖷 *880·1007*

This Helderberg winery with its honeyed stone walls, clementine trees, lavender hedges and dozing dogs, and central square with a tinkling fountain, conjures up images of the Old World, especially the Mediterranean. The theme continues into the cellar and the vineyard, where varieties such as mourvèdre, grenache and tempranillo have been established or are planned. With 28 vintages in the Stellenbosch area behind him, Kevin Arnold's quest is still an estate blend which, he assures, 'is in the making and will be bottled in a few years time'. Arnold was honoured to be invited to present an overview of 'SA Shiraz and its Blending Partners' at the first International Shiraz Alliance held in Australia last year. Another fine moment was when Oprah Winfrey chose his Kevin Arnold Shiraz to accompany the main course at her celebrity-studded 50th birthday bash.

★★★★ **Cabernet Sauvignon 02** quintessential cab with added sex appeal from ±10% cab f/merlot/malbec; aged 20 mths Fr/Am oak (80/20, 40% new) as blend. Sweet cassis, eucalyptus, herbaceous nose. All this & choc/black fruit on palate. Sensuous, regal tannins; mineral finish. 13.5% alc. **01** had classic cab complexity — undergrowth, tomato; fine tannins complemented by blackcurrant, spice nuances.

★★★★☆ **Kevin Arnold Shiraz** Benchmark Cape Rhône-style red (10% mourvèdre) **02** named for son 'Michael Ian'. Strong farmyard whiffs obscure fruit on nose, palate more generous with beef & brambles. Built for long haul. **01** VDG. Boasts pure red fruit, polished by 60/40 Am/Fr oak, half new. Cellar at least 5 yrs. 14% alc.

★★★★★ **Cape Winemaker's Guild Blend** 🆕 **03** regal cab-dominated blend (40%) with 6 other Bdx/Rhône varieties ranging from dollop shiraz (28%) to drop petit v (2.5%). Closed & brooding, throbbing with potential. Strapping tannins from 12 mths Fr oak, some new; long fennel finish. 14.5% alc. Will reward cellaring.

★★★★ **Chardonnay** Exotic fruit, spice-&-toast style far cry from ultra-buttery examples; suppressed malo evident in fine fruit-acid focus. Fermented/matured Fr oak, ±65% new. **04** (with 3% chenin) retiring, moreish tangerine/lime palate; 13.5% alc; needs time. Tauter than **03**, which gaining waxy/honey complexity from bottle age. 14% alc. Drink these 3-5 yrs from harvest.

★★★★☆ **Sauvignon Blanc 04** shy & dusty nose; like pvs, palate brims with gooseberry & zesty acids; sustained dry mineral finish. 13.5% alc.

★★★★☆ **Family Reserve 'Heatherleigh'** Their first dessert, cross-vintage blend 65% 03 muscat d'A, 35% 04 chenin, sauvignon, chardonnay. Apricot & fennel notes with teasing sweetness (65g/ℓ sugar), arresting acidity. 17% natural alc. Promises to develop beautifully. Muscat fermented/11 mths new Am oak. 375ml. NV.

Pecan Stream range

Classily attired 2nd label. **Cabernet Sauvignon-Shiraz** ★★★ New name (pvsly 'Red') reflecting make-up change: **03** 50/42 blend with splashes cab f, mourvèdre, cinsaut, merlot. With juicy fruit & light wooding, ideal al fresco lunch-mate. **Chenin Blanc** ★★★ Easy-drinking fun wine. **04** more floral than fruity; 13.5% alc; zesty, but seems leaner than flavourful **03**, with nicely balanced acidity; 14% alc. — *CvZ*

Waterkloof see False Bay Winery

Webersburg Wines 🍷

Stellenbosch ▪ *Est/1stB 1996* ▪ *Visits by appt Mon-Fri 9-4* ▪ *Closed public holidays* ▪ *Owner Fred Weber* ▪ *Winemaker Rudi de Wet, advised by Giorgio Dalla Cia (Feb 2004/1996)* ▪ *Viticulturist Braam Steyn (Apr 1996)* ▪ *20 ha (cabs, merlot)* ▪ *±3 000 cs 100% red* ▪ *PO Box 3428 Somerset West 7129* ▪ *weber@iafrica.com* ▪ *www.webersburg.co.za* ✆ *851·7417* 🖷 *852·5280*

Following a deal with golfer-turned-vintner Ernie Els, Webersburg Wines have relocated to nearby Groenerivier, the original farm on this stretch of the Helderberg. Its manor house was built in 1786 and the cellar, now being restored, dates back to 1796. Winemaker Rudi de Wet and consultant Giorgio Dalla Cia had decided they'd be too busy with the move to make wine in 2004 but, says marketer Marta Dalla Cia, 'we got the opportunity to make some, so we did'. Webersburg 04, she promises, will be unique.

★★★★ **Cabernet Sauvignon** Cellar's commitment to classicism, consistency is antithesis of market trend to jolly immediacy ('vulgar', suggests GDC); expresses place & vintage, needs time to unfurl. Big, opulent **01**: waves of rich cassis fruit woven into fresh oak frame, plush finish. Likely to be ready for release before brooding, meaty **00** (★★★★★), still secured by sentinel tannins, whereas **99** approachable earlier. No **02**. Alcs up to 14%; 18 mths Fr oak, 70% new.

★★★★ **Cabernet Sauvignon-Merlot 02** Work-in-progress due 2006 so unrated. Smoky, butcher-shop sniffs hint at fruit confined in tannin for now; elegance, restraint bodes well. — *DS*

Wedderwill Country Estate

Stellenbosch (see Helderberg map) ▪ Est/1stB 1997 ▪ Visits by appt ▪ Owners Georg-Ludwig von Loeper & Neil Jowell ▪ Vini consultant Nico Vermeulen (2004), with Johan Manson ▪ Viticulturist Johan Manson, advised by Dawie le Roux (1997) ▪ 24 ha (cabs s/f, merlot, shiraz, sauvignon) ▪ 1 300 cs 90% red 10% white ▪ PO Box 75 Sir Lowry's Pass 7133 ▪ w@lfgang.de ▪ www.wedderwill.co.za Ⓒ/🖷 858·1402

Having provided significant input during 2003, Havana Hills's Nico Vermeulen is now also winemaker for Wedderwill farm in the Helderberg. In 2004 he oversaw a tricky harvest with his trademark equanimity ('there simply are no shortcuts'), and the fruits are currently maturing at KWV (a purpose-built cellar on Wedderwill is planned for 2006). With business graduate Wolfgang Johann von Loeper (son of co-owner Georg) settling on the farm to manage and actively market the wine, this niche label is set to grow. By next year it will comprise Shiraz, Sauvignon and a Bordeaux-style blend.

Welgedacht see Baarsma, Dominion

Welgegund Farm

Wellington ▪ Est 1800s ▪ 1stB 1997 ▪ Tasting & sales by appt ▪ B&B ▪ Owners Alex & Sheila Camerer ▪ Winemaker Corlea Fourie (Siyabonga) ▪ Viticulturist Johan Smit (Winecorp, 2004) ▪ 30 ha (cab, carignan, cinsaut, merlot, pinotage) ▪ 1 000 cs own label 100% red ▪ PO Box 683 Wellington 7655 ▪ Alex.Camerer@welgegund.co.za ▪ www.welgegund.co.za Ⓒ 082·554·7871 🖷 873·2683

Having extracted himself from the hurly-burly of Johannesburg, Alex Camerer says, he's blissfully happy giving his full attention to Welgegund. The move comes at an auspicious time for the farm: pinotage from 'Sheila's Block', an 11 year old vineyard named after Camerer's politician wife 'who showed more faith in it than anybody else', under another label helped clinch the category trophy at the 2004 FCTWS. Encouraged, they're thinking of adding a Pinotage to their own line-up. This to join a Merlot, already decided upon. Making the wines, including the original Carignan and the recently inaugurated Cab, is Siyabonga's Corlea Fourie.

Cabernet Sauvignon Two vintages tasted: **01** (★★★) smoked meat/salami on nose; blackcurrant jam notes; chewy, mouthfilling, chunky tannins needing time. **04** (sample) completely different style: exuberant minty nose; mint-choc palate loaded with plummy fruit, sweet finish (4.4g/ℓ); still clumsy mid-2004 but promising ★★★★. Mix new/used oak. **Carignan** ★★★★ Features dash shiraz for extra heft. **03** red brambly fruit with hints tomato jam, spice & potpourri; light bodied, juicy. Lunchtime wine, serve chilled. **04** sampled from barrel, seems slightly fuller, deeper coloured. Portion fruit ex-Swtlnd. — *TM*

Welgeleë

Paarl ▪ Est 1999 ▪ 1stB 2003 ▪ Visits by appt ▪ Owners/viticulturists Liris Trust (Chris & Lidea Meyer) ▪ Vini consultant Morné Kemp (Jan 2003), with owners ▪ 3 ha (shiraz) ▪ 300 cs 100% red ▪ PO Box 439 Klapmuts 7625 ▪ welgelee@absamail.co.za Ⓒ/🖷 875·5726

Joie de vie, with a bacchanalian bias, inspired Chris and Lidea Meyer to purchase and develop their boutique winery in Paarl. Surrounded by their many pets, this enthusiastic couple ventured into winemaking 'with heaps of love and gusto'. Morné Kemp vinified the first crop off a small shiraz block in 2003 (2 more ha planted and another 17 planned, including cab, shiraz and 'a snip of chardonnay for the family'). With the next Shiraz in bottle and a Cab maturing in barrel, the focus is on fine reds for the local and export market. 'And if we make a buck or two in the process, whoopee!'

★★★★ **Shiraz Reserve** Elegant **03** offers nutmeg, cassia aromas, black berry fruit. Fine tannins, with good, unobtrusive support from 9 mths Fr oak. 13.8% alc. **04** has started on its promisingly spicy way.

Cabernet Sauvignon 04 sample too young to rate, but blackcurrant fruit, fine tannins, concentrated but not massive, all auguring well. — *MF*

Welgemeend Estate

Paarl ▪ 1stB 1979 ▪ Tasting Wed 2–4 Sat 9–12.30 ▪ Sales during office hours only by appt ▪ Closed public holidays ▪ Privately owned ▪ Winemaker Louise Hofmeyr (Jul 1991) ▪ Manager/viticulturist Ursula Hofmeyr ▪ ±11 ha (cab s/f, grenache, malbec, merlot, 'petit mystery', pinotage, shiraz) ▪ 3 500 cs 100% red ▪ PO Box 1408 Suider-Paarl 7624 ▪ welgemeend@worldonline.co.za ▪ www.welgemeend.co.za Ⓒ 875·5210 🖷 875·5239

There will be less cab in the Estate Reserve 04, advises winemaker Louise Hofmeyr, because what ripened later was disappointing. Generally, however, she was happy with the harvest. Registration is on the cards for a new label, Upelation, for the 25 or so cases made in 2003 by long-time cellar assistant Abraham Suse, nicknamed 'Uppie'. What's in a name? Bad news, according to the winemaker: 'A large producer has taken the name Soopjeshoogte and registered it in the Benelux countries. It kind of says how little the industry cares and how the big guys like chewing the smaller ones.' On trends, she's trenchant: 'Recently more people comment on how dry our wine is. Welgemeend is no drier than before.' The reason, she suggests, is today's currency: over-extracted wines with higher residual sugar and alcohol, which have a sweet finish.

★★★★★ **Estate Reserve** ✓ The first Cape Bdx blend — cab, merlot, cab f — with loyal following around the wine world over 25 yrs. **01** predominantly merlot; marked by cellar's signature elegance, finesse. Like pvs & below, needs time & patience to offers its best. Retasted **00** shows hallmark austere intensity; brambly flavours in harmony with svelte wood & firm tannin backbone; great persistence. Moderate alc (±13%) & bone-dry finish. Oaked for the long haul (18 mths, 30% new barriques).

★★★★★ **Pinotage-Shiraz 01** Finally emerges in bottle as tribute to Billy Hofmeyr (1929–2000), the label with one of his paintings. Unlike many modern, opulent composites of these varieties, this very fine, without overt reference to its grape provenance. Fluid tannin structure still houses silky ripe fruit; bigger than above. 20 mths oak, 50% new for first yr. Unusually bold (for cellar) 13.5% alc. Mere 50 cs.

★★★★ **Douelle** ✓ A fragrant, different nod to Bdx, mostly malbec with cab, merlot & soupçon cab f, 18 mths in oak. **01** savoury, herb-infused character to sappy muscular scaffold, fine-grained tannin will need time to open. **00** deeply coloured, cab contributing cassis & brambles. 13.5% alc.

★★★☆ **Amadé** ✓ Idiosyncratic pioneering Cape interpretation of Rhône-style blend: pinotage, shiraz & grenache in 40/35/25 ensemble on **01**; ripe earthy texture, insistent vinosity to fine-tailed frame. Food-friendly, 13% alc. 18 mths older oak.

★★★☆ **Soopjeshoogte** ✓ Cab-based blend includes dash 'petit mystery' — once thought to be p verdot, still an ampelographic enigma. **01** elegant build with some cassis flesh making appearance, linear without austerity. **00** drinking well with grip. 12.5% alc.

Upelation **03** Work-in-progress (so not rated) of senior farmworker and cellar assistant Abraham Suse (nicknamed 'Uppie', hence provisional punning name). Single 300ℓ barrel cab bearing herbaceous fruit in restrained frame. ★★★★ promise. — *DS*

Welgevonde see Daschbosch

Wellington Cellar

Wellington ▪ Est/1stB 1934 ▪ Tasting & sales Mon-Fri 8-1; 2-5 ▪ Owners 46 members ▪ Winemakers Gert Boerssen, Koos Carstens & Bertus Albertyn (1980/1990/2001) ▪ Viticulturist Bertus Albertyn (2001) ▪ 1 600 ha (cinsaut, pinotage, chard, chenin, sauvignon) ▪ ±11 000 tons ±6 500 cs own label ▪ PO Box 520 Wellington 7654 ▪ wellingtoncellar@ iafrica.com ▪ www.wellingtoncellar@co.za ✆ 873·1163 🖷 873·2423

The general swing toward making a greater proportion of red wines has caused its own challenges for this winery. With reds requiring longer time in the tanks, they've had to provide more storage facilities at considerable cost. Wellington Cellar has recently joined forces with four other wineries to form a new marketing company, Cape Coastal Wines, initially targeting the US market. All five member wineries have agreed to change production styles to suit the export requirements, if necessary.

Cinsaut-Ruby Cabernet ☺ ★★★ 75/25 combo, partly Fr oaked. **03** very light textured, chill slightly & enjoy with a braai.

Cabernet Sauvignon ★★★★ ✓ **02**, retasted, still has fairly puckering tannins — give more time; well structured with cassis fruit. 9 mths Fr oak. 14% alc. **Merlot** ★★★ Back in the guide with **03**, aged 9 mths Fr oak; mix of red & black berries, healthy acid/tannin backbone, lively & ripe. **Pinotage** ★★★★ ✓ **03** deeper colour than most of these reds, fairly forthcoming aromas of raspberry & strawberry, softly gripping tannins; briefly oaked. 14.5% alc. **Shiraz** ★★★★ ✓ **02** pleasing middle-of-the-road style; fair amount of tannins but they're ripe. 8-9 mths Fr oak. **Pinotage Rosé** ★★★ Scented semi-sweet with firming touch tannin; **04** tastes dry despite 10g/ℓ sugar, has some body; more of a food style. **Chardonnay** ★★★ No **04**; lightly oaked **03** was full & lively, & for early enjoyment. **Chenin Blanc** ★★★ **04** notes of pear, apple & guava; clean & easy to drink. **Sauvignon Blanc** ★★★ Bouncy, lightish **04** offers subtle gooseberry aromas/tastes, modest 13% alc. **Late Harvest** ★★★ Semi-sweet chenin with pear tones & hint of tangerine, not too sweet; light 12% alc. **Hanepoot Jerepiko** ★★★ No **04** version of this delicate & charming fortified dessert; **01** had a perfume-counter bouquet. **Port** ★★★ Still-available ruby-style **02** is from tinta, fruity & balanced, with traditionally low fortification (17.5% alc). — *JN*

Welmoed see Stellenbosch Vineyards

Weltevrede Estate

Robertson ▪ Est 1912 ▪ 1stB 1975 ▪ Tasting & sales Mon-Fri 8-5 Sat 9-3.30 ▪ Tours by appt ▪ Under the Vines Bistro for lunch Tue-Sat (closed Jun/Jul) or BYO picnic ▪ Weltevrede Guest Cottage (see Stay-over section) ▪ Conservation area ▪ Walks ▪ 4x4 trail ▪ Mountain biking ▪ Owner Lourens Jonker ▪ Winemaker Philip Jonker (1997), with Riaan Liebenberg (Sep 1999) ▪ Viticulturist Philip Jonker, advised by Francois Viljoen ▪ 100 ha (cab, merlot, shiraz, chard, colombard, sauvignon) ▪ 150 tons 25 000 cs own label 15% red 75% white 10% other ▪ PO Box 6 Bonnievale 6730 ▪ info@weltevrede.com ▪ www.weltevrede.com ✆ (023) 616·2141 🖷 (023) 616·2460

Fourth-generation vintner Philip Jonker can feel *wel tevrede* (well-satisfied) with recent achievements. He got off to a crackling start when his 99 MCC won the *Wine*/Amorim Cork bubbly award. A 100% chardonnay, it seals this quietly ambitious young man's reputation as a skilled artisan when working with a variety that can produce either ordinary or overstated examples. His Chardonnays, like most of his wines, emphasise expression of specific sites (the newly named Travelling Stone Sauvignon being a case in point). Though synonymous with white, Weltevrede also hits a high note with its first single-varietal red, a Syrah. Two new Tricolore blends are tailor-made for their farm-bistro's 'home cooking with a touch of flair'.

Oude Weltevreden range

★★★★ **Chardonnay** Expression of the limestone origin of the farm's oldest vyd site. Retasted **02** opulent butterscotch/toffee girth, grapefruit flavours. Bright acid freshens coconut/crème brûlée richness, sweet hint. Fermented/10 mths Fr oak. 14. 6% alc.

Merlot-Cabernet Sauvignon Barrel sample **03** (likely ★★★★) signals comeback for label. 55% merlot. Meaty, chocolate fullness & soft tannins combine for character, approachability; eschews muscularity of many competitors. 14 mths Fr oak.

Weltevrede range

★★★★ **Syrah** NEW Full name pending for estate's first single varietal red, but the character's already etched into its generous frame. Sample dark **03**, purple plum/mulberry fruits laced with pepper spice; gentle tannins afford access in youth. Yum… 14 mths oak, 80:20 Fr:Am.

★★★★ **Poet's Prayer Chardonnay** Impressive attention — wild yeast ferment (which lasted a full yr in barrel!), 20 mths Fr oak, further yr in bottle, etc — rewarded. **02** (★★★★★) scintillating golden patina, stunning chalky aromas complex rather than bold; beautifully integrated fruit/oak in lingering 14.4% alc tail. **01** marmalade, opulent palate (±15% alc) — truly rich. Not for the faint-hearted. Only 30 cs.

★★★★ **Place of Rocks Chardonnay** From broken shale rock, taut, less exuberant than cellar-mates. Next **03** (★★★★) evinces bristling minerally citrus fruit, with integrated oak (fermented/aged 10 mths), excellent length. 14% alc.

★★★★ **The Travelling Stone** ✓ Pvs 'Sauvignon Blanc' New name for **04** hand-harvested *vine* selection from quartzite stony vyd which originally 'rolled down the surrounding mountains'. Sample rushes out ringing nettles, brisk herbaceous edginess leavened by tropical flesh. Pvs **01**, featuring minty fig, still firm, holding.

★★★★ **Rhine Riesling** ✓ Renewed verve, interest in (just-) dry **01**, backed by Jonker for demure ageing. Well-developed by mid-2004; orange sheen, dusty dried herbs & dried apricots on honeyed palate. Foil for spicy food. 13% alc.

★★★★ **Gewürztraminer** For many, synonymous with the property, And with reason: off-dry **03** beautifully intense Turkish Delight features, enduring, elegant dry feel. Sample **04**'s classic rose-petals/litchi in youth, also promises good development.

★★★★ **Philip Jonker Brut** MCC from chardonnay, 3 yrs on lees, garnered Cap Classique Challenge with **99**. Label upgraded to reflect its hand-made identity with next **00**: developed, broad butterscotch tones, braced with racy acid zing. Ready on release.

★★★★ **Oupa Se Wyn** ✓ Succulent fortified dessert from red muscadel & m de Hambourg, partly ex-bushvines planted 1926. **01** light mahogany; enormous raisiny nose, rich, almost unctuous; orange-rind/roasted nuts in silky finish. VDG, MIWA gold. 17% alc. 375ml.

★★★★ **Cape Muscat** Luscious full-sweet dessert, from well-aged (red) m de Hambourg vyd, traditionally vinified & handsomely packaged. **01** smoked meat & raisin flavours; mature gamey/spicy bouquet. 375ml. Not retasted for this ed.

Tricolore Duo of three-way blends destined for 'upmarket housewine'. **White** ★★☆ **04** cheerful medley sauvignon, colombard fleshed out with semillon. Overt guava tamed by fresh grip, figgy, just-dry finish. **Red** ★★☆ **03** black cherry tint to herby/earth tones, gentle tannins. Merlot, syrah & smidgen cab. 14% alc. **Privé du Bois** ★★★ Stalwart brand/blend of oaked chardonnay/sauvignon; last **01** developed, ready for table. **Ovation Rhine Riesling** ★★★ 'Natural Sweet' in pursuit of crossover style: botrytis richness but drier than NLH. **99** striking orange-gold hue mid-2004; dried-fruit & terpene whiffs; cling-peach palate. Ready for enjoyment. 32g/ℓ sugar; 12.5% alc. **Ouma se Wyn** ★★★

Consistently delicious, from single white muscadel vyd; **01** grapey aromas, honeycomb/ dried peach; lighter, less viscous style. MIWA Grand Medaille d'Or. 15% alc. 375ml.

River's Edge range

Chardonnay ☺ ★★★ **04** billows melon/banana allure, delivers concentrated lemon/ lime freshness. Unwooded, pure fruit for enjoyment before the next harvest.

Colombard ★★★ **04** zesty floral/lemongrass whiffs, lemon palate, off-dry, enjoy in flush of youth. **Sauvignon Blanc** ★★ **04** perky poolside quaffer with tropical/grapefruit tones. **Blanc de Blanc** discontinued.—*DS*

Welvanpas

Wellington ▪ Tasting & sales Mon-Fri 9-12.15; 1-5 Sat 9-1 ▪ Owners D Retief & Son Cellars ▪ Winemaker/viticulturist Dan Retief Jnr ▪ ±500 tons (15-30 for own range, 75% red 25% white) ▪ PO Box 75 Wellington 7654 ▪ welvanpas@xsinet.co.za © 864·1238/ 082·498·5145/082·393·6268 ☐ 864·1239

This historic farm celebrated its 300th anniversary last year. The Retiefs have been connected with it since its establishment, making it one of the oldest family farms in the Cape. Most of the grapes grown here go to Bovlei Winery, though Dan Retief Jnr does vinify a small batch of selected grapes to bottle under the farm label.

Weskus see Winkelshoek

Westbridge Vineyards

Stellenbosch ▪ Est 1998 ▪ 1stB 1999 ▪ Tasting & sales Mon-Sat 8-6 (phone ahead on public holidays) ▪ B&B ▪ Owner JC Starke & Muldersvlei Estates ▪ Winemaker Ian Starke ▪ Viticulturist Julian Starke ▪ 17 ha (cab, pinotage, chenin) ▪ 60 tons 4 000 cs 85% red 15% white ▪ PO Box 66 Muldersvlei 7607 ▪ wine@muldersvlei.co.za © 884·4433

Their name may have changed (previously known as Starke Wines), but their enthusiasm not a jot. Winemaker Ian Starke — an old hand at 23, he made his first wines at 18 — dad Julian (the dairy and fruit orchards his domain) and mom Helen (marketing and the B&B hers) handle the daily running of their estate; Juliette, who's 'sweet 16', lends her name to the blend. 'The Starke name is synonymous with agriculture,' they proudly say, and the new labels, which pay homage to their prized dairy herd, unusually depict a prize-winning cow. An experimental native yeast fermented Cab promises to be a 'very interesting' wine, and a new tasting room in the old barrel cellar is on the cards.

★★★★ **Pinotage Reserve** Two vintages to date: **99** introduced characterful, full-flavoured style with pronounced savoury edge; **00** attractively rustic in character. **Shiraz** ★★★ **02** retasted, characteristic shiraz spice, plus house's earthy touches; tannins still stern, need further cellaring. 3rd fill Fr oak. **Merlot** Last tasted was **03**, too young to rate but showing extraordinary concentration. **Pinotage** ★★★★ **03** individually styled, as were pvs; tropical fruit whiffs & touches tobacco/earth, tannins less daunting than pvs. Oak chip fermented/aged. **Juliette** Sparingly wooded blend changes with vintage; vinified/matured separately & blended just before bottling; **02** (★★★) cab, merlot, shiraz, mid-2004 shows touch good bottle-age, appealing roundness; **03** (★★★★) gets 22% pinotage injection, shows as fruitier, more satisfying.—*DH*

WestCorp International

Olifants River (see Vredendal Cellar on Olifants River map) ▪ Est 2002 ▪ Tasting & sales Mon-Fri 8-5 Sat 8.30-12 (sales close 30 mins later) ▪ Closed public holidays ▪ Tours at 10 & 3 during harvest ▪ Light meals by appt or BYO picnic ▪ Tourgroups (±42 people) ▪ Conferencing ▪ Audio-visual presentation ▪ Gifts ▪ Owners 224 members ▪ Winemakers Alwyn Maass, Pieter Verwey, Driaan van der Merwe & Len Knoetze (1997/1999/2000/ 2002), with Koos Thiart, Johan Weideman & Renier van Greenen (all Jan 2004) ▪ Viticul-

turists Koos van der Merwe, Marina Bruwer & Hein Jansen van Rensburg (Dec 2002/Jan 2004/Jan 2004) • 4 990 ha (cab, merlot, pinotage, ruby cab, shiraz, chard, chenin, colombard, sauvignon, hanepoot) • 86 000 tons 610 000 cs 20% red 80% white • www. westcorp.co.za Vredendal Cellar: PO Box 75 Vredendal 8160 • info@westcorp.co.za © (027) 213·1080 ☎ (027) 213·3476 • Spruitdrift Cellar: PO Box 129 Vredendal 8160 © (027) 213·3086 ☎ (027) 213·2937

This West Coast colossus (Vredendal cellar and satellite Spruitdrift) can bandy about some serious numbers: roughly 5 000ha under vine (five times more than the entire UK), close to 90 000 tons of grapes, and a total case output of more than 600 000 a year. Clearly they are not (yet) into hand-crafting terroir-drenched soupçons for the titillation of the vinous elite. They *are* into making easy-drinking, budget-priced wines in a production environment which meets globally accepted criteria, hence their delight at simultaneously passing three important quality control and food safety audits, ISO, HACCP and BRC. Out in the market, their Gôiya range (one of SA's top-selling wines in the UK) has had a facelift, and is raising its profile further as exclusive two-season wine sponsor to the official English cricket test grounds. Extensive television coverage is part of the deal, valued at £500 000. Local punters who have yet to sample the previously export-only Gôiya wines can do so in the comfort of their own homes — they are now available locally — or at the revamped tasting locale at the winery. 'Definitely worth a visit,' they declare.

Gôiya range
Pronounced 'Hoya', meaning 'First'. Reds unwooded; new versions of **Merlot** (★★★), **Pinotage** (★★★★) & **Shiraz** (★★★) not tasted. **Merlot-Cabernet Sauvignon** ★★★ Going back in time to vintage **02**; ripe cassis aromas, sweet, plump choc flavours. 14% alc. **Shiraz-Pinotage** ★★★ Formerly known as Gôiya G!aan; made in very large quantities (±300 000 cs) **04** shy gamey/smoked meat aromas; medium body, decidedly slippery finish thanks to 8g/ℓ. Latest bottlings of **Chardonnay** (★★★) & **Sauvignon Blanc** (★★) not tasted. **Chardonnay-Sauvignon Blanc** ★★★ The renamed Gôiya Kgeisje, winery's top seller (500 000+ cs); equal blend, unwooded; just off-dry; meant to be uncorked as fresh as possible. **04** fragrant floral bouquet, hints of apple; peachy fruit-salad flavours; limy acidity strikes good balance. **Inanda Brut** ★★★ NV. Top selling sparkling in its category in the UK. On sweet side of brut at ±14g/ℓ sugar.

Namaqua range
Following all NVs, available in restyled 3/5ℓ bag-in-boxes; red unwooded. **Dry Red** ★★☆ Blend shiraz, pinotage, ruby cab, merlot; nice dried-fruit/gamey nose with hint fennel; Mediterranean-style food friendliness. **Rosé** ★★★ Not tasted. Pvs was semi-sweet blend colombard/pinotage. **Grand Cru** ★★ Quite full & juicy, undemandingly dry; mix chenin, colombard. **Stein** ★★★ From chenin, colombard; shy, lightly floral aromas; creamy/appley flavours, pleasant lifted finish. **Late Harvest** ★★ Chenin, colombard, would you believe? Soft & semi-sweet. **Johannisberger** ★★★ Slightly spicy rose-petal intro, hint of honey, surprisingly generously flavours for low 10.5% alc, balanced. **Extra Lite** ★★ Weigh-Less approved for its low (9%) alc; lemon-zest/herb tones, quite full, refreshing & dry. **B4 Play Sparkling** ★★ The playfully renamed 'Vredendal Spumanté' ('B4 you start an occasion you have to drink some'); low-alc (±8%) carbonated fizz. Soft, fruity & sweet, fairly energetic bubble, Turkish Delight prettiness. **Johannisberger Red** 🆕 ★★★ Healthy ruby colour; smoky strawberry nose, sweet but a firm structure from touch tannin courtesy of merlot, pinotage & ruby cab.

Spruitdrift range
Retasted for this ed unless noted; reds unwooded. **Cabernet Sauvignon** ★★★ **03** typical cassis with some leafy notes; house dryness, tobacco touch on finish. **Merlot** ★★★ **03** smoked bacon & dried fruit on nose, potpourri/tobacco flavours, appealingly lean & savoury, food friendly. 14% alc. **Pinotage** ★★★ **03** notes of mulberry, pepper & smoke; sour-plum finish; nice grainy tannins. Selected by WOM. **Shiraz** ★★★ Uncomplicated **03**, smoky plum notes, medium bodied, dark plum & tobacco flavours. **Blanc de Noir** From red muscadel; latest not ready for tasting. **Premier Grand Cru** ★★☆ NV from chenin,

colombard; bland, slightly coarse & dry. **Johannisberger** ★★ Faint scents jasmine & Turkish Delight; supple, undemanding semi-sweet. NV. **Natural Sweet** ★★★ None since light bodied/toned **02**, with tropical fruit-salad tastes. — *TM*

Western Wines

*Stellenbosch ▪ Est 1981 ▪ 1stB 1995 ▪ Closed to public ▪ Winemaker Ben Jordaan (Jul 2002) ▪ 25 ha (Journey's End – cab, shiraz, chard; Kumala – cab, cinsaut, merlot, pinotage, ruby cab, shiraz, chard, chenin, colombard, sauvignon, semillon) ▪ 5 500 cs (Journey's End) + 2.4m cs (Kumala) 45% red 50% white 5% rosé ▪ PO Box 769 Stellenbosch 7599 ▪ ben@ westernwines.co.za james@westernwines.co.za ▪ www.kumala.com ✆ **882·8177** ⊠ 882·8176*

What happens when 'Top Gun' meets 'Big Cannon'? Not a boom or a crash, but an amicable convergence of interests in the case of Western Wines, the Stellenbosch-based export blunderbuss which fires off an astonishing 2.4m cases of SA wine a year into mainly European markets, and Vincor, 8th largest wine company in the New World and 13th largest overall. The latter's takeover of Western Wines in 2004 is a win-win for both companies — and for fans of W-Ws multi-tiered Kumala and high-end Journey's End ranges. With Vincor's financial muscle and long reach into world markets, 'we can take our brands to the next level and play on the global stage,' says local operations director, James Reid. 'We're tremendously excited.' As are W-W's base of key partners (from the Swartland, Lutzville, Worcester, Paarl and Stellenbosch areas), now part of the Kumala Growers Club, and raring to take the next step. Seems that Kumala — 'wines that make the moment' — will continue to do so… worldwide.

Journey's End range

★★★★ **Cabernet Sauvignon** Grapes for this range sourced from Journey's End farm in S/West. **01** was bold, full & vividly flavoured; firmly, supportively oaked. Classy wine yet unpretentious. No **02**. Delicious **03** (sample) ripe mulberry fruit, sniff of mint, fleshy & well rounded, some attractive dry tannins on finish. Fr/Am oak, 70% new.

★★★★ **Shiraz** We last tasted the accessible yet firm **03**.

★★★★★ **Chardonnay 03** (★★★★) much quieter than arresting **02**. Glimpses of ripe peach & vanilla custard; fleshy build enhanced by ultra-soft acidity, generous oatmeal flavours. 9 mths oak, 50/50 new Fr/2nd fill Am. Above WO Stbosch; most below W-Cape.

Winemakers Selection

★★★★ **Shiraz-Cabernet Sauvignon** From selected vyds in Stbosch/Paarl, barrel-aged (contrast with ranges below, which staved/chipped). **02** 50/50 blend now integrated, well balanced in mid-2004, hence higher rating.

Kumala Reserve range

Unless noted all **03**, ★★★★; reds 20-30% Fr staved ±6 mths. **Cabernet Sauvignon** Chewy, structured with fine concentration. Mint & sage whiffs on rounded palate with fine length & some nascent complexity. WO Stbosch. Some Am oaking, ditto for ... **Merlot** Lavender & violet perfumes; well upholstered though still fairly tannic mid-2004, lacks balance, re-rated to ★★★. Fr/Am oak. **Pinotage** Nicely tamed version: plum & cinnamon spice first impressions; full & firm, tannins soft & approachable. **Shiraz** Ripe mulberry, touches spice, game, scrub; smooth & plump, hardly any tannin to ruffle the palate. 30% staves, 14% alc. **Chardonnay 04** attractive toasty oak, citrus flavours, smooth acidity for soft silky palate. 30% staved. **Sauvignon Blanc** ★★★ **04** hints new-mown grass, capsicum, quite light & easy at 11.5% alc.

Kumala range

> **Ruby Cabernet-Merlot** ☺ ★★★ 03 80/20 blend, attractive mulberry flavours mid-2004, slightly firmer than reverse blend below, more varietal punch & style. **Pinotage-Cinsault** ☺ ★★★ 04 to same 70/30 formula, plummy ripe, firm fleshed, quaffable. **Sauvignon Blanc-Colombard** ☺ ★★★ 04 light, easy sipping 50/50 blend, citrusy with tang of lemon, perfect for poolside.

Cabernet Sauvignon-Shiraz ★★★ Plummy shiraz with dryness & firmness from cab, 04 seems drier & less overtly fruity than other reds, more serious. **Pinotage-Shiraz** ★★★ 70/30 blend, pinotage-led taste-wise, too. 2 mths staves. 04 plummy, fat, juicy, sweet finish. **Merlot Ruby-Cabernet** ★★★ 60/40 blend, 30% staves. 04 seems fruitier, lighter & less tannic than pvs; none of the meaty/savoury tone. **Chardonnay** ★★ 04 light textured, with lively citrus tang. 20% barrel-aged. **Chardonnay-Semillon** ★★ Chardonnay-borne peaches & cream tone in 04, soft acidity, smooth, tiny portion oaked. **Chenin Blanc-Chardonnay** NEW ★★ 04 slightly more plump than above though still lightish, tropical fruits with sprinkling spice, modest oak influence. **Colombard-Chardonnay** ★★★ 04 successful 70/30 blend, some oaked; chardonnay pulling its weight, literally, imparting pleasing fullness. **Sauvignon Blanc-Semillon** NEW 04 untasted.

Kumala Organic range

Pinotage-Shiraz ★★★ 04 pinotage dominant, taste-wise, in 60/40 blend. Ripe, plummy, brush dry tannins on finish. Staves 2 mths. **Colombard-Chardonnay** ★★ 04 gentle grassy, guava notes, softish acidity, fresh & dainty. Modest oak influence. — *IvH*

WhaleHaven Wines

Hemel-en-Aarde Valley (see Walker Bay map) ▪ Est/1stB 1995 ▪ Tasting & sales Mon-Fri 9. 30-5 Sat & non-religious holidays 10.30-2 ▪ Fee R10 for groups of 10+ ▪ Closed Easter Fri/ Sun, Dec 25 & Jan 1 ▪ Tours by appt ▪ BYO picnic ▪ Owners Bottega family ▪ Winemaker Paul Engelbrecht, with Kath Simm (Sep 2003/May 2004) ▪ Viticulturist Tim Clark (Feb 2001) ▪ 80 tons 6 500 cs own label 70% red 25% white 5% rosé ▪ Private Bag X14, Suite 1D, Hermanus 7200 ▪ whwines@hermanus.co.za ✆ (028) 316·1633 🖷 (028) 316·1640

Things are coming together for this Walker Bay winery. Sole ownership resides with the Bottega family, whose Sir Lowry's Pass farm Buitenzicht supplied grapes for earlier WhaleHaven releases. Ex-Blaauwklippen winemaker Paul Engelbrecht handled the 2004 vintage. Helping him establish WhaleHaven as one of SA's 'top boutique wineries', and check out new Asian markets (including Japan and India) is winemaker/marketer Kath Simm. New to a streamlined range is an unwooded viognier/chardonnay blend. The former comes from Buitenzicht, planted with mostly merlot plus cab, cab franc, shiraz and experimental sangiovese, mourvèdre and primitivo (zinfandel). These will be vinified/bottled separately under the apt moniker Idiom (a form of expression peculiar to a language — read: 'terroir'). Visitor-friendly winery upgrades Winery upgrades include a big garden for picnics and boule games.

★★★★ **Pinot Noir** Elegant & restrained, but also succulent, well-wooded (usually mix new/older Fr barrels, 16-18 mths): the charm is in the texture or 'mouthfeel' of good pinot. Big, more rustic 01 (pvs ed) not retasted. 00 violets & delicate red-berry fruit well synchronised with oak's vanilla & tannins. 99 revisited: tannins a trifle stalky, ready for table accompaniment. ±13% alcs. WO W Cape.

★★★★ **Cabernet Sauvignon 01** (★★★★ pvs ed) not reviewed. 98 retasted mid-2004: peppery edge to brambly nose, Elgin fruit shored up by assertive, tight-knit tannins.

★★★★ **Cabernet Franc 01** returns to range, last was 97 ('Chelene' in pvs eds.) Latest: sappy, 'greenstick' varietal fruit hemmed in by massive tannins, needs time to unveil savoury best. Elgin grapes, 18 mths small Fr oak. 13% alc.

★★★★ **Merlot 01** (★★★) with curious tomato nose, sour cherry palate; carrying huge oak (2 yrs Fr) mid-2004. Balanced, persistent **99**; minty, meaty, red-berry flavours. **00** not tasted.

★★★★ **Chardonnay** Fermented, matured mix new/older oak, ±yr on lees. **01** more rustic, woodier than pvs; good weight of fruit (W Bay) still in attendance on review. **00**, (Overberg) from Kaaimansgat near Villiersdorp, has peaked.

★★★★ **Chardonnay Unwooded** Last tasted was appealing **02**.

Old Harbour Red ☺ ★★★ ('Baleine Noire' pvsly.) Versatile NV blend, lightly oaked, offers earthy, tarry fullness to merlot-based fruit. For pizza & parties, better lightly chilled.
Rosé NEW ☺ ★★★ Rubenesque, berries dominate medium-bodied, crisp, refreshingly dry, firm mouthful. Ripe Stbosch fruit; 15% alc may induce an after-lunch nap.

Viognier-Chardonnay NEW ★★★ Novel blend; tank sample **04** offers peach, pear angles to interesting mouthful; as ripe (14.5% alc) but less flamboyant than others in the genre.

Idiom range NEW

Sourced from Helderberg grapes, all unfinished samples so not rated. **Sangiovese 03** ripe but toned, juicy red/blue-black berry fruits bursting through yr new oak, tang to chewy tail. Treads middle road between opulent overripe pulp and dusty austerity. **Shiraz-Mourvèdre 03** in tank after yr oak, 30% new Am. Piercing peppery nose, pimento/ anise edginess to full palate anchored by firm tannins. **Wooded Viognier 04** destined for ±yr in cask, offers butterscotch/toffee fullness, muscular palate cloaking apricot/peach fruit mid-04. All 14.5% alc & potential ★★★★. — *DS*

White River see Bergsig
Wide River see Robertson Winery

Wildekrans Estate

Walker Bay ▪ Est/1stB 1993 ▪ Tasting & sales: Farm cellar Mon-Fri 9-5 (closed public holidays unless gate is open); Wildekrans Wine Shop & Art Gallery at Orchard Farmstall, Grabouw, daily (except Dec 25) 8.30-5.30 (Sep-May) 9.30-5.30 (May-Sep) ▪ Cellar tours on request ▪ Meals, snacks, gifts, farm produce at farmstall, or BYO picnic to farm by appt ▪ Guest house ▪ Play area for children ▪ Conservation area ▪ Owners Bruce & Jo Elkin ▪ Winemaker Bruce Elkin, with William Wilkinson (2001/2003) ▪ Viticulturist Bruce Elkin, advised by Danie Conradie ▪ 50 ha (cabs s/f, merlot, pinotage, shiraz, chard, chenin, sauvignon, semillon) ▪ 450 tons 10 000 cs own label 50% red 50% white ▪ PO Box 200 Elgin 7180 ▪ bruce@wildekrans.co.za ▪ www.wildekranswines.co.za ℂ *(028) 284-9829* 📠 *(028) 284-9902*

No, no road-signs as yet but the open-gate invitation still holds on holidays (see above). On normal working days, the tasting room on this Bot River farm welcomes visitors; otherwise, the Orchard Farm Stall near Elgin. Harvest 2004 delivered an interesting maiden: one batch of shiraz from the B-River property and another from the Elkins' fruit farm in Elgin (where there's accommodation in the homestead or Cape-style cottages). 'Once the wines have developed a bit we'll decide whether to keep them separate or to blend,' says Bruce E. His new Caresse Marine Red is for 'the discerning wine drinker who regularly has a red with his meals'.

★★★★ **Pinotage Barrel Selection** From low-cropped bushvine vyd improbably named 'Cinderella', densely & forwardly fruity. Features new Fr/Am oak, ± yr. **01** sweet plum-jam whiffs, stewed flavours, oak quite obtrusive. **02** (★★★★) retasted mid-2004 lighter, softer, less savoury & tannic; flavours deepening & darkening, but still needs time.

★★★★ **Pinotage 02** retasted for this guide, has settled into bottle nicely, shows mulberry & smoked beef intro; warm sweet ripe black cherry fruit, soft tannins, very approachable. This in contrast to reds below thanks to lower acidity, softer tannins & tiny dab sugar. 9 mths Fr/Am oak. 13.5% alc.

★★★☆ **Cabernet Sauvignon** Firm-tannined, spicy & herbal. **00** mid-2004, green olive tinge to blackcurrant fruit, attractive touch eucalyptus, tannins still brusque. 10 mths oak, some new. 13.5% alc. **99** more conventional cab, sans green tones.

★★★★ **Merlot 00** ripe & elegant; fruit pastille/Ribena tones on soft, sweet palate; finishes savourily. 14% alc. Mid-2004 still needs 2-3 yrs.

★★★★ **Warrant** Educated & classy Bdx blend, **01** retasted mid-2004, opening up to show loads dusty cedary fruit, sweet vanilla oak, still tannins grippy. Mainly new Fr oak-matured. Assemblage 40/40/20 cab, merlot, cab f, harmonious, well-behaved. Alc. 14%.

★★★★ **Semillon 03** distinctive lanolin of the variety with asparagus; creamy notes mingle with sweet vanilla spice. Stylish, individual. 14% alc not out of kilter.

★★★☆ **Chenin Blanc** ✓ Latest **04** sample (★★★) fresh out of barrel (3 mths used Fr) oak still to integrate but dry, lean, good firm acidity. Fresh green apple flavours, touch of tannin. **03** was stylish & multi-layered.

Sauvignon Blanc ☺ ★★★ Sprightly, food-friendly style; newest **04** distant echoes of grass, nettle; bone dry, but easy to drink — perfect for fresh oysters, calamari or plain fish 'n chips. Alc a pleasing 12.5%.

Cabernet Franc-Merlot ★★★ Inviting 80/20 blend; latest **03** fragrant oak, black cherry & whiff mint; palate relaxed with soft tannins & fleshy fruit. 9 mths 2nd-/3rd-fill Fr oak. **Caresse Marine Red** ★★★ 𝗡𝗘𝗪 Interesting oaky/minty introduction to **03**, charming properly dry red still with youthful tannin; blend pinotage, cabs f & s, 58/24/18, 9 mths oak, used Fr. Alc 13%. **Chardonnay Reserve** ★★★ **03** marzipan & toast; smooth, lightly caramelised nuts; livened by citrus acidity; properly dry. Barrel-fermented/aged 4 mths. Alc 13.5%. **Caresse Marine White** ★★★ Lively blend chenin, chardonnay, sauvignon to be enjoyed young; **04** (sample) sunny ripe flavours, touch apricot fruit, tart & zingy. **Semillon Reserve** discontinued. — *IvH*

Wild Rush see Rietvallei

Wilhelmshof see Nico van der Merwe

William Everson Wines

Paarl ▪ Est/1stB 2001 ▪ Tasting, sales & tours by appt ▪ BYO picnic ▪ Owner/winemaker William Everson ▪ 300 cs 80% red 20% white ▪ 7 Prospect Street Somerset West 7130 ▪ we@ intekom.co.za ✆ 082·554·6357 ☏ (021) 851·2205

Things are moving for transport company owner William Everson, who makes his wine in a shared cellar on Paarl's Main Street. Within its cool depths a Rhône-style blend from shiraz, mourvèdre and viognier is maturing. When he's not oeno-philing, you'll most likely find the part-time winemaker somewhere in the Onrus area, catching a wave, or a crayfish, or just free-ranging on his Harley-Davidson.

★★★★ **Pinotage** Flamboyant **01**, from intensely ripe Agter-Paarl fruit, followed by **02** from Mbury grapes, matured yr in Am oak. Forward, showy & very appealing; cherry/banana tones, supportive oaking, subtle earth undertone, juicy tannins. Good prospects for development. ±14.7% alc.

★★★★ **Shiraz 01** featured well-structured Swtlnd fruit, picked super-ripe, hence hefty 14.9% alc. **02**, at 15.5%, makes pvs seem positively ethereal. Masses of everything, yet well composed & controlled, & underpinned by dense but juicy tannins, so should age well over 5-6 yrs. Oaking as above.

★★★★ **Chardonnay 02** (★★★) stave-fermented fruit ex-Rville. Retasted, attractively honeyed but needs drinking up, whereas **03** only now in its stride; another big number (14% alc) but well-fruited too with peach/citrus; firm acid backbone maintains liveliness. Bot R grapes, vinified in 3rd fill barrels. — *DH*

Windfall

Robertson ▪ Est 2000 ▪ 1stB 2001 ▪ Closed to public ▪ Owner Rob Alexander ▪ Winemaker Helmard Hanekom (2001) ▪ Viticulturist Jaco de Wet (2001) ▪ ±14 ha 100 tons 2 000 cs own label 75% red 25% white ▪ PO Box 802 Robertson 6705 ▪ windfallwinefarm@webmail.co.za ℃ *(023) 626·4498* 🖷 *(033) 342·2531*

KwaZulu-Natal property developer Rob Alexander bought this farm in tucked-away Agterkliphoogte Valley from veteran cricketer Eddie Barlow in 2000. The vines are tended by Jaco de Wet and the wines vinified by Helmard Hanekom at nearby Agterkliphoogte Winery. Alexander's goal is to 'make Windfall picture perfect' and increase the area under vine to about 24 ha. The wines were not tasted for this edition, but previous included a Pinotage, Ruby Cabernet and Merlot-Ruby Cabernet blend.

Windmeul Cellar

Paarl ▪ Est 1944 ▪ Tasting & sales Mon-Fri 8-5 Sat 9-1 ▪ Closed public holidays ▪ Tours during tasting hours by appt ▪ Owners 48 members ▪ Winemakers Danie Marais & Hugo Lambrechts, with Danie Geldenhuys (Dec/Aug 1999, Dec 2003) ▪ Viticulturist Paul Malan, advised by Paul Wallace (Dec 2001/Jan 1997) ▪ 1 700 ha (cab, merlot, shiraz, chard, chenin, sauvignon) ▪ 10 500 tons 6 000 cs own label 52% red 48% white ▪ PO Box 2013 Windmeul 7630 ▪ windmeul@iafrica.com ▪ www.windmeulkelder.co.za ℃ ***869·8043/ 8100*** 🖷 *869·8614*

A difficult growing season resulted in uneven ripening, and winemakers Danie Marais and Hugo Lambrechts had to draw on all their collective experience to figure out the most appropriate harvesting dates. Reporting for duty just as the games began was new winemaking assistant, Danie Geldenhuys, fresh from Elsenburg. Cab and shiraz fared best, the team reports, though merlot and pinotage suffered. In the end, 'serious canopy management and green harvesting' (culling not yet ripe bunches to promote final flavour intensity) saved the day. Amidst all the activity they found time to convert a few small open *kuipe* to allow for traditional punching down of the skins. 'The experiment showed that they must have made good wine back in the old days', Hugo Lambrechts sums up.

★★★★ **Cabernet Sauvignon-Merlot** Unpretentious example with many Veritas plaudits. **02** 70/30 blend, as was pvs; 20% new Fr oak portion enhanced elegant tone (which not compromised by big 14.8% alc). **03** (★★★) charming rather than impressive; cassis & sweet spice; very juicy, lively, ready but should go ±2 yrs.

★★★★ **Cabernet Sauvignon** Usually a crowd-pleaser with forward fruit, though **02** showed some restraint, less overt oak (yr Fr, 40% new). **03** (sample) mineral & lead pencil aromas, plummy flavours; firm, slightly furry tannins; on current showing ★★★. 6 mths wooded.

★★★★ **Cabernet Sauvignon Reserve** ✓ Longer oaking distinguishes this from version above; **02** (sample) was stylish, seductive; plump black fruit harmonised with vanilla-oak & mouthfilling alc (15%). **03** (sample) rich fruitcake aromas, layered cassis fruit, ripe tannin; sample still youthfully firm, dry. Yr Fr barriques. 14% alc.

★★★★ **Merlot** Fleshy **02** (sample) was crammed with macerated plums; almost over the top but appealing. **03** (unrated work-in-progress) tightly boarded up; palate overpowered by charry/spicy oak. 6 mths oak. 14% alc.

Pinotage ★★★ **03** (sample) black fruit, dried banana whiff; fruit just prevailing against heavy oaking (6 mths, 50% Am). 14% alc, as is... **Shiraz Reserve 03** wild berries & fynbos, beautiful intense berry fruit, lively on palate, creamy vanilla finish. Sample promises ★★★★ quality. Yr oak, 40% Am. **Mill Red** 🆕 ★★ Smoky floor polish aromas, bit blunt; savoury/smoky flavours; NV blend of **03** shiraz & **04** shiraz, cinsaut, cab f. **Chenin Blanc** ✓ **04** pungent aromas of grass & apple, very fresh & appealing; palate to match: good crisp appley fruit-salad concentration. Delightful. 13.6% alc. **Sauvignon Blanc** ★★★ **04** restrained asparagus/celery combo; zinging acidity which cries out for food. **Mill White** 🆕 ★★★ Melon & hay aromas, crisp tropical flavours. NV sample tasted. Chenin/sauvignon (50/50), plumped by chard. **Late Harvest** ★★ **03** from chenin

(90%), white muscadel; glacé pineapple scent; soft, rounded, uncomplicated & easy. **Cape Ruby Port** NEW ★★★ Deeply dark **03** (sample) rich Xmas cake bouquet; concentrated, sweet but juicy flavours, eminently drinkable now; traditional low fortification (17. 2%). Ruby cab, yr Fr barriques. WO Coastal, all others Paarl.—CR

Winds of Change see African Terroir
Wine 4U see Le Manoir de Brendell

Wine Concepts

Cape Town ▪ Tasting & sales Mon-Fri 9-6 Sat 9-5 ▪ Cardiff Castle cnr Kildare & Main St Newlands 7000 ▪ sales@wineconcepts.co.za ▪ www.wineconcepts.co.za ℂ 671·9030 ⊠ 671·9031

No new releases of their in-house budget range, Sommelier's Choice, but Cape Town fine-wine merchants Mike Bampfield-Duggan and Murray Giggins continue to stock a range of interesting and often unusual wines at their shops in Newlands and Kloof Street (see also Specialist wine shops section).

Winecorp

Stellenbosch ▪ Closed to public ▪ Group winemaker Frans Smit ▪ Winemakers Kobie Viljoen (red) & Eleonor Hoogendijk (white), with Etienne le Roux ▪ Group viticulturist Johann Smit, with Orlando Filander ▪ PO Box 99 Lynedoch 7603 ▪ winecorp@iafrica.com ▪ www.winecorp.co.za ▪ ISO 9001 & BRC certified ℂ 881·3690 ⊠ 881·3699

A 2004 JSE de-listing and merger between Winecorp Holdings (winery and brand owners) and Winecorp Private Label Services (producer of buyers' own brands) has streamlined what is now Winecorp (Pty) Ltd. Marketing man Vernon Davis (former KWV International MD) is the new CEO. His mission: establishing a 'focused marketing approach; concentrating on trade, rather than production through brand building'; developing Winecorp as a 'prominent, leading player in the SA wine industry' and taking it to the international market. Their two cellars meet different requirements. Longridge is the 'boutique' winery drawing on Helderberg vineyards for the premium Longridge label (and mainly exported Bay View). Spier sources from own-vineyards and mostly Stellenbosch sites for its ranges — Private Collection, Classic, Discovery (new entry-level easy-drinkers) and Inspire (export-only cellarmaster's choice of unusual varieties, special blends). The Spier cellar also handles Savanha wines from contracted growers for the Premium and export-only Sulanga line. Winecorp's Private Label Services continue to blend/bottle for buyer's own brands using their Ashwood facility in Simondium. Johan de Villiers procures wine and vinifies bought-in fruit, with group cellarmaster Frans Smit overseeing quality.

Dumisani range

Joint venture with Winecorp's UK agent Private Liquor Brands; now also distributed in the US & Ireland. Meaning 'Praise' in Xhosa. Strikingly attractive labels, each with individual motif. **Pinotage** ★★★ Uncomplicated, tasty. Revisited **02** undiminished berry piquancy, satisfying lively zesty palate. Lightly oaked. 14.5% alc. **Pinotage-Shiraz** ★★★ Early drinking 70/30 blend. **03** unoaked, reveals unadorned truth of varieties: herbaceous, fresh-picked wild berries, tangy smooth texture, juicy ripe finish. 14.5% alc. **Ruby Cabernet-Merlot** ★★ Quaffable 70/30 blend. Retaste finds **02**'s red berry appeal undiminished, remains pleasantly light-toned & juicy. 14% alc. **Pinotage Rosé** NEW ★★★ Charmer from top to toe: pale cerise colour, vibrant crushed berry/fruit pastille character, friendly touch sugar on finish. **04** not serious; ideal summer quaffer. 13% alc. **Chardonnay** ★★★ **03** early drinking, but offers something extra: tangy freshness, rounded peach-toast flavours from deft oaking. Now with slightly more serious label. 14% alc. **Chenin Blanc-Chardonnay** ★★★ **04** while chenin dominates (65%), chardonnay intrudes in delightful way: whiffs lemon zest in summer fruits nose, slight biscuit tone, plump palate. Lightly oaked. 13% alc. **Chenin Blanc** NEW ★★★ Good ambassador o/seas for tasty, easy-drinking chenin. Guavas, crunchy apples, fresh & light, roundly appealing. 12.5% alc. **Cinsaut-Merlot** & **Brut** discontinued.

Fat Ladies range

Uncomplicated, easy-drinking wines, all with screwcaps. Delightfully corpulent ladies on labels by local artist Roland West. Nicely done.

> **Sauvignon Blanc** ☺ ★★★ 04 vibrant Cape gooseberries & kiwi fruit, ripe, fragrant. Long, aromatic, mouthfilling finish. 13.5% alc.

Cabernet Sauvignon-Merlot ★★★ 02 fruit is main focus in this 70/30 blend; fresh-picked berries/cherries, zinging with fleshy, juicy appetite appeal. Unwooded. 14% alc. **Pinotage Rosé** ★★ 04 Goes down easily; fruit pastille, candyfloss aromas, palate-lengthening sugar (12g/ℓ). 13.5% alc. All above WO W-Cape. — CR

Wine of the Month Club

Est 1986 ▪ Founder Colin Collard ▪ MD Tai Collard ▪ 200 000 cs 50% red 49% white 1% sparkling ▪ Private Bag X2 Glosderry 7702 ▪ wineclub@wineofthemonthclub.co.za ▪ www.wineofthemonth.co.za ✆ 657·8100 🖷 657·4992

Colin Collard started this enduring mail-order, door-to-door delivery wine venture in 1986. It now handles some 200 000 cases a year. Besides wines selected by the club's panel for distribution to 40 000 customers, WOM also supplies its own-label wines. Among these is the Select Winemakers Collection Limited Release, an exclusive range by big names Hempies du Toit (Annandale), Bruce Jack (Flagstone), Bruwer Raats (Zorgvliet/Raats Family) and Gesie Lategan (Domaine Brahms), none retasted for this ed.

Wines of Charles Back see Fairview, Goats do Roam, Spice Route
Wine Society see International Wine Services, Rudera

Wine Village-Hermanus

Walker Bay ▪ Est 1998 ▪ 1stB 2004 ▪ Tasting & sales hours: see Specialist wine shops section ▪ Owners Paul & Cathy du Toit ▪ Winemakers Reino Thiart & Hester Havenga ▪ ±1 000 cs 50% red 50% white

This delightful country wine shop, run by Paul and Cathy du Toit, has its housewine back on the shelves under the Wine Village label (previous labelled 'Hermanus Heritage'). With a couple of friends and enthusiastic staff members, they've produced two blends in their artisanal back-stoep operation. 'Winemaking is a pretty risky business,' they jest, 'but we plan to have a lot of fun while stressing about the possible results of our labours.'

Dry Red ★★★ All-sort blend led by cab; smoked meat & currant jam aromas, some damp earth notes; elegant, shows pleasant touch of bottle-age. **Dry White** ★★★ Lively, light & refreshing, from Stanford semillon, 2 mths new Fr oak; nice sherbety acidity, interesting & attractive rhubarb twist to finish. Both NEW, NV. — TM

Winkelshoek Wine Cellar

Piketberg (see Swartland map) ▪ Tasting & sales Mon-Fri 9-4 Sat 9-12 ▪ Fee R5 ▪ Restaurant daily 7.30am-6pm ▪ Gifts ▪ Owners Hennie Hanekom & Jurgens Brand ▪ Winemaker Hennie Hanekom (1984) ▪ PO Box 395 Piketberg 7320 ▪ info@winkelshoek.co.za ✆ (022) 913-1092 🖷 (022) 913·1095

This cellar's easy-drinking Weskus range is available for tasting and sale from the restaurant/visitor centre at the N7/R44 intersection near Piketberg. The wines, untasted for this ed, include Dry Red, Grand Cru, Blanc de Blanc and Late Harvest.

Withoek

Calitzdorp (see Little Karoo map) ■ Est/1stB 1996 ■ Tasting & sales Mon-Fri 9-4 ■ Closed Mar 21, Easter Fri, Apr 27, May 1, Jun 16, Aug 9, Sep 24 ■ Tours by appt ■ Self-catering cottages ■ Farm produce ■ Walks ■ Conservation area ■ Owner/winemaker/viticulturist Koos Geyser, with Fanie Geyser (1996/2000) ■ 20 ha (cab, petit v, ruby cab, shiraz, tinta, touriga, chenin, colombard, hanepoot, muscadel) ■ ±300 tons 400 cs own label 50% red 50% fortified ■ PO Box 181 Calitzdorp 6660 ■ withoek@telkomsa.net stabilpave@mweb. co.za ©/✉ (044) 213·3639

Several recent changes have made this small Calitzdorp cellar more attractive to visitors, including the establishment of a new, modern tasting and sales venue just off the main road (R62), and the opening of the adjoining Jakkalskop Succulent Plant Route, inaugurated during the recent World Conference on Succulents. The changes have brought the winery within easy walking distance of the town centre. Also tourist-friendly are the Spekboom self-catering cottages on the premises.

Dry Red ☺ ★★★ Spicy, leafy notes on **03** nose with cinnamon whiff; dry, savoury; interesting cinnamon/vanilla twist on finish from Yr 3rd fill oak; tinta, ruby cab.

Cape Ruby ★★★ Very soft & friendly ruby-style port from above varieties, 2 yrs oaked. **01** ripe, spicy rum & raisin nose; soft, silky, medium-sweet. 17% alc, low for style. — TM

Withof see Kosie Möller Wines
Witteboomen see Thorntree
Wolvenbosch see Jason's Hill

Wolvendrift Private Cellar

Robertson ■ Est 1903 ■ 1stB 2002 ■ Tasting & sales Mon-Fri 9-4.30 Sat 10-1 ■ Closed Easter Fri-Sun, Dec 25/26 & Jan 1 ■ Tours by appt ■ Picnic baskets by appt or BYO ■ Farm produce ■ Walks ■ Owner Michael Klue ■ Winemakers Michael & Jan Klue (Jan 1973/Jan 2003) ■ Viticulturist Jan Swart (Jan 2000) ■ 120 ha (cab, merlot, chard, chenin, colombard, sauvignon) ■ 45% red 45% white 10% fortified ■ PO Box 24 Robertson 6705 ■ wolvendrift@ lando.co.za ■ www.wolvendriftwines.co.za © (023) 616·2890 ✉ (023) 616·2396

Now a century old, the Klue family cellar is due for expansion to accommodate more red wine barrels. It should be an attractive alteration: the new section will overlook the Breede River, whose banks make an ideal vantage point for bird-watching, picnic spot (BYO or book ahead to buy) and 'braai plek' (you might catch something for the pot!). The philosophy of father-and-son team Michael and Jan K is akin to that of Slow Food devotees: 'It requires handling'. The grapes are harvested with care at night, and the winemaking process is slowed down to reduce stress. It's working: they've added more metal to the bronze won for their very first Wolvendrift wine in 2002.

Cabernet-Sauvignon-Merlot 'Red Wolf' in pvs ed. **04** (early sample) sweetish ripe plum jam aromas; bright zippy fruit, touch jammy but redeeming dry finish, some charred oak on back palate. Provisional ★★★. **Chardonnay** ★★★ Unshowy, easy drinking **03**, now pleasantly honeyed but peaking, must drink. Briefly oaked. **Sauvignon Blanc** ★★★ **04** quiet pear-drop aromas, slight dustiness; lightweight, flinty & bone dry. **Muscadel** ★★★★ Red (which it doesn't say on the charming label); **03** retasted, limpid coppery hue, complex rose-petal & tea-leaf interplay, good red-fruit taste. Preview **04** effusive raisin/muscat aromas; well-judged fortification but very sweet; provisional ★★★. ±17% alc. — TM

Woolworths

Category manager William Fakude © 407·3683 ■ Selection manager Allan Mullins © 407·2777 ✉ 407·3946 ■ AllanMullins@woolworths.co.za ■ Buying manager Ivan Oertle © 407·2762 ■ IvanOertle@woolworths.co.za

Like its other good living essentials — clothing, homeware, food — Woolworths' wines represent style, quality and value. And exclusivity, without being off-puttingly 'exclusive'. Testimony to winebuyer Allan Mullins' and aide-de-camp Ivan Oertle's success is a double anniversary: 20 years for Woolies wines; 20 for Oertle with Woolworths. Stocktaking reveals 136 stores selling wine, five with cafés offering wine by the glass. 80% of wine sold is consumed within two days, and 80–90% is repeat business. 'You'd be surprised how many people come into our stores to buy the same wine on the same day of the week,' Allan M says. 'We're hugely flattered, given the vast selection of wines on retail shelves generally.' Sophisticated information systems supplying such data now allow stocking of specific outlets according to area demographics. Demand for screwcaps is being met on their standard ranges. There's a new imported selection (French, Italian, Australian, US). Yet Mullins remains quietly proud that most wines are his own blends.

Signature Series
Flagship range, featuring special selections from exceptional vintages.

★★★★★ **The Cape Blend 01** still available; bold striking, broad-shouldered wine (nudging 15% alc); blend pinotage, shiraz, cab (45/37/18) — the majority partner's bright ruby lights & perfume (incl some ripe banana) evident among the succulent fruit-cake. Balanced & well-wooded (14 mths Fr, mainly 2nd/3rd fill). From Warwick.

★★★★ **Merlot-Cabernet Sauvignon** To date the **00**. Spicy & austere claret, 20 mths in Fr oak, merlot eclipsed by strident, still rather uptight junior partner cab (35%). From Morgenhof.

★★★★★ **Chardonnay** From one of Mullins' longest-standing suppliers, Neil Ellis. Scrumptious **02** retasted mid-2004, intensified citrus vein, holding freshness intact. Layers of interest: buttered toast, roasted nut flavours, tangy orange peel finish, smooth-textured structure. Fermented/aged in cask 10 mths. 13.5 % alc. **02** rivetted attention with full-blown citrus & hazelnuts array; incredibly lively orange-zest finish.

Reserve range
★★★★ **Cabernet Sauvignon** Shows Villiera's restrained generosity; **02** overall impression is of richness & depth: spice-infused plums & mocha-choc; creamy texture, elegantly structured, with oak supportive; everything geared for enjoyment. Could age 3-4 yrs, but why wait? Fr oak, yr, quarter new. 13.5% alc. **01** was also soft & ready, with credentials to age 3-4 yrs. **00** rich, ripe & spicy.

★★★★ **Founder's Reserve Cabernet Sauvignon** Moves here from above Signature range, where **01** continues to impress. Mid-2003 still deeply coloured, weighty & concentrated; plum pudding & cream from 60% new oak (70/30 Fr/Am), 15 mths. Barrel selection from Diemersfontein, owned by Wlwrths' founding family.

★★★★★ **Pinotage** From Bellevue, showcasing that estate's singular essence-of-pinotage style, from vines up to 50 yrs old. Stylish **02** proves how compatible this variety & Am oak can be (10 mths small barrels, half new): perfumed coconut/vanilla-spice & macerated plums; balanced, with friendly reined-in tannins, lithe structure. Good 5+ yr potential. 14.5% alc. **01** was a paean to ripe black fruit.

★★★★ **Groenekloof Shiraz** Full, rich, almost extravagant version from Darling Cellars. Latest **02** beguilingly explores savoury spectrum: smoky, roasted spice, whiffs of espresso, dried herbs, on a dark fruit base. No rough edges, just creamy, delicious ripeness. Yr Fr oak, 40% new. 14.9% alc. Pvs **00** very ripe & broad textured. **99** had hot-earth & leather nuance, ripened into opulence in bottle.

★★★★★ **Cabernet Sauvignon-Merlot** Reflects vintage variations through mirror of Neil Ellis' classicism. **02** layered complexity: dark fruit, spice-threaded smoked meat, mocha-choc, whiffs of underbrush. Elegant structure retains generosity of fruit, easily accommodates fine-grained tannins. Misleadingly accessible, has 5+ yr ageing potential. 15 mths Fr barrels, 25% new. 13.5% alc. 61/39 blend. Silky elegance characterised **01** (★★★★), for earlier enjoyment.

★★★★ **Shiraz-Cabernet Sauvignon** In classic La Motte mould. **01**'s slight shiraz dominance (53%) comes through in peppery, brambleberry aromas, flavours; in structure, cab takes over: elegant, sinewy ripe tannins, with good 5+ yr ageing potential. Seasoned Fr barrels, touch Am, 21 mths. 14.5% alc. **00** tad more ripe-fruited than pvs.

★★★★ **Chardonnay** All since 97 by Neil Ellis. Current **03** shows bold New World style at its best: tangy citrus peel & buttered toast, exotic shading of lime; palate's food-friendly freshening acidity tempered by nutty overlay. 80% blend Fr oak-fermented/aged 9 mths, third new. 13.5% alc. **02** returned to form with a food-cordial style. **01** (★★★★) more workmanlike.

★★★★★ **Limestone Hill Chardonnay** Prized by fans both of De Wetshof's Danie, who makes it, and the oak-free style he does so well. **03** (★★★★) quieter than pvs: gentle peach ripeness, freshened by citrus edginess, brisk acidity. For tasty solo drinking or food partnership. 13.5% alc. **02** returned to racier mode of **00**; lively lemon/orange-zest palate ends with a citrus fanfare. **01** slightly softer.

★★★★ **Barrel Chenin Blanc** These delicious on release, sustain interest for good few yrs. **03** mellow, ripe, honeyed tropical fruit, spiced by 9 mths half-portion barrel maturation. Full-flavoured, vibrant; finishes with invigorating citrus zestiness. 14% alc. **02** was tangy, full yet crisp-finishing. Native-yeast fermented. Ken Forrester does the styling.

★★★★ **Sauvignon Blanc** From Buitenverwachting. Beautifully balanced & delicious **03** back to form: draws you in with intense passionfruit/gooseberry fruit expression; ripe, tangy, full-bodied palate. 12.9% alc.

★★★★ **Noble Late Harvest Chenin Blanc Barrel Reserve** From Ken Forrester. Latest **03** (★★★★) deeply ripe, tropical fruit, honeycomb & barley sugar tones; sweetness (123g/ℓ) tempered by racy acidity, but no mistaking wine's richness. Natural ferment in barrels. 11.5% alc. Pvs was **00**, light & quite sweet, probably for early drinking.

Founder's Reserve Cabernet Sauvignon, Grenache-Syrah & Noble Late Harvest Weisser Riesling discontinued.

Art of Blending range

★★★★ **SCC** Syrah, cabs s/f blend (73/25/2) from Boekenhoutskloof. **02** unmistakeably shiraz on entry, savoury, spiced meat, black plums, but cabs kick in on palate to temper exuberant ripeness; fine-grained tannins, touch herbaceous on finish. 15 mths Fr barriques, cabs' portion new. Will reward 5+ yrs cellaring. 14.7% alc.

★★★★ **CPMS** Youthful assembly cab, pinotage, merlot, shiraz (40/30/15/15) by Diemersfontein. **03** pinotage in charge of aromas (beetroot, dark fruit, dried banana), thereafter varieties in concert: red berry/ plum flavours, chewy tannins, needing few yrs to show full potential. Fr /Am oak 11 mths. 14% alc.

★★★★ **MCP** Harmonious malbec, cab franc, petit v blend (50/30/20) from Spier, as are following trio. **03** emphasis on red currant fruit, but artful touches violets, 'wet heath', even mint strengthen on palate. Classically structured, refined; oak a supple, important presence for 6+ yr longevity. 13 mths small Fr, third new.

★★★★ **NSB** Strikingly perfumed nebbiolo, sangiovese, barbera creation (78/17/5), **03** violets, Parma ham, wild berries draw you in, seduce. Classic sturdy dry tannins from nebbiolo, will develop, unfold over time. 9 mths older Fr barrels. 14.3% alc.

★★★★ **SMV** Individual, impressive shiraz, mourvèdre, viognier amalgamation (72/25/2). As with siblings, **04** wondrously aromatic: strawberry/red berry base, with tantalising leaf, meat extract, pepper nuances, & yes, hint of viognier's peach. Smoky/gamey flavours complete the experience. 13 mths small Fr barrels, third new provide 6+ yrs ageing credentials. 15.1% alc.

★★★★ **SVC** Attractively exotic mix sauvignon, viognier, chardonnay (50/26/24). **04** layers of interest: peachy, floral intro, sauvignon shows dominance on palate with lemony, cut-grass freshness, crisp finish. All varieties barrel fermented/matured together (7 mths small Fr oak, 20% new), but wood plays subtle role, lets aromas shine through. 13% alc.

Limited Release range

★★★★ **Chardonnay Sur Lie** Beautiful wine. Jordan Winery's Gary & Kathy deserve a trophy for coaxing so much flavour out of the unwooded grape; **03** full, poised, marvellously rich yet focused/sharpened by racy citrus acidity. 3 mths on lees.

★★★★ **Semillon** Now made by Nitida. Sample **04** (★★★★) good partnership between well-judged oak (half barrel-fermented, some new) & variety's tantalisingly ethereal fruit: lemongrass, citrus peel, grated apple. Light-textured, subtle, poised. Food-friendly crisp finish. 14% alc. Classy & classic **01** was from Spier.

Merlot ★★★ **02** attractive mint-choc, café latte character; generous, roundly accessible. Likely to make many friends. Yr Fr oak, qtr new. 14.4% alc. Ex-Villiera. **Pinotage** ★★★ Supplier changes to Diemersfontein in **03**, wine shows that cellar's wood-driven style (loved by Woolies' customers, Allan M notes). plummy fruit copes well, manages a dry finish. **Pinot Noir** ★★★★ Pvs quirky versions now replaced with a more conventionally delicious offering from BWC Wines; **03** rasp- & other fat fresh berries join creamy spice on nose/palate; full-ripe style (no farmyards/fungi) with elegance, texture. Only 12% alc. **Sauvignon Blanc** NEW **04** from Cape Point Vineyards. Unfinished sample, yet already beautifully captures invigorating essence of sauvignon: grapefruit, interleavings of capsicum, fresh asparagus, nettles/herbs. Racy, intense, impossibly long finish. A lesson in flavour concentration. 13.5% alc. Likely ★★★★★. **Gewürztraminer** ★★★ **04** from Bergsig, as usual. Classic rose-petal, litchi perfume, softly aromatic off-dry flavours; easy, friendly. 12.5% alc. **Weisser Riesling** NEW ★★★★ From Paul Cluver. Elegant **04** (sample) delicate pineapple, floral, spicy aromas; brisk acidity (7.8g/ℓ) gives drier finish than 11g/ℓ sugar promises. 12.4% alc. Screwcap. **Chenin Blanc**, **Semillon** & **Pinotage** sold out.

Grapes of the World Collection

Mullins & co aiming for varietal typicity with this range. **Malbec** ★★★☆ Open-textured **02** from Bellevue, with that winery's signature curvaceousness; brambleberries & touch mint; melded oak; **03** (preview) same profile, more overt mintiness. 14% alc. **Viognier** NEW ★★★☆ Clean, forthcoming peach aromas/flavours on **03**; grain sugar (6g/ℓ) subsumed in sherbety acidity, amenable & beguiling. By Spier; 6 mths in Fr oak.

Organic range

Merlot NEW ★★★ **02** fruit-powered for early enjoyment; concentrated cassis aroma/flavour; juicy & soft. Made by Stellar Winery. **Shiraz** ★★★ Unwooded **04** with spicy & savoury dry flavours; smoky/herbaceous notes gravitate towards char-grilled foods; from African Terroir. **The Red Blend Reserve** ★★★ Standout in range by virtue of its strong tannic grip; **03** needs yr/2 for core of wild berry fruit to unfurl; should give lots of pleasure for several more yrs. Merlot-led blend with cabs f/s (64/19/17), by up-and-coming Laibach. Yr Fr oak. **Sauvignon Blanc** ★★ Unremarkable but light, pleasant **04** with gentle pear-drop & boiled sweet tone, tangy finish. By African Terroir. **Chenin Blanc Sulphur Free** NEW ★★★ Preservative-free but not lacking charm, flavour; 04 (sample) gentle fruit salad taste, perky sour-sweet finish. From Stellar Winery; carries 6-mth sell-by date.

Premium range

★★★★ **Chardonnay-Pinot Noir** Cream-textured food wine from Cabrière (moderate 12.5% alc a plus for long lunches); **04** (sample) equal blend, bunch-pressed for fruitiness; aromas of lemon butter on toast; tangy lemon-lime flavours.

★★★☆ **Rhine Riesling** Youthfully charming but cellarable version from Villiera. **04** showcases riesling's aromatic charm: floral scents, tropical fruit aromas/flavours; friendly off-dry finish. 13.5% alc. **03** had a lovely floral bouquet; racy fruity acid for food partnering.

Merlot ★★★★ Made by La Motte. **03** a step up, thanks to warmly engaging ripeness toned with lead-pencil oak; savoury black choc flavour. 14.3% alc. **Shiraz** ★★★ **03** nose promises seriousness, palate delivers quaffability via bouncy cherry-berry flavours. 14% alc. From Rooiberg. **Grand Rouge** ★★★★ ✓ Popular, consistent Sunday lunchtime red by La Motte. **02** serious but friendly; clarety cassis & cedar on nose; plum pudding & custard flavours; refreshing lifted finish.

Premier range

Shiraz ★★★ **03** one for traditionalists: old-style savoury palate with liquorice nuance, peppery dusting on nose. Made by Swartland Wine Cellar. **Founder's Shiraz-Cabernet Sauvignon** ★★★ **02** from Diemersfontein; partly wooded, Fr/Am casks. **02** retasted, richly toned with mocha oak & choc; smooth pruney flavours; charcterful. 'Founders' name to be dropped from future releases. **Sauvignon Blanc** ★★★ Lightish, refreshing **04** (sample), forthcoming zingy nose, herbaceous green palate. Ex-Darling Cellars.

House Wines

Charming easy-drinkers by Franschhoek Vineyards; simply but well packaged. **Red** ★★★ Spiced fruitcake aromas; accessible berry fruit; **03** just enough tannins to go with saucy pasta. **White** ★★★ Warmly ripe tropical fruit salad tone on **03**, refreshing & uncomplicatedly flavourful.

What range

Quaffable version of Grapes of The World, 'wines chosen to represent their varieties as closely as possible'.

> **Chenin Blanc** ☺ ★★★ Surprisingly well structured & full flavoured, taste seems to last forever. **04** (sample) tangy, juicy, lemon-apple combo, crisp dry conclusion.

Pinotage ★★★ **04** telltale dark, creamy brambleberry fruit, lip-smacking finish; also less obviously pinotage whiffs pepper & wet heath. This, above, from Ken Forrester. **Chardonnay** ★★★ Unadorned by oak, to showcase varietal character. **04** tasty peaches & tropical fruit; crisply dry, light-textured for easy drinking. From Weltevrede.

Longmarket Range

Mid-priced cork-closed range; some also in 'Flexible' line-up below.

Pinotage ★★★★ Long-time customer favourite from Rooiberg, unobtrusively oaked. **03** has rhubarb & banana on nose, smoky black fruit flavour, lively, juicy & well knit. **Chardonnay-Semillon** ★★★★ Appetite-whetting food wine from Delheim. **03**, yr on, dominated by semillon's beeswax breadth, chardonnay a tangy palate-lifter; **04** unfinished/unrated sample very well structured; lively citrus freshness. Portion 4–5 mths Fr casks.

> **Cabernet Sauvignon** ☺ ★★★ The sort of wine to chill & consume lots of. **03** retasted this ed. Oodles of flavour, red berries & toasty oak, satisfyingly accessible. 13.5% alc. From Bergsig. **Gamay Noir** ☺ ★★★ Unwooded, to capture variety's fruity character, created by partial carbonic fermentation. **04** pulpy, freshly crushed cranberries; lighttoned, dry. Delicious chilled. 13,5% alc. By Villiera, as are next 2 wines. **Rosé** ☺ ★★★ **04** step up. Redcurrant, wine-gum aromas leap out of glass; light-toned structure & red berry focus make perfect al fresco dining companion. Friendly touch sugar. 12.5% alc. **Blanc de Blanc** ☺ ★★★ Zesty dry white. **04** bursting with freshness, asparagus, Granny Smith apples. Tasty early drinking. 13.5% alc. **Spicy** ☺ ★★★ From Weltevrede; **03** gently aromatic melon & honey tones; good sugar/acid balance presents dry finish without losing roundness. Friendly 10.7% alc.

Merlot ★★ **03** spice & creamy plum fruit on nose, lively but very dry, demands a hearty stew. From Simonsvlei. **Merlot-Cabernet Franc** ★★★ Made by Simonsvlei. Cab f's herbaceous top-note on retaste of 02, plus merlot's red berries; **02** still quite firm, dry. Could do with further ageing. **Blanc de Noir** ★★ **04** (sample) soft, generously proportioned offdry from Swartland Wine Cellar, light cerise shade, pretty strawberry wafts. **Chardonnay** ★★★ **03** from Robertson Winery. Has broadened pleasantly since last tasted; ripe melon palate, sparingly wooded. **Chenin Blanc** ★★ Light everyday tipple; **04** offers quiet fruit salad flavours/aromas. From Rooiberg. **Sauvignon Blanc** ★★★ Lightish quick gulp from Robertson Winery; **04** more character/refreshment than pvs; whiffs asparagus & green leaves. **Maison Rouge** discontinued.

Selected range

Also available in 1 & 5ℓ packs. From Simonsvlei: **Cape Red** ★★ Four-way unwooded blend, **03** more fruity than pvs; lively red berry flavours; pizza-friendly dry finish. **Late Harvest** ★★★ **03** pineapple taste, juicy & fresh, not over-sweet. From Rooiberg: **Cape White** ★★ **04** fresh hay/guava on nose, grain sugar plumps out palate. From colombard.

Sweet & Lite range

> **Bianca Light** ☺ ★★★ Never insipid, as low-alc wines can be. **04** appealing & pretty; peardrop & pink sweets on nose; crisp melon on taste. 9.5% alc. From Delheim.

Bel Rosso Sweet Red ★★ Med-bodied NV; works because fruit is the hero: berry-rich, softly rounded, semi-sweet, light quaffing fare. 13% alc. By Bergsig.

Zesties

Juicy Red ★★ Juicy, yes, & good natured, with berry-toned winegum ripeness. 13% alc. **Zesty White** ★★ Guava-rich summer fruit salad, lively, crisply refreshing. Friendly 12% alc. **Perky Pink** ★☆ Uncomplicated, pretty-hued & -flavoured; fruit pastilles, with off-dry, tangy finish. 12% alc. **Sassy Sweet** ★★ Perfume of sun-drenched sultanas; roundly ripe melon-flavours, simple quaffing fare. These NVs all from Bergsig.

Cap classique sparklers

★★★★ **Vintage Reserve Brut** Excellent 60/40 pinot/chardonnay *cuvée*, traditionally made & matured 5 yrs on lees, further yr on cork. Delicious **97** beguiling layers biscuit, citrus peel, red berry fruit, bursting with tangy freshness. Generous mousse, mouthfilling flavours, good length: has all the right ingredients. 12.3% alc. **96** at peak, no need to hold back. All by Villiera, 12–12.5% alc.

★★★☆ **Brut** Easy, affordable celebratory NV bubbles from mainly chardonnay, some pinot, pinotage, ±2 yrs on lees. Classic chalky nose, tasty, exuberantly refreshing palate, plumped up by slightly higher sweetening dosage (9g/ℓ) than above.

★★★☆ **Brut Rosé** Partridge-eye-pink NV with vigorous frothy bubble. Generously flavoured, cranberries, redcurrants, dry, aperitif-friendly finish. Pinot, pinotage, chardonnay (45/40/15); 18 mths on lees, 6 on cork, sugar as for Brut.

Basic sparklers

Spumante Rosé ★★☆ Aromatic sweet pink; clean & fruity. Latest version has lovely ripe red berry character through to finish. **Brut** ★★☆ Soft & semi-dry rather than brut; fruitily fizzy with apple & fruit salad tones. **Spumante** ★★★ Sweet but lively foam, lots of balanced grapey scents/tastes. 9.5% alc. All NVs, from Rooiberg.

Bag in boxes/Flexibles

These 1ℓ, 2ℓ 'flexibles', and 3ℓ, 5ℓ boxes, filled on demand for freshness.

> **Semi-Sweet** NEW ☺ ★★★ Lovely jasmine bouquet; light texture but generous tropical flavour, crisp finish.

Merlot ★★ **03** creamy/spicy plum aromas; lively body, very dry finish, needs food. **Dry Red** ★★★ Four fruity grapes showing lots of plummy freshness & verve, soft food-friendly dry finish. **Chardonnay** ★★★ **04** warm, ripe & generous; baked apple whiffs, crisp citrus flavours; lightly wooded. Note high alc: 14%. From Robertson Winery, as is... **Sauvignon Blanc** ★★★ **04** more satisfying than pvs; figgy nose, fairly pronounced crisp grassy/herbaceous flavours. **Blanc de Blanc** ★★ Best seller in range, from chenin. Peardrops & guava, uncomplicated but lively, lots of juice. **Crisp White** ★★ As the label says: crisp — with tart, green apple finish. From Robertson Winery. **Stein** ★★ Delicately fruity, light semi-sweet chenin, with appley aromas/flavours. **Late Harvest** ★★ Delicate tropical/boiled sweet tonés; drier than style would suggest. All NV from From Simonsvlei unless noted. **Bouquet Blanc** discontinued. — *CR*

Wozani see Oranjerivier
Yellow Cellar see Helderkruin
Yammé see Overhex

Yonder Hill Winery

Stellenbosch (see Helderberg map) ▪ *Est 1989* ▪ *1stB 1993* ▪ *Tasting, sales & tours Mon-Fri 9-4* ▪ *Closed public holidays* ▪ *Owners Frikkie & Danila Naudé* ▪ *Winemaker/viticulturist David Lockley (Jul 1998)* ▪ *10 ha (cabs s/f, merlot, chard)* ▪ *85 tons ±12 600 cs 97% red 3% white* ▪ *PO Box 914 Stellenbosch 7599* ▪ *wines@yonderhill.co.za* ▪ *www.yonderhill.co.za* ② *855·1008* ▤ *855·1006*

'All varieties did well,' says David Lockley, nicely satisfied with the 2004 vintage. He's also content with the state of the vineyards: they're 'well spaced', with even growth and 'the ducks are doing a great job with the snails'. Wine news is that a third range, named 'Y' and produced mainly from Robertson fruit, was launched. If all goes well, the winemaker will bottle 200 cases of a Reserve blend. Somehow he finds time to travel: two weeks in Europe in 2003 and then six weeks in Romania, making 9 000 tons of wine. No lack of energy here – consumers should take a leaf from the Lockley book: 'Anyone who buys wine off the supermarket shelf has a boring life,' he opines. 'One needs to get out.'

★★★★ **iNanda** 'Beautiful Place'. Heir-apparent, for now, until a 'Reserve Blend' (6 yrs in the crafting) takes throne. Currently a cab, merlot, cab f blend with dash shiraz (to be replaced by petit v in time). **02** survives 'difficult year', a little leaner than pvs, but enough juicy fruit for firm length. **01** (★★★★) bulky; big dry tannins. 14% alc.

★★★★ **Merlot** 'We're pushing the boat out on this one,' says David L of his flagship, from 1.2 ha (recent plantings will only qualify at 8 yrs). Sample **03** polished, restrained. Complex, serious structure, carrying bright fruit needing several yrs to bloom. **01** (★★★★) integrated pencil box notes. IWC gold. No **02**. 16 mths Fr oak. 14.6% alc.

★★★☆ **Shiraz-Merlot** NEW **03** As loud as cellar-mate above is restrained. Intense milled peppercorn focus jostles with well-juiced huckleberry fruits, near-electric tension to tannins. House merlot (25%) & Stbosch shiraz, 16 mths oak. 13.5% alc.

Cabernet Sauvignon ★★★ **02** herbal, scrubby nature & stalky tannins weighing heavily on cab fruit. Mature vine fruit, 20% new Fr oak. 13.5% alc. **Chardonnay** ★★★ Breezily unoaked **03**, exuberant youthful fruit (quinces, limes), brisk dry finish freshened by 10% sauvignon.

Y range

Shiraz-Merlot NEW ★★★ **03** snazzily packaged, destined for fun. Pretty serious frame, though, plumped full of bright choc/mulberry fruits, tannins spear spiced finish. 13 mths old wood. **Merlot** ★★★ **03** snappy vanilla-spiked plum, hints choc in uncomplicated, grippy mouthful. 13.5% alc. **Muscadel** NEW ★★★ **03** bottled sunshine, in a 500ml pack. Aromatic, full sweet, moreish. 18.5% alc; 99g/ℓ sugar. – *DS*

Zandberg Farm

Stellenbosch (see Helderberg map) ▪ *1stB 2001* ▪ *Tasting & sales daily 10-6* ▪ *96 Winery Road Restaurant (see Eat-out section)* ▪ *4-star guesthouse & other amenities (see intro)* ▪ *Owner Ernst Heusser* ▪ *Winemaker Anton Bredell* ▪ *Viti consultants Kobus van Graan & Johan Wiese* ▪ *±12 ha (cab & merlot)* ▪ *2 200 cs 100% red* ▪ *PO Box 5431 Helderberg 7135* ▪ *wine@zandberg.co.za* ▪ *www.zandberg.co.za* ② *082·323·6367* ▤ *842·1505*

Steady progress and a string of successes characterised the past year for Zandberg farm. An AA 'Highly Recommended' rating for their country guesthouse; 96 Winery Road again featuring among *Wine* magazine's Top 10 SA restaurants and the maiden Cab receiving a medal at the FCTWS. Particularly pleasing to Ernst Heusser is the strong appreciation shown by Johannesburg clientele for his food-friendly wine, together with continuing exports to Germany, Switzerland and Ireland. In defiance of the pace of the wine label's symbolic tortoise, the newly planted cab vines show astounding, super-charged growth. The secret: a special seaweed potion into which the roots were dipped, prior to planting!

Cabernet Sauvignon ★★★ Classic & individual **02** step up on pvs, richer plum/fruit pastille tone; bigger wine (14% alc) yet retains house's trademark linearity; will benefit from further bottle-ageing. Yr Fr oak. — *DH*

Zanddrift Vineyards

Paarl ▪ Est 1995 ▪ Closed to public ▪ Owner Windsharp Trading 23 (Singapore) ▪ PO Box 1302 Suider-Paarl 7624 ▪ zanddrift@xsinet.co.za © *863·2076* 🖷 *863·2081*

These vineyards succumbed to 'black goo', a virulent fungus, which led to the vines being removed. Some nine hectares have since been redeveloped — cabernet and shiraz being the focus — and production is planned to kick off again this harvest.

Zandvliet Estate

Robertson ▪ Est 1867 ▪ 1stB 1975 ▪ Tasting & sales Mon-Fri 9-5 Sat 9-1 ▪ Closed Easter Fri/ Sun & Dec 25 ▪ Tutored tastings by appt for small groups (12-30) with snacks/light meals; BYO picnic ▪ Owners Paul & Dan de Wet ▪ Winemaker Johan van Wyk (Apr 2000), advised by Paul de Wet ▪ Viticulturist Dan de Wet, advised by Francois Viljoen & Phil Freese ▪ 150 ha (cab, shiraz, chard) ▪ 1 350 tons 60 000 cs own label 50% red 45% white 5% rosé ▪ Export brands: Cogmans/Kogmans Kloof, Cogmans River & Sandy River ▪ PO Box 36 Ashton 6715 ▪ shiraz@lando.co.za ▪ www.zandvliet.co.za © *(023) 615·1146* 🖷 *(023) 615·1327*

The De Wet brothers (winemaker Paul and vineyardist Dan) on this gracious farm celebrate 40 years of bottling this year. Though wines still proudly carry the 'estate' appellation, ever-outspoken Paul deW questions the ongoing value internationally of this much-legislated Cape concept. And Zandvliet has long been a successful global brand: recent awards include a Chardonnay-du-Monde gold, and a Japan Wine Challenge gold (and best SA entry accolade) for the Shiraz. Now the Zandvliet label is being re-branded in English-speaking markets (UK, US) as Enon (to include Sauvignon and a Cab-Shiraz blend). Meanwhile, ongoing exploration of terroir and techniques produced the Kalkveld Hill of Enon 'Smallberry Pick'.

★★★★ **Kalkveld Shiraz French Oak Matured** 'Shiraz', to be distinguished from version below; both from low-yielding single vyds, fruit selected to focus/reflect the lime-rich 'kalkveld' terroir; barrelled ±18 mths. Persistence & seamlessness are keynotes reflected in current (reviewed) **00**. Scented spice nose & red stone-fruit flavours; fairly muscular. 14% alc. More intense, vinous than unflamboyant **99**.

★★★★ **Kalkveld Syrah American Oak Matured** Current **99** developing glowing-ember smoke interest, blue-black/loganberry richness broods in still-youthful tannin frame. No gauche Am oak sweetness (although 100% new). No **00**. 14% alc.

★★★★ **Kalkveld 'Hill of Enon' Shiraz** 🆕 Sample 'small berry pick' — yielding minuscule 2 t/ha — **03** dominated by billowing oak vanilla mid-2004, exciting spicy fruit in soft, creamy finish. Delicious young, promises great future. New Am oak. 13.5% alc.

★★★☆ **Shiraz** Fruit-focused but not opulent, blowsy style. **02** shows wood-smoke, white pepper tinges to well-toned mouthful; fruit, oak, acid & 14% alc all in unison, no clashing cymbals to measured finish. **01** weightier. Seasoned barrels.

★★★☆ **Chardonnay** ✓ Standout **03** (★★★★) retasted: golden hue, stony ring to fresh brioche nose; almond & coconut on palate lifted by striking mineral tang. Fermented 30% new Fr casks. 14% alc. Chardonnay-du-Monde 2004 gold.

Cogmans Kloof Shiraz Export label discontinued.

Astonvale range

Sauvignon Blanc ☺ ★★★ **04** bristles with bluegum/asparagus, fresh fillip to firm finish. Aperitif, lunchtime pick-me-up, 11.9% alc. **Crème** ☺ ★★★ **04** refreshing, poolside medley of fruity colombard & tropical sauvignon. Dry; genteel 12% alc.

Shiraz ★★★ **00** Very attractive, dusty/savoury interest to firm but yielding mouthful; unwooded, bottle matured. 13.6% alc. **Old Paddock Cabernet Sauvignon-Shiraz** ★★★ Easy-drinking, 50/50 mix **00** not retasted. No further releases to date. **Ruby Cabernet** ★★★ Unwooded **03** stewed fruits & cinnamon, with earthy, sweet finish. 13.8% alc. **Chardonnay** ★★★ 'Wild' individuality; mature **03**, honeysuckle, almonds & substantial alc (14%). Drink up. **Férent** ★★★ **03** off-dry colombard/chardonnay, no **04**. — *DS*

Zandwijk see Kleine Draken
Zantsi see Darling Cellars
Zaximus see Citrusdal Cellars
Zebra Collection see Rooiberg
Zellerhof see Huguenot Wine Farmers

Zevenwacht

Stellenbosch ▪ Est 1800 ▪ 1stB 1983 ▪ Tasting & sales Mon-Fri 8.30-5 Sat/Sun 9.30-5 ▪ Fee R17 ▪ Closed Dec 25 ▪ Tours by appt ▪ Restaurant & picnics daily (see Eat-out section) ▪ Luxury country inn, vineyard cottages & self-catering chalet ▪ Conferences/banqueting ▪ Tourgroups ▪ Children's play park ▪ Farm produce ▪ Conservation area ▪ 4×4 trail ▪ Owner Harold Johnson ▪ Winemaker Karl Lambour, with Jacques Viljoen (both Jan 2000) ▪ Viti adviser Kevin Watt (Jan 2001) ▪ 200 ha (cab, merlot, pinotage, shiraz, chenin, sauvignon) ▪ ±1 000 tons 65 000 cs 50/50 red/white ▪ PO Box 387 Kuils River 7579 ▪ info@zevenwacht. co.za ▪ www.zevenwacht.co.za © **903·5123** ☎ 903·3373

'The longest, most mixed-up harvest I've ever worked,' says Karl Lambour of 2004. Yet individual parcels of grapes proved remarkable, the winemaker says. Aromatic sauvignon reminiscent of 97; a rich, almost oily wine from one chardonnay block; an exceptional viognier (bought in); shiraz and merlot that shone. (With said chardonnay and viognier earmarked for the lower-priced Tin Mine blend, it's understandable why Lambour reckons Zevenwacht over-delivers at its price-point.) To highlight a style-change for the flagship range (riper picking, only free-run juice), a striking new front-label has been launched. Lambour is looking forward to 2005: new farm manager Phillip Myburgh's attention to aesthetics/vineyard management augurs well; as does new cheesemaker André Kruger — his commitment to hygiene and precision 'has paved the way to increased awareness of the same in our cellar'.

★★★★ **Syrah** ('Shiraz' in pvs ed.) A standout, especially **02** bearing new label & with 13% Mbury zinfandel. Heady roast pimento & gentian evoke Rhône styling, excellent delivery in finish, despite potentially loud occupants, including 14% alc. **01** intense spicy warmth to rich plum, round tannins. Now 40% new Fr oak, 10% new Am.

★★★★ **Cabernet Sauvignon** Still current **01** (★★★★) minerally, restrained; leafy/vegetal notes to dry tannins, finishes trifle hard. Yr Fr oak, 30% new. **00** more fruit-driven.

★★★★ **Merlot** ✓ Serious treatment (14 mths 60% new Fr oak), serious result. **02** deftly integrated contributions from succulent red berry fruit, fine-grained tannins, a fresh seam of acid & 14% alc, polished by dark-choc weight. Curvaceous **01** commenced step-up from pvs in 'more of everything' mode.

★★★★ **Pinotage** 'Awesome' suggests cellarmaster of first offering from virus-purged vines. **03** (★★★★) glistening black cherry & wild berry/liquorice; unambiguous composite reigned in by firm tannins. Yr 2nd fill Fr oak. 13.5% alc. More balanced than beefier (14.2% alc) **02**'s green banana whiffs, heavy tannin grip.

★★★★ **The Tin Mine Red** Partner of white blend below, maiden **03** shiraz, merlot, cab (51/26/23) melange offers structure & grip without overt varietal character, as well as relatively keen pricing. 50/50 Am:Fr oak. 14.6% alc.

★★★★ **The Tin Mine White** ✓ (Pvs Tin Mine label included once-off **01** Chenin Blanc.) Enterprise of miners operating on the property in early 20th century reflected in both name & innovative contents. Tank-fermented sauvignon & barrelled chardonnay, viognier (77/18/5) melded into striking balance of **03**. Herbaceous scrub characters fleshed out by ample, & scented, fruits. Refreshingly moderate 12.5% alc.

★★★★ **Gewürztraminer** 'Extreme gewürz,' ventures Lambour. Striking package (Alsatian elegance) at a premium price. **03** (★★★★★) raises goose-flesh: a censer of potpourri, great texture, finely structured. Super now, likely to develop extra complexity over 2-3 yrs. Like **02**, fragrant passionfruit & honeysuckle melange. Single vyd, barrel-fermented/on lees 6 mths, 14% alc, bone dry.

★★★★ **Sauvignon Blanc** 'The best sauvignon grapes I've worked with,' says Karl L of **04**: a sleeper on release; substantial grip of structure suggests *fynbos* scrub tones with mineral tints likely to come out to play over next yr. **03** (★★★★) gear up on pvs, similar herbal whiffs lead to tangy grapefruit palate. 13% alc.

Zevenrood ☺ ★★★ **02** no-nonsense value: baked plum aromas, solid chewy red berry fruit unobscured by tannins. Pleasant, versatile shiraz/cab blend, dash merlot; 10 mths oak. 13.5% alc. **Bouquet Blanc** ☺ ★★★ **03** off-dry charmer, aromatic marriage equal parts gewürz, riesling with honeysuckle girth, more substantial than pvs.

Zevenblanc ★★★ A duo of blancs, sauvignon & chenin, revamped with **03**; former partner dominant with herbal scrub, latter brings flesh to bear. Refreshingly dry. **Chenin Blanc** ★★★ **04** quiet nose, rich fruity palate unhinged by 14.5% alc. 25% barrel-fermented/aged. Discontinued: **Cabernet Sauvignon-Merlot**; **Chardonnay**. — DS

Zidela Wines

Stellenbosch ▪ Est 2001 ▪ 1stB 2002 ▪ Closed to public ▪ Owners/winemaker: see intro ▪ 50% red 50% white ▪ Export brands: Suikerbosch & Gordon's Bay ▪ PO Box 3021 Matieland 7602 ▪ info@zidelawines.co.za ▪ www.zidelawines.co.za ✆ 880·2936 🖷 880·2937

Danie Kritzinger and Herman Nell are joint owners of this wine services company (Zidela, from the Zulu, meaning to give of oneself to help others), now with its own ranges of wines. Stuart Buchan, Distillers-seasoned like Kritzinger, brings his considerable marketing skills to the venture which he recognises as a challenge, given that the company is launching into 'a world market flooded with wines and labels'. The winemaker is Danie K's eldest son, Jaco.

Shiraz ★★★ Unwooded **03** with elegant allspice, ground pepper whiffs, & raspberry-fruited palate gently supported by light tannins, comfortable 13.8% alc. WO W-Cape (Rbtsn fruit) as is... **Cabernet Sauvignon-Merlot** ★★ Boiled sweet, ripe blackcurrant notes on 60/40 blend **02**, seems light, rather insubstantial despite 13.3% alc; this too without oak support. Also two **04** whites untasted by us: **Sauvignon Blanc**, **Chenin Blanc**. — MF

Zomerlust

Carefree quaffers in 500ml and 2/5ℓ packs by Robertson Winery for Vinimark.

All agreeably light (±11% alc unless mentioned), NV. **Dry Red** ★★ Easy-drinking *vin ordinaire*; fruity, with light tannins. **Blanc de Blanc** Untasted. **Stein** ★★ Honeyed semi-sweet with gentle tropical tone. **Late Harvest** ★★ Similar to Stein, slightly richer. — DH

Zondernaam

These wines may be 'Without name', but certainly not without cachet. They are made at the big-budget Tokara Winery on Helshoogte by Miles Mossop (Gyles Webb, of neighbouring Thelema, in an advisory role), from Tokara grapes and selected vineyards further afield. While uncompromising selection has seen no wines released under the Tokara label, punters should look here for second-brand wines at surprisingly reasonable prices.

★★★★ **Cabernet Sauvignon** ✓ Re-visited **01** gaining in flesh & complexity; additional bouillon dimension to cedar/cassis; accessible yet with vibrancy for further 3-4 yrs; savoury dryness enhances overall graceful, serious demeanour, nullifies big 14.3% alc. Own (Tokara), Devon Vlly vyds. 35% new Fr oak, 18 mths.

★★★★ **Pinotage** ✓ Extra yr has expanded savoury sophistication of **01**. Refined, textured wine, more vinous than fruity. Splash cab strengthens backbone. Diners Club Winemaker of Yr finalist. Oaked 18 mths, ±15% Am, 40% new.

★★★★ **Shiraz** [NEW] **02** bears thumbprint seamless refinement, excellent oaking (14 mths, 30% new, some Am). Modern meaty, dark spice notes complement full body, gently-muscled texture; balanced freshness, grip & savoury finish enhance finesse. Exceptionally drinkable; further ±3 yr staying power. Grapes ex-Warwick.

★★★★ **Chardonnay 03** first from 100% home vyds; careful oaking plays up delicate, young-vine fruit; pickled lime/lemon zest, buttered toast hints; bright, succulent flavours, with weight, freshness balancing 14.5% alc. Fermented/10 mths Burgundy barrels, 25% new. **02** (★★★★) delicate fruit, beautifully judged oak/lees.

★★★★ **Chenin Blanc** [NEW] Barrel-fermented **03**, pleasant mellowing notes reflected in palish-gold hue. Big, broad-based; quite luscious, though dry; botrytis-brushed, floral, honeyed filling in tandem with toasty oak. Bought-in Stbosch grapes; natural ferment; 18% new oak. 14.5% alc.

★★★★ **Sauvignon Blanc** ✓ After agreeable **03**, **04** showing variety's zesty best. Cascade ripe gooseberries/figs; bouncy & rich with pulsating thread cool acid. 60/40 mix Hldrberg/Paarl/Vdorp & home vyds.—*AL*

Zonnebloem

Stellenbosch ▪ *Owner Distell* ▪ *Cellar manager Callie van Niekerk (1972)* ▪ *Winemakers Michael Bucholz (reds, Dec 2000) & Louw Engelbrecht (whites, Feb 2001), with Justin Corrans & Deon Boshoff (Dec 2001/Jan 2002)* ▪ *Viticulturist Henk van Graan (Jan 1996)* ▪ *9 000 tons ±220 000 cs 59% red 41% white* ▪ *PO Box 46 Stellenbosch 7599* ▪ *www. zonnebloem.co.za* ℂ **808·7911** ℂ **883·2603**

This is the André Agassi of the wine brands in the Distell portfolio: a little more mature (actually somewhat older than the tennis star at 60, but it doesn't show), appreciated and respected by those in the know, always impeccably behaved. And still able to do the business, thanks to the unflashy Michael Bucholz (reds) and Louw Engelbrecht (whites), and their seconds Justin Corrans and Deon Boshoff. 'Zonnebloem', say its creators, 'is accessible and easy on release, but also shows varietal character, and in the case of the reds, lasts for 5–10 years.' So the familiar, angst-free styling continues, along with realistic pricing. Fans will be pleased and reassured.

★★★★ **Cabernet Sauvignon** Impressive quality for commercially successful label; **02** less forthcoming on nose, but palate handsomely cloaked in dark mulberry ripeness, contrasts with fine-grained dry tannins, lingering dry finish. 14.1% alc. **01** retasted mid-2004, muscular & firm but generously flavoured, dry tannic comeback on finish. 14.3% alc. Over 50% oaked, balance staves.

★★★★ **Merlot** One of the more attractive versions, **02** (★★★★) understated appeal, good dark choc taste, softish tannins but the vintage strikes again. 13.6% alc. Only 55% oaked. Firmer (no less likeable) **01** had a minty edge.

★★★★ **Pinotage** ✓ Stalwart of range, savoury **02** (★★★★), hints of varietal redcurrant, lighter than previous, victim of difficult vintage, still some sleekness, shows hallmark drinkability. 55% barrel-aged, mixture of oak. **01** ripe, already accessible.

★★★★ **Shiraz** ✓ Latest **02** (★★★★) some depth & well-groomed dark berries, supple & inviting, supportive oak. 13.2% alc. **01** firmish tannins well balanced by excellent dark-berried fruits, fine oak & whiff varietal woodsmoke.

★★★★★ **Lauréat 02** (★★★★) sleek & refined, rather more classic cab-led blend with same varieties as **01**. Distinct claret flavour & feel, some pleasing plumpness, but also some the vintage's austerity. **01** was first to include shiraz with familiar Bdx varieties (cabs s/f, merlot, malbec, petit v) for stylish, pinotage-free attempt at a 'Cape blend'. Retaste mid-2004 ripe fruit, intriguing scrub fragrance, tiny sprig mint; seamless melding of smooth, sleek flavours. 14.2% alc. 10 mths oak, equal parts 1st-3rd fill, all Fr. Good maturation prospects over 4-6 yrs.

★★★★ Chardonnay ✓ Has definitely put on weight since last year: **03** full flavoured, lime marmalade edge to citrusy fruit & toasty notes to oak, but mouthwatering, fresh, with creamy length. 13.9% alc. **02**, attractive despite difficult yr. More cruiser- than heavy-weight. These ±50% fermented/aged new casks, mix oak/coopers.

Blanc de Blanc ☺ **★★★** Enduring favourite, **04** deliciously soft & accessible chenin/sauvignon. Fresh green apple, touch tropical lime; slender build, ideal lunchtime drink. Best young. **Premier Grand Cru** ☺ **★★★** Light summer tipple, ever delightful, with fresh citrus tang, bone-dry. Lighter still in **04** at 12% alc. Colombard/chenin (50/50).

Sauvignon Blanc ★★★ 04 whiff gentle gooseberry; tangy, bone-dry. 12.7% alc. Fine Art range discontinued, last were **Shiraz Malbec** & **Cabernet Sauvignon-Shiraz**. — *IvH*

Zonneweelde see Slanghoek

Zorgvliet Wines

Stellenbosch ▪ Est/1stB 2000 ▪ Tasting & sales Nov-Apr: Mon-Thu 9-5 Fri 9-6 Sat 10-7 Sun 10-5 May-Oct: Mon-Fri 9-5 Sat 10-3 Public holidays Jan-Dec 10-3 ▪ Fee R10 ▪ Closed Easter Fri, Dec 25 ▪ Herenhuis 1692 Restaurant Sep-Apr: Mon-Sat 9-11 Sun 9-5 May, Jun, Aug (closed Jul): Wed/Fri/Sat 9-11 Sun 9-5 ✆ 885·2580 ▪ Le Pommier Restaurant & Country Lodge: see separate entry ▪ Cellar tours by appt ▪ Facilities for children ▪ Gifts ▪ Conferencing ▪ Banhoek Vineyard Lodge ✆ 885·1791 ▪ Owners Mac & Marietjie van der Merwe ▪ Winemaker Bruwer Raats, with Neil Moorhouse (Aug 2002/Jan 2003) ▪ Farm managers Essie van Heerden & Rudolf Jansen van Vuuren, advised by Kevin Watt ▪ 70 ha (cabs s/f, merlot, shiraz, chard, sauvignon, semillon, viognier) ▪ 380 tons 12 000 cs own label 70% red 25% white 5% rosé ▪ PO Box 1595 Stellenbosch 7599 ▪ info@zorgvliet.com ▪ www.zorgvlietwines.co.za ✆ 885·1399 🖷 885·1318

'Let your sorrows flee' is the meaning of the name of this revitalised spread in the Banhoek area, owned by entrepreneur Mac van der Merwe and his wife Marietjie. 'Amazement' rather than sorrow last year, as vine-minders Essie van Heerden and Rudolf Jansen van Vuuren recorded the latest harvest date (May 1) since their founding in 2000. The 500-ton cellar is complete, and winemakers Bruwer Raats and Neil Moorhouse now enjoy generous barrel maturation facilities. 'Spend as much time in our vineyards as possible', is their maxim. 'Don't try to force anything. And don't lose touch with what people like to drink.' They certainly haven't: their local fan base is expanding, and they assure they will first serve this market before they venture abroad.

Silver Myn range

- **★★★★☆ Cabernet Franc 03** wonderfully expressive, big, dark nose with tickly pepper; cedar, blackberry & blueberry explode on palate — well balanced in spite of 14.5% alc. 14 mths oak, third new. Will benefit from ±5 yrs' cellaring.
- **★★★★ Petit Verdot** Characterful **03** mixes in 15% merlot, with spice & white pepper; firm palate with tannins galore, but finishes a bit short. Massive 15% alc. 14 mths older oak, none new. Should keep 5+ years.
- **★★★☆ Merlot-Cabernet Franc 03** 57/43 blend offers spicy nose & elegant cab f flavours; let down by jammy element. Hefty 14.8% alc. 14 mths oak, third new.
- **★★★☆ Sauvignon Blanc** Pineapple, grapefruit peek out of a basket of tropical fruit in **04**. Lingering crisp flavours. 13.5% alc. WO W-Cape.

Cabernet Sauvignon ★★★ Shy nose, typical black fruit flavours but **03** more over-extracted than deeply rich. Yet another enormous alc: 14.6%. 14 mths oak, third new.
Shiraz ★★ 03 with admixture of 15% cab. Barnyardy aromas, plus disturbing metallic character. Rather out of balance. 13.6% alc. 14 mths in wood, third new. **02** FCTWS gold.
Chardonnay ★★ 04 showing vegetal, cabbagey notes, a little stale & flabby. 14% alc. WO Coastal.

Spring Grove range
★★★★ **Viognier** NEW Flowers & fruit aromas on **04**, but not over-perfumed. Fine, dry finish. Typically, not for maturation: drink within yr/2. 13.3% alc.
★★★★ **Shiraz 02** leathery nose & palate, perked with peppery spices. 14 mths oak, third new; 13.8% alc. In same showy style as very ripe **01**. – *NP*

A-Code Numbers

Many wines appear on the market under brand names, with, at first glance, no reference to their producers or purveyors. However, consumers need not buy 'blind', and may trace a wine's provenance by checking the official 'A-number' which appears on the bottle or pack. This identity code tells you either who has produced the wine, or who has acquired it. In the latter case, an enquiry to the purveyor should elicit the source. The list keeps growing and being revised, and the version below is the latest supplied by the National Department of Agriculture, Liquor Products Division. For the further information contact Marian Honing, marianh@nda.agric.za ✆ 809·1687 🖷 887·6396/2.

Bdale = **Barrydale** B/West = **Beaufort West** Bville = **Bellville** Bfn = **Bloemfontein** Bspruit = **Bronkhorstspruit** Bkfl = **Brackenfell** Bnvale = **Bonnievale** Cdorp = **Calitzdorp** Citrd = **Citrusdal** Constia = **Constantia** CT = **Cape Town** Dbnville = **Durbanville** Dbn = **Durban** EL = **East London** Frhoek = **Franschhoek** Fgrv = **Firgrove** G/Bay = **Gordon's Bay** Gwood = **Goodwood** Grt Drknstn = **Groot Drakenstein** Hmsdrp = **Humansdorp** H/Hse = **Halfway House** Jnb = **Johannesburg** Kdorp = **Krugersdorp** Khof = **Koelenhof** K/River = **Kuils River** Kvoogds = **Klaasvoogds** Kim = **Kimberley** K/Gdns = **Killarney Gardens** K/Park = **Kempton Park** Kpmuts = **Klapmuts** KDorpN = **Krugersdorp North** Ldoch = **Lynedoch** L/Ridge = **Lynnwood Ridge** Mbury = **Malmesbury** M/gdns = **Montague Gardens** Mvlei = **Muldersvlei** Mtgu = **Montagu** N/Paarl = **Noorder-Paarl** Ouh = **Oudtshoorn** Pville = **Porterville** Plet = **Plettenberg Bay** PE = **Port Elizabeth** Pta = **Pretoria** Pmb = **Pietermaritzburg** Rbg = **Randburg** Rbktl = **Riebeek Kasteel** Rbtson = **Robertson** Rville = **Rawsonville** Stbosch = **Stellenbosch** S/Paarl = **Suider-Paarl** Sville = **Sinoville** S/West = **Somerset West** Smdm = **Simondium** T/Valley = **Tyger Valley** Tbgh = **Tulbagh** Utn = **Upington** Vdal = **Vredendal** Vdorp = **Villiersdorp** Vng = **Vereeniging** Vltburg = **Vlottenburg** Wdville = **Wadeville** Wllngtn = **Wellington** Wstr = **Worcester**

Code

A001-A017 Cancelled **A018** E W Sedgwick & Co, CT **A019** Gordon's Dry Gin Company, Wdville **A020-A022 A024 A027-A028 A030-A031 A033-A039 A041-A044** Distell, Stbosch **A023** Bergkelder, Stbosch **A025** Drostdy Winery, Stbosch **A026** Castle Wine & E K Green, Stbosch **A029** Henry C Collins & Sons, Stbosch **A032** Paarl Wine & Brandy Co, Stbosch **A040** Durbanville Hills Wines, Dbnvlle **A045** Martell & Cie (SA), CT **A046** Cancelled **A047** Erven Lucas Bols, CT **A048** Zonnebloem Wines, Stbosch **A049-A055 A057-A058** Distell, Stbosch **A056** Plaisir de Merle, Stbosch **A059** Cancelled **A060** JC Botha, Wllngtn **A061 A078** DGB, Wllngtn **A062 A082** Kersaf Investments, Rbg **A063-A067 A079** Guinness UDV SA, T/ Valley **A068-A077** Distell, Stbosch **A080 A083 A085 A087** Cancelled **A081** Henry Taylor & Ries, Florida **A084** Ladismith Co-Op, Ladismith **A086** Saxenburg Wine Farm, K/River **A088** Natal Wholesale Wine & Spirit Merchants, Dur **A089** Distell, Stbosch **A090-A094** Cancelled **A095** Kanu Vineyards, Stbosch **A096** Superior Imports, CT **A097** Boland Vineyards, Paarl **A098** Rustenberg, Stbosch **A099** Mooiuitsig Wine Cellars, Bnvale **A100** KWV, S/Paarl **A101 A126 A128 A133 A153 A178** Cancelled **A102** Culemborg Winery, Wllngtn **A103** Cancelled **A104** Jonkheer Farmers Winery, Bnvale **A105** Langeberg Associated Wineries, Rbtsn **A106** Anglo American Farms, Grt Drknstn **A107** Blue Ridge Vineyards, Khof **A108** Cancelled **A109** Cancelled **A110** Simonsig, Khof **A111** Mecklenberg, Jnb **A112** Cancelled **A113** E Snell & Co, Isando **A114-A115** Drop Inn Group, Plumstead **A116** DGB, Midrand **A117** Cancelled **A118** South Western Tvl Agricultural Co-Op, Jacobsdal **A119** Cancelled **A120** Romansrivier Wine Cellars, Wolseley **A121** Boland Wine & Brandy Merchants, Paarl **A122** Cancelled **A123** StellenHills, Vltburg **A124** Rooiberg, Rbtsn **A125** Fairview, S/Paarl **A129** Simondium Wine Cellars, Smdm **A130** Kanonkop, M/Vlei **A131** Koelenhof Winery, Khof **A132** Constantia Negociants, Garden View **A134** Weltevrede, Bnvale **A135** Simonsvlei, S/Paarl **A136** Roodezandt, Rbtsn **A137** Backsberg, Kmuts **A138**

Retief Bros, Kvoogds **A139** Bottelary Winery, Khof **A140** Stellenbosch Vineyards, Ldoch **A141** Bainskloof Wine Cellar, Breërivier **A142** Hartswater Wine Cellar, Hartswater **A143** Hamilton Russell Vineyards, Hermanus **A144** Swartland Winery, Mbury **A145** Spruitdrift Wine Cellar, Vdal **A146** Cancelled **A147** Perdeberg Wine Farmers, Paarl **A148** Badsberg Wine Cellar, Rville **A149** Groenkloof Wholesalers, Darling **A150** Slanghoek Wine Cellar, Rville **A151** Landskroon, S/Paarl **A152** Nuy Wine Cellars, Nuy **A154** Botha Wine Cellar, Wstr **A155** Goudini Wine Cellar, Rville **A156** Blaauwklippen Agric Estates, Stbosch **A157** Brandvlei Wine Cellar, Wstr **A158** Aan de Doorns Winery, Wstr **A159** Merwida Winery, Rville **A160** Barrydale Winery, Bdale **Frhoek** Drie Berge Farm Cellar, Mtgu **A162** Lievland, Kmuts **A163** Louwshoek Winery, Rville **A164** Picardi Liquors, CT **A165** Allied Shippers, Isando **A166** Tulbagh Winery, Tbgh **A167** Waboomsrivier Winery, Wstr **A168** Cancelled **A169** Whitby Distillers & Liquor Wholesalers, Grabouw **A170** Southern Cape Vineyards (Boplaas), Cdorp **A171** Aufwaerts Winery, Rville **A172** Wellington Wine Farmers, Wllngtn **A173** Neethlingshof, Stbosch **A174** Kango Co-Op, Ouh **A175** Franschhoek Vineyards, Frhoek **A176** Cancelled **A177** Bon Courage, Rbtsn **A179** Rietrivier Winery, Mtgu **A180-181 A183 A199** Cancelled **A182** Stark-Condé, Stbosch **A184** Douglas Co-Op, Douglas **A185** Ashton Winery, Ashton **A186** Le Grand Chasseur, Rbtsn **A187** Du Toitskloof Winery, Rville **A188** Calitzdorp Fruit & Winery Co- Op, Cdorp **A189** Montpellier du Sud, Tbgh **A190** Danie de Wet (De Wetshof), Rbtsn **A191** Eikendal Vineyards, Stbosch **A192** Kaapzicht, Stbosch **A193** North West Liquor Merchants, Vdal **A194** Stettyn Winery, Wstr **A195** J Parker, Dbnvlle **A196** Baumker's Hotel (Alexander Hotel), Caledon **A197** Woolworths, CT **A198** Namakwaland Winery, Klawer **A200** Zevenwacht, K/River **A201** Team Liquor World, Pinetown **A202** Opstal, Rville **A203** Mouton Excelsior, Frhoek **A204** De Wet Winery, De Wet **A205** Simonsig Sales (Coastal Wines), Khof **A206** Die Krans, Cdorp **A207** Kersaf Investments, Rbg **A208** CJ Meyer & Son, Ouh **A209** Whitby Distillers & Liquor Wholesaler, Grabouw **A210** Lutzville Vineyards, Lutzville **A211** De Doorns Winery, De Doorns **A212** Stellenbosch Vineyards, Vltburg **A213** Buitenverwachting, Constia **A214** Soetwyn Farmers, Mtgu **A215** Winkelshoek Winery, Eendekuil **A216-A217** Cancelled **A219** Chasapy (Hotel Brandwacht), Wstr **A219** Porterville Cellar, Pville **A220** Rhine Ruhr Holdings (Morgenhof), Stbosch **A221** Stellenbosch Vineyards, Fgrv **A222 A226 A229 A231-233 A235** Cancelled **A223** Citrusdal Liquor Merchants, Citrd **A224** Citrusdal Winery, Citrd **A225** Vredendal Winery, Vdal **A227** McGregor Winery, Rbtsn **A228** Agterkliphoogte Winery, Rbtsn **A230** Groot Eiland Winery, Rville **A234** Uiterwyk, Vltburg **A236** Wamakersvallei Winery, Wllngtn **A237** Cancelled **A238** Saxenburg Wine Farm, K/River **A239** Montagu Winery, Mtgu **A240** Delaire Wines, Stbosch **A241** Klawer Winery, Klawer **A242** Makro, Jnb **A243** Van Riebeeck Cellars, Wllngtn **A244** Rozendal Farm, Stbosch **A245** Pinetown Bottle Store, Pinetown **A246** Oranjerivier Winery, Utn **A247** Rooiberg Liquor Merchants, K/River **A248 A249 A251 A253 A256** Cancelled **A250** Riebeeck Wine Farmers, Rbktl **A252** Clos Cabrière, Frhoek **A254** Domein Doornkraal, De Rust **A255** Cape Vintners, Stbosch **A257** Vredenheim, Stbosch **A259** Cancelled **A260** Bovlei Winery, Wllngtn **A261 A263-A267 A269 A271 A273-274** Cancelled **A262** Trawal Winery, Klawer **A264-7** Cancelled **A268** Delheim Wines, Khof **A270** Villiersdorp Moskonfyt & Fruit Co-Op, Vdorp **A272** Zandwijk, Paarl **A275** Hartenberg, Khof **A276** Highveld Bottle Store, Ermelo **A277** Cancelled **A278** Rust & Vrede, Stbosch **A279** Vinimark, Stbosch **A280** Robertson Winery, Rbtsn **A281-284 A286 A288** Cancelled **A285** Rhebokskloof, Windmeul **A287** Onverwacht, Wllngtn **A289** Du Toit Bros, Herold **A290** Distell, Stbosch **A291-A293** Cancelled **A294** OK Bazaar, Jnb **A295** Cancelled **A296** Klein Constantia, Constia **A297-A298** Cancelled **A299** ES Ratcliffe (Warwick), M/Vlei **A300** Cancelled **A301** Glen Garlou Vineyards, Kmuts **A302** Cancelled **A303** Overgaauw, Vltburg **A304** De Wet Bros, Ashton **A305** Cancelled **A306** Karoo Wine Distributors, Cradock **A307** La Rochelle Wine Depot, Bnvale **A308** Constantia Nek Restaurant, Constia **A309** Cancelled **A310** Beyerskloof, Khof **A311** Kaapsche Wijn & Brandewijn, Stbosch **A312** Cancelled **A313** JP Coetzee (Bloemendal), Dbnvlle **A314** Diemersdal Farmers, Dbnvlle **A315** Cancelled **A316** McLeod's Wines & Spiritis, N/Paarl **A317-A319** Cancelled **A320** Overhex Winery, Wstr **A321** Twee Jonge Gezellen, Tbgh **A322** NMK Schultz, Jnb **A323** Muratie Wine

Farm, Khof **A324** Avontuur Winery, S/West **A325** Neil Ellis Wines, Stbosch **A326** JPW Jonker, Albertinia **A327** Merwespont Winery, Bnvale **A328** De Lucque & Dieu Donne Vineyards, Frhoek **A329** Hemel-en-Aarde, Hermanus **A330** Prof RK Belcher, S/Paarl **A331** Clos Malverne, Stbosch **A332** Groot Constantia, Constia **A333** AH Pillmann, Botrivier **A334** Pick 'n Pay Hypermarket, Bkfl **A335** Big Daddy's, Centrahill **A336-A340** Cancelled **A341** R Fehlmann, Tbgh **A342** JRC Jorgensen, Wllngtn **A343** Cancelled **A344** Kangra Holdings, Rbtsn **A345** Cancelled **A346** EBR Products, S/Paarl **A347** Breeriver Valley Wine Distributors, Wstr **A348** Aan de Doorns Winery, Wstr **A349** Mulderbosch Vineyards, Stbosch **A350** Montestell, Stbosch **A351** Villiersdorp Liquor Merchants, Vdorp **A352** Bordelais Distributors, Wittebome **A353** Mooivallei Wines, Wstr **A354** Eikehof Wines, Frhoek **A355** Tollgate Vintners, Wynberg **A356** Cancelled **A357** Lateganskop Winery, Breërivier **A358** DSA Liquor Wholesalers, H/Hse **A359** Rob's Liquor, EL **A360** Aroma Fine Wine Centre, Bkfl **A361-A362** Cancelled **A363** Anglo American Farms, Grt Drknstn **A364** Longridge, Stbosch **A365** Cancelled **A366** HSJ Coetzee, Ficksburg **A367** Klein Gustrouw, Stbosch **A368-A370** Cancelled **A371** Vinfruco, Stbosch **A372** Cancelled **A373** Wine Warehouse, CT **A374** Cancelled **A375** Vinicor International Wine & Spirit, Howard **A376** Vriesenhof, Stbosch **A377** Grangehurst Winery, Ldoch **A378-A380** Cancelled **A381** African Terroir, Stbosch **A382** Hazendal, Stbosch **A383** Manikas Trading, Brixton **A384** Bacchus Bros, Newlands **A385** Niblock Properties, Elgin **A386** Fredericksburg, Smdm **A387** Diamant, S/Paarl **A388-A391** Cancelled **A392** SA Cultural History Museum, Rayton **A393** Wine of the Month Club, Constia **A394** The Hyperama, Jnb **A395** Cancelled **A396** Robertson Winery, Rbtsn **A397** Watergang, Khof **A398** L'Avenir, Stbosch **A399** Cape Chamonix, Frhoek **A400** Constantia Uitsig, Constia **A401** Zanddrift, Frhoek **A402** Louisvale, Stbosch **A403** Worcester Museum, Wstr **A404** Goedverwacht, Bnvale **A405-A406** Cancelled **A407** La Petite Ferme, Frhoek **A408** Nietvoorbij, Stbosch **A409** Cancelled **A410** Alternative Beverage Corp, Malvern East **A411** Northside Packing & Marketing, Ventersdorp **A412** Jordan Vineyards, Vltburg **A413** Cancelled **A414** Trauve Estates, Frhoek **A415** Napier Winery, Wllngtn **A416** Cancelled **A417** Spier Winery, Stbosch **A418** Paddagang Vignerons, Tbgh **A419** Cancelled **A420** Wine Industries International, Airport Industria **A421** Cape Bay Wines, Hermanus **A422** Haute Provence Vineyards, Frhoek **A423** DD Wholesalers, Lions River **A424** Von Ortloff, Frhoek **A425** Van Zylshof, Bnvale **A426-A427** Cancelled **A428** Mont Fleur, Stbosch **A429-430** Northside Packing & Marketing, Ventersdorp **A431** Windmeul Co-Op, Windmeul **A432-A433** Cancelled **A434** Veenwouden, N/Paarl **A435** Simonsvlei Liquor Merchants, S/Paarl **A436** JP Bredell Wines, Helderberg **A437** Shoprite Checkers, Parow **A438** Worcester Co-Op, Stbosch **A439-A440** Cancelled **A441** Albertinia Poort Farms, Albertinia **A442-A447** Cancelled **A448** Williston Liquor Wholesalers, Williston **A449** Mooiuitsig/Overberg Co-Op, Bnvale **A450** Sabasco Wholesalers, Jnb **A451** Môreson, Frhoek **A452** Hartswater Wine Cellar, Hartswater **A453-A457** Cancelled **A458** Bellmount Liquor Store, Ceres **A459** Huguenot Wine Farmers, Greyville **A460** Môreson, Frhoek **A461** La Motte, Paarl **A462** Morgenzon, Vltburg **A463** Cancelled **A464** Riverside Distillers, K/Park **A465** Grundheim Wines, Ouh **A466** Cancelled **A467** La Lucia Liquor Shop, La Lucia **A468** Cancelled **A469** Midmar Liquor Store, G/Wood **A470** Thelema Mountain Vineyards, Stbosch **A471** Cancelled **A472** Krugels Buiteverbruik, Lydenburg **A473** Allan Nelson Vineyard, Windmeul **A474-A475** Cancelled **A476** Bodega Farm, Khof **A477** Tanbee Properties, Khof **A478-A479** Cancelled **A480** Jacaranda, Wllngtn **A481** La Lucia Liquor Shop, La Lucia **A482** Somersbosch, Stbosch **A483** La Brie, Frhoek **A484** Cancelled **A485** Irina Botha, Rosebank **A486** Perdeberg Vineyards/Sonop Wine Farm, Windmeul **A487** Cancelled **A488** Jade Liquors, Atlantis **A489** Stellenbosch Wines Direct, Stbosch **A490** Springfield, Rbtsn **A491** Meerdendal, Dbnvlle **A492** Papegaaiberg Cellars, Windmeul **A493** Imandi Cellars, Windmeul **A494** Kersfontein Farm, Windmeul **A495** Beaumont Wines, Bot River **A496-497** Cancelled **A498** Excelsior Farm, Rville **A499** Ruitersvlei, S/Paarl **A500** Cancelled **A501** Pernod Ricard, Stbosch **A502** Penaltembe, Turffontein **A503** Goede Hoop, K/River **A504** Dawilla Mampoer, Pta **A505** Cancelled **A506** Steppe Buzzard Partners, Dbnvlle **A507** Cancelled **A508** Cape

Wine Cellars, Wllngtn **A509** Central Liquor Store, B/West **A510** M&M Liquor Cellars, Houghton **A511-A512** Cancelled **A513** Savanha Wines, CT **A514** Robertson Valley Wines, Stbosch **A515** Nampini Cellars, Bfn **A516** Coppoolse & Finlayson, Bkfl **A517** Cancelled **A518** L'Ormarins, S/Paarl **A519** Helderenberg, Stbosch **A520-A523** Cancelled **A524** Paarl Bottling Trust, Paarl **A525** Cancelled **A526** Watervliet Farm, Smdm **A527** Wilreza, Jacobsdal **A528** Cancelled **A529** DeWetshof, Rbtsn **A530** Steenberg Vineyards, Steenberg **A531-A532** Cancelled **A533** Steven Rom Liquor Merchants, CT **A534** Royal Africa Intnl, Pmb **A535-A536** Cancelled **A537** Langverwacht Cellar, Bnvale **A538** Van Nyathi, Falcon Ridge **A539** Nu-Ced Liquor Distributors, Hatfield **A540** Lemberg,Tbgh **A541-A542** Cancelled **A543** Marico Valley, Groot Marico **A544** Whalehaven Wines, Hermanus **A545** Simonstown Bottle Store, Simonstown **A546** Hawekwa Cellars, Wllngtn **A547** Cancelled **A548** Unique Wholesalers, Alexandria **A549** Etienne le Riche Wines, Stbosch **A550** Diamond Discount Liquor, Maitland **A551** Cancelled **A552** Rozendal Distillery, Stbosch **A553** Chapmans Peak Liquor Store, CT **A554** Exclusive Label & Liquor Gifts, Kocksvlei **A555** Wild Cape Liqueurs, S/West **A556** Cancelled **A557** Brown Forman Beverages, Rondebosch **A558** Cancelled **A559** Lanzerac Wines, Stbosch **A560** Klipspruit Farm Cellar, Leeudoringstad **A561** Fairseat Cellars, Kenilworth **A562** Cancelled **A563** Camberley Wines, Stbosch **A564** Cancelled **A565** Mooiplaas, K/River **A566-A567** Cancelled **A568** Hermitage Van Zyl Family Trust, Swellendam **A569** Mont Rochelle, Frhoek **A570-A572** Cancelled **A573** Amani Farm, Vltburg **A574** Bot River Hotel, Bot River **A575-577** Cancelled **A578** Good Success Farm, Stbosch **A579** Stilwaters Distributors **A580** Cancelled **A581** Stellenbosch Vineyards, Ldoch **A582** Elsenburg Wine Cellar, Stbosch **A583** Bonnievale Wine Cellar, Bnvale **A584** Cancelled **A585** Devonhill Winery, Stbosch **A586-A587** Cancelled **A588** Lebensraum/Deetlefs, Rville **A589-A591** Cancelled **A592** Bloupunt Wines, Mtgu **A593** Paul Cluver Wines, Grabouw **A594** Wine Direct, Rivonia **A595** Lost Horizons, Paarl **A596** Fort Simon, K/River **A597** De Villiers Wines, N/Paarl **A598** Boschkloof Cellar, Stbosch **A599** Happy Valley Farm, S/West **A600-A601** Cancelled **A602** Hoopenburg Wines, Stbosch **A603** Cancelled **A604** Du Preez Wines, Stbosch **A605** Kleine Zalze, Stbosch **A606** R Manson Trading, Steenberg **A607** D'em Distributors, H/Hse **A608-A611** Cancelled **A612** RJ Superior Liquors, Silverton **A613** Cancelled **A614** Oude Wellington, Wllngtn **A615** Green & Gold, Pta **A616-7** Cancelled **A618** Forresters Winery, Plet **A619-A620** Cancelled **A621** Cape Vineyards, Rville **A622** Barto Eksteen Wines, Hermanus **A623** Cancelled **A624** Philadelphia Liquor Suppliers, Klein Dassenberg **A625** Purlikur, Bville **A626** Cancelled **A627** Cape Vintages, S/West **A628** Ashanti, Klein Drakenstein **A629** Cape Viticultural Holdings, Khof **A630** Cancelled **A631** Withoek Cellar, Cdorp **A632** Cancelled **A633** De Meye Wines, Elsenburg **A634-A637** Cancelled **A638** Nobunto Liquor Wholesalers, Rville **A639** Helderfontein Mampoer, Pietersburg **A640** Somerset Wine & Spirit Company, S/West **A641** Perseverance Liquors, Swartkops **A642** Cancelled **A643** Remhoogte Wines, Stbosch **A644-A645** Cancelled **A646** Viljoensdrift Farm, Kvoogds **A647** Die Baken Farms, Wllngtn **A648** Tansiedor Een, Stbosch **A649** Awethu Liquor Wholesalers, Rivonia **A650-A651** Cancelled **A652** Peninsula Wine, Bville **A653** Duplenia Farms, Stbosch **A654** Spice Route Wine Company, Mbury **A655** Luca De Luca, Honeydew **A656-A660** Ready Tot, Honeydew **A661** Cancelled **A662** The Beverage Business, Westville **A663** Excelsius Wines, Vdal **A664** Middelvlei, Stbosch **A665** Clear Mountain Wines, Dennesig **A666** Niel Joubert, Kmuts **A667** Intra International Trading, Westlake **A668** South Western Free State Liquor Wholesalers, Jacobsdal **A669** Cancelled **A670** Rietrivier Distributors, Jacobsdal **A671** Bonnie Wines, Stbosch **A672** Haskins Bottle Store, Hmsdrp **A673** Flagstone, S/West **A674** Black Sheep Brewery, M/Gdns **A675** Diamonds Discount Liquor, Maitland **A676** Wine Concepts, CT **A677** Bonsteen Wholesalers, Bloubergsands **A678** Groene Cloof, Darling **A679** The Spar Group, Dbn **A680** Midmar Liquors, Parow **A681** Long Chan Distillers, Bfn **A682** Mijn-Burg Wines, Kmuts **A683** Calvinia Drankwinkel, Calvinia **A684** Mellasat Wine & Fruit, Paarl **A685** Cederberg Kelders, Clanwilliam **A686** African Wine & Spirits, Constia **A687** Nordale Winery, Bnvale **A688** Liquor Ranch Goodwood, G/Wood **A689** Die Kelder, Calvinia **A690** Cancelled **A691** Audacia Wines, Stbosch **A692** District Township Bottle

Store, K/DorpN **A693** Cancelled **A694** Parade Café, Stbosch **A695** Metro Cash & Carry, Jnb **A696** Hildenbrand Wines, Wllngtn **A697** Cancelled **A698** Mountain Range, CT **A699** Cancelled **A700** Wel d'Mer Winery, Stbosch **A701** Cancelled **A702** Hoopenburg Wines, Stbosch **A703** JBC Liquor Distributors, Bothasig **A704** Clos Du Toit, Wllngtn **A705** Darling Cellars, Darling **A706** Ben Nevis Cellar, Clocolan **A707** Frangelo, Jnb **A708** Roodezandt Winery, Rbtsn **A709** Silver Hill Wines, S/Paarl **A710** BSA Wholesale & Bottling, Midrand **A711** Pacific Distributors, CT **A712** Matlaplan Architects, Hatfield **A713** Old Rock Wine & Liquor Wholesalers, Roodepoort **A714** Eastern Cape Liquor, PE **A715** Akho Property Investments, Frhoek **A716** Paulinas Dal Farm Holdings, Frhoek **A717** ZS Wines, Plankenbrug **A718** Vintage Liquor Merchants, Centurion **A719** Retail Brands Interafrica, Wdville **A720** The House of Coffees, Jnb **A721** Drews Brew, Milnerton **A722** Free State Distillers, Fauresmith **A723** Starpack, Alberton North **A724** Southern Liquors, CT **A725** Oasis Liquor Wholesalers, Benoni **A726** Leebri Wholesalers, Jnb **A727** Windsor Discount Liquor, Windsor Glen **A728** De la Querre, Stbosch **A729** Fixtrade, Malvern **A730** Dyasonsklip Wine Cellar, Dyasonsklip **A731** Northern Natal Liquor Distributors, Newcastle **A732** The Avondale Trust, Paarl **A733** G&M Manufacturers, Prieska **A734** Bulmer SA, Centurion **A735** De Wet Cellars, Bfn **A736** Gewalisa Bottlers, Pinetown **A737** Kevin Kitley, Stbosch **A738** Rolon Beverages, Glendale **A739** Stormberg Trust, Wllngtn **A740** Cancelled **A741** Plodimex Liquor Wholesalers, Benoni **A742** Cancelled **A743** Breevallei Co-Op, Wstr **A744** Onderkloof, Sir Lowry's Pass **A745** Herberts Associated Berries, Kmtn Prk **A746** Cancelled **A747** Davnat Liquor Wholesalers, Jnb **A748** Mahers Bottling, George **A749** Donkerhoek Fruit Syndicate, Frhoek **A750** Klein Karoo Wines, Bdale **A751** Maiden Wines, Kmtn Prk **A752** Nicholson Smith Agencies, Rbg **A753** Bafana Wines, Dbnvlle **A754** Gants Wholesale Liquor, Strand **A755** Vaalharts Brewery, Hartswater **A756** Yonder Hill, S/West **A757** Winkelshoek Cellar, Piketberg **A758** Cancelled **A759** Wine Village, Hermanus **A760** Von Regen Wines/Geelkop, Keimoes **A761** Vendôme, Huguenot **A762** Handi-Pak, S/West **A763** Midlands Distillers, Pmb **A764** Cancelled **A765** Jordaan Bros/Theuniskraal Partnership, Tbgh **A766** Springbok Liquor Store, PE **A767** Cormard Spirit Blenders, New Germiston **A768** Hennie Reynecke, Kvoogds **A769** Central Liquor Store, Fraserburg **A770** Cancelled **A771** Black Sheep Beverage Distributors, M/Gdns **A772** Liq 'O' Mac, Utn **A773** Kapland Wines, G/Bay **A774** Cancelled **A775** New Cape Wines, Wstr **A776** Greeff's Liqueurs, Mowbray **A777** PR Kelder, Prieska **A778** Monate Citrus Cellar, Brits **A779** Tokara, Stbosch **A780** Diablo Trade 200, Jnb **A781** Bilton Wines, Ldoch **A782** Divan's McGregor Liquor, McGregor **A783** Cool Products, Pinetown **A784** Mafilas Liquor Stores, Jnb **A785** Swartland Wines, Mbury **A786-7** Cancelled **A788** Embiteni Wholesalers, Nelspruit **A789** CBC International Trading, Parow **A790** Millennium Liquors, K/Park **A791** Intombi Liqueurs & Fine Foods, Dbn **A792** Ultramix 21, CT **A793** Cancelled **A794** Cancelled **A795** Independent Liquor Marketers, Elandsfontein **A796** Thirsty Now Beverages, Centurion **A797** Hanzet Muti, Vredefort **A798** Emerald Glen Vineyards, Stbosch **A799** Esancha Liquors, Van Riebeeckstrand **A800** Verdun/Asara, Vltburg **A801** FC Distributors, Kim **A802** High Constantia, Constia **A803** Stellenbosch Bottling Co, Ldoch **A804** Appelsdrift Winery, Rbtsn **A805** Brenthurst Winery, S/Paarl **A806** Bowe Vineyards, Stbosch **A807** Myburgh Winery, M/Vlei **A808** De Heuvel, Tbgh **A809** Bernheim Winery, N/Paarl **A810** Mooreland Trading, Woodstock **A811** Meerlust Trust, Faure **A812** Lammershoek Cellar, Mbury **A813** Cancelled **A814** Meerhof Winery, Mbury **A815** Muldersvlei, Stbosch **A816** Leeuwvally Mampoer, Burgersfort **A817** Arctic Rivers, Boksburg **A818** Cancelled **A819** SLD Liquor Manufacturers, Epping **A820** Trackstar Trading, Paarl **A821** Vleiland Wines, Vdal **A822** Winco Trade Twenty Eight, M/gdns **A823** Agave Distillers, Graaff-Reinet **A824** Baarsma SA, Stbosch **A825** Shikari Fine Taste, Jhb **A826** Dellrust Wines, Fgrv **A827** Stelvest BK, Wllngtn **A828** Tindwa Distillers, Nylstroom **A829** Droogfontein, Kim **A830** Vilafonte Wine Farms, Kmuts **A831** Big 5 Wines, Thornton **A832** Havana Hill Cellar, Koeberg **A833** Sterhuis Trust, Bottelary **A834** Sands Traders, Bkfl **A835** Die Vlakte Boerdery, Rbtsn **A836** Cape Vintners International, CT **A837** Jasonsfontein, Rville **A838** Southern Cape Vineyards, Cdorp **A839** Spooky Mountain Vineyards, Frhoek **A840** South

African Breweries, Sandton **A841** Cancelled **A842** Tomorrow Wine Co, Dbnvlle **A843** Klompzicht, Frhoek **A844** Harvest Bottling, Midrand **A845** Wilgenhof, Vdal **A846** Grahamstown Wholesale Liquors, Grahamstown **A847** Ridder's Creek Wines, Wllngtn **A848** Cape Wine Works, Milnerton **A849** Spirits of Cape Town, Gwood **A850** Eilandtzicht, Thornton **A851** Jubilee Distillers, Vng **A852** Billsons Coutts, PE **A853** Keerweder (Franschhoek) Fhoek **A854** Clovelly Wines, Stbosch **A855** Cover Collections, Dieprivier **A856** Bay Export, Salt River **A857** M Jackson, Stanford **A858** Mountain River Wines, Paarl **A859** Garden Route Cellars, George **A860** Purple Rain, George **A861** Makadas Drankwinkel, Calvinia **A862** Oaklands Wine Exporters, Stbosch **A863** Sumaridge Wine, Hermanus **A864** Rosslo Wines, Vdal **A865** Cancelled **A866** The Wine Society, Constia **A867** Janèza Private Cellar, Rbtsn **A868** Tradequick 1024, Alberton **A869** Paul Roux, Fhoek **A870** Glenhurst Wine Farm, Stbosch **A871** Bon Cap, Eilandia **A872** False Bay Winery, Wllngtn **A873** Eikestad Vintique, Stbosch **A874** Zidela Wines, Stbosch **A875** Anura Vineyards, Kmuts **A876** Eldorado Wines, Windmeul **A877** Siyabonga Wines, Wllngtn **A878** Puma Beverages, Evander **A879** Philippi Liquor Wholesalers, Philippi **A880** Vinum, Sir Lowry's Pass **A881** Ingwe Wine, S/West **A882** De Franchi Wines, Stbosch **A883** Annandale Distillers & Vintners, Stbosch **A884** Cowal Alcoholic Fruit Beverages, Pinetown **A885** De Compagnie Landgoed, Wllngtn **A886** Paarl Valley Wines, Paarl **A887** African Pride Wines, Constia **A888** Bluetrim Senior Liquors, Germiston **A889** Kirabo Private Cellar, Rville **A890** Fontenay, Fhoek **A891** JJ Streicher, Dbnvlle **A892** Cancelled **A893** Egoli Liquor Store, Northriding **A894** Konza Investments, Shakaskraal **A895** Cape Rock Wines, Van Rhynsdorp **A896** Flare Beverages, Bkfl **A897** Meerrust Farm, Constia **A898** Southern Vineyards, Granger Bay **A899** Antel's Distributor, Baynersfield **A900** Magicolix Distributors, S/West **A901** Mitchell's Waterfront Brewery, CT **A902** Far Horizons Wine Estate, Agter-Paarl **A903** Montpellier de Tulbagh, Tbgh **A904** Oubenheim Wine Estate, Vdal **A905** Koekenaap Cellars, Koekenaap **A906** Hot Tot Distribution, Sandton **A907** Remarkable Vineyards, Fhoek **A908** Major's Hill Winery, Rbtsn **A909** Thabani Wines, Stbosch **A910** Best Cape Cellars, Stbosch **A911** Avalon Vineyards, Wllngtn **A912** Beins Wines, Vltburg **A913** Western Investment Company, Paardeberg **A914** De Zoete Inval, Paarl **A915** Bergwater Vineyards, Prince Albert **A916** Teslaarsdal Winery, Caledon **A917** TCB Wines, Rville **A918** Imperial Liquor Wholesalers, Brakpan **A919** Post House, Raithby **A920** Bar Bella's Trading, Claremont **A921** Origin Wines, Stbosch **A922** Journey's End Vineyards, S/West **A923** Olsen Wineries, Paarl **A924** Ventulus, Delmas **A925** PA Mostert (Dispore Kamma), Caledon **A926** Koelenhof Boerdery, Khof **A927** Vin de Stel Wines, Khof **A928** Rainbow's End, Stbosch **A929** Trio Wholesalers, Jan Kempdorp **A930** Waterford Wines, Stbosch **A931** Earl Buntmann Wines, Breërivier **A932** Liris Trust, Kmuts **A933** Grand Union Properties, Bot River **A934** Top 200 Liquors, Carletonville **A935** Luddite Wines, Bot River **A936** Winecorp Private Label Services, Smdm **A937** Welgemeend Estate, Kmuts **A938** Western Wines, Stbosch **A939** Wedgewood Wine, Wllngtn **A940** Mega Wholesale Liquors, Diep River **A941** Questev Wines, Stbosch **A942** Houmoed Plase, Vdal **A943** Embev Marketing, Durban North **A944** Houdamond Trust, StBosch **A945** Domaine William, Rbtsn **A946** Buitehof, Rbtsn **A947** Lorraine Trust, Wstr **A948** Mostert Boerdery, Koringberg **A949** Topaz Wine, S/West **A950** Wine Culture, CT **A951** Allesverloren, Riebeek West **A952** Mount Rozier Wines, S/West **A953** Agricola Farming, Fhoek **A954** Jacoline Haasbroek, Fhoek **A955** Nyloewer Padstal, Nylstroom **A956** Hillcrest Farm, Dbnvlle **A957** Portmore Wine Company, Stbosch **A958** Cilliers Family Trust, Rbtsn **A959** Keukenhof, Koekenaap **A960** Bloem Wynverspreiders, Bloemfontein **A961** Signal Hill, CT **A962** Rampac, Paarl **A963** Manley Private Cellar, Tbgh **A964** Vrede & Lust Farms, Smdm **A965** David Frost Wines, Agter-Paarl **A966** Du Von Wines, Rbtsn **A967** Schalkenbosch Wines, Tbgh **A968** AW Eksteen Boerdery, Noorder-Paarl **A969** West Coast Organics, Vanrhynsdorp **A970** Diemersfontein Wines, Wllngtn **A971** Leshata Distilleerders, Soutpansberg **A972** Christoph Dornier Wines, Stbosch **A973** ZFL Distributors, Strand **A974** Matzikama Wine Cellar, Vanrhynsdorp **A975** La Chataigne, Fhoek **A976** Waltco Distributors & Exporters, Malmesbury **A977** Hemel & Aarde, Hermanus **A978** Ormonde Vineyards, Darling **A979** Beau Soleil, McGregor **A980** Langkloof Vineyards, George **A981** Cader

Groothandel, Kimberley **A982** Gallop Hill, Agter-Paarl **A983** JE Lambrechts, Malmesbury **A984** Marklew Wines, Stbosch **A985** Moddervlei Boerdery, Bredasdorp **A986** Artica Trading, Jacobs **A987** Kareedouw Bottle Store, Kareedouw **A988** Koningsrivier Wines, Rbtsn **A989** Stellentia Liquor Store, Dbnvlle **A990** Wrapsa, Centurion **A991** Mystery Wine Corporation, Maitland **A992** Breede Valley Wines, Rbtsn **A993** Mother City Wine Logistics, Montague Gardens **A994** Mountain Oaks Winery, Wstr **A995** Kleinrivier Belleggings, Stanford **A996** RWV Liquor Distributors, Bloemhof **A997** Sp Frost Dormershire, Kuils River **A998** Sir Lowry's Pass Inn, Sir Lowry's Pass **A999** Rayner Hotels (Proprietary) Ltd, Gouritsmond **A1000** Fullimput 146 T/A Cygna, CT **A1001** The Oak And Vigne Café, Greyton **A1002** Wederom Boerdery Trust, Rbtsn **A1003** DL De Waal, Paarl **A1004** Vinbott T/A Wine Worx, Stbosch **A1005** Olyvenbosch Vineyards, Wllngtn **A1006** Hogmeister T/A Prestige Cellars, Strand **A1007** D C Hidden T/A Hidden Valley Wines, Stbosch **A1008** L L Hughes, Stbosch **A1009** Joubert-Tradauw, Tradouw Valley **A1010** Rudera Wines, Khof **A1011** Oude Molen Tavern, CT **A1012** Leiberg Estate, Stbosch **A1013** NJT de Villiers Boerdery, Caledon **A1014** Seven Falls Trading, Midrand **A1015** Bromar Import & Export, Wllngtn **A1016** Cradock Farm, Herold **A1017** SA Bulk Wine, S/West **A1018** Clouds Vineyards, Stbosch **A1019** Doornhoek Stokery/Distillery, Lydenburg **A1020** Anatu Wines, Northcliff **A1021** Saronsberg Cellar, Tbgh **A1022** Doolhof Wine Estate, Wllngtn **A1023** Sixbar Trading, Khof **A1024** Haut Espoir, Frhoek **A1025** Domaine Brahms, Paarl **A1026** Cape First Wines, S/West **A1027** Black Pearl Wines, Suider-Paarl **A1028** Leeuberg Private Cellar, Swellendam **A1029** Skilpadvlei, Vlottenburg **A1030** Barfly Beverages, Durban **A1031** Intertrade 15, Frhoek **A1032** Adamastor & Bacchus (Main Ingredient), CT **A1033** Kleinvallei Winery, Paarl **A1034** Cape Classics Global Exports, Stbosch **A1035** Vrolykheid, Rbtsn **A1036** Brinkhof Wines, Riebeek West **A1037** Stellar Winery, Trawal **A1038** Vansha Farming, Paarl **A1039** Agterplaas, Stbosch **A1040** Rusticus Wine Cellar, Rbtsn **A1041** Sanctum Wines, Khof **A1042** Fransie Conradie Trust, Rbtsn **A1043** Feiteiras Wine (Roodeheuvel Farm), Bot Rivier **A1044** Lourensford Winery, S/West **A1045** Quagga Schnapps, George **A1046** Britz Vineyards (Under Oaks), Paarl **A1047** Grand Provence Properties, Frhoek

General Index

Here we combine a summary of the wines featured in the A-Z, with their ratings, sorted first by wine style, in alphabetical order, and then by producer or brand. New wines in bold. **NT** = not tasted; **NR** = tasted but not rated; **VS** = vintage skipped; **D** = discontinued. Multiple versions of wines indicated in brackets after the name, e.g. (2).

Barbera
★★★☆ Altyd

Blanc de noir
★★★ Aan de Drns, Boschndl, Btnvrwchtng, Cabrière, KWV, Van Lvren ★★★ Ashton, **Belbon Hills**, Chamnx, Du T'kloof, Hzndal, Lndskrn, Swrtland, Van Lvren ★★ Boplaas, Goudini, Jonkhr, Oude Wllngton, Wlworths ★★ Grt Cnsttia, Klawer, Oranje ★ Country C, **NT:** Cltzdorp, Ltzvlle, Picardi, **D:** Citrus, Frost, Horse Mtn, Montpllr Sud

Blends – see 'Red blends' and 'White blends'

Bukettraube
★★★ Cedrbrg ★★★ Du T'kloof, Klnhof, Smnsvlei ★★ Bovlei, Swrtland ★★ Citrus, **D:** Rooibrg

Cabernet franc
★★★★★ **Zrgvliet**

★★★★ Bellnghm, High C, Philip J, Warwick

★★★☆ Avntuur, Boschndl, Chrsto Wiese, **Cpe Grace**, Ekndal, Le Pommier, Makro, Ndrburg, Raats Fam, Whlhaven

★★★ Lvland, Nthlingshof ★★★ Lndskrn, **NR: Rainbow**, **D:** Uiterwyk

Cabernet sauvignon
★★★★★ Verglgn

★★★★☆ Alto, Asara, Bknhtskloof, Blue Creek, Carisbrke, Cedrbrg, De Traf, Delaire, Ekndal, Havana, **Kaapzicht**, Kanu, KWV, Le Riche (2), Mrgnhof, Neil E (2) Ovrgaauw, Rstnberg, **Rudera**, Sprgfield (2), Stark-C, Stkaya, **Stony B**, Thelema, Verglgn

★★★★ Agusta, Annandale, Anura, Avndale, Bellnghm, Bertrams, Bilton, Blwklppn, **Boland**, Bon Crge, Bonfoi, Boschndl, Btnvrwchtng, Cedrbrg, Coleraine, **Crows Nest**, Darling C, Delheim (2), Dmrsfntn, Eaglevlei, Eikehof, Fleur dC, Flgstone (2), Frost, G Beck (2), Gracelnd, Grnghurst, Grnghurst, Havana, Hidden V, Hpnbrg, Hrtnberg, Jordan, K Constantia, Kaapzicht, Kleine Z, Knonkp, Knrhoek, **KWV**, L'Avenir, La Bri, Lndskrn (2), L'Ormarins, L'rdge, Lvland, **Lynx**, Makro, Mooipls, Môreson, Muratie, Ndrburg, Rbtson, Rhbsklf, Rijk's, Rmhoogte, Rooibrg, Rust en V, Sbosch Vyds, Sbsoch Hills, Signal H, Spier, Stark-C, Stellnzcht, Stnwall, Stony B, Swrtland, Sxnburg, Vljsdrift, Vrgnoegd, Waterfd, Wbrsburg, Western, Wlworths (2), Wndmeul, Zndrnaam, Zonneblm

★★★☆ Afrcn Pride, Altyd, Ashton, Assegai, Audacia, Avntuur, Bcksbrg, Bergsig, Bknhtskloof, Bloemndal, Bnnievle, Boland, Bon Cap, Boplaas, Boschndl, Bschklf, **Chrsto Wiese** (2), **Cilandia**, Citrus, Clmborg, **Cloof**, Clovelly, Cls Mlvrne, Darling C, Dbn Hills, De Compagnie, De Wetsh, Devon H, Dmrsdal, Domaine B, **Drnrshire**, Ekndal, Exclsor (2), Fleur dC, **Fort S**, Grt Cnsttia, Grt Eilnd, High C, Hildenb, IWS, Jonkhr, **JP Bredell**, K Constantia, Klnhof, KWV, L'Avenir, La Motte, **La Petite F**, Laborie, Laibach, Ldrsburg, Le Bonh, Le Grand C, Linton P, L'rdge, Lushof, MAN Vintners, Marklew, McGreg, Mdlvlei, Meerend, Mischa (2), Mnt Rochelle, **Mnt Rozier** (2), Mntn River, Môreson, Mostrtsdrift, Mouton (2), Mrgnhof, Ndrburg (2), Newton J, Nitida, Nthlingshof, Ntvbij, Onderklf, Oracle, Ormonde, Oude Wllngton, Paul C, **Perdebrg**, Plaisir, Post Hse, Prtrville, **Pulpit Rock**, Rbtson, Rickety, Riebeek (2), Rietvallei, **Royle Fam**, Rtrsvlei, **Rusticus**, Savanha (2), Sbosch Vyds, **Schlkbnbsch**, Seidel (2), Sentinel, Smnsig,

Cape 'Bordeaux' – see under Red blends

Cape 'port' – see under Fortifieds

Carignan

Chardonnay, unwooded

Chardonnay, wooded

Chenin blanc, unwooded, dry

★★★☆ Brndvlei, Dellrust, **Grndheim**, Mooitsg, Vlrsdorp, Wamaker

★★★ De Krans, Jacaranda, **Kango**, Prtrville, Swrtland ★★ Mns Ruber, **NR:** Drnkraal, **Prtrville, NT:** Cltzdorp, Drnkraal (2), Huguenot, Mooitsg, Oranje

Morio muscat

★★★★ Lndskrn

Muscadel, red

★★★★★ Boplaas, Monis, Nuy, Rietvallei

★★★★ Avndale, De Wet, Du T'kloof, Jonkhr, Kango, **KWV**, Ldismth, Rietrvr, Rietvallei, Rooibrg, Van Lvren

★★★☆ Aan de Drns, Ashton, Badsberg, Boland, KWV, McGreg, Merwida, Nordale, Seidel, W'drift, Wltvrede

★★★ Grndheim, Mns Ruber, Mooitsg, Oranje, **Ovrhex**, Rdezandt ★★☆ Klawer, Slnghoek ★★ Douglas, **NT:** Agterklip, De Doorns, Grndheim, Lndzicht, Montagu, Uitvlucht, **D:** Gdveld, Louiesnhf

Muscadel, white

★★★★ Avndale, Boland, Bon Crge, De Krans (2), De Wetsh, Deetlefs, G Beck, **Jonkhr** (3), **KWV**, Nordale, Nuy

★★★☆ Ashton, Boplaas (2), Citrus, Clairvx, Mns Ruber, Rooibrg, Thelema

★★★ Grndheim, McGreg, Mns Ruber, Oranje, Rbtson, Rdezandt, Rietrvr, Wltvrede ★★☆ Kango, Mooitsg, **Ovrhex**, **Yonder** ★★ Klawer, **NT:** Barrydale, Cltzdorp, Kango, Lndzicht, Ltzvlle, Montagu, Uitvlucht

Muscat de Hambourg

★★★★ Sbsoch Hills

★★★☆ Wltvrede

Non-muscat, red, fortified

★★★★ Drnkraal, Laborie

★★★ Boplaas, Mooitsg, Perdebrg ★★ Mooitsg ★ Mooitsg

Port, red

★★★★★ Axe Hill, Boplaas, JP Bredell

★★★★★ Allesvlrn, Bergsig, Boplaas, De Krans, Ovrgaauw, Vrgnoegd

★★★★ Boplaas, De Krans (3), Drnkraal, JP Bredell, KWV (2), L'Avenir, Lndskrn, Riebeek, Swrtland

★★★☆ Annandale, Bergsig (2), Boplaas (3), **Botha**, De Wet, Dellrust, Du T'kloof, **Flgstone**, Grt Cnstntia, Jonkhr, Linton P, Louiesnhf, Monis, Mrgnhof (2), Muratie, Villiera, Waboom

★★★ Ashton, Beaumnt, Bertrams, Boland, Goudini, **Kango**, KWV, McGreg, Mns Ruber, Muratie, Rstnberg, Slnghoek, **Smrbsch**, Withoek, Wlington, **Wndmeul** ★★☆ Aan de Drns, Coppoolse, Grndheim, Oranje, Padda, Rbtson, Rdezandt, Sentinel, Swrtland, Tulbagh (2), Vlrsdorp ★★ Badsberg, Bovlei, De Zoete, Douglas, F'hoek Vyds, Kango, Rooibrg ★★ Citrus ★ Clairvx, Hldrkruin, Mooitsg, **NT:** Barrydale, Cltzdorp (3), Drnkraal, Gdveld (2), Grndheim, Hrtswater, Huguenot (2), Klnhof, Lmrshoek, Makro, Ntvbij, Wamaker, **D:** Daschbsch, Glen C, Nutwd Grove

Port, white

★★★☆ Asara

★★★ Boplaas ★★★ De Krans, **NT:** Drnkraal, Mooitsg

Non-muscat, white, fortified

★★★★ Daschbsch

Gamay noir

★★★ Asara, Kleine Z, Wlworths, **D:** Rhbsklf, Signal H

Gewürztraminer

★★★★★ Zevnwacht

★★★★ Nthlingshof, Smnsig

★★★☆ Bergsig, Delheim, **Ndrburg**, Paul C, Wltvrede

★★★ Altyd, Oude Wllngton, **Thirty-two S**, Villiera, Wlworths ★★☆ Bon Crge, Klnhof, Rietvallei, **NT:** Bovlei, Douglas, Lndzicht, **D:** Meerend

Grenache
★★★★ **Signal H**

★★★☆ Signal H

★★★ Citrus, Signal H ★★☆ **Van Z'klf**, **D:** Mnt Destin

Hanepoot – see under Fortifieds

Hárslevelü
D: Lemberg

Icewine
★★★★ Signal H

Kosher wines
★★★☆ K Draken, Zndwijk

★★★ K Draken (4), Zndwijk (3) ★★☆ Bcksbrg, K Draken, Zndwijk ★★ K Draken, **NT:** Bcksbrg (3), Zndwijk

Late harvest
★★★★ Waboom

★★★ **Bnnievle**, Boplaas, Delheim ★★☆ Ashton, De Zoete, Du T'kloof, Ovrmeer, **Wllngton**, Wlworths ★★ Cellr Csk, Citrus, Drostdy, **Jnkersklf**, Kango, K'prinz, Mooitsg, Pick 'n P, Rvnswood, Westcrp Int, Wlworths, Wndmeul, Zomerlust ★☆ Bernheim, Carnival, Rbtson, Rietrvr, Tulbagh ★ McGreg, **NT:** De Doorns, Douglas, Grndheim, Hrtswater, Huguenot (2), Klawer, Montagu, Oranje, Picardi, Rdezandt, Swrtland, Uitvlucht, Wnklshk, **D:** Gdveld, Hrnhof, KWV, Prtrville

Light & low-alcohol wines
★★★ Cold Duck (3), Grünb (2), Twee JG, Wlworths ★★☆ Darling C (2), Fleur dC, Grünb, Hrtswater ★★ Drostdy, **Jnkersklf**, Pick 'n P, Rbtson (2), Rvnswood, Swrtland, Tulbagh ★☆ Darling C (2), Odyssey (2), Rbtson (3), Westcrp Int ★ Country C (4), Rbtson, **NT:** Bergsig, Oranje, Riebeek, **Swrtland**, Bergsig

Malbec
★★★★ Ashanti, Bellevue, **Bellevue**, **Hildenb**, Makro, Ndrburg, Umkhulu, Wlworths

★★★ Bellevue, Fview ★★☆ Bcksbrg, **NR: Signal H**

Merlot
★★★★★ Avndale, Havana, KWV, Ovrgaauw, Sbosch Vyds, Slaley, Spice R, Stnberg, Thelema, Veenwdn, Verglgn

★★★★ Amani, Anura, Asara, Bein, **Bellnghm**, Bilton, Boschndl, Btnvrwchtng, Chrsto Wiese, Cmbrly, Coleraine, Cordoba, De Traf, Delheim, Du Preez, Ekndal, Fleur dC, **Grt Cnstntia**, Havana, Hrtnberg, Jordan, Kanu, Kleine Z, **KWV**, **L'Ormarins** (2), L'rdge, Lvland, **Major's Hill**, Meerend, Meinert, Mrgnhof (2), Mrlust, Ndrburg, Plaisir, Quoin, Ridgeback, Rmhoogte, Rust en V, Savanha (2), Sbsoch Hills, Seidel, Stony B, Sxnburg, The Winery, Thelema, Von O, Yonder, Zevnwacht, Zonneblm

★★★☆ **Afrcn Terroir**, Altyd, Assegai, Audacia, Avntuur, Bcksbrg, Bellnghm, Bknhtskloof, Bloemndal, **Blubrry Hill**, Blwklppn, Boschndl, Bovlei, Bowe, Bschklf, Clmborg, Coppoolse, Cowlin, **Cpe Grace**, Darling C, Dbn Hills (3), Deetlefs, Devon H, Dmrsfntn (2), Dominion, Douglas G, Drostdy, **Eaglevlei**, **Ernst Co**, Exclsor, F'hoek Vyds (2), Fleur dC, Fort S, Frost, Goedvrwcht, Gracelnd, Grdian Pk, Grt Cnstntia, Grt Eilnd, Grte Pst, Hippo, Hpnbrg, Hzndal, **Iona**, IWS, JP Bredell, Kaapzicht, Kango, Ken F, Kleine Z, **Klmpzicht** (2), **Koelfntn**, Krnskop, KWV, L'Avenir, La Couronne, Laborie, Laibach, **Lindiwe**, Linton P, L'rdge, Lushof, Makro, Marklew, **Mischa**, Mnt Rochelle, Môreson, Mouton, Nelson, Nico vdM,

Méthode cap classique – see under Sparkling wines

Morio muscat – see under Fortifieds

Mourvèdre

Muscadel – see under Fortifieds

Muscat d'Alexandrie

Muscat de Frontignan

Natural sweet

Nebbiolo

Noble late harvest

★★★★ Boschndl, Btnvrwchtng, Con Uitsig, Cpe Point, Delheim, Fleur dC, Jordan, K Constantia, Ndrburg (4), Rbtson, Rstnberg, Signal H, Slnghoek, Spier, Villiera, Wlworths

★★★☆ Beaumnt, Bergsig, Du T'kloof, IWS, **Jason's**, L'Avenir, Mrgnhof, **Nuy**, Waterfd

★★★ Boland, **Thirty-two S**, **NT:** Afrcn Terroir, **D:** Wlworths

Non-muscat, red/white, fortified — see under Fortifieds

Nouveau

★★☆ Oranje

Organic wines

★★★☆ Afrcn Terroir (3), Bcksbrg, Bon Cap (5), Fierte, Laibach, Stellr Orgs (2)

★★★ Afrcn Terroir (5), Bon Cap, Stellr Orgs, Wlworths (3) ★★☆ Afrcn Terroir (2), Stellr Orgs (3), Wlworths ★★ Stellr Orgs (3), Wlworths, **NT:** Black Eagle (2) **D:** G Beck

Perlé wines

★★★ De Wet, Grünb, Lost H, **Lost H** ★★ Ashton, Riebeek, **NT:** Bergsig (2), Lost H

Petit verdot
★★★★☆ Smnsig
★★★★ **Du Preez**, Ndrburg, Signal H, **Zrgvliet**
★★★☆ **Bellevue**

Pinotage
★★★★☆ **Allee B**, Bellevue, Bergsig, Byrskloof, Cls Mlvrne, Cmbrly, Dmrsfntn, Fview, Kaapzicht, Knonkp (2), L'Avenir, L'rdge, Nelson, Nthlingshof, Reyneke, Sbosch Vyds, Smnsig, **Sthrn Rght** (2), Tukulu, Uiterwyk (2), Umkhulu, Wlworths

★★★★ Altyd, Ashanti, Avntuur, Beaumnt, Bellnghm, Boplaas, Cloof, Darling C, **Domaine B**, Flgstone, G Beck, Grnghurst, Hidden V (2), Horse Mtn, Jacobsdal, Kaapzicht, KWV, L'Avenir, **Lyngrove**, Mauroma, Mdlvlei, Mnt Destin, Mooipls, Môreson, Mrgnhof, Ndrburg, Neil E, Nelson (2), Newton J, Perdebrg, S'bonga, Seidel, Sentinel, Signal H, Spice R (2), Spier, Stellnzcht, Stony B, Sxnburg, Sylvnvle, Wamaker, Warwick, Zndrnaam, Zonneblm

★★★☆ **Afrcn Terroir** (2), Asara, Assegai, Boland, **Bon Cap** (2), Botha, Chrsto Wiese, Citrus, **Cloof**, Cls Mlvrne, Coppoolse (2), Cpe Classics, Darling C, Dbn Hills, Deetlefs, Delheim, Dmrsdal, Douglas G, Eaglevlei, Fleur dC, Goede H, Grt Cnstntia, Grt Eilnd, Hill & Dale, Hldrkruin, Hrtnberg, Hzndal, IWS, Jonkhr, Klawer, Kleine Z, Klnhof, Knrhoek, **Kosie M**, Ktzenbrg, KWV, Laborie, Laibach, L'Auberge, Lmrshoek, Lyngrove, **Major's Hill**, Manley, Meerend, Migratn, **Mntn Oaks**, Niel J, Onderklf, Oracle, Patrys, Perdebrg, Rbtson, Rijk's, **Romans**, Rooibrg, Sbosch Vyds (2), Scali, Seidel, **Slaley** (2), Smnsig, **Smrbsch** (2), Stettyn, Swrtland (2), Uiterwyk, Van Lvren, Vljsdrift, Wamaker, **Wdlands** (2), Western, Wldekrans (2), Wlington, Wlworths, Wm Everson, Wstbrdge, Zevnwacht

★★★ Aan de Drns, Afrcn Terroir, Anura, Badsberg, Bcksbrg, Beaumnt, Bellnghm, Bergheim, Bianco, Bon Crge, Boplaas, Botha, Bovlei, Byrskloof, Chrsto Wiese, Citrus, **Cloof**, Cpe Bay, **Cpe Vyds** (2), De Krans, **De Zoete**, Deetlefs, Dellrust, Dieu D, Dmrsfntn, Drostdy, F'hoek Vyds, Fort S, Fview, G Beck, Goudini, Hippo, Hldrkruin, Jason's, Kango, Ken F, Kleine Z, Kosie M, **KWV**, Ldismth, Le Grand C, Lndskrn, L'rdge, Lyngrove, Makro, Malan, MAN Vintners, McGreg, Mellasat, Millstrm, **Mnt Rozier**, Môreson, Mouton, Mrhof, Ndrburg, New Begin, Nitida, Nthlingshof, Ntvbij, Origin, Oude Kaap, Prtrville, **Pulpit Rock**, **Raka**, Riebeek, Rtrsvlei, **Rusticus**, Sbosch Hills, Seidel, Slnghoek, Smnsvlei, Smook, Spice R, Spier, Stnwall, Sxnburg, Tarentaal, Thelema, **Thirty-two S**, **Tulbagh** (2), Villiera, Vinfruco, Vrdnheim, **Wdlands**, Westcrp Int, **Wlworths** (2), Wndmeul
★★★ **Avntuur**, Barrydale, Blue Creek, Cpe Wne Cllrs, Du T'kloof, F'hoek Vyds, G Beck, Hpnbrg, IWS, **K Draken**, Klnvallei, **Kosie M** (2), Lndhorst, Louieshht, **Main Str**, Mellasat, **Mnt Rozier**, Mntn River, **Mrgnhof**, Obikwa, Paradysklf, Rhbsklf, Rietrvr, Two Oceans, **Van Z'klf**, Vinfruco, Waboom, Winecorp, **Zndwijk** ★★ Bernheim, Citrus, Devon

H, Drknsig (2), Eshkl Kshr, Fair Valley, **Fort S**, Long Mntn, **Rbtsn Wd Rver** (3), Stellr Orgs (2), Thorn ★★ **Lindiwe**, Prtrville, Rbtsn Wd Rver (3), Rietrvr, Sumardg ★ Le Mnoir Brndel, **Vinus Via, NR:** Doolhof, **Marklew, NT:** Anthill, Bcksbrg, Bodega, Chamnx, Daschbsch, Detendu, Goede H, Huguenot, Keerweder, Kln DasBsch, Lemberg, Lndzicht, Ltzvlle, Mdlpos, Old Brdge, Oranje, **Oubenhm**, **Pulpit Rock**, Vljsdrift, Windfall, **D:** Afrcn Terroir (2), Cedrbrg, Cloof, Devon H, Gdveld, Horse Mtn, JP Bredell, Louisvle, Mijn-B, Mnt Rochelle, Paradysklf, Sable V, Sbsoch Hills, Villiera

Pinot Blanc
★★ Chrsto Wiese

Pinot gris
★★★☆ L'Ormarins (2)

★★☆ Van Lvren

Pinot noir
★★★★★ HRV

★★★★★ Bchrd-F (2), Flgstone, Mrlust

★★★★ BWC, Cabrière, Kln Optnhrst, Newton J, Paradysklf, Paul C, Topaz, Whlhaven

★★★☆ Chamnx, De Traf, De Wetsh, Flgstone, Grte Pst, **Herold**, K Constantia, Muratie, Newton J, Signal H, Sumardg, Wlworths

★★★ Barrydale, **Bellevue**, Btnvrwchtng, Flgstone, Glen C, Goedvertw, Hpnbrg, **Rusticus**, Thandi ★★★ **Ashton** ★★ **Cpe First** ★ Montpllr Tbgh, **NR: The Winery, NT:** Gdveld, Lemberg, **D:** Montpllr Sud

Pontac
D: Hrtnberg

Red blends
Cape Bordeaux
★★★★★ Ernie Els, Verglgn

★★★★☆ Boschndl, Btnvrwchtng, Byrskloof, Capaia, Cordoba, Dbn Hills, De Toren, Glen C, Grnghurst, Havana, High C, Jean D, Jordan, Knonkp (2), Mrgnhof, Mrgnster, Mrgnster, Mrlust, Nthlingshof, Ovrgaauw, Paradysklf, Sprgfield, Veenwdn, Verglgn, Warwick, Welgemnd, Wlworths

★★★★ Asara (2), Avntuur, Bcksbrg (2), Beaumnt, Bellevue, Bschklf (2), Chamnx, Cmbrly, Con Uitsig, De Toren, Delaire (2), Ekndal, Flgstone, Frost, Goede H, Goedvrwcht, Grt Cnstntia, Havana, Ingwe, Jean D, **Jonkhr**, Jordan, Kanu, Kln Gustrw, KWV, La Bri, La Motte, Laibach, Le Bonh, Le Riche, L'Ormarins, Louisvle, Lvland, **Lynx**, Makro (3), Meerend, Meinert, Môreson, **Mulderb**, Muratie, **Nabyglgn**, Ndrburg (2), Neil E, Nelson, Paradysklf, R&R, Raka, Rhbsklf, Rickety, **Ridgeback**, Rstnberg, S'bonga, Sbosch Vyds, **Sbsoch Hills**, Seidel, Smnsig, Smrbsch, Stellnzcht, Stony B, Swrtland, Sxnburg, Umkhulu, Veenwdn, Verglgn, Villiera, Von O, Vrgnoegd, **Wbrsburg**, Welgemnd, **Wlworths** (2), Yonder

★★★☆ **Afrcn Terroir**, Amani, Bertrams, Blwklppn, Bnnievle, Bovlei, Btnvrwchtng, Bwland, Capaia, Chrsto Wiese, Cls Mlvrne (2), **Cmbrly**, Cowlin, Cpe Vyds, Crows Nest, De Compagnie, **Fierte**, **Fryer**, Ghrd Britz, Gusto, **Hegewisch**, **Helshoogte**, Hillcrest, Jordan (2), Joubert-T, K Constantia, Kosie M (2), **Krnskop**, KWV, La Couronne, Laborie, **Laibach** (2), Lmrshoek, Lndskrn, Makro, Mnterosso, Mntn River, Mulderb, Napier, Nico V, Nthlingshof, Ntvbij, Ovrhex, Paul C, **Romond**, Sbosch Vyds, Seidel, Slaley, Slnghoek, Smook, Stnwall, **Tangara**, Two Oceans, Van Z'hof, Vendôme, Vrede en Lust, Welgemnd, Wldekrans, Wltvrede, Wlworths, Zonneblm, **Zrgvliet**

★★★ Agusta, Audacia, Avntuur, Bellnghm, **Bon Cap**, Cloof, Coleraine, Cpe Bay, **Cpe First**, **Cpe Grace**, Detendu, Dominion (2), **Dornier**, **El Dorado**, Grte Pst, Jacaranda, Jonkhr, K Draken, Kango, La Couronne, Leopard's, **Lost H** (2), Louiesnhf, **Lyngrove** (2), **MAN Vintners**, **Merwespnt**, Migratn, **Mooitsg**, Môreson, **M'pont**, New Cape, Nitida, **Ormonde**, Oude Kaap, Perdebrg, Raka, Rhbsklf, Rooibrg, Rtrsvlei, Sbosch Vyds, Seidel

(2), Shoprite, Smnsvlei, Stellndrft, **Swrtland**, **Ultra Liq**, W'drift, Westcrp Int, Wldekrans (2), Wlworths, Wndmeul, Zndwijk ★★★ Avntuur, Bovlei, Crghall, **Daschbsch**, De Wet, Dieu D, Hldrkruin, Jacaranda, **Jonkhr**, La Petite F, Malan, Paradysklf, Roothman, Swrtland, **The Winery**, **Winecorp** ★★ Bernheim, McGreg, Nuy, **Ultra Liq** ★★ Cpe First, **Zidela**, **NR:** Hldrkruin, **Horse Mtn**, Klfzicht, **Linde**, Niel J, **Saronsbrg**, **NT: Adler**, **Bergwater**, Bottlry Hills, Brnthrst, Conspirare, Hrtnberg, Klnhof, **Koningsrvr**, Old Brdge, Rozendal, **Schlkbnbsch**, Thabani, Uva Mira, **Vilafonte**, **D:** JP Bredell, Le Riche, Lemberg, Romans, Rstnberg, Vlrsdorp, Zevnwacht

Other cabernet-based blends

★★★★★ Rust en V

★★★★ Alto, **Black Pearl**, Bonfoi, **Carisbrke**, Cloof, Cls Mlvrne, De Meye, Dmrsdal, **Dmrsfntn**, Dornier, **Flgstone** (2), Joostnbrg, Ndrburg, Plaisir

★★★☆ Bon Crge, **Chrsto Wiese**, Cpe Bay, Doolhof, Grdian Pk, **Havana**, Hill & Dale, Hrtnberg, Ingwe, JP Bredell, Kaapzicht, **Mnt Destin**, Ndrburg, Rstnberg, Slaley, Smnsig, Vrdnheim

★★★ **Cloof**, Clovelly, **De Zoete**, Flgstone, **Goede H**, **Gracelnd**, Mrgnhof, **Opstal**, Rickety, Rijk's, Uitkyk, Van Lvren, Waterfd, Western, **Wine Vllge**, Zndvliet ★★★ **Agterplaas**, Douglas, Glen C, **Klnvallei**, Vinfruco ★★ De Zoete, **Fierte**, **NR: Ernie Els**, **Lushof**, **NT:** Drostdy, Eshkl Kshr, Rbtson

Other red blends

★★★★★ Makro, **The Winery**, **Waterfd**

★★★★ Avndale, **Boplaas**, De Traf, **Fview**, Mnt Destin, Mnt du Toit, Stnberg, **Stony B**, The Foundry

★★★☆ Annandale, Avndale, Blyde, Boschndl, **De Krans**, Dellrust, Douglas G, Du Preez, Ekndal, Grt Eilnd, Hill & Dale, Hzndal, Joostnbrg, Ken F, KWV (2), Merwida, **Mrgnhof**, Signal H, Stkaya, Vaughan J, Vrgnoegd

★★★ Ashanti, Beaumnt, Bergsig, Boschndl, Botha, Brndvlei, Ch Lib, Citrus, Coppoolse, Cpe Bay, Cpe Vyds, Darling C, Douglas G, Du Preez, Goudini, Grt Cnstntia, H Boom, **IWS** (2), Janéza, Kaapzicht, **Kanu** (2), Klawer, KWV, Le Grand C, **Main Str**, Nordale (2), Raka, Rdezandt, Ridder's, Rtrsvlei, Sbosch Vyds, Swrtland, Sxnburg, Thnskraal, **Two Oceans**, Van Lvren, Vaughan J, Vinfruco, Vljsdrift, Vrede en Lust (2), Waboom, **Wdlands** (2), Western, Whlhaven, Withoek, Wllington ★★★ Afrcn Terroir, Barrydale, Bcksbrg, Blwklppn, **Bnnievle** (2), Boland, Citrus, Coleraine, Cordoba, Dominion, Douglas G, F'hoek Vyds, **Kln Optnhrst**, Leopard's, Lndskrn, Long Mntn, Millstrm, Mnt du Toit, Mostrtsdrift, Muratie, Ndrburg, Patrys, **Prmium Cpe Wnes**, Rtrsvlei (2), **Schlkbnbsch**, Tassenbrg, **Thirty-two S**, **Ultra Liq**, **Ultra Liq**, Van Lvren, Vaughan J, Western, Wltvrede, **Wlworths** (2) ★★ Aan de Drns, Boplaas, Citrus, **Crows Nest**, **Jnkersklf**, Ltzvlle, Mouton, Pick 'n P, Rbtson (2), **Rietvallei**, Rvnswood, Schlkbnbsch, Winecorp, Wlworths (2), Zomerlust ★★ Cellr Csk, **Crows Nest**, Ovrmeer, **NR:** Bcksbrg, **Fredine le Roux**, Lvland, **NT:** Country C, De Doorns, Douglas (2), Drostdy (2), Fairseat, Grndheim, Hrtnberg, Kango, Keerweder, KWV, Mnt du Toit, Montagu, Oranje, Picardi, Rdezandt, Riebeek, Swrtland, Uva Mira, Vlrsdorp, Windfall, Wnklshk, **D:** BWC, Cloof, Hrnhof, Knysna, Mijn-B, Sbosch Vyds, Winecorp, Wlworths, Zonneblm

Red blends with pinotage

★★★★★ Kaapzicht

★★★★★ Byrskloof, Darling C, Grnghurst, **Kaapzicht**, Meinert, Welgemnd, Wlworths

★★★★ Asara, Ashanti, Assegai, Cls Mlvrne (3), Dellrust, Devon H, **Dmrsfntn**, Fleur dC, Flgstone, G Beck, **Goats**, Kaapzicht, Ken F, Knonkp, Marklew, Nthlingshof, Paradysklf, Quoin, **Rmhoogte** (2), Smnsig, **Stkaya**, Uiterwyk, Villiera, Warwick, **Wdlands**

★★★☆ **Bianco**, Blwklppn, Byrskloof, **Cloof** (2), Devon H, **Dmrsfntn**, Du Preez, Flgstone, Klfzicht, **Kosie M**, KWV, Leopard's, Lyngrove, Mdlvlei, **Mnt Rochelle**, Rmhoogte, **Romans**, Umkhulu, Welgemnd, **Wlworths**, Wstbrdge

★★★ Afrcn Terroir, Asara, Ashton, **Assegai**, **Belbon Hills**, **Bellevue** (2), Bknhtskloof, Cedrbrg, **Chrsto Wiese**, Clairvx, **Cls Mlvrne** (2), Coppoolse, Country C, **Cpe First**, **Cpe Grace**, Deetlefs, Domaine B, Drostdy (2), Du T'kloof (2), F'hoek Vyds, Flgstone, **Fort S** (2), Goats, Goedvertw, **Horse Mtn**, **Jonkhr**, Kleine Z, Klnhof, **Kosie M** (2), L'Avenir, Leopard's, **Lmrshoek**, **Lost H** (3), Mdlvlei, Mntn River, Mooitsg, New Cape, **Oaklnds Exprtrs**, Opstal, R&R, **Sbosch Vyds**, **Stellnzcht**, **Thirty-two S**, Two Oceans, Villiera, Vinfruco, Waboom, **Wdlands**, Western (2) ★★★ Boland, Chamnx, Coppoolse (3), Cpe Classics, **De Krans**, Delheim, Goudini, Grt Cnstntia, Hrtswater, **IWS**, **Kosie M**, KWV, Mdlvlei, Mystery, Nelson, Ntvbij, **Origin** (3), Oudeklf, Padda, Rhbsklf, **Riebeek**, Rooibrg, S/SW, **Slaley**, Slnghoek, **Smnsvlei** (2), Smrbsch, Stellr Orgs, **Tulbagh**, Uiterwyk, **Ultra Liq**, Vinfruco, Wamaker, **Westcrp Int** (3), **Western**, Winecorp, **Wldekrans** ★★ Bon Crge, Bovlei, Carnival, Douglas G, Drnkraal, KWV, Malan, Merwespnt, M'pont, Prtrville, Rietrvr, Sbosch Hills ★★ Rietrvr, **NR: Gallop Hill**, **L'Avenir**, **NT:** Bottlry Hills, **Drostdy**, Drostdy, Huguenot, Maiden, Makro, **D:** Carneby, Fleur dC, Horse Mtn, Louisvle, Mnt Rozier, Nutwd Grove, Ovrgaauw

Shiraz-based blends

★★★★★ Bknhtskloof, **Cmbrly**, Nico vdM, **Spice R**

★★★★ G Beck, Goats, Grdian Pk, Havana, Hzndal, Klmpzicht, **La Motte**, Lmrshoek, Ndrburg, **Newton J**, Ovrgaauw, Sbosch Vyds, Sxnburg, **Wlworths**

★★★★ **Anura**, Doolhof, G Beck, Havana, KWV, Ovrhex, Reyneke (2), Rstnberg, Stettyn, Stllnhills, **Sxnburg**, Western, **Whlhaven**, **Wlworths** (2), **Yonder**, **Yonder**, Zevnwacht

★★★ Afrcn Terroir, **Barton**, **Chrsto Wiese**, **De Wet**, Fview, Lndhorst, Long Mntn, Merwida, **Prospect**, **Riebeek**, Sbosch Vyds, Smnsvlei, **Swrtland**, **Tarentaal**, The Winery, Vinfruco, Wlworths, Zevnwacht ★★★ Afrcn Pride, Barrydale, Old Vines, Padda ★★ Douglas, **Slaley**, **Wndmeul**, **NR: Saronsbrg**, **The Winery**, **D:** G Beck, Lmrshoek, Swrtland, Zonneblm

Riesling, Cape or SA

★★★ Bon Crge, Thnskraal ★★★ Ndrburg ★★ Boland, De Wet, Du T'kloof, KWV, Van Lvren ★★ Ldismth, Nuy ★ Bovlei, Le Mnoir Brndel, **NT:** Rooibrg, **D:** Boschndl, Goudini

Riesling, Rhine or weisser

★★★★ De Wetsh, K Constantia, Paul C, Rhbsklf, Thelema, Villiera, Wltvrede

★★★★ Btnvrwchtng, Grt Cnstntia, Hrtnberg, Jack & Knox, Ndrburg, **Wlworths** (2)

★★★ Bergsig, Deetlefs, Jordan, Lvland, Wltvrede ★★★ Rooibrg ★★ Montpllr Tbgh, **D:** Montpllr Sud

Rosé dry

★★★★ Bloemndal, **Cloof**, Goats, Newton J, **Schlkbnbsch**, Sumardg

★★★ Asara, **Bknhtskloof**, Cabrière, Cloof, Darling C, Dominion, Flgstone, High C, **IWS**, **L'Avenir**, Le Pommier, Origin, Raka, Rtrsvlei, **Signal H**, Sylvnvle, Vljsdrift, Vrede en Lust, Waboom, **Whlhaven** ★★★ Ashanti, Bernheim, Chrsto Wiese, Coppoolse, Cpe Bay, De Krans, **Drostdy**, F'hoek Vyds, Goedvrwcht, **Mrgnhof**, **Mrhof**, Nelson, **Prmium Cpe Wnes**, **Riebeek**, **Slaley**, Slnghoek ★★ Afrcn Terroir, Bellnghm, Deetlefs, Hill & Dale, Horse Mtn, Opstal, **Rbtsn Wd Rver**, **NR: Tangara**, **NT:** Jason's, **Môreson**, **Rbtsn Wd Rver**, **Swrtland**, **VS:** Byrskloof

Rosé, off-dry/semi-sweet

★★★ Bergsig, **Bnnievle**, Grünb, Hildenb, **Kanu**, **Kosie M**, Ndrburg, **Origin**, **Ovrhex**, Seidel, Shoprite, Wlington, Wlworths ★★★ Badsberg, Darling C, De Zoete, Delheim, Dieu D, Douglas G, **G Beck**, Goudini, Graca, Grt Eilnd, Hrtswater, L'Avenir, Ldismth, Le Grand C, Louiesnhf, Ltzvlle, Millstrm, Prtrville, **Riebeek**, **Rietrvr**, **Sbosch Vyds**, Seidel, Smnsvlei, Two Oceans, Vinfruco, Vrdnheim, **Winecorp** ★★ Bcksbrg, Cellr Csk, Citrus, Clairvx, Country C, **De Wet**, Klnhof, **Kosie M**, Oude Kaap, Rbtson, Swrtland, Van Lvren, **Winecorp** ★★ **Jnkersklf**, Mooitsg, Odyssey, Pick 'n P, Rbtson, Rvnswood, Tulbagh,

Wlworths, **NT: Agusta**, Bovlei, Douglas, Drostdy, Lndzicht, **Long Bch Café**, McGreg, Oranje, Riebeek (2) **D:** Gdveld, Rhbsklf

Ruby cabernet

★★★★ Flgstone
★★★☆ Daschbsch, Goudini, Merwida

★★★ Belbon Hills, Lngvrwacht, Ltzvlle, Rbtson ★★★ Ldismth, Long Mntn, McGreg, **Mnt Rozier**, Oranje, Oude Wllngton (2), Rbtson, Waboom, Zndvliet ★★ Drostdy, Hrtswater, **Rbtsn Wd Rver** (6) ★☆ **Rusticus**, **NT:** Agterklip, Fairseat, Gdveld, Uitvlucht, Windfall, **D:** Afrcn Terroir, Vlrsdorp

Sacramental wines

★★★ Mooitsg ★★ Citrus ★☆ K Draken, **NT:** Huguenot

Sangiovese

★★★★ L'Ormarins, **Whlhaven**

★★★ Ashanti, **D:** G Beck

Sauvignon blanc, unwooded

★★★★★ Stnberg
★★★★☆ Bartho E, Cpe Point, Dbn Hills, Fleur dC (2), Fryer, Iona, Mulderb, Neil E, Nitida, **Nitida**, **Oak Valley**, Ormonde, Spier, Verglgn, **Wlworths**
★★★★ Avndale, Bartho E, Bellevue, Bloemndal, Btnvrwchtng, Cedrbrg, **Cloverfld**, Con Uitsig, Dbn Hills, Delaire, **Elgin Vntnrs**, Flgstone, Fview, Grt Cnstntia, Havana (2), Hillcrest, Ingwe, Jordan, K Constantia, **KWV**, **L'Ormarins**, Lushof, Môreson, Ndrburg (3), Newton J, Oracle, Plaisir, Quoin, Raka, Ridgeback, Rijk's, **Saronsbrg**, Sbosch Vyds, Spice R, Sprgfield, Sthrn Rght, Stnberg, Sxnburg, Thelema, Uiterwyk, Verglgn, Villiera, Wltvrede, Wlworths, Zndrnaam
★★★☆ Altyd, Amani, **Amavara**, Bchrd-F, Beaumnt, Boland, Boschndl (2), Botha, **BWC**, Chamnx, **Chrsto Wiese** (2), Cls Mlvrne, Cpe Point, Darling C (2), Daschbsch, Dbn Hills, Deetlefs, Devon H, Ekndal, Fleur dC, Flgstone, Fort S, Frost, G Beck, Glnwood, Goede H, Gusto, **Hemlzcht**, Hill & Dale, Hpnbrg, Hrtnberg, Hzndal, IWS, K Draken, Kanu, Ken F (2), Kleine Z, Klnhof, L'Avenir, La Motte, Land's E, Landau, **Ldrsburg**, Leopard's, **Lmrshoek**, L'Ormarins, **Major's Hill**, Meerend, Mnt Rochelle, Mnt Rozier, Mooipls, Mouton (2), Nabyglgn, Ndrburg, New Cape, Nthlingshof, **Oaklnds Exprtrs**, Onderklf, Ovrgaauw, Paul C, Quando, Rbtson, **Ross G**, Savanha, Spier, Sprgfield, Stellnzcht, Uitkyk, Vinfruco, Von O, Warwick, Waterfd, Zevnwacht, Zndwijk, **Zrgvliet**

★★★ Afrcn Pride, **Afrcn Terroir** (2), Anura, Asara, Assegai, Avntuur, Badsberg, Barrydale, Bellevue, Bellnghm, Bergsig, Bknhtskloof, Bnnievle, Boland, Bon Crge, Bonfoi, Bovlei, Bowe, Capaia, Clouds, **Cpe Bay** (2), **Cpe First**, Dalla Cia, De Wetsh, Delheim, Dieu D, Dmrsdal, **Dombeya**, Dominion (2), Du Preez, Exclsor, Goedvrwcht, Grte Pst, Hippo, Hldrkruin, Inglewd, IWS, **K Draken**, Kaapzicht, **Kanu**, Knrhoek, **KWV** (2), La Couronne, Laborie, Laibach, Le Grand C, Linton P, Louiesnhf, L'rdge, Lyngrove, **Main Str**, **Mnt Rozier**, Mntn River, Mouton, Mrgnhof, Nelson, New Cape, Niel J, Ntvbij, Obikwa, **Ormonde**, Ovrhex, **Prmium Cpe Wnes**, Reyneke, Rietvallei, Rstnberg, **Rtrsvlei**, Sbosch Vyds, Sbosch Hills, Schlkbnbsch, Seidel, Sentinel, Slaley, Smnsig, Smnsvlei, Smrbsch, Sterhuis, Stettyn, Stony B, Swrtland, Table Mtn, Tarentaal, The Winery, Two Oceans, **Ultra Liq**, **Usana**, Uva Mira, Van Z'hof, Villiera, Vlrsdorp, **Wdlands** (2), Western, **Winecorp**, Wldekrans, Wlworths, Zndvliet ★★★ Afrcn Terroir, **Agterplaas**, Ashton, B&E, Bcksbrg, Boplaas, Bovlei, Chrsto Wiese, Coppoolse, Country C, Cpe Classics, Cpe Vyds, Douglas G, Drmrshire, Drostdy, Du Preez, Du T'kloof, **Ernst Co**, F'hoek Vyds (2), **Fierte**, **Fort S**, Goedvertw, Goudini, Grt Eilnd, Janéza, Jason's, Jonkhr, Klnhof, KWV, Le Pommier, **Lindiwe**, **Lost H** (2), Ltzvlle, **Main Str**, Malan, MAN Vintners, McGreg (2), Merwespnt, Merwida, Migratn, **Mnterosso**, M'pont, Nordale, Nuy, **Opstal**, **Origin** (2), Rbtson, Romans, Rtrsvlei, Sbosch Vyds, Shoprite, Slnghoek, Sumardg, **Thirty-two S**, Thorn, Umkhulu, Urbane, Van Lvren, Vinfruco, Vljsdrift, Wamaker, W'drift, Wlington, Wlworths

Kosie M, Krnskop, **KWV** (2), La Petite F, Land's E, Le Grand C, Linton P, Lndhorst, Lndskrn, Lngvrwacht, L'rdge, **Lushof**, **Lyngrove**, Main Str, Makro, MAN Vintners, Mason's, Migliarina, Migratn, Mischa, **Mnt Destin**, **Mnt Rochelle**, Mooipls, Mouton (2), **Mulderb**, Ndrburg, Nelson, Nico vdM, Niel J, Nitida, **Oaklnds Exprtrs**, Oracle, Origin, **PAX Vrbtm**, Prtrville, Rainbow, Rbtson, Rhbsklf, Riebeek (3), Rooibrg, **Sanctum**, Savanha, Sbosch Vyds (2), Scali, Seidel, Slaley, Slnghoek, Smnsig, Smook, Stellr Orgs, Stony B, Swrtland, Tarentaal, Twee JG, Umkhulu, Van Lvren, Veenwdn, Verglgn, Villiera, Vinfruco, **Vinus Via**, **Wdlands**, **Welgelee**, Western (2), Wlington, **Wltvrede**, Zndvliet, **Zrgvliet**

★★★ Afrcn Terroir, **Andy Mtchell**, Angora, Anura, Assegai, B&E, Badsberg, Belbon Hills, Bnnievle (2), Cameradi, Clairvx, Cordoba, Cpe Vyds, Cpe Wne Cllrs, **De Zoete**, Deetlefs, Dieu D, **Douglas G**, Drknsig, Drmrshire, Du T'kloof, Eikehof, F'hoek Vyds, Flgstone, Glnwood, Goudini, Gracelnd, Hldrkruin, Hpnbrg, IWS, Kosie M, **KWV**, **Laborie**, **Ltzvlle**, Lyngrove, **Main Str**, Makro, MAN Vintners, McGreg, Meerend, Mellasat, Merwida, Mntn River, Nelson, New Cape, Nordale, Obikwa, Origin, **Oudeklf**, Perdebrg, Raka, Royle Fam, Sbosch Vyds, Sbsoch Hills, Seidel, Shoprite, Smnsvlei (2), Smrbsch, Spier, Stellnzcht, Stellr Orgs, The Winery, **Thirty-two S**, **Thorn**, Tulbagh, **Two Oceans**, Urbane, Vrdnheim, Wamaker, **Wdlands**, Wlworths (2), Zndvliet ★★★ Afrcn Pride (2), Bovlei, Buthelezi, Coppoolse, Fort S, Hldrkruin, Jason's, **Kosie M**, Le Pommier, Matzikama, New Cape, Oranje, **Origin** (3), Patrys, **Rbtsn Wd Rver** (3), Ridder's, Savanha, Shoprite, Tulbagh, Vinfruco, **Wdlands**, Westcrp Int, Wlworths, Wstbrdge, **Zidela** ★★ Citrus, **Lindiwe**, Rbtsn Wd Rver (3), Stellr Orgs, **Zrgvliet** ★ Barrydale, Rietrvr, **Rusticus**, **NR:** Botha, Doolhof, **Horse Mtn**, **Marklew**, **Quoin**, **Romans**, Rtrsvlei, **Saronsbrg**, **NT:** Agterklip, **Arendsig**, **Bergwater** (2), Bernheim, **Blue Crane**, Bottlry Hills, De Hoopen, Eshkl Kshr, **Excelsious**, Ht Espoir, **Koningsrvr**, Le Mnoir Brndel, Libertas, Lndzicht, Old Brdge (2), **Oubenhm**, **Pulpit Rock**, Rdezandt, **Schlkbnbsch**, **Sthrn Sky**, Thabani, Tulbagh, Vljsdrift, **D:** Afrcn Terroir, Citrus, G Beck, Havana, Jason's, Kosie M, Louiesnhf, Nutwd Grove, Zndvliet

Sparkling wines

Méthode cap classique, red
★★★ G Beck

Méthode cap Classique, rosé
★★★★ Cabrière, G Beck, JC le R
★★★☆ Villiera, Wlworths

Méthode cap classique, white
★★★★☆ Bon Crge, G Beck, High C, Villiera
★★★★ Ambeloui, Avntuur, Bon Crge, Boschndl, Cabrière (2), Chamnx (2), G Beck, JC le R (3), Laborie, Mrgnhof, **Old Vines**, **Smnsig** (4), Stnberg, Twee JG, Villiera, Wlworths
★★★☆ Boschndl, Btnvrwchtng, Cabrière (2), Deetlefs, Grt Cnstntia, Hzndal, JC le R (3), **Long Mntn**, **Rstnberg**, Rtrsvlei, Sbosch Vyds, Villiera, Vinfruco, Wltvrede, Wlworths
★★★ Montpllr Tbgh, Môreson ★★ Bloemndal, **NT:** Dieu D, Sxnburg, **D:** Bcksbrg, Montpllr Sud, Ndrburg

Non-MCC, off-dry/semi-sweet
★★ Rooibrg (2) ★★ Rbtson, (2), **NT:** De Krans, Kango, Montagu, **D:** KWV

Non-MCC, red
★★★ JC le R, **D:** Cinzano

Non-MCC rosé, dry
★★★ Laborie, Twee JG ★★☆ Boplaas

Non-MCC rosé, off-dry/semi-sweet

★★★ Cold Duck, Le Grand C, Waboom ★★☆ Wlworths ★★ Bon Crge, Drnkraal, **NT:** Klnhof, Swrtland, **D:** Jason's

Non-MCC white, dry

★★★★ Bergsig

★★★ **Bnnievle**, Botha, Dominion, Ekndal, Goudini, Lyngrove, Rhbsklf, Swrtland, **Westcrp Int** ★★☆ Citrus (2), Du T'kloof, JC le R, McGreg, Merwida, Ndrburg, Wlworths ★★ Brndvlei, Makro, Riebeek, Rooibrg, Tulbagh, Van Lvren ★★ Mooitsg, Rbtson, **NT:** Bovlei, Delheim, F'hoek Vyds (2), **D:** Boland, KWV, Winecorp

Non-MCC white, off-dry/semi-sweet

★★★ Boplaas, Botha, Rietrvr, Wlworths ★★★ Badsberg, Citrus, F'hoek Vyds, Grand Msx, JC le R, Nuy, Slnghoek, Tulbagh, Vrdnheim ★★ Capnheimr, Cinzano, Grand Msx, JC le R, Makro (2), Mooitsg, Van Lvren (2), Wamaker, Westcrp Int, **NT:** Aan de Drns, Bovlei, De Doorns, Hrtswater, Klnhof, Lndzicht, Ltzvlle, Oranje, Uitvlucht (2), Vlrsdorp, **D:** Boland, Goudini, Grand Msx, Ndrburg (2), Smnsvlei

Special late harvest

★★★★ Bon Crge, Ekndal, Paul C

★★★ Bergsig, Drostdy, Ndrburg, Rbtson, Van Lvren ★★★ Du T'kloof, Rdezandt, Slnghoek ★★ Ashton, Badsberg, Botha, De Wet ★★ Goudini, **NT:** Bovlei, Douglas, Hrtswater, Merwespnt, M'pont, Oranje, **D:** Bcksbrg, Hrtnberg

Sweet red

★★★★ Sylvnvle

★★★ Fview ★★★ **Prmium Cpe Wnes**, Taverna ★★ Avntuur, **Prmium Cpe Wnes**, Rbtson (2), Tulbagh, Wlworths ★★ Cellr Csk, **NR:** Douglas G, **Van Z'klf**, **D:** Gdveld

Sylvaner

★★★★ Ovrgaauw

Tempranillo

★★★★ De Krans

Tinta barocca

★★★★ Allesvlrn, Lmrshoek

★★★Boplaas, De Krans, Louiesnhf, Swrtland, **D:** Signal H

Touriga nacional

★★★★ Boplaas, De Krans

★★★ Allesvlrn

Vin de paille

★★★★★ De Traf, Fview, Fview, Rstnberg, Stellr Orgs

★★★★ **Hzndal**, Signal H

★★★ Stettyn, **NR:** Mellasat, **NT:** Lmrshoek

Viognier

★★★★ Bcksbrg, Bellnghm, Fview, **Ridgeback**, Seidel, Spier, **Zrgvliet**

★★★★ Bon Cap, G Beck, Lmrshoek, Rstnberg, Sbosch Vyds, Uiterwyk, **Whlhaven**, **Wlworths**, **NR:** Merwida, **Niel J**, **The Foundry**, **NT:** Boschndl

White blends

Chardonnay-based blends, unwooded

★★★★ KWV

★★★★ Cabrière, Thnskraal, Wlworths

★★★ Jean D, Vaughan J, **Vinfruco** ★★★ Ashanti, Bellnghm, Boplaas, Clairvx, **Cpe Grace**, Crghall, Mooitsg, Rhbsklf (2), S/SW, **Vinfruco**, Westcrp Int ★★ **IWS**, Mouton, Ntvbij ★ Barrydale, **NR:** Meerend, **D:** Knysna, Vendôme

★★★★ Quoin
★★★★ Boschndl

★★★ Chamnx, **Jason's**, Le Grand C ★★☆ Douglas G, **Fierte**, Western ★★ **Western**, **NT:** Bnnievle

Sauvignon blanc-based, unwooded

★★★★ Fort S, Jordan

★★★ Asara, De Wetsh, Deetlefs, **Horse Mtn**, Hrtnberg, La Couronne ★★★ **Cpe Grace**, Malan, **Mooitsg**, Western, Wltvrede, Zevnwacht, **NT:** Drostdy, Tulbagh, **Western**, **D:** Paradysklf, Rickety, Umkhulu

Sauvignon blanc-based, wooded

★★★★ Ndrburg

★★★☆ **Ndrburg**, Nico V, **Nico vdM**, **Wlworths**

★★★ Ndrburg

Semillon-based, unwooded

★★★☆ **Glnwood**, **Grt Cnstntia**, **Raka**

★★★ Sbosch Vyds, The Winery ★★★ Leopard's, Long Mntn, **D:** Dbn Hills, Grt Cnstntia

Semillon-based, wooded

★★★★ **Allee B**, Con Uitsig

★★★ **Stettyn** ★★★ Afrcn Terroir, F'hoek Vyds, **Origin** ★★ Two Oceans

Zinfandel

★★★★ Hrtnberg

★★★☆ Blwklppn, Fview, Glen C

★★★ Ashanti, **VS:** Lmrshoek